THE ATMOSPHERE AND THE SEA IN MOTION

CARL-GUSTAF ROSSBY

1898—1957

THE ATMOSPHERE AND THE SEA IN MOTION

SCIENTIFIC CONTRIBUTIONS TO THE ROSSBY MEMORIAL VOLUME

Edited by BERT BOLIN

THE UNIVERSITY OF STOCKHOLM

New York

THE ROCKEFELLER INSTITUTE PRESS

in association with

OXFORD UNIVERSITY PRESS

1959

LIBRARY OF CONGRESS CATALOGUE CARD NUMBER 59-14858

PRINTED IN SWEDEN BY ESSELTE AB, 1959

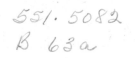

Preface

In July 1957 invitations were extended to colleagues and former students of Professor Rossby, to submit scientific contributions for a special volume to commemorate Professor Rossby's sixtieth birthday anniversary, 28 December 1958. A month later, on 19 August 1957, Professor Rossby died suddenly after a heart attack, in his office at the Institute of Meteorology in Stockholm. His death, at the age of 58, deprived the world of science and his many friends of a man who, by force and charm of personality, power of intellect, and indomitable spirit and energy was a central figure in the explosive development of meteorology that has taken place during the past three decades.

Fate thus has altered the title of this volume, but not its purpose, which is to provide a permanent testimony of the remarkable impact of a man who has been an enormous source of inspiration as a teacher and an international leader in science and scientific cooperation.

The five persons whose names are listed below are responsible for the organization of the Rossby Memorial Volume, and for any defects which may be found in the final publication. Apart from the editorial work, which has been carried out entirely by Dr. Bolin, the most difficult aspect of our responsibilities has been the selection of contributors. The aim which guided us in this selection was to seek contributions that could be grouped around the general theme "The atmosphere and the sea in motion" — the subtitle of the Volume, which epitomizes the scientific work of Professor Rossby. However, the number of close colleagues or former students who could make suitable contributions was so great that we were forced to exclude many prominent names in order to satisfy the rather stringent requirements of economy.

During the months preceding his death, Professor Rossby completed an article entitled *Aktuella Meteorologiska Problem,* which was published in the 1956 yearbook of the National Science Research Council of Sweden. This essay which has been translated into English by Staff Members of the International Meteorological Institute in Stockholm, is presented here in its entirety, under the title "Current problems in meteorology." Written for the non-specialist, it is a penetrating appraisal of many of the dominant problems of meteorology and exemplifies the characteristically broad sweep of Professor Rossby's vision.

We wish to express our appreciation to all those whose contributions made this Volume possible. We are particularly grateful to two of Professor Rossby's life-long associates, Professor Tor Bergeron of the University of Uppsala and Professor Horace R. Byers of the University of Chicago, for their biographical sketches.

March 1959

BERT BOLIN
The University of Stockholm

JULE G. CHARNEY
Massachusetts Institute of Technology

ARNT ELIASSEN
Institute of Theoretical Meteorology, Oslo

GEORGE W. PLATZMAN
The University of Chicago

HENRY STOMMEL
Woods Hole Oceanographic Institution

Contents

Current Problems in Meteorology[1]

C.-G. Rossby

Introduction

The following survey of current problems in meteorological research deals primarily with the classical problem of meteorology, the quantitative analysis of the state and motion of the atmosphere based upon the laws of physics. In addition we shall discuss some recent problems concerning the role played by the atmosphere as a carrier of insoluble minerals, soluble condensation nuclei and industrial pollutants, problems of importance for understanding the role of the atmosphere in certain geological processes, and as a milieu for the biological processes at the surface of the earth. Investigations on such problems in the past have been considered to be of peripheral interest to meteorology, partly because the feed-back of these windborne substances on the general circulation of the atmosphere is usually insignificant. It has, however, become apparent lately that one of the important tasks for applied meteorology will be to forecast the effects of large-scale diffusion processes in the atmosphere. In addition, a systematic study of the distribution of air-borne particles can give us valuable information concerning the tracks of individual air particles, and thereby also the dynamics of the atmosphere. Such information cannot always be obtained through the analysis of the daily meteorological observations at our disposal. For these reasons more attention lately has been devoted to trajectory and diffusion problems in the atmosphere.

One essential criterion which will show that the classical task of meteorology has been solved will be our ability to compute objectively the future state and motion of the atmosphere on the basis of theoretical principles; in other words to issue numerical forecasts of the weather. By and large this means trying to find an answer to the question: "What will the wind direction, wind speed, pressure etc. be at a given place at a given instant in the future?" The diffusion problem, on the other hand, which more and more engages the attention of meteorologists, can be formulated in a prognostic question of the type: "Where will a given air particle be at a given instant in the future?" To the extent that it is possible to solve these two problems with the aid of the basic equations of hydrodynamics, the diffusion problem means one additional time integration and therefore puts far greater demands on the accuracy of both theory and meteorological observations.

It is hardly necessary to stress that the following survey is both incomplete and subjective in the choice of problems discussed. The incompleteness is a result not only of the lack of space but also depends upon the fact that it is hardly possible any longer for one meteorologist to acquire detailed knowledge of the whole front along which meteorological research is carried out today. This research includes a large number of special problems and problems of a local character which are of great theoretical and practical importance. Such questions have been disregarded here for the problems of a more global character.

In the first part of the review certain problems concerning the atmosphere as a whole and its interaction with the ocean are briefly considered. A discussion of the general circulation of the atmosphere follows, and in this connection an analysis of the present status of numerical forecasting is given. In connection with problems of forecasting, certain aspects of trajectories in the atmosphere are presented, followed by a discussion of some circulation and diffusion problems in the field of atmospheric chemistry. The review is concluded with some brief comments concerning the possibility of controlling some atmospheric processes artificially. The mutual dependence of various branches of geophysics as well as the similarity of the problems in these different fields is everywhere stressed as being

[1] This article is a translation of "Aktuella meteorologiska problem», published in *Svensk Naturvetenskap 1956* by the Swedish Natural Science Research Council.

particularly true for meteorology, oceanography, hydrology and geochemistry. Sooner or later these intimate connections must be considered by those who have the responsibility for the future training of geophysicists and for the planning of purposeful and responsible geophysical research.

In the preparation of the following review the writer has received many valuable suggestions and critical comments from his associates at the International Meteorological Institute in Stockholm, in particular from Dr. BERT BOLIN, who has been in charge of the work in numerical forecasting at the Institute for a number of years, and has also played a role in other research activities at the Institute.

Planetary problems of balance and circulation

A. *Radiation balance and heat storage*

During the decades which have passed since meteorology first took shape shortly after the beginning of this century, the network of meteorological stations which is at our disposal for the study of the daily changes in state and movements of the atmosphere, has been extended in an impressive way. It is now possible to give a rather satisfying picture of the air movements of the troposphere and the lower stratosphere twice a day over the major part of the northern hemisphere. At the same time our knowledge of the dynamics and physics of the atmosphere has to some degree become more profound. In spite of, or perhaps because of this better knowledge, one finds that certain fundamental postulates, which earlier were regarded as so self-evident that they were not even dealt with in the meteorological textbooks, now must be looked upon as rather uncertain. The heat balance of the atmosphere serves as a good example.

The solar radiation falling perpendicularly upon a surface of one square centimeter at the outer edge of the atmosphere, amounts to about 1.95 cal min^{-1}. This value, the "solar-constant", is of course uncertain, as it is determined by extrapolation to the outer border of the atmosphere from measurements within the atmosphere. However, for the particular estimates which are given here, this uncertainty can be regarded as unimportant. Because the surface of the earth is four times greater than its cross-section, it follows that about 0.49 cal cm^{-2} min^{-1} is available to maintain the circulations of the atmosphere and the sea. It is generally supposed that between 30 and 40 per cent of this amount of energy is reflected back to space as short-wave radiation by the upper surfaces of the clouds, snow covered areas, to some degree by the sea surface, and finally by the atmosphere itself (Rayleigh scattering). The exact amount of the total reflection is still uncertain. The remaining amount of energy, of the order of 0.3 cal cm^{-2} min^{-1}, thus represents the effective solar radiation which keeps the air (and the sea) in motion. It is assumed, usually without discussion, that our planet as a whole is in radiation balance with its surroundings, so that the same amount of energy, 0.3 cal cm^{-2} min^{-1}, thus will be sent back to space as long wave (infrared) radiation from the earth's surface, from the upper surfaces of the clouds and, even of more importance, by the water vapour in the atmosphere. How precisely the equilibrium condition must be maintained is, however, uncertain and should, as the following calculations indicate, depend strongly upon the time interval taken into consideration.

In three extremely interesting papers at the end of the 1920's G. C. SIMPSON investigated the radiation balance of the atmosphere and calculated the geographical and yearly variation of the outgoing long-wave radiation. Simpson found that this outgoing radiation was very evenly distributed both in space and in time, and that within the accuracy of the computations the total outgoing radiation from our planet as a whole, during each of the months of the year, was balanced by the total effective incoming solar radiation. Simpson does not deal with the total amount of heat stored in the sea and the solid surface of the earth, and these questions are generally ignored by the meteorologists studying the radiation balance. Thus the good agreement between the calculated incoming and outgoing radiation indicates that it is possible to neglect variations of the stored heat even for as short a period as one year or even a few months, as long as one limits oneself to the entire planet. This result is really rather astonishing, if one takes into account the great uniformity in space and time of the outgoing radiation found by Simpson. Such uniformity indicates that the atmosphere is rather incapable of adjusting locally the outgoing radiation to the very great variation in space and time of the incoming effective solar radiation.

Qualitatively Simpson's result may be explained in the following way. The intensity of long-wave radiation in the atmosphere is determined primarily by the vertical distribution of water vapour and temperature. The minor deviations, which are due to carbon dioxide absorption and emission may be neglected in a first approximation. If one disregards a gap between 8.5 μ and 11 μ in the absorption spectrum of water vapour where Simpson considers a cloudless atmosphere to be completely transparent, the water vapour atmosphere is rather opaque, and therefore the major part of the radiation which goes out into space must be emitted from the middle or upper parts of the troposphere and from the upper surfaces of clouds. Because of the permanent convective mixing in the atmosphere and the upper limit of the water vapour concentration, which for each temperature is determined by the saturation vapour pressure, the vertical distribution of water vapour will be very closely tied to the vertical temperature distribution; as a matter of fact Simpson starts his calculations from an empirical formula, by which the relative humidity is uniquely determined by the temperature. The temperature at the top of the clouds is supposed to be the same everywhere. Since the outgoing radiation, because of the atmosphere's absorption, in this way almost entirely emanates from the upper parts of the water vapour atmosphere where the temperature is given, it does not matter at what height above the surface this layer is situated, or in other words, what temperature there is at the earth's surface. Thus, outgoing radiation flow is almost uniquely determined.

Since Simpson's time much work has been done on a detailed study of the selective absorption spectrum of water vapour and in developing graphical methods for reliable calculations of the atmospheric long-wave radiation flow from the observed vertical temperature and humidity distribution. The leading name in this branch of research was for many years W. ELSASSER.

A fundamental advantage of these graphical methods is that they eliminate the analytic connection between the water vapour and temperature distribution, which served as a starting point for the calculations of Simpson. It has been shown above that this forms a constraint which hinders the local adjustment of outgoing radiation to the incoming solar radiation. On the other hand one must remember that the connection between temperature and water vapour content is an empirical, statistical fact, which therefore ought to show up even in graphical estimates based upon observations of the vertical stratification. Thus it is rather doubtful whether these more refined methods now available can lead to large fundamental differences from the uniformity and the lack of adaptation of the outgoing radiation as found by Simpson. A few years ago H. G. HOUGHTON published a new computation of the annual heat (radiation) balance, based upon recent data concerning cloud distribution and light reflection, and applying Elsasser's graphical method to the upper-air data now available from a rather great number of radiosonde stations. According to Houghton both the incoming and the outgoing radiation are considerably higher than the results of Simpson indicate, but the question concerning the ability of the atmosphere to adapt to the outgoing long-wave radiation to the effective incoming radiation remains unanswered.

In the study of post-glacial climatic fluctuations, it has been assumed to be of great importance to know how the radiation exchange between our planet and space adapts to possible variations of the solar constant. Simpson's answer is that as the outgoing radiation can hardly be modified to any great extent, the adaptation must take place in form of variations in total cloudiness in such a way that increasing incoming radiation causes increasing cloudiness by increasing evaporation from the sea surface, thus causing greater reflection of incoming radiation. This conclusion seems at first to be rather surprising when considering the relatively small changes of the planetary cloud cover from winter to summer. On the other hand, as a support of his hypothesis, Simpson develops an extremely interesting comparison between the radiation balances of the planets Venus, the Earth and Mars. If the cloudiness is expressed in terms of tenths of the total cloudiness, one finds that this figure varies from 10/10 on Venus, to about 5/10 on the Earth and 0/10 on Mars. The resulting differences in the ability of these planets to reflect the incoming radiation of the sun (albedo) is to a large degree enough to compensate for the differences in the incoming radiation depending on the mean distance of the planets from the sun.

Our knowledge of the variations in the total solar radiation which reaches the outer border of the atmosphere, is for obvious reasons very rudimentary, but it is likely that variations of one or a few per cent of the total energy occur. The greatest part of this variation is probably to be found in the ultra-violet part of the incoming radiation, which is absorbed almost totally in the upper parts of the atmosphere and therefore is not directly able to influence the lower atmosphere and its circulation. Variations in the absorbed solar radiation must, because of the extremely low density of the atmosphere at these high altitudes, lead to strong local temperature fluctuations. Many attempts have been made to construct mechanisms by which such fluctuations in their turn could influence the circulation of the troposphere. These efforts have not yet led to the goal, but considering the strong vertical stability which characterizes the lower layers of the stratosphere (15—35 km) it is very unlikely that variations of the temperature and structure of the higher atmosphere should have any noticeable influence on the circulation of the troposphere. But it ought to be pointed out that this personal opinion of the writer is not shared by all meteorologists.

It has already been observed that Simpson's work does not touch on the possibility of secular changes in the stored heat. The yearly cycle of the heat which is stored in the solid earth's crust and the sea, was dealt with for the first time extensively in 1934 and 1935, by F. BAUER and H. PHILLIPS, who considered the heat balance of the atmosphere in a renewed treatment along the same lines as Simpson, but starting from much more accurate values of the parameters. Bauer and Phillips assume, however, that the local storage has an annual cycle prescribed in such a way that the net accumulation for one year vanishes everywhere. Because of the very low heat conductivity of the earth's crust, variations in its heat storage must be rather unimportant, which is shown for instance by the fact that the temperature climate of isolated desert regions follows the sun very closely. The ability of the atmosphere to store heat is also rather limited. As an illustration it can be mentioned that if during one year 1 % of the total effective solar radiation, i.e. 0.003 cal cm^{-2} min^{-1}, should be stored instead of being sent back to space, this would lead to an increase of the mean temperature of the atmosphere of about 6.3° C, but as the capacity of the atmosphere to absorb water vapour from the sea would increase at the same time, the resulting temperature increase would probably amount to only half this value.

The magnitude and character of the variations of the total heat, both realized and latent, stored in the atmosphere is not known. In spite of the well organized international meteorological network there is at present no international organization responsible and equipped for the enormous statistical work which current computations of this kind would demand.

In the surface layer of the sea the perpetually shifting winds cause mixing and a vertical homogeneous layer of water, the medium depth of which is of the order of magnitude of 50—100 m. If the heat capacity of this layer is taken into account, it is found that a storage of 1 per cent of the effective incoming solar radiation would lead to a mean temperature increase in the entire storage layer (the atmosphere plus the homogeneous surface layer) of only a few tenths of a degree.

It is not difficult to demonstrate that the storage of heat in the turbulent surface layer ought to be taken into account in local radiation balance computations. For this purpose one can choose the surroundings of Bermuda, where the advection of warm and cold water masses is of very secondary importance. It is easily found that the excess of the incoming, effective solar radiation in the warm season is more than sufficient to explain the increase with time of the heat stored in the surface layer, which reaches its maximum about three months after the summer solstice. At the same time Simpson's tables, as well as Bauer's and Phillips' calculations, show that the outgoing radiation in that part of the world is practically independent of the season.

The heat stored in the surface layer of the ocean in the southern hemisphere is decreased at the same time as the heat storage in the northern hemisphere is increased, and the surface layer is perhaps of minor importance of the total heat balance of the earth, which would very well agree with the results of Simpson. Considering, however, the difference between the hemispheres in regard to the distribution of land and sea, it is not self-evident that such an equalization occurs.

The role of the sea as a secular heat reservoir assumes quite a different character at the moment that one takes up the question of secular changes of the total heat balance, taking into account the circulation of the deeper layers. An elementary calculation gives the result that even as much as 1 % of the total incoming heat radiation could be stored in a layer of 1,000 m thickness in the interior of the sea, without producing a temperature increase greater than 0.015° C per year; for thicker layers the temperature increase would become proportionally smaller. — *These deeper layers are insulated from the atmosphere by stably stratified warmer watermasses near to the sea surface and are not able directly to restore the radiation balance by means of an increased evaporation and cloud formation.* The figure mentioned above should be increased by 50 per cent in order to correct for that part of the earth's surface which is covered by continents and continental shelves, but the correction is of course unimportant for these rough estimates.

The deep water is produced along the borders of the Antarctic, especially along the Atlantic sector and during the colder season possibly even in some limited regions of the northern Atlantic near Greenland. Furthermore it is certainly necessary to take into account that water in the northern parts of the North Atlantic is forced into the deep ocean by the prevailing wind system in the whole North Atlantic Ocean, which ordinarily forces the surface water to the north. The deep water masses formed in this way gradually spread to the other oceans by the Antarctic circumpolar currents, and finally end up in the Pacific Ocean, where the "oldest" water masses are found. The cycle is probably closed by the very slow mechanical mixing of the superimposed warmer layers with the stagnated deep layers, which in this way are able to rise to the sea surface again. As the intensity of the mechanical mixing must necessarily decrease with increased temperature contrast between the surface water and the deep water, i.e. with increased vertical stability, it is not unlikely that the intensity of the whole thermohaline cycle mentioned above must undergo strong and probably rather irregular, slow fluctuations. The total volume of the water masses normally taking part in this cycle is not known, but its order of magnitude lies probably between 10 and 100 million m^3 per second, corresponding to a circulation period for the whole sea of 4,000 years in the former and 400 years in the latter case. A period of about 400 years fits fairly well into the values which have been deduced e.g. from instantaneous "age measurements" of the deep sea with the aid of C^{14}-analyses and from estimates of the oxygen consumption in the deeper layers of the sea.

On the basis of these (admittedly loose) estimates, one is probably justified in expressing the following two suggestions:

a) The assumption that our planet as a whole stands in firm radiation balance with outer space cannot be accepted without reservations, even if periods of several decades are taken into account.

b) Anomalies in heat probably can be stored and temporarily isolated in the sea and after periods of the order of a few decades to a few centuries again influence the heat and water-vapour exchange with the atmosphere.

If this latter assumption is correct, it does not seem unlikely that the problem of post-glacial climate fluctuations lasting a few hundred years can take on new aspects. But it must be pointed out that if these anomalies in heat which are stored in the interior of the sea are gradually distributed in greater water masses, they must, when they finally reach the sea surface again, be characterized by very small temperature amplitudes. How such exceedingly small variations in temperature could possibly have a significant influence on the atmosphere is still an unanswered question. It is perhaps more likely that the changes by no means take place at a constant rate but fluctuate so that the contrast in temperature between the surface water and the deep water shows strong variations with time.

Considering what has been said above, it is obvious that measurements or reliable estimates of the heat exchange between our planet and outer space must be looked upon as a major question for meteorologists and oceanographers interested in the global circulation systems of the sea and atmosphere and their fluctuations. Our knowledge of long-wave radiation streams which penetrate the atmosphere is yet too uncertain to permit more reliable numerical estimates of their intensity. For easily understandable reasons oceanography has not yet become a synoptic science, and large parts of the interior of the sea are yet too little explored to permit any computations of secular variations of stored heat. An attempt to examine the possible existence of such variations is, however, being made during the International Geophysical Year by measurements in some parts of the Atlantic Ocean, which were investigated by the Meteor Expedition in the 1920's.

It is obviously of great importance for both meteorology and oceanography that some preparatory instrumental work has been started in order to measure the total heat exchange of the earth with space by means of satellites, which will be sent up during the International Geophysical Year. In order to determine the heat exchange it is necessary to measure simultaneously not only the incoming radiation (the solar constant) and the earth's albedo (reflection power), as was originally planned, but also the total outgoing longwave radiation. As we are mainly interested in what are probably very small differences between the amounts of incoming and outgoing radiation, the technical difficulties are enormous, but as the problem is now accepted as being of fundamental importance, certainly intensive work will be conducted in order to solve the problems connected with such measurements.[1]

B. *Carbon dioxide and its cycle*

The circulation of water between the surface and the deep layers of the sea, and especially its period of circulation, is of fundamental importance when studying another global meteorological problem of great interest to climatology, i.e. the increase of the carbon-dioxide content of the atmosphere. This increase seems to be a result of the steadily increasing consumption of fossil fuel in the last 50 to 100 years. How large this increase really is must to a great degree depend upon whether the sea, particularly the deep layers, is able to absorb slowly or quickly the excess of carbon dioxide constantly supplied to the atmosphere.

It has been pointed out frequently that mankind now is performing a unique experiment of impressive planetary dimensions by now consuming during a few hundred years all the fossil fuel deposited during millions of years. The meteorological consequences of this experiment are as yet by no means clarified, but there is no doubt that an increase of carbon-dioxide content in the atmosphere would lead to an increased absorption of the outgoing infrared radiation from the earth's surface thus causing an increase of the mean temperature of the atmosphere. As we know, SVANTE ARRHENIUS was first to point out that variations in the carbon-dioxide content of the air, resulting from the volcanic activity of the earth, could explain the variations in climate, which characterize the geological history of our plante. Quite recently G. N. PLASS calculated that, assuming all other factors to be constant, a doubling of the carbon dioxide in the atmosphere would lead to a mean air temperature increase of about 3.6° C, while a reduction of the carbon dioxide to half its value would lower the temperature by 3.8° C. It is almost certain that these figures will be subjected to many strong revisions, depending mainly on the fact that those complicated processes, which finally determine the mean temperature of the atmosphere, cannot be dealt with as independent, additive phenomena. For instance, a higher mean temperature caused by carbon dioxide must lead to

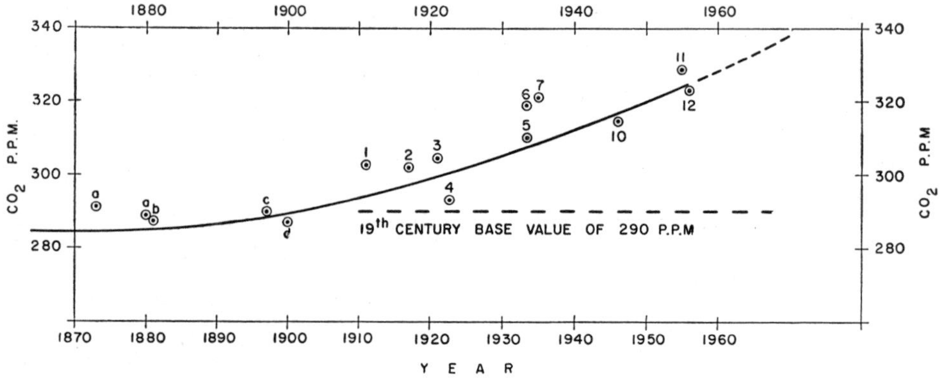

Fig. 1. In this diagram by G. S. CALLENDAR an attempt is made to illustrate the increase, in recent years, of the content of carbon dioxide in the atmosphere by means of observational series which were critically selected. The continuous ascending line represents the theoretically estimated content of carbon dioxide under the assumption that none of the carbon dioxide liberated through combustion is stored in the sea or in increased vegetation.

[1] In this connection it ought to be mentioned that Simpson's as well as Houghton's calculations of the outgoing long-wave radiation from different latitudes have been corrected by multiplication with a factor common for all latitudes and chosen in such a way that complete balance is obtained between the total incoming and outgoing radiation. Considering the imperfection of the methods of calculation this procedure is, of course, completely justified, as the deviations resulting from the computations have no physical significance, whatsoever. On the other hand, it must be emphasized that in fact real deviations of this order of magnitude (1—3 per cent) could be of outstanding importance from the paleo-climatological point of view.

an increase of atmospheric water vapour content and therefore of the infrared absorption by the water vapour but probably also to an increased cloudiness.

Has there really been a considerable increase in the content of carbon dioxide in the air during the very much expanded industrial activity of the last decades? In 1940 G. S. CALLENDAR thought it possible to show that the carbon-dioxide content of the atmosphere had increased by approximately 10 per cent since the beginning of the century. The observational material at this disposal was very extensive but of very uneven quality with a highly unsatisfactory geographical distribution of the observation sites (most of them were situated at places in central Europe, which were highly polluted by industrial activity). Callendar selected the series of observations that he thought were most reliable and representative, but an inspection of the material used with its enormous spread gives a strong impression of the uncertainty which necessarily characterizes his estimates. In a paper published recently, however, and based on a critical review of older as well as more recent data Callendar maintains his opinion about the rapid increase of the atmospheric carbon dioxide.

An increase by 10 per cent of the total carbon-dioxide content of the air would, according to Callendar, approximately correspond to the amount of carbon dioxide liberated through the consumption of fossil fuel during the three or four first decades of this century. In order to explain this high value of the increase of carbon-dioxide content, one must assume that only a very small fraction of the amounts released to the atmosphere has been absorbed in the sea in spite of the fact that the capacity of the marine reservoir is about sixty times greater than that of the atmosphere. Thus one is immediately faced with a great number of difficult problems. How should measurements of the total carbon-dioxide content of the atmosphere be conducted in the best way? How should measurements or estimates be made in order to gain increased knowledge of the carbon-dioxide exchange at the sea surface. Finally, how rapid is the exchange between the surface layer and the deep sea?

For almost two years a small group of Scandinavian scientists has maintained a network consisting of 15 stations on the Scandinavian peninsula, Denmark and Finland from which air samples for carbon dioxide analysis have been taken three times every month. The sampling stations and times are chosen to suppress the local sources of error as much as possible. Nevertheless it is found that the carbon-dioxide content varies so much with the origin of the prevailing air masses that it possibly could be used as a diagnostic, synoptic element. It is not unusual to find variations of 10 per cent across a well-developed front. Therefore it seems almost hopeless to arrive at reliable estimates of the atmospheric carbon-dioxide reservoir and its secular changes by such measurements in limited areas.

In order to overcome this difficulty to some extent it has been suggested that regular carbon-dioxide analyses of the air near the surface should be performed in some synoptically inactive parts of the world far from industrial regions, the sea, and densely vegetated regions where also the assimilation could influence locally the values obtained. Carbon-dioxide determinations in the free atmosphere and in desert regions, mainly in the not yet too heavily industrialized southern hemisphere ought therefore to be of special interest, but they must, of course, be made concurrently and during a great number of years in order to establish secular changes in the total carbon-dioxide content of the atmosphere.

As a contribution to the study of these important problems, a rather extensive observational program will be conducted during the International Geophysical Year. In addition to the rather modest Scandinavian network meteorologists and oceanographers have planned an extended network of synoptic carbon-dioxide stations in North and South America, the Artic and the Antarctic. Carbon-dioxide determinations will furthermore be made on a great number of islands in the Pacific and the Atlantic, and on mountain stations in North and South America. Furthermore, there will be regular flights along certain meridians in order to determine the carbon-dioxide content in the free atmosphere.

In spite of the rich material which will thus be collected, it is very likely that great difficulties will be encountered in every attempt to compute the content of carbon dioxide in the atmosphere and its secular changes from such scattered observations. For this reason it is of special interest that a new, perhaps more promising method, is being developed based upon comparative determinations of the content of the atmosphere and the biosphere of radioactive carbon (C^{14}). The first attempt to determine the secular change of the carbon-dioxide content of the atmosphere by this method were made by

H. SUESS in 1953, and the problem has later been taken up by others.

In principle, this method is based upon the fact that the carbon dioxide, which is brought to the atmosphere by the combustion of fossil fuel, must be free from radioactive carbon, the half-life of which is 5,568 years. By comparison of the C^{14} content of annual tree rings from the middle of the last century with the youngest annual rings in trees recently felled one can thus determine whether the assimilated carbon dioxide originates from the earlier "natural" carbon dioxide reservoir of the atmosphere, in which the C^{14} content represents an equilibrium between the production and decay of radioactive carbon, or from the extra supply of "dead" carbon dioxide which originates from the fossil fuel consumed.

The method has the great advantage that it is very likely to eliminate local synoptic variations in the atmospheric carbon-dioxide content. However, the industrial consumption of industrial fuel shows very great geographical variations with a minimum in the southern hemisphere. Therefore it is obvious that definitive conclusions concerning secular variations can be drawn only when samples from widely separated parts of the world have been analysed.

It should perhaps be stressed that investigations concerning such problems as the total variation of the heat stored in the sea, or of the total content of carbon dioxide in the atmosphere, biosphere or the sea, mean a completely new class of questions in theoretical meteorology and oceanography. In these investigations one is hardly interested in geographical distributions. As a first approximation the problem consequently may be reduced to systems of simultaneous ordinary and usually nonlinear differential equations, which express the interplay between the different reservoirs. Under special conditions thermomechanical systems of this type are able to maintain nonlinear oscillations of finite amplitude, as if their self-regulating properties were defective in some way. E. ERIKSSON and P. WELANDER have recently suggested that the combined carbon dioxide system should be characterized by such oscillations. Their result depends to a great extent on some much debated assumptions about the interior properties of the system, but it is obvious that the possible existence of such oscillations in the total heat balance system, including the heat storage in the sea, would be of great climatological interest.

C. *Tritium and the hydrologic cycle*

Water vapour, which evaporates from the sea surface, is transported over the continents by maritime winds to condense and finally precipitate as rain or snow. A part of this precipitation is perhaps temporarily stored in lakes or in the ground water and another part is restored to the atmosphere by the transpiration of vegetative cover or by evaporation from the ground, but on the average as much water must flow into the sea by streams and rivers as the net amount which is brought inland by the maritime wind systems. A careful analysis of this complicated hydrologic cycle with its many epicycles is an important prerequisite for a rational treatment of climatology. In some highly industrialized regions in the world, where in recent years the industrial per capita consumption of water has increased very rapidly, the knowledge of the hydrologic cycle has become of increasing practical importance, e.g. in connection with the many experiments now performed in order to increase the water supply by artificially initiated precipitation or by suppression of the evaporation from lakes and reservoirs.

The evaporation from the sea is supposed to be of the order of 2—3 mm water per day. A systematic estimate of average supply of water vapour in the atmosphere has not been made, but should lead to a value of one or a few $g\,cm^{-2}$. Thus the residence time of water vapour in the atmosphere as a whole must be of the order of a few days or at most one week. It is, however, obvious that the small fraction of the water vapour evaporated from the sea which is brought over the continents and is stored in the ground water, must have a circulation time of quite another order of magnitude. W. F. LIBBY and his students have recently shown that radioactive tritium (H^3), which is normally formed in the atmosphere by cosmic ray activity and which is furthermore produced in much greater amounts by hydrogen-bomb explosions, could be used for determinations of the average storage time of water as ground water.

Tritium has a half-time of 12½ years and is very well suited for studying such cycles, the circulation times of which are of the same order of magnitude. Libby and his collaborators determined the tritium content of the precipitation in Chicago and of Mississippi-river water in the years 1953—56. Shortly after the hydrogen-bomb explosion "Castle" in spring 1954 the tritium content rose by a factor of 10^2, and then began to fall exponentially to a value, which, however, was much higher than the one observed before "Castle". The exponential decrease of the "Castle" tritium in the precipitation indicates an average residence time of "Castle" tritium in the atmosphere of about 40 days. This value is explained by Libby to be due to the fact that the

After the bomb explosion the tritium content in the Mississippi stayed at a fairly constant high level for almost one year. From this value and from an estimate of the total amount of tritium per unit area, produced by the bomb, it is easy to calculate the total amount of ground water per unit area, assuming total mixing. With the aid of the yearly precipitation values one is then able

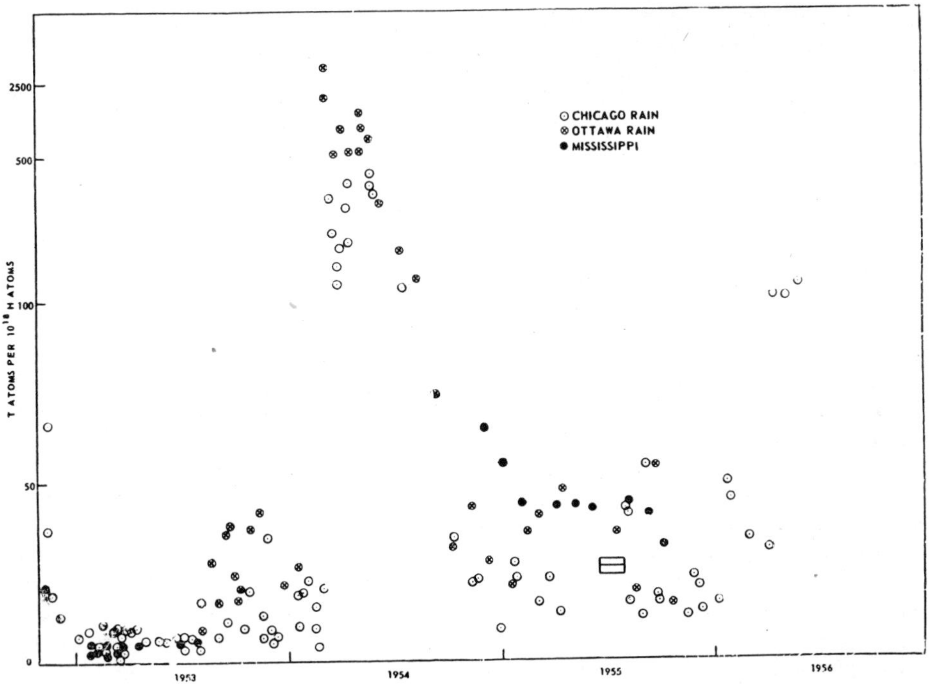

Fig. 2. The picture shows the result of a series of tritium analyses of rain and river water from the Mississippi Valley in the years 1953—1956. After the hydrogen bomb-explosion "Castle" in 1954 the concentration of tritium increased by a factor of one hundred. A great part of the tritium produced in the explosion was probably transported up into the stratosphere in the form of rather large droplets which in a few months sank back into the troposphere; the washing out in the troposphere probably took only a few days. From a paper by F. Begemann and W. F. Libby.

main part of the tritium produced in the explosion is transported far up into the stratosphere as water vapour, where it is condensed in relatively large droplets or crystals. Within a few months these nuclei then fall down through the tropopause into the troposphere, where after a few days they are precipitated in the usual way as rain. In contrast, it ought to be mentioned that very finely distributed, minute radioactive particles or material in the gaseous state is assumed to need several years to penetrate the stable border layer between the stratosphere and the troposphere, but this extremely important problem cannot yet be considered fully analysed.

to calculate the average residence time of ground water (about eight years). Starting from a comparison of the tritium content of the Mississippi water and the precipitation a few months after the Castle explosion, it is finally possible to calculate whether the rain in the Mississippi Valley has its origin in the maritime wind systems or from water vapour locally brought back to the atmosphere by evapo-transpiration. In this special case Begemann and Libby have the opinion that about 33 per cent of the precipitation originates from evapo-transporation.

It is obvious that tritium and some other natural or artificial radioactive elements could give valuable information about numerous cycles which take place entirely or partly in the atmosphere. Various objections can be raised against the special interpretations and figures given by Begemann and Libby in the investigation mentioned above, but this only means that a completely satisfying interpretation of these radioactivity measurements requires collaboration between meteorologists, hydrologists and geochemists. To be able to utilize the extraordinary possibilities and obligations, produced by radiochemistry, it is, however, necessary to establish satisfactory laboratories for systematically planned, routine determinations of the tritium content of precipitation.

The general circulation of the atmosphere

The main task for meteorology is of course to describe the general circulation of the atmosphere, its variations and superimposed secondary systems of motion in accordance with the basic principles of hydrodynamics and thermodynamics. A rational solution of this problem must be considered as a necessary prerequisite condition for building up reliable numerical theories of prognosis. On the whole, in order to be able to formulate the problems to which one is led through the study of available data, it is necessary to give a brief description of the observed circulation in the atmosphere. Due to the geographical distribution of the observational material this description must refer mainly to the northern hemisphere. A series of charts and diagrams are reproduced in this article in order to give the reader a clearer picture of the planetary circulation and the superimposed larger and smaller disturbances which together give rise to the never ceasing variation of the motion of the atmosphere. This marked variability of the observed state of motion deserves a few introductory comments.

During the time of one year the earth and its atmosphere receive more heat from the sun in the equatorial regions than is sent back to space, while the opposite is true in high northerly and southerly latitudes. In order to transport the excess heat from the equatorial regions to the regions of outgoing radiation in the north and the south, it is necessary to have an exchange of air between the tropics and the polar regions. The intensity of this exchange of air varies of course with seasons and with the amounts of heat which must be transported to the polar regions, and reaches its minimum in the summer hemisphere.

During the summer the continents (and thereby the lowest layers of air) are heated more than the surrounding seas, where part of the incoming excess heat is stored in the homogeneous wind-mixed surface layer having an average thickness of 50—100 m. Opposite conditions prevail during the winter. This temperature contrast between continents and sea gives rise to a "monsoon circulation" which changes sign at the transition from summer to winter with inflow of maritime air over the peripheral parts of the continents during the summer and with outflow of continental air across the coasts during the winter.

The external factor which ultimately controls the planetary circulation and the monsoon systems, i.e. the solar radiation which during the course of one day passes a unit area just outside the atmosphere exposed at right angles to the sun's rays (the geometric insolation), varies slowly and regularly with the seasons but beyond this it probably shows only insignificant energy variations in the parts of the spectrum which reach the atmospheric layers ($<$ 20 km above the surface) we are interested in. However, the character of the resulting circulations varies from week to week and even from day to day. A certain instability is thus "built in" in the dynamics of the atmosphere. This instability means that one certainly can hope for the possibilities of developing theories and methods in order to analyse objectively, and forecast numerically, the propagation and further development of already existing *transient* systems of motion, in any case the larger and more long lived ones, but probably very great or almost insuperable difficulties will arise in finding general methods for forecasting the development of entirely new systems. The speed of progress toward the solution of this latter problem becomes ultimately an economic question, the answer to which will depend upon the scientific and practical importance of the solution, upon the access to scientific talent, and upon the availability of the required observations.

The simplest picture of the general circulation is obtained by studying the air currents in the upper part of the atmosphere, i.e. at the 500-mb surface or higher. During the colder season west winds usually dominate and the strongest currents are normally observed in middle latitudes. Superimposed on these west winds one finds a number of quasi-horizontal wave-shaped disturbances (varying from 3 to 7), which generally move slowly eastwards while constantly changing shape.

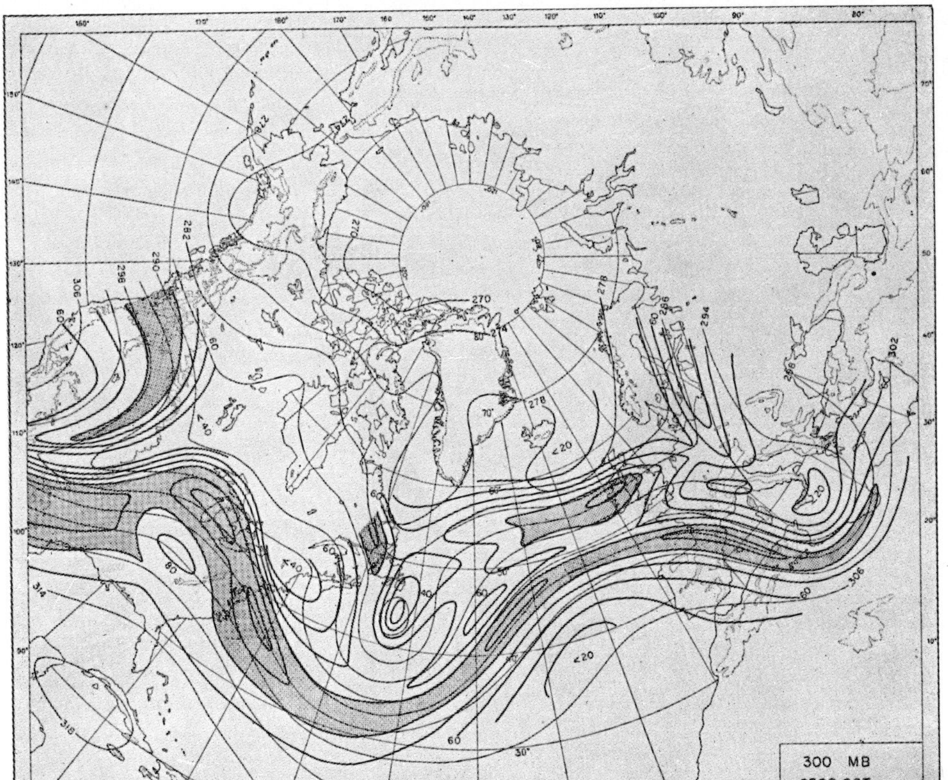

Fig. 3. This picture shows a characteristic flow pattern at the 300-mb level during a period of well-developed zonal wind. The thin lines give the topography of the 300-mb surface at intervals of 400 feet. They can also be interpreted as streamlines. The heavy lines are drawn for constant wind speed at intervals of 20 knots. Regions of wind speed greater than 100 knots are indicated by shading. (From a paper by W. J. HUBERT.)

In spite of the very regular variation of the geometric insolation with latitude, the temperature contrast between the pole and the thermal equator is not uniformly distributed over the earth's surface but is usually concentrated in a few narrow zones ("fronts") oriented almost parallel to the prevailing winds. In intimate connection with this property of the temperature field, it is found that the air currents still higher up at the border between troposphere and stratosphere have the character of narrow bands with a width of 300 km to 700 km, in which the wind velocity at times can reach values of 100 m sec^{-1} or more (jet streams).

It is worth while to observe that in the individual cases where it has been possible to determine the horizontal velocity profile across individual well-developed jet streams, it is almost always found that the wind speed increases more and more rapidly when approaching the center of the stream, where the derivative of the velocity changes sign almost discontinuously. Especially during the summer, "jet streams" are observed in which the motion also is concentrated vertically to a thin layer at the transition between stratosphere and troposphere.

By and large it seems that the circulation of the middle troposphere varies between two extreme types. On the one hand is a zonal type ("high index") with a well-developed and fairly broad westerly current in middle latitudes with insignificantly developed long waves. Opposite this is a meridional type ("low index"), characterized by the compression of the west-wind belt to one (or several) narrow bands (jets) and a displacement southwards, with the superimposed long waves now reaching very large horizontal amplitudes. The last phase in this

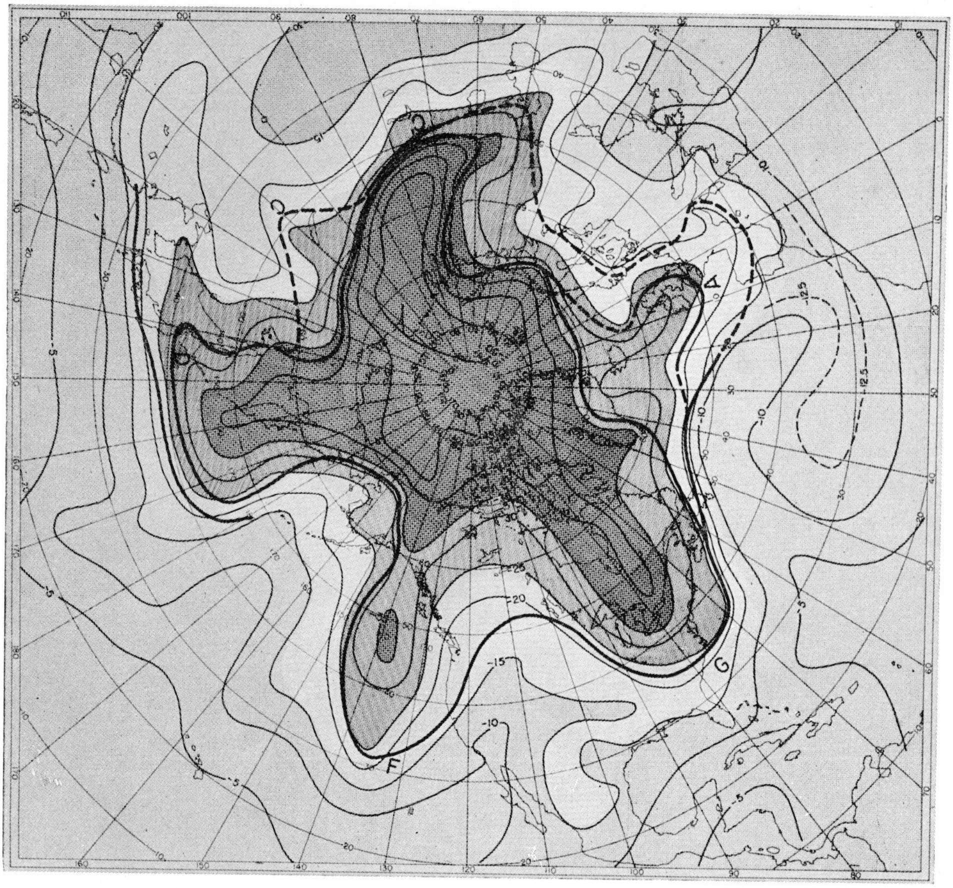

Fig. 4. The temperature distribution at the 500-mb level during a period when the circumpolar circulation was characterized by a well-developed five-wave pattern. Isotherms are drawn at intervals of 5° C, and the different temperature intervals are marked by different shading. The solid and dashed heavy lines indicate the positions of the strongest windbelts (from a paper by F. DEFANT.)

process seems to be that the meandering waves finally break up in closed cyclonic or anticyclonic cells at the same time as a new west-wind belt starts to develop far northward. The time scale for this whole "index cycle" is of the order of magnitude of 3—6 weeks, but it must be emphasized strongly that the description given above is extremely simplified.

The wave shaped quasi-horizontal disturbances of the fronts at the ground, which for the first time were thoroughly described accurately by meteorologists during the years around 1920, thereby giving rise to modern synoptic meteorology, are often a much shorter wave length than the long waves which dominate the circulation at the 500-mb level or higher. The long waves correspond more to a family of cyclones in the Norwegian terminology while the individual frontal waves usually move considerably faster to the east or northeast than the long upper-level waves. The latter follow a frontal zone embedded in the south-westerly current on the east side of a long wave in the free atmosphere. This difference in dimension between the two types of quasi-horizontal waves (long waves and frontal waves), however, is not always well marked.

Owing to the long waves, the cut-off cyclonic and anticyclonic cells and the individual frontal waves, the horizontal circulation in middle (and high) latitudes is of a very irregular character. A fairly rough estimate shows that at least in the lower troposphere the necessary exchange of heat between lower and higher latitudes, to a very great extent, has to take place thro ughcold (northerly) and warm (southerly) air currents which move side by side. Farther south, in the

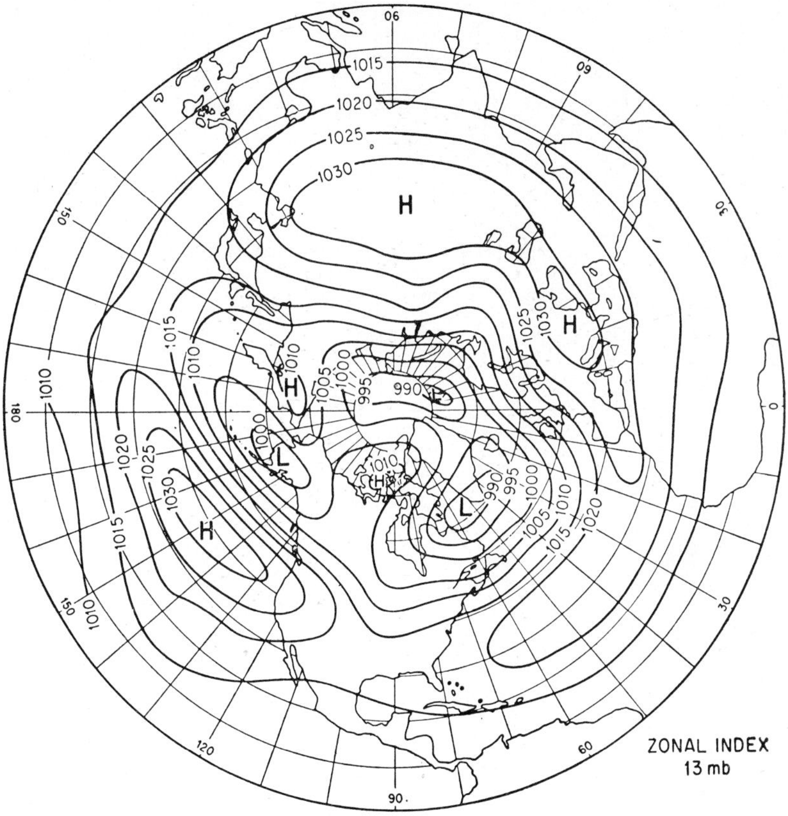

Fig. 5. Pressure distribution at sea level during a period of strong zonal motion in the middle troposphere ("high index"). The exchange of air between different latitudes is insignificant and the temperature anomalies weak in this weather situation (from H. C. WILLETT, Descriptive meteorology, Academic Press 1944).

trade-wind belt, the prevailing circulation in the lower part of the troposphere takes a much simpler and more stable and symmetric shape, with flow towards the heat-equator (the intertropic convergence zone) close to the surface by northeasterly winds and outflow by southwesterly winds in the higher levels.

To what extent can it now be said that the thermodynamic and hydrodynamic processes, which finally give rise to these extremely complicated, closely linked circulation systems, really are understood? The answer depends to a great extent on what is meant by an explanation. The speculations and the theories regarding the general circulation and its thermo-hydrodynamics goes back to the first half of the eighteenth century, when G. HADLEY in a classic work gave the first explanation for the almost permanent trade-wind systems. According to Hadley, the air close to the ground in the equatorial regions must ascend to higher levels because of the maximum insolation in these latitudes and thereby be replaced by colder air which streams in towards the equatorial zone from the north and the south. This inflow is symmetric with respect to the earth's axis and the inflowing air masses therefore seek to conserve their initial absolute *rotation around the earth's axis.* The friction at the ground or sea surface gives rise to a certain equalization of the rotation between the atmosphere and the earth but a certain lag is unavoidable and as a result, the air masses which flow towards the equator are characterized by easterly wind components. Thereby northeasterly trade winds are created north of the heat-equator and southerly trade winds south of it. The compensating air masses which higher up are transported from the equatorial regions

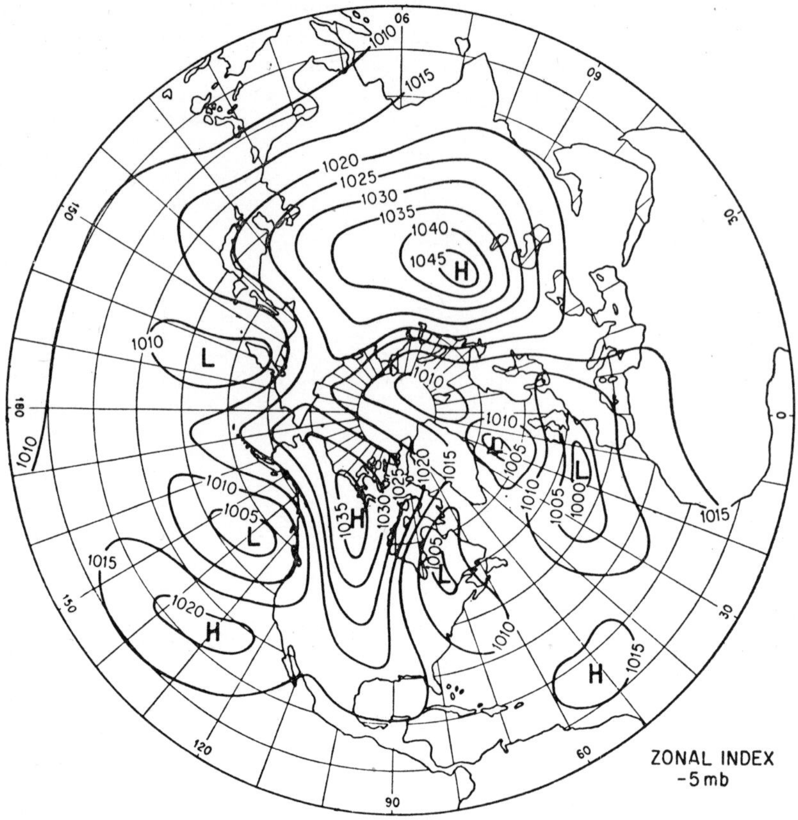

Fig. 6. Pressure distribution at sea level during a period of weak zonal motion in the middle troposphere ("low index"). In this situation there is a strong exchange of air between high and low latitudes near sea level; strong cold-air outbreaks from the north and warm air from the south appear side by side at the same latitude (from H. C. WILLETT, Descriptive Meteorology, Academic Press 1944).

northwards (or southwards) must therefore at some distance from the equator give rise to southwesterly (or northwesterly) winds.

In analyses of Hadley's type, the general circulation is considered to be the direct result of convection between an axially-symmetric heat source and two symmetrically situated cold sources to the north and to the south. The convective circulation is modified by the earth's rotation but remains symmetric if the effects of the symmetric distributions of land and sea and the resulting monsoon systems are disregarded. It is obvious that in each theory based on these starting points such phenomena as the long waves and their products in the form of cut-off cyclonic and anticyclonic cells must be considered as disturbances, whose main task at most can be to consume the kinetic energy which constantly is created through the primary symmetric convective circulation.

H. JEFFREYS indicated in the 1920's that every attempt to construct symmetric models of the general circulation must lead to fundamental theoretical difficulties. In modern terminology the objections may be summarized in the following way: The earth's rotation around the vertical, which in a striking way is demonstrated by the slow turning of the plane of the Foucault pendulum, exerts a strong influence on the horizontal streams of the atmosphere which tend to be deflected in opposite direction relative to the earth's own rotation. Thus, every newly formed air current in the northern hemisphere is deflected a little to the right. This deflection causes in turn a piling up of air, i.e. leading to high air pressure on the right side of the stream and to low air pressure on the left side until the resulting pressure gradient across the current prevents further deflection. This adjustment of the pressure distribution to the state of motion is a fundamental property of the atmosphere and leads to the fact that the streamlines of the air by the large follow the lines of equal pressure ing that similar laboratories have been established at a number of other institutions. Among other things, Fultz studied the relative motion of a thin rotating fluid with a free surface bounded by concentric walls, the outer heated and the inner cooled. As long as the velocity of rotation is low and the temperature difference between

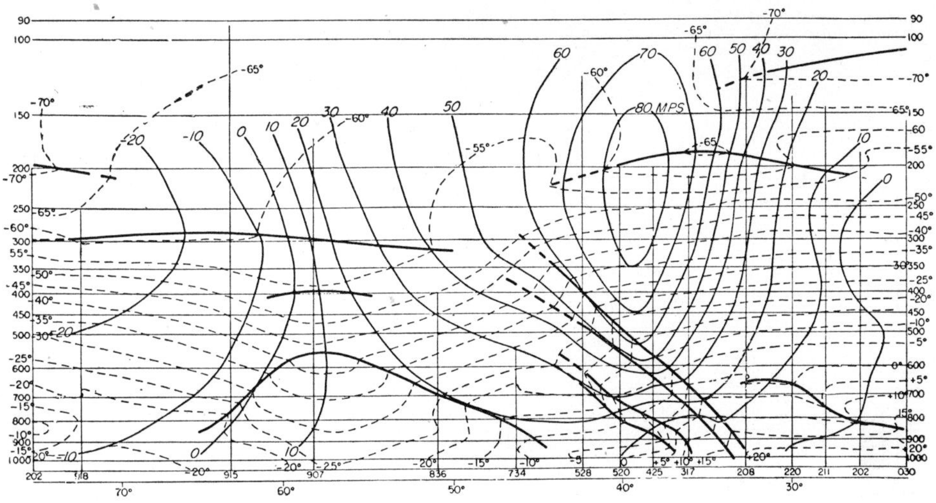

Fig. 7. Vertical section through the atmosphere along the meridian 90° W. The dashed lines show the temperature distribution and the solid lines indicate the speed in metres per second of the wind component perpendicular to the section. In the picture two frontal zones are indicated by two sloping pairs of solid heavy lines. A concentrated speed maximum of more than 80 m.s^{-1} is situated at the 200-mb level, approximately at the latitude where the main front cuts the 500-mb level (from a paper by E. PALMÉN).

(isobars). It is now easy to see that a symmetric convection cell in the northern hemisphere with southerly motion at the earth's surface and northerly motion in higher levels must be accompanied by the air pressure at the sea surface everywhere rising to the west while at higher levels it must rise to the east. Because of the necessarily cyclic continuity in the air pressure, such an axially-symmetric pressure adjustment obviously is not possible. The adjustment must therefore in one way or another lead to a breakdown of the symmetric convection regime and a transition to an asymmetric regime, in which northerly and southerly air streams exist side by side at the same level.

What has been said above may be illustrated in a very effective way with the aid of the model experiments which have been set up during the years after the war in order to study the dynamics of rotating fluids under the influence of heat- and cold sources. This research was first developed at the University of Chicago under direction of D. FULTZ but the results have been so stimulating the walls high, the resulting circulation in the fluid is symmetric and corresponds to Hadley's picture of the trade wind circulation. For a given value of the velocity of rotation, which in each case is determined by the temperature difference between the walls, the symmetric solution becomes unstable.

In the top surface layer horizontal, slowly progressive waves are now formed which in shape resemble the long waves in the free atmosphere. For a given temperature difference the wave number increases with the angular velocity of the system. Since the angular velocity of the earth's rotation around the vertical, which is the critical parameter for the circulation of the atmosphere, increases from infinitely low values in the equatorial regions to a maximum value at the poles, it is reasonable a priori that convective circulations of the Hadley type can be developed in the equatorial regions, while the circulation in higher latitudes necessarily must be characterized by asymmetry and of northerly and southerly currents side by side at the same level. In the asymmetric type of circulation the "disturbances", i.e. the horizontal long waves — and their forms of degeneration, the closed cyclonic and anticyclonic cells—play quite a different role than the one which they must be allotted, if one starts from the symmetric Hadley circulation as the primary mentum in the zones where the strongest west-winds occur.

This complicated interaction with respect to energy and momentum between the observed disturbances of the atmosphere and the zonal motion has in recent years been clarified through

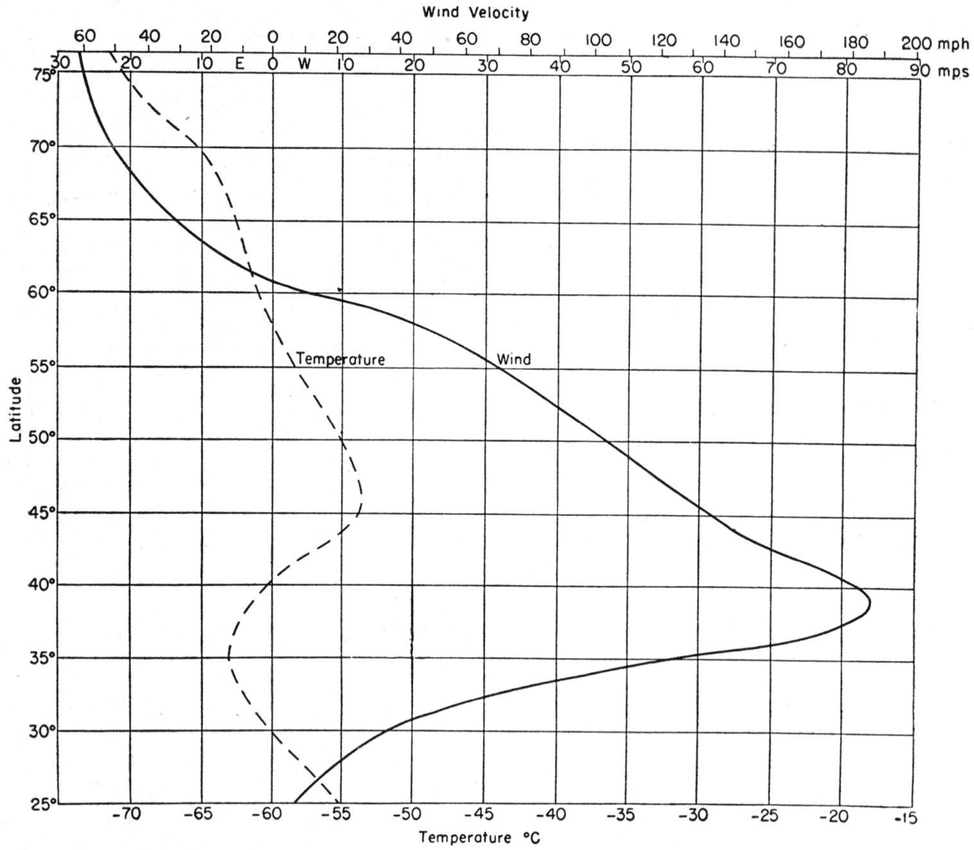

Fig. 8. Distribution of zonal wind velocity and of temperature with latitude at the 200-mb level for the same section and same day as in preceeding figure. The picture shows a concentrated jet stream with a maximum wind speed of 85 m.s^{-1} at 39° N (from a paper by E. PALMÉN).

phenomenon. As a matter of fact it is found in the asymmetric case that the cold and warm air masses, which side by side build up the big disturbances, represent sources of potential energy. When this energy is released through sinking of the cold air, at least part of the available energy is used to build up and maintain the zonal west-wind current. It is also found that because of their asymmetric character the disturbances are able to transport angular momentum with respect to the earth's axis (west-east momentum) in north-south direction. The transport varies with latitude and leads to an accumulation of west-east mo- two big "book-keeping" studies of the general circulation at the Massachusetts Institute of Technology under the direction of V. STARR and at the University of California under the direction of J. BJERKNES. With the aid of the large amounts of aerological material now available, these two groups have, for the northern hemisphere, statistically investigated the balance of both angular momentum and energy and especially the relative importance of the direct Hadley circulation and of the quasi-horizontal, asymmetric disturbances for the maintenance of the zonal west-winds in middle latitudes.

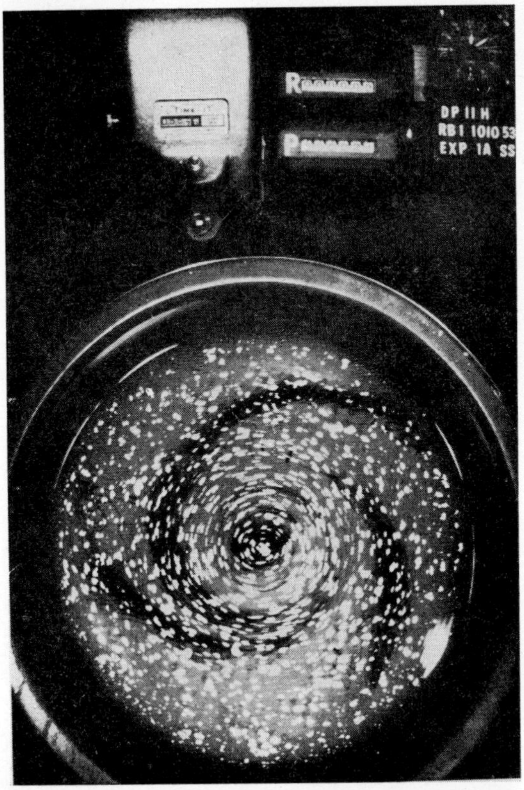

Fig. 9. The water in this rotating dishpan is heated from below at the rim of the pan and cooled through evaporation at the free surface. The temperature difference between the center and the rim thus obtained in this particular experiment is great; the pan rotates slowly counterclockwise. The result is a symmetric circulation with counterclockwise spiral shaped inflow at the free surface, and clockwise spiral shaped outflow along the bottom (picture by D. FULTZ, University of Chicago).

Fig. 10. In this experiment the water is heated from below at the rim of the rotating pan, and is cooled by means of a coolant at the center. The temperature contrast between the outer and inner side is in this case fairly small, while the rotation velocity (counterclockwise) is great. A symmetric circulation between the periphery and the center is no longer possible; a system of almost stationary horizontal waves forms which resemble in many particulars the long waves in the atmosphere (picture by D. FULTZ, University of Chicago).

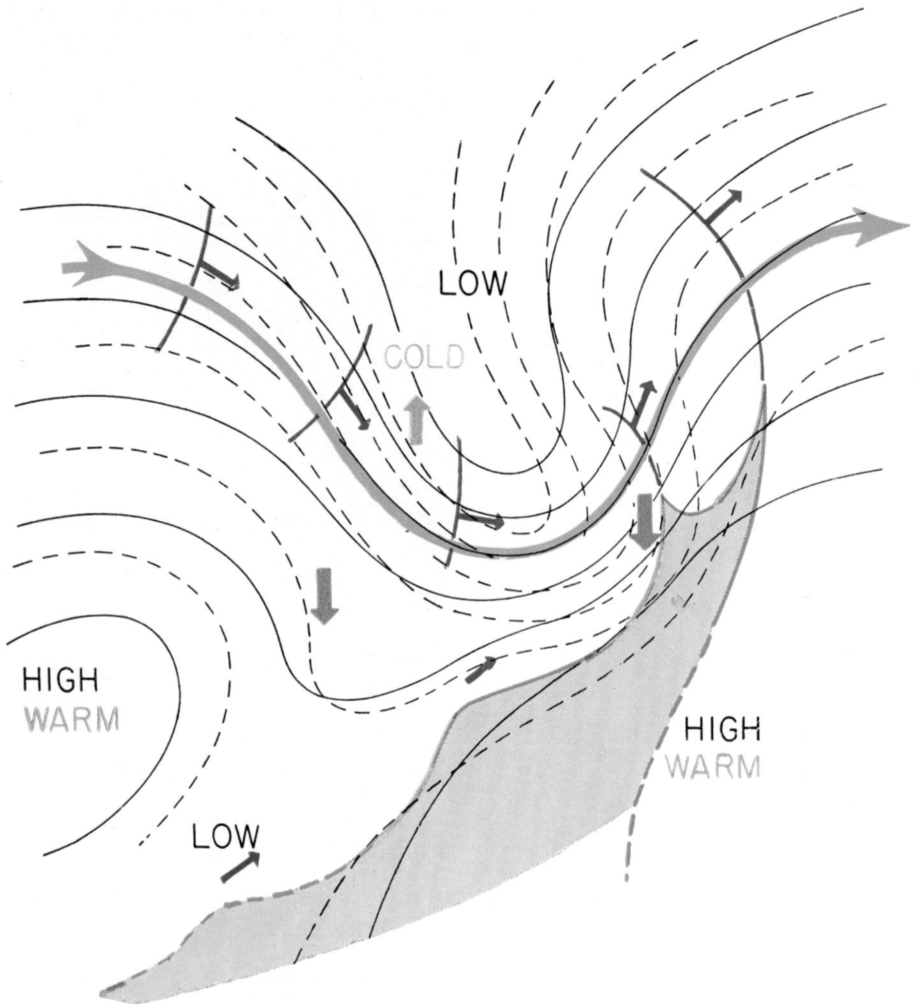

Fig. 11. Schematic representation of the relationship between the flow pattern in the middle of the troposphere and at the ground, as deduced from data for North America. The picture shows a long wave at the 500-mb level, represented by means of solid black lines which indicate the height above sea level of this surface. The temperature distribution at the 500-mb level is indicated by the dashed black isotherms. A depression of the 500-mb surface (i.e. low pressure in a fixed level) and low temperatures go together. In this case the center of the wave can be assumed to be situated in the Mississippi valley. The strongest wind at the 500-mb surface blows along the green band. This strong current is often characterized by weak disturbances which move very rapidly eastwards and is in some degree reflected in the wind and pressure distribution at the ground. These disturbances are indicated by purple lines and arrows in the direction of the motion. A front (blue and red line) is observed further south at the ground which separates the cold air in the north and north west and the warm air in the south (red). Along the surface front a series of polar front waves move northeastwards, where they are retarded and occluded when the warm air is lifted from the ground. The vertical motion in the 500-mb surface is indicated by blue and red arrows.

It must be emphasized that the statistical investigations referred to above leave a number of fundamental questions unanswered, among others the problem of why the atmospheric circulation tends to swing between a predominantly zonal ("high index") and a predominantly meridional ("low index") type of motion ("index cycle"), climatologically so different from each other: the meridional type of motion is characterized by strong positive and negative temperature anomalies side by side in the same latitude, while the zonal type is associated with a considerably weaker but zonally distributed temperature anomalies of which the most important may be the temperature deficit in high latitudes. It is known that certain winters are mainly characterized by zonal and other mainly by meridional circulation types. H. C. WILLETT even goes so far as to describe the post-glacial climatic variations as a consequence of the first and sometimes the second type of circulation dominating during a long sequence of years. It is therefore of fundamental importance to try to clarify the role which these oscillations between zonal and meridional types of motion ("index cycle") play in the dynamics of the atmosphere, and still further to investigate to what extent the variations in the index cycle, i.e. variations in its amplitude and frequency, can be explained without resorting to extra-terrestical factors, for example through coupling between the atmospheric circulation and the above-mentioned, probably variable, slow thermohaline cycle in the ocean.

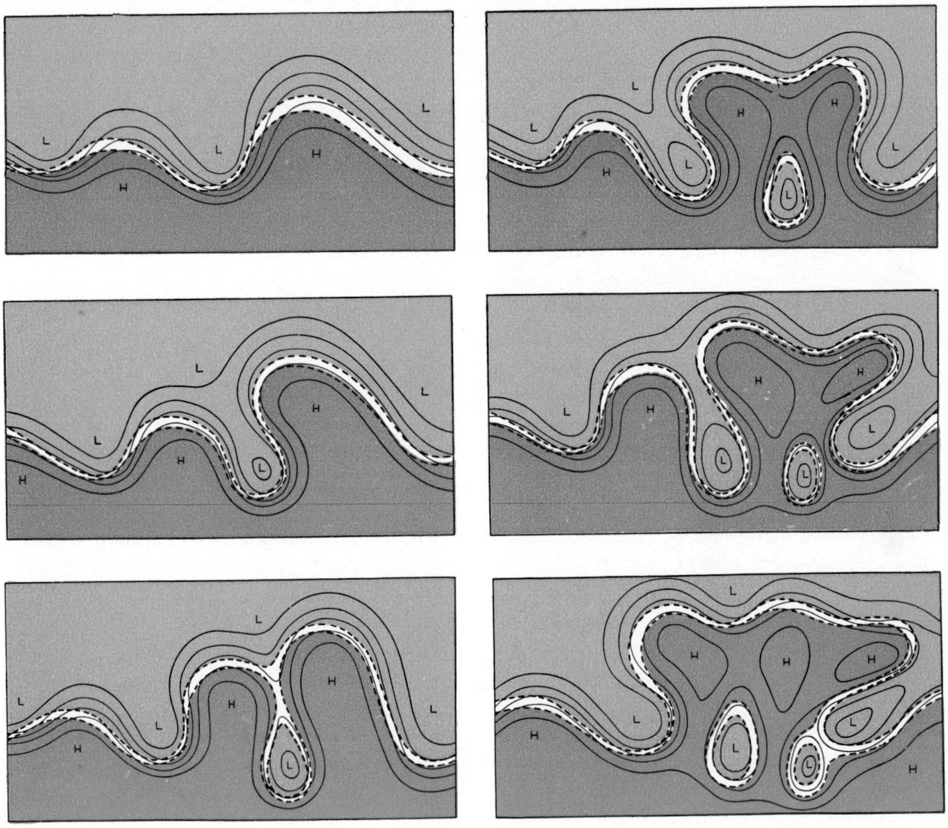

Fig. 12. Schematic representation of the consecutive stages of the break-down of a zonal flow in the 500-mb surface; the development takes place during a period of eight to ten days and the chart picture can be assumed to extend from the Mississippi Valley in the west to the Ural Mountains in the east. The flow in the 500-mb surface is indicated by the thin black contour lines, and the temperature distribution by the colours. The strongest current coincides with the white band, in which the temperature contrast between the warm air in the south (red) and the cold air in the north (blue) is concentrated. The long waves move eastwards towards Europe where the westwind is considerably weaker. In this weaker flow the waves retard, and at the same time their horizontal amplitude grows approximately in the same way as surface waves do on their way towards shallow water. (From a paper by BERGGREN, BOLIN and ROSSBY.)

NORMAN PHILLIPS recently has made an attempt to approximate the index cycle by means of a theoretical-numerical investigation of the circulation in a hypothetical atmosphere bounded to the north and to the south by rigid walls, heated in the south and cooled in the north through a net supply of heat which is independent of time but varies linearly with latitude. The basic equations are nonlinear and it was therefore necessary to perform all computations with a high-speed electronic computer of large capacity. In spite of this the problem required a machine time of about thirty hours. In the beginning of the computations the atmosphere is assumed to be at rest relative to the earth's surface. After a time interval which in nature should correspond to 130 days, the system was characterized by a zonal flow with a fairly concentrated west-wind belt in the upper parts of the troposphere. At that instant Phillips puts random disturbances into the system in which all scales are represented and the numerical computations are continued. Then it appears that disturbances of a certain scale begin to dominate and finally waves are developed which in a striking way resemble the long waves of the atmosphere with respect to dimensions, structure and further development. When it has been possible to perform computations of this type for a whole index cycle, including the cut-off processes and the development of a new zonal current, the road may be open for numerical forecasts of the general state of motion of the real atmosphere for one or perhaps two weeks. However, it should be emphasized that such forecasts necessarily must be of a very general character and can hardly give more than very general statements concerning weather and wind.

The dynamics of the long waves and the index cycle do not stand alone as insufficiently understood phenomena. The same is true for the concepts of atmospheric fronts and frontal waves with which the Norwegian meteorological school started its victorious progress. The discovery of the fronts gave the practical working meteorologists a diagnostic tool of extremely high efficiency when the object was to follow individual air masses and especially the tracks of individual precipitation areas. With a starting point from the meteorological observations at the earth's surface, one was led to consider the fronts as borders between air masses of different temperature in relative motion to each other; a well-developed west-east surface front thus usually was represented as the border between a westerly warm air stream to the south and a cooler air stream with easterly or weaker westerly motion to the north. This picture was assumed to be valid at higher levels with the cooler air wedge-shaped pushed in below the warmer and lighter air mass. T. BERGERON developed early an attractive theory for the origin of fronts (frontogenesis) as a final result of certain horizontal fields of motion (fields of deformation) by which the isotherms in certain areas must be packed together, but this theory did not explain why the surface fronts are characterized not only by a temperature but also by a wind discontinuity. A dynamic theory for frontogenesis was never formulated by the Norwegian school.

The problem of frontogenesis has lately again come under study owing to the extension of the network of meteorological observations in the vertical direction with the aid of radiosonde and radar wind soundings. The higher one goes in the troposphere, the more one finds that the frontal zones, and their strong concentration of the horizontal temperature gradient, coincide with the areas with the strongest winds, i.e. the fronts are no longer to be considered as borders between air masses in differential motion. The motion is instead concentrated in or in the vicinity of the frontal zone itself. The picture thus obtained from the new aerological material leads to a more satisfactory agreement between our concepts of the structure of the free air streams and the quasi-permanent sea currents. Both the Gulf stream and the Kuroshio stream may thus be considered as concentrated streams, in which the strong motion coincides with a zone of strong contrast between the warm water masses over the open sea and the cooler water masses above the continental shelf.

It can be demonstrated without too much difficulty that the horizontal wind velocity (in the sea the current velocity) as a result of the earth's rotation must increase with height proportionally to the horizontal temperature gradient across the direction of the flow from the right to the left. This elementary rule does not, however, explain the tendency of the temperature field to bring together the contrasts between high and low latitudes to a few narrow zones and thereby giving rise to fronts and the extremely concentrated jet streams in the upper troposphere. There can hardly be any doubt that the earth's rotation in combination with the vertical stability of the air must be responsible for the fact that the free atmosphere at a certain distance from the earth's surface prefers to flow in such narrow bands rather than in broad rivers, but a satisfactory theory for this fundamental phenomenon is still missing.

The theoretical studies of frontal waves (polar-front cyclones) are in a similar state. The surface maps show that in an early stage they rapidly move along the frontal zone, usually from southwest to northeast, and that their horizontal amplitudes at the same time grow rapidly. The increase of the amplitude, however, is accompanied by a strong retardation in the phase velocity of the waves. This finally leads to a state, where two successive tongues of cooler air reach each other. The wave thereby loses its character of a wave and is transformed to a quasi-stationary vortex, which gradually rolls up the front. Accordingly, the theoreticians of the Norwegian school considered the frontal wave as an unstable surface wave, generated in the sloping boundary surface between two media with different motion and density. During the '20s and '30s much labour was devoted to creating a satisfactory theory for such surface waves, but it can hardly be said that the results correspond to these efforts. It is true that the surface fronts have served as the diagnostic tool whereby it has been possible effectively to demonstrate the existence of frontal waves, but this is far from saying that the surface front is the dynamically decisive factor in the generation of these waves. At great heights above a frontal zone along which rapid frontal waves move, a well-developed jet stream usually is found. Analyses of observations from the free atmosphere in this region show that the jet undergoes marked changes in structure with the passage of individual frontal waves below. It seems fairly unlikely that surface waves generated in the lower levels of the troposphere could influence the structure of the winds at the base of the stratosphere, especially because these surface waves often seem to come from the southwestern part of the frontal zone, where the frontal surface is almost horizontal and the available potential energy supply therefore is very limited. For these and other reasons it seems much more probable that the origin of the frontal waves is to be found in some kind of progressive transversal vibrations in the jet which later show up at the surface through the resulting displacements of the surface front and associated vertical motions.

Weather forecasts

Considering our limited knowledge of the planetary and secondary circulation systems of the atmosphere, it is rather obvious that very much —maybe the most—still remains to be done concerning the development of methods for circulation and weather forecasts based on physical principles. In the beginning of this century V. Bjerknes defined the main problem in theoretical meteorology the computation of the state and motion of the atmosphere at a given instant from observations of the corresponding state and motion at a previous time. Bjerknes was possibly the last great representative of the classical school in theoretical physics, which flourished in the nineteenth century, and which was governed by almost unlimited belief in the equations of mechanics and their immediate application to problems in nature. Later students of this school have too often depended upon a rather sterile manipulation of the linearized partial differential equations, which became their chief tool. Bjerknes, on the other hand, had exceptional ability to think simply, to see the basic problem and to create enthusiasm around himself. His work became of extraordinary importance, partly because his strong belief in the formulation of the problem gave theoretical studies in the following decades a well defined goal, and partly because he, as preparation to a systematic attack on the forecast problem, succeeded in carrying through an important rationalization of the methods by which we describe the three dimensional distribution of the scalar and vector quantities, which together determine the physical state of the atmosphere.

The basic hydrodynamic and thermodynamic equations can all be written in such a form that the left side represents the instantaneous change in time at an arbitrary fixed point of one of the atmospheric variables (for example, the momentary change in time of the atmospheric pressure at a given point, or the instantaneous increase of the force of the west-wind component at the 5,000 m level over a certain place) while the right side consists of a rather complicated, nonlinear combination of the different variables of state for the same point, and their space derivatives in horizontal and vertical directions. The right sides of the equations consist, therefore, of quantities which in principle can be measured without the change of the system in time. With certain assumptions it is possible to transform these differential equations to difference equations. By doing this we replace the time and splace derivatives with differences of finite magnitude (for example, 1 hour for the time increment, 300 km for the horizontal space differences and 1 km for the vertical increments). We shall later return to a discussion of the principles on which the choice of these units is based. The meteorological problem is then given, and consists of describing the change in time of the state of the atmosphere by the values of the fundamental parameters, hour after hour in the three dimensional network so defined.

It has already been pointed out that the right side of the atmospheric equations consists of measurable quantities, and it is therefore possible, in principle, to compute the expected changes in the succeeding hour from the momentary distribution in the network. By adding these changes to the original values one gets a new distribution in the net and the procedure can now be repeated until one gets a 12- or 24-hour prognosis. This is in fact the method now used in the routine numerical weather prediction services.

A heroic and isolated effort to perform a numerical integration of the atmospheric equations along the lines indicated above was attempted in 1922 by L. F. Richardson. In a great work of continuing value he made a profound analysis of the physical processes which the atmospheric equation must express and then prepared, through very laborious hand computations, a 12-hour prognosis for the British Isles. The agreement between the observed and computed state was very unsatisfactory. According to Richardson this depended upon the fact that the prognostic equations are of such a type that the computed changes always appear as small differences between terms of equal magnitude; consequently it should be necessary to know the meteorological initial values with an accuracy not available at this time, and which cannot be obtained, or aimed at, even now. The fact that 12- and 24-hour prognoses of a conventional type are regularly prepared in weather centrals all over the world and that these, by and large, give satisfactory results means that the changes in the atmospheric circulation possibly do not depend to a great extent upon the fact that, for example, the wind velocity is given with an accuracy of 0.1 m sec^{-1}. The reasons for the failure of Richardson's prognosis must therefore be more fundamental.

Real progress in the problem of numerical prediction did not come until after the last World War and has now resulted in the preparation of numerical forecasts as a daily routine in Washington and on a limited scale also in Stockholm; similar centrals for numerical predictions probably will be started in the near future in Dunstable (the headquarter of the British weather service), in Frankfurt, Oslo and Tokyo. It is of interest to investigate, a little more closely, the historical background for the fast development in this field in recent years.

The weather maps supply the material on which theoretical meteorologists finally must base their considerations. As late as the 1930's, the national weather services used synoptic surface maps of a rather limited geographical extent. In Scandinavia these maps in general covered Europe and part of the neighbouring Atlantic Ocean. A certain telegraphic exchange of observations between North America and Europe took place, and certain weather services, in particular the German one, paid some attention to the daily maps for the northern hemisphere. However in general the transatlantic observational material played only a rather insignificant role in the daily European weather service, among other things for the practical reason that the scarcity and poor quality of the ship observations from the Atlantic made it almost impossible to connect the detailed pattern on the maps in Europe with the corresponding patterns in North America. Daily observations from the upper atmosphere, where the atmospheric flow patterns have a somewhat simpler and more large-scale character, were missing almost entirely. Attention was therefore almost exclusively concentrated on the small-scale waves on the polar front and their motion.

The German meteorologists were an exception in this respect as shown by the fact that they introduced, very early, the concept of "Grosswetterlage". This term indicates that the frontal zones, to which the individual frontal waves are bound, do not always have the same position, but are displaced slowly and change orientation and intensity in connection with the displacements of the quasi-permanent centers of action of a mixed planetary and monsoonal character (for example the Azores high, the Islandic low). The concept "Grosswetterlage" means naturally an understanding of the fact that horizontal circulation system of quite different dimensions can exist at the same time in the atmosphere, the smaller superimposed on the larger and partly steered in the direction of their movement. But the German ideas were never put on a rational theoretical foundation and were therefore rather unimportant for the coming development.

Apart from this exception, it is very striking that articles and textbooks in the years between the two world wars hardly touch the question of the scale of atmospheric phenomena. Why do the travelling cyclones at the surface of the earth have radii of the order of magnitude 10^3 km and not 10^2 or 10^4 km? Questions of this type were never brought forward. This is perhaps easier to understand if one remembers that the dense network of surface stations, organized through the initiative of V. Bjerknes at the end of the First World War, was based on the fundamental assumption that detailed observations from a limited region could replace data from a more extended, but sparser net.

In the later part of the 1930's a research project was organized at the Massachusetts Institute of Technology, the main purpose of which was to develop methods, if possible, for the extension of the weather forecasts in time from one or two days, to five days or a week.

The scientists responsible for this project immediately recognized that since an individual frontal wave can develop within a week, move several thousand kilometers, and finally dissipate slowly as a dying cyclonic vortex, it was rather hopeless to try to extend the period of validity for conventional forecast methods without at the same time radically changing their character. Starting from thoughts of this kind, which guided the Germans to introduce the concept "Grosswetterlage", but otherwise independently, they therefore decided to eliminate the transient and small-scale phenomena on the maps from more slowly moving large scale circulation systems. This was achieved by forming progressive five-day time averages of five consecutive daily synoptic surface maps. In this way the pattern obtained on the map showed only the larger phenomena and their slow changes and displacements. These larger systems still had the character of closed cyclonic and anticyclonic systems, but it was already evident at this point that an extrapolation of the pressure field to the 5-km level in the middle troposphere most often showed a system of slow progressive waves superimposed on a westerly current in middle latitudes.

The horizontal flow systems found in this way have linear dimensions of the order of 5,000 km. The vertical extension of the troposphere and the lower part of the stratosphere, which seems to be closely coupled in a dynamic sense with the troposphere, is around 20 km or 1/250 of the horizontal scale. It was therefore rather natural to try to formulate a preliminary theory for the motion of these large systems as if they represented inertial motions in a shallow, two-dimensional layer covering the surface of the earth. The dynamics for the inertial motions in a two-dimensional layer of this kind can be condensed to a single equation (the vorticity theorem), which expresses the fact that individual fluid elements conserve their absolute vorticity around the vertical. This absolute vorticity consists of the vorticity of the fluid element relative to the earth and the vertical component of the vorticity of the earth itself. The latter has a maximum at the pole and is zero at the equator. The fact that the absolute vorticity is conserved during the motion means therefore that *a fluid element which moves to the south experiences an increase in vorticity relative to the earth and vice versa.* The distribution of vorticity can be determined from a given velocity field and consequently the distribution at a later time (for example one hour) can be computed with the aid of the vorticity theorem discussed above. The distribution of vorticity obtained in this way determines in turn the new wind field, and from this one can compute the distribution of vorticity in the following time interval. Apart from certain difficulties at the boundaries of the region considered, a two dimensional fluid in inertial motion represents a dynamically closed system, the future motion of which in principle can be computed from a single equation, the vorticity theorem. This equation is linear with respect to the time derivative but non-linear with respect to the horizontal derivatives of the velocity field. This theorem is still the basis for the numerical forecasts prepared routinely.

At this time theoretical meteorology was still governed by intensive experiments to find solutions to linearized atmospheric differential equations of such character that they could be used to describe the phase, speed, structure, and amplitude changes of frontal waves. In these investigations the complete three-dimensional character of the atmospheric flow pattern was usually stressed. After Richardson's experiment in 1922 little thought was given to the idea of integrating the general atmospheric equations of motion through numerical hand computations. Even the brutally simplified, purely two dimensional picture of the large-scale atmospheric motions developed by the group working at the Massachusetts Institute of Technology leads to an equation requiring extremely extensive numerical computations if a stepwise integration from an arbitrary initial situation is tried. It was therefore necessary to work with still simpler models which one could believe to have some similarity to the observed smoothed motions in the atmosphere. A theory for certain simple, transverse horizontal waves superimposed on a zonal current, constant in time and space, was developed. Systematic experiments were performed in order to apply this theoretical model to the atmosphere. Equations thus derived for the phase velocity of the long atmospheric waves, and especially for the dependence of this velocity on the force of the zonal wind and the wave length, proved to be of certain practical use in the study of the motions as observed on the upper-level maps of limited geographic extent, which by now, in the beginning of the 1940's, were possible to construct. The observed motion on the upper-level maps deviated so often from the simple wave type, however, that one was forced to look for other very approximative methods for the integration of the vorticity equation from arbitrary initial values, but these received very limited application and will not be further discussed here.

In the real atmosphere the stationary long waves are above all formed in the lee of the large mountain ranges (the Himalayas and the Rocky Mountains), and over the western part of the oceans as a result of the very violent thermal contrasts to which the zonal current is exposed when passing from the continent to the ocean. The dimensions of these stationary waves are determined by the intensity and the width of the zonal current and by the latitude. When the wind decreases or increases the forced waves are displaced to the west or to the east. It is above all important that the theory based upon the vorticity theorem leads to a specific expression for the linear dimensions of the large-scale horizontal flow pattern in which the frontal zones and the frontal waves are embedded. For the first time one began to realize how different the atmospheric flow patterns on different scales are. The energy spectrum of the atmospheric motions caught the interest of the meteorologists.

This extension of the perspective of the meteorologists would not by itself have led to general numerical forecasting methods, but the occurrence at the same time of the development of fast electronic computers caused outstanding mathematicians and hydrodynamicists to consider seriously the possibilities of numerical integration of the general hydrodynamic equations of motion.

A small group of theoreticians with a mathematical and hydrodynamical meteorological education was collected in the late 1940's at the Institute for Advanced Study in Princeton. This group was assembled by the late mathematician, J. von Neumann, for a serious attack on the meteorological integration problem. First among these collaborators must be mentioned J. Charney and his younger colleague, N. Phillips, mentioned earlier in this article. After some years of orientation it was obvious that the preliminary numerical integration experiments had to be restricted to the large atmospheric flow patterns, which to a first approximation possibly could be treated as if the atmosphere was a two-dimensional fluid in inertial motion. Starting from this assumption the first four numerical 24-hour predictions were computed and published in 1950. It is perhaps worth while mentioning that every prediction meant nearly ten million elementary numerical operations and required a computation time of about 24 hours. Corresponding computations for a region of the same size today require only a few minutes.

If one wants to approximate the atmosphere by a two-dimensional fluid layer, it is obvious that one must make a dictionary, so to speak, for translating the initial situation in the real three dimensional atmosphere to a corresponding situation in the hypothetical two dimensional model and for translating the final prediction to an expression for the state of the real atmosphere after 24 hours. The MIT-group had intuitively supposed that the motions at the 500-mb level, which by and large divide the atmosphere horizontally into two layers of equal mass, could be supposed to behave as if they represent the motions in a two-dimensional fluid layer. Charney now succeeded in giving a rational explanation for this choice of the 500-mb level.

Numerical predictions, which can be computed with the aid of the vorticity equation for an "equivalent" two-dimensional atmosphere, are in general somewhat more reliable than the conventional prognoses, especially in the northwestern part of Europe, where sharp thermal contrasts and strong orographic perturbations of the horizontal motion of the atmosphere do not play a dominant role. In Sweden, the computations are carried out for 24, 48 and 72 hours, but at this latter time the errors become in general so great that the predictions often loose practical meaning. The numerical predictions offer a further advantage which should not be forgotten. Knowledge and experience, formulated in a rational way, can once and for all be incorporated in the computational program, while a meteorologist working in a traditional way in his predictions must constantly keep old accepted methods in mind as he at the same time must be aware of new methods and results. This later difficulty is especially noticeable in educating new meteorologists in the conventional predicition techniques.

The two-dimensional (in meteorological terminology, "barotropic") forecasts do not give the weather directly but only the large-scale perturbations on the 500-mb surface, which, however, to a large extent govern the motion of the active weather systems and also, but to a less extent, their development. The changes between "nice" weather and precipitation depend upon the vertical motion of the air; sinking motion leads by and large to a disappearance of the clouds, rising motion to formation of clouds and precipitation. The fact that the two-dimensional model is able to describe the very large scale flow systems rather well, means that the vertical motions connected with these systems are generally small. Usually the rule is valid that the vertical motion in the atmosphere becomes greater, the smaller the horizontal extension of the synoptic system is; one finds in fact the very strongest vertical velocities in thunderstorms, where vertical and horizontal dimensions are approximately the same. The long waves and closed cells which are treated by the barotropic forecasts may therefore be looked upon as the "infrared", degenerated and practically speaking purely two-dimensional part of the whole rich spectrum of atmospheric motions.

Even these relatively simple barotropic systems offer, however, great problems for the theory of numerical prediction, partly of a surmountable technical nature, but also of a more fundamental nature. When barotropic predictions are made for a region of limited geographical extent, the solution to the theoretical prediction problem is not completely given by the vorticity equation itself. One needs, furthermore, certain information concerning the state of motion at all points on the closed line which encloses the region considered, and then in principle information must be available during the entire time over which the prediction is computed. Because in general the wind has a component across the artificially drawn boundary line, new air masses with varying vorticity are constantly imported and exported, and because these changes of the vorticity distribution in the forecasting region influence the velocity distribution, one has to know the vorticity transport across the boundaries of the region, i.e. one has to know the vorticity and the normal component of the wind at all points on the boundary during the entire prediction interval. This information is, however, not available (for in that case the prediction problem would already be solved), and one must therefore make certain plausible assumptions concerning the boundary conditions (for example, the normal component of the wind and vorticity transport across the boundaries remain unchanged during the prediction interval). The errors which are introduced in the system through an arbitrary assumption of this kind increase in time inwards over greater and greater areas, and it is therefore necessary to start the computations with data from a very much larger region than the one for which one wishes a reliable prediction. The problem could be solved perhaps by extending the computations to the greater part of the northern hemisphere with the boundaries located in the inactive subtropical highs. But here one meets with other difficulties, first of all deficiencies in the observational network, poor telecommunications from remote regions and finally limitations in the capacity and speed of the electronic computers available to meteorologists.

A relatively small number of the radiosonde stations, which give us our initial material for the numerical predictions, measure wind speed and wind direction. Methods of prognoses are therefore based upon the assumption that the wind field and the quantities derived therefrom, for example the vertical component of the relative vorticity, in general can be computed with sufficient accuracy from the pressure field, assuming the validity of the previously discussed balance between the horizontal pressure gradient, and the deviating force arising from the rotation of the earth. In such a balanced state the wind blows along the lines of equal pressure in the horizontal plane (the isobars) and its force is proportional to the magnitude of the horizontal pressure gradient ("geostrophic wind"). The assumption made above means that the pressure field everywhere and at all times immediately and completely adjusts to the wind field in such a way that the properties of the latter can be computed with sufficient accuracy from the pressure field. An exact theoretical analysis shows that the adjustment in the purely two dimensional case certainly is immediate but deviates in a characteristic way somewhat from the "geostrophic" adjustment defined above, and if one tries to consider these deviations, certain new difficulties

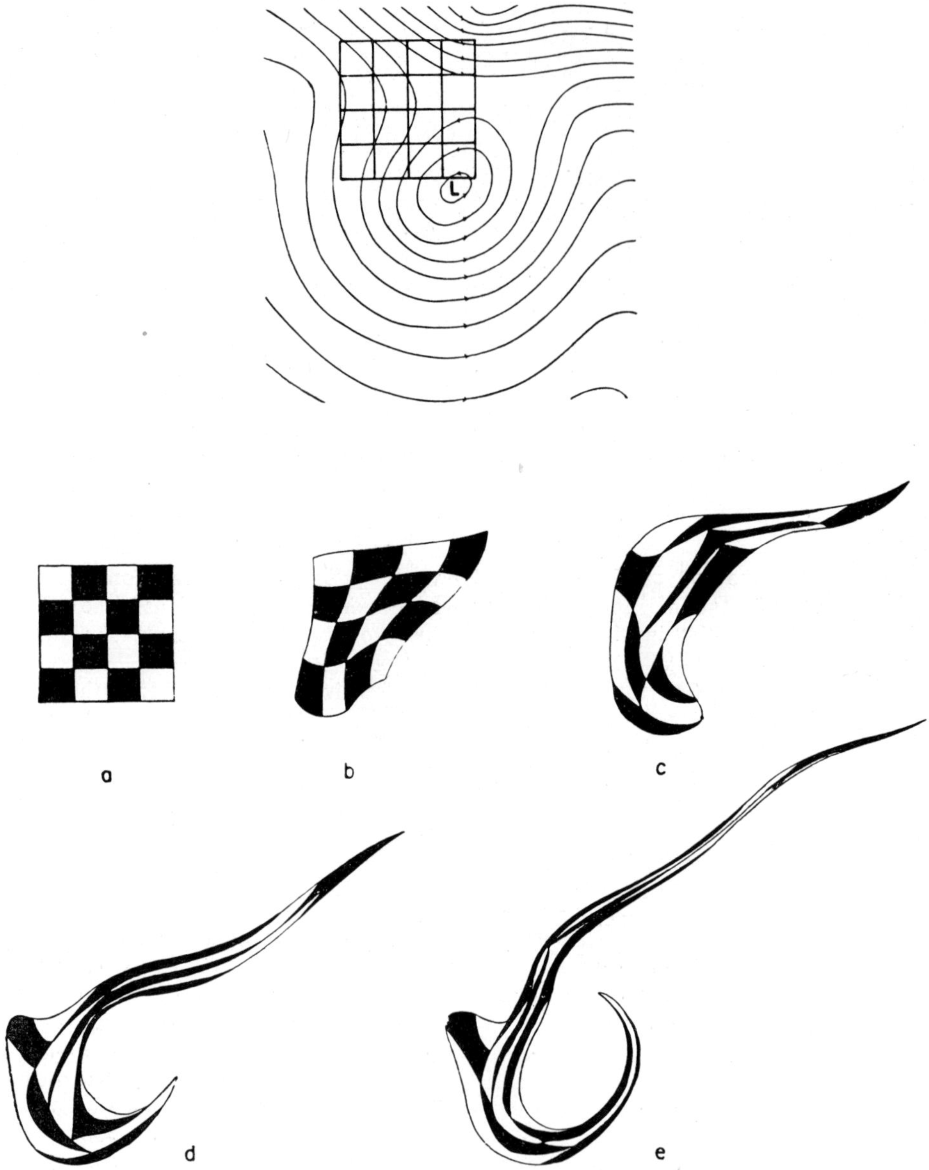

Fig. 13. In the upper part of this figure a square grid is superimposed on a 500-mb map. The following pictures show the progressive deformation of the square grid during four consecutive 12-hour intervals, computed under the assumption that the material points, which originally coincided with the corner points in the squares, follow the motion in the 500-mb surface. If one systematically describes the state of the atmosphere by means of a fixed net, which with regard to grid size, coincides with the original grid, certain details in the state between the grid points evidently must disappear as time passes. The figure indicates also one of the reasons that the aerosols released in a limited region, sooner or later tend to stretch into narrow bands (from a paper by P. WELANDER).

arise with respect to the boundary conditions. The question about the "geostrophic" adjustment is, however, far more important in connection with the three dimensional models of atmospheric motions which are being developed now for possible use in the numerical prediction services, but it would carry us too far to enter into this problem here.

For the determination of the vorticity changes at a given point, the wind and the gradient of vorticity computed with the aid of values at the surrounding grid points are used. It is obvious that a time derivative obtained in this way is not representative for a time period longer than it takes the air to travel from the nearest grid points to the grid point in question. This means that the ratio between grid size and time unit must never be smaller than the maximum wind velocities which we experience in the atmosphere.

The grid size in the network depends upon several factors of practical and theoretical nature. The initial distribution of the meteorological parameters in the net must be obtained from some kind of interpolation procedure between the aerological stations, and it is not economical to introduce a finer grid than necessary for extracting the information needed from the original observations. The finer the grid size one introduces, and the more details one tries to describe, the greater the risk is that the two-dimensional theory, on which the computations are based, becomes insufficient and must be replaced by a three-dimensional prognostic theory. As yet a reliable theory of this kind does not exist. In this case the time steps must further be decreased, and this may mean that the capacity of the computer is surpassed and that the time necessary for the computations becomes too long. It is such considerations which have led to the choice of 300 km and 1 hour as suitable units in space and time.

If one assumes purely two-dimensional motion and then from a series of consecutive 500-mb maps computes the individual displacements of air particles, which originally coincide with the corner points in a square of the grid, one finds that the circumference of the elementary region defined in this way is already very much deformed in 12 hours and usually stretched to a narrow band which falls between the points in the fixed grid. From this it follows that detailed pictures of the same order of magnitude as the grid size very soon are lost, and that the methods therefore by and large are limited to giving information and predictions about systems of such large dimensions that they extend from the beginning over a great number of grid intervals.

It is usually assumed that turbulent friction in the atmosphere will destroy the available kinetic energy in a few days. (The estimates vary, but generally a week is assumed to be more than enough for this purpose.) In spite of this strong dissipation, one often observes in the 500-mb surface some nearly stationary systems—for example closed cyclonic and anticyclonic cells, which can be followed or observed for several weeks. In order to understand this persistence completely, one must assume that such systems give rise to some kind of transversal circulations or vertical motions through which a part of the potential energy can be released to cover frictional losses. In such a case the prediction theory now in use gives correct results only by neglecting the dissipation as well as the addition of energy.

It has already been pointed out that the synoptic systems, which are directly responsible for the changes in weather from day to day, are of a considerably smaller scale than the long waves or cut-off cells which can be treated by means of the barotropic theory. In order to understand these smaller systems better it is necessary to pay attention to the vertical motion of the air. This has been attempted by dividing the atmosphere in a number of horizontal layers and applying a somewhat generalized vorticity theorem to each of these. The generalization means that if one considers the fact that in a region where the troposphere has rising currents, the lower layers are characterized, because of mass continuity, by convergent flow, and the upper layers by divergent flow. In regions where there is sinking motion the distribution of horizontal convergence and divergence is opposite. Divergence and convergence in turn influence the vorticity distribution in such a way that convergence increases the vorticity, divergence decreases it. By means of thermodynamic arguments and assuming geostrophic balance and hydrostatic equilibrium at all levels, it is finally possible to form a closed dynamic system. The resulting prediction theory has been tested for some time on a routine basis in Washington. Using this theory rather unexpected sudden cyclonic deepening has been successfully predicted at the surface of the earth, but in certain other cases the results of the theory have been rather misleading. It is probable that the defects so far lie in our understanding of the dynamics of these smaller systems. Every numerical theory must for practical reasons and in order not to include a number of phenomena which are meteorologically uninteresting, make a selection of the terms in the hydrodynamic equations which should be included in the computations. Such a selection presupposes, however, previous and thorough knowledge of the structure and dynamics of the system. It is by no means certain that a complete general selection of the sort mentioned above can be made, in other words it is quite possible that the observed three-dimensional smaller systems in the atmosphere represent a whole series of very different phenomena from the dynamic view point. Comparisons of certain patterns at the base of the stratosphere and the characteristic systems in the lower layers of the troposphere, support this hypothesis. The modern aerological network in this respect has done very much to eliminate dogmatic and conventional thinking, which to a large extent dominated synoptic meteorology between the wars.

The progress in the elaboration of a rational theory for detailed wind and weather predictions of shorter duration (up to 24 hours) may be rather slow for the reasons mentioned above. To this the fact must be added that the now existing, three-dimensional net of observations over the northern hemisphere is still in large areas too sparse for describing smaller atmospheric systems, which in this connection are most important. In the United States efforts have been made to solve the practical prediction problem of the violent tornadoes which plague the Middle West. This has been done through the organization of a coördinated net of surface stations furnished with radar equipment having a range of several hundreds of kilometers. This is cutting the Gordian Knot instead of untying it. On the other hand it is quite probable that observations from this net will make a valuable contribution to our understanding of the morphology and dynamics of the tornadoes.

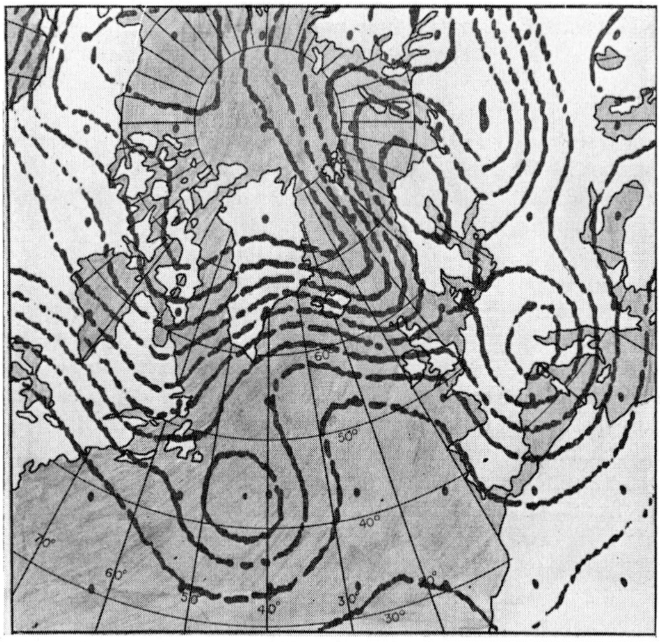

Fig. 14. The electronic computer BESK has been used to analyze the observations from the 500-mb surface at a given time, and the result has been projected in form of a conventional 500-mb map on the screen of a cathode ray tube, connected to BESK. The electronic computer may in the future take over the job of sorting and checking incoming observations, analyzing them and projecting the result of the analysis on such screens. In principle it would be possible to correct the analysis continuously by means of the latest observations to arrive and at the same time project on another screen a prognostic map for a later time (for example 24 hours). Such continuously corrected analyses and prognostic maps should lead without doubt to significant improvements in the quality of the weather predictions (from a paper by B. Döös and M. Eaton).

With respect to the part of the atmospheric spectrum which lies between the dimensions of a tornado and the large barotropic disturbances, there is at present no such short cut. It is, however, of interest to point out that recently at White Sands, New Mexico, using a rocket at a height of approximately 100 miles, a photograph was obtained mapping a well-defined cloud system, organized as a cyclonic vortex, the existence of which was unknown at the time the photograph was made. Shortly afterwards the system gave very violent local rains and floods. The example demonstrates the fact that we as meteorologists working with conventional tools are constantly hampered by the structure-dissolving, frog's-eye view, which is forced upon us. On the other hand photographs from great heights might help us to develop a bird's eye view. It is naturally still too early to say to what degree such photographs from rockets and satellites can be applied to routine operations. It is not unreasonable that a suitable combination of an extended radar network with photographs or other measurements taken from suitable platforms at great heights will be of great importance for solving the practical problem of issuing short range, detailed weather predictions.

Very great progress has been made lately in the problem of letting electronic computers take over the very laborious job of analyzing daily synoptic maps. The 500-mb maps, which form the basis for the numerical forecasts in Stockholm, are being analyzed by the electronic computer in such a way that the preceding day's 24-hour prediction is selected as the start for and the first approximation to the day's map. This approximation is then corrected by means of observations from the day in question. During the last winter in Stockholm conventionally analyzed maps have been introduced into the prediction scheme only once a week. In principle one can incorporate in the objective numerical analysis, all the rational empirical rules which the experienced synoptician uses in the map analysis. In Washington the teleprinter tapes which contain the meteorological observations are introduced directly into the electronic computer which sorts the data wanted, checks them for internal consistency, discards faulty observations, and then stores approved observations in the machine for final analysis. The development of a method for numerical analysis of the surface map with its much more detailed structure is of course an extremely laborious problem but not unsolvable.

Regarding the fundamental barotropic prognosis there is at present no principal reason why one could not combine the meteorological communication net (the teleprinter lines) with an electronic computer, and this in turn with two television screens in such a way that the incoming observations could be automatically sorted and analyzed in the machine, and the current maps so obtained shown on one television screen, while at the same time the other screen shows the probable situation 24 or 48 hours later.

Distribution of matter in the atmosphere

A. *Air trajectories*

It was already pointed out in the introduction to this article that the role of the atmosphere as a carrier and distributing agent for matter such as maritime salts, dust, and industrial pollutants, including radioactive debris, is likely to demand the attention of the meteorologists to an ever increasing degree. The fundamental dynamic problem connected with these questions is to determine the future path (trajectory) that will be followed by an air particle which, at a given moment, is situated at a given point. It may seem, at first, as if one would have solved this problem once the principles of numerical forecasting have been established. The solution could then be found simply by moving the air parcels hour after hour according to the instantaneous values of wind speed and direction provided by the numerical forecasting procedure. The general forecasting problem in three dimensions has, admittedly, not been solved so far, but the general character of the flow at the 500-mb level by now is reasonably well understood, and one could possibly utilize this to compute trajectories of particles that stay in the 500-mb surface and move within it with the speed and direction of the wind. Such trajectories would by no means represent a projection onto the 500-mb surface of the real, three-dimensional, air trajectories. The horizontal winds normally exhibit a marked variation in the vertical both with regard to speed and direction. Air particles with the same horizontal coordinates of origin may, consequently, follow widely different paths depending upon the level at which they are moving. It has already been pointed out that the simplified theory of 500-mb forecasting is inherently incapable of giving accurate information regarding isolated details at the fixed points of the basic grid. Attempts to verify barotropically forecast wind at prescribed points will, accordingly, in general give quite discouraging results. This, in turn, implies that the agreement between the "real" 500-mb trajectories and those computed barotropically may be entirely unsatisfactory even in cases where a good forecast of the development of the atmospheric circulation has been produced. This has been demonstrated effectively in the computations of

500-mb trajectories that have been made recently by D. Djuric and A. Wiin-Nielsen of the International Meteorological Institute in Stockholm.

One of the greatest difficulties encountered in studies of this kind lies in the determination of the "real" trajectories that are to be compared with those computed from the forecast. Aerological observations are in most places made only twice a day and many stations do not report winds at the 500-mb level. It is therefore necessary to construct the "real" trajectories on the basis of weather maps that are, in some suitable way, interpolated between the observed twelve-hourly maps. It will also, in general, be necessary to utilize geostrophically computed wind in addition to the observed ones.

We have already mentioned P. Welander's investigation of the deformation fields in the 500-mb level. His case, as well as those computed lately by D. Djuric and A. Wiin-Nielsen, shows that already within twelve hours the paths computed for neighbouring points in the basic grid diverge widely. As a result, one finds that a square defined by four such points in the initial state will in general soon be deformed into a long streak covering the same total area. We cannot expect to be able to forecast the exact position of such a streak very accurately but there is no reason to doubt the existence in nature of such strong deformation fields, as have been indicated in the investigations mentioned. It seems likely then that aerosols released over a limited area would spread in the form of narrow bands without necessarily losing too much in concentration. The deformation fields, and thus the tendencies to form streak-patterns, are even stronger in the uppermost parts of the troposphere and in the lowest stratospheric regions, where the strongly concentrated jet streams occur.

The lack of direct observations of air trajectories clearly constitutes a primary difficulty in all attempts to attack the problems mentioned here. However, during recent years some data of this type have been collected by the meteorological agencies of the U.S. Armed Forces. Use has been made of free balloons equipped with automatic control gear designed to keep them at a predetermined constant pressure level, moving with the winds at that level. The position of the balloons was then determined at regular intervals with the aid of radio direction finders. This observational material has not been made generally available so far for detailed analysis, but it should in due time give valuable information regarding the possible systematic deviations of the actual winds from those computed geostrophically. Investigations of air temperatures, and other properties such as humidity, measured along the trajectory of such balloons undoubtedly would increase our knowledge about the vertical motions connected with the larger synoptic systems as well as about the importance of the radiation balance for changes in air temperature.

It is regrettable from many points of view that such an extremely valuable observational program should lie in the hands of military authorities. The problem of distribution of matter in the atmosphere will no doubt be of fundamental importance to all of us. It is unlikely that it could be solved completely in a theoretical way or with the aid of conventional aerological observations. It seems desirable, therefore, and it will no doubt prove necessary sooner or later to conduct trajectory experiments regularly through the agencies of the international civil meteorological organization, WMO.

The spreading of aerosols, naturally, takes place not only through the purely advective processes discussed above, but also through various processes of turbulent diffusion. The velocity of vertical diffusion in the middle and upper parts of the troposphere is controlled in general by the mechanical turbulence brought about by the vertical wind shear and the consequent relative motions of the superimposed air layers. This mechanical turbulence is suppressed to some extent by the static stability in the vertical that is found generally in the atmosphere. The order of magnitude of the more or less isotropic turbulent mixing can be expressed through a kinematic coefficient of diffusion, the magnitude of which is normally found to lie between 10^5 and 10^6 cm^2 sec^{-1}. This coefficient has the dimensions of length times velocity, and could be looked upon as representing a characteristic dimension of 10 to 100 metres and a characteristic velocity of 1 m/sec in the turbulent elements. In the relatively limited areas dominated by thermal convection, both of these numbers have to be multiplied by one power of ten. It is evident from these numbers that isotropic mechanical turbulence cannot play the decisive role in the spreading out of aerosols that have been introduced into the atmosphere over areas of the scale of hundreds of kilometres and depths of one or several kilometres.

Turbulence of characteristic scales much larger than the above mentioned occurs in the atmosphere also. This turbulence must necessarily be anisotropic, because of the dimensions and stability characteristics of the troposphere. We know, however, too little about its structure to be able to make definite statements regarding its importance. It seems likely, for theoretical reasons, that cylindrical turbulent elements with their axis oriented along the direction of the wind should form in the vicinity of well-developed jet streams. This idea is supported by observations of analogous concentrated currents in the oceans, e.g. the Gulf Stream. *Anisotropic turbulence of this kind will probably lead to a tendency of aerosols to concentrate in narrow horizontal streaks in regions of concentrated upward motion.*

It has been pointed out before that the rotation of the earth tends to cause a certain dynamic stability of the large-scale horizontal motions of the atmosphere. This is shown above all in the capability of the atmosphere to build up quickly a balance between the horizontal pressure gradient and the deflective force caused by the interaction of the wind and the earth's rotation. It is probable that this stability exerts a strongly damping influence on the occurrence of turbulence elements with a vertical axis and characteristic dimensions of the order of magnitude of 10 to 100 km. The resulting gap in the turbulence spectrum will increase the tendency to develop streakiness of the atmospheric distribution patterns.

B. *Distribution and circulation of maritime salts*

The previous discussion has been primarily concentrated on the prognostic problems connected with the streaky distribution in the upper layers of the troposphere of aerosols from instantaneous, geographically limited sources. During recent years the attention of meteorologists has also turned to certain climatological distribution processes in the lower troposphere, involving more or less permanent sources of aerosols. The local processes connected with the transport of air pollutants from individual industrial sources belong among others to this class. We shall confine ourselves here to somewhat more general questions concerning the redistribution by the wind of salts originating from the sea. Such questions are not only of meteorological interest but have also given rise to a series of significant microchemical and geochemical problems.

When the wind over the sea is strong enough to form white-caps, air is captured by the collapsing wavecrests and rises to the surface afterwards as tiny bubbles. When these bubbles burst, a jet of water is ejected into the air where it breaks up into small droplets. Some of these droplets fall back to the water surface. Others are carried away with the winds and after evaporation produce new salt particles. These particles of maritime salts can act at some later time as condensation nuclei and are therefore of essential importance in the formation of clouds.

The northwestern part of Europe is ventilated by and large by winds from the sea, carrying both water vapour and sea salts. The rain falling from the clouds in these maritime air currents sweeps out a part of the salt particles in the lower air layers. The intensity of this washing-out is proportional to the number of salt particles per unit volume as well as to the intensity of the precipitation. Consequently, the amount of precipitated salts will, by and large, decrease with increasing distance from the coast. This elementary result can be verified easily by studying the chemical-climatological maps recently constructed for northwestern Europe. The basis for these maps is data obtained from the chemical analysis of monthly samples of precipitation, collected at a great number of stations. These stations are organized and supported by the Royal College of Agriculture and the International Institute of Meteorology in Stockholm in collaboration with a number of foreign organizations and scientists.

In earlier geological considerations these airborne salts have in general been neglected. It has been assumed generally that salts which were transported to the sea by the rivers consisted of the products of chemical erosion. Provided this reasoning were correct and the transport of salts into the sea by running waters were known and could be assumed constant, we could estimate the age of the oceans. Such an estimate has been made, yielding a value of about 60 million years. This absurdly low age makes the entire reasoning doubtful. We must ask ourselves whether the transport by the rivers really represents a supply of products of chemical erosion.

Erik Eriksson of the International Institute of Meteorology in Stockholm has made an effort to throw light on this problem by comparing the quantities of chlorides supplied to the soil by precipitation with those transported to the sea by the water courses of Sweden. Some 30 years ago, water samples collected from a large

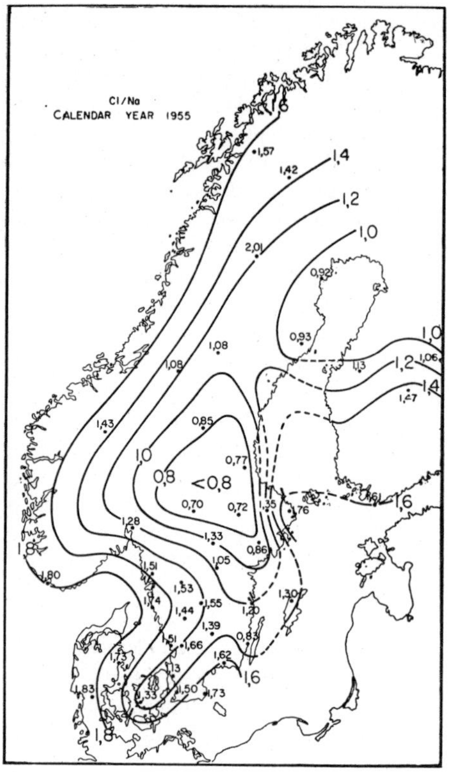

Fig. 15. Weight ratio of chloride and sodium ions in precipitation during the calendar year 1955.

number of places in the Swedish river system were chemically analyzed. By multiplying the measured concentrations of chlorides with the yearly amount of outflow one can easily determine the transport of chlorides at each place. These values can be reduced to the loss of salts per annum per unit area by a division by the area of the corresponding drainage basin. In this way it is possible to obtain data for a hydrological-chemical map indicating the removal of chlorides in kilograms per hectare per annum.

The general outlines of this map coincide strikingly with the map of chlorides supplied by precipitation and by contrast are apparently independent of the character of the bedrock. One feels therefore strongly tempted to conclude that the salt content of the rivers must to a large extent consist of salts transported over land by the winds and thereafter carried back to the sea. A fact which contradicts this hypothesis is, that the quantities removed are in general two or three times as large as those supplied by the precipitation. Eriksson has tried to overcome this difficulty by pointing out that the Swedish forests, especially those of conifers, may during dry periods "filter" the winds thus collecting a considerable part of the aerosols of the lowest atmospheric layers, which are constantly renewed by a supply from the west. Experiments have been carried out at the Institute of Forestry as well as abroad, which support this hypothesis. It is, however, not yet possible to make a reliable estimate of the quantities of salts collected in this way over a unit area.

For the arid and semi-arid zones, especially for those having no drainage to the sea, the supply of salts to the soil by sporadic rain showers and by direct gravitational sedimentation can gradually lead to a destruction of the soil and existing water reservoirs. Western Australia is at the present fighting these problems. The collection of reliable data concerning the precipitated salts are of great practical interest. In addition the systematic observations of the chemical composition of the precipitation, carried out during recent years in northwestern Europe,[1] have given rise to a renewed discussion of the geological history of the great salt deserts. It has been generally assumed earlier that the salt deposit of the deserts is built up by marine invasions. Considering, however, the large amount of salts which, during geological ages, were transported into these areas by the winds and precipitated there, one can no longer exclude the possibility that much of these salt deposits is due to the accumulation of airborne salts.

C. *The circulation of sulphur and ammonia*

Compared with the apparently simple and easily interpreted geographical distribution of the actual sea salts transferred to the soil by precipitation, the maps for other elements, as for example sulphur and ammonia, show a far more complicated pattern. Sulphur found in the sea water has an average volume proportion compared to sodium of 0.08. Since precipitation usually contains rather large quantities of sulphur it has been assumed that these originate from sources of industrial pollution. The quantities of sulphur transferred to the soil from precipitation over Denmark and Sweden decrease in a fairly regular way with increasing distance from the Western Ocean, apart from some entirely local dis-

[1] A similar chemical network has been in operation in North America for about one year under the leadership of CHRISTIAN JUNGE.

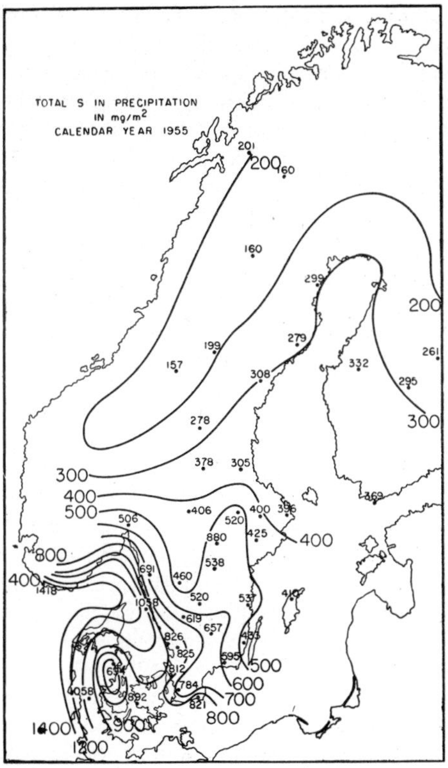

Fig. 16. Distribution of sulphur from precipitation during the year of 1955 (mg/m²). Notice the high concentration in southwestern Sweden which probably can be explained as a combined effect of maritime sulphur and sulphur from the industries in western Europe.

turbances.[1] One can try to eliminate the sulphur of maritime origin in the precipitation by subtracting from the latter the fraction (i.e. 0.08) of the simultaneously transferred amounts of sodium corresponding to the sulphur contribution of the seas. The resulting map will still show a fairly smooth decrease of the "non-maritime" amounts of sulphur from southwest to northeast. A tongue of high concentration extending from southernmost Sweden northwards indicates with good probability that there is an airborne contribution to Sweden's sulphur provision from Germany's industry. This map nevertheless gives rise to certain questions of geochemical importance. If the industries and coal combustion of the British Isles and Western Europe are really responsible for this "non-maritime" part of the sulphur transfer, it seems difficult to understand the strong concentration of the horizontal gradients over Scandinavia, several thousands of kilometres away from the sources of pollution in question. One can hardly avoid the impression that one part of this "non-maritime" sulphur, after all, emanates from the sea. Hereby we arrive at the question of whether the process discussed above is the only one capable of transferring chemical components from the sea to the air. One possibility put forward much earlier is that a major part of the maritime sulphur leaves the sea as hydrogen sulfide (H_2S). The shallow, so-called "shelf-areas" should be in this case the most important source areas of this hydrogen sulphide.

The examples shown above demonstrate the wide geographic separation of the sources of the various chemical substances in precipitation. The

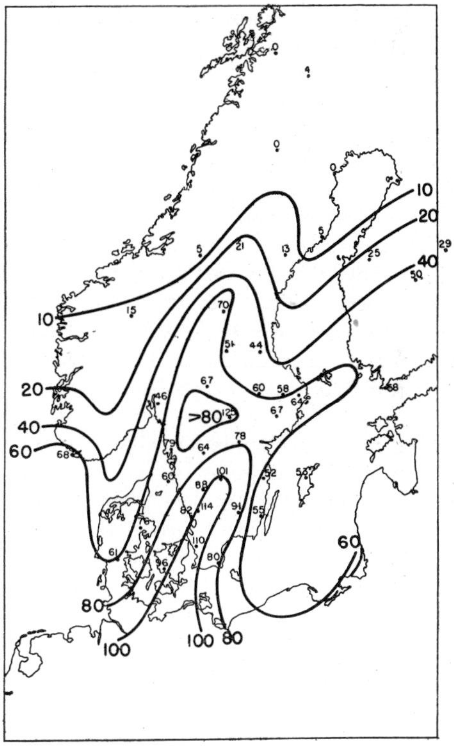

Fig. 17. Non-maritime sulphur in precipitation during the month of May 1955. The maritime part has been eliminated by subtraction of a correction, which was computed from the sodium in precipitation and with the aid of the existing weight ratio between sulphur and sodium in the ocean. Note the tongue of high sulphur content, probably from western Germany, extending northwards through southern Sweden.

[1] It should be pointed out that the northwest European chemical network was organized for the study of distribution phenomena on a synoptic scale and that the stations have in general been established at places where one could hope to avoid effects from purely local pollution sources.

relative chemical composition of precipitation should therefore vary with the origin of the air mass from which it precipitates. The chemical composition of precipitation during a certain time interval could possibly be used in this way as an indication of the predominant circulation pattern during the same interval. In peat-bogs, nourished exclusively from the air, certain constituents of the precipitation are so intimately bound to organic matter that a chemical stratification is formed in the course of the years. This should to some degree reflect the composition of precipitation at the time of formation of the strata. By coordinated determinations of the chemical structure of geographically well-distributed, "air-nourished" (ombrogenous) peat-bogs possibly one should be able to obtain a picture of the relative chemical composition of precipitation, and thus also changes in the type of circulation during different postglacial periods. Extensive experiments in this direction have been started during the summer of 1957 by the International Institute of Meteorology in Stockholm under the leadership of E. Eriksson. The study of the extensive material, which not only has to be analyzed chemically but also dated with the aid of C^{14} and pollen analysis, has not yet been completed. It should, however, be pointed out that from a study of an "air-nourished" peat-bog in southern Halland, SANTE MATTSON has been able to prove that the well-documented climatic deterioration which occurred approximately simultaneously with the transition from the bronze-age to the iron-age, is clearly reflected in the vertical chemical stratification of this peat-bog.

Since nitrogen compounds are of interest to agriculturalists and foresters, these compounds have been investigated in detail since the middle of the last century or still earlier. Several, and in some cases fairly long, series of measurements were made at agricultural experimental stations such as Rothamstead in England. As a rule, these measurements have been carried out without attention to meteorological viewpoints, and therefore cannot yield the necessary information we need for a fairly complete analysis of the circulation of nitrogen compounds. Such an analysis should also lead us far beyond the boundaries of meteorology. E. HUTCHINTON during recent years has made valuable contributions to the discussion of this question in articles on the bio-geochemistry of nitrogen compounds.

Already in the middle of the last century T. SCHLÖSING suggested that the ammonia in precipitation originates in the sea, and that after having taken part in the organic circulation in the biosphere, this ammonia is transported back to the sea by the rivers in the form of nitrates and of nitrogeneous organic decay products. Schlösing's theory was abandoned when it turned out that the nitrogen content of maritime air masses was lower than that of continental air masses. The discovery of nitrogen fixing bacteria on legumes indicates that the sources of the ammonia in the atmosphere and precipitation should be sought in the cultivated areas of the continents.

The data which now are available from the chemical-climatological networks in northwestern Europe and in the USA have not yet been analyzed conclusively. The fairly irregular pattern of the maps for ammonia in the precipitation in Sweden indicates that the greater part of the circulating quantities of ammonia passes through fairly short, locally controlled circuits, during which the quantities of ammonia liberated by decay processes return directly to the atmosphere as gases. This impression of local control is strengthened by some material from America. Chr. Junge recently found that the precipitation over southeastern United States, south and east from a line connecting the Mississippi delta with Virginia, contains exceedingly small quantities of ammonia. This part of the country is, however, characterized by certain acid, red soils, whose low pH apparently prevents the ammonia liberated by decay processes from returning to the atmosphere. Thus, the advection of ammonia from more distant parts of the country seems to play a relatively insignificant role.

No doubt one must presume the existence of a slower circulation, involving much larger regions of the world, but reflecting considerably smaller concentrations than produced locally, in addition to these shortlived, local circuits. Sporadic analyses of the precipitation in tradewind zones at island stations, more than 2,000 miles away from the nearest continent, have yielded values of ammonia concentration which are comparable to those obtained from eastern Sweden in the absence of strong local sources of pollution. One must therefore probably assume that small quantities of ammonia are liberated at the sea surface in gaseous form and eventually precipitated over the continents as Schlösing suggested. We still do not know the periods of these different cycles and of the magnitudes of quantities of ammonia involved finally. It should be of considerable bioclimatological interest to settle the question whether at present there is a balance between bacteria-controlled processes which fix ammonia and those which reconvert nitrogen compounds into molecular nitrogen.

The amount of nitrates in precipitation is in general considerably lower than the content of ammonia. Nitrogen bound in the nitrates amounts roughly to 50% of the nitrogen in ammonia compounds. This number is, however, by no means constant and the two elements are distributed in an entirely different way. It has often been assumed that a great part of the nitrates in precipitation is created by direct oxidation of nitrogen in air by lightning discharges. Hutchinson has tried to determine this effect by comparing the concentration of nitrates and ammonia in precipitation obtained from rain with and without simultaneous lightning discharges at certain stations in Oklahoma, where thunderstorms are both common and intense. The results are not convincing and the effectiveness of thunderstorms as producers of nitrates is still an open question. In Sweden the largest concentration of nitrates is found in the precipitation from the west coast: the gradients in toward the center of the country are steep and more concentrated than in the case of the "proper" sea salts. The circulation of the nitrates must be considered as an unsolved problem.

Keeping in mind that probably the nitrates and the ammonia in the precipitation are formed in completely different ways, an investigation has been made at the International Institute of Meteorology in Stockholm of the relative abundance of the stable isotopes N^{14} and N^{15} in ammonia and in nitrates, respectively. This should indicate systematic differences with regard to fixation. The results are almost entirely negative. However, this should only indicate that the amount of recently fixed nitrogen is small in comparison with the total quantity of nitrogen in the circulation of ammonia and nitrates in the biosphere.

We have pointed out above the geochemical and bio-geochemical questions arising from the study of the chemical composition of the precipitation obtained from the chemical-climatological network. These questions, however, are closely connected to certain physical-chemical problems. These problems deal partly with the exchange at the sea surface itself and partly with the processes acting on condensation nuclei after the latter having been carried up into the air by turbulent winds. One typical problem is the relative abundance of chloride versus sodium ions in precipitation in Sweden. The mass ratio of these two ions is 1.8 in sea water and 1.5 in a solution of pure sodium chloride. On the Swedish west coast it is found that the corresponding ratio in the yearly precipitation is closer to 1.5; the ratio decreases systematically with increasing distance from the west coast attaining values between 1.0 and 0.8 in the eastern parts of central Sweden. It is likely that the results obtained during different years would be different depending on the prevailing circulation. The general characteristics of these results, however, are always the same. The simplest explanation is, of course, that the salt-transporting westerlies become enriched with other sodium salts from the ground during their movement inland over Sweden. This viewpoint especially has been maintained by the German chemist and oceanographer K. KALLE, who has studied thoroughly the observational material from the two first years of the Swedish chemical network. Another possibility is that the nuclei of condensation are subjected to certain processes which lead to a partial elimination and substitution by other ions of chloride. Based on certain observations collected on board German submarines and over central Europe during the second world war, H. CAUER some years ago suggested that the small quantities of ozone normally present in the lowest atmospheric layers could contribute to a chain of events which eventually results in small amounts of gaseous hydrogen chloride in the atmosphere. According to Cauer, the chloride ions of condensation nuclei should hereby be substituted by carbonate or bicarbonate ions from atmospheric carbon dioxide. It is now regarded for theoretical reasons as well as from conclusions based upon certain experiments arranged to varify this hypothesis, that atmospheric ozone is considered not to play the role suggested by Cauer. It is, however, of some interest to point out that Junge claims to have found free hydrogen chloride in air samples from Hawaii, which previously had been deprived of their condensation nuclei.

D. *The exchange of matter at the sea surface*

A comparison of the ratio between chloride and sodium ions for different types of circulation has indicated that, especially during the late autumn in the presence of humid, southerly or southwesterly winds, one can obtain values of the mass ratio of these two ions which exceed 3.0 whereas an analysis of air samples (with condensation nuclei included) should in similar circumstances have yielded values of 4.0 or more. Values of the chloride content of the air in the neighbourhood of the Black Sea have during recent years been published by Russian investigators who indicate values of the order of magnitude of 100 micrograms per cubic meter of air as far as 100 km, or more, from the coast. The ratio of chloride ions to sodium ions in the water of the Black Sea hardly deviates from the corresponding ratio in the oceans. Its water masses, being very stably stratified and only slowly renewed, on the other hand contain large quantities of hydrogen sulphide below a depth of 200 m. The possibility has been suggested that the uppermost layer of water could be "swept aside" by powerful storms, thus giving the hydrogen sulphide in the lower layers a chance to diffuse into the atmosphere. This hydrogen sulphide must, with the cooperation of the sun, fairly quickly become oxidized to SO_2 and further on to SO_3, which may be able to expel the chloride ions from condensation nuclei, leading to a formation of gaseous hydrogen chloride. This latter may in its turn be carried over long distances, while the corresponding condensation nuclei, now mainly sodium sulphate, should precipitate fairly quickly.

It is evident from what has been said here that the chemical constituents of cloud water and precipitation have left the sea in different proportions than those characteristic for sea water. It has been pointed out already that small quantities of ammonia as well as gaseous hydrogen sulphide probably escape to the atmosphere in gaseous state. There may exist an additional process which could lead to differentiation in the delivery of marine salts to the atmosphere. The sea surface is, in the presence of weak winds, often characterized by the existence of a thin organic film, probably consisting of certain fatty acids. These fatty acids possess the property of being able to bind cations, such as calcium and magnesium, to a higher degree than sodium and potassium. During the generation of bubbles, which has been described earlier, a part of the organic film is carried off with the droplets. As a result this should carry calcium and magnesium into the air in higher proportions than their abundance in sea water. We still do not know the importance of this differentiated transport of salts. It is, however, conspicuous that the content of calcium in precipitation, to which we should by and large like to ascribe the widespread occurrence of highly calcine rocks over continents, is equally high along the western coast of Scandinavia and farther in over the country. Similarly, the occurrence of organic matter in the snow over Finland, far away from sources of pollution, has been interpreted as a proof of the regular formation of organic films on the sea surface, and removal of it by the bubbling process.

From what has been said above it should be clear that the transport of salts from the sea to the air is by no means a simple mechanical process as earlier supposed. A final example of the physical-chemical problems connected with this process can be found in the hydroxylionconcentration (pH) of precipitation. Sea water is basic having a pH of about 8.0. The precipitation at Scandinavian coastal stations has a fairly stable pH between 4.5 and 5.0. Farther inland this value increases slowly, becoming at the same time more variable geographically and with time. The low pH near the coast cannot be ascribed to carbonic acid in the air, which, being in equilibrium with cloud droplets and precipitation, should not be able to depress the pH from 8.0 to less than about 5.7.

Attempts to control atmospheric processes

With our increasing understanding of the structure and motion of the atmosphere meteorologists have been looking also into the possibilities of influencing or controlling some atmospheric processes. It has become more and more apparent that water supply will become the most important limiting factor for economic development in many parts of the world. It is hardly surprising, therefore, that the atmospheric cycle of water vapour has been the object of some very intense research, culminating in certain field experiments designed for the development and the testing of methods to interfere, locally, with this cycle. For some ten years experiments have been conducted to stimulate the local release of precipitation. The next step was taken a few years ago considering the problem of evaporation from natural and artificial water reservoirs, and the possibility of reducing this evaporation with the aid of certain surface films. An investigation of the possible utilization of similar methods on snow fields also has recently been initiated. The results gained so far along these two lines of research on the hydrologic cycle are rather modest and, in particular regarding the release of precipitation, to some extent debatable. The potential economic importance even of limited advances in this field of work is, however, so great that, in spite of temporary setbacks, the experimental work in this field may be expected in the long run to intensify rather than die away.

Our possibility to stimulate, artificially, the local release of precipitation is ultimately dependent upon the apparent fact that, while the normal atmospheric condensation process is extremely efficient, this seems not always to be the case. This is indicated by the fact that not all clouds give rain or snow. Condensation nuclei, mainly salt particles of maritime origin, are normally abundantly present in the lower air strata. Cooling of the air caused by lifting or by radiation, results in condensation of the atmospheric water vapour onto these nuclei. The numerous cloud droplets formed in this way are quite small (typically around 10 microns diameter) and have too low a velocity of fall to cause measurable quantities of precipitation to fall out (about 1—2 cm/sec). The release of precipitation thus requires some special process capable of converting a large number of cloud particles into a much smaller number of raindrops. The raindrops are normally of the order of millimeters in diameter and have fall speeds up to 6—7 m/sec. An efficient process for the release of precipitation should accordingly be capable of quickly combining all the water in a large number (up to a million) of cloud droplets into a single raindrop.

It was suggested by Bergeron in a classical paper in 1933 that the natural release of precipitation should depend almost completely on the occurrence of a limited number of ice crystals in a cloud otherwise composed of supercooled water droplets. These snow or ice crystals would then grow rapidly because of the difference in saturation water vapour pressure over liquid water and ice. This difference reaches its maximum of about 0.27 mb at a temperature of — 12° C. Finally, when the crystals have grown sufficiently to start sweeping up the surrounding cloud droplets due to their higher fall velocity, the growth is accelerated rapidly and the particles fall out as snow, sleet or rain, according to the temperature conditions in lower air layers. This theory was quite generally accepted, and it agreed, by and large, with the experience gathered at middle latitudes. There is in fact little doubt that the heaviest rains fall from clouds reaching well above the 0°-isotherm.

Some doubt regarding the general validity of the Bergeron theory arose during and after World War II as a result of the meteorologist's acquaintance with tropical conditions. Experience accumulated clearly indicating that large amounts of rain may be released from clouds that never reach the atmospheric freezing level. The quite detailed investigation of the meteorological conditions of the Hawaiian Islands that has been made during the last ten years has added particularly valuable data regarding this type of precipitation. It is, however, not only at the lower latitudes that the Bergeron theory has had to give way to some extent. Special radar equipment has been utilized especially in the U.S.A. and Great Britain to study the development of rain, particularly in convective clouds. The level and time of the formation of raindrops is easily distinguishable as the intensity of the radar echo is strongly dependent upon the size of the reflecting particles. It has been observed on many occasions that the first raindrop echo occurred at levels where solid phase cloud particles could not possibly have existed, and that the echo, i.e. the region occupied by rain drops, spread vertically upwards as well as downwards.

Naturally, the results briefly indicated above only mean that in addition to the Bergeron process some other mechanism must exist that is capable of a rapid transformation of cloud droplets into raindrops. Langmuir, and before him Findeisen, has suggested that this could happen if cloud droplets of different sizes collide and coalesce because of their different fall velocities. The larger more rapidly falling drops are in this way capable of collecting a large number of the smaller droplets, thereby growing into raindrop size. With this theory in mind a number of theoretical investigations have been made of the efficiency with which this sweeping up of smaller droplets takes place (collection efficiency). The fact that many clouds do not produce precipitation indicates that some stabilizing factors may exist in nature that tend to counteract, or at least to slow down the coalescence process. Such a stabilizing influence is exerted e.g. by unipolar electric charges. In general, one gets the impression that rapid formation of rain only occurs when a sufficiently wide spectrum of droplets is present in the cloud already from the beginning. Some workers (A.

Fig. 18. Effect of cloud seeding by means of dry-ice pellets upon a supercooled stratus cloud (photograph by Dr. V. SCHEAFER).

WOODCOCK in particular) maintain that this critical width of the droplet spectrum is produced in nature by the presence in the population of condensation nuclei of (comparatively) very large sea salt particles, "giant nuclei". The droplets formed on such nuclei would grow much faster than the major part of the cloud droplets because of the depression of the equilibrium vapour pressure caused by the dissolved salts.

The theoretical estimates that have been made of the collection efficiency are highly dependent upon special assumptions e.g. about the aerodynamics of the collision process. It is hardly surprising, in view of this, and keeping the above mentioned stabilizing influences in mind that the theoretical results gained so far have been somewhat contradictory, and that they can hardly be used as a sound foundation for extensive and costly field experiments. One has further not distinguished, in the theoretical investigations, between collision and coalescence. The assumption that each collision leads to coalescence cannot be accepted without experimental support, in particular since organic matter in the condensation nuclei may change the physical surface properties of the water and so may influence the coalescence process. It seems necessary therefore thoroughly to reconsider the theoretical investigations made so far and to conduct an extensive and systematic program of experimental studies particularly of the coalescence process. Such investigations made with the aid of ultra high speed motion cameras and other special equipment would be highly desirable in order to guide us out of the chaos of the moment to a point where we get a more clear and reliable picture of the microphysical processes in the interior of the clouds.

Accepting the Bergeron theory one should be able to stimulate the release of precipitation from clouds consisting of supercooled droplets by introducing ice crystals into the supercooled layers or by causing some of the droplets to freeze with the aid of special freezing nuclei (artificial cloud seeding). A similar process (natural cloud seeding) occurs in nature, according to Bergeron, when tiny snow crystals from higher clouds fall or get mixed into a supercooled water cloud thereby rapidly transforming it into a precipitating system.

The earliest controlled experiments of this kind were carried out in 1948 by LANGMUIR and SCHAEFER at Schenectady. They "seeded" a relatively thin supercooled stratus layer from an airplane simply by spreading out dry ice particles in an easily recognizable pattern. Each dry ice particle rapidly cools the air in its vicinity past the point where droplets freeze spontaneously and leaves a trail of ice crystals behind it as it falls through the air. In this way the proper initial conditions for a Bergeron type precipitation release were set, and 15 to 20 minutes later the effect could be clearly observed as a nearly complete dissipation of the cloud in the seeded area, while ground observers reported a light snow fall. Several experiments of similar character have been performed since then, and the possibility of dissipating thin supercooled stratus layers in this way is clearly established, which might be of some value for aviation purposes.

One cannot, however, say that the possibilities of releasing precipitation artificially in amounts significant to agriculture or hydroelectric power production have been demonstrated to the extent that they have been accepted by most meteorologists. A vertical column of air at North European latitudes rarely contains more than one gram of precipitable water per cm^2, of which only a fraction could be condensed out without excessive lifting of the air. It is thus necessary to have large convergence of the air in order to produce significant amounts of precipitation from layer type clouds. However, once such large scale convergence is present, then it is also highly probable that precipitation would be released in a natural way either through natural freezing of the droplets in the upper parts of the clouds or through the constantly proceeding process of coalescence in the turbulent interior parts of the growing cloud system. The latitude for artificial influence on the precipitation process thus becomes very narrow. One is more or less forced, in spite of our incomplete knowledge of the microphysical processes in the clouds, to adopt the idea that once the convergence necessary to produce intense precipitation is present, then nature has at its disposal not one but several microphysical processes for its release. If, on the contrary, this convergence does not exist, then the amounts of precipitation that could be released artificially would normally be quite insignificant. It has been suggested that the release of latent heat caused by the precipitation process should be sufficient to cause intensified vertical development of the cloud and in this way would set up the convergence necessary for intensive precipitation formation. This requires that the vertical structure of the atmosphere be characterized by a certain potential lability while at the same time the natural disturbances in the air have to be so weak that a release of the available energy does not occur. It is quite certain that such conditions exist, but it is also quite certain that they are exceptions.

The difficulties mentioned above are quite well illustrated by the work on the release of precipitation from convective clouds that has been performed at various places. Experiments with this type of clouds have been carried out on a large scale both in Australia and in the U.S.A. To attempt a release of precipitation from widely scattered cumuli by dry ice seeding from airplanes is obviously both a time consuming and a costly way of operation. It was therefore a very important step forwards when B. VONNEGUT, one of Langmuir's collaborators, in 1947 discovered and demonstrated the capability of microscopic silver iodide crystals to cause a rapid transformation of a supercooled water cloud into a cloud of glittering ice crystals. The silver iodide was tried because of the similarity between its crystal shape and dimensions with those of ice, but the actual way in which it works is not yet completely understood. Smoke of silver iodide can be produced by generators placed at suitable points on the ground. It is then expected that turbulence and the general vertical motion of the air would carry it up into the critical supercooled cloud layers, where it could initiate a Bergeron type precipitation release. The weakness of this relatively simple and inexpensive method of cloud seeding obviously lies in the impossibility to control the distribution of the smoke and thus to direct the silver iodide crystals to a specified cloud.

The attempts that have been made so far to release precipitation from convective clouds with dry ice or silver iodide, have given a few positive and highly dramatic results, but the majority of the experiments has been rather inconclusive.

In one of the earliest Australian experiments conducted by G. C. BOWEN and P. SQUIRES one single cloud out of a population of several hundred apparently similar cumulus clouds was treated with dry ice. A few minutes later strong vertical development of the treated cloud was observed together with typical signs of transformation into an ice cloud in its upper parts. No other cloud in the neighbourhood exhibited the same type of development.

It is found in most cases, however, that sooner or later also some untreated clouds will undergo the same development as the seeded ones, and it becomes necessary to resort to long series of experiments carefully designed for statistical analysis in order to decide the efficiency of the seeding operations. It is thus probable that some possibilities exist to accelerate the release of precipitation from convective clouds, and in that way to influence the distribution of showers, but we do not at present possess any method of estimating the efficiency of such operations. In spite of all these difficulties commercial enterprises have been operating for some time in the semiarid parts of the southwestern USA attempting to promote convective release of precipitation. Even a minor increase in rainfall may of course be of immense value on a cattle ranch and may motivate rather expensive experimentation even if that does not produce any considerable rise in the precipitation over larger areas.

Of all weather systems the orographic precipitation, i.e. rain or snow from humid air that is forced to rise and cool on the passage over hills or mountain ranges, probably offers the best possibility for control. The orographic cloud cover stays on the upwind side of the obstacle and above its highest parts as long as the humid wind presists. If the stratification of the air stream is relatively stable, then the clouds get quite thin and they are readily dissipated in the subsiding air stream on the lee side of the mountain. Under suitable circumstances a series of lee waves may occur, each carrying a stationary cloud on its crest.

It may well happen under these circumstances that the time spent by an individual cloud particle in traversing the cloud is quite short. If at the same time the cloud is quite thin and thus free from strong vertical turbulence elements, then there will not be time enough for the coalescence mechanism to build up the droplets to raindrop size. Such orographic cloud systems are relatively common. In Sweden one may find them for example in western Jämtland, where maritime air flows into the country through relatively low passes in the Scandinavian mountain range.

Stable orographic clouds of this type and occurring at temperatures from —10° C up towards 0° C always consist of supercooled droplets under natural condition. It should be possible to cause a certain release of precipitation from such clouds with the aid of silver iodide smoke released from ground generators on the windward side of the mountain. Preliminary plans for such experiments in the Ovik mountains in Jämtland, Sweden, have been worked out by F. LUDLAM as leader of the cloud physics group at the International Meteorological Institute in Stockholm, but personnel shortage has inhibited the further development of the project.

Extensive attempts to increase orographic precipitation have been running during several years in the Sierra Nevada range in California, sponsored by the hydroelectric power interests. The correlation between the run-off from two catchment areas, one seeded and the other not seeded, is being used for estimating the efficiency of operation. A positive result should show up as an anomaly in the relation between the total run-off from the two basins. It is unfortunately impossible to find two basins with a perfect correlation between the run-off data, and so a number of years are required to establish the results firmly, especially as the effect looked for is relatively limited.

Nothing has been mentioned above about the rather primitive and preliminary experiments that have been performed so far in order to stimulate the release of precipitation from warm clouds, i.e. clouds that do not reach the 0° C isotherm. It ought to be mentioned, therefore, that a team from the University of Chicago conducted by prof. H. BYERS has been experimenting with shallow cumulus clouds in the West Indian trade wind region. They have tried to stimulate the coalescence process by injecting water into the clouds, but their results have to be looked upon as so far rather inconclusive. One has tried in other parts of the world to stimulate the release of precipitation by injection of "giant" salt nuclei but the results of these experiments are also open to debate. In general one gets the impression that the whole field needs some investment in the form of new ideas.

It has been known for considerable time that evaporation from water surfaces can be reduced under laboratory conditions by the application of monomolecular films of certain organic substances, particularly polar ones with straight carbon chains. Some experiments using fatty acids in particular were performed in the twenties. In 1943 Langmuir and Schaefer published a paper in which the properties of fatty alcohols in this respect were described. Particularly cetyl alcohol, i.e. the fatty alcohol with a saturated chain of 16 carbon atoms, exhibits the properties of rapid spreading combined with a relatively strong effect of evaporation suppression. This result brought up to the possibility of decreasing the evaporation losses from natural and artificial water reservoirs. In 1953 this problem was taken up by a team conducted by W. W. MANSFIELD of the CSIRO in Australia. Systematic experiments of the same kind have later been taken up in Kenya and also since 1955 in the southwestern U.S.A. under supervision of the Bureau of Reclamation.

Cetyl alcohol is a waxy substance and it emits spontaneously a monomolecular film when it is kept in contact with a water surface. It is thus possible to apply such a film to a dam reservoir by allowing it to spread from small beads of the substance floating on the water. It will in general prove more feasible, however, to dissolve it in a volatile solvent substance and then simply to pour it out in suitable amounts on the surface.

Various properties of the film material other than its capability of suppressing evaporation are of course also important, e.g. the persistence of the film against the action of wind and waves and its possible effect on water quality and biological conditions. The information on these points is incomplete, but it indicates that the cetyl alcohol is harmless both to water quality and to lake biology but that wind and waves tend to break the film up and to carry it away so that a continuous renewal is necessary as long as the wind is blowing.

Reliable data on the field efficiency of the method are not available yet, but an average reduction of the evaporation by 18 % has been reached in pan experiments according to oral communications from the U.S. Geological Survey.

Recently K. GROTH in Sweden suggested the use of similar methods on snow surfaces. Considerable evaporation losses may occur from snow surfaces during the melting period, especially where Foehn effects are common. In northern Sweden the evaporation losses are estimated to be approximately 10 % of the accumulated snow cover while the corresponding figure in some regions of the Sierra Nevada and the southern part of the Rocky Mountains is stated to be near 50 %.

The application of cetyl alcohol to snow involves several new problems including the question of whether the film would spread under the low temperature conditions found at the snow surface. In order to overcome this difficulty Groth suggested that the fatty alcohol should be mixed with a pigment, ordinary red iron oxide. The pigment particles would then serve as absorbers of solar radiation and thus help in supplying the energy necessary for the film formation. The effect of the application of this mixture is a complex one consisting of a change in the albedo and at the same time of a shift in the energy budget in favour of the melting of the snow. Some field experiments have been carried out to study the possibilities of the method, but the marginal character of the evaporation losses under Swedish conditions make a quantitative evaluation virtually impossible. It would be highly desirable in view of this, to try out the method in a suitable region of the Rockies or the Sierra Nevada.

The method mentioned may of course be used also with the aim of speeding up melting of the snow cover. It may compete favourably in this application with the well known methods of spreading coal dust or gravel onto the snow, partly because the substance is hydrophobic and thus stays on top of the melting snow layers, where it is most useful, partly because of the small amounts required (50 kg/km^2), which is a great advantage when larger areas are to be treated and which may thus outweigh the higher cost of the material. In addition the coal dust method is bound to introduce evaporation losses.

It is useful for some purposes to divide the hydrometeorological processes in the atmosphere into three classes: The microphysical processes, concerning the constitution and history of individual cloud particles, the mesophysical processes, covering the development of individual clouds, their culmination and final dissipation, and finally, the macrophysical or synoptic processes dealing with the cyclones and anticyclones and the cloud systems connected with them. The very brief discussion above has indicated that interference on the microphysical level may have mesophysical consequences, but there exists no reliable and generally accepted evidence for similar effects on the synoptic scale. Admittedly, Langmuir has maintained that certain experiments in periodic cloud seeding performed in the southwestern U.S.A. had caused the release of precipitation in the Mississippi Valley to occur with the same period (one week) as the seeding operation and with a lag of two or three days. However, most meteorologists have not been prepared to accept these results at face value. If it were really true that one could control the development of the synoptic systems through relatively limited micrometeorological manipulations, then this would indicate an extraordinary sensitivity to small disturbances to be a characteristic of these systems. Such a lability is contradicted, however, by the fact that their development can be forecast quite successfully in most cases even with methods that completely neglect the microphysical processes. It stands clear in any case that the interconnections between the various scales of atmospheric processes in this and other respects is badly in need of a thorough and systematic investigation. One may ask oneself if it would be possible to turn the whole question upside down and to proceed in a direction exactly opposite to the present path of the cloud physicists. In other words would it be possible in some way to try to interfere with the general circulation of the atmosphere and in that way indirectly also with the meso- and micrometeorological processes? It should be pointed out in this connection that we already have some observational evidence and experience that indicates the possibility of unintentional or intentional human interference with the general circulation mechanism of the atmosphere and consequently on the climate at the earth's surface. One indication of that kind has already been discussed, namely the effect on the mean temperature of the atmosphere of the increased carbon-dioxide content caused by the continuously increasing consumption of fossile fuel. Another example was set by the eruption of the volcano Krakatoa in 1883. Fine dust particles from this single eruption were thrown all the way up into the stratosphere. Because of their small velocity of fall and the strong lateral mixing at these levels, the particles spread quite evenly around the earth increasing the reflectivity of the upper atmosphere to solar radiation to such an extent that for several years the average yearly temperature was depressed by an amount between one half and one degree C below its normal value.

The general circulation of the atmosphere is driven by the temperature contrast between the polar and the equatorial regions that is maintained by the radiative energy exchange between the earth and space. The Krakatoa eruption indicated that this temperature contrast could be adjusted by the spreading out in suitable regions of the stratosphere of finely divided dust thereby increasing the reflection losses of solar energy in these regions. Another way of affecting the radiation balance would be to cover the polar caps with coal dust. It is true that great progress has been made in the studies of the hydrodynamics and thermodynamics of the atmosphere, but we are as yet far from the point where we could forecast more precisely the probable consequences for the synoptic and the mesometeorological processes of such a hypothetical experiment. Our understanding of the general circulation of the atmosphere is increasing rapidly, however, and the expenses that would go with a large scale experiment of changing the albedo of the earth do not seem unsurmountable. It is perhaps not surprising then that some very outstanding scientists consider the question of climatic control to be a real and practical task for meteorological research. As an example the highly judicious mathematician J. von Neumann who was cited already earlier in this presentation, made this statement in 1955: "Probably intervention in atmospheric and climatic matters will come in a few decades and will unfold on a scale difficult to imagine at present." (Fortune, June 1955.) Most meteorologists would be reluctant perhaps to accept von Neumann's forecast today, but one should remember that during the last decades the technological development has time after time shown the dreams of a visionary mind to be closer to reality than the common sense judgement of the realists.

The Young Carl-Gustaf Rossby

By Tor Bergeron

When only a youngster, Carl-Gustaf Rossby and one of his schoolmates made a Sunday trip on skis in the surroundings of Stockholm, their home town. Carl-Gustaf was in no way an athlete and certainly not a trained skier, but when they came to a well-known ski-jump (at Lilla Fiskartorpet) he just darted down the slope, and did not give up until he could pass the jump . . . and make it! He had never done anything of the sort before.

Such was, in a way, the character of his life, the mark of his personality. Many, if not most, of his decisive steps in life as a man and a scientist were daring jumps into the unknown that succeeded, and admirably so.—His pluck was remarkable. To be "brave" when one ignores the danger, or lacks enough imagination and sensitivity to perceive it, is no real bravery. We all know, though, that with Rossby there was no lack of imagination; moreover, he had a very sensitive disposition and his constitution was not robust. But his spirit was strong, his gifts and interests manifold, and thanks to his extraordinary ambitions he also managed to accomplish his multifarious intentions. His indefatigable brain was exceedingly receptive and yet capable of producing a wealth of fruitful ideas, two faculties that do not often go together.

*

Carl-Gustaf Rossby's father was a Stockholm engineer, quiet and jovial, and a good negotiator. His mother—still living at 84—was the daughter of a well-to-do pharmacist at historic Visby, the romantic capital of the island of Gotland in the Baltic Sea. Carl-Gustaf was the eldest of four brothers and a sister, and he was in many respects his mother's son, inheriting her keen and mobile brains and an intellectual tradition of the old Gotlandic pharmacy. The writer can still remember her as a youngish lively and ready-witted lady.

The four brothers have all done well in intellectual professions, but there is no doubt that the eldest differed fundamentally from the others. He must have led a life a little aside from that of ordinary boys, not being good at sports and having so many queer interests: music, geology, botany etc.—Gotland is famous for its orchids, and Rossby became an orchid-fan. Those of his American friends whom he took to Gotland can vouch for that.—Together with three schoolmates, kindred spirits, he formed a small private "club" where all sorts of intellectual sports were pursued. They kept together all throughout school, and even later, meeting for endless discussions of music, literature, art, science and politics; thus, Darwinism and religion were treated at length and in detail. He had a way—so his old schoolfriend tells, and those who knew him from Bergen will confirm—to vindicate any rather absurd or extreme statement to the bitter end . . . and then suddenly to give in, or sometimes even to go over to the opposite view, with a most amiable and puckish smile. He could give long "lectures" in subjects unknown to him, and when found out he would laugh.

Not only was Rossby very interested in botany but also in music. He liked to play the piano, and played it often as quite young. And yet this writer, having the very same interests, never came to know anything about Carl-Gustaf's studies or accomplishments in these fields. Occasionally, though, he would display a surprisingly good judgement of music we had heard together, without betraying his familiarity with this art.—His great ambition when grown up seems to have induced a strong desire not to give himself away when he suspected himself not quite up to the mark. This may also explain why nobody outside the circle of his family and schoolmates knew of his heart-weakness, until rather late. He had acquired it as a boy, after a rheumatic fever, and it had exempted him from military service.

He was not at all secretive in the negative sense of the word, but evidently he possessed a strong natural pride, which had built up a reserve around such parts of his personality and life that he from some reasons wanted to keep for himself. This is perhaps why, in later years, he showed a marked dislike to references to his young days at Bergen.

In the spring of 1917 C.-G. Rossby passed his matriculation examination, and in spite of his intense interests in natural science he did it on the Latin side. But he had evidently studied the modern side subjects too, since he could pass this complementary examination just one week later. — Now, many ways opened to young Rossby; the choice was evidently not an easy one since he had interests in most fields of learning. He first chose one of the most human of all: medicine. However, due to certain personal events, his progress in this career was suddenly interrupted, and he turned to the mathematical sciences. In less than a year he acquired his bachelor's degree (filosofie kandidat) with Astronomy, Mathematics and Mechanics as subjects, a phenomenal result since this study was supposed to take three years and it often lasted much longer.

*

These then were some important constituent parts of the mental equipment and education of young Carl-Gustaf Rossby, when on the 20th June 1919, not yet of age, he entered the circle around the famous Vilhelm Bjerknes at Bergen, Norway. He was then still without any knowledge of Meteorology; therefore, it would be interesting to learn how he had been induced to become V. Bjerknes' Carnegie assistant.

In the last year, before coming to Bergen, Rossby had pursued his studies of Mechanics (with Prof. Ivar Fredholm, famous for his work on integral equations) and of Astronomy. — But nobody seems to know any longer what had first brought him into contact with the field where he later could reap his laurels. The following conjecture, though, is certainly better than a guess. Even at the University, Rossby evidently differed considerably from his comrades, not only by his receptivity, but also by not being afraid of talking and asking. His professors could not help noticing this very young, very eager and very inquisitive student. One of the professors of mathematics was Ivar Bendixon, a close friend of V. Bjerknes' ever since the latter's days at the Stockholm University in 1893—1907. V. Bjerknes, in the winter of 1918/19, was talent-scouting Sweden for students willing to join the sprouting Bergen

The Bergen Weather Service, 14 Nov. 1919.

An attic-room, Allégaten 33, formerly a wealthy man's house, bestowed on Meteorology in 1918.—At the barograph: J. Bjerknes, chief.—At the left hand table (from left to right): T. Bergeron, C.-G. Rossby, S. Rosseland, junior meteorologists.—At the other tables: The technical staff.

School at its work, since Norway, at that time, could not provide a sufficient number of them. Bjerknes may have asked Bendixon to recommend a really keen young student, and Rossby will have been *the* one answering to the description . . . So Bendixon's choice, if this conjecture is right, made history in Meteorology.

Already Rossby's first days at Bergen revealed to us what a remarkable addition our synoptic-hydrodynamic team had received. This boy of 20 had an amazing persuasive and organizing faculty; his far-reaching ideas and high-flying plans often took our breath away. Soon he was also able to make practical suggestions of value for the experimental weather service that was connected with the Geophysical Institute at Bergen (having J. Bjerknes and his father V. Bjerknes as chiefs, respectively). This does not mean, however, that Rossby was "practical" in the commonplace sense of the word—among his family and schoolmates he was rather regarded as "impractical", i.e. not so dexterous with his hands and the like. In fact, the practical map work was not his favourite job or speciality even at Bergen.

At that time, instead, one saw glimpses of the talent that gives part of the clue to his great influence and rise to fame within Meteorology. —Several young Swedish Carnegie assistants boarded with the Bjerknes family during the eventful year 1919—when the Polar front and Life cycle of cyclones were discovered—serving also as hands in the new Weather Service in the same building. Before Christmas some of us were to leave Bergen, and we wanted to present our landlady, Mrs. Bjerknes, with a pair of silver candlesticks. Our speaker on the occasion was, of course, Rossby, although he was the youngest of us; the gift was delivered with a masterly little speech.—Many other incidents could be told, from that time and later, showing his budding eloquence and power to persuade people to do the things they least of all had intended to.

However, it is also evident that Rossby had not yet, at Bergen, found the time and place, and the branch of Meteorology, where his special capacity as a scientist and organizer could prosper. The work at Bergen, being to a great extent of a practical-technical kind, could not satisfy Rossby's searching spirit, in spite of the fact that within this very group of young men at the Weather Service the foundations of the Bergen School were then laid by the discoveries mentioned above—a challenging and fascinating task in itself.

It will not reduce the greatness of Carl-Gustaf Rossby, when we state that he made no direct contribution to this scientific development. Several reasons concurred to this result. Firstly, he was entirely a blank page meteorologically when he turned up at Bergen.—True enough it was favourable to Meteorology that the triumvirate V. Bjerknes, J. Bjerknes and H. Solberg knew so little of classical meteorology when they started to reform our science; thanks to this circumstance their minds were open to innovations On the other hand, they had received a good training in treating meteorological data from their time in the Leipzig School 1913/17. Rossby did not even possess this minimum knowledge beforehand.—Decisive in this respect, though, was most likely the fact that Rossby had no great faculty for, or interest in, scanning, combining and mapping all the concrete data appearing on synoptic maps, or at following the evolution of the sky. His map analyses at Bergen were generally most summary, to say the least.—His forte appeared, instead, already then in being a constant source of penetrating general ideas, especially in the more hydrodynamical part of geophysics, in being a master to concentrate on things of main importance, and in making himself and other people work with these problems and develop these ideas.

In many ways V. Bjerknes was the ideal teacher of theoretical hydrodynamics, a field that later proved to take possession of Rossby's ingenium and interest to an extent that Weather Service never could have done. However, during Rossby's Bergen year, 1919/20, hydrodynamics were pushed a little aside even with V. Bjerknes, in favour of the technical and empiric-physical work of the advancing Bergen School. Moreover, thanks to his receptive mind, Rossby had probably managed to absorb the main aspect of V. Bjerknes' theoretic-hydrodynamic message already during this one year.

Thus, in the summer of 1920 Rossby was ready to leave Bergen and to go over the hills and far away, where he might learn more and later be his own master.—At first, though, he did not go very far: only to Leipzig, to the Geophysical Institute, founded and furthered by V. Bjerknes in the period 1913/17. Thereby, he became even more closely attached to this kind of meteorology, and his later development showed that he, after all, bore the stamp of V. Bjerknes' general attitude towards our science, and that the Bergen year had left a lasting impression on him. He also kept and deepened the contact with his Bergen mates during a life-time.

It would be entirely wrong to believe that Rossby was uninterested in the empiric side of the Bergen work. Already when visiting Bergen again in the summer of 1922 — after a stay at the Prussian Aerologic Observatory of Lindenberg — he tried to induce J. Bjerknes to start some aerologic ascents from a flat island outside Bergen. This was apparently one of the few occasions when Rossby's persuasive power did not work. — The interest in organizing direct aerology appeared earlier and more manifest with him than with any one else of the Bergen group. This is amply proved by his very first scientific publication, dated Dec. 1922: *Den nordiska aerologiens arbetsuppgifter. En återblick och ett program* (Tasks of Scandinavian Aerology. A retrospect and a program). In this paper he proposes a network of aerologic stations around the Norwegian Sea that has not been realized until during the very last years — and one station of it is even now missing: Trondheim! This farsighted project of Rossby's was put forth when he had been only three years in Meteorology, and at a time when Arctic aerology was still non-existent. —The study of the Polar-air cap as a whole and its dynamics was already then a pet theme of his, at discussions and speculations. These early ideas thus, later, in a ripened shape formed an important part of the basis of the Chicago School work.

Part of the period 1922—1925 Rossby worked at the Swedish Meteorological and Hydrological Institute (Stockholm) as a junior meteorologist. His hibernation in a service of this type, which hardly could satisfy his very speculative, active and restless nature, was evidently made endurable by simultaneous studies at the University of Stockholm. He continued to work at Mechanics with Professor Fredholm. The Swedish "licentiat" degree (corresponding to a Ph.D.), achieved in 1925, meant a thorough education in this field and gave Rossby an indispensable fundament and tool for his later scientific work.

He would not have been the man he was, had he not during these years also taken part in some more or less unusual, or even risky enterprises. There may have been several, but two of them are well-known: the voyage in 1923 with the oceanographic vessel "Conrad Holmboe" through the pack-ice near East Greenland (which might have ended then and there), and the summer-cruise around the British Isles on the training-ship "af Chapman" in 1924. These diversions were not sufficient, though, to prevent Rossby's biggest "ski jump"—over to the U.S. in 1926 on a one-year fellowship from the Swedish-American Foundation. — That one year had grown to more than 20 years when he again became more than a transient visitor in his old country.

Carl-Gustaf Rossby's true fortitude was united with, or even conditioned by, his extraordinary enthusiasm. Together with a very marked intellectual and speculative disposition it determined his actions and development throughout life to organize and carry out work based on brilliant ideas and schemes begotten in the world of thought. This is the kind of ambition that hurts nobody and may help many, and together with Rossby's well-known personal charm it worked wonders. He was born to be a leader.

*

Rossby's further development—on the basis sketched above—and life-work in his new country, and back in Sweden, will be described in the following article. Therefore, only certain features from this later epoch, having roots in his youth and background, will be touched here. —In 1935 the writer met him again in Sweden. Rossby was now a man with an established position in the U.S. and an American family, his wife already an invaluable support to him. He was no longer the slender and almost over-sensitive youth of some 15 years earlier, but somewhat stocky and ripened—still full, though, of boyish enthusiasm.—These were the concrete data and outward appearances. But was there also an inward change as to his scientific standing?

Yes, there was.—Unlike the rest of us, Rossby had had the pluck of breaking away altogether from the tradition of his young days at Bergen, which had by now, at last, in a way become fashion in Meteorology. (The air-mass methods were officially introduced into American weather service in 1930.) This time he performed the real scientific "ski-jump" into the unknown. Instead of becoming an apostle of the Bergen School in the U.S., his zeal had driven him to try to start something of his own over there; and this attitude was clearly visible already during this visit to Sweden. He was evidently well on his way to lay the foundation of a new School in

Meteorology that might partly replace, partly supplement the Bergen School.

To the Bergen School the Polar front was (at that time) still the central concept, to which all its other entities were more or less attached. In a lecture at Stockholm in 1935 Rossby, on the other hand, positively declared that he offered another basic system for the middle-latitude weather processes, where the upper westerly air-flow was the fundamental entity, and where one did not need the Polar front. The rest of his system was at that time in many respects quite different from what it became some five years later, but the nucleus of his later truly Lagrangian study of the jet-stream and its long waves was already there.

V. Bjerknes, in his famous program of 1904, had outlined the goal of our science. L. F. Richardson had attempted, in 1910—1922, strictly to apply these principles to one trial case, but had failed. Only Rossby, in 1938/40, could achieve this next, much longed-for, break through, thanks to his extraordinary combination of a good mathematical-mechanical education, an intense desire to do better than his forerunners, and his ingenious faculty of ruthlessly simplifying a problem until it becomes solvable—i.e. his practical sense in the world of thought. One might even say that the very fact that Rossby had failed to play a rôle in the Bergen School and in the first significant meteorological advance of this century, goaded him into making the utmost of his great endowments and to found a new School built on methods that suited his special gifts, thereby initiating a second great meteorological advance.

*

There is still a long and dreary way to go in Meteorology before we can really begin to compete with the other physical sciences as to results, because our problems are so utterly complex and unsurveyable. However, C.-G. Rossby has taught us the lesson, afresh, that, to ensure progress, theoreticians and empiricists must go hand in hand at their work. Thanks to him we have again been able to force a difficult section of the road. He could achieve this because of his rare combination of faculties and a life that acted as a mighty stimulus to these gifts, thereby also stimulating all those who came within his sphere of action. By this capacity and by his charming personality he won innumerable followers and friends who shall always thankfully remember the great scientist and man Carl-Gustaf Rossby.

Carl-Gustaf Rossby, the Organizer

By Horace R. Byers

Carl-Gustaf Rossby not only was impatient with the progress of meteorology but was determined from the start that he personally had to do something about it. How could a man in his twenties move weather services, foundations and universities into the kind of action he felt was necessary? His stocky build and thinning hair made him look older than his years, but administrators were only slightly amused or downright annoyed by his unbounded, youthful enthusiasm.

Some who have assessed his career maintain that the free-going attitude of Americans toward progress enabled him to make his way. This factor may have helped at some points on his route to success, but in the beginning he could not have found a worse place for a young man than the Central Office of the U.S. Weather Bureau, where he first went in 1925 after finishing his Swedish education. Under an accomplished but short-sighted chief and lesser officials chosen for their loyalty and administrative ability rather than their scientific outlook, the Weather Bureau put up an impenetrable barrier to the young Swede's exuberant schemes. In fact, when he left Washington after 2½ years there, Rossby was literally *persona non grata* to the Weather Bureau and word went out to all stations to that effect.

Rossby was undaunted. He had been making some very valuable friends in Washington through his personal charm, enthusiasm and obvious knowledge of modern meteorology. While still in the good graces of the Weather Bureau after his first year in Washington, his appointment as Research Associate in Meteorology (assigned to the Weather Bureau) of the Daniel Guggenheim Fund for the Promotion of Aeronautics was accomplished. The Fund needed his help in planning flights such as those of Richard E. Byrd. Harry F. Guggenheim, President of the Fund and Government aviation officials such as I. M. Cone, Edward P. Warner, Jerome C. Hunsaker and Francis W. Reichelderfer, saw in Rossby a man of great promise. In 1927 Rossby's carreer as an organizer began, when he was appointed chairman of the Fund's Committee on Aeronautical Meteorology.

His first big organizing task came at the end of that year when the Fund decided to establish a model airline between San Francisco and Los Angeles. Rossby was asked to develop an experimental weather service for the area. He walked into the district office of the Weather Bureau in San Francisco a few days after the letter warning against him had been received from Washington. The official in charge was the late Edward H. Bowie, politically astute, more forward looking than most of his cohorts and unimpressed by the Washington bureaucrats, over most of whom he held seniority. He chose to ignore the letter and welcomed the 29-year-old Rossby to the Golden State.

With a generous expense account and an Army airplane and pilot at his disposal, Rossby was in his glory as he flew around the state setting up the dense network of stations. The interest in the future of aviation at that time, a few months after Charles A. Lindbergh's famous trans-Atlantic solo flight, was intense. Rossby and his Army pilot often were met at the edge of towns by the mayor and president of the Chamber of Commerce and driven to a banquet at the town's best hotel.

In the late spring of 1928 the system was ready to be operated. It was then that the author of this piece became associated with Rossby at the weather collection center at the Oakland Airport. Meanwhile, Rossby's remarkable persuasive and organizing ability, aided by an awakening of the Weather Bureau as to what was going on and by pressure from Washington officials, resulted in the Bureau's consent to operate the service for the Guggenheim Fund. Later that summer Rossby and the Fund presented the system directly to the Weather Bureau, where it became the model around which subsequent airways weather services in the United States were built. Rossby then stepped out; for even greater things were about to happen.

In connection with the Daniel Guggenheim Aeronautical Laboratory which the Fund had established at the Massachusetts Institute of Technology, it was decided that a graduate course of instruction in meteorology, aimed mainly at training Navy officers, should be established.

Rossby was appointed Associate Professor of Meteorology, responsible to his friend Dr. Edward P. Warner, Head of the Aeronautical Engineering Course, at M.I.T. He left San Francisco in September 1928 to take up his new post in Cambridge, leaving Delbert M. Little, Edward M. Vernon and the author to run the operations at Oakland, with George M. French holding up the Los Angeles end of the line at old Vail Field.

Before starting at M.I.T., Rossby persuaded Hurd C. Willett, a Weather Bureau employee who had obtained his doctor's degree in physics with specialization in meteorology at George Washington University under William J. Humphreys, to join him as an assistant professor. The two of them taught a group of four Navy officers the first year. Later in the year the group was joined by Chaim L. Pekeris, an M.I.T. civilian student, who was later to become the first to receive a doctor's degree under Rossby, and who is now a well-known theoretical geophysicist.

Rossby also used his persuasive powers that year on Harriet Alexander, of Boston, and they were married just at the beginning of the second year.

The course in meteorology grew rapidly; Rossby became a full professor; a small body of civilian students augmented the military group, and the outstanding research under his guidance was carried on. In describing the years with Rossby at M.I.T., I can only repeat the words used in an obituary piece written for the American Meteorological Society, as in the following paragraph.

"At M.I.T. Rossby exhibited that leadership for which he was famous. Those who studied under him practically worshipped him. They were participating in his great crusade—to bring modern meteorology to America where the science had been existing in a stifling atmosphere for many years. The experience of studying under Rossby was most exhilarating. His lectures were carefully prepared and given with enthusiasm and his informal discussions over luncheon or a cup of coffee in the neighborhood lunch room across the street on Massachusetts Avenue were nothing less than an inspiration."

At M.I.T. Rossby also directed his attention to physical oceanography, which was in a state of neglect in America. A friendly atmosphere for this interest existed in connection with the fisheries work in the Museum of Comparative Zoology at Harvard under H. B. Bigelow and Columbus O. D. Iselin. It was only natural that with the founding of the Woods Hole Oceanographic Institution Rossby became a part-time associate. He insisted that his meteorology students at M.I.T. should learn physical oceanography, and some of his graduates, notably Raymond B. Montgomery and Athelstan F. Spilhaus have devoted part or all of their time to this field. The great master himself retained his interest in oceanography throughout his career as is well known to readers of this volume. His influence most certainly was felt in the decisions involving the long sojourn in the United States of the late Dr. Harald U. Sverdrup.

In his years at M.I.T. Rossby found himself engaged in the type of conflicts with administrators which everywhere created turbulence in his career. There was the question of an independent department for meteorology in the face of a drive by the administration to have fewer and larger academic units; there were regulations concerning degrees and other academic affairs which Rossby applied only to the extent that he felt they were good for the science of meteorology; and there were the ever-present budgetary difficulties. An academic institution could hardly be big enough to contain the great schemes of Rossby.

He found a partial outlet for his expansive vision in the position he took in 1939 as Assistant Chief for Research and Development of the U.S. Weather Bureau. Having just been naturalized as a U.S. citizen, he was not considered to be eligible for the vacant position of Chief of the Bureau. That post went to F. W. Reichelderfer who, with Rossby's help, began to build a more modern Weather Bureau. Rossby found a special interest in trying to improve the Bureau's manpower situation. The lack of meteorological training centers in the United States had resulted in the staffing of the Bureau with poorly trained personnel. Rossby inaugurated an intensified in-service training program and used a variety of devices to send qualified personnel to the existing meteorological schools—M. I. T. and New York University, the latter organized in the late 1930s. With the invasion of Norway, J. Bjerknes was more or less stranded in the United States. Rossby persuaded him to remain and also convinced the University of California that it should build a Department of Meteorology around Bjerknes. Thus the group in Los Angeles came into being in 1940.

Meanwhile also in 1940, the University of Chicago, influenced by the writer, established an

Institute (later called Department) of Meteorology and invited Rossby to come to Chicago as its head. He left the Weather Bureau in 1941 to begin his famous Chicago period of approximately ten years.

Pearl Harbor and the United States involvement in World War II brought new scope to Rossby's activities. He was immediately in Washington fighting for the kind of training program for meteorologists which he knew the military services needed. His activities in those hectic days defy description. He became almost a commuter between Chicago and Washington and other military centers. The result was the establishment of what was considered to be the best military educational program of its time. Thousands of young graduates were trained in one-year intensified courses, about 1,700 at Chicago alone under Rossby's general direction. The organization of the University Meteorological Committee which recruited the men and guided the program was due to Rossby, with a great deal of help from the renowned physicist-geophysicist Joseph Kaplan and from Eldon L. Johnson, now President of the University of New Hampshire. The program was developed to include pre-meteorological studies in basic education and science as well as the more advanced professional course. Convincing the military that this could be done best at universities was possible only through the Rossby charm.

This writer has the feeling that even to this day administrators and colleagues in other departments of the University of Chicago do not believe that Rossby could have done high-grade research work during this period of preoccupation with the world crisis. But the record shows that he did.

In the middle of the war word came back from the tropical regions that the young officers were not prepared to cope with the strange meteorological problems of the low latitudes in which a major part of the war was being fought. To Rossby the obvious solution was to establish an Institute of Tropical Meteorology. This was done in the spring of 1943 at the University of Puerto Rico with the help of the New Zealand tropical specialist Clarence Palmer. After this start Herbert Riehl rose to fame there, developing the models of tropical disturbances. A nucleus of Air Corps and Navy officers learned the techniques there and the tropical weather problems of the military were on their way toward solution.

Word came back from other areas of difficulties the young officers were having with weather in unusual situations. Rossby organized teams of university meteorologists and better-trained officers to "trouble-shoot" and consult in these areas, going to the most distant places. The great master himself went on the trans-Atlantic flights, then difficult and arduous, appeared in Africa, Italy, the South Pacific and points beyond, always full of ideas for improving the situation.

With the close of the war, Rossby already had plans under way for the post-war era. He and some of his colleagues felt that the American Meteorological Society needed reorganizing to become a really high-grade scientific society, and he set himself to this task with the usual vigor. Among the personal effects found in his apartment in Stockholm after his death is a log or diary for the period October 1944 to January 1945 which is full of entries relating to the reorganization of the Society. This is the only diary, however brief, that he ever kept, and it is recalled that his associates at Chicago wondered at the time what possessed him to do such an un-Rossby-like thing. We are thankful for it, because it shows the agonizing details, the personal quibbling, the play and interplay of personalities involved when a man tries to do someting momentous. He was highly successful, and the Society and its Journal of Meteorology, as existing today, were largely carved out by this man.

In connection with the American Meteorological Society he also saw that it was his duty to provide greater opportunities in meteorology for the vast numbers of young men who would be leaving the military service. Industrial meteorology as an outlet for this young talent attracted his attention, and he spent many hours and days, including much travel in the interest of this development. What success this field of application has had in America is due to a considerable extent to his efforts.

Among other organizing actions during this period were those in connection with studies of Hawaiian weather and climate, in cooperation with the Pineapple Research Institute, starting much valuable research in that area. At Chicago intense efforts to bring world scientists together again after their war-time separation resulted in an amazing collection of meteorologists—Palmén, Bergeron, Nyberg, Quéney, Van Mieghem for extended stays, Sekera, Bolin, Yeh, Hsieh, Kuo and others of distinction. These were the great days of the Chicago School.

Then came the Stockholm period. Having made his world-wide reputation, Rossby now was listened to with great respect in his native land. How different from his student days when all of Sweden and even the world seemed to be against this overly eager young man! He was now about 50 years of age and Sweden was good to him and good for him. His organizing ability was found helpful in assessing the country's needs in meteorological services and education and in establishing research goals. But Rossby would not stop there. He saw in Sweden the opportunity for better international cooperation in a war-torn world. The need, as he saw it, was for an international institute of meteorology.

The work in organizing the International Institute which he directed until his untimely death, forms perhaps too recent a story to be recounted here. Many of his efforts are only now bearing fruit. The disappointments in obtaining the kind of international recognition and support he would have liked, the financial instability accompanying the expansion at the breath-taking Rossby rate, the indifference encountered in some quarters, were more than compensated by the great success of the Institute as an international force in meteorological research. The founding of the high-grade geophysical research journal Tellus was an accomplishment that will live as a monument to his efforts.

During the months before he died, the great master was thinking of other areas where he could practice his magic touch. He thought of the Middle East. Yes, he was going to settle somewhere in that area and found an institute of meteorology where the regional need for scientific development could be met, and met by the dynamic impact of Rossby. One can only conjecture as to what would have happened in that rapidly awakening region had Rossby lived another ten years.

Publications by Carl-Gustaf Rossby

1923 Den nordiska aerologiens arbetsuppgifter. En återblick och ett program. Ymer, Vol 43; 364.

1924 On the origin of travelling discontinuities in the atmosphere. Geogr. annaler, Vol VI; 180—189.

Thermisches Gleichgewicht in der Atmosphäre. Arkiv f. mat., astr. och fys., Bd 18; No. 11 and 20.

1925 Meteorologiska resultat av en sommarseglats runt de brittiska öarna. M. H. A., Medd., Bd 3; 1.

Not beträffande teorin för Flettner-rotorn, Tekn. Tidskr., H 2.

1926 On the solution of problems of atmospheric motion by means of model experiments. Monthly Weather Rev., Vol 54; 237—240.

The vertical distribution of atmospheric eddy energy. Monthly Weather Rev., Vol 54; 321—332.

(with R. H. Weightman) Application of the polarfront theory to series of American weather maps. Monthly Weather Rev., Vol 54; 485—496.

1927 Convection in the free atmosphere and over a heated surface. Monthly Weather Rev., Vol 55; 1—5.

The theory of atmospheric turbulence—an historical résumé and an outlook. Monthly Weather Rev. Vol 55; 6—10.

Zustandsänderungen in atmosphärischen Luftsäulen, I. Beitr. z. Phys. d. fr. Atm., Bd. 13; 164—174.

1928 Airways and the weather. Western Flying Magazine, April 1928, No. 4.

Zustandsänderungen in atmosphärischen Luftsäulen, II. Beitr. z. Phys. d. fr. Atm., Bd 14; 65.

Studies in the dynamics of the stratosphere. Beitr. z. Phys. d. fr. Atm., Bd. 14; 240—265.

1929 (with C. M. Alvord and R. H. Smith). The tephigram, its theory and practical uses in weather forecasting. M.I.T. Met. Prof. Notes, No. 1; 7—13.

1930 On the effect of vertical convection on lapse-rates. Journ. Wash. Acad. Sci., Vol. 20 No. 3; 33—35.

1932 Thermodynamics applied to air mass analysis. Papers in Phys. Oceanogr. and Met., Vol. I, No. 3.

A generalization of the theory of the mixing length with applications to atmospheric and oceanic turbulence. Papers in Phys. Oceanogr. and Met., Vol. I, No. 4.

1934 Comments on meteorological research. Journ. Aeronaut. Sci., Vol 1; 32—34.

1935 (with R. Montgomery) The layer of frictional influence in wind and ocean currents. Papers in Phys. Oceanogr. and Met., Vol. III, No. 3.

1936 (with R. Montgomery) On the momentum transfer at the sea surface. Papers in Phys. Oceanogr. and Met., Vol. IV, No. 3.

Dynamics of steady ocean currents in the light of experimental fluid mechanics. Papers in Phys. Oceanogr. and Met., Vol. 5, No. 1.

1937 Isentropic analysis. Bulletin of the Amer. Met. Soc. Vol 18; 201—209.

On the mutual adjustment of pressure and velocity distributions in certain simple current systems. Journ. of Mar. Res., Vol. 1; 15—28.

Aerological evidence of large-scale mixing in the amosphere. Trans. Am. Geophys. Union 1937 I; 130—136.

Rate of turbulent mixing. In paper by F. B. Wood: The formation and dissipation of stratus clouds beneath turbulence inversions. M.I.T. Met. Prof. Notes, No. 10; 9—15.

1938 On the mutual adjustment of pressure and velocity distributions in certain simple current systems. II. Journ. of Mar. Res., Vol. I; 239—263.

Solenoidal circulations resulting from lateral mixing. Trans. Am. Geophys. Un., Vol 19; 159—162.

On temperature changes in the stratosphere resulting from shrinking and stretching. Beitr. z. Phys. d. fr. Atm. B. 24; 53—60.

On the role of isentropic mixing in the general circulation of the atmosphere. Proc. of the Fifth International Congress of Applied Mechanics. 1938; 373—379.

(with J. Namias, R. G. Simners) Fluid mechanics applied to the study of atmospheric circulations. On the maintenance of the westerlies south of the polar front. Papers in Phys. Oceanogr. and Met., Vol. VII, No. 1.

Note on shearing stresses caused by large-scale lateral mixing. Proceedings of the Fifth International Congress of Applied Mechanics, 1938; 379—382.

(with G. Grimminger, C. L. Pekeris, J. Namias and H. Wexler). Applications of fluid mechanics to the problem of the general circulation of the atmosphere. Trans. Am. Geophys. Union, 1938; 159—170, 174—176.

1939 Relation between variations in the intensity of the zonal circulation of the atmosphere and the displacements of the semi-permanent centers of action. Journ. of Mar. Res., Vol. 2; 38—55.

1940 Planetary flow patterns in the atmosphere. Toronto 1940. Quarterly Journal of the R.M.S., Vol. 66, Suppl. 1940; 68—87.

1941 Comments on the Weather Bureau's experiment in five-day weather-forecasting. Trans. Am. Geoph. Union. 1941; 437—437 b.

The scientific basis of modern meteorology. U.S. Yearbook of Agriculture, Climate and Man; 599—655. (Chinese edition, Formosa 1947.)

Amateur forecasting from cloud formations. U.S. Yearbook of Agriculture. Climate and Man; 656—661.

1942 (with V. J. Oliver and M. Boyden) Weather estimates from local aerological data. A Preliminary Report. Univ. of Chicago, Inst. of Met., Miscellaneous Reports No. 2, Chicago.

Kinematic and hydrostatic properties of certain long waves in the westerlies. Univ. of Chicago, Inst. of Met., Miscellaneous Reports, No. 5.

Forecasting of flow patterns in the free atmosphere by the trajectory method. Appendix Victor P. Starr: Basic Principles of Weather Forecasting; 268—284.

1943 Boundary layer problems in the atmosphere and ocean. New York 1943. Introduction to the conference and some applications of boundary-layer theory to the physical geography of the Middle West. New York Acad. Sci. 44, Art. 1; 3—12.

Specific evaluation of pilot balloon data in single station forecasting. In Univ. of Chicago, Inst. of Met., Miscellaneous Reports, No. 7.

1944 Horizontal motion in the atmosphere. Journal of Meteorology, Vol. 1; 109—114.

1945 On the propagation of frequencies and energy in certain types of oceanic and atmospheric waves. Journal of Meteorology, Vol. 2; 187—204.

The earth sciences and the undergraduate liberal arts curriculum. Bull. Am. Met. Soc., Vol 26; 1—4.

1947 On the general circulation of the atmosphere in the middle latitudes. Staff of the Dept. of Met., Univ. of Chicago, Bull. Am. Met. Soc., Vol. 28; 255—280.

Notes on the distribution of energy and frequency in surface waves. Journ. of Mar. Res., Vol. 6; 93—103.

On the distribution of angular velocity in gaseous envelopes under the influence of large-scale horizontal mixing processes. Bull. Amer. Met. Soc., Vol. 28; 53—68.

Recent advances and probable future trends in basic and applied meteorology. Proc. of the third Hydraulics Conf., Bull. 31, Univ. of Iowa Studies in Engineering; 103—120.

1948 Nyare riktlinjer inom meteorologien: De atmosfäriska rörelsesystemens skala och struktur. Kosmos Bd. 26; 162—182.

(with H. C. Willett) The circulation of the upper troposphere and lower stratosphere. Science, Vol. 108; 643—652.

On displacements and intensity changes of atmospheric vortices. Journal of Marine Research, Vol. 7; 175—187.

(with R. Berggren, B. Bolin) On the mechanism of changes in the upper flow pattern. Union Géodésique et Géophysique International. Huitième Assemblée Générale, Oslo 1948.

1949 On a mechanism for the release of potential energy in the atmosphere. Journal of Meteorology, Vol. 6; 163—180.

On the dispersion of planetary waves in a barotropic atmosphere. Tellus, Vol. 1, Nr. 1; 54—58.

On the nature of the general circulation of the lower atmosphere. In Kuiper. The Atmospheres of the Earth and Planets. Chicago 1949; 16—48.

(with H. Ertel) Ein Neuer Erhaltungs-satz der Hydrodynamik. Sitzungsberichte der Deutschen Akademie der Wissenschaften zu Berlin. Mathematisch-naturwissenschaftliche Klasse, Jahrgang 1949, Nr. 1, Akademie-Verlag, Berlin.

(with H. Ertel) A new conservation-theorem of hydrodynamics. Geofisica Pura e Applicata, Milano. Vol. XIV; 189—193.

(with V. P. Starr) Interpretations of the angular-momentum principle as applied to the general circulation of the atmosphere. Journal of Meteorology, Vol. 6; 288.

Glaciers and Climatology; Hans W:son Ahlmann's contribution. Glaciers and Climate, Geografiska Annaler 1949, No. 1—2; 11—13.

(with R. Berggren, B. Bolin) An aerological study of zonal motion, its perturbations and break-down. Tellus Vol. 1, No. 2; 14—37.

1950 On the dynamics of certain types of blocking Waves. Journal of the Chinese Geophysical Society. Vol. 2; 1—13.

1951 Ueber die Vertikalverteilung von Windgeschwindigkeit und Schwerestabilität in Freistrahlbewegungen der oberen Troposphäre. Archiv für Meteorologie, Geophysik und Bioklimatologie, Serie A, Vol. 4; 3—23.

Note on cooperative research projects. Tellus Vol. 3; 212—216.

On the vertical and horizontal concentration of momentum in air and ocean currents. Tellus, Vol. 3; 15—27.

1952 Wanted: A government policy towards research. Statens Naturvetenskapliga Forskningsråds Årsbok 1951/52.

1953 A comparison of current patterns in the atmosphere and in the ocean basins. Un. Geod. et Geophys. Int., 9th Gen. Ass., Procès-Verbaux, Assoc. de Météor., Brussels 1951; 9—30.

1955 (with H. Egnér) On the chemical climate and its variation with the atmospheric circulation pattern. Tellus, Vol. 7; 118—133.

1957 Aktuella meteorologiska problem. *Svensk Naturvetenskap, 1956*. Statens Naturvetenskapliga Forskningsråds Årsbok; 15—80. (Translation: Current problems in meteorology. Reprinted in this volume; 9—50).

THE SEA IN MOTION

The Recent Warming of the North Atlantic

By J. Bjerknes
University of California, Los Angeles

Historical Note

Among the many problems that fascinated Rossby during his outstandingly active and distinguished research career the question of the mutual influence of atmosphere and ocean ranked high. In recent years, when his planning for the future was no less active than before, he repeatedly spoke of a possible joint oceanographic-meteorological project that would aim at building a broad base for the subsequent establishment of a general geo-and-solar-physical theory for climatic change. In the spring of 1957 at U.C.L.A. he suggested to me the Geophysical Institute in Bergen, Norway, as the appropriate headquarters for that project. He wanted to see it develop in the town where Fridtjof Nansen and Björn Helland-Hansen (1917) had made their pioneering maritime meteorological study and where Rossby himself had received his first inspiration in research from V. Bjerknes. I was strongly moved by Rossby's suggestion, promised my support and, as a preliminary step for my participation in the project, began collecting data for the present article. Our next contact was to have been somewhere in Scandinavia in the fall of 1957.

Abstract

The maximum rate of rise of sea surface temperature is found along the Gulf Stream from Cape Hatteras to the edges of the Newfoundland Banks. It has persisted there from the eighteen-nineties to the present. A belt from Ireland to the edge of the Labrador current was not warmed up during the same period although it is traversed by the northern branches of the Gulf Stream. North of that belt the warming started around 1920 together with the spectacular amelioration of climate in Greenland, Iceland and Scandinavia. Most of the observed secular changes in ocean temperature south of 50° N can be interpreted as having been caused in part by increasing wind drag, which has speeded up the Antilles Current and the Gulf Stream and possibly also by the increasing thickness of the warm surface layer in the areas of increasing anticyclonic wind drag. Between 50° and 57° N the corresponding surface cooling, connected with a thinning out of the surface layer by increasing cyclonic wind drag, partly also assisted by increasing cold winds from North America, must have been strong enough to overcompensate the advective warming in the belt from Ireland to the edge of the Labrador Current.

1. Data for the present study

The possibility of studying the fluctuations of Atlantic sea surface temperatures has of late improved appreciably through the publication by Bullig in 1954 of the statistics covering sea surface temperatures, winds, and cloudiness along the Europe to South America shipping lane during the periods 1906—13 and 1922—38, and the pamphlet by Riehl (1956) presenting the preliminary statistics on North Atlantic sea surface temperatures observed on board ships having reported to the U.S. Weather Bureau during the period 1887—1936. The northern limit of this coverage is 50° N. North of that line we have available the statistics of sea surface temperatures from 1876 up to the present published under the auspices of the Conseil Permanent International pour l'Exploration de la Mer, in Copenhagen. The latter valuable record goes back to the period covered by the Hoffmeyer daily synoptic maps of the North Atlantic region published jointly by the Danish Meteorological Institute and the Deutsche Seewarte in Hamburg. The present surveys of the Conseil International are mainly based on the data collected by the Danish Meteorological Institute and published in its Nautic-Meteorological Annual. The historical summary used in this article was published by SMED (1952).

The subject of the present essay is, first, a condensed description of the observed secular change of temperature of the North Atlantic and, secondly, an attempt at assigning the responsibility for those temperature changes to a selection of known physical processes.

2. The trend of North Atlantic sea surface temperatures

The more or less standard procedure in looking for a climatic trend goes by way of forming overlapping time averages, preferably as long as 30 years if the data permit. Since the American data collection does not cover more than 50 years, and does have gaps during and after World War I, the method of over-lapping averages is unsuitable. As a second choice we can compare a selected test period near the beginning with one near the end of the fifty years. Test periods of eight years were selected, namely 1890—97 and 1926—33. That choice trims the fifty years by the first three and the last three years during which the coverage was somewhat poor. The choice of the eight year length of the test periods was a matter of convenience arising from the fact that the German data cover two separate periods, one of eight and one of seventeen years. Anyway, eight year periods average out well enough the short period ups and downs which we are not studying at this stage.

The published material consists of sea surface temperature anomalies computed for five-degree squares. The anomalies refer to the fifty-year average in those squares where a record of that length is available, elsewhere to shorter periods. An anomaly map therefore does not present a quite homogeneous set of information, but the difference between two anomaly maps illustrates the real change from the one test period to the other. Fig. 1 represents that kind of a map showing the change of sea surface temperature that has taken place between the two test periods 1890—97 and 1926—33.

The map shows in the low latitudes of the western Atlantic and in the Sargasso Sea a slight upward trend of less than 0.5° C. The rising trend dates mainly from the period after 1920.

In marked contrast hereto the narrow region of the Gulf Stream shows big positive trends of temperature. In the particular section from Cape Hatteras to the southern escarpment of the Newfoundland Banks the upward trend has lasted since the beginning of the published data in the late eighteen-eighties.

The drawing of the iso-lines of anomaly change can of course be made in many different ways on the basis of the quite open grid of data plotted at the centers of five-degree squares. The admittedly subjective solution given in Fig. 1 is based on the assumption that the maximum positive changes should be clearly aligned along the average position of the oceanic polar front. Our analysis then inevitably arrives at values exceeding two or even three degrees centigrade along the center line of the zone of maximum rise between 70° W and 50° W. Further quantitative refinement in that part of the analysis can only be achieved if it proves possible to make the statistics of sea surface temperature apply to smaller squares. In the region of great ship density near 40° N that would seem well feasible.

The warming of the Atlantic waters continues in a tongue extending eastward from the edge of the Banks over toward the southern European coast. The weak and diffuse branches of the Gulf Stream occupying that part of the Atlantic apparently also profit by the secular warming of the main stem of the current.

Between 50° N and 57° N the trend in the sea temperature has been slightly negative. That is, in fact, the only region within the whole Gulf Stream system where the long range trend of warming fails to show up. This belt of negative trend of temperature is traversed by the strongest, farthest left branch of the Gulf Stream system which is heading for Iceland. The explanation of the surprising lack of secular temperature rise along that branch and its ramifications, will be attempted in the following section.

North of about 57° N the trend in sea temperature has been slightly upward. Actually that secular change results from a brief but strong upward trend in the nineteen-twenties which overcompensates the accumulated effect of a preceding long and slow downward trend. A

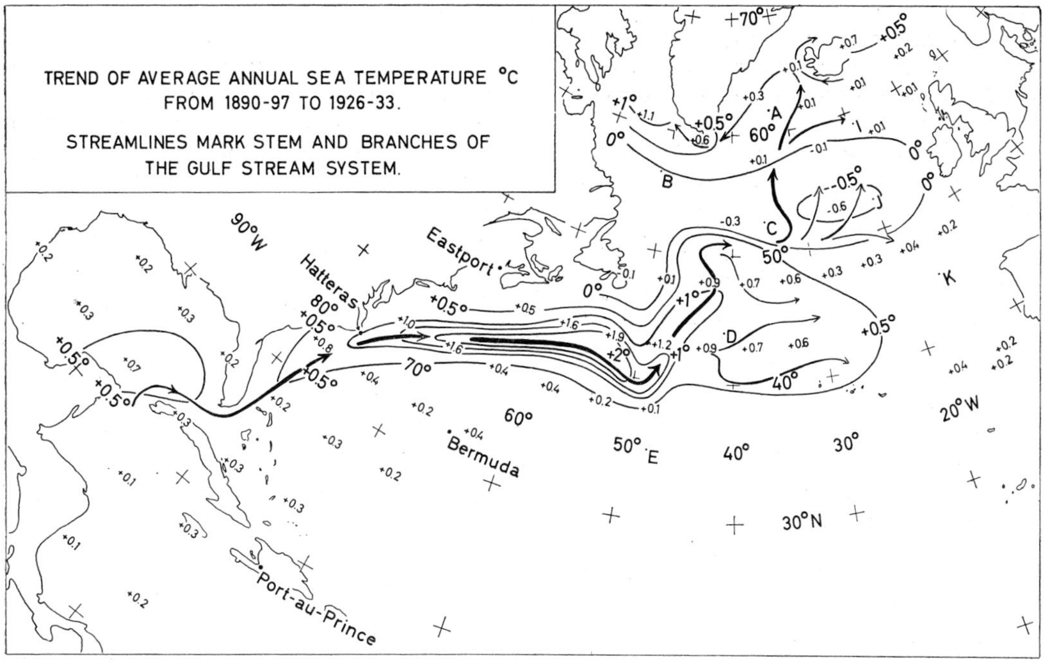

Fig. 1. Streamlines of the Gulf Stream system, and isallotherms in °C of annual sea surface temperature from 1890—97 to 1926—33. Positions of present weather ships marked with capital letters.

somewhat similar brisk upward trend, starting as late as 1920, is found in the Labrador current on the Newfoundland Banks in close proximity to the main stem of the Gulf Stream, where the rising trend got under way at least thirty years earlier. The surface temperature contrast at the oceanic polar front south of Newfoundland was thus rising from 1890 to 1920 and later became more constant.

3. The physical interpretation

The primary energy for all meteorological and oceanic processes comes from the sun. An increase in the rate of delivery of that energy to the ocean would raise its surface temperature and, more indirectly, the temperature of the superjacent atmosphere. Such a process may perhaps be responsible for most of the slow rise in ocean temperature in the part of the low latitude belt mapped in Fig. 1, but it is unlikely that any of the bigger rises occurring in higher latitudes could be simply a direct effect of increased insolation. And it is of course quite impossible to interpret the narrow strip of big temperature rises along the oceanic polar front except as an effect of a change in the oceanic circulation. Such a secular trend in oceanic circulation is most likely dictated by changes in atmospheric circulation, which in their turn ultimately may have solar causes.

This article will only deal with a discussion of the relationship between the secular changes of atmospheric and oceanic circulations. The secular change of the atmosphere circulation over the North Atlantic from 1890—97 to 1926—33 is represented in Fig. 2 by the observed change with time of sea level pressure. Denoting that quantity by Δp, we have for the corresponding secular change Δu_g and Δv_g of the two cartesian components u_g and v_g of the annual average of the geostrophic wind

$$\Delta u_g = -\frac{\alpha}{2\Omega \sin \varphi} \frac{\partial \Delta p}{\partial y}$$

$$\Delta v_g = \frac{\alpha}{2\Omega \sin \varphi} \frac{\partial \Delta p}{\partial x}$$

The relationship of the "anomaly wind" to the isallobar field in Fig. 2 is thus the same as that of the wind itself to the field of isobars. It is a logical assumption, established by several earlier researchers in this field, that the change in geostrophic wind with time should also provide the explanation for most of the secular change of the surface temperature of the ocean. The underlying reasoning can briefly be summed up as follows.

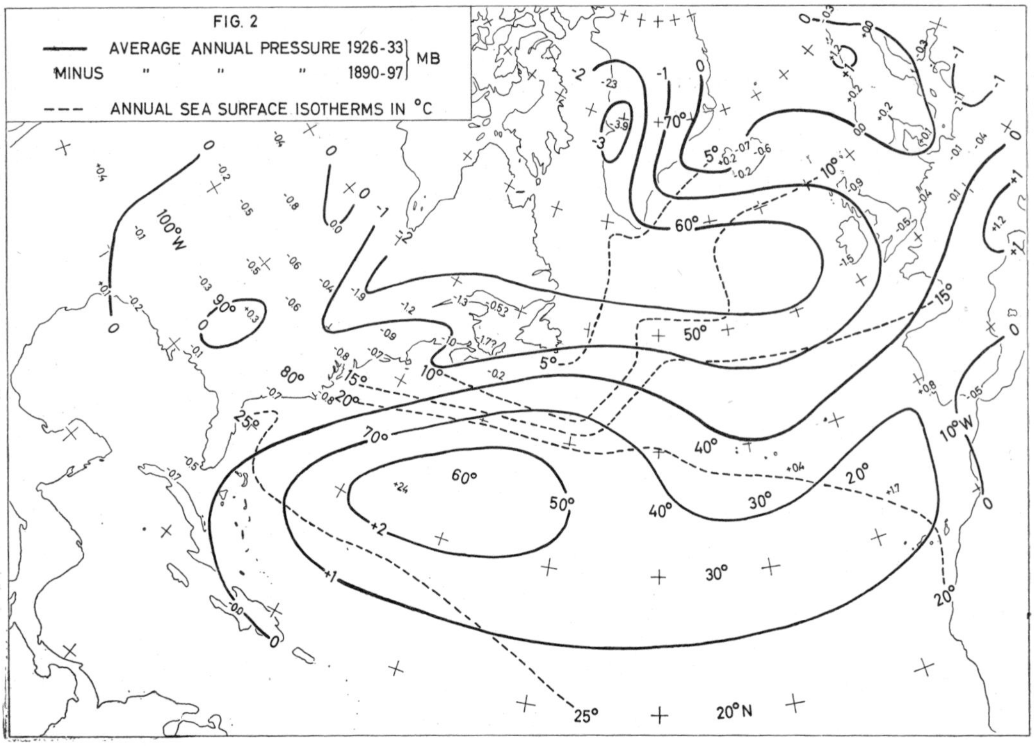

Fig. 2. Change in mb of average annual sea level pressure from the period 1890—97 to that of 1926—33 (full lines), and average annual sea surface isotherms (dashed lines).

The wind stress exerted on a level ocean surface produces in the northern hemisphere a water displacement to the right of the wind direction. In a closed anticyclonic wind system the water displacement therefore converges toward the center of the anticyclone until a tilt of the ocean surface outward from the center has been built up sufficiently to stop the water convergence. The new mass distribution, with dome shaped isobaric surfaces under the dome shaped ocean surface, provides the field of force necessary to keep the water mass in anticyclonic circulation. Since the change to a new mass distribution was caused by wind stress, it is justified to speak of the resulting geostrophic ocean current as a wind-driven one. A further adjustment to the final steady state comes as shown by STOMMEL (1948), from the tendency of the anticyclonic water vortex and the corresponding mass field to travel westward due to the local piling up of water in northgoing geostrophic motion and local depletion of water in southgoing motion (change with latitude of the Coriolis factor). The final anticyclonic water vortex is therefore centered farther west than the center of the atmospheric anticyclone and maintains a jet-like ocean current on its western and northern side. In that way the Gulf Stream in the Atlantic, and the analogous Kuroshio in the Pacific, are maintained indirectly by the prevailing anticyclonic wind stress on the ocean surface in the latitudes below 40° N. Both jet currents run along the tilting "cold wall" of water masses not belonging to the subtropical anticyclonic circulation. The corresponding temperature discontinuity of the Atlantic "polar front" is seen in Fig. 2 in the crowding of the annual ocean surface isotherms from Cape Hatteras to the perimeter of the Newfoundland Banks. Since the whole large scale current system is ultimately wind-driven, any secular change in the winds, as represented geostrophically by Fig. 2, will be accompanied by a slight secular change in the currents and in their advection of heat. Later we will discuss how the rate of heat loss down to the colder deepwater also depends on the winds, but first let us consider the direct advective effects.

The isallobars in Fig. 2 show, as far as the

latitudes up to 50° N are concerned, a distribution of values rather like that of the map of average annual pressure. Hence, the subtropical anticyclone has been strengthened from 1890—97 to 1926—33, and to the original anticyclonic wind circulation has been added an anomaly circulation to strengthen the anticyclonic wind drag on the ocean. The isallobaric gradient is particularly strong around the western end of the isallobaric high. The correspondingly strengthened winds run approximately parallel to the Antilles current and the Gulf Stream both of which must have been secularly accelerated.

The pressure difference at sea level from Bermuda roughly south-southwestward, to Port au Prince (Haiti), west-northwestward to Hatteras and northward to Eastport (Me) increased from 1890—97 to 1926—33 as tabulated.

Profiles	1890—97			1926—33		
	p. diff.	Geostr. wind		p. diff.	Geostr. wind	
	mb	$m\ sec^{-1}$	$m^2\ sec^{-2}$	mb	$m\ sec^{-1}$	$m^2\ sec^{-2}$
Bermuda—Port au Prince	3.68	3.3	10.9	6.12	5.5	30.2
Bermuda—Hatteras	—0.05	0	0	3.16	3.2	10.2
Bermuda—Eastport	2.80	1.7	2.9	6.24	3.8	14.4

In the eighteen-nineties the average pressure distribution was characterized by a bridge of high pressure from Bermuda to the American mainland, whereas later the average Bermuda high was more separated from the mainland high. The former type of pressure distribution is the one used by HIDAKA (1949) and MUNK (1950) in their attempts at constructing the large scale features of the ocean currents from an assumed purely zonal system of wind drags, westward in the belt of tradewinds and eastward in middle latitudes. Also that model leads to the jet structure of the Kuroshio, and of the Gulf Stream, where they go through the latitude of zero wind stress between easterlies and westerlies. According to the Bermuda—Hatteras data in the above table an average wind stress in the direction of that northgoing current has been added since the eighteen-nineties. The effect must have been some added strength of that jet current and the weaker northgoing current on its right flank (the northward continuation of the Antilles current).

However, of far greater importance must have been the secular increase of the easterlies of low latitudes, and the westerlies of middle latitudes, exerting their drag over long stretches of the corresponding ocean currents. In this connection it may be of interest to remind of the observed response of the Florida current to the annual variation of wind velocity east of the Windward Islands, where Atlantic water is forced through the island chain into the Caribbean Sea. (DIETRICH & KALLE 1957, p. 442). To the annual oscillation of these winds, from an average of 6 $msec^{-1}$ in June to one of 5 $msec^{-1}$ in November, corresponds, with about one month's lag, an oscillation of the Florida current from a maximum of 140 to a minimum of 105 $cmsec^{-1}$ resulting from the build-up of excess ocean level in the Caribbean and the Mexican Gulf (FUGLISTER, 1951). The strength of the current between Florida and the Bahamas, and probably also its downstream continuation for a considerable distance, thus responds to the fluctuations of distant winds in the equatorial easterlies more or less independently of the local winds.

The same must have been true for the secular increase of the speed of the Florida current in its response to the increase of the trade winds, which most likely must have taken place together with the strengthening of the Bermuda high. Quantitative estimates of that effect cannot be made because of the lack of old, and sufficiently complete, climatological records from the Windward Islands. The nearest substitute record of sufficient length and completeness is that quoted for the Bermuda-Port au Prince profile in the above table. That profile, which cuts across the Antilles current, shows indeed a remarkable secular increase of cross-profile geostrophic wind from 3.3 $msec^{-1}$ in 1890—97 to 5.5 $msec^{-1}$ in 1926—33. If the wind drag on the ocean were proportional to the square of that geostrophic wind (actually that estimate is too high), it would have tripled during the interval under consideration. The lack of corroborative evidence from other station profiles compels us to accept these figures with great caution, they may be off by a wide margin of error.[1] But the sign of the secular increase can hardly be wrong.

The gradient of ocean surface temperatures along the streamlines of the Antilles current, and its northern continuation, is very weak, so that an increasing speed of water motion will only produce a small secular warming at fixed points. This is shown clearly in Fig. 1 together with the very much stronger local warming at the left rim of the subtropical water along the Atlantic polar front.

The strong secular heating recorded at the Atlantic polar front may be due to: (a) the increased warm water advection parallel to the front in the jet maximum, where speeds up to 3 $msec^{-1}$ may occur, (b) a northward displacement of the front, and (c), on the cold side of the front, a possible increase of average temperature due to increasing meandering. Our data at 5° grid points are far too crude to enable us to separate the three effects. They have probably all been partly responsible for the production of the maximum strip of local secular warming of 2° or 3° C shown in Fig. 1.

In favor of (b), in particular, can be quoted, first, that a very small displacement of the front is sufficient to produce the observed temperature rises and, secondly, that a component of the secular change of winds is directed across the front from its warm side in the section from Cape Hatteras to the Newfoundland Banks. The part of that front section which is situated over deep water is known to be relatively mobile in its meandering and could possibly adjust its average position a little northward on a secular time scale too. On the other hand, where the front follows the brink of the continental shelf, or the escarpment of the Newfoundland Banks its position must be rather rigidly tied to bottom topography.

Passing on to the region in Fig. 1 east of the Newfoundland Banks we probably see the advective effect of the branching of the Gulf Stream toward the right of the main current. The secular warming has there been greater than in the Sargasso waters that flank the Gulf Stream to the right over the first part of its course.

The zone of negative trend in sea surface temperatures between 50° N and 57° N is also within

[1] Most likely the secular rise of pressure at Bermuda has not been as great as shown in Fig. 2.

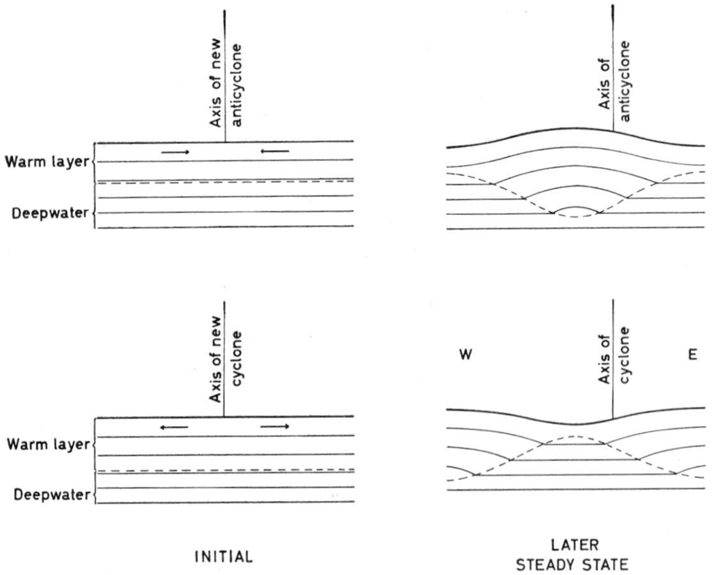

Fig. 3. Zonal, vertical profiles showing schematically the creation and maintenance of maximum thickness of the warm oceanic surface layer under the influence of anticyclonic wind stress, and minimum thickness of same layer under cyclonic wind stress.
Full lines: sea surface and interior isobaric surfaces.
Dashed line: density discontinuity surface.

the warm water advection of the Gulf Stream system, as is visible from Fig. 1. The process, or processes, responsible for the secular net cooling therefore must have been quite strong and systematic. In order to present a tentative explanation of the secular cooling we must again digress a little into oceanographic dynamic theory.

The wind can influence the sea surface temperature also in other ways than by the pure advection operating through the wind-driven current. This second kind of influence comes about through a change in the vertical temperature distribution in the water masses near the surface as shown in principle in Fig. 3.

An anticyclonic vortex in the ocean which is decreasing in intensity with depth must be of the warm core type, in other words, the warm surface layer must have maximum thickness near the center. In that way the anticyclonic winds around the Bermuda high do maintain in a permanent fashion a downward bulge of the lower limit of the warm surface water. Anticyclonic anomaly winds, more or less concentric with the anticyclonic ocean current, would add more depth to the warm surface water at the center. That inflation of the warm layer would tend to raise very slightly the equilibrium temperature of the ocean surface, because the water there would have become a little less exposed to mixing with the cold deepwater.

Conversely, a cyclonic current system decreasing with depth will be characterized by minimum thickness of the warm surface layer. The only major cyclonic vortex of the North Atlantic ocean currents (excluding the Norwegian Sea) is centered south of Greenland and corresponds to the Iceland low in the atmosphere. The surface water of the cyclonic vortex is mainly of old Gulf Stream origin, but at the vortex center it forms a very thin layer in accordance with the above reasoning. It can be taken for granted that a cyclonic anomaly circulation concentric with the normal Iceland low would reinforce the cyclonic vortex of oceanic flow and make the layer of warm surface water thinner, thus exposing the water at the ocean surface to more mixing with the cold deepwater.

The above discussion of the closed circulations of anticyclonic or cyclonic sense in atmosphere and ocean can be further refined by taking into account the variation of the Coriolis factor with latitude. The oceanic vortex then establishes itself a little to the west of the atmospheric vortex as indicated in Fig. 3. It is also possible to extend the rules for deflation or inflation of the surface layer to apply to any system of surface stress with cyclonic or anticyclonic vorticity such as is produced, for instance, by troughs or ridges in the atmospheric distribution of pressure anomaly.

If the wind stress had been directly proportional to the geostrophic wind, the final wind-driven current would have been the vectorial sum of the initial wind-driven current and the current propelled by the anomaly wind. In reality the relationship is not quite that simple. If we accept the old empirical rule that the stress on the ocean surface is proportional to the square of the anemometer wind, it would be proportional to a power of the geostrophic wind speed less than two but higher than one. In cases of cyclonically curved air paths and strong winds typical of the cyclone belt, that power would be shifted even more toward one. How much, can only be decided by painstaking and extensive statistical work with day-to-day data. In our present discussion we must accept the makeshift method of roughly superimposing the separate stress effects of the initial average geostrophic wind field and that of the geostrophic anomaly wind in order to make conclusions about the altered stress effects at the end of the time interval.

Applying such reasoning to Fig. 2, we can conclude that the belt of cyclonic vorticity of the anomaly wind, extending along the W—E trough from Labrador to Ireland, must have had the effect of deflating the warm surface layer. The associated cooling by increased mixing with cold water beneath, seems to be one of the most important processes contributing to the secular decrease of ocean surface temperature shown in Fig. 1 for the same belt. It is of course to be expected that the deflation of the always rather thin surface layer in the cyclonic area, with subsequent churning under the influence of strong winds, should make the surface temperature much more sensitive to a change than what may be observed in the case of the inflation of an already rather thick surface layer in an anticyclonic region with light winds.

Another contributing cooling effect of the surface water lies of course in the direct transfer of heat and moisture to the air of winter time cold waves from North America. Actually, the air advection from North America during the time interval under consideration has increased relatively more in winter than for the year as a whole. The secular increase of the rate of heat loss to the atmosphere must have had its maximum in the zones of maximum ocean-to-atmosphere heat transfers near the American coast (SVERDRUP 1942, pp. 228—235, JACOBS 1951). It has obviously below 50° N fallen short of compensating for the secular increase in warm water advection. North of 50° N the increasing cold advection from the American continent, together with increasing vertical stirring, produce a net surface cooling despite the warm water advection which most likely must have been increasing also in that zone.

North of the 57th parallel, where the secular change of sea temperature again turns positive, there is no definite cyclonic vorticity of the stress of the anomaly wind. Around the southern point of Greenland the stress vorticity is even strongly anticyclonic and is accompanied by the biggest temperature rises. In favor of a temperature rise are also the easterly, and in part southerly, anomaly winds, which may have produced anomaly currents in the ocean of similar directions leading to more warm water advection toward Iceland and Greenland. This kind of development did not start until 1920, but was thereafter accompanied by much stronger easterly anomaly winds than those shown in Fig. 2 averaged for the whole period from 1890—97 to 1926—33.

4. Later trends

A few years after the end of the period investigated in this article World War II interrupted the regular observation of sea surface temperatures over the major portion of the North Atlantic. The statistical treatment of the data collected after 1945 is available for the area north of 50° N in the publications of Conseil Permanent International pour l'Exploration de la Mer, but the data from the area south of 50° N still await publication. From the northern data collection can be seen that the sea surface temperatures near Greenland culminated in the early nineteenthirties, while from Iceland to the British Isles the maximum water temperatures seem to have occurred in the early nineteenforties. Despite the irregular downward trend, following the culmination, the general level of sea surface temperatures remains well above the low recorded in the northern areas around 1920.

Rodewald, in a series of papers from 1952 to 1956, has made ingenious use of the sea temperature measurements on fixed weather ships for the purpose of extending the study of the climatic change in the oceans up to present time. The map he published in 1956 (RODEWALD, 1956, p. 297), showing the distribution of approximate average sea surface temperature anomalies around 1950, is very similar to Fig. 1 in this article. In particular, the warming of the Gulf Stream waters at weather ship D is shown by Rodewald to have reached +1.5° C, while practically no long range warming has taken place at weather ship C (− 0.1° C) and J (+0.2° C) just north of 50° N. The warming of the Gulf Stream waters south of 50° N and the lack of significant warming in a belt north of 50° N have thus formed part of a systematic trend of at least sixty years duration, from 1890 to the 1950's. Rodewald's quoted map also shows that in the North Pacific an analogous system of temperature anomalies can be derived from weather ship data, probably indicating that the same long trend has been operating there as in the North Atlantic. It is, by the way, not surprising that the Pacific shows a pattern of secular change similar to that of the Atlantic. Already since the studies of SCHERHAG (1936) it has been known that all major centers of action of the atmosphere, both highs and lows, intensified together in the climatic change that got started around 1920. But Rodewald's recent work with sea surface temperatures has again focussed attention on that hemisphere-wide nature of climatic change.

The warming of the waters in the far northern Atlantic (to which the Pacific has no parallel) was much more sudden and short range than that farther south. Essentially, it lasted only from 1920 to 1930 in Greenland waters and from 1920 to the early 1940's in Iceland and northern British waters. It seems that in each case the changing wind regimes can be made responsible for most of the changes in sea surface temperature. It is possible, however, that further studies may enable us to isolate specifically oceanic long range fluctuations tied to the thermo-haline deepwater circulations, which in winter intermittently extend all the way up to the surface in the waters south of Greenland. Such fluctuations, which would bring into play the exchange of heat between the great heat capacity of the deepwater, the smaller heat capacity of the surface layer, and the still much smaller heat capacity of the atmosphere, may very well, as often suggested by Rossby in recent years, give the clue to the understanding of climatic trends of duration into the centuries or millenia.

REFERENCES

BULLIG, H. J., 1954: Atlas der Monatswerte von Wassertemperatur, Wind und Bewölkung auf dem Seeweg Europa—Südamerika. *Deutscher Wetterdienst, Seewetteramt, Einzelveröffentlichungen Nr.* **5**, pp. 1—25.

DIETRICH, G., 1957: Ozeanographische Probleme der Deutschen Forschungsfahrten im Internationalen Geophysikalischen Jahr 1957/58. *Deutsche Hydrographische Zeitschrift,* **10**, Heft 2, pp. 39—61.

DIETRICH, G. & KALLE, K., 1957: *Allgemeine Meereskunde,* Berlin, Gebr. Borntraeger.

FUGLISTER, F. C., 1951: Annual variations in current speeds in the Gulf Stream system. *Journal of Marine Research* **10**, pp. 119—127.

HELLAND-HANSEN, B., and NANSEN, F., 1917: Temperaturschwankungen des Nordatlantischen Ozeans und in der Atmosphäre. *Videnskapsselskapets Skrifter, Mat.-Naturv. klasse* 1916 No. 9, pp. 1—341, Kristiania. Contains thorough references to earlier literature.

HIDAKA, K., 1949: Mass transport in ocean currents and lateral mixing, *Journal of Marine Research* **8**, pp. 132—136.

JACOBS, W. C., 1951: The energy exchange between sea and atmosphere and some of its consequences, *Bulletin of the Scripps Institution of Oceanography.*

MUNK, W. H., 1950: On the wind-driven ocean circulation, *Journal of Meteorology* **7**, pp. 79—93.

RIEHL, H., 1956: Sea Surface Temperature of the North Atlantic 1887—1936. Contract No. N6ori—02036 *Project NRO* **82—120**, pp. 1—9, *Office of Naval Research,* Washington D.C.

RODEWALD, M., 1956: Beiträge zur Klimaschwankung im Meere, 7, Beitrag: Die Wassertemperaturen und ihre Anomalien bei den Japanischen und Nordamerikanischen Wetterschiffen im Nordpazifischen Ozean. *Deutsche Hydrographische Zeitschrift,* **9**, Heft 6, pp. 289—298.

SCHERHAG, R., 1936: Die Zunahme der Atmosphärischen Zirkulation in den letzten 25 Jahren. *Annalen der Hydrographie und Maritimen Meteorologie,* pp. 397—407.

SMED, J., 1952: Variation of the Surface Temperature in the North Atlantic during 1876—1952. *Conseil Permanent International pour l'Exploration de la Mer, Annales Biologiques,* Vol. IX, pp. 17—21. Copenhagen.

STOMMEL, H., 1948: The westward intensification of wind-driven ocean currents, *Transactions, American Geophysical Union* **29**, pp. 202—206, Washington, D.C.

SVERDRUP, H. U., 1942: *Oceanography for Meteorologists,* New York, Prentice Hall.

(Manuscript received 1 April, 1958)

On the Thermal Unrest in the Ocean

By

BERNHARD HAURWITZ
New York University

HENRY STOMMEL
Woods Hole Oceanographic Institution[1]

WALTER H. MUNK
Scripps Institution of Oceanography, La Jolla[2]

Abstract

ROSSBY (1937, 38) has argued from theoretical grounds that there should be a great deal of thermal unrest in the deep ocean, partly due to variable wind-stresses associated with storms. DEFANT (1936, 1950, etc.) has suggested that internal tidal waves are a practically ubiquitous feature of the ocean, and has presented many analyses of rather short series of observations in evidence. As HAURWITZ (1954) has indicated, the chief uncertainty involved in all discussions to date has been the result of the series of observations being too short: often only a few days. The purpose of this paper is to present a preliminary analysis of portions of temperature data obtained since Dec. 8, 1954 on two resistance thermometers located on the bottom off Bermuda at depths of 50 and 500 meters, the data being recorded regularly for several years now. The analysis for tidal periods, inertial periods, and shorter periods of the Brunt-Väisälä type is described.

I. Introduction

In two pioneer studies of the response of the ocean to transient wind-stresses, ROSSBY (1937—38) demonstrated theoretically that internal inertial gravity wave motions are induced in the deep stratified layers of the sea, thus suggesting a mechanism for stirring deep water. These theoretical results are of fundamental importance as indicative of a process of mixing which may play a central role in the general circulation of the deep ocean: " —because of the variability of the surface stresses it appears probable that vigorous inertia oscillations must develop in stratified media and express themselves as a marked intensification of the large scale horizontal turbulence . . ." (ROSSBY 1938, p. 248). These investigations stimulated theoretical studies by CAHN (1945), and others, the latest being a study by VERONIS and STOMMEL (1956) which contains a summary of other studies.

In addition there is a very large literature concerning internal tidal waves in the ocean, among

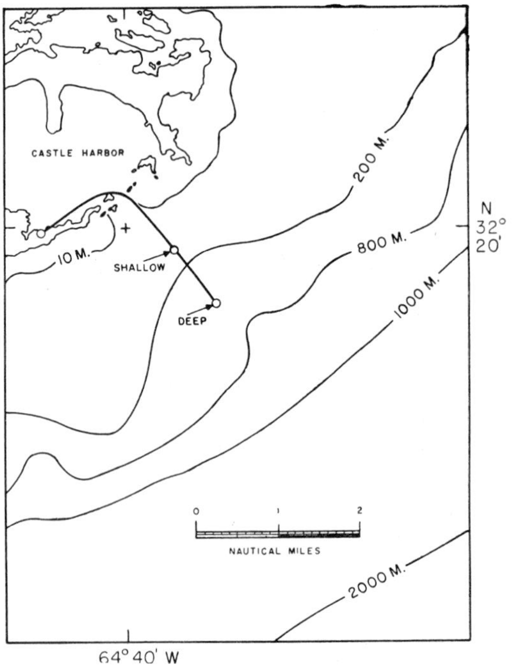

Fig. 1. Bathymetric Chart of Portion of Bermuda showing approximate location of the shallow and deep thermistors, the cable, and of the shore installation.

[1] Contribution No. 954 from the Woods Hole Oceanographic Institution and No. 229 from the Bermuda Biological Station.

[2] Contribution from the Scripps Institution of Oceanography, new series.

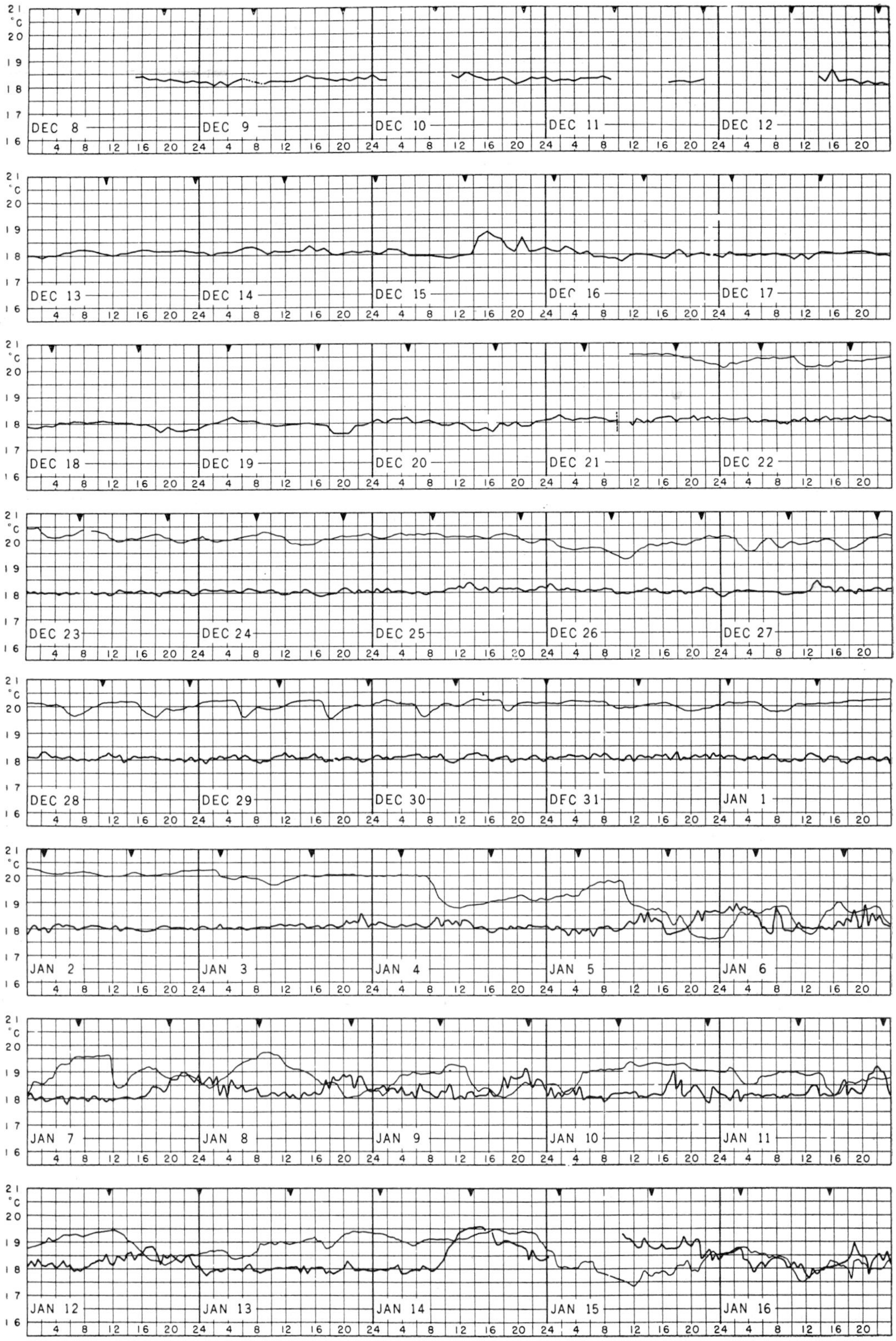
21 °C
20
19
18
17
16
DEC 8
DEC 9
DEC 10
DEC 11
DEC 12
DEC 13
DEC 14
DEC 15
DEC 16
DEC 17
DEC 18
DEC 19
DEC 20
DEC 21
DEC 22
DEC 23
DEC 24
DEC 25
DEC 26
DEC 27
DEC 28
DEC 29
DEC 30
DEC 31
JAN 1
JAN 2
JAN 3
JAN 4
JAN 5
JAN 6
JAN 7
JAN 8
JAN 9
JAN 10
JAN 11
JAN 12
JAN 13
JAN 14
JAN 15
JAN 16
4 8 12 16 20 24

Fig. 2a.

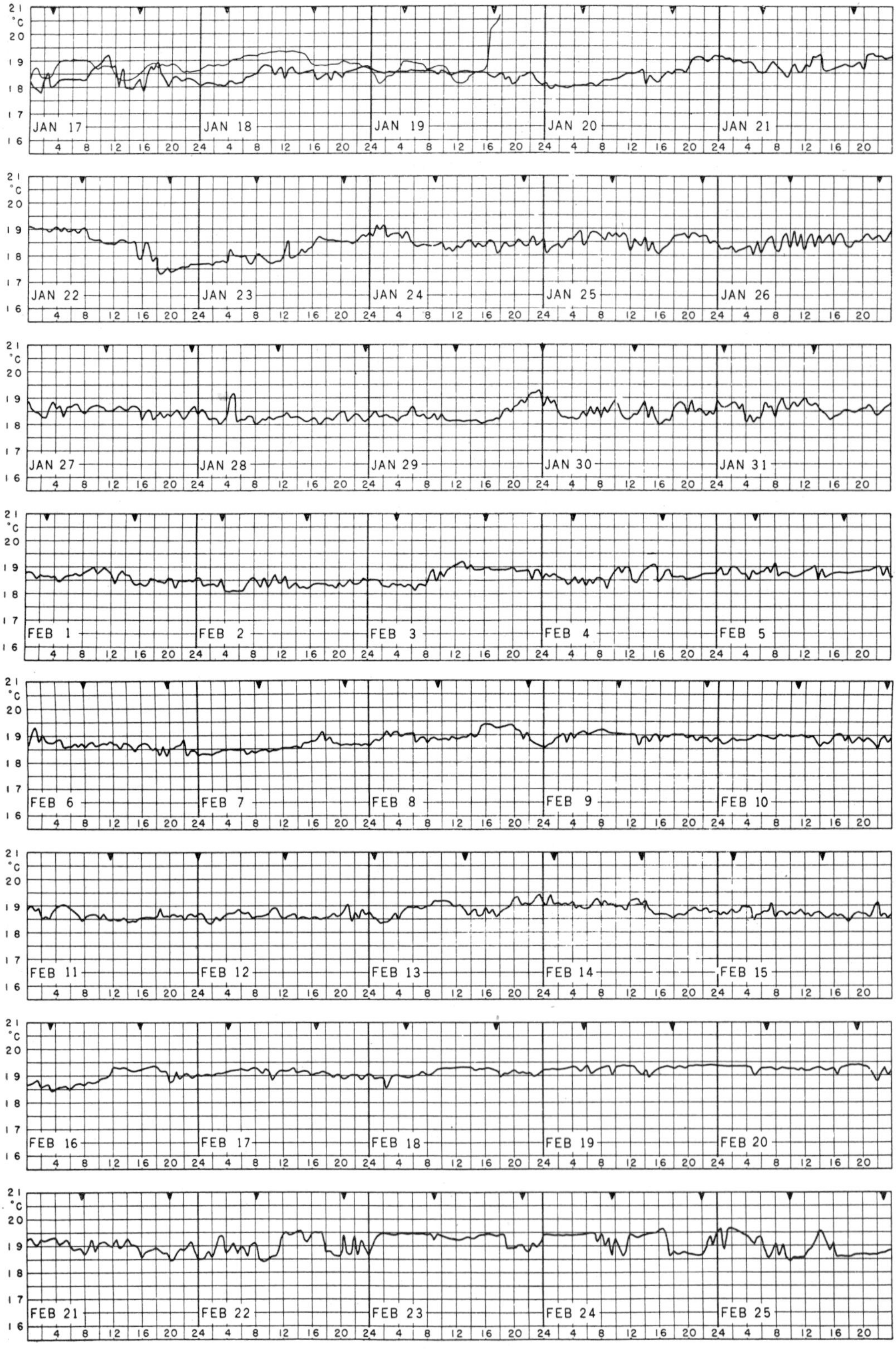
21
°C
20
19
18
17
16
JAN 17
JAN 18
JAN 19
JAN 20
JAN 21
JAN 22
JAN 23
JAN 24
JAN 25
JAN 26
JAN 27
JAN 28
JAN 29
JAN 30
JAN 31
FEB 1
FEB 2
FEB 3
FEB 4
FEB 5
FEB 6
FEB 7
FEB 8
FEB 9
FEB 10
FEB 11
FEB 12
FEB 13
FEB 14
FEB 15
FEB 16
FEB 17
FEB 18
FEB 19
FEB 20
FEB 21
FEB 22
FEB 23
FEB 24
FEB 25
4 8 12 16 20 24

Fig. 2b.

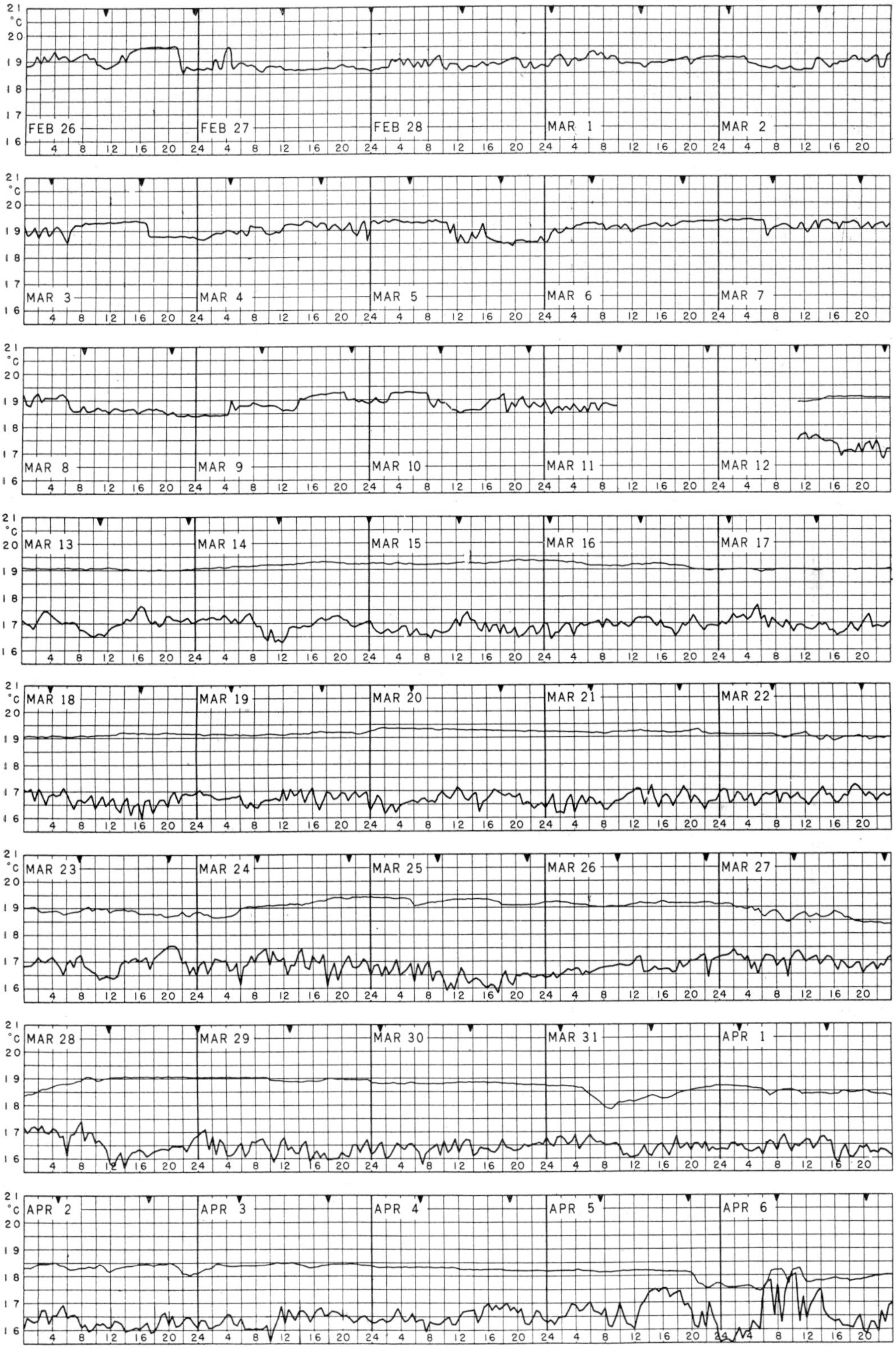
°C
21
20
19
18
17
16
FEB 26
FEB 27
FEB 28
MAR 1
MAR 2
MAR 3
MAR 4
MAR 5
MAR 6
MAR 7
MAR 8
MAR 9
MAR 10
MAR 11
MAR 12
MAR 13
MAR 14
MAR 15
MAR 16
MAR 17
MAR 18
MAR 19
MAR 20
MAR 21
MAR 22
MAR 23
MAR 24
MAR 25
MAR 26
MAR 27
MAR 28
MAR 29
MAR 30
MAR 31
APR 1
APR 2
APR 3
APR 4
APR 5
APR 6
4 8 12 16 20 24

Fig. 2c.

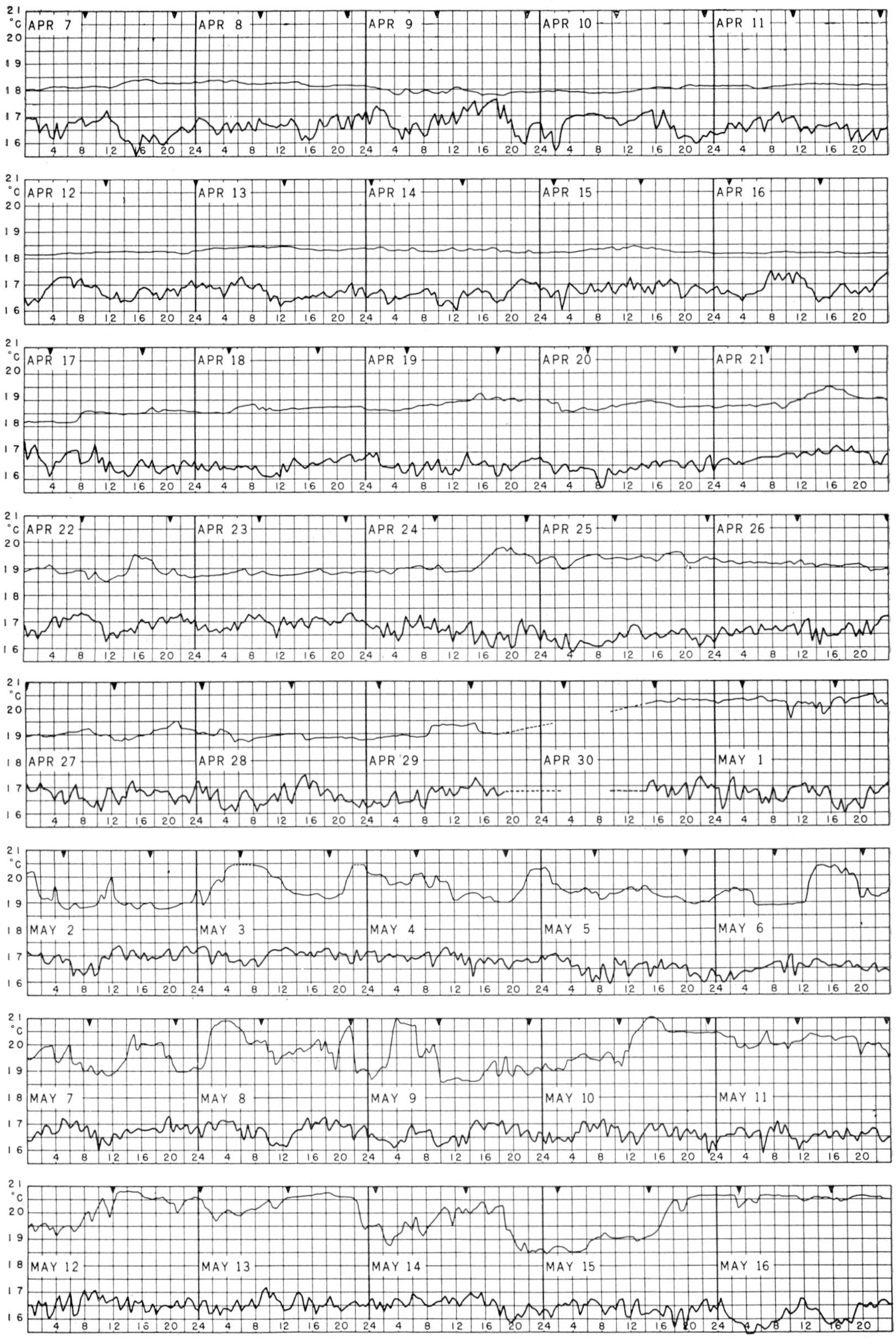
°C
APR 7
APR 8
APR 9
APR 10
APR 11
APR 12
APR 13
APR 14
APR 15
APR 16
APR 17
APR 18
APR 19
APR 20
APR 21
APR 22
APR 23
APR 24
APR 25
APR 26
APR 27
APR 28
APR 29
APR 30
MAY 1
MAY 2
MAY 3
MAY 4
MAY 5
MAY 6
MAY 7
MAY 8
MAY 9
MAY 10
MAY 11
MAY 12
MAY 13
MAY 14
MAY 15
MAY 16

Fig. 2d.

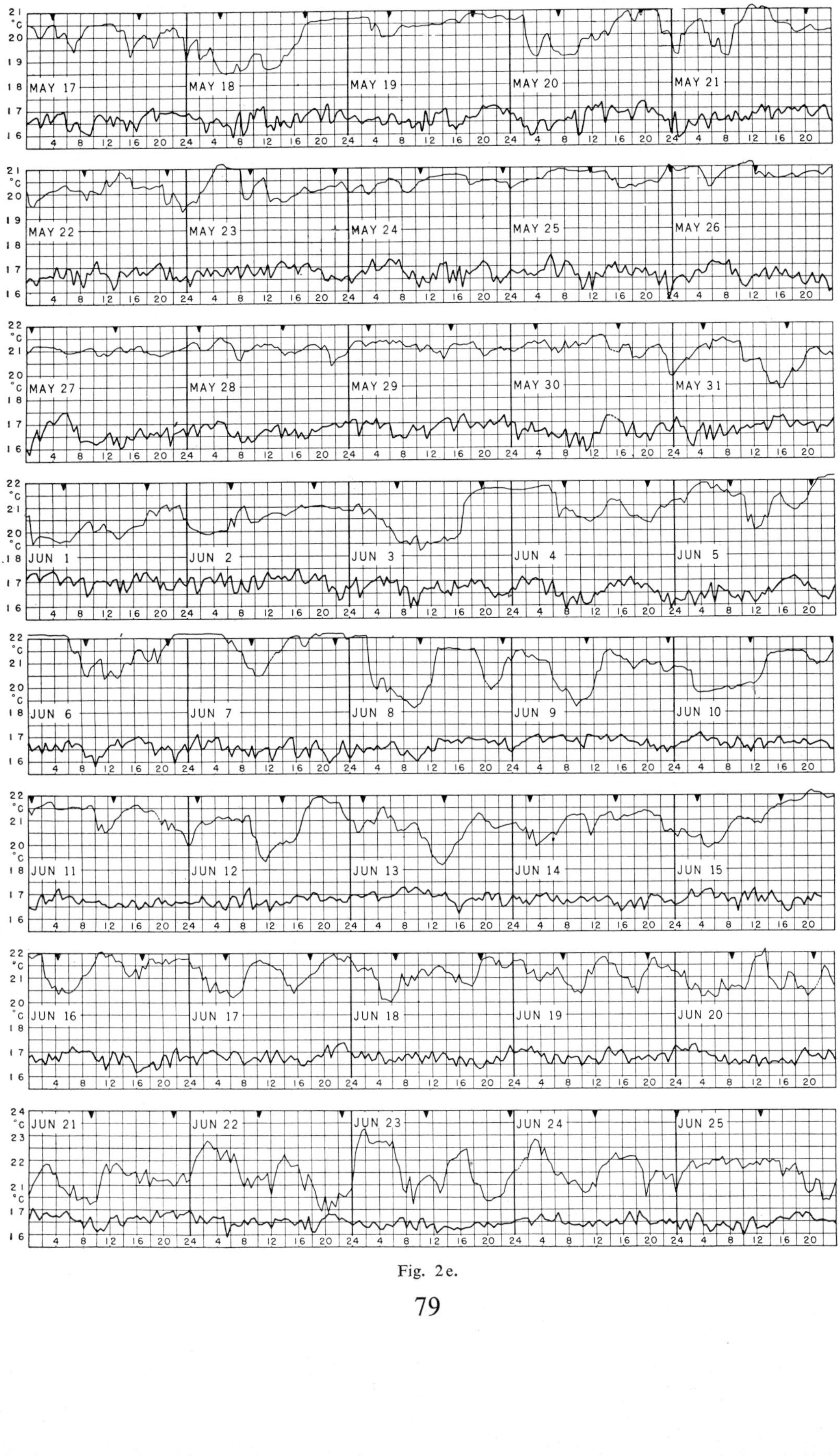
MAY 17
MAY 18
MAY 19
MAY 20
MAY 21
MAY 22
MAY 23
MAY 24
MAY 25
MAY 26
MAY 27
MAY 28
MAY 29
MAY 30
MAY 31
JUN 1
JUN 2
JUN 3
JUN 4
JUN 5
JUN 6
JUN 7
JUN 8
JUN 9
JUN 10
JUN 11
JUN 12
JUN 13
JUN 14
JUN 15
JUN 16
JUN 17
JUN 18
JUN 19
JUN 20
JUN 21
JUN 22
JUN 23
JUN 24
JUN 25
°C
4 8 12 16 20 24

Fig. 2e.

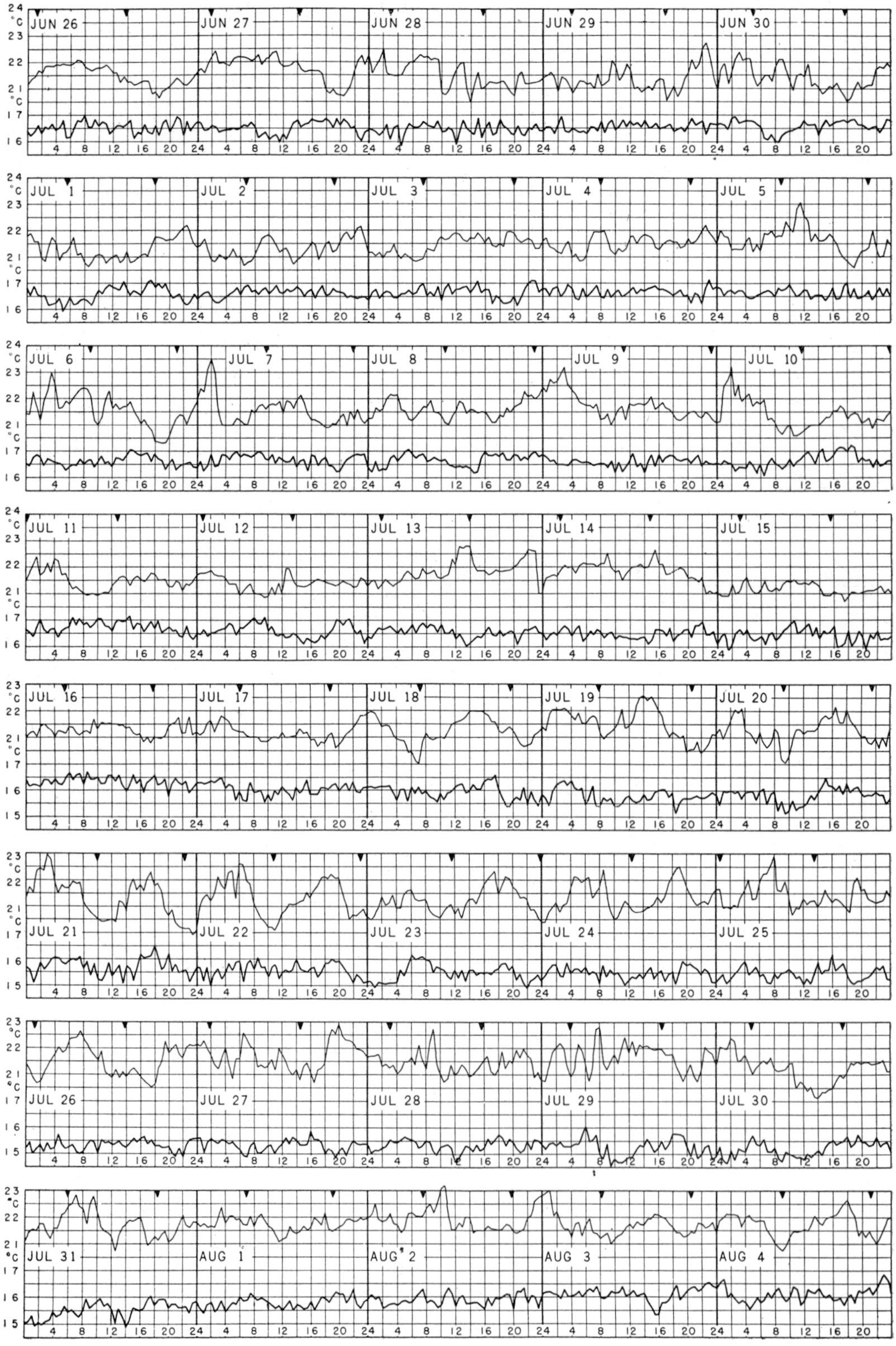
JUN 26
JUN 27
JUN 28
JUN 29
JUN 30
JUL 1
JUL 2
JUL 3
JUL 4
JUL 5
JUL 6
JUL 7
JUL 8
JUL 9
JUL 10
JUL 11
JUL 12
JUL 13
JUL 14
JUL 15
JUL 16
JUL 17
JUL 18
JUL 19
JUL 20
JUL 21
JUL 22
JUL 23
JUL 24
JUL 25
JUL 26
JUL 27
JUL 28
JUL 29
JUL 30
JUL 31
AUG 1
AUG 2
AUG 3
AUG 4
°C

Fig. 2f.

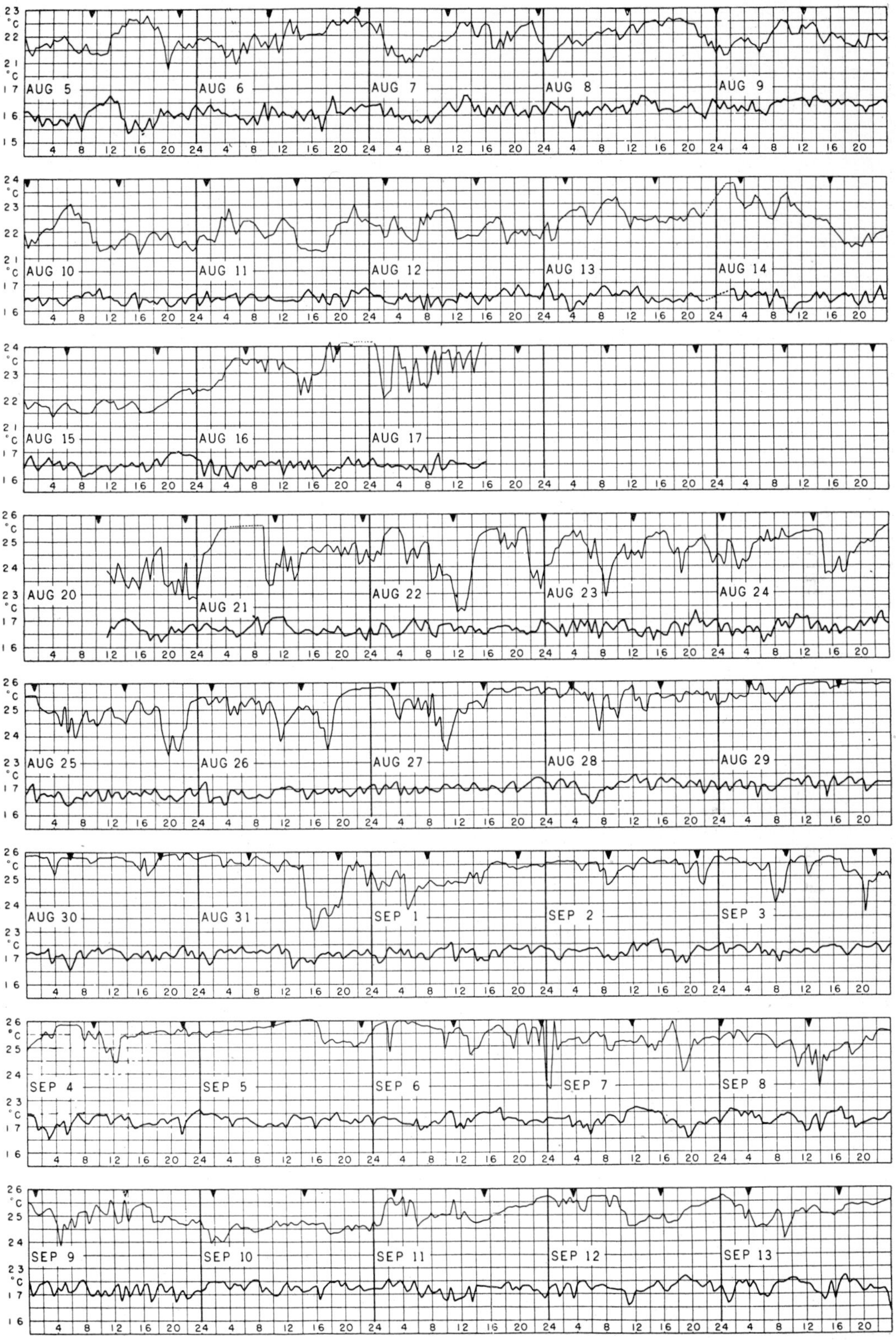
AUG 5
AUG 6
AUG 7
AUG 8
AUG 9
AUG 10
AUG 11
AUG 12
AUG 13
AUG 14
AUG 15
AUG 16
AUG 17
AUG 20
AUG 21
AUG 22
AUG 23
AUG 24
AUG 25
AUG 26
AUG 27
AUG 28
AUG 29
AUG 30
AUG 31
SEP 1
SEP 2
SEP 3
SEP 4
SEP 5
SEP 6
SEP 7
SEP 8
SEP 9
SEP 10
SEP 11
SEP 12
SEP 13
°C

Fig. 2g.

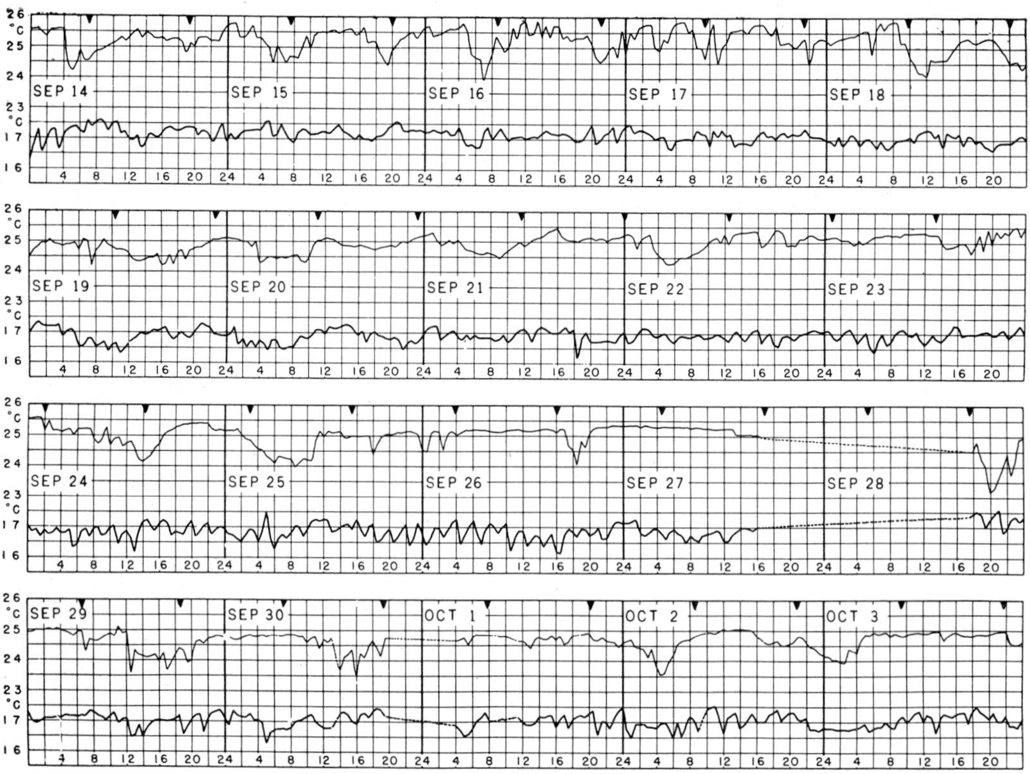

Fig. 2. The thermistor records from Dec. 8, 1954—Oct. 3, 1955 showing temperatures at the shallow and deep thermistors (light and heavy lines respectively). A new cable was installed March 12, with thermistors at slightly different depths. The small black triangles at the top show time of Bermuda high water, the time at the bottom is 60° W meridian time.

the most recent being papers by DEFANT (1950) and HAURWITZ (1954). These studies have been largely based upon the analysis of very short series of data, usually of no more than a few days' duration. As HAURWITZ (1954) has pointed out, one of the main obstacles to obtaining a more certain knowledge of the existence of internal waves in the ocean has been the lack of a truly long series of records of temperature in the deep water. As a first attempt to help supply such data, a submarine cable was laid from a recording Wheatstone bridge on the shore at Bermuda to two resistance thermometers offshore: one lying on the bottom at a depth of 50 meters, the other at 500 meters. (See Fig. 1 for location.) The shallow one was therefore approximately at the depth of the seasonal thermocline; the deeper one near the top of the main thermocline. Records have been obtained on this cable from Dec. 8, 1954 to Oct. 3, 1955 at intervals of one-half hour. From October 3, 1955 to May 7, 1957 records were obtained at five minute intervals. Since May 7, 1957 records have also been obtained from another resistance thermometer at 500 meters depth, but located five miles away from the original thermometer at a point further to the southwest along the coast of the island.

II. Qualitative presentation of data for the first period of observation

Portions of the cable data are presented in Fig. 2. The temperatures in degree Centigrade are given as ordinate, the dates and 60° W time are given as abscissa. The heavy line is the temperature as indicated by the deep thermometer: the light line indicates the shallow-element temperature. Occasionally, in order to keep the graph on scale, the origin of the ordinate is shifted (for example, see shift from June 20 to June 21, or July 15 to July 16). Also the scale is often broken in the middle to accommodate both thermistors (the first date at which the broken scale occurs is May 27). The little black triangles indicate time of predicted Bermuda high water. Two cables were used, one from December 8, 1954 to March 11, 1955; the second cable, from March 12 through October 3, 1955. The first cable was unarmored and soon began to fail—the shallow thermistor was lost on January 19, 1955, and it seems likely that the slow increase of the average deep temperature from 18.4° C near December 8 to 19.0° C in March, was also due to progressive cable failure. The deep thermistor of the second cable was placed somewhat deeper than that of the first as can be seen from the lower deep temperature beginning March 12. Readings at first were made every hour, but after December 22 were made every half hour. The readings were scaled off and replotted as shown in Figure 2.

In addition to the cable data, hydrographic data were also obtained over the same period by the PANULIRUS, the research vessel of the Bermuda Biological Station, and these data are exhibited in Figures 3 and 4. The vertical lines represent actual PANULIRUS stations—the rest of the contours are interpolated. Inasmuch as the variations of deep thermal structure indicated by the hydrographic data are no more than the high frequency variations revealed on the cable, it seems probable that the monthly fluctuations implied by the method of contouring in Figures 3 and 4 are simply the result of sampling errors. The seasonal variation above 500 meters is of course real. The main usefulness of the hydro-

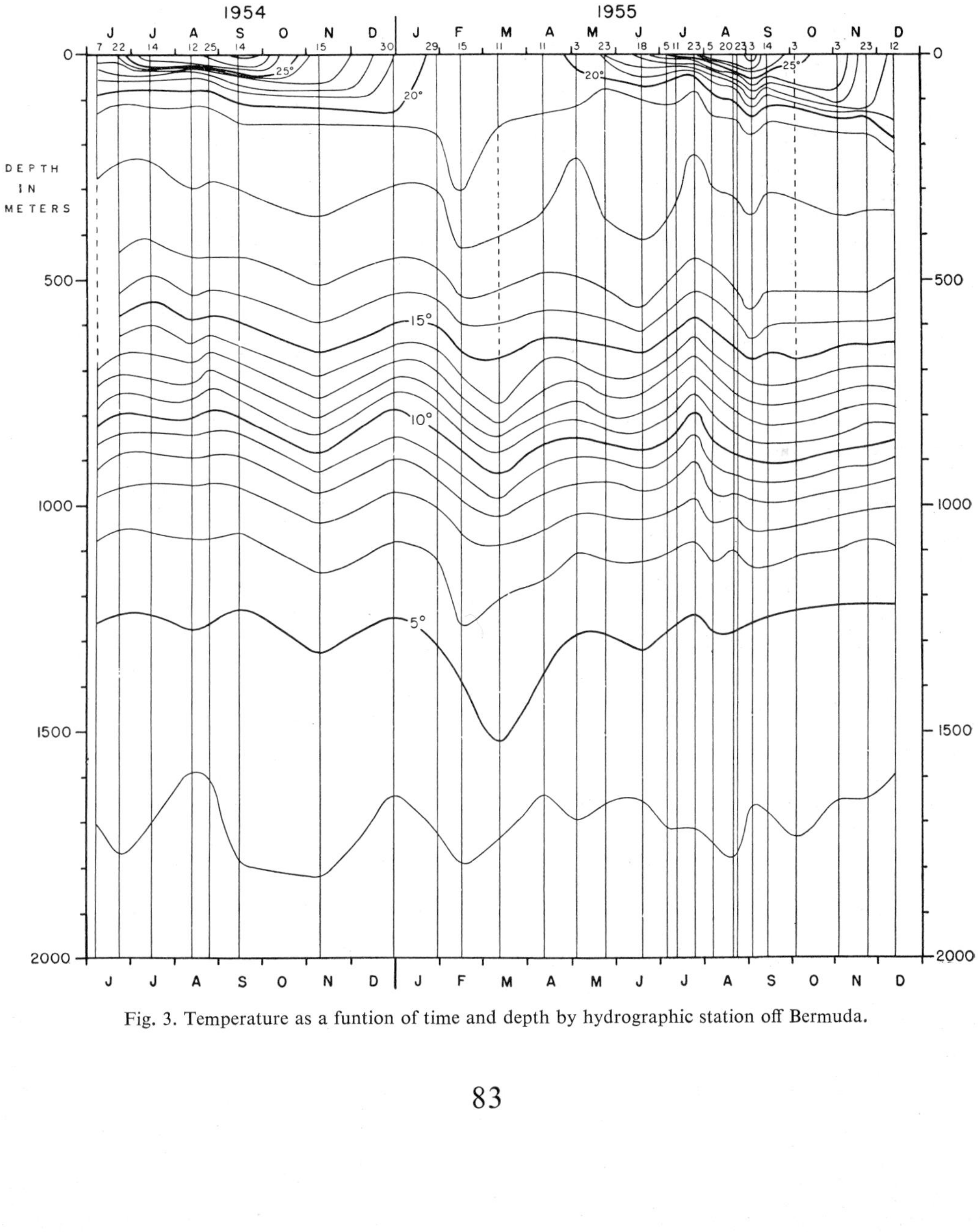

Fig. 3. Temperature as a funtion of time and depth by hydrographic station off Bermuda.

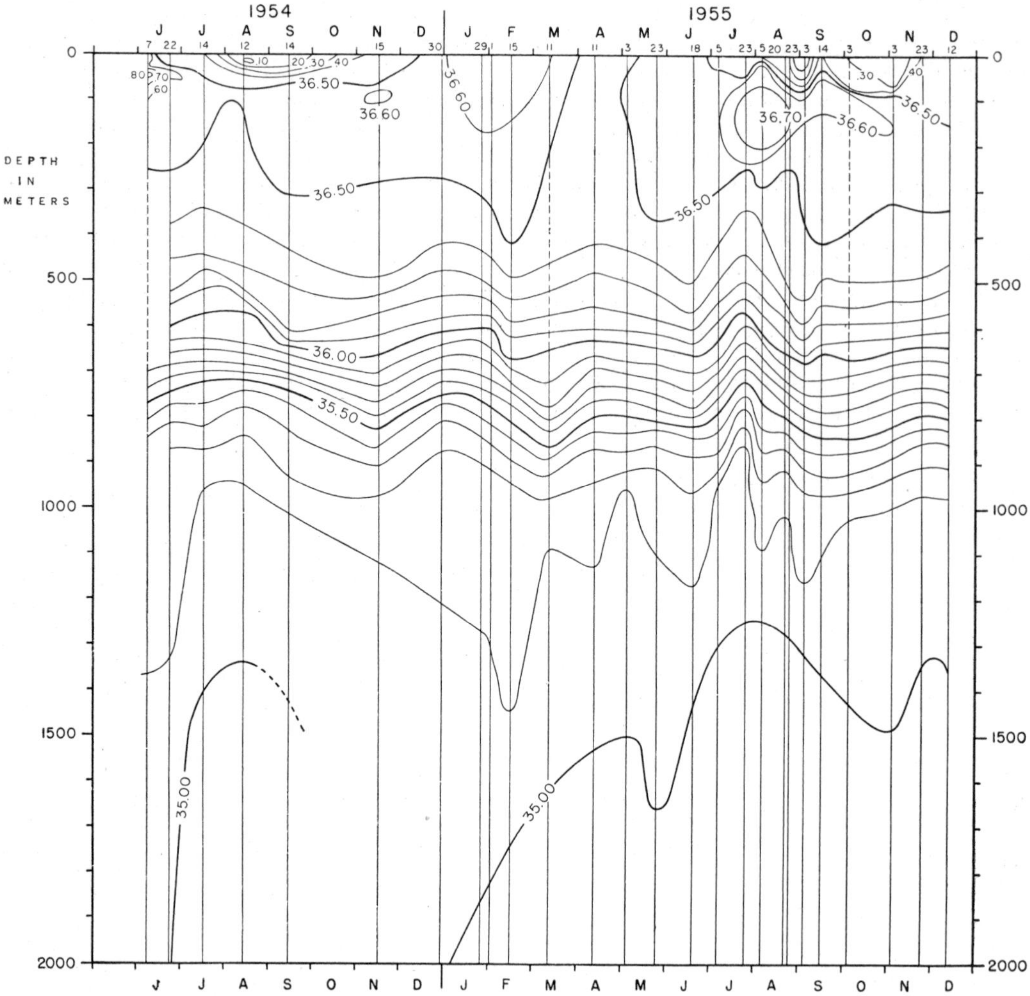

Fig. 4. Salinity corresponding to Fig. 3.

graphic data in Figures 3 and 4 is that it gives an idea of the *mean* vertical distribution of properties at various seasons near the cable, so that a rough estimate of vertical displacements of water can be obtained from the thermistor cable data.

From December 8 to January 3 there are few large disturbances on the shallow or deep thermistor. From December 26 to January 1 there is a slight drop in temperature of the shallow thermistor slightly after low water. Inasmuch as this is unassociated with any similar tidal fluctuation in the deep thermistor, and this is a period when the upper layer is fairly well mixed (Figure 4) we are inclined to explain this as evidence of cascading along the bottom slope of cold water from Castle Harbour (see BODEN 1952, 1953), which just manages to reach the shallow thermistor, but does not penetrate deeply enough to reach the deep one.

On January 2 a violent series of storms commenced over the North Atlantic, and by January 4, major disturbances at both thermistors were evident. During January 6 to 12 a pronounced long period, of somewhat less than 24 hours—perhaps an inertial period—can be seen on the deep thermistor record. Gradually the record becomes more and more confused or jagged—and during the period January 15 to February 15 even longer periods make an appearance. Above all, the deep records do not bear any resemblance to a tidal phenomenon—the phases appear to be quite randomly distributed with respect to time of high water. Isolated portions of the record (say February 24—25) look very much like tides—but they fail to persist and the similarity is doubtlessly fictitious. During this period the upper water became more and more mixed, the shallow thermistor was destroyed, and electrical tests indicated a gradual failure of insulation on the deep thermistor. On March 12 a completely new—and this time armored—cable was put into operation.

The violent temperature oscillations of the deep thermistor, starting on April 5 seem to be related to an intense storm just north of the island. During late April and May the growing amplitude of fluctuation on the shallow element appears to be associated with increasing vernal heating and growth of the seasonal thermocline (Figure 4), and gradually appears to be connected with surface tides. By mid-July there can be no doubt that the shallow temperature fluctuations are tied in with the surface tides. The deep thermistor appears to become more steady as the seasonal thermocline forms above it. Perhaps the seasonal thermocline shelters the main thermocline in some way, from disturbances at the surface—even hurricanes. Very remarkable long period fluctuations in deep temperature are indicated during the summer season, however, for example during July the average deep temperature dropped 1.5° C over a period of about three weeks and then rose again.

The hurricane which passed to the SW of Bermuda August 15th apparently caused the major disturbance at the shallow thermistor on August 16, without having any discernible effect at the deep one. A weak hurricane was passing to the east of Bermuda on August 31.

III. Preliminary search for tidal and inertial periods

A complete analysis of the large amount of data represented by the temperature records obtained off Bermuda is best carried out by cross-spectrum analysis. Such an analysis has been performed on the data obtained from November 1955 through February 1956. Its results are discussed in Section IV. But, since the records show some intervals during which periodicities appear fairly clearly it appeared worth while to make a simple preliminary investigation of the material.

In this section the results will be described which have been found in this manner. Attention has mainly been paid to the time interval up to the summer of 1955 when most of the work was done on which this section is based.

If the inspection of the temperature timegraphs indicated that during a certain time interval a period or periods appeared in the data its statistical significance, and hence by inference its physical reality, was studied on the basis of periodogram analysis, harmonic analysis, and expectancy test. For some time intervals the tests for periodicities were made even though an inspection of the curves did not show that the periods to be looked for were present. This was done in particular for the lunar semidiurnal tidal period since it was thought that a demonstration of the presence or absence of this, the tidal period with the largest theoretical amplitude, was of intrinsic interest.

The methods employed here in the investigation of periodicities are all standard statistical procedures. They will therefore be described only very briefly in order to demonstrate specifically how they were used in this study. The temperatures are given at intervals of one-half hour. Since only periods of at least a few hours' duration are to be investigated the data were first smoothed by forming the means for each two-hour period. Only in the analysis of the 500 m records for the period 16—29 March 1955 such a smoothing was not performed.

With a few exceptions to be noted below for each selected record interval a periodogram analysis was first performed to determine the predominant amplitudes. Since no great accuracy was required a simplified method of periodogram analysis was used as a rule, as described by WHITTAKER-ROBINSON (1944, p. 356). In this simplification one takes for a given trial period the difference between the highest and lowest value in the line of mean values and plots this as abscissa.

After the predominant period or periods in the selected record interval have been determined the data were subjected to a harmonic analysis, with the determined period or an integral multiple of it as the analysis interval. Harmonic analysis will, of course, always give an amplitude for an assumed period even if the computation is based on random numbers. It is therefore necessary to ascertain how much larger the actually computed amplitude is than an amplitude resulting from an analysis of random numbers. This can be done by the expectancy test. Let A_i with the components a_i and b_i denote the amplitudes by harmonic analysis of the n individual periods.

Then

$$E^2 = \frac{1}{n^2} \sum_{i=1}^{n} A_i^2$$

the expectancy, is a measure of the amplitude of the mean period which should be expected in random data. Let $\overline{A}$ be the actual mean of the amplitudes,

$$\overline{A}^2 = \frac{1}{n^2} \left[\left(\sum_{i=1}^{n} a_i \right)^2 + \left(\sum_{i=1}^{n} b_i \right)^2 \right]$$

Then the probability p that

$$\overline{A} = kE$$

is

$$p = e^{-k^2}$$

If p is small it can be concluded that the computed mean amplitude is not likely to appear in random data; in other words it is likely that $\overline{A}$ is statistically and hence physically significant.

A difficulty in the application of the expectancy test in the present study is that the investigated time intervals are not selected arbitrarily, but because they showed fairly well developed temperature oscillations. This biased selection decreases the probability p, but it is impossible to state to what extent p is affected by this selection. It can only be said that with large p it is highly probable that the data are randomly distributed, and that the computed amplitudes are not significant. To be sure that a low value of p indicates non-random data and significance of the amplitude one would wish to find lower values of p than in those cases when the data are not pre-selected.

In the following the analyses of the various intervals will be discussed briefly.

a) *6—18 January, 1955*

During this time some pronounced oscillations occurred at the 50 m and 500 m recorders. The periodogram analysis for the 50 m record suggested periods of 24 hours and 30 hours, for the 500 m level a period of 23 hours, close to the inertia period. Accordingly expectancy tests were performed for these periods, and also for a 12-hour period because of its proximity to the theoretically largest lunar tidal period. The results are summarized in Table I. An inspection of the harmonic coefficients of the 24-hourly oscillation at both levels for the individual days shows a much greater regularity during the first six days than later. Therefore, the expectancy test was also applied separately to this time interval. None of the computed probabilities is small enough to state that the periods under consideration are not statistical accidents, especially in view of the manner in which this time interval was selected for analysis. In particular the values for the 12-hour period indicate that the 12-hourly tidal period was not contained in the data. Further, the harmonic coefficients for the 12-hourly period, based on the temperature on the individual days, which are not reproduced here did not show the systematic phase change which would be present if a lunar period of 12 hours 25 minutes existed. At 500 meters depth the lower probability associated with the 23 hour period favors an inertial oscillation over a diurnal tide, at least during 6—11 January 1955, but the statistical significance of this result remains in doubt because of the selection of the data.

b) *16—29 March 1955; 1—29 June 1955*

Although the time interval from 6—18 January 1955 did not show either the 12-hourly or 24-hourly lunar tidal period it was thought that statistically significant values for the amplitudes of these two tidal oscillations might perhaps be obtained if a longer series of data were chosen. First, the temperatures registered at 500 meters during the epoch from 16 March to 29 May,

Table I. Expectancy Test, 6—18 January 1955, 50 m and 500 m

Period	50 meters			500 meters		
	Ampl.	Expect.	Prob.	Ampl.	Expect.	Prob.
30 hrs.	0.26° C	0.15° C	0.05	—	—	—
24 hrs.	0.15	0.13	0.33	0.13° C	0.10° C	0.18
12 hrs.	0.09	0.06	0.10	0.08	0.14	0.67
24 hrs.*	0.28*	0.16*	0.05*	0.23*	0.11*	0.013*
23 hrs.*	0.26*	0.17*	0.08*	0.22*	0.10*	0.009*

* First six days.

1955 have been studied. This time interval was chosen because about the middle of March 1955 a new and more satisfactory cable was installed. The data were plotted on a time graph with solar time as the abscissa. On this graph the upper lunar transits (local lunar noon) were marked so that the temperatures for each lunar hour could be read off without difficulty. For this particular computation no smoothing by averaging was performed here. The data were then combined into groups each of which consisted of four consecutive lunar days, in order to reduce the amount of computational work. Altogether 17 such groups were available; the period April 26—30 had to be omitted because of insufficient data.

The 17 four-day mean daily ranges were then harmonically analyzed. The results of the expectancy test for the harmonics 1 and 2 are shown in Table II.

Table II. Expectancy test for time interval 16 March —29 May 1955, 500 meters

Period length	Amplitude	Expectancy	Probability
24 lunar hours	0.038° C	0.026° C	0.10
12 lunar hours	0.034° C	0.020° C	0.27

The probabilities that the 24-hourly and especially the 12-hourly amplitudes are due to random data are large. Thus it must be concluded that these two main lunar periods are not present in these data. Because of the negative result for the 500-m depth the temperature at the 50-m depth has not been studied.

In order to see whether a different result would be obtained for another time interval an expectancy test for the two main lunar tidal periods was also made for 1—19 June 1955, both for the 50 and 500-m depths. The difference between lunar and solar time was allowed for by a rearrangement of the solar hours in the computation schedule. In order to reduce the numerical work the data were averaged in groups of four consecutive lunar days prior to the harmonic analysis. The results are summarized in Table III. Only the semidiurnal lunar period at 50 m can possibly be considered as appearing in the temperature data. The amplitudes of the diurnal lunar period at both depths and of the semidiurnal lunar period at 500 m are not statistically significant.

Table III. Expectancy tests for time interval 1—29 June 1955, 50 m and 500 m

Depth	Period length	Amplitude	Expectancy	Probability
50 m	24 lun. hrs	0.12° C	0.14° C	0.51
50 m	12 lun. hrs	0.28° C	0.13° C	0.01
500 m	24 lun. hrs	0.012° C	0.031° C	0.85
500 m	12 lun. hrs	0.057° C	0.044° C	0.19

During this period the temperature at 500 m depth showed some pronounced oscillations. Therefore a simplified periodogram analysis was performed beginning with a period of 10 hours and extended in steps of two hours, to 42 hours (Fig. 5). The periodogram shows a peak for a period of 20 hours, and another one for 40 hours

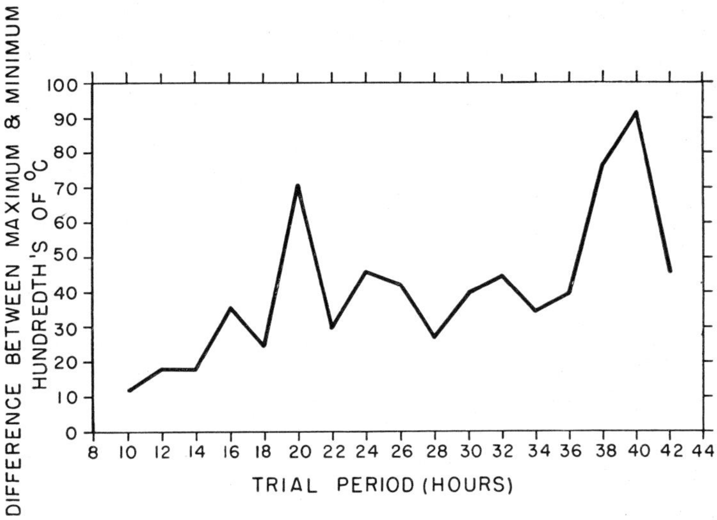

Fig. 5. Periodogram of temperature records at 500 m depth off Bermuda, April 5—13, 1955.

which is a reappearance of the maximum at 20 hours.

This 20-hour period is evidently not of tidal origin. The inertia period at the latitude of Bermuda is 22.4 hours, considerably longer than 20 hours. A direct expectancy test showed furthermore that a period of 22 hours is not indicated in the data (see Table IV below). Thus it must be concluded that the 20-hour period has no connection with the inertial period. It does not appear fruitful at this time to speculate on the physical origin of the 20-hour oscillation; it may be that it is excited by the storm in the vicinity of Bermuda at the beginning of the time interval under investigation, and that the length of its period is determined by the physical state of the waters around Bermuda. But this is admittedly pure speculation.

For the sake of completeness this same time interval has also been searched for periods of 24 and 12 hours because these periods are very close to the lunar tidal periods. The results together with the relevant expectancy test data for all the periods studied for this interval are shown in Table IV. The probabilities that the 24-hour and especially the 12-hour oscillations as expressed by their amplitudes are of real physical significance are evidently very low. Since it is actually the lunar tidal periods which are in general strongest and not the solar tidal periods it might be thought that the test is not conclusive since the analysis has been performed for solar hours. It is possible to apply a correction for the phase shift which arises if a set of data containing the lunar period is analyzed according to 24 solar hours. This has been done but the resulting corrections do not alter the computed probabilities significantly. Hence it appears that the lunar periods are definitely not observable during the time interval under investigation.

Table IV. Expectancy test for time interval 5—13 April 1955, 500 meters

Period length	Amplitude	Expectancy	Probability
20 hours ...	0.31° C	0.13° C	0.003
22 hours ...	0.09° C	0.12° C	0.613
24 hours ...	0.16° C	0.12° C	0.14
12 hours ...	0.05° C	0.09° C	0.70

d) *7—12 May and 3—7 June 1955, 500 m*

These time intervals were investigated because the temperature graphs showed some fairly regular oscillations during these times. Periodogram analyses extending from trial periods of 10 to 42 hours indicated peaks at 12 hours, 24 hours, and 36 hours. The expectancy test was performed only for the 12 and 24 hour periods because its result showed immediately that the periodogram peaks at 24 hours, and by inference those at 36 hours, are merely repetitions of the twelve-hour peak. The results of Table V make it appear possible that the 12-hourly periods are real, but it must be remembered that the time intervals were chosen because they showed regular oscillations. While the analysis was carried out according to solar time it is likely that the 12-hourly periods discussed here are in reality lunar 12-hourly periods, since the lunar tidal force is larger than the solar tidal force. If the lunar tides were more strongly developed and not as much disturbed by superimposed variations it would be possible to differentiate between lunar and solar tidal oscillations by studying the phase shift of the harmonic constants as determined for each day. But the superimposed noise makes this procedure inapplicable.

Table V. Expectancy tests for time intervals 7—12 May and 3—7 June 1955, 500 m

Epoch	Period length	Amplitude	Expectancy	Probability
7—12 May	24 hours	0.03° C	0.06° C	0.80
	12 hours	0.14° C	0.08° C	0.035
3—7 June	24 hours	0.07° C	0.07° C	0.32
	12 hours	0.23° C	0.12° C	0.019

In summary of the discussion in this section it can be said that from time to time periodicities appear in the record with periods whose lengths are 30, 24, 23, 20, and 12 hours. The 24-hourly and 12-hourly oscillations are presumably the lunar tidal periods, the period of 23 hours may be the inertial period (more accurately 22.4 hours at Bermuda). No explanation is offered for the 30 and 20-hourly periods. None of these periods can be regarded as definitely established, except perhaps the 12-hourly lunar tidal period at 50 m depth during June 1955 (Table III) whose chance occurrence has a probability of only one in one hundred. Other periods with equally low or lower probability, 20 hours

(Table IV), 23 hours (Table I) are not as significant because they were found in pre-selected data. Even the 12-hourly period is not always clearly indicated in the data, as shown by the expectancy tests. Physically, it would seem quite plausible that even these periodicities for which causes are known, such as the tidal and inertial periods, are not always clearly shown in the observation material because they may often be completely obscured by other periodic and unperiodic variations.

To make an over-all test concerning the reality of various periodicities in the Bermuda data it is oecessary to extend the analysis to a larger body nf data. It becomes then desirable to compute cross spectra using high-speed computers. This part of the investigation will now be discussed. The resulting gain of higher resolution and statistical reliability is offset in part by the implied assumption that many months of record can be treated as a "stationary time series".

IV. Spectra of the records

A) THE METHOD

The method is essentially the one given by Tukey (TUKEY, 1949; PANOFSKY and McCORMICK, 1954). From the cosine transform of the autocorrelations one obtains the spectra S_d and S_s of the deep and shallow temperature records. The cosine and sine transforms of the cross-correlation are the cospectrum C and quadrature spectrum Q. From these we obtain the coherence Co and phase Θ between the two records according to

$$Co^2 = \frac{C^2 + Q^2}{S_d S_s}, \qquad \tan \Theta = \frac{Q}{C},$$

with Θ taken between 0° and 180° for positive Q, and between 180° and 360° for negative Q. With this convention Θ designates the phase *lead* of shallow record with respect to the deep one.

For each of the six analyses the four quantities S_d, S_s, Co^2 and Θ are plotted without smoothing against frequency in cycles per hour. The highest frequency in Fig. 6 is 2.5 c.p.h., exactly half the sampling frequency of 5 readings per hour. The frequency range from 0 to 2.5 c.p.h. is divided into $m = 62$ equal frequency intervals $\triangle f = 2.5/62 = .0432$ c.p.h. (see Table VI). S_d, S_s, Co^2 and Θ are plotted for all but the first of these intervals.

S_d and S_s are in units of °C²/c.p.h. This can be interpreted as follows. The r.m.s. value of the deep record A: 1 is .25 °C (Table VI); the variance thus equals .0625 °C². The plotted values give the contribution towards this variance from a unit frequency band (width 1 c.p.h.) centered at the plotted frequency. The reliability of the plotted values depends on the degrees of freedom, $\gamma = (2\,N/m) - {}^1/_2$, where N is the total number of values used in the analyses. Analyses A:1, A:2, and A:3 are each based on 2,355 readings, thus $\gamma = 75$. The vertical arrows on Fig. 6 and 7 give the 95 per cent confidence limits. For 75 degrees of freedom these are 0.76 to 1.40; i.e., there is one chance in twenty that the correct value be less than 0.76 or larger than 1.40 times the computed value. The logarithmic plot enables one to plot a single "confidence arrow" for all values in an analysis.

The mean phase relation throughout the record length is given by Θ for each of the frequency bands. Co^2 is a measure of the variability in Θ at this frequency. If Θ were constant throughout the analyzed record, then $Co^2 = 1$; if it were randomly distributed, then $Co^2 = \Theta$. Clearly the reliability of the computed Θ depends on coherence. The 95 per cent confidence limits that Θ lies within the limits $\Theta - \Delta\Theta$ and $\Theta + \Delta\Theta$ are as follows (from GOODMAN, 1957):

Table VI. Information concerning the two charts that were analyzed. Data extend from Nov. 1955 to Feb. 1956

	Prefilter	Δf c.p.h.	E °C deep	E °C shallow	N	ν
A: 1 Nov. 9: 0800—Nov. 28: 2200...	12^m H 12^m	.04032	.25	.11	2355	75
A: 2 Nov. 28: 2200—Dec. 18: 1200...	12^m H 12^m	.04032	.31	.15	2355	75
A: 3 Dec. 18: 1200—Jan. 7: 0200....	12^m H 12^m	.04032	.32	.22	2355	75
B: 1 Jan. 11: 1300—Feb. 2: 0700	12^m H 12^m	.04032	.25	.20	2610	84
A: 4 Nov. 11: 0500—Jan. 5: 0500....	12^m L 48^m H 48^m	.001008	.28	.23	1650	53
B: 2 Jan. 13: 1000—Jan. 31: 1000 ...	12^m L 48^m H 48^m	.01008	.29	.32	540	17

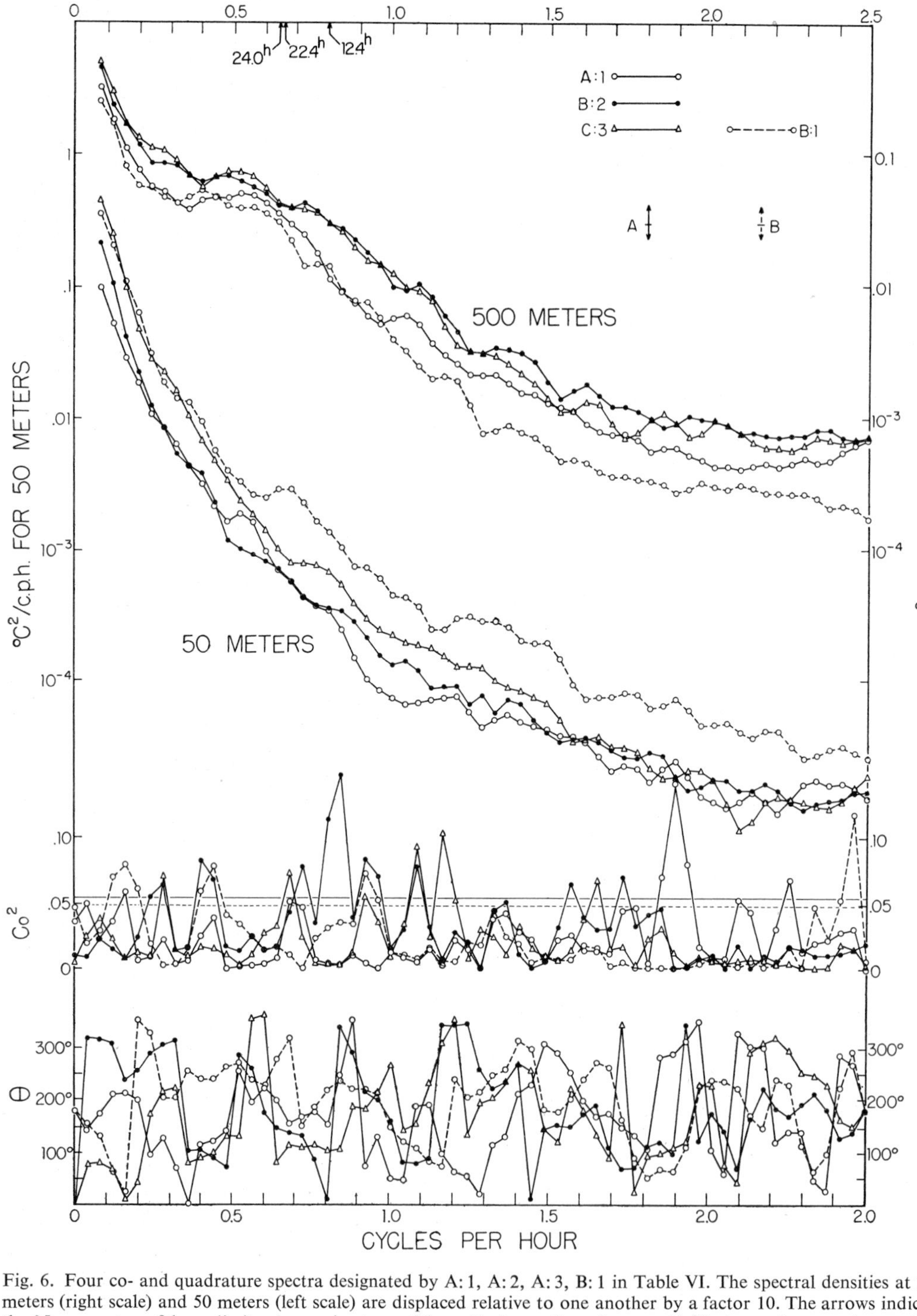

Fig. 6. Four co- and quadrature spectra designated by A: 1, A: 2, A: 3, B: 1 in Table VI. The spectral densities at 500 meters (right scale) and 50 meters (left scale) are displaced relative to one another by a factor 10. The arrows indicate the 95 per cent confidence limits. Approximate confidence limits on the coherence Co² between the records are given by the horizontal lines. Evidently there is no significant coherence, and accordingly the phase relation Θ between the records is not significant.

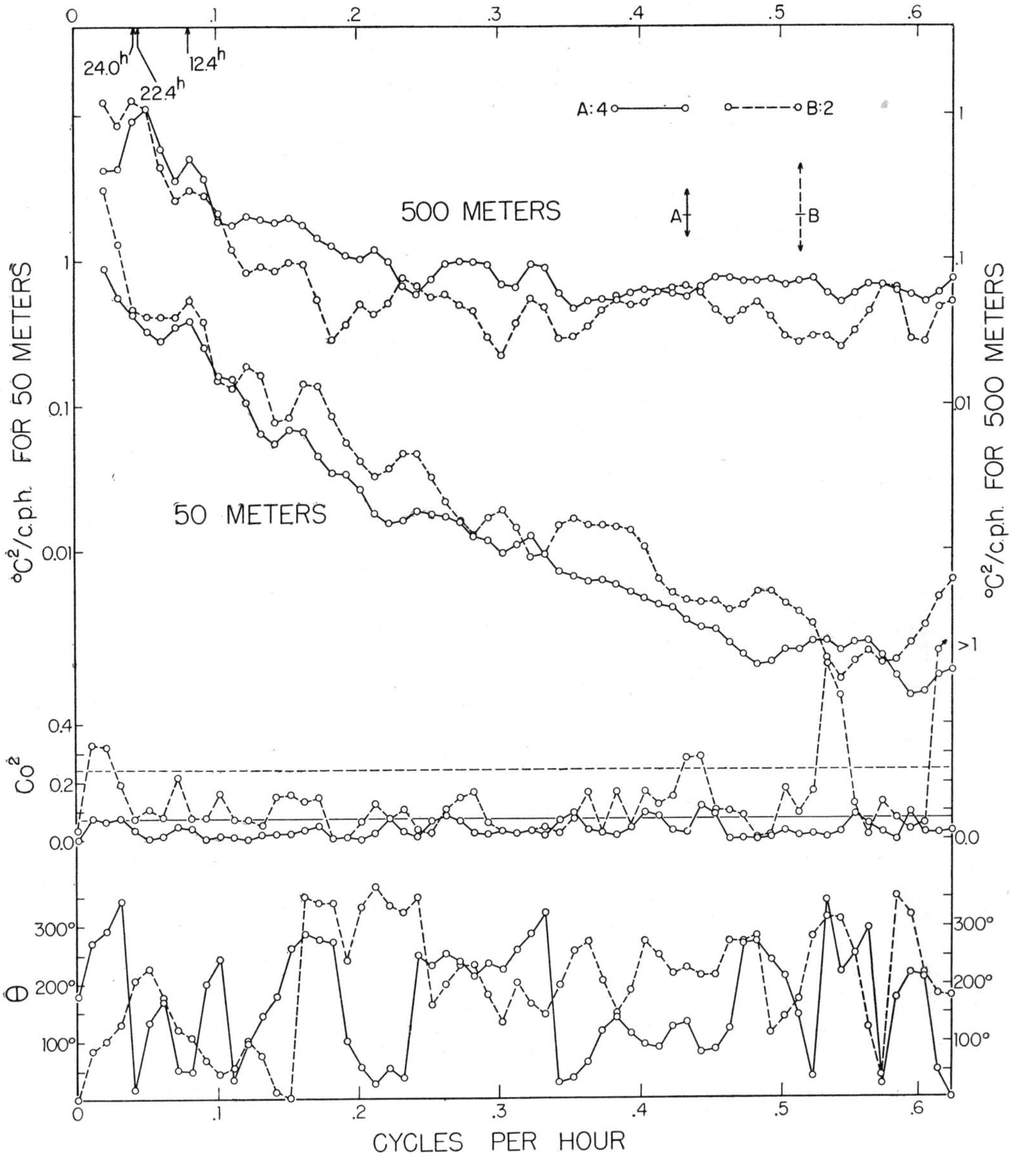

Fig. 7. Similar to Figure 6 except for a lower frequency range.

Table VII. Values of $\Delta\theta$ for stated coherence Co^2 and degrees of freedom

		ν 84	75	53	17
Co^2	.50	16°	17°	20°	40°
	.25	28°	30°	37°	—

The corresponding limits on Co^2 are roughly $4/\nu$, so that only the largest values of coherence are significant, and only for those can a meaningful phase relation be inferred.

The procedure adopted was as follows. Record A was read every 12 minutes to the nearest 0.01 chart-inch (0.005° C); each reading is in doubt by something like .02 chart inches (.01° C). The data were put on punchcards and a numerical high-pass filter applies (designated by $12^m H\ 12^m$ in Table VI). In this way long-term temperature drifts are suppressed without appreciably affecting the frequencies here under consideration. If the high-pass filtering were not done, then the spectrum would be seriously contaminated by the relatively high "energy" associated with this drift. Fifteen hours of record are lost at each end by virtue of the high-pass filtering. The remaining portion was split up into three equal lengths as shown in Table VI, and the spectrum analysis performed. Prefiltering was done on an IBM 650 computer, the spectrum on a Remington Rand 1103 computer.

In addition, the complete record was analyzed in another way in order to improve the resolution at low frequencies (Table VI, A: 4). By a suitable set of weighting functions the high-frequency wiggles were reduced, and the smoothed record tabulated at an interval of 48^m, four times that of the original record. This low-pass filtering was again performed on an IBM 650 computer. The 48^m readings were then high-passed and analyzed as before. The prefiltering is designated by 12^mL 48^mH 48^m in Table VI. The result is that the smoothed spectra (Fig. 7) extend only over one-fourth the frequency range as compared to the original spectra (Fig. 6), from 0 to 0.625 c.p.h. instead of 0 to 2.5 c.p.h. The reduced frequency range is again divided into 62 intervals, and in this way the frequency resolution is quadrupled. The improved resolution is at the expense of reliability. In the case of record A, the reduction in ν is moderate, from 75 to 53, because A: 4 is based on roughly three times the length of records as the other analysis. In the case of B the length of record was too short for subdivision, and the reduction in ν is severe, from 84 in B: 1 to 17 in B: 2. (Note the uncertainty arrows in Fig. 7.)

In any analyses based on observations at discrete intervals, the "aliasing problem" is severe (Tukey, 1949): frequencies in the vicinity of the sampling frequency appear in the alias of a low frequency. Thus for reading every 12^m a 13^m wave would have the appearance of $13^m \times 12^m = 156^m$ wave. The problem is particularly acute when going from the 12^m readings to the 48^m reading, and the low-pass filter is designed to alleviate the difficulty. First order corrections for aliasing were made for A: 4 and B: 2, and the final results were corrected for slight modifications due to filtering. The procedures are cumbersome and dull. A full discussion is in preparation (Munk, Snodgrass, and Tucker, in press).

B) THE RESULTS

i. *The high frequency cut-off*

For frequencies in excess of 0.75 c.p.h. all spectra drop towards high frequency by something like 10 db per octave, that is, somewhat more sharply than f^{-3}. The computed cut-off is actually weaker than the true cut-off for a number of reasons: (1) In any steep spectrum the calculation leads to a diffusion of spectral energy from the high to the low regions. (2) More important, random errors in chart reading introduce a white noise which materially boosts the high frequency values. Suppose the rms error is .02 chart inches = .01 °C. The error variance is then 10^{-4} °C^2, and if this is uniformly distributed across the entire range of frequencies, from 0 to 2.5 c.p.h., the resulting spectral density is $10^{-4}/2.5 = 4 \times 10^{-5}$ °C^2/c.p.h. This is roughly the value reached at the high frequency and by the shallow spectra. The deep spectra at the high frequency end are ten times higher and may be real. A reliable determination of the spectra for $f > 2$ c.p.h. would require some elaboration in the recording scheme.

In all events the monotonic high-frequency cut-off is a real feature and needs to be explained. For each of the four spectra the *trends* are reproducible within the limits of statistical uncertainty. Actual values may vary from record to record by a factor three. B: 1 record has the lowest densities of the deep spectra and the highest of the shallow spectra. A noteworthy feature is that the deep spectrum is ten times the shallow spectrum.

In a general way this can be accounted for in terms of the stability of the water column. A thorough analysis of the internal wave motions possible in the waters around Bermuda does not seem warranted by the available data. But certain conclusions can be drawn by means of the Väisälä (or Brunt) frequency,

$$N = \frac{1}{2\pi}\sqrt{\frac{g}{\varrho}\frac{d\varrho}{dz}}$$

Fig. 8 shows $N(z)$ for winter conditions in 1955. A maximum $N_m = 5.6$ c.p.h. at 200 meters is associated with the seasonal thermocline, a second, weaker maximum at 850 m with the permanent thermocline. N_s and N_d are local values of the frequency at the depths of the shallow and deep instruments, respectively. At any depth we should expect no frequencies larger than N_m; a greatly reduced spectral density for frequencies larger than the local Väisälä frequency, and a relatively large spectral density for frequencies less than the local Väisälä frequency. An extrapolation of the computed curves bears out the first prediction of no significant spectral density at 5.6 c.p.h.; the second prediction might account for the relative absence of high frequencies in the shallow record. The spectral densities at the local Väisälä frequencies is 10^{-3} °C²/c.p.h. for both the deep and shallow records.

This geometric argument has been developed by Eckart (personal communication) and will be discussed in detail in his forthcoming book.[1] It would be out of place to reproduce the argument here. There is, however, some doubt concerning the applicability of the argument to a situation as complex as the one found at Bermuda, with two maxima of N. Judging by the three-layer case, one expects the oscillations at the two thermoclines to be only weakly coupled, with the shallow instrument responding largely to modes associated with the seasonal thermoclines, and the deep instrument to modes associated with the permanent thermocline. This situation could account for the virtual absence of coherence between the records. At no frequency range is there a significant coherence, and it is significant that this should be so.[2]

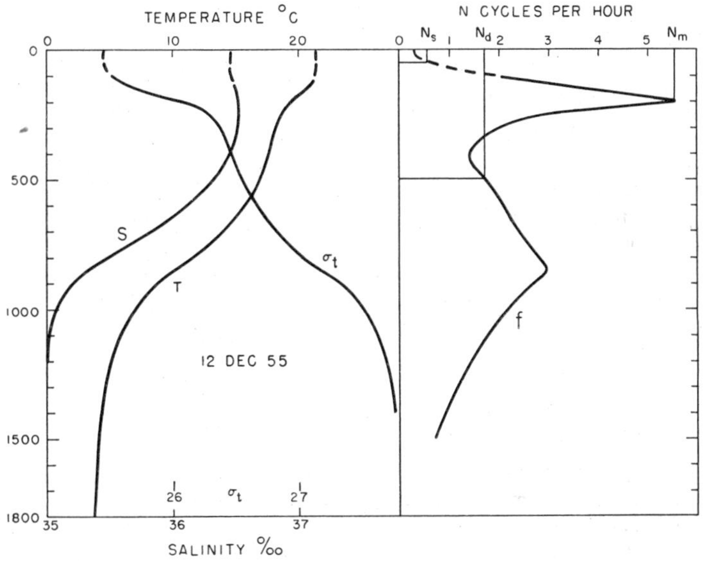

Fig. 8. The Väisäla (or Brunt) frequency $2\pi\,(g\varrho^{-1}\,d\varrho/dz)^{1/2}$ on December 12, 1955. The upper maximum (N_m= 5.6 c.p.h.) is associated with the seasonal thermocline; the lower, weaker maximum with the permanent thermocline; N_s and N_d are the local values of this frequency at the depths of the shallow and deep recorders, respectively.

ii. *The 0.5 c.p.h. plateau*

All four deep records show a weak maximum (or at least a plateau) of spectral density between 0.4 and 0.6 c.p.h. There is no corresponding feature on the shallow records. The feature can be seen on both the low and high-frequency spectra, and there can be no reasonable doubt of its reality. The surprisingly low frequency involved, 1 cycle in two hours, is an embarrassing aspect of the situation. Nowhere beneath the seasonal thermocline does the Väisälä frequency reach such low values, except depths below 2,000 m. Could it be that the Väisälä frequency associated with the deeper half of the ocean contributes appreciably to the thermal unrest in the permanent thermocline?

iii. *The lunar tide*

Both spectra show a peak for both the shallow and deep records at the frequency of the principal lunar tide (see Fig. 7). For the deep spectrum the area under the peak corresponds to roughly

[1] The earliest discussion of the cut-off frequency (a far as we know) has been given by GROEN (1948).

[2] Widely separated low-frequency surface wave records have yielded coherences up to $Co^2 = 0.9$ (MUNK, SNODGRASS and TUCKER, in press). Two components of currents as determined by a long GEK series taken by J. Reid also had coherences up to 0.9.

.004 °C^2 above background, somewhat more for the shallow spectrum. The corresponding amplitude is $\sqrt{.008} \approx 0.1$ °C, or 10 meters of vertical displacement. The internal tide contributes only a small fraction of the energy in the band centered at .008 c.p.h., and for that reason the coherence must remain low; still a coherent harmonic embedded in an incoherent noise could have been expected to give some enhancement in Co^2 at this frequency. The fact that it is not so indicates that the relative phase of the two instruments for the 12.4^h internal tides does not remain fixed!

With regard to the possible existence of discrete tidal modes, the present method of analyzing into relatively wide frequency bands cannot compete with the resolution obtained by Fourier Series methods employed in earlier parts of this paper.

iv. *Diurnal oscillation*

A significant peak in spectral density for the two shallow records at .04—.05 c.p.h. can be ascribed to either a 24.0^h tide or a 22.4^h inertial oscillation.

Whether or not this is due largely to internal tides could be decided by the use of the expectancy test. If the peak is due chiefly to inertial motion which decays in, say, tenperiods, then the resolution by the present method is adequate.

Remarks

The authors have tacitly assumed an explanation in terms of internal waves rather than drifting convection cells. To settle this point decisively the cross-spectrum of two records at 500 m depth would be required.

Acknowledgements

The authors are greatly indebted to a number of people who generously gave their help to us, in particular: (B.H.) to Mr. Frank Haurwitz for his help in carrying out the harmonic analyses; (H.S.) to Messrs. Brunel Spurling and Sloat Hodgson for collaboration in putting out the thermometric cable at Bermuda and the preliminary preparation of the data; and (W.H.M.) to Mr. Ferber, Mrs. Shumway and Mrs. Covher of Convair Corp. for their help in programming and carrying out the computations involved in the cross-spectrum analysis.

REFERENCES

CAHN, A. J., 1945: An Investigation of the free oscillations of a simple current system. *J. Meteorology,* **2**, p. 113—119.

DEFANT, A., 1932: Die Gezeiten und inneren Gezeitenwellen des Atlantischen Oceans. *Wissensch. Erg. d. Deutschen Atl. Exp. »Meteor«*, 1925—27, Bd. VII, Teil I, 1—318.

— 1950: On the origin of internal tide waves in the open sea. *J. Mar. Res.* IX, **2**, 111—119.

GOODMAN, N. R., 1957: On the joint estimation of the spectra, cospectrum and quadrature spectrum of a two-dimensional stationary Gaussian process. *New York University: Scientific Paper* No. 10, Engineering Statistics Laboratory.

GROEN, P., 1948: Contribution to the theory of internal waves. *Kon. Ned. Met. Inst. de Bilt. Med. en Verh.*, **2**, 11.

HAURWITZ, B, 1954: The occurrence of internal tides in the ocean. *Arch. Meteor. Geophys. und Bioklimat,* **7**, 406—424.

MUNK, W. H., SNODGRASS, F. E., and TUCKER, M. J., 1959: Spectra of low frequency ocean waves. To be submitted to the *Bulletin of the Scripps Institution of Oceanography* (in press).

PANOFSKY, H. A., and MCCORMICK, R. A., 1954: Properties of spectra of Atmospheric turbulence at 100 meters. *O,. J. Roy, Meteor. Soc.*, **80**, 546—564.

ROSSBY, C.-G. 1937—38: On the mutual adjustment of pressure and velocity distribution in certain simple current systems. *Jour. Mar. Res.* Part I, **1**, 15—28, Part II, **1**, 239—263.

TUKEY, J. W., 1949: The sampling theory of power spectrum estimates. *Symposium on applications of autocorrelation analysis to physical problems*, Woods Hole, Mass., 13—14 June 1949, p. 47—67 (printed by Office of Naval Research).

VERONIS, G. and STOMMEL, H., 1956: The action of variable wind stresses on a stratified ocean. *Journ. Mar. Res.* **15**, p. 43—75.

(Manuscript received 15 March, 1958)

On the Vertically Integrated Mass Transport in the Oceans

By Pierre Welander

International Meteorological Institute in Stockholm

Abstract

A computation is made of the Sverdrup transport in the oceans between 50° N and 35° S using the annual mean wind-stress field given by *Scripps Institution of Oceanography* and by *Hidaka*. It is pointed out that the Sverdrup model calls for the existence not only of boundary currents at the western edges but also of a system of free "jets". One may thus expect an essential non-Sverdrup transport even in the open parts of the oceans. For further use a more general transport equation is derived. This equation does not only include the lateral friction but also the effects of time-variation, noncompensation of the horizontal pressure gradient and Ekman bottom friction.

1. The Sverdrup transport

For the mass transport in a stratified ocean, integrated from the surface to the bottom, Sverdrup (1947) derived the simple equation

$$\beta \frac{\partial \psi}{\partial x} = \text{curl } \tau^w \tag{1}$$

Here x and y are quasi-cartesian coordinates in the eastern and northern directions, respectively, β is the y-derivative of the Coriolis parameter, and $\text{curl } \tau^w = \frac{\partial \tau_y^w}{\partial x} - \frac{\partial \tau_x^w}{\partial y}$, where τ_x^w, τ_y^w are the components of the wind-stress at the sea surface. ψ is the mass transport stream-function increasing to the right of the transport direction. The equation can be derived from the equations of motion, the hydrostatic equation and the equation of continuity, provided the following assumptions are made:

1. the motion is steady,
2. the mass transport is divergence-free (evaporation-precipitation neglected),
3. the lateral friction and the non-linear accelerations are neglected,
4. the horizontal pressure gradients due to surface slope and density stratification compensate at great depths.

Equation (1) was applied by Sverdrup (1947) to account for the equatorial transports in eastern Pacific, and at least qualitative agreement was obtained. Sverdrup started the integration of the equation at the eastern boundary, where the normal transport was put equal to zero. Munk (1950) computed the transport in a closed rectangular ocean basin using the same model with addition of lateral friction. The friction term allowed him to satisfy the condition of zero normal transport also at the western boundary. Munk was able to show that the Sverdrup equation was a good approximation except near the western boundary where a narrow, frictionally driven boundary current appeared. This was another demonstration of the westward intensification due to the β-term which had been predicted earlier by Stommel (1948). Further studies of the nature of the boundary current were carried out by Charney (1955) and Morgan (1956) introducing non-linear acceleration terms instead of lateral friction.

It would certainly be of interest to extend the previous transport computations to the total water globe, introducing the realistic shape of the boundaries. In principle such models as are used by Stommel, Munk and Charney could be integrated numerically over an ocean basin of complicated form, using a relaxation technique. Such

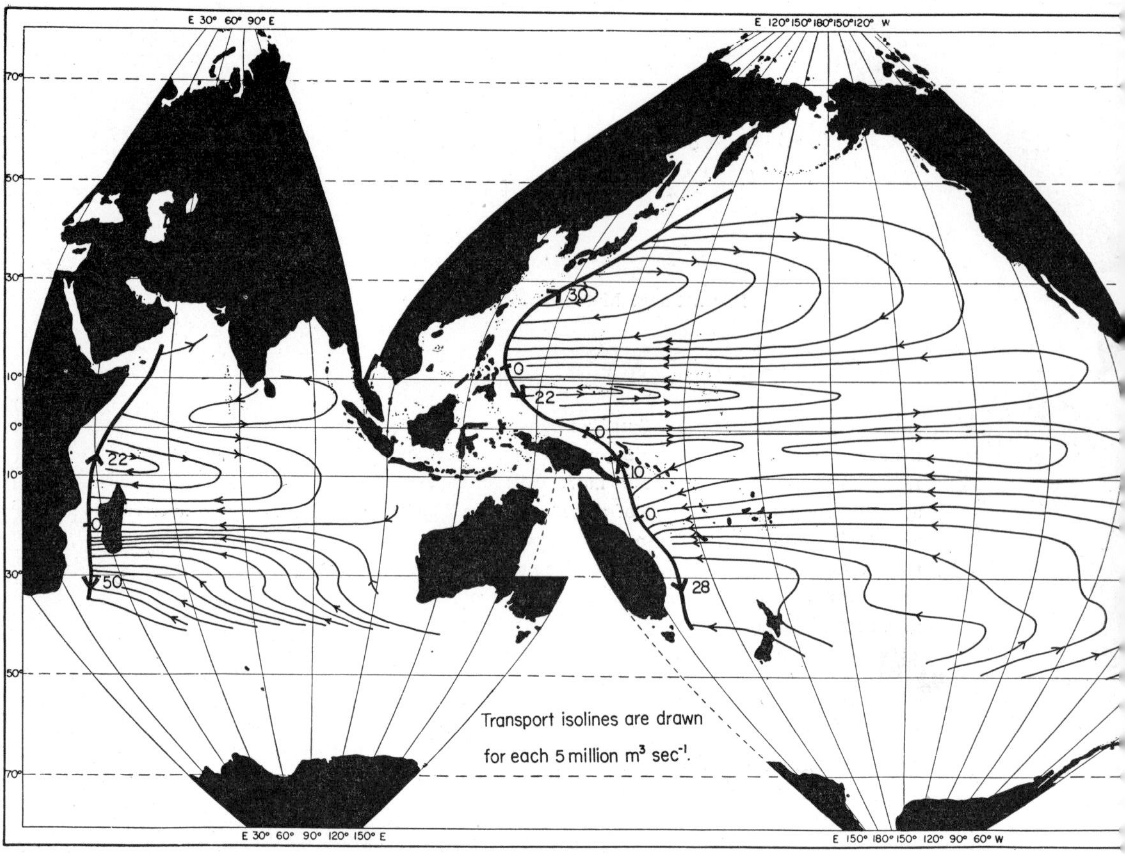

Plate I. The Sverdrup transport and the boundary currents in the oceans corresponding to the annual mean wind stress field. The figures give the transport in million m^3s^{-1} in different parts of the boundary currents. The wind stress field has been computed by Scripps Institution of Oceanography (1948) and by HIDAKA (1958).

computations would, however, become quite tedious. Probably one could get a fairly good picture of the main circulation simply by applying the Sverdrup equation to the entire basin and then add at the western boundaries narrow currents that balance the total meridional Sverdrup transport. The transport in the boundary currents predicted by this model is not likely to differ much from the value given by the more complicated models. Of course, nothing can be said about the details of the boundary currents.

As a first step towards such a global mapping a computation of the Sverdrup transport between 50° N and 40° S has been carried out, using meridional and zonal wind stress data published by *Scripps Institution of Oceanography* (1948) and by HIDAKA (1958). These data are based on the Pilot Chart of wind roses for 5° squares of the U.S. Hydographic Office. The resulting transport is seen in Plate I. The values of the transport in the boundary currents are also indicated.

A characteristic feature of the map is that the boundary currents on the northern and the southern hemispheres have comparable transports. This seems to contradict earlier observations, according to which the boundary currents of the northern hemisphere are essentially stronger than those of the southern hemisphere. These measurements included, however, only the uppermost layer of the ocean. More recent measurements revealing the existence of "under-currents" at the western boundaries seem to change the actual transport values in a direction which gives an improved agreement with the computed Sverdrup transport.

Another feature in the map which deserves special attention is the zonal jets that seem to form

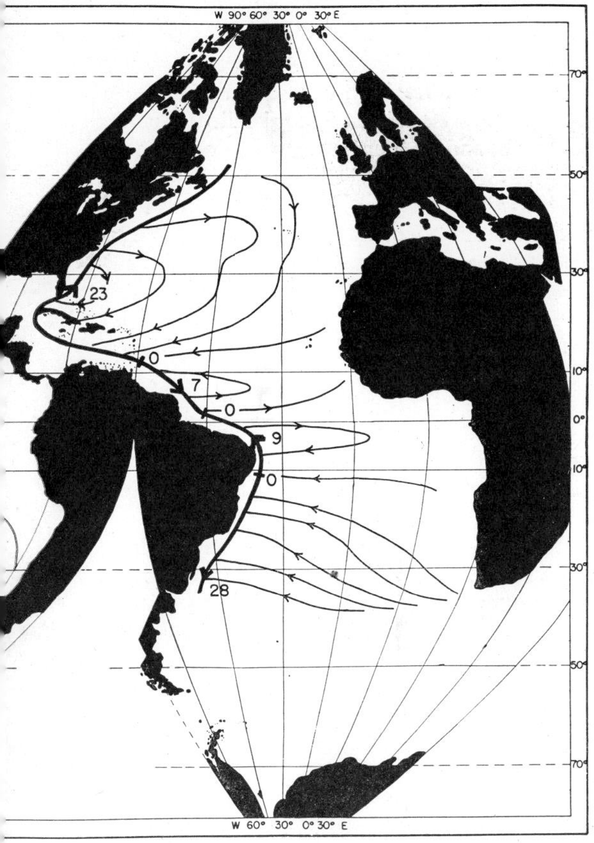

in the southern Atlantic and Indian Oceans. The explanation of these jets is as follows. In a closed basin the boundary current will vanish both at the northern and the southern ends of the basin, and a continuous Sverdrup regime can persist in the interior region (Fig. 1 A). In the semi-

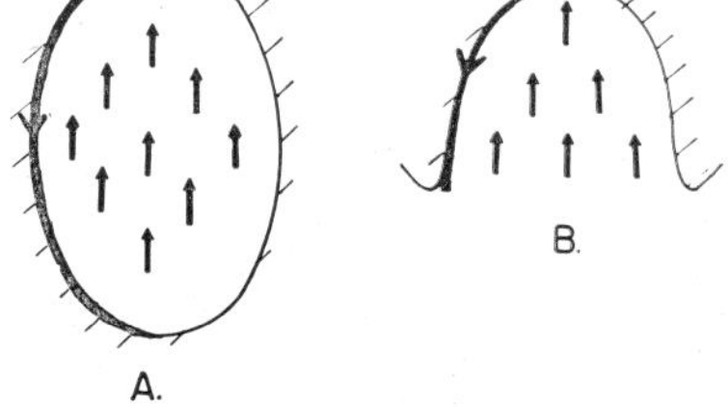

Fig. 1. The meridional Sverdrup transport and the boundary current A) in a closed basin, B) in a semiclosed basin.

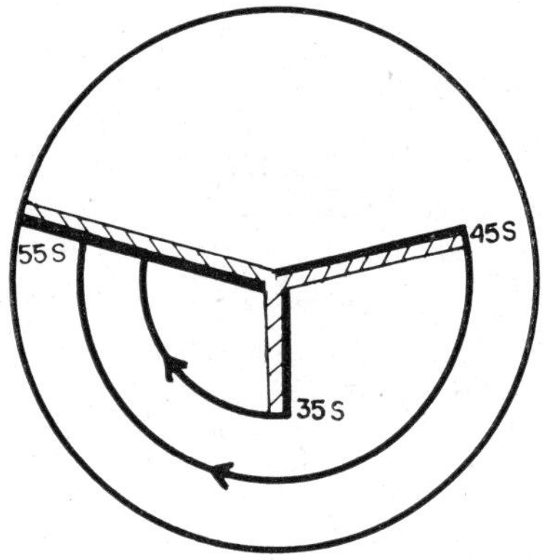

Fig. 2. The system of boundary currents and free jets implied by the Sverdrup model.

closed ocean basins we have in reality, the situation is complicated by the fact that the total Sverdrup transport into the basin does not generally vanish. This transport calls for a compensating boundary current at the end point of the western boundary (Fig. 1 B). Since eastern boundary currents are excluded and since the meridional transport is already fixed by the wind-stress curl, this water can only proceed out in the open sea in the form of a zonal jet, ending at another boundary current[1]. If the total water globe is considered one would accordingly find, in the Sverdrup model, a system of boundary currents and free sharp jets of the form schematically indicated in Fig. 2. In the figure is also indicated the Antarctic circumpolar current, the transport of which cannot be determined by help of the Sverdrup theory (see MUNK and PALMÉN 1950).

Contrasting the above picture with the observed ocean transport we know that the boundary currents and the circumpolar current certainly are there, while no sharp jets are known to exist at 35° S and 45° S in the Atlantic and Indian Oceans. This must mean that the boundary currents that reach the southern tips of Africa and Australia spread into the open sea by help of some other mechanism and join a large-scale non-Sverdrup circulation. This circulation should involve quite large transports, certainly comparable to the pure Sverdrup transports. Thus, the Sverdrup model does not perhaps apply so well to the open sea as has been assumed earlier.

[1] The existence of such jets in the Sverdrup regime has recently been confirmed by experiments carried out at the Woods Hole Oceanographic Institute (private communication).

There are also other arguments that points in the same direction. If one considers the actual wind-stress field this will vary in time. The response of the pure Sverdrup model to these variations is quite rapid. If one includes the local time derivatives in the equations of motion and still considers the mass transport to be approximately divergence-free, Sverdrup's equation is changed into the form

$$\frac{\partial}{\partial t}(\nabla^2 \psi) + \beta \frac{\partial \psi}{\partial x} = \text{curl } \tau^w \tag{2}$$

where

$$\nabla^2 = \frac{\partial^2}{\partial x^2} + \frac{\partial^2}{\partial y^2}$$

Assuming a horizontal scale of the motion of the order L, the time of response will be of the order $\frac{1}{\beta L}$. For scales of the order of a few thousands of km the response time would be of the order of one or a few days. Thus, if the Sverdrup model is a good approximation the transport would follow, say, the annual variation of the wind-stress very well. A computation of the theoretical variation in the transport between the months January and July has now been made, using zonal wind-stress data given by PRIESTLEY (1951). The resulting mean-square variation in the transport is, in the open sea, about 10 million $m^3 s^{-1}$, and the variation in the boundary currents is even larger. Such a large variation is certainly not observed in the real oceans, and the reason for this seems also to be clear. In Sverdrup's model it is assumed that the sea surface slope and the density field compensate so as to give a negligible horizontal pressure gradient at great depths. When the wind-stress varies the surface slope may follow quite quickly, while the rearrangement of the density field needed to compensate the surface slope will develop more slowly. In fact, if this rearrangement involves an appreciable advection of the density field a response time of several years seems not to be unlikely. One may thus expect that the assumption of compensation at great depths is not very well fulfilled at each moment, and that noticeable velocities may occur near the bottom.

2. A generalized transport equation

The previous discussion has raised the question of the importance of the non-Sverdrup terms in the open sea. The effects of such terms as the lateral friction and the non-linear accelerations have been discussed by earlier investigators and have been found to be important for the understanding of the detailed structure of the boundary currents. In the open sea it seems, however, more likely that the incomplete compensation at great depths is the most important effect to be added to the Sverdrup model. Such an incomplete compensation will manifest itself in two ways. Firstly, the velocities set up at the bottom will create a bottom stress that should be subtracted from the wind-stress in equation (1). Secondly, if there exists a bottom slope, the vertically integrated horizontal pressure gradient is not curl-free, and an extra pressure term appears in the Sverdrup equation. Some discussion of the effect of a sloping bottom in a baroclinic ocean has been given by NEUMANN (1955) and HANSEN (1958). Hansen has also discussed the effect of friction, but his frictional law (bottom stress + integrated lateral friction proportional to the transport vector) may not be sufficiently realistic. In the present section a more general derivation of the mass transport equation will be given which includes all linear effects: local acceleration, lateral friction, Ekman bottom stress, the curl of the integrated horizontal pressure gradient and also the divergence in the mass transport due to evaporation-precipitation. Non-linear terms are not included. These terms require a specification of the whole three-dimensional velocity field and cannot be simply expressed in the mass transport stream function. Some simplifications that should not be very critical are introduced in the course of the derivation. The transport is assumed to be almost divergence-free so that it could still be represented well enough by a stream function, except in the divergence-terms. The mass transport due to changes in the sea surface elevation is neglected everywhere. This will exclude certain types of wave-motions but it is hoped that it will not affect critically the large-scale adjustment processes in the open sea that is of interest to us.

We start out from the following equations of motion

$$\varrho \frac{\partial u}{\partial t} - f\varrho v = -\frac{\partial p}{\partial x} + A_H \nabla^2 u + A_v \frac{\partial^2 u}{\partial z^2} \tag{3}$$

$$\varrho \frac{\partial v}{\partial t} + f\varrho u = -\frac{\partial p}{\partial y} + A_H \nabla^2 v + A_v \frac{\partial^2 v}{\partial z^2} \tag{4}$$

the hydrostatic equation

$$0 = -\frac{\partial p}{\partial z} - g\varrho \tag{5}$$

and the continuity equation

$$\frac{\partial \varrho}{\partial t} + \frac{\partial}{\partial x}(\varrho u) + \frac{\partial}{\partial y}(\varrho v) + \frac{\partial}{\partial z}(\varrho w) = 0 \tag{6}$$

Here p is the pressure, ϱ the density, g the acceleration of gravity, and A_H, A_v the coefficients of lateral and vertical viscosity, respectively. A_H and A_v are considered as constants. We integrate these equations from the bottom ($z = -h\,[x, y]$) to the surface ($z = \zeta\ [x, y, t]$). $z = 0$ is the undisturbed sea-surface. We replace $\varrho \frac{\partial u}{\partial t}$ by $\frac{\partial}{\partial t}(\varrho u)$ etc., $A_H \nabla^2 u$ by $\frac{A_H}{\bar{\varrho}} \nabla^2(\varrho u) = A'_H \nabla^2(\varrho u)$ etc. where $\bar{\varrho}$ is a mean density, which simplifications are permitted in view of the restriction to linear terms. We further neglect the lateral friction in the layer from $z = 0$ to $z = \zeta$, and we also neglect the effect of atmospheric pressure. Equations (3) and (4) non takes the form

$$\frac{\partial}{\partial t} M_x - fM_y = -\frac{\partial}{\partial x}\int_{-h}^{\zeta} p dz + \frac{\partial h}{\partial x} p_{-h} + A'_H \nabla^2 M_x$$
$$- A'_H \left\{ \frac{\partial h}{\partial x}\left[\frac{\partial}{\partial x}(\varrho u)\right]_{-h} + \frac{\partial h}{\partial y}\left[\frac{\partial}{\partial y}(\varrho u)\right]_{-h} \right.$$
$$\left. + \nabla^2 h (\varrho u)_{-h} + \frac{\partial h}{\partial x}\frac{\partial}{\partial x}(\varrho u)_{-h} + \frac{\partial h}{\partial y}\frac{\partial}{\partial y}(\varrho u)_{-h} \right\}$$
$$+ \tau_x^w - (\tau_x)_{-h} \tag{7}$$

$$\frac{\partial}{\partial t} M_y + fM_x = -\frac{\partial}{\partial y}\int_{-h}^{\zeta} p dz + \frac{\partial h}{\partial y} p_{-h} + A'_H \nabla^2 M_y$$
$$- A'_H \left\{ \frac{\partial h}{\partial x}\left[\frac{\partial}{\partial x}(\varrho v)\right]_{-h} + \frac{\partial h}{\partial y}\left[\frac{\partial}{\partial y}(\varrho v)\right]_{-h} \right.$$
$$\left. + \nabla^2 h (\varrho v)_{-h} + \frac{\partial h}{\partial x}\frac{\partial}{\partial x}(\varrho v)_{-h} + \frac{\partial h}{\partial y}\frac{\partial}{\partial y}(\varrho v)_{-h} \right\} +$$
$$+ \tau y^w - (\tau y)_{-h} \tag{8}$$

where we have introduced the components of the mass transport

$$\left.\begin{aligned} M_x &= \int_{-h}^{\zeta} \varrho u dz \\ M_y &= \int_{-h}^{\zeta} \varrho v dz \end{aligned}\right\} \tag{9}$$

The terms in the brackets of the above transport equations give the effects of lateral viscosity and non-compensation in a product form. If we agree to consider our theory as one giving the first order correction to Sverdrup's model it may be justified to neglect these. Taking $-\frac{\partial}{\partial y}$ of (7) and $\frac{\partial}{\partial x}$ of (8) and adding gives

$$\frac{\partial}{\partial t}\left(\frac{\partial M_y}{\partial x} - \frac{\partial M_x}{\partial y}\right) + f\left(\frac{\partial M_x}{\partial x} + \frac{\partial M_y}{\partial y}\right) + \beta M_y =$$
$$= -J(h, p_{-h}) + A'_H \nabla^2 \left(\frac{\partial M_y}{\partial x} - \frac{\partial M_x}{\partial y}\right) +$$
$$+ \text{curl}\,\tau^w - \text{curl}\,(\tau)_{-h} \tag{10}$$

where J denotes the Jacobian with respect to x, y. The vertically integrated continuity equation may be written, in the linear approximation,

$$\frac{\partial M_x}{\partial x} + \frac{\partial M_y}{\partial y} = -\bar{\varrho}\frac{\partial \zeta}{\partial t} - P \tag{11}$$

where P is the vertical mass flux due to evaporation minus precipitation. Here we introduce the simplifications mentioned of earlier: $\frac{\partial \zeta}{\partial t}$ is being neglected and P is considered only in terms proportional to the divergence. Introducing the mass transport stream function through $M_x = -\frac{\partial \psi}{\partial y}$, $M_y = \frac{\partial \psi}{\partial x}$ equation (10) can now be written

$$\frac{\partial}{\partial t}(\nabla^2 \psi) + \beta \frac{\partial \psi}{\partial x} - A'_H \nabla^4 \psi =$$
$$= fP - J(h, p_{-h}) + \text{curl}\,\tau^w - \text{curl}\,(\tau)_{-h} \tag{12}$$

It remains to express $J(p_{-h}, h)$ and curl $(\tau)_{-h}$ in terms of ψ and the density distribution. The hydrostatic equation gives after a vertical integration

$$p = g\bar{\varrho}(\zeta - z) + g\int_z^0 \varrho' dz \tag{13}$$

where ϱ' denotes the deviation of ϱ from its mean value. The contribution of ϱ' in the layer from $z = 0$ to $z = \zeta$ is neglected. One finds

$$J(h, p_{-h}) = g\bar{\varrho} J(h, \zeta) + gJ(h, \overline{Q}) \tag{14}$$

where

$$\overline{Q} = \int_{-h}^{0} \varrho' dz$$

The stress components $(\tau_x)_{-h}$ and $(\tau_y)_{-h}$ are determined by the relations

$$\left.\begin{aligned}(\tau_x)_{-h} &= -D\left[\left(\frac{\partial p}{\partial x}\right)_{-h} + \left(\frac{\partial p}{\partial y}\right)_{-h}\right]\\ (\tau_y)_{-h} &= -D\left[-\left(\frac{\partial p}{\partial x}\right)_{-h} + \left(\frac{\partial p}{\partial y}\right)_{-h}\right]\end{aligned}\right\} \quad (15)$$

where $D = -\sqrt{\dfrac{A_v}{2f}}$ is $\dfrac{1}{2\pi}$ times the Ekman depth of frictional influence (EKMAN, 1905). D is considered to be a constant. The above relations hold well when the variation of the pressure gradient over the Ekman depth is small and there is no direct contribution from the surface stress. With these values one finds

$$\begin{aligned}\text{curl}\,(\tau)_{-h} &= D\left\{\frac{\partial}{\partial x}\left(\frac{\partial p}{\partial x}\right)_{-h} + \frac{\partial}{\partial y}\left(\frac{\partial p}{\partial y}\right)_{-h} + \frac{\partial}{\partial y}\left(\frac{\partial p}{\partial x}\right)_{-h} - \frac{\partial}{\partial x}\left(\frac{\partial p}{\partial y}\right)_{-h}\right\} =\\ &= Dg\left\{\varrho\,\nabla^2\zeta + \left(\frac{\partial \overline{Q}_x}{\partial x} + \frac{\partial \overline{Q}_y}{\partial y}\right) - \left(\frac{\partial \overline{Q}_y}{\partial x} - \frac{\partial \overline{Q}_x}{\partial y}\right)\right\}\end{aligned} \quad (16)$$

where

$$\overline{Q}_x = \int_{-h}^{0} \frac{\partial \varrho'}{\partial x}\,dz \quad \text{etc.}$$

Values of $\dfrac{\partial \zeta}{\partial x}$ and $\dfrac{\partial \zeta}{\partial y}$ in terms ψ and ϱ' may be obtained from the vertically integrated equations of motions (7, 8), after introducing (13) and (15).

Inserting the values of $\dfrac{\partial \zeta}{\partial x}$ and $\dfrac{\partial \zeta}{\partial y}$ in the expressions for $J(h, p_{-h})$ and curl $(\tau)_{-h}$ (14) and (16) and introducing the stream function ψ everywhere, equation (12), after complicated reductions, takes on the form

$$\boxed{\begin{aligned}&\left(\nabla^2 - \alpha_1\frac{\partial}{\partial x} - \alpha_2\frac{\partial}{\partial y}\right)\frac{\partial \psi}{\partial t} - A'_H\,\nabla^4\psi +\\ &+\left[A'_H\left(\alpha_1\frac{\partial}{\partial x} + \alpha_2\frac{\partial}{\partial y}\right) + \frac{D}{h}f\right]\nabla^2\psi +\\ &\left[\beta\left(\frac{\partial}{\partial x} + \frac{D}{h}\frac{\partial}{\partial y}\right) - f\left(\alpha_2\frac{\partial}{\partial x} - \alpha_1\frac{\partial}{\partial y}\right)\right]\psi\\ &= F_{\text{ev.}} + F_{\text{wind}} + F_{\text{dens.}}\end{aligned}} \quad (17)$$

with

$$\left.\begin{aligned}F_{\text{ev.}} &= \left(f + \frac{D}{h}A'_H\,\nabla^2\right)P - \frac{D}{h}\frac{\partial P}{\partial t}\\ F_{\text{wind}} &= \alpha_2\tau_x^w - \alpha_1\tau_y^w - \frac{D}{h}\,\text{div}^w + \text{curl}\,\tau^w\\ F_{\text{dens.}} &= g\Big\{-\alpha_2\overline{Q}_x - \alpha_1\overline{Q}_y + \alpha_3\overline{Q}_x +\\ &+\alpha_4\overline{Q}_y + \left(\alpha_5\frac{\partial}{\partial x} - \alpha_6\frac{\partial}{\partial y}\right)\overline{Q} +\\ &+ D\left(-\frac{\partial \overline{Q}_x}{\partial x} - \frac{\partial \overline{Q}_y}{\partial y} + \frac{\partial \overline{Q}_y}{\partial x} - \frac{\partial \overline{Q}_x}{\partial y}\right) +\\ &+\frac{D}{h}\left(\frac{\partial \overline{\overline{Q}}_x}{\partial x} + \frac{\partial \overline{\overline{Q}}_y}{\partial y}\right)\Big\}\end{aligned}\right\} \quad (18)$$

and

$$\alpha_1 = \frac{1}{h}\left[\left(1 + \frac{D}{h}\right)\frac{\partial h}{\partial x} - 2\frac{D}{H}\frac{\partial h}{\partial y}\right]$$

$$\alpha_2 = \frac{1}{h}\left[\left(1 + \frac{D}{h}\right)\frac{\partial h}{\partial y} + 2\frac{D}{h}\frac{\partial h}{\partial x}\right]$$

$$\alpha_3 = \frac{D}{h}\left(\frac{\partial h}{\partial x} + \frac{\partial h}{\partial y}\right)$$

$$\alpha_4 = \frac{D}{h}\left(-\frac{\partial h}{\partial x} + \frac{\partial h}{\partial y}\right)$$

$$\alpha_5 = \frac{\partial h}{\partial y} \qquad \alpha_6 = \frac{\partial h}{\partial x}$$

Finally, $\overline{\overline{Q}}_x = \int_{-h}^{0}\int_{z}^{0} \dfrac{\partial \varrho'}{\partial x}(dz)^2$ etc. In the derivation it has been assumed that $D \ll h$, so that terms of the order $\left(\dfrac{D}{h}\right)^2$ and higher can be neglected. The present equation includes such effects as are caused by non-compensation, by a variable depth and by the local time-variation. To get an idea about the relative importance of these different effects one cannot, however, rely upon a direct estimate of the order of magnitude of the different terms. As example, one cannot merely from the fact that the terms $f\alpha_1$ and $f\alpha_2$ are of the order of magnitude of β conclude that bottom slope is as important a factor as the β-effect. Obviously the role of the bottom slope is coupled to the question of the compensation: if the compensation is perfect the bottom slope will not enter the problem at all, meaning that in this case the slope-terms in the left hand side of the equation are balanced by corresponding terms in F_{dens}.

The difficulty to discuss the significance of the different terms in (17) is primarily due to the fact that this equation only gives part of the theoretical solution, relating the transport to the wind-stress, the evaporation-precipitation, and the density field. The density field is, however, no forcing function given from outside in the same way as wind and evaporation-precipitation, but is related to the velocity field by an equation expressing the balance of density advection and diffusion.

The complete theoretical model will, be very difficult to handle mathematically, due to the occurrence of non-linear advection terms. For the present one can only try to test equation (17) by introducing the measured density field. Provided the density data are good enough such an investigation is, however, likely to throw some further light on the equation of the validity of the Sverdrup equation and the importance of the new effects mentioned of.

The auther finally wants to thank Professor Hansen at the University of Hamburg who gave the impulse to the investigation of Sect. 2. This part of the work should be considered as a direct extension of an earlier work by Professor Hansen, that is also published in this volume.

REFERENCES

CHARNEY, J. G., 1955: The Gulf Stream as an intertial boundary layer. *Proc. Nat. Acad. Sci.* 41: 10, p. 731—740.

EKMAN, V. W., 1905: On the influence of the earth's rotation on ocean currents. *Arkiv Mat. Astr. Fysik* **2**, No. 4.

HANSEN, W., Wind und Massenverteilung als Ursache der Meeresströmungen (contribution no. 4 in this volume, p. 102—106.)

HIDAKA, K., 1958: Computation of the wind-stress over the oceans, *Geophysical Notes* 11: 1, p. 77—123.

MORGAN, G. W., 1956: On the wind-driven Ocean circulation. *Tellus,* **8: 3**, p. 301—320.

MUNK, W., 1950: On the wind-driven ocean circulation, p. 79—93, *Journal Meteorology,* 7: 2.

NEUMANN, G., 1955: Dynamics of wind-driven ocean currents. *New York Univ. College of Eng., Meteor. Pap.* vol. 2/4, August 1955.

Scripps Institution of Oceanography, 1948: The field of mean wind-stress over the North Pacific Ocean. *Oceanographic Report* No. 14, p. 1—12.

STOMMEL, H., 1948: The westward intensification of wind-driven ocean currents. *Trans. Amer. Geophys. Union,* 29, p. 202—206. *Proc. Nat. Acad. Sci.,* 33, p. 318—326.

SVERDRUP, H. U., 1947: Wind-driven currents in a baroclinic ocean; with application to the equatorial currents of the eastern Pacific.

(Manuscript received 1 October, 1958)

Wind und Massenverteilung als Ursache der Meeresströmungen

Von WALTER HANSEN

Institut für Meereskunde, Universität Hamburg

(Received 10 June, 1958)

Zusammenfassung

Der Zusammenhang zwischen Geschwindigkeit und Druck als Unbekannten und dem Wind- und Massenfeld als gegebenen Grössen im Ozean wird dargestellt und in speziellen Fällen die Gestalt der Meeresoberfläche als Funktion der Dichteverteilung angegeben. Dabei ist es nicht notwendig, wie etwa beim dynamischen Verfahren, eine Null- oder Bezugsfläche einzuführen. Beispiele erläutern diese funktionalen Beziehnungen und zeigen den Einfluss verschiedener Parameter auf die Ausbildung der Stromgeschwindigkeit.

I. Einleitung

Die vorhandenen Beobachtungen der Stromgeschwindigkeiten reichen bei weitem nicht aus, um Karten der Meeresströmungen im offenen Ozean zu entwerfen, so wie es etwa im wesentlich einfacheren Fall der Gezeiten- und Gezeitenströme in der Nordsee geschehen ist. (HANSEN 1952.) Deshalb ist die Ozeanographie bei der Erforschung der Meeresströmungen auf hydrodynamische Methoden angewiesen. Eine besondere Rolle spielt das dynamische Verfahren, das auf Bjerknes, Sandström und Helland-Hansen zurückgeht und von Defant auf den gesamten Atlantischen Ozean angewendet worden ist. Der grosse Vorteil dieser Methode liegt in der einfachen Handhabung, ist aber mit dem Nachteil verknüpft, dass die Gestalt der Meeresoberfläche und die Geschwindigkeit durch die bekannte Dichteverteilung allein nicht eindeutig bestimmt sind.

Die im folgenden abgeleitete Theorie, die an Hand sehr einfacher Beispiele erläutert wird, vermeidet diese Schwierigkeiten.

II. Die hydrodynamischen Grundlagen

Die hydrodynamischen Gleichungen werden in der folgenden Form verwendet:

$$-fv - \nu\frac{\partial^2 u}{\partial z^2} - A\Delta u + \frac{1}{\varrho}\frac{\partial p}{\partial x} = 0,$$

$$fu - \nu\frac{\partial^2 v}{\partial z^2} - A\Delta v + \frac{1}{\varrho}\frac{\partial p}{\partial y} = 0,$$

$$\frac{1}{\varrho}\frac{\partial p}{\partial z} = -g, \quad \frac{\partial u}{\partial x} + \frac{\partial v}{\partial y} + \frac{\partial w}{\partial z} = 0,$$

$$\Delta = \frac{\partial^2}{\partial x^2} + \frac{\partial^2}{\partial y^2} \qquad (1)$$

Es sind: x, y, z Koordinaten in Ost-, Nord- und Vertikalrichtung, f Coriolisfaktor, A, ν virtuelle Viskositätszahlen (horizontal, vertikal), g Schwerebeschleunigung, $\varrho = \varrho(x, y)$ die Dichte (bekannt aus Beobachtungen). Ausserdem werden verwendet:

$$\nu\frac{\partial u}{\partial z} = \tau^{(x)}, \quad \nu\frac{\partial v}{\partial z} = \tau^{(y)}.$$

als Komponenten des Schubes. Die ungestörte Oberfläche des Meeres liegt bei $z = 0$, die Abweichung davon wird durch $z = \zeta$ (Wasserstand) und der Meeresboden durch $z = -h$ beschrieben. Die Gesamttiefe ist $H = h+\zeta$. Funktionswerte an der Oberfläche werden durch den Index *ob*, am Boden durch den Index *B* gekennzeichnet.

Unbekannt sind die Komponenten der Stromgeschwindigkeit u, v, w und der Druck p. Diese Funktionen sind durch das Gleichungssystem (1) erst dann eindeutig bestimmt, wenn für sie eine Anzahl von Randbedingungen vorgeschrieben werden. So muss am Meeresboden und an der Küste die Normalkomponente der Geschwindigkeit Null sein. An der Meeresoberfläche sind $\tau_{ob}^{(x)}$ und $\tau_{ob}^{(y)}$ durch den Stress des Windes gegeben.

Durch Integration vom Meeresboden $z = -h$ bis zur Oberfläche $z = \zeta$ kann aus der Kontinuitätsgleichung w eliminiert und unter Berücksichtigung der Randbedingungen eine Stromfunktion ϕ mit

$$\int_{-h}^{\zeta} u dz = \frac{\partial \phi}{\partial y}, \int_{-h}^{\zeta} v dz = -\frac{\partial \phi}{\partial x}$$

in die gleichfalls integrierten Bewegungsgleichungen — nach Vernachlässigung von Termen, die bei der Vertauschung von Integration und Differentiation entstehen und von höherer Ordnung klein werden — eingesetzt werden:

$$f\frac{\partial \phi}{\partial x} + \tau_B^{(x)} - A\Delta\frac{\partial \phi}{\partial y} + \int_{-h}^{\zeta} \frac{1}{\varrho}\frac{\partial p}{\partial x} dz = \tau_{ob}^{(x)},$$

$$f\frac{\partial \phi}{\partial y} + \tau_B^{(y)} + A\Delta\frac{\partial \phi}{\partial x} + \int_{-h}^{\zeta} \frac{1}{\varrho}\frac{\partial p}{\partial y} dz = \tau_{ob}^{(y)} \qquad (2)$$

Dieses Gleichungssystem verknüpft die Stromfunktion ϕ und den Wasserstand ζ mit der Massenverteilung und den tangentialen Schubkräften. Wegen der komplizierten Form — ζ tritt implicit auf — sollen das System (2) zunächst etwas spezialisiert und dann einige einfache Fälle diskutiert werden.

III. Die Ermittlung des Wasserstandes aus dem Dichtefeld

Zunächst werden die von der Reibung herrührenden Terme in den Gleichungen proportional den Komponenten des Transportes und umgekehrt proportional der Wassertiefe gesetzt, Reibungskoeffizient r:

$$\tau_B^{(x)} - A\Delta\frac{\partial \phi}{\partial y} = \frac{r}{h+\zeta}\frac{\partial \phi}{\partial y},$$

$$\tau_B^{(y)} + A\Delta\frac{\partial \phi}{\partial x} = -\frac{r}{h+\zeta}\frac{\partial \phi}{\partial x}.$$

Eine weitere Vereinfachung wird erzielt, wenn angenommen wird, dass die Dichte ϱ nur von x, y, aber nicht von der Tiefe z abhängt, dann gilt $\int_{-h}^{\zeta} \frac{1}{\varrho}\frac{\partial p}{\partial x} dz = g(h+\zeta)\left(\frac{\partial \zeta}{\partial x} + \frac{\zeta + h}{2\varrho}\cdot\frac{\partial \varrho}{\partial x}\right)$ und Entsprechendes für die y-Komponente des Druckgradienten. Wird weiterhin überall zwecks Linearisierung ζ gegen h vernachlässigt, dann folgt an Stelle von (2) das System

$$\frac{f}{h}\frac{\partial \phi}{dx} + \frac{r}{h^2}\frac{\partial \phi}{dy} + g\frac{\partial \zeta}{\partial x} + \frac{gh}{2}\cdot\frac{\partial}{\partial x}(\log \varrho) = \tau_{ob}^{(x)},$$

$$-\frac{r}{h^2}\frac{\partial \phi}{\partial x} + \frac{f}{h}\frac{\partial \phi}{dy} + g\frac{\partial \zeta}{\partial y} + \frac{gh}{2}\cdot\frac{\partial}{\partial y}(\log \varrho) = \tau_{ob}^{(y)} \qquad (3)$$

Hier lässt sich ζ eliminieren durch kreuzweise Differentiation, mit den Abkürzungen

$$F = \frac{\partial}{\partial y}\left(\frac{\tau_{ob}^{(x)}}{h}\right) - \frac{\partial}{\partial x}\left(\frac{\tau_{ob}^{(y)}}{h}\right),$$

$$G = \frac{g}{2}\left(\frac{\partial h}{\partial x}\cdot\frac{\partial}{\partial y}(\log \varrho) - \frac{\partial h}{\partial y}\cdot\frac{\partial}{\partial x}(\log \varrho)\right)$$

folgt:

$$\Delta\phi + \frac{\partial \phi}{dx}\left[\frac{\partial}{\partial x}\left(\frac{1}{h^2}\right) + \frac{\partial}{\partial y}\left(\frac{f}{rh}\right)\right]h^2 +$$

$$\frac{\partial \phi}{\partial y}\cdot\left[\frac{\partial}{\partial y}\left(\frac{1}{h^2}\right) - \frac{\partial}{\partial x}\left(\frac{f}{rh}\right)\right]h^2 = \frac{h^2}{r}(F+G) \qquad (4)$$

Die Stromfunktion ϕ ist in jedem Meeresgebiet eindeutig bestimmt, wenn ϕ auf dem Rande dieses Gebietes bekannt ist. Speziell wird längs einer Küste $\phi = 0$.

Ist nun die rechte Seite der Gleichung (4) Null, — das ist der Fall, wenn der Wind Null, die Tiefe konstant oder die Dichte homogen sind — dann folgt aus der Randbedingung, dass $\Phi \equiv 0$. Im gesamten Meeresgebiet verschwindet die Stromfunktion. Dieser Schluss kann aber nur gezogen werden, wenn die Reibungszahl r nicht Null ist — damit keine Singularitäten auftreten, muss immer $h \gg c > 0$ sein. Für $r = 0$ wird die Differentialgleichung (4) von der ersten Ordnung und die Randbedingungen können nicht mehr erfüllt werden. Das Problem ist dann nach Courant (1937) nicht mehr sachgemäss. So ist in einem geschlossenen Meeresgebiet zu fordern, dass die Strömung parallel der Küste erfolgt und die Normalkomponente dort verschwindet. Wird aber in (4) $r = 0$ gesetzt, so kann diese Randbedingung allgemein nicht erfüllt werden. Diesem prinzipiellen Mangel unterliegt auch das dynamische Verfahren, das unter der Voraussetzung abgeleitet ist, dass die Reibung verschwindet. Die

Reibung mag noch so klein sein, immer lässt sich die Gleichung (4) eindeutig lösen, sie darf nur nicht Null werden.

Es wird gesetzt: $\phi = \varphi + \psi$

dabei ist φ die vom Wind-, ψ die vom Massenfeld herrührende Stromfunktion. Separation führt zu den Gleichungen

$$\Delta\varphi + \frac{\partial\varphi}{\partial x}\left[\frac{\partial}{\partial x}\left(\frac{1}{h^2}\right) + \frac{\partial}{\partial y}\left(\frac{f}{rh}\right)\right]h^2 + + \frac{\partial\varphi}{\partial y}\left[\frac{\partial}{\partial y}\left(\frac{1}{h^2}\right) - \frac{\partial}{\partial x}\left(\frac{f}{rh}\right)\right]h^2 = \frac{h^2}{r}F \quad (5)$$

und

$$\Delta\psi + \frac{\partial\psi}{\partial x}\left[\frac{\partial}{\partial x}\left(\frac{1}{h^2}\right) + \frac{\partial}{\partial y}\left(\frac{f}{rh}\right)\right]h^2 + + \frac{\partial\psi}{\partial y}\left[\frac{\partial}{\partial y}\left(\frac{1}{h^2}\right) - \frac{\partial}{\partial x}\left(\frac{f}{rh}\right)\right]h^2 = \frac{h^2}{r}G.$$

Ist am Rande $\phi = \varphi = \psi = 0$, dann können hieraus die vom Windschub herrührende Stromfunktion φ und die vom Massenfeld stammende Stromfunktion ψ eindeutig bestimmt werden.

φ und ψ sind nur dann im Innern des Meeresgebietes von Null verschieden, wenn $F, G \neq 0$. Sind dagegen $F, G = 0$, dann auch $\varphi, \psi = 0$. Ist speziell $\psi \equiv 0$, dann folgt aus den (3) entsprechenden Gleichungen

$$\frac{\partial\zeta}{\partial x} + \frac{h}{2}\frac{\partial}{\partial x}(\log \varrho) = 0, \quad \frac{\partial\zeta}{\partial y} + \frac{h}{2}\frac{\partial}{\partial y}(\log \varrho) = 0.$$

und wegen $G = 0$ ist auch

$$\frac{\partial h}{\partial x}\cdot\frac{\partial}{\partial y}(\log \varrho) - \frac{\partial h}{\partial y}\cdot\frac{\partial}{\partial x}(\log \varrho) = 0.$$

Die letzte Gleichung besagt entweder, die Tiefe h ist konstant oder eine Funktion der ortsveränderlichen Dichte ϱ nämlich $h = h(\log\varrho)$. Für konstante Tiefe $h = h_0$ wird

$$\zeta = -\frac{h_0}{2}\log\frac{\varrho}{\varrho_0}$$

und für h ($\log \varrho$) folgt:

$$\zeta = -\frac{1}{2}\int_{\varrho_0}^{\varrho}\frac{h(\varrho)}{\varrho}\,d\varrho$$

Die willkürlichen Konstanten sind so gewählt, dass ζ in dem durch den Index 0 gekennzeichneten Punkt Null ist.

Damit ist die Gestalt der Meeresoberfläche aus dem Massenaufbau und der Tiefe bestimmt. Im Gegensatz zum dynamischen Verfahren ist bei der hier gegebenen Ableitung kein Gebrauch von zusätzlichen Annahmen etwa über eine Null- oder Bezugsfläche gemacht worden.

Die Gleichungen zeigen, dass bei anwachsendem ϱ die Wasseroberfläche ζ abfällt und umgekehrt. Besitzt die Dichte ϱ im Punkt Null ein Minimum, dann hat die Wasseroberfläche dort ein Maximum. An der Ostflanke des Golfstroms erreicht die Dichte Minimalwerte. Die von DEFANT (1941) für dieses Gebiet angegebene Topographie weist hier ein Maximum auf. Ähnliches wird südlich des Äquator vor der brasilianischen Küste festgestellt.

Diese einfachen Beziehungen geben aber auch quantitativ für den Bereich des Golfstroms Höhenunterschiede der Meeresoberfläche von etwa ein Meter, ein Wert, der mit Defants Angaben recht gut übereinstimmt.

Die Ermittlung des Wasserstandes ist immer dann besonders einfach, wie das vorstehende Beispiel zeigt, wenn die Stromfunktion identisch verschwindet. Das ist aber nur dann der Fall, wenn G identisch Null ist und somit die Tiefe und der Wasserstand ζ Funktionen sind, die nur von der Dichte ϱ abhängen. Dann sind längs den Isodensen auch die Wasserstände und die Tiefen konstant. Helland-Hansen und Ekman (EKMAN, 1923) haben allgemein dieses »law of parallel solenoids« formuliert, das im Ozean näherungsweise erfüllt ist.

Nach dem Vorstehenden lässt sich sagen: Ist dieses Gesetz streng erfüllt, dann ist die Stromfunktion identisch Null, gilt es dagegen nur approximativ und ist $G \neq 0$, dann existiert auch eine Stromfunktion $\psi = 0$, und es finden Massentransport statt. In diesen Fällen muss also der Bestimmung des Wasserstandes die Lösung der elliptischen Differentialgleichung für ψ voraufgehen. Da aber das Gesetz der parallelen Felder im Ozean angenähert gilt, besteht die Hoffnung, ζ aus der einfachen Beziehung $\psi \equiv 0$ zu ermitteln.

Das obige Beispiel unterstützt diese Vermutung. Abschliessend soll noch ein sehr einfacher Fall betrachtet werden, der zeigt, dass bei Tiefenänderungen Konzentrationen der Geschwindigkeit auftreten, die eine gewisse Ähnlichkeit mit denen haben, die in den grossen Stromsystemen der Ozeane beobachtet werden.

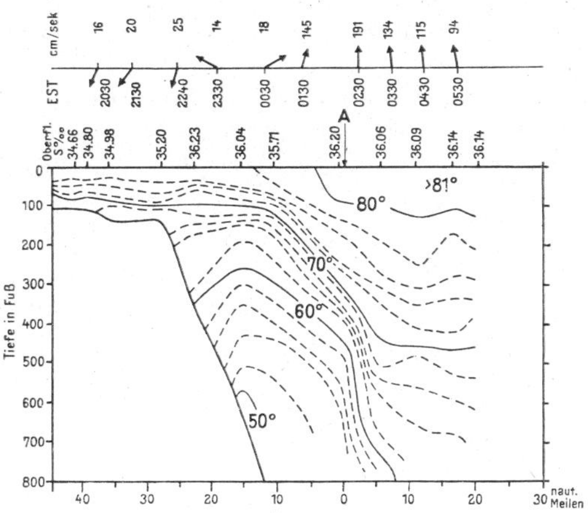

Abb. 1. Temperatur und Geschwindigkeit (GEK) in einem Golfstromschnitt nach v. Arx.

Es wird vorausgesetzt, dass für die Dichte des Meerwassers $\frac{\partial \varrho}{\partial y} = 0$ und für die Tiefe $\frac{\partial h}{\partial y} = 0$ gilt und der Windschub Null ist. Ausserdem soll die Ostwestkomponente des Transportes $\frac{\partial \phi}{\partial y} \equiv 0$ sein. Damit folgt aus Gleichung (4), da $G \equiv 0$ ist:

$$\frac{\partial^2 \phi}{\partial x^2} + \frac{\partial \phi}{\partial x}\left[\frac{h}{r} \cdot \frac{\partial f}{\partial y} - \frac{2}{h} \cdot \frac{\partial h}{\partial x}\right] = 0.$$

Für die Grössenordnung gilt:

$$\frac{\partial f}{\partial y} = 10^{-11} \text{ (m sec)}^{-1}, \quad r = 10^{-2} \text{ m sec}^{-1}$$

Zur Abkürzung wird $\frac{1}{r}\frac{\partial f}{\partial y} = \alpha$ und $\frac{\partial \phi}{\partial x} = -hv$ gesetzt, wo v die mittlere Stromgeschwindigkeit bedeutet. Nun ist die Gleichung zu lösen:

$$\frac{\partial v}{\partial x} + v\left[\alpha h - \frac{1}{h}\frac{\partial h}{\partial x}\right] = 0$$

Diese Lösung lautet:

$$v = v_0 \frac{h}{h_0} e^{-\alpha \int_0^x h dx} \tag{6}$$

Hier sind die Werte im Punkte $x = 0$ durch den Index Null bezeichnet.

Ist die Tiefe $h = h_0$ konstant, dann ist

$$v = v_0 e^{-\alpha h_0 x}$$

Die Geschwindigkeit nimmt exponential von West nach Ost ab und zwar umso stärker je grösser $\frac{\partial f}{\partial y}$ und je kleiner r ist. Sehr grosses r kann die westward intensification verringern, diese ist auf tiefem Wasser auch grösser als auf flachem Wasser. Für eine lineare Tiefenänderung

$$h = h_0 + (h_1 - h_0)\frac{x}{x_1}$$

lautet die Lösung der Gleichung (6)

$$v = v_0\left(1 + \left(\frac{h_1}{h_0} - 1\right)\frac{x}{x_1}\right) \cdot e^{-\alpha h_0 x_1\left(\frac{x}{x_1} + \frac{1}{2}\left(\frac{h_1}{h_0} - 1\right)\left(\frac{x}{x_1}\right)^2\right)}$$

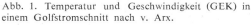

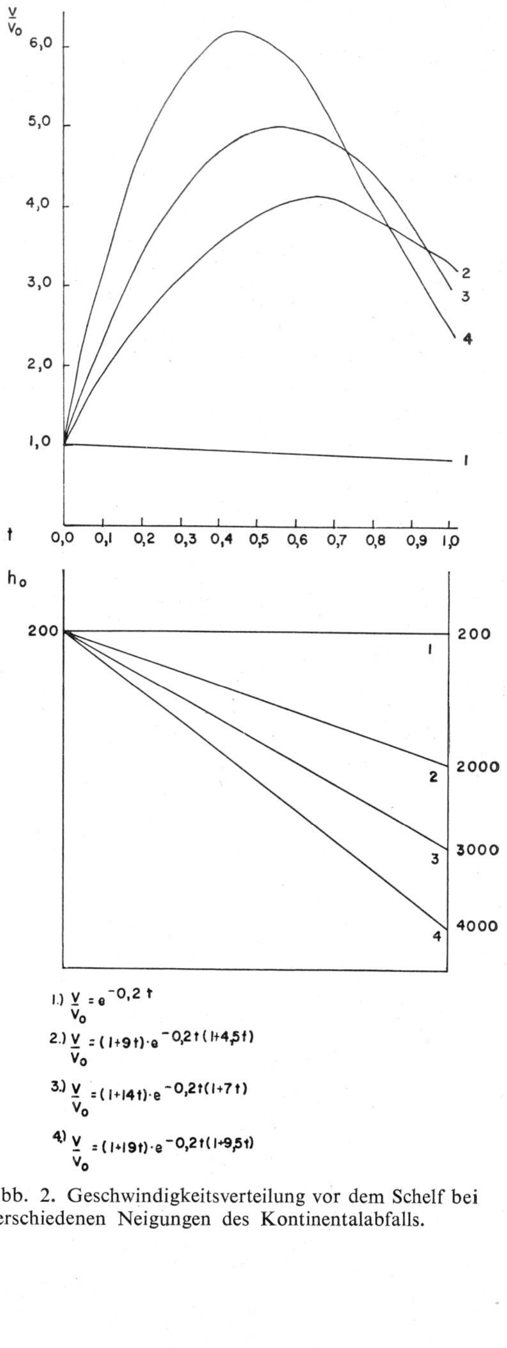

Abb. 2. Geschwindigkeitsverteilung vor dem Schelf bei verschiedenen Neigungen des Kontinentalabfalls.

Der Punkt $x = 0$ möge am Schelfrand liegen, dann ist h_0 die Tiefe des Schelfs, von hier fällt der Schelf steil ab und erreicht im Punkt $x = x_1$ den Tiefseeboden mit der Tiefe h_1.

Zur Abkürzung werden noch eingeführt:

$$\frac{h_1}{h_0} - 1 = \delta, \qquad \frac{\delta}{\alpha h_0 x_1} = \varkappa, \qquad \frac{x}{x_1} = t$$

dann wird v

$$v = v_0 (1 + \partial t) e^{-\frac{\partial}{\varkappa}\left(t + \frac{1}{2}\delta t^2\right)} \tag{7}$$

Diese Funtion v erreicht an der Stelle

$t_m = \frac{\sqrt{\varkappa}}{\partial} - 1$ einen Extremwert v_m

$$v_m = v_0 \sqrt{\varkappa} e^{-\frac{1}{2} + \frac{1}{2\varkappa}}$$

Unter den ausserordentlich einfachen Verhältnissen des vorliegenden Beispiels tritt durch das Zusammenwirken von Corioliskraft, Reibung und Tiefe sowie der Änderungen dieser Grössen auf dem Kontinentalabfall auf den Westseiten der Ozeane eine Konzentration der Stromgeschwindigkeiten auf, so wie sie auch in der Natur beobachtet wird. VON ARX et. al. (1955) hat Messungen (vgl. Abb. 1) der Stromgeschwindigkeit und der Temperatur über dem Kontinentalabfall im Bereich des Golfstroms geliefert. Die Geschwindigkeit zeigt einen Verlauf, der dem aus Gleichung (7) folgenden ähnlich ist (Abb. 2). Diese qualitative Übereinstimmung legt die Vermutung nahe, dass die oben bei der Ableitung der einfachen Lösung (7) berücksichtigten Faktoren bei der Ausbildung der Maxima der Stromgeschwindigkeit vor den Kontinentalabhängen auf der Westseite der Ozeane eine wichtige Rolle spielen. Diese Faktoren sind: die Reibung, die Corioliskraft und die Tiefe. Entscheidend für das Zustandekommen eines Extremwertes ist es, dass diese Grössen nicht konstant, sondern ortsveränderlich sind. Das hängt offenbar damit zusammen, dass in den Bewegungsgleichungen die Reibung im offenen Ozean um mehrere Grössenordnungen kleiner ist als der Coriolisbeitrag. In der hieraus gewonnenen Vorticity-Gleichung (4) treten die Differentialquotienten der Reibung und der Corioliskraft auf. Diese sind nun aber von der gleichen Grössenordnung. Gelegentlich kann sogar der Reibungseinfluss die dominierende Rolle spielen.

Schlussbemerkung

Wesentliche Ursachen der grossräumigen Stromsysteme in den Ozeanen sind der Tangentialschub des Windes an der Oberfläche und der Massenaufbau im Ozean. Dementsprechend treten zwei Stromfunktionen φ und ψ auf, eine φ ist dem Driftstrom, eine ψ ist dem Gradientstrom zugeordnet.

Beide genügen den Differentialgleichungen (5), die sich allein durch die rechten Seiten unterscheiden. Es liegen eine Reihe von Untersuchungen der Gleichung für φ vor unter der Voraussetzung, dass die Tiefe h konstant ist. Die aus dem Massenaufbau folgende Stromfunktion scheint bisher noch nicht betrachtet worden zu sein. Da im Ozean in erster Annäherung das von Helland-Hansen und Ekman aufgestellte Gesetz der parallelen Felder gilt, kann mit gleicher Genauigkeit in der Gleichung für ψ das $G \equiv 0$ gesetzt werden. Für ein geschlossenes Meeresgebiet wird der Satz formuliert: Gilt das Gesetz der parallelen Felder, dann verschwindet die zum Massenfeld gehörige Stromfunktion ψ. Das hat zur Folge, dass die Gestalt der Meeresoberfläche in einfacher Weise aus der Dichteverteilung ermittelt werden kann. Ein einfaches Beispiel erläutert diese Zusammenhänge. Ein weiteres Beispiel als spezielle Lösung der Gleichung (5) zeigt den Einfluss, den die Tiefenänderung auf die Struktur der Geschwindigkeit, die der des Golfstroms ähnlich ist, besitzt.

Allgemeiner scheinen die obigen Gleichungen geeignet, sowohl die Stromfunktionen als auch die Wasserstände aus Wind- und Massenfeldern zu ermitteln. Es liegt in der Natur der Sache, dass zu diesem Zweck Randwertaufgaben gelöst werden müssen, im Gegensatz zu dem bisher vornehmlich verwendeten dynamischen Verfahren.

(Manuscript received 10 june, 1958)

LITTERATURNACHWEIS

HANSEN, W., 1952: Gezeiten und Gezeitenströme der halbtägigen Hauptmondtide M_2 in der Nordsee. *Deutsche hydrogr. Zeitschrift* Hamburg 1952, 1. Ergängzungsheft.

COURANT-HILBERT, 1937: *Methoden der Mathematischen Physik* Band II. S. 176. Berlin 1937.

DEFANT, A., 1941: Die absolute Topographie des physikalischen Meeresniveaus. *Wiss. Ergebnisse der Meteor-Expedition*, Band VI, 2. Teil, 5. Lief. Berlin.

EKMAN, V. W., 1923: Über Horizontalzirkulation bei winderzeugten Meeresströmungen, *Arkiv f. Mat. Astr. och Fysik*, **17**, 26.

VON ARX, BUMPUS, and RICHARDSON, 1955: On the finestructure of the Gulf Stream Front. *Deep Sea Research*, Vol. 2, p. 46.

The Antarctic Convergence–or Divergence?

By H. Wexler

U.S. Weather Bureau, Washington, D.C.

Abstract

Bathythermograph (BT) data available in the past decade reveal the existence of a narrow cold core of water embedded in the Antarctic Circumpolar Current at the Antarctic "Convergence." This cold core is explained by upwelling of cold water from below. The upwelling itself results from horizontal divergence impressed on the sea surface by the frictional stress of the strong winter westerly winds on the open water just north of the northern limit of the pack-ice surrounding Antarctica.

In recent years, increased use of the bathythermograph (BT) has revealed strong horizontal temperature gradients within the ocean surface at unexpected places. For example Cromwell and Reid (1956) showed the existence in the mid-Pacific (1° N, 120° W and 2° N, 172° W) of surface temperature gradients of 5° F in 1 mile. Later at 3° N, 120° W, Knauss (1957), by taking BT's 50 seconds apart as the ship drifted at one knot, found a temperature gradient of 5° F in less than 200 feet. In all three cases the strong temperature gradient extended to about 100 feet below the surface. It is not known how characteristic these discontinuities are of their particular localities and how they compare with similar phenomena found in other oceanic areas far removed from land.

One of the best known and permanent oceanic temperature discontinuities, the "Antarctic Convergence", has been studied since 1923 [Meinardus (1923), Schott (1926), Wust (1928), Defant (1928), Sverdrup (1934), Deacon (1937)]. The best summary of its location and properties, based on pre-BT data, has been made by Mackintosh (1946).

Mackintosh defines the Antarctic Convergence "... as the line at the surface along which Antarctic surface water sinks below the less dense sub-Antarctic water, and it is distinguished by a more or less sharp change of temperature at the surface." The temperature gradient varies with longitude but the Antarctic Convergence is probably continuous around the Southern Ocean. It is essentially a feature of the surface but where surface conditions are ill-defined, Mackintosh goes on to say, the Antarctic Convergence "can usually be assumed to lie in the latitude at which the coldest part of the Antarctic surface layer sinks below 200 meters."

Deacon's compilation of the mean position of the Antarctic Convergence as determined by the latitude reached by Antarctic bottom water was drawn on a circumpolar chart in 1937. Mackintosh had more data on which to base his average position and while his curve agreed quite closely in the main with Deacon's curve it did show some significant deviations and also greater variations in latitude than formerly believed.

In figure 1 is shown a somewhat smoothed copy of Mackintosh's average position of the Antarctic Convergence (an exact reproduction is given in figure 6). This curve, while roughly zonal, has waves and varies in latitude from 48° S to 62° S. The principal meanders occur east of Australia and South America.

In this same figure there are plotted 13 triangles in the South Atlantic showing positions of the Antarctic Convergence as determined by whalers (Vowinckel and Oosthuizen, 1953). The criteria used in identifying the Antarctic Convergence were not described by the authors. There are also 11 black dots in the figure, 6 between New Zealand and the Ross Sea, 2 in the eastern South Pacific and 3 in the Scotia Sea. These dots show the locations of the Antarctic Convergence as determined by a new criterion for the Antarctic Convergence made possible by BT profiles taken by various ships listed in Table 1.

New Definition of the Antarctic Convergence

The criterion used in identifying the Antarctic Convergence listed in Table 1 arose as follows:

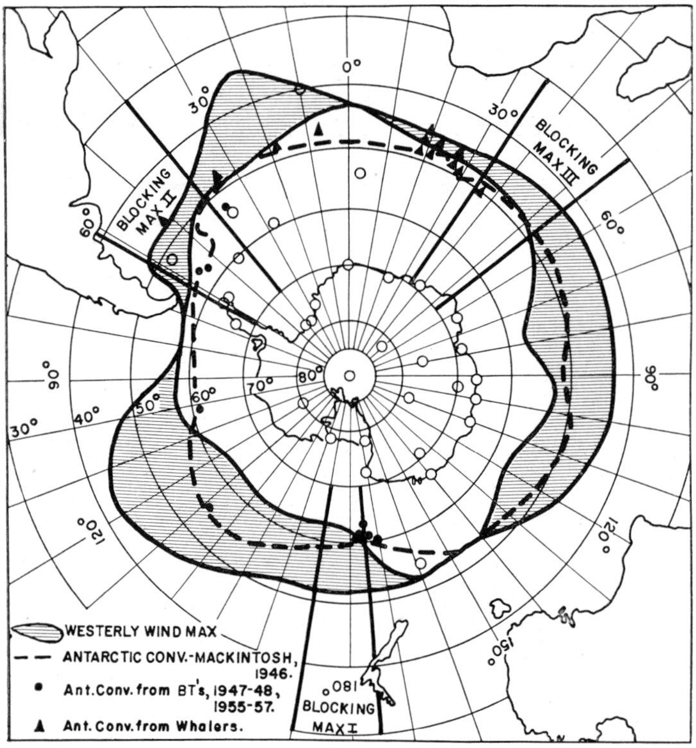

Fig. 1. Positions of the Antarctic convergence: Average (Mackintosh, 1946) shown by dashed line; individual positions computed from BT's, shown by solid circles; from data supplied by whalers, shown by triangles. Shaded area refers to the zone of maximum westerly winds.

it was noted that the strong surface temperature decrease southward, which is called for by the classical definition of the Antarctic Convergence, terminated in a temperature minimum followed by an increase of 1° to 3° F as one proceeded a short distance south. That this temperature minimum was not restricted to the surface is shown by the hourly BT soundings which revealed the existence of a "cold core" extending downward for several hundred feet, with similar temperature increases to the north and south. In figures 2 and 3 there are shown two examples of this phenomenon*—both based on BT data taken by the USS *Glacier* on 13 Nov. 1956 and 14 Dec. 1956. In each case the cold cores had centers with temperatures below 36° F and extended to the bottom of the BT dips, −450 feet and 650 feet, respectively. To the South there existed a distinct wall of warmer water (temp. > 39°) separating the cold cores from the below 32° F Antarctic water.

Previous investigators of the Antarctic Convergence have not drawn attention to this minimum temperature zone south of the strong temperature gradient, although it does show up to some extent on 6 of the 15 "Discovery" sections which formed the basis of Deacon's 1937 plot of the mean position of the Antarctic Convergence. Only by a combined use of a recording of sea surface temperature and frequent (at least once an hour) BT dips could the narrow zone (usually less than 50 miles) of minimum temperature be detected with certainty.

Although the packing of isotherms leading to a strong horizontal temperature gradient has generally been interpreted in terms of horizontal convergence and sinking of surface water, its presence just to the north of a zone of temperature minimum might denote just the opposite—an upwelling of colder sub-surface water induced by horizontal divergence. This particular point will form the principal theme of this paper to be discussed in greater detail later.

Comparison with Average Winds

Referring again to figure 1, the shaded area denotes the belt of the maximum westerly winds as computed from average sea-level barometric pressure data taken from three different sources:

* The writer is greatly indebted to Dr. Willis L. Tressler of the U.S. Navy Hydrographic Office for furnishing these and other data in advance of publication.

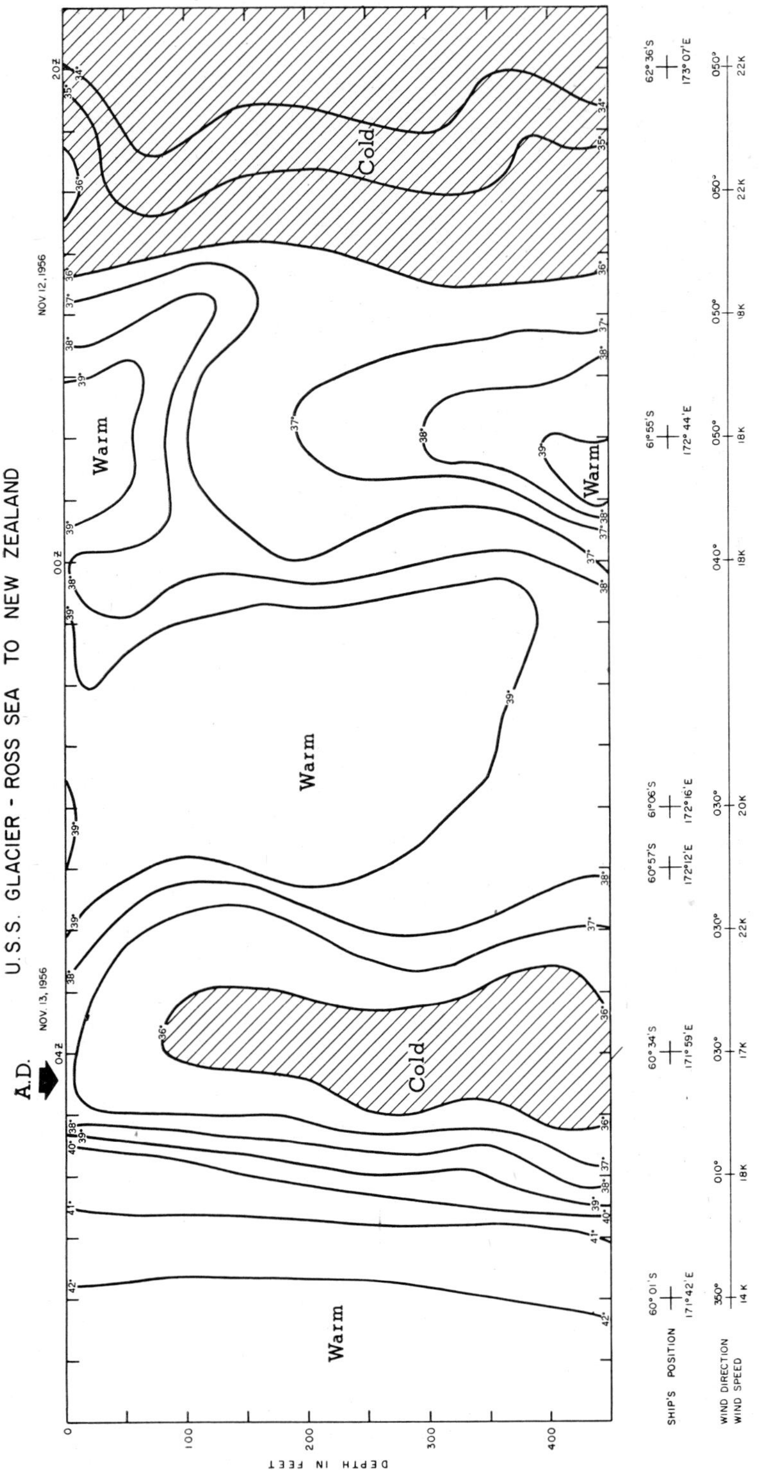

Fig. 2. Bathythermograph cross-section, Ross Sea to New Zealand, Nov. 12—13, 1956, U.S.S. *Glacier*. (Shaded area shows temperatures below 36° F.)

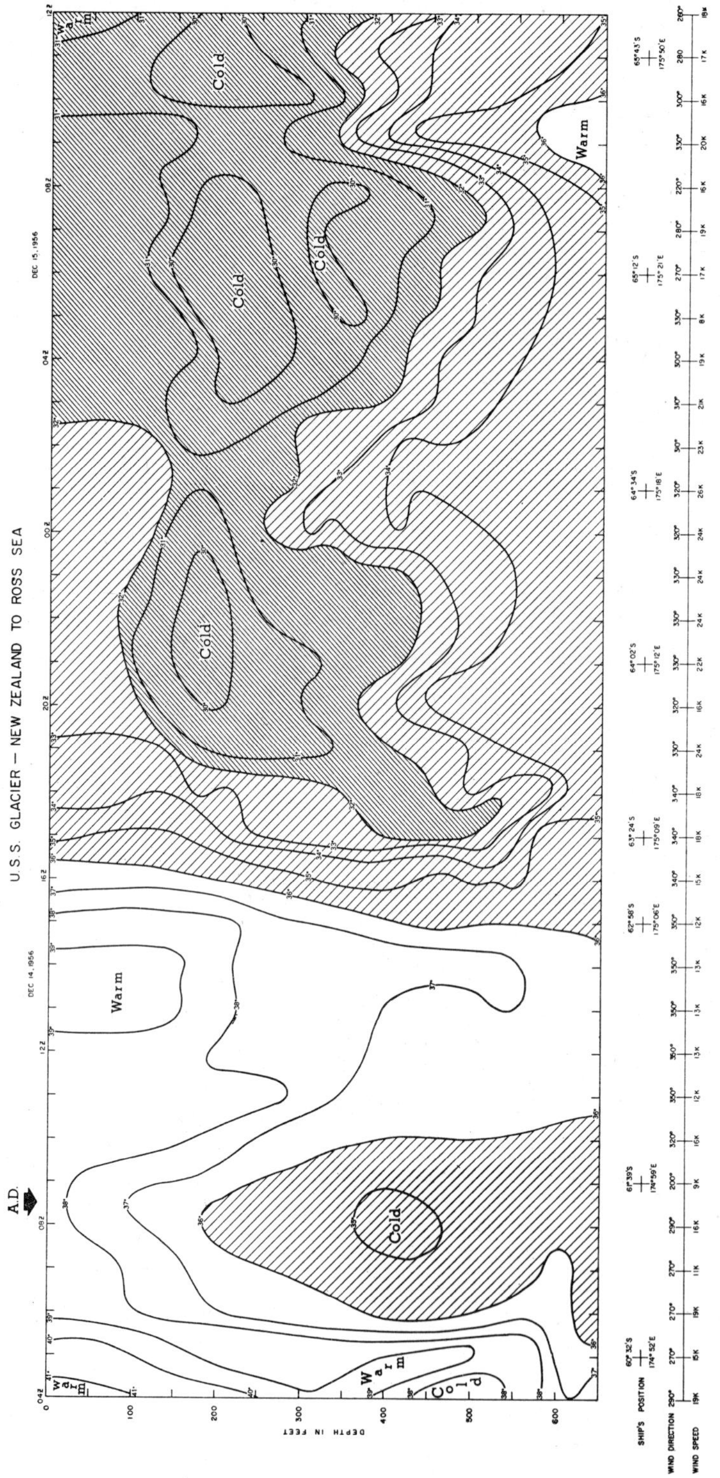

Fig. 3. Bathythermograph cross-section, New Zealand to Ross Sea, Dec. 14—15, 1956, U.S.S. *Glacier*. (Shaded areas show temperatures below 36° and 32° F respectively.)

Assur (1951), Vowinckel (1955), and Lamb and Britton (1955). Meridional pressure profiles were drawn for each 20° of longitude beginning with 0° and the latitudes of the maximum westerly winds determined. The shaded area was then drawn in to encompass the maximum points of all three determinations.

For the most part the maxima of westerly winds were found over a considerable spread of latitude,—10° to 25°. But there are three regions, south of eastern Australia, South America and South Africa, where the maximum westerlies are confined to a very narrow latitudinal belt. Downwind (east) of these three regions where the belt of maximum westerlies widens considerably, are found the three areas of maximum atmospheric blocking according to van Loon (1956). Atmospheric blocking in the Southern Hemisphere as defined by van Loon is a long-lived (at least 6 days) quasi-stationary anticyclone which is displaced at least 10° south of the normal position of the sub-tropical high pressure belt as given by Vowinckel (1955). According to van Loon, blocking action in the Southern Hemisphere is largely limited to these three regions listed in order of decreasing importance: I, eastern Australia-western South Pacific; II, the Scotia Sea (east of southern South America); and III, the Marion-Crozet Island area east of South Africa. When these blocks become established the maximum westerly winds are displaced far south of their normal latitudes, which is in agreement with the observed southward displacement of the southern edge of the shaded westerly wind maximum areas in two of the three regions shown in figure 1.

Judging from the location of these circulation blocks east of regions where the westerly winds emerge from the relatively narrow channels between Antarctica and the three main continental masses, it would appear that these blocks arise as a result of a horizontal "hydraulic jump" as suggested by Rossby (1950) to explain the North Atlantic blocks.

It is interesting to note that the maximum meridional deflections of the Antarctic Convergence are also found in the vicinity of the atmospheric blocks. These large-scale meanders of the Antarctic Convergence have been ascribed by Sverdrup et al. (1942) to the passage of the associated current system over submarine ridges with consequent Coriolis deflections. This implies that the current system associated with the Antarctic Convergence extends at least to the 3,000 meter depth. But it would also be tempting to postulate an analogy between the atmospheric westerly "jet-stream" and a wind-induced oceanic "jet-stream", in which the Antarctic Convergence is embedded; however a discussion of this and other possible causes of the Antarctic Convergence will be deferred until later.

Fine Structure and Changes of the Antarctic Convergence

As shown in Table 1 twelve days after the second *Glacier* section of Dec. 14, 1956, another section was made by the H.M.N.Z.S. *Pukaki* along nearly the same meridian. The Antarctic Convergence was crossed at nearly the same latitude but was characterized by cold temperatures as much as 6° F lower than those observed by the *Glacier*. This section, shown in figure 4, was kindly provided to the writer by Mr. R. W. Burling of the New Zealand Oceanographic Institute, Department of Scientific and Industrial Research, in advance of publication. The remarkable feature of the *Pukaki* cold core is not only its low temperature of —1° C but also its vertical extent downward, so that below 200 meters it is colder even than the water at the same depths found just off Antarctica. The source of this water deserves comment. Deacon's temperature data at latitude 62° S show that water of that low temperature is found below 3,000 meters. Since it is inconceivable that upwelling of that magnitude could have occurred in 12 days, the source of the cold water must have been horizontal motion northward from the cold sub-surface Antarctic water, shown in figure 4, a breaking-off of this water mass from its source region, and a strong vertical stretching of the water column to produce cooling both in the surface layer and at depths below 200 meters.

To the well-known horizontal concentration of the sea-surface isotherms thus should be added these additional properties of the Antartic Convergence:

i) a temperature minimum to the south of the strong temperature gradient (figs. 2, 3 and 4),
ii) extension of these properties downward at times to at least the 300-meter depth (e.g., *Pukaki* section),
iii) rather large temperature changes of the order of 5° F can occur across the Antarctic Convergence within a few weeks with but little change in location,

Table 1. BT Profiles Across the Antarctic Convergence

Ship	Date	Position	Min. Sfc. Temp.	Reference
A. *New Zealand-Ross Sea Section*				
U.S. Navy Operation High Jump				
Section C-2..........	13—16 Feb. '48	62° 40′ S 176° E	39.7° F	Dietz, 1948
Section C-3..........	27 Feb.— 1 Mar. '48	61° 50′ S 176° E	40.6° F	Dietz, 1948
USS ATKA...............	Jan. '55	61° 00′ S 177° 54′ E	38° F	H. O. Misc. 16331, 1956
USS GLACIER............ (Operation Deep Freeze II)	13 Nov. '56	60° 34′ S 171° 58′ E	37.2° F	Priv. Commun. Tressler, 1957
USS GLACIER............	14 Dec. '56	61° 24′ S 175° 10′ E	38.1° F	Priv. Commun. Tressler, 1957
H.M.N.Z.S. PUKAKI......	25—26 Dec. '56	62° 5′ S 176° 55′ E	<36° F	Burling, 1959
B. *Eastern South Pacific*				
U.S. Navy Operation High Jump				
Section A...........	23—25 Dec. '47	65° S 100° W	34° F	Dietz, 1948
Section B...........	25—28 Dec. '47	55° S 131° W	39.2° F	Dietz, 1948
C. *Scotia Sea*				
USS ATKA...............	25—26 Feb. '55	52° 30′ S 37° 20′ W	36° F	H.O. Misc. 16331, 1956
USS STATEN ISLAND...... (Operation Deep Freeze II)	10 Dec. '56	57° 03′ S 57° 44′ W	36.5° F	Priv. Commun. Tressler, 1957
USS STATEN ISLAND...... (Operation Deep Freeze II)	22 Feb. '57	56° 37′ S 55° 17′ W	39.8° F	Priv. Commun. Tressler, 1957

iv) at times a multiple structure of the Antarctic Convergence appears to exist,—see for example fig. 2 here and figs. 15 and 16 (DIETZ, 1948).

Movements of the Antarctic Convergence

The Antarctic Convergence appears to be remarkably fixed geographically. Mackintosh found that although a displacement of 50 miles or so either way is not uncommon, its location is rarely found more than 100 miles from its mean position but sometimes it has twists and loops that extend 100 miles north or south. There appears to be a slight seasonal deviation from the mean position, from 16 miles north in November to 28 miles south in February.

The Antarctic Convergence, as defined by the position of the "cold core", moved approximately 28 nautical miles south in the 12 days from 14 Dec. 1956 (second *Glacier* section) to 26 Dec. (*Pukaki* section). Large temperature changes accompanied this shift. But in the 31 days from the first *Glacier* section (13 Nov.) to the second section (14 Dec.) the southward shift of the

Antarctic Convergence was only 50 nautical miles or 70 % of the speed of movement southward from Dec. 14 to 26 and its temperature remained practically unchanged.

This acceleration southward of the Antarctic Convergence appears to be related to the winds at 60° S, 170° E as shown in Table 2:

Table 2. Average Resultant Surface Winds at 60° S, 170° E

Period	Wind from	Speed	Source
1956			
Nov. 8—13	330°	16 K	Weather Charts
Nov. 16—21	280°	20 K	USS BROUGH
Nov. 22—28	285°	13 K	USS BROUGH
Dec. 9—14	340°	8 K	USS BROUGH
Average resultant	305°	13 K	
Dec. 14—19	23°	11 K	USS BROUGH
Dec. 20—26	45°	16 K	Weather Charts
Average resultant	35°	14 K	

Unfortunately no reliable winds were available for the periods Nov. 14—15 and Nov. 29—Dec. 8. Nevertheless it appears quite clear from the resultant winds shown in Table 2, that there were predominantly west-northwesterly winds between the first *Glacier* Section of Nov. 13 and the second *Glacier* Section of 14 Dec. (average resultant wind from 305°, 13 K) and predominantly northeasterly winds between Dec. 14 and Dec. 16 (average resultant wind from 35°, 14 K). The mean component of wind from north to south in the latter period was 53 % greater than that of the earlier period, — in good agreement with the accelerated displacement of the Antarctic Convergence southward. The increased winds from the north in December were associated with a strong blocking anticyclone which persisted through December and extended from New Zealand to the western Ross Sea.

Suggested Explanations for the Antarctic Convergence

Before attempting to explain the Antarctic "Convergence" we must first make up our minds whether it is a horizontally *convergent* or *divergent* phenomenon. While it is possible to explain a north-south packing of isotherms by horizontal convergence it would appear difficult to explain by the same process the temperature minimum observed in the surface layer just to the south of the strong temperature gradient. However horizontal divergence, operating sufficiently long in the surface layer of an ocean where the temperature decreases with depth (under a thin homogeneous layer), could account for both a surface temperature minimum and a strong temperature gradient to the north, since the resulting upwelling of cold, sub-surface water in a restricted zone would lower the surface temperature in this zone and thus increase the normal north-south temperature gradient to the north and reverse it to the south.

Thus the detailed temperature data available from BT's seem definitely to point in the direction of a narrow band of horizontal divergence encircling Antarctica, at a position very close to that given by Mackintosh for the Antarctic "Convergence". The problem now is to explain the existence of such a narrow circumpolar zone to be referred to henceforth as the "Antarctic Divergence".

The possible explanations can be divided into two categories: (i) Internal and (ii) External:

Internal—It appears difficult to find a strictly internal explanation for such a sharp fixed line as the Antarctic Divergence. Thermohaline-induced vertical meridional circulations, analogous to the Hadley (low-latitude) and Ferrel (mid-latitude) atmospheric circulation cells, could be visualized to produce horizontal divergence along the wavy line shown in figure 1, but one would first have to explain how such oceanic circulation cells arise in the first place.

Internal waves along the thermocline, similar to those noted in Antarctic waters by DIETZ (1948) might well become unstable and bring cold deep water to the surface but again it is difficult to see why this process should prefer the particular wavy line shown in figure 1 unless some external influence enters.

External—The frictional drag of the winds on the ocean surface would seem to be the principal means of introducing an external influence to cause a line of divergence. The rough correspondence between the broadening of the belt of maximum westerly winds and the meandering of the Antarctic Divergence plus the fact that on the average the Antarctic Divergence is found slightly to the south of the maximum westerlies leads one to suspect a connection. However the contrast between the well-known variability of the winds and the stability of location of the Antarctic Divergence would tend to discourage a search for a relationship unless the great inertia of the ocean masses makes them responsive only to winds averaged over long periods of time—weeks and months.

If we apply to an average north-south profile of winds from the west the results of the Ekman theory, where the transport of the wind-induced current is proportional to the square of the wind speed and directed to the left of the current in the Southern Hemisphere, this leads to a divergence south of the latitude of the maximum winds and a convergence to the north. A computation of this nature, based on ASSUR's (1951) average sea-level pressure distribution over the Southern Hemisphere, has been performed by KOOPMAN (1953).

Koopman arrives at a series of convergent and divergent lines; the one which he believes corresponds to the Antarctic "Convergence" is found some 5° of latitude to the *north* of Assur's maximum westerly winds, and *farther north* still of Mackintosh's average position of the Antarctic "Convergence". Koopman also finds a short line of divergence along latitude 64° S, extending from 145° W westward to 175° E and a nearly circumpolar line of divergence farther south at the boundary between the polar easterly winds and the temperate westerlies. The divergence at the 180° meridian between 62.5° S and 67.5° S, computed from Assur's data, yields an average upwelling of $^1/_4$ meter per day.

Koopman's computations neglect lateral frictional stresses which according to HIDAKA and TSUCHIYA (1953) must be exceptionally large in the Antarctic Circumpolar Current. Their analysis, taking into account both lateral and vertical frictional forces within an homogeneous ocean subjected to a maximum wind stress of 2 dynes cm^{-2} at the surface, yields a horizontal convergence just to the south of the westerly wind maximum (taken at 57° 30′ S) and horizontal divergence to the north (fig. 5). The meridional motions are confined to the top few hundred meters and the vertical motions to the north and south of the latitude of the wind maximum are of the order of 10 centimeters per day. This value which amounts to only 3 meters per month, would appear at first sight to be too small but before continuing with further analysis of this frictional explanation let us examine two more possibilities.

Another likely explanation might be sought in the reaction of the ocean to sudden changes in wind. If the ocean has an internal surface across which the density varies as observed at the

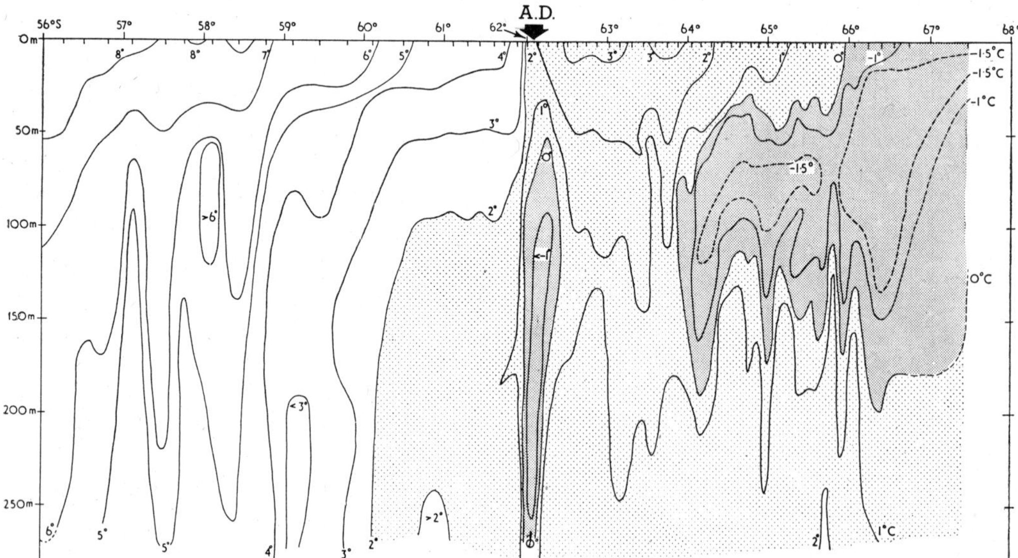

Fig. 4. Bathythermograph cross-section, New Zealand to Ross Sea, Dec. 25—26, 1956, H.M.N.Z.S. *Pukaki.* (Shaded areas show temperatures below 2° C (35.6° F) and 0° C, respectively.) (After Burling, 1959.) The arrow marked "AD" has been superimposed by the present writer.

thermocline, then an inertial (north—south) oscillation caused by fast inputs of momentum by frictional transfer from rapidly accelerating winds, would introduce a vertical distortion of the thermocline. Following the initial analyses of this effect by ROSSBY (1937, 1938) and CAHN (1945), the problem, relieved of certain artificial restraints, was tackled anew by BOLIN (1953), VERONIS and STOMMEL (1956) and VERONIS (1956).

Using Rossby's simple model, a 2-layer fluid at latitude 60° was investigated—composed of a 100 meter thick upper homogeneous layer of density ϱ over a 3,900 meter thick lower layer of density ϱ' with the density difference ratio, $(\varrho' - \varrho)/\varrho'$, at the interface equal to $2 \cdot 10^{-3}$. A 200 km wide strip of the surface water layer was set into motion impulsively by a sudden west wind so that the maximum speed of the water surface rose suddenly to 1 meter per second and decreased discontinuously to zero on either side of the strip. After equilibrium was reached the thermocline south of the maximum westerly acceleration showed an upward displacement of the order of 25 meters and a downward displacement of equal magnitude to the north. This computed distortion of the thickness of the homogeneous layer bears a remarkable resemblance to the observed distortion noted on the *Pukaki* Section (see fig. 4). Repeated accelerations of the winds in response to passing storms* could finally bring the thermocline very close to the surface where it could be destroyed by wind mixing, thus creating a zone of cold water.

There is another possible explanation which cannot be analyzed quantitatively at this time but which, by analogy, appears to be worthy of serious consideration. This has to do with the phenomenon of "streakiness" which seems to be characteristic of geophysical fluid motion over a wide range of scales. Some of the BT sections such as Section B, 25—28 Dec. 1947 (DIETZ, 1948) convey a most pronounced impression of horizontal thermal streakiness but in this particular case it may be due in part to the oblique ship's track from 55° S, 131° W to 65° S, 156° W. The *Atka* Section from New Zealand to the Ross Sea in Jan. 1955 (see figs. 11 and 12 in H. O. Misc. 16331) shows a streaky thermal field from 58° S, 176° 30′ E to 61° S, 177° 50′ E, where at least three horizontal temperature minima were observed extending from the surface to the bottoms of the BT dips at 600 feet.

These observations remind us of a much smaller scale (meters) of streakiness observed in the motion of water surfaces by LANGMUIR (1938) and WOODCOCK (1942). A still larger scale of streakiness (100's of kilometers) has been observed in the Gulf Stream by FUGLISTER (1951). In the atmosphere streakiness has been manifest as cumulus cloud streets (FORBES, 1945), cold front striations (WEXLER, R., 1947), banded structure of hurricanes (WEXLER, H., 1947) and in multiple jet-stream structure of the upper westerlies (ENDLICH, R. M., et al. 1954).

The cause for these highly organized concentrations of momentum is not known but by analogy one would expect it to be present in a well-marked oceanic "jet-stream" in the Antarctic Circumpolar Current (ACC). Since the examples of streakiness cited above all have a system of horizontal divergences and convergences arranged along the axis of the current, it would appear that this should also be characteristic of the ACC.

The characteristic structure of the waters surrounding Antarctica in summer shows a subsurface layer of cold (<32° F) water from 200 feet to 500 feet which on the 180th meridian extends northward to near latitude 62° South. A system of alternate horizontal convergences and divergences impressed on the ocean surface layer in this zone could cause alternate warm and cold surface layers of water. Once the longitudinal vortices of opposite rotation are set into motion in the surface layer by the winds they may continue for some time and thus create the thermal streakiness which might persist even after the emergence of a new wind regime. However, the contrast between a relatively fixed thermal streaky pattern of the ocean surface and what must be rather large changes in surface wind pattern does not render this explanation very reasonable.

The Pack-Ice Effect

We come now to what, in the writer's opinion, appears to be the most reasonable explanation of the Antarctic Divergence. This is based on combination of the Rossby inertial oscillation and the HIDAKA-TSUCHIYA (H-T) (1953) frictional analysis applied to an open ocean extending from 45° S to 70° S. In the latter case, as we have seen from figure 5, a *convergent* region is found to the south of the wind maximum, which is at

* At the author's suggestion a non-linear analysis of this effect is being undertaken by his colleague, Dr. M. Tepper.

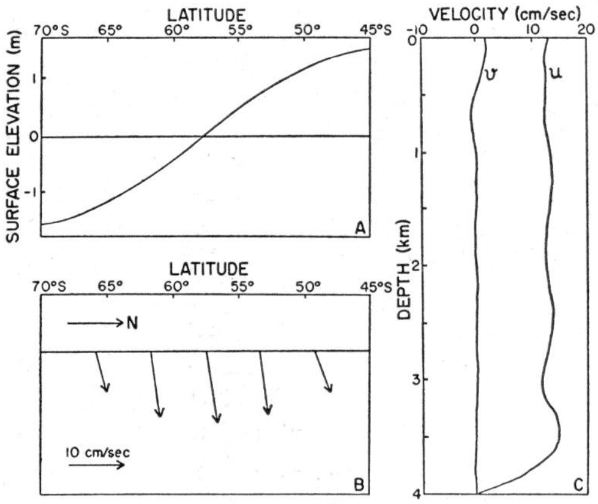

Fig. 5. Computed wind-driven current and surface elevation for lateral and vertical mixing coefficients of 10^{10} and $2 \cdot 10^{3}$ gm cm^{-1} sec^{-1}, respectively, and maximum surface frictional stress of 2 dynes cm^{-2}. A. Surface profile. B. Vector diagram of surface currents. C. Vertical distribution of the current velocity along the median line (57° 30′ S). (After Hidaka and Tsuchiya, 1953).

variance with the oceanic *divergence* observed in this region. However at the extreme southern boundary of the westerly winds the H-T analysis shows a weak divergence as the wind-induced surface current moves northward. But if we compare the theoretical position of this strong upwelling with the observed position of the Antarctic Divergence we encounter a discrepancy of the order of 10° of latitude.

We get around this difficulty in the following way: In late winter, as shown in fig. 6, the mean northern limit of the Antarctic pack-ice according to Mackintosh and Herdman (1940) is 5° to 15° north of the 70° S latitude circle which marked the southern limit of the "open" ocean analyzed by H-T. This means that in winter there must be a corresponding shift northward of the west wind-induced divergence.

Mackintosh (1946) has already pointed out the rough parallelism of the mean northern limit cf the pack-ice (September—October) and the Antarctic "Convergence" which, however, are separated by distances varying from 120 miles in the Scotia Sea to about 550 miles in the Indian Ocean section with an average separation

* The cruise of the USS *Glacier* in October 1956 just north of the pack-ice edge from 118° W to 180° showed this edge extended as much as 180 miles (with average of 100 miles) north of and parallel to Mackintosh and Herdman's position shown in figure 6. (See Techn. Report, Operation Deep Freeze II, 1956—1957, U.S. Navy Hydrographic Office, Oct. 1957, figures 18 and 19.)

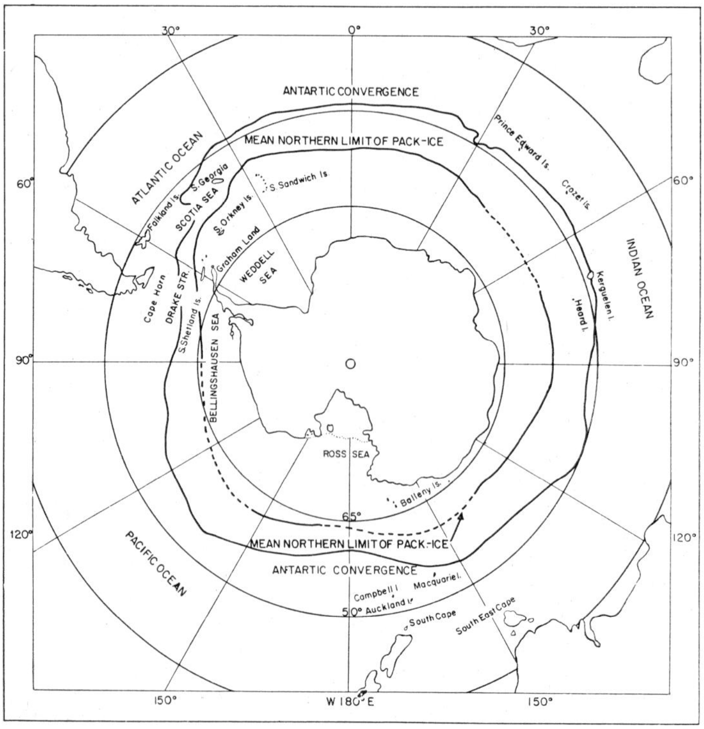

Fig. 6. Estimated mean position of the Antarctic Convergence (Mackintosh, 1946) and mean northern limit of the pack-ice for September (Mackintosh and Herdman, 1940).

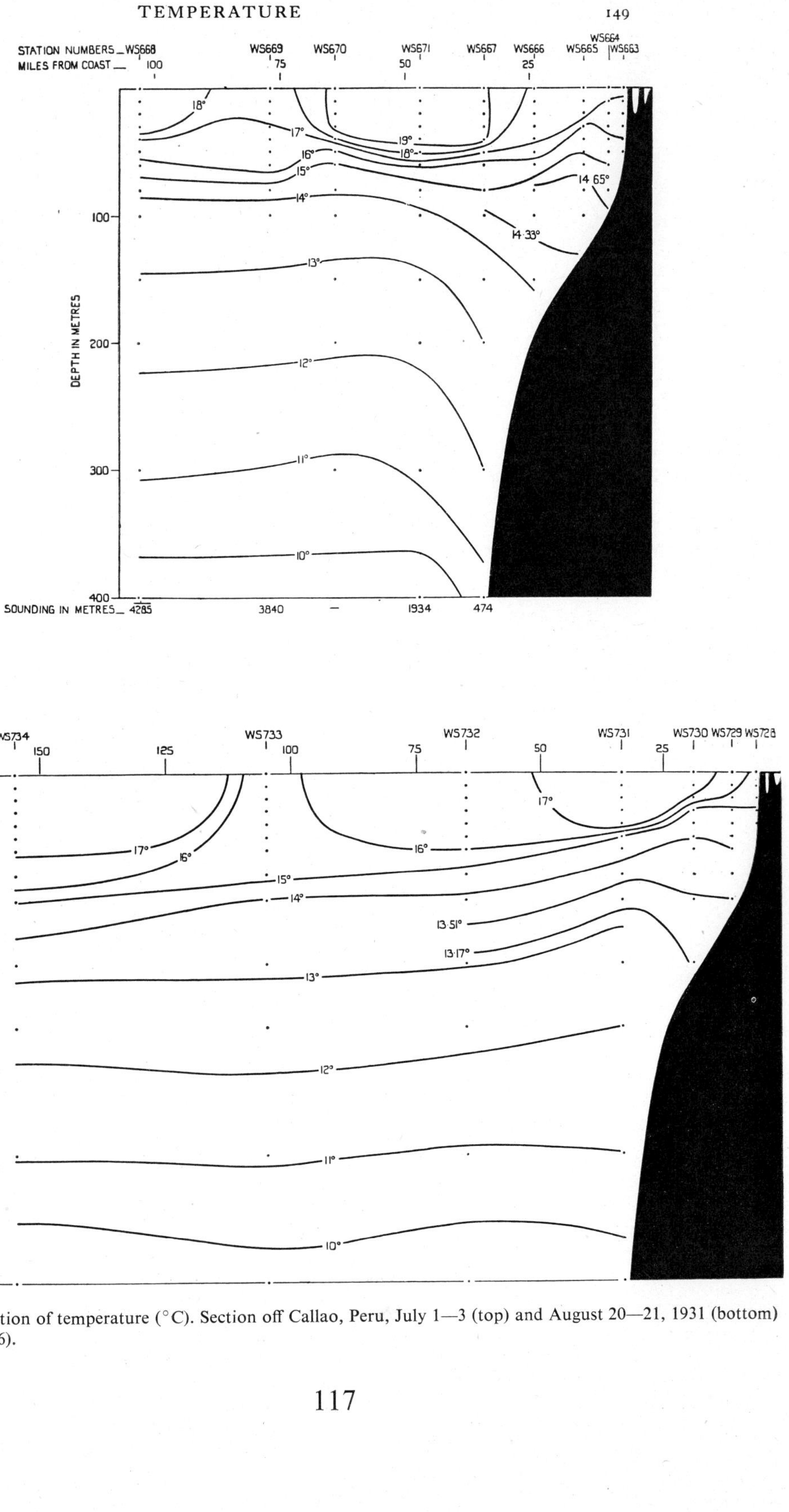

Fig. 7. Distribution of temperature (°C). Section off Callao, Peru, July 1—3 (top) and August 20—21, 1931 (bottom) (GUNTHER, 1936).

of 370 miles or 6° of latitude (figure 6).* The strict interpretation of the H-T theory would call for the maximum divergence at the edge of the pack-ice whereas in reality it is found 2° to 10° farther north. How do we get around this discrepancy? The writer can only proceed by analogy with another great oceanic divergent region, such as is found off the west coast of South America. This region has been studied intensively, especially by SCHOTT (1931) and GUNTHER (1936), and the pattern of upwelling determined.

As the predominantly southerly winds move parallel to the west coast of South America the wind-driven surface water moves westward and induces upwelling of colder sub-surface water. Again, from purely theoretical grounds one would expect the maximum upwelling and minimum surface temperatures to be located at the coast but Schott and Gunther show that another region of low temperature is found 100 or more miles off the coast. Gunther further emphasizes that this multiple structure is remarkably persistent (see figure 7). Both temperature minima extend to the 100 meter depth and are separated by warm-water wedges 1° to 2° C warmer. Unfortunately Gunther's vertical sections do not extend sufficiently far to the west to see if the alternating warm and cold pattern continues.

The same warm and cold pattern has also been observed off the coast of Southern California by SVERDRUP and FLEMING (1941). These authors interpret this pattern as a result of circulation cells forming normal to the wind-driven current flowing parallel to the coast and extending to a depth of some 80 meters. The ascending branches of these cells have speeds of the order of 4 meters per day. Beneath the cell closest to the shore is a broad region of upwelling extending from 80 to 150 meters in depth where the speed is about 1 meter per day. The cell closest to the coast extends westward for 100 km and 30 km beyond is the ascending branch of another cell whose horizontal dimension is not given because of lack of observations sufficiently far off-shore.

The similarity between the Peru and California current temperature sections and those across the Antarctic Divergence seems striking enough to proceed with the analogy between the wind-induced divergence of water some 100 or more miles west of the South and North American west coasts—for the case of southerly and northerly winds respectively—and some 100 or more miles north of the mean northern limit of the Antarctic pack-ice—for the case of westerly winds. The temperature contrasts in the latter case are much greater than in the former case but this is to be expected because of the large supply of cold water available near the edge of and underneath the pack-ice.

Now assuming we have satisfactorily explained the winter-time formation of a strongly divergent region some 100 miles or so north of the northern limit of the Antarctic pack-ice why does not this region follow the summer retreat southward of the pack-ice edge; e.g., on the 180° meridian, from 64° S in September—October to near 70° S in February—March, (MACKINTOSH and HERDMAN, 1940)? In the first place I think the answer is to be found in the fact that the winter combination of the ice-pack edge not far south of the average position of the most strongly developed and fluctuating westerlies leads to a formation—by the purely frictional effect of H-T, and the inertial effect described earlier—of a strongly divergent region that cannot be destroyed or even moved significantly during the brief summer season (see Table 2). Nor can another equally strong divergence form in summer some distance to the south of the winter position because in summer the westerlies are weaker and are located much farther north from the ice-pack edge.

The cold Antarctic sub-surface current, observed in summer and illustrated in figures 3 and 4, and which is found approximately 100 to 500 feet below the surface as it moves northward and descends, is believed to have its origin in the wind-induced water drift to the north as called for in the H-T theory. The summer warming of the upper 100 feet of this current is undoubtedly a result of heating by solar radiation in relatively ice-free water.

Summary

The fine thermal structure of the Antarctic "Convergence" reveals the existence of a narrow cold core,[1] extending downward at least 200 or 300 meters, which can only be explained by up-

[1] An analysis of four *BT* sections south of New Zealand made in 1957—58 by Garner (*N. Z. Jour. Geol. and Geophys.*, Vol. 1, No. 3, Aug. 1958, fig. 7) revealed absence of cold cores so markedly present the year before. This suggests perhaps a vast difference in properties of the westerlies (strength, persistence, position, etc.) in the two years which will be looked into when *IGY* meteorological data for this area become available.

welling induced by horizontal divergence of the surface layer. In winter, when the Antarctic Continent is expanded horizontally by the formation of ice so that its new "coast" is found not far south of the strong winter westerlies, the horizontal divergence and upwelling are most strongly developed. The upwelling is caused by

i) frictional transport northward of surface water
ii) and, in the case of accelerating winds from the west, by an inertial displacement northward of surface water (Rossby).

The thermal structure of the Antarctic Divergence appears similar to those found off the west coast of Chile and Southern California.

The brief summer season does not appear to affect materially the winter-formed cold-core and in summer neither the ice condition nor the weaker westerly winds encourage the formation of an equally strong cold-core farther south, although weak cores are occasionally found.

Special Remarks

The author's interest in the problem of the Antarctic Circumpolar Current was first aroused by remarks made by Professor C.-G. Rossby at a meeting of the United States National Committee for the International Geophysical Year held in Washington on April 8, 1954. Professor Rossby suggested an extensive coordinated investigation of the Antarctic Circumpolar Current during the IGY because this current was unobstructed by continents and might therefore be expected to be similar to the atmospheric westerlies, with respect to jet-stream structure, meandering waves, and eddy formation.

Because of the commitment of available oceanographic research vessels to other oceans during the IGY, it was not possible to realize Professor Rossby's dream of coordinated research in Antarctic waters although individual investigations carried on by IGY Antarctic expeditionary ships have produced valuable results.

It is hoped that the post-IGY Antarctic research plans now being formulated by the ICSU Special Committee on Antarctic Research (SCAR) in consultation with the Special Committee on Oceanographic Research (SCOR) will result in a coordinated synoptic investigation of the ACC extending around the Antarctic Continent to be carried out during specially designated international periods. When such observations become available they will cast much light on the Antarctic "Convergence" and other properties of the ACC.

REFERENCES

ANONYMOUS, 1956: Field Report, Oceanographic Observations, U.S. Navy Antarctic Expedition, 1954—55, USS *Atka* (AGB-3), H. O. Miscell. 16331, U.S. Navy Hydrographic Office, Washington, D.C.

ASSUR, A., 1951: Ein Beitrag zur Untersuchung der planetarischen und monsunalen Zirkulation. Dissertation, Universität Hamburg.

BOLIN, B., 1953: The Adjustment of a Non-Balanced Velocity Field Towards Geostrophic Equilibrium in a Stratified Fluid. *Tellus*, **5**, no. 3, pp. 373—385.

BURLING, R. W., 1959: To be published in *New Zealand Jour. Geol. and Geophys.*

CAHN, A., 1945: An Investigation of the Free Oscillations in a Simple Current System. *J. Meteorol.*, **2**, No. 2, pp. 113—119.

CROMWELL, T., and REID, J. L., JR., 1956: A study of Oceanic Fronts, *Tellus*, **8**, no. 1, pp. 94—101.

DEACON, G. E. R., 1937: Hydrology of the Southern Ocean, *Discovery Reports*, XV, pp. 1—124.

DEFANT, A., 1928: Die systematische Erforschung des Weltmeeres, *Gesellsch. f. Erdkunde, Zeitschrift*, Jubiläums-Sonderband, pp. 459—505, Berlin.

DIETZ, R. S., 1948: Some Oceanographic Observations on Operation HIGH-JUMP, U.S. Naval Electronics Lab., Rep. No. 55 (portions of this report are included in *Proc. 7th Pacific Science Conference*).

ENDLICH, R. M., et al., 1954: Project Jet Stream—The Observation and Analysis of the Detailed Structure of the Atmosphere near the Tropopause, *Bull. Amer. Met. Soc.*, **35**, no. 4, pp. 143—153.

FORBES, A., 1945: Photogrammetry applied to aerology. *Photogrammetric Eng.*, **11**, no. 3, pp. 181—192.

FUGLISTER, F. C., 1951: Multiple Currents in the Gulf Stream System. *Tellus*, **3**, no. 4, pp. 230—233.

GUNTHER, E. R., 1936: A Report on Oceanographical Investigations in the Peru Coastal Current, *Discovery Reports*, XIII, pp. 107—276.

HIDAKA, K., and TSUCHIYA, W., 1953: On the Antarctic Circumpolar Current. *Jour. of Marine Res.*, **12**, no. 2, pp. 214—222.

KNAUSS, J. A., 1957: An Observation of an Oceanic Front, *Tellus*, **9**, no. 2, pp. 234—237.

KOOPMAN, G., 1953: Entstehung und Verbreitung von Divergenzen in der oberflächennahen Wasserbewegung der Antarktischen Gewässer. *Deut. Hydrogr. Zeit.* Ergänzungsheft 2, Deut. Hydrogr. Inst., Hamburg.

LAMB, H. H., and BRITTON, G. P., 1955: General Atmospheric Circulation and Weather Variations in the Antarctic, *Geogr. Jour.*, CXXI, part 3, pp. 334—349.

LANGMUIR, I., 1938: Surface Motion of Water Induced by Wind. *Science*, **87**, pp. 119—123.

Mackintosh, N. A., 1946: The Antarctic Convergence and the Distribution of Surface Temperatures in Antarctic Water, *Discovery Reports*, XXIII, pp. 177—212.

Mackintosh, N. A., and Herdman, H. F. P., 1940: Distribution of the Pack-Ice in the Southern Ocean, *Discovery Reports*, XIX, pp. 287—296.

Meinardus, W., 1923: Ergebnisse der Seefahrt des Gauss. *Deutsche Südpolar-Expedition* 1901—03 III. Meteorologie 1, 1, 544.

Rossby, C.-G., 1937—38: On the Mutual Adjustment of Pressure and Velocity Distribution in Certain Simple Current Systems I, II. *Jour. Mar. Res.*, **1**, no. 1, pp. 15—28; **1**, no. 3, pp. 239—263.

— 1950: On the Dynamics of Certain Types of Blocking Waves. *Jour. Chinese Geophys. Soc.*, **2**, no. 1, pp. 1—13.

Schott, G., 1920: *Geographie des Atlantischen Ozeans*, Hamburg.

— 1931: Der Peru-Strom und seine nördlichen Nachbargebiete in normaler und anormaler Ausbildung. *Ann. d. Hydrogr. u. Mar. Met.*, **59**, pp. 161—169, 200—213, 240—252.

Sverdrup, H. U., 1934: Wie entsteht die Antarktische Konvergenz? *Ann. d. Hydrogr. u. Marit. Met.*, **62**, pp. 315—317.

Sverdrup, H. U., and Fleming, R. H., 1941: The Waters Off the Coast of Southern California March to July, 1937. *Bull. Scripps Inst. Ocean.*, U.C.L.A., **4**, no. 10, pp. 261—378.

Sverdrup, H. U., et al-, 1942: *The Oceans*, Prentice-Hall Inc., New York.

Tressler, W. L., 1957: Private Communication of BT data published later in Report of Operation Deepfreeze II (see reference in footnote on p. 000).

van Loon, H., 1956: Blocking Action in the Southern Hemisphere, Part I, *NOTOS*, **5**, pp. 171—178.

Veronis, G., 1956: Partition of Energy between Geostrophic and Nongeostrophic Oceanic Motions. *Deep-sea Res.*, **3**, pp. 157—177.

Veronis, G., and Stommel, H., 1956: The Action of Variable Wind Stresses on a Stratified Ocean. *J. Mar. Res.*, **15**, no. 1, pp. 43—75.

Vowinckel, E., 1955: Southern Hemisphere Weather Map Analysis: Five-year Mean Pressures. Part II. *NOTOS*, Pretoria, **4**, pp. 204—216.

Vowinckel, E., and Oosthuizen, C. M., 1953: Weather Types and Weather Elements over the Antarctic Ocean During the Whaling Season, *NOTOS*, **2**, no. 3, pp. 157—182.

Wexler, H., 1947: Structure of Hurricanes as Determined by Radar. *Ann. N.Y. Acad. Sci.*, XLVIII, Art. 8, pp. 821—844.

Wexler, R., 1947: Radar Detection of a Frontal Storm 18 June 1946. *J. Meteor.*, **4**, no. 1, pp. 38—44.

Woodcock, A. H., 1942: Soaring Over the Open Sea, *Science*, LV, pp. 226—232.

— 1950: Subsurface Pelagic *Sargassum*, *J. Mar. Res.*, **9**, no. 2, pp. 77—92.

Wust, G., 1928: Der Ursprung der Atlantischen Tiefenwasser, *Gesellsch. f. Erdkunde, Zeitschrift*, Jubiläums-Sonderband, pp. 506—534, Berlin.

(Manuscript received 15 March, 1958)

Climatic Records on the Ocean Floor

By Gustaf O. S. Arrhenius
Scripps Institution of Oceanography, La Jolla

(Received 30 September, 1958)

Abstract

A close relation is found between the wind driven circulation in the Equatorial Current System in the Pacific, and the distribution on the ocean floor of minerals produced by organisms in the surface layer of the ocean. The large variations in time of rate of accumulation of such solids is discussed in terms of corresponding changes of trade wind intensity in the past. Special attention is given to the validity of time estimates, and a comparison is made between the Atlantic and the Pacific records.

Climatic changes on continents and in polar areas mostly have such catastrophic effects on the geological record that in a quantitative study the intensity and time factors involved are difficult to ascertain. The bottom deposits of the tropical ocean far away from continents and polar areas therefore appear promising as records of such climatic changes.

1. Significance of carbonate accumulation

The first attempt at a large-scale study of the stratification of such deposits was undertaken by W. Schott (1935), using the extensive material of sediment cores collected during the German Meteor-Expedition in the Atlantic Ocean. The areas studied by Schott are mostly covered with foraminiferal ooze, a sediment which essentially consists of a minor fraction of silicate minerals and varying amounts of calcium carbonate in the form of tests of foraminifera. These are protozoa, which are largely planktonic and live from the phytoplankton produced in the surface layer of the ocean. At reproduction or upon death, the calcareous tests sink to the bottom. Another contribution of sedimentary calcite comes from planktonic flagellates with minute calcareous plates, coccoliths, secreted from the protoplast. Due to the lack of saturation of the deep water with respect to calcium carbonate, a varying fraction of the accumulated carbonate goes back into solution in the bottom water. The final rate of accumulation of calcium carbonate is therefore found as the difference between the rates of production and dissolution of calcareous skeletal material.

The production of skeletal calcium carbonate in the surface layer of the ocean is an unknown function of food supply, temperature (acting through the carbon dioxide system and perhaps also in a direct way), competition factors and other unknowns. The food supply, in its turn, appears in the tropical ocean to be regulated by the intensity of vertical mixing which brings inorganic nutrients from the deep water up into the surface layer where radiation from the sun makes photosynthesis possible. The amount of post-depositional dissolution varies considerably and depends on the time of exposure of the calcite in the surface layer of the sediment and therefore on the total rate of deposition, and further on an intensity factor. This intensity factor depends on the amount and state of dissociation of the carbon dioxide in the bottom water, and is therefore influenced by the temperature, pressure and past history of the bottom water, and on the production of carbon dioxide by respiration of organisms living in the sediment. The pattern of distribution of calcium carbonate on the ocean floor is thus a complex result of oceanic circulation, depth and temperature distribution, and the interpretation of changes in space and time has to be based on our knowledge of these variables.

Schott (op. cit.) was able to show that in large parts of the Equatorial Atlantic Ocean the Recent sediment stratum is relatively high in calcium carbonate, with foraminifera known to thrive in warm water forming a large part of the fossil assemblage. Below this stratum he found another one much lower in calcium carbonate, and with a larger fraction of tests of foraminifera, known to prefer lower surface water temperatures. Schott interpreted this lower layer as laid down during the last glacial age, assuming that the Equatorial surface water temperature was lowered by decreased insolation during this time, and that hence the production rate of foraminifera was decreased. SCHOTT's work, later on extended, (1952) was of basic importance in demonstrating the use of the oceanic sedimentary record for the study of climatic change, and a number of similar studies have since been carried out by other workers (BRAMLETTE, BRADLEY, 1940; CUSHMAN, HENBEST, 1940; HAMILTON, 1957; OVEY, 1950; PHLEGER, 1939, 1942, 1947, 1948; PHLEGER et al., 1946, 1951, 1953), in the Equatorial Atlantic especially by Ericson (ERICSON et al., 1955, 1956). However it appears at the present time uncertain whether the decreased carbonate content in the glacial strata of the Equatorial Atlantic was due to a decrease in the productivity, to an increase in the rate of dissolution depending on the northward flow of Antarctic water along the bottom of the Atlantic Ocean, or to an increased influx of fine grained detrital matter, diluting the pelagic biogenous carbonate in the Atlantic Ocean. Evidence for this latter effect has recently been presented (BROECKER et al., 1958).

Another most promising approach to this problem has been made possible by the development by Urey, Lowenstam, Epstein and Mc Kinney (see references in EMILIANI, 1955), of a method for determination of the temperature of ocean water from the oxygen isotope ratio in carbonate, laid down in equilibrium with the water. Pioneer studies of paleotemperature distribution in ocean sediments have been carried out by these workers and by EMILIANI (op. cit.), the latter employing Atlantic and Caribbean

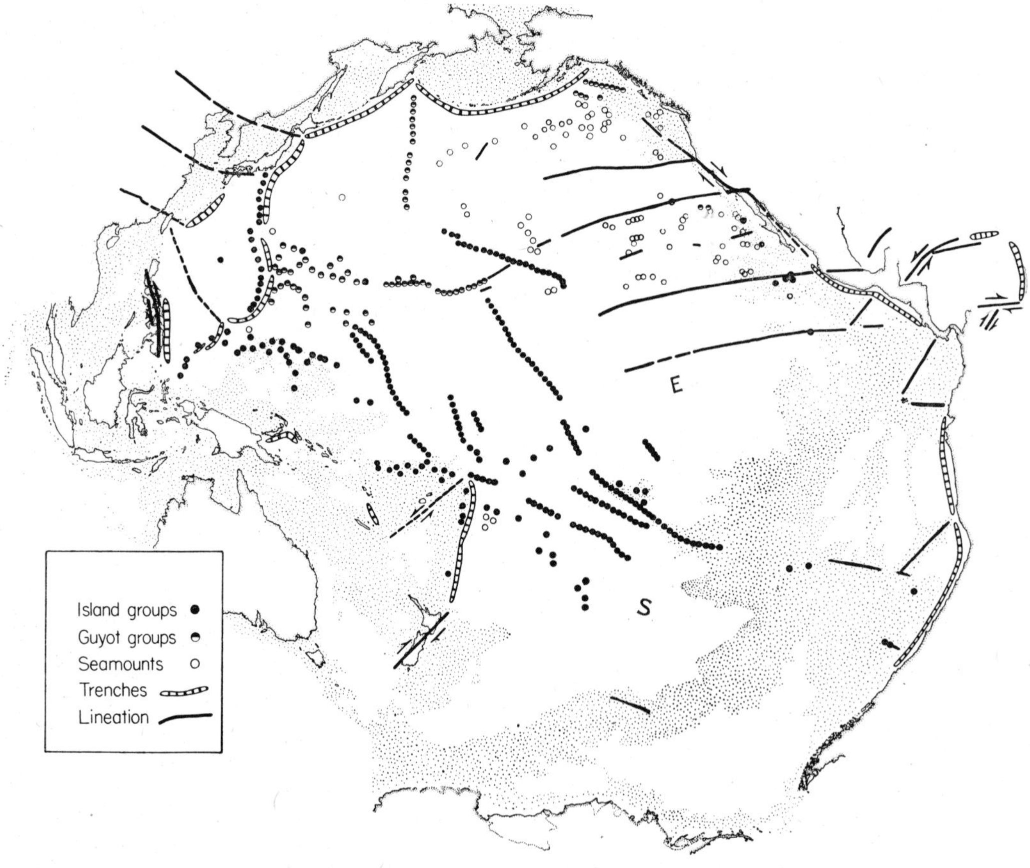

Fig. 1. Structures in the Pacific influencing sedimentation. Stippled area indicates depth less than 4000 m. Two basins appear especially well protected from turbidity inflow from the continents; the East Equatorial Basin, E, and the South Pacific Basin, S. — From Menard and Fisher, J. Geol. *66*, 250, 1958.

sequences of the same type as those used by Schott, but much longer, due to the improved coring technique. Emiliani's investigations confirm in general SCHOTT's and ERICSON's (op. cit.) conclusions regarding the variations in temperature of the surface water based on the frequency of cold and warm water species of foraminifera. Emiliani's record extends back into the Lower or Middle Pleistocene, and includes a series of oscillations of the surface water temperature, as indicated by the oxygen isotope ratios in tests of planktonic foraminifera. Emiliani also reports Washington radiocarbon dates from several levels in the upper part of the sequences. He has further attempted to extrapolate the time scale for this upper part downward in the sequence, and to correlate the temperature oscillations found, with the glacial events recorded on the continents.

2. The sedimentary record below the Equatorial Divergence

The stratification of the Late Tertiary, Pleistocene and Recent sediments has been extensively studied, in the Equatorial Pacific (ARRHENIUS, 1952). This area has been explored in great detail, because the sedimentation basins are located far away from the disturbing influence of the continents, and are surrounded by trenches and rises which prevent inflow of sediments along the bottom (fig. 1). Secondly, there exists in the surface layer of the ocean a wind driven circulation mechanism which controls the production and sedimentation of organic matter, and therefore the biostratigraphy. It appears possible in this area to establish a relationship between the changes in geologic time of trade wind intensity, and simultaneous changes in the composition of the sediment.

The mechanism of sedimentation in the East Equatorial Pacific is schematically illustrated in fig. 2. The central diagram of this figure shows a meridional cross section through the surface layer of the ocean in the East Equatorial Pacific at longitude 120—130° W, where the features of the vertical circulation are well developed, and where the regularity of the sedimentation makes possible a quantitative study of the variations in time of inorganic components.

The temperature distribution is in this middle diagram indicated by the isotherms for 15, 17, 20, 25 and 27° C. The cold, nutrient-rich intermediate water is marked by a dotted surface, and the vertical circulation pattern is shown by arrows. The Equatorial Countercurrent, running eastward, is limited by the South Equatorial Current at about 5° N, and by the North Equatorial Current at about latitude 10° N, both moving in the opposite (westward) direction. Divergence of these wind drift currents produces upwelling along the equator (see discussion in CROMWELL, 1953). The rise of the intermediate water, which is high in nutrient salts, into the surface layer, where most of the sunlight is absorbed, leads to a strongly increased production of algae, sustaining an increased production of higher members of the food chain. At higher tropical latitudes the lack of a mechanism which enriches the euphotic layer, keeps the productivity low.

The rate of production of skeletal calcium carbonate from coccolithophorids and foraminifera is illustrated in the upper diagram, where the full line curve, marked "Pleistocene minimum circulation (interglacial)" corresponds to present time conditions. The abscissa scale is the same as in the middle graph. The inferred rate of dissolution of calcium carbonate before final burial of the fossils is indicated by the curve "Pleistocene minimum production of cold deep water (interglacial)", and shows an increase under the Equatorial productivity maximum, indicating the effect of carbon dioxide produced by the respiration of bottom living animals feeding on the rain of organic detritus.

The resultant rate of accumulation of calcium carbonate corresponds to the ordinate difference between the two curves. At the intersection of these between latitude 7 and 9° N the carbonate accumulation accordingly drops to zero. Siliceous clays cover the bottom of the ocean north of the present loci of this intersection, the carbonate compensation line.

Paleotemperature measurements have been made using the calcium carbonate tests of both benthonic and pelagic foraminifera (EMILIANI, 1955), and the results for the present sediment surface are indicated at the present-time curve in the diagram. The benthonic tests indicate a temperature of about 1° C in good agreement with the directly measured temperature of the bottom water. The planktonic tests, in accordance with the observed temperature distribution in the surface layer, display a gradient, with rising temperature from the Equator to the north (14.8° at the Equator, 15.3° at latitude 2° N and 15.6° C at latitude 7° N). The temperature values obtained from the oxygen distribution would, however, if they represented the habitat

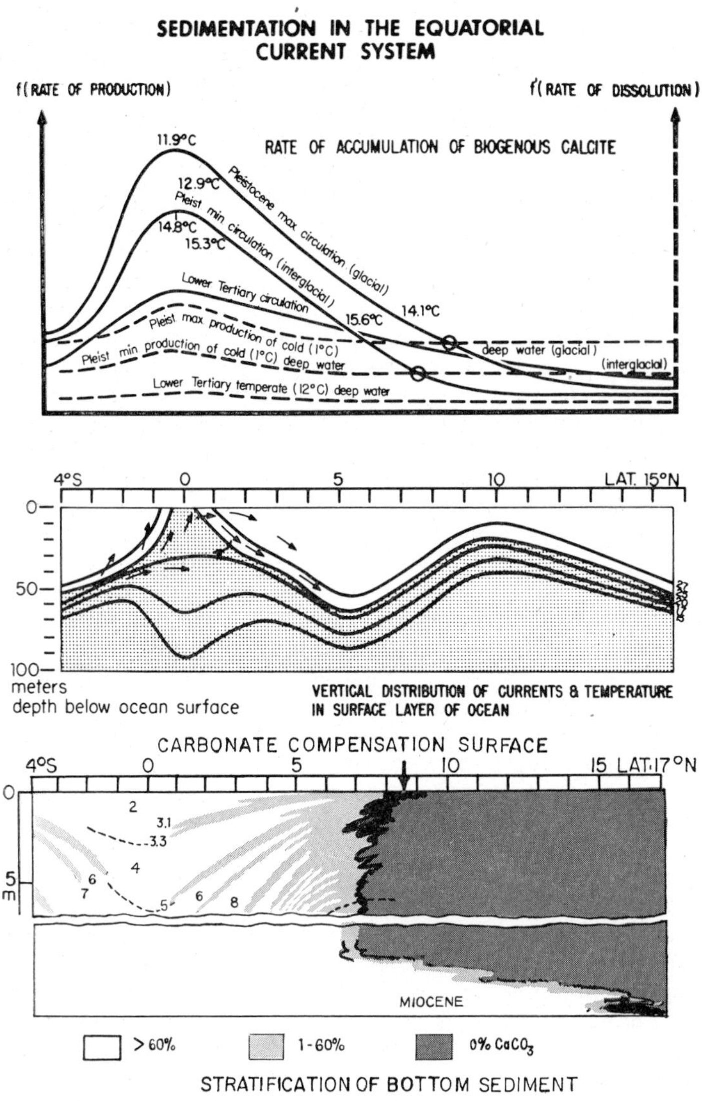

Fig. 2. Meridional profile at approx. long. 130° W. in the Pacific Ocean, showing the distribution of properties in the surface layer of the ocean (middle graph), the stratification of the bottom sediment (lower graph), and the interpretation of the sedimentary record in terms of rates of production, dissolution and accumulation of calcium carbonate from planktonic organisms (upper graph). (From Arrhenius 1959.)

of the foraminifera, place these below the thermocline. If this were the real condition, it is difficult to understand the meridional gradient in temperature, indicated by the isotopic composition of the calcite tests. Although well developed in the surface layer of the ocean, no such gradient is found below the thermocline. As is shown below, the isotopic gradient displayed by the foraminiferal tests exists and is even more marked during past ages (11.9° C at the Equator, 12.9° at latitude 2° N and 14.1° at latitude 7° N, during maximum circulation which occurred during the Riss [Illinoian] Glacial Age). The present conclusion is that the paleotemperature data from planktonic foraminifera show a trend which is in good agreement with the observed surface temperature distribution. The data therefore probably furnish indications of the relative temperature variations with time. However, the absolute values are difficult to reconcile with the actual distribution of water temperature. Investigations of the vertical distribution of the species in question in the surface layer of the ocean and of the relation between the oxygen isotope ratio of the tests on the one hand and the ambient water temperature on the other, appear needed for an interpretation in terms of absolute temperature.

Before the discussion of the other curves in the upper graph, representing the conditions in the past, the lower diagram in fig. 2 will be explained. This diagram is a generalized cross section through the bottom deposits along the same meridian as in the upper graphs. The ordinate has arbitrarily been chosen = 0 for the present sediment surface. The lower, detached half of the graph, showing the stratification of the Middle Tertiary sediments lacks greatly in detail due to the paucity of observations. The vertical scale is, in this case, relative and reference to the zero level is not available.

The distribution of carbonate concentration along the intersection of the profile with the present sediment surface reflects the productivity distribution in the surface layer of the ocean with the superimposed effect of dissolution. From high values below the Equatorial Divergence, the concentration drops toward higher latitudes, and the present northern carbonate compensation line is found between latitude 7 and 9° N.

The profile also demonstrates in a generalized way the marked stratification of the calcareous deposits. Below the surface layer, which is characterized by relatively low carbonate concentrations, lies a stratum (2), high in carbonate, and coinciding in time with the last glaciation in higher latitudes. This stratum is preceded by another low carbonate unit (3) with a small subordinate maximum (3.2, between the subordinate minima 3.1 and 3.3). Below this is a high-carbonate stratum (4) indicating extraordinarily high rates of accumulation of biogenous carbonate and silica. Altogether about nine major carbonate maxima occur in the Pleistocene part of the sequence. The underlying Pliocene sediments are characterized by less variability with time of the carbonate content. The Pliocene-Pleistocene transition is characterized by a rapid drop in the temperature of the bottom water, indicated by the oxygen isotope distribution in benthonic foraminifera (EMILIANI, EDWARDS, 1953), and by a marked change in the fossil assemblages of coccolithophoridae (BRAMLETTE, RIEDEL, 1954). This transition is shown as a dashed line crossing over the carbonate compensation surface near the break in the profile.

From measurements in the stratum 4 the full line curve marked "Pleistocene maximum circulation (glacial)" in the top diagram and the dashed curve marked "Pleistocene maximum production of cold deep water (glacial)" have been constructed. The productivity appears to have been largely increased, especially in the Equatorial Divergence and probably to some extent also the dissolution due to respiration of benthonic animals, although not enough to counterbalance the greatly increased rate of deposition of calcareous skeletal remains. As a result the overall rate of accumulation of calcium carbonate reaches a maximum during this time. The greatest increase occurs at the equator, where values of the order 3—10 $g \cdot cm^{-2} \cdot millennium^{-1}$ of calcium carbonate are found.

Although the amount of calcium carbonate relative to the inorganic components of the sediment is an analytically convenient measure of the organic productivity, varying with geologic time, it is not the only one. The variations, described above, are closely connected with still more marked changes in the relative amounts of phosphate from fish debris and of opaline silica from diatoms (ARRHENIUS et al., 1957; ARRHENIUS, 1959). The diatoms also display characteristic changes in their reproductive cycle (ARRHENIUS, 1952 chapters 1.5, and 1.9). The original amounts of diatomaceous opal and skeletal apatite are modified to a lesser extent than the calcite by secondary dissolution, and the distribution of silica and phosphate thus gives a still better approximation of the productivity in the past than the distribution of calcium carbonate.

As already mentioned above the paleotemperature data in the top graph indicate a steepening of the temperature gradient away from the Equator, which is taken as additional evidence for an increased rate of upwelling in the divergence as the cause of the increased productivity. The reason for this intensified vertical circulation occurring during the glacial ages is believed to be an increase in the tropical atmospheric circulation depending on a displacement toward the Equator of the high pressure centers now located between latitude 20 and 35°. Under these conditions the stratification of biogenous components in the Equatorial Pacific provides a direct and undisturbed record of the climatic evolution of the Earth during the last few million years. An estimate of the relative variations in trade wind intensity in the past, and a discussion of the time factor on the basis of the sedimentary record is given in the last part of this paper.

Due to the higher production of biogenous calcite and opal in the Equatorial Divergence, the time-rock units are thickest under the Equator, and thin out toward the north and south as is schematically indicated in the lower graph of fig. 2. A detail correlation of the Pleistocene strata has been carried out within the zone of high productivity around the Equator, and with less certainty to the bordering compensation surfaces (ARRHENIUS, (1952).[1] A stratigraphic subdivision of the Pleistocene clay formation is still lacking, mainly because of the great uniformity of most sections through this formation. The directly underlying Pliocene clay sediments are characterized by a higher and varying manganese and phosphorous content (ARRHENIUS, 1952, REVELLE et al., 1955), and by a lower content of detrital minerals like quartz (Rex, GOLDBERG 1958), indicating a lower total rate of deposition of detrital minerals in Tertiary than in Quaternary time.

Apparently due to tectonic disturbances of Tertiary age, seamounts and ridges were created in the area in question. Due to their elevation above the sedimentary basins, many of these topographic highs have not received any accumulation of sediment since the time of disturbance. Tertiary sediments of varying age thus outcrop on these highs, and a reconstruction can be made of the sedimentation during the early part of the Cenozoic era. It appears that the northern carbonate compensation line in Lower Tertiary was located much farther north than at present, probably north of latitude 45°. However, it was gradually displaced southward, passed latitude 16° N in Miocene time, and reached its approximate present location in Upper Miocene or Pliocene time. Lower Tertiary conditions are illustrated by the corresponding curves in fig. 2. Oxygen isotope measurements of benthonic foraminifera from these strata indicate bottom water temperatures of approximately 10° C as compared to 1—2° throughout the Pleistocene (EMILIANI, 1955; EMILIANI, EDWARDS, 1953). It is believed that the large meridional extent of carbonate sediments in Lower Tertiary time was due to a decreased rate of dissolution rather than to an increased over-all rate of production. This interpretation is supported by

[1] Near these surfaces the carbonate content has been found to be influenced by postdepositional dissolution and small fluctuations in the location of the compensation line to such an extent that correlation of the strata becomes difficult, unless a large number of sections are available. For this reason the previous correlation of the strata of core 58 near the northern compensation surface can not be trusted in detail.

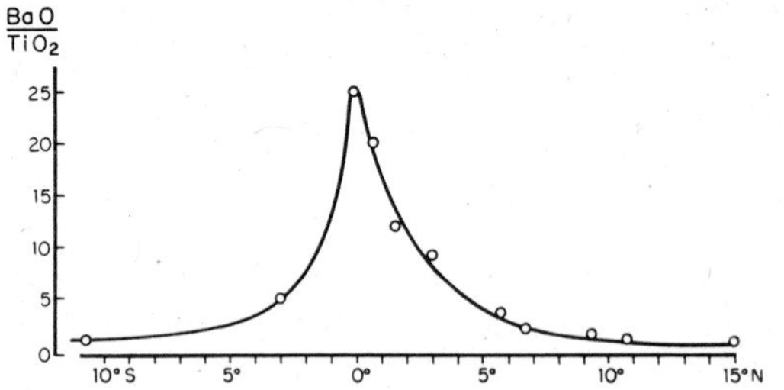

Fig. 3. Relative rate of accumulation of barium as a function of latitude, across the equatorial zone of high organic productivity. The rate is represented by the ratio BaO/TiO_2 in the Postglacial sediments. (From Goldberg, Arrhenius 1958.)

the observation of a low relative barium content in the calcareous Tertiary as compared with the Pleistocene sediments below the Equatorial Divergence (GOLDBERG, ARRHENIUS, 1958, par. 5.4). Barium is concentrated by marine organisms before or after death, and the barium concentration relative to the inorganic fraction of the sediment is another parameter, indicative of the rate of organic productivity in the surface layer of the ocean (fig. 3).

3. The time element

The stratification of the Equatorial calcareous Pleistocene, and the correlation of the strata throughout the Equatorial zone from long. 90° W to long. 180°, makes it possible to compare the variation in space of the content in each time-rock unit of specific fossils, minerals or elements. Such investigations have demonstrated (ARRHENIUS, 1952) that in the shielded sedimentation basins of the East Equatorial Pacific (fig. 1), the integral of the titanium content from the present surface to any given isochronous level in the Pleistocene strata, is subject to but small variations in space. The titanium content is assumed proportional to the total amount of inorganic matter in the sediment, and the results consequently indicate that in spite of the large variation in thickness of the time-rock units due to varying admixture of biogenous silica and calcium carbonate, the rate of accumulation of non-biogenous matter can, as a first approximation, be regarded as constant in space within the area in question during any given Pleistocene-Recent time interval. Therefore, the relative rate of accumulation over the area of any component during a given time interval can be expressed as the ratio of concentration of the component in question to the concentration of titanium. Such computations form the basis for the curves in the top diagram of fig. 2, expressing the rate of accumulation of carbonate as a function of latitude.

As has been mentioned above, the Pleistocene formation north of the northern compensation surface consists of a uniform, buff clay with practically no variation in the titanium content above the level of the analytical error (GOLDBERG, ARRHENIUS, 1958 par. 5.7). This clay sediment is known to consist of several components with a different mode of formation or transportation. Quantitatively the most important of these components are probably windborne and waterborne detrital minerals and pyroclastics from the continents, and marine hydrogenous minerals. These components are known to differ markedly in their titanium content, and variations of this content by more than a factor of two are observed in sedimentary sequences with large changes in the proportions of the components in question. The uniformity in titanium content and thus, presumably in the relative proportions of inorganic components in the Upper Pleistocene clay sediments in the East Equatorial Basin, may consequently be interpreted in two ways: either the rates of these components varied in such a way that the proportions remained constant, or they did not vary above the limits of detectability. The former alternative appears highly improbable. It is thus concluded that in the area and during the period in question, the rate of accumulation of inorganic components did not vary in a detectable way and this rate is therefore as a first approximation taken as constant (ARRHENIUS, 1952). This approximation is extended to the adjacent zone of equatorial carbonate sediments as these belong to the same physiographic province (fig. 1).[1]

This implies that a unit mass per surface area of aluminum, titanium, or other element proportional to the total of silicate phases, required approximately the same amount of time for accumulation during different Upper Pleistocene stages, and that the relative rates of accumulation within each time-rock unit can be compared with the rates found in other time-rock units.

[1] For reasons specified in GOLDBERG, ARRHENIUS (1958), it is difficult, at the present time, to estimate quantitatively the limit of detectability of variation in the rate of accumulation of one of the inorganic components mentioned. It is believed, however, that a change by a factor of two would be well above this limit.

This approximation is valid only under the uniform conditions of sedimentation within the basins in question, and cannot be directly applied to other areas of the ocean. Near and on topographic highs and in areas without protection against turbidity flow, the uniformity of sedimentation often appears to be disturbed and age estimates on the basis of the total amount

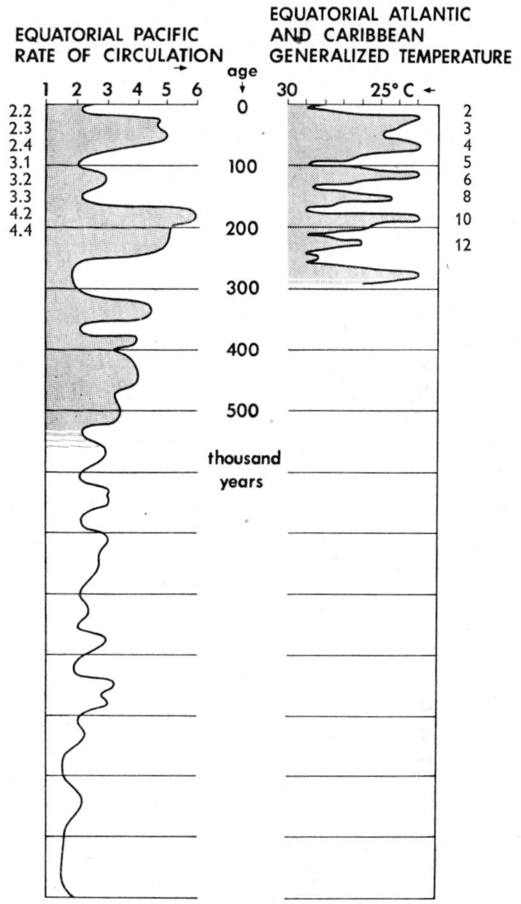

Fig. 4. Left. Relative rate of low latitude atmospheric circulation during the Pleistocene, estimated from the rate of accumulation of biogenous solids below the Equatorial Current System in the Pacific. The time scale is based on the total accumulated amount of titanium calibrated by radiocarbon. The Pliocene-Pleistocene boundary falls within the lowest two sections of the graph. (After Arrhenius 1952.)

(Right.) Atlantic surface water temperature from oxygen isotope data. The extrapolation of the time scale beyond 30,000 years is based on Emiliani's assumption that each climatic cycle had the same duration. (Compiled from Emiliani 1955.)

The numbers in the graphs refer to the stratigraphic subdivisions used in Pacific and in the Atlantic sedimentary sequences.

of any component in a column of unit cross section become uncertain.

Attempts have been made to date the different strata of the Atlantic and Pacific sequences, most of the recent ones using the carbon-14 method. The age information in the Pacific is derived from the measurement of one core carried out by Libby in 1950 (ARRHENIUS, KJELLBERG, LIBBY, 1951). The Atlantic cores are covered by a number of later and more accurate measurements by Suess and Rubin (EMILIANI, 1955).[1] Due to the short halflife of C^{14}, only the very top strata could be measured, corresponding to a few 10,000-year periods. In order to estimate the age of older strata, extrapolation techniques have been used. In the Equatorial Pacific these are based on the observation mentioned above of relative uniformity in space and time of the rate of accumulation of inorganic components. In a column of constant cross section, a given mass of these components under such circumstances corresponds to a definite length of time, which can be determined by calibration with radiocarbon. On this basis, the time-scale for the Pacific events, shown in the left diagram in fig. 4, has been constructed. This chronology can only be regarded as a first approximation, as the error is cumulative. However, it is believed that extrapolations like the present one, and the one made by Emiliani, represent the best estimates of the Pleistocene time-scale available at the present time, with the exception of the last Glaciation, and Postglacial time, where the continental record from high northern latitudes is known with greater precision.

4. The Atlantic record

Emiliani observed that in the Atlantic and Caribbean cores investigated by him, each major temperature cycle corresponds to a sediment layer of relatively constant thickness. This implies that in contrast to the conditions in the Pacific, approximately the same amount of both biogenous calcium carbonate and silica, and non-biogenous components were deposited during each one of the Pleistocene climatic cycles recorded. On the basis of this observation, Emiliani makes the assumption that the cycles all occupy an equal length of time, and that the age of the different strata is directly proportional to their depths below the surface. The estimate of the proportionality factor is based on a number of radiocarbon measurements in the surface layer.

The right-hand diagram in fig. 4 shows in a generalized way the temperature of the surface water from oxygen isotope data as a function of time according to Emiliani's estimate. Comparison with the left-hand graph shows a satisfactory agreement between the Atlantic-Caribbean and the Pacific records for the last 100,000 years, and Emiliani's stages 2, 3 and 4 appear to be isochronous with Arrhenius' stages 2.2, 2.3 and 2.4. Below the 100,000-year level, corresponding to Emiliani's stage 5, and Arrhenius' substage 3.1, it is difficult to attempt a realistic correlation of the strata on the basis of the present time information. If it were assumed that both time-scales were correct, Emiliani's stages 6 and 8 could correspond to substages in Arrhenius' stage 3, which could be better resolved in the Atlantic than in the Pacific, due to the higher rate of deposition of non-biogenous minerals in the Atlantic. Emiliani's stages 10 and 12 could in such a case correspond to 4.2 and 4.4 in the Pacific.

Another possibility, which at the present state of information appears worthwhile considering, is that the assumptions used in the extrapolation systems are such crude approximations that they lead to apparent discrepancies in the ages of corresponding time-rock units in the two oceans when the extrapolation is carried further back in time than 100,000 years. This opinion is shared in part by Emiliani (l.c., p. 561—562) insofar as he suggests that the Atlantic chronology is correct, and the Pacific invalid, and that time scale of the Pacific record should be shrunk by a factor of 1.8. However, the justification of such a modification necessitates substituting the titanium rate value from a core with a high rate of biogenous deposition, and therefore with a relatively good stratigraphic resolution, by a value from a poorly correlated sequence near the northern carbonate compensation surface (see footnote, p. (7). Further, the strata above the 100,000-year level, which appear to correlate well between the Atlantic and Pacific, would be brought out of phase.

[1] Among his chronological references Emiliani also includes age determinations based on the radium content of the sediment. However the observation of secondary redistribution of radium in the sediment (ARRHENIUS, 1959; ARRHENIUS, GOLDBERG, 1955; KOCZY, 1956; BROECKER et al, 1958) indicate that age determinations based on the distribution of radium are unreliable, unless support of the parent element ionium (Th 230) is proved in each individual case.

In view of the conflicting evidence, it appears desirable at the present time to assign the chronology of Pleistocene strata older than a hundred thousand years to the realm of order of magnitude, pending direct dating of these sediments by their ionium and thorium content, or by other absolute methods. Such attempts are being made at the present time.

REFERENCES

ARRHENIUS, G., KJELLBERG, G., and LIBBY, W. F., 1951: Age determination of Pacific chalk ooze by radiocarbon and titanium content. *Tellus* **3**, 222—229.

ARRHENIUS, G., 1952: Sediment cores from the East Equatorial Pacific. *Rep. Swed. Deep Sea Exp.*, **5**.

ARRHENIUS, G., BRAMLETTE, M. N., and PICCIOTTO, E., 1957: Localization of radioactive and stable heavy nuclides in ocean sediments. *Nature* **180**, 85—86.

ARRHENIUS, G., 1959: Sedimentation on the ocean floor. *Researches in geochemistry* (ed. Ph. H. Abelson), Wiley, N. Y.

ARRHENIUS, G., and GOLDBERG, E., 1955: Distribution of radioactivity in pelagic clays. *Tellus* **7**, 226—231.

BRAMLETTE, M. N., and BRADLEY, W. H., 1940: Geology and biology of North Atlantic deep-sea cores between Newfoundland and Ireland. *USGS Prof. paper* 196 A. Pt. I.

BRAMLETTE, M. N., and RIEDEL, W., 1954: Stratigraphic value of discoasters and some other microfossils related to Recent coccolithophores. *Jour. Paleont.* **28**, 385—403.

BROECKER, W., TUREKIAN, K., and HEEZEN, B., 1958: The relation of deep sea sedimentation rates to variations in climate. *Am. J. Sci.* **256**, 503—517.

CUSHMAN, J. A., and HENBEST, L. G., 1940: *USGS Prof. paper 196 A.*, Pt. 2.

CROMWELL, T., 1953: Circulation in a meridional plane in the Central Equatorial Pacific. *Jour. Mar. Research* **12**, 196—213.

EMILIANI, C., 1955: Pleistocene temperatures. *J. Geol.* **63**, 538—377.

EMILIANI, C., and EDWARDS, G., 1953: Tertiary ocean bottom temperatures. *Nature* **171**, 887.

ERICSON, D. B., EWING, M., HEEZEN, B. C., and WOLLIN, G., 1955: Sediment deposition in deep Atlantic. *Geol. Soc. Am. Spec.* Paper 62, 205—220.

ERICSON, D. B., and WOLLIN, G., 1956: Correlation of six cores from the Equatorial Atlantic and the Caribbean. *Deep Sea Research* **3**, 104—125.

GOLDBERG, E., and ARRHENIUS, G., 1958: Chemistry of Pacific pelagic sediments. *Geochim. Cosmochim. Acta* **13**, 153—212.

HAMILTON, E., 1957: Planktonic foraminifera from an Equatorial Pacific core. *Micropaleont.* **3**, 69—73.

KOCZY, F., 1956: Vertical eddy diffusion in deep water. *Nature* **178**, 585.

OVEY, C. D., 1950: On the interpretation of climatic variations as revealed by a study of samples from an Equatorial Atlantic deep-sea core. *Roy. Met. Soc.*, Centennial Proc., 211—215.

PHLEGER, F. B., 1939: Foraminifera of submarine cores from the continental slope. *Geol. Soc. Am. Bull.* **50**, 1395—1422.

PHLEGER, F. B., 1942: Foraminifera of submarine cores from the continental slope. *Geol. Soc. Am. Bull.* **53**, 1073—1097.

— 1947: Foraminifera of three submarine cores from the Tyrrhenian Sea. *Göteborgs Kungl. Vet. o. Vitterh. Samh. Handl.* 6, ser. B, Bd 5, No. 5.

— 1948: Foraminifera of a submarine core from the Caribbean Sea. *Ibid.* No. 14.

PHLEGER, F. B., and HAMILTON, E. A., 1946: Foraminifera of two submarine cores from the North Atlantic Basin. *Geol. Soc. Am. Bull.* **57**, 951—965.

PHLEGER, F. B., and PARKER, F. C., 1951: Ecology o foraminifera northwest Gulf of Mexico. *Geol. Soc. Am. Mem.* 46.

PHLEGER, F. B., and PEIRSON, J. F., 1953: North Atlantic foraminifera. *Rep. Swed. Deep Sea Exp.* 1947—1948, **7**.

REVELLE, R., BRAMLETTE, M., ARRHENIUS, G., and GOLDBERG, E., 1955: Pelagic sediments of the Pacific. *Geol. Soc. Am., Spec. Paper* **62**, 221—236.

REX, R., and GOLDBERG, E., 1958: Quartz contents of pelagic sediments from the Pacific Ocean. *Tellus* **10**, 153—159.

SCHOTT, W., 1935. Die Foraminiferen in dem aequatorialen Teil des Altantischen Ozeans. *Wiss. Ergebn. d. Deutsch. Meteor-Exp.* 1925—1927, **3**, T 3.

SCHOTT, W., 1952. On the sequence of deposits in the Equatorial Atlantic Ocean. *Göteborgs Kungl. Vet. o. Vitterh. Samh. Handl.* 6, ser. B, Bd 6, No. 2.

(Manuscript received September 25, 1958)

DISTRIBUTION OF MATTER IN THE SEA AND ATMOSPHERE

Changes in the Carbon Dioxide Content of the Atmosphere and Sea due to Fossil Fuel Combustion[1]

By BERT BOLIN and ERIK ERIKSSON

International Meteorological Institute in Stockholm

Abstract

The dissociation equilibrium of carbon dioxide in the sea is discussed with particular emphasis on the buffering effect of sea water, when changes of the partial pressure of CO_2 in the gas phase take place. The results are used in a study of the changes of the carbon dioxide content of the atmosphere and the sea that occur as a result of release of CO_2 to the atmosphere by fossil fuel combustion. It is shown that the steady state considerations given by previous authors hereby are considerably modified. Thus an increase of the CO_2 content of the atmosphere of about 10% as reported by Callendar may be compatible with a Süess effect of only a few percent. Because of the small buffering effect of the sea it seems likely that the biosphere on land may play a more important role for the changes actually occurring in the atmosphere due to release of CO_2 by combustion than previously believed. This problem warrants further investigation, but already the present treatment indicates that an appreciable increase of the amount of CO_2 in the atmosphere may have occurred since last century. This increase will continue and should be detectable with present techniques for measuring CO_2 in the atmosphere within a few years in areas with little or no local pollution due to fossil fuel combustion as in the Antarctica or on Hawaii.

1. Introduction

Fossil fuel combustion has added considerable amounts of carbon dioxide to the atmosphere during the last 100 years. In view of the great importance of CO_2 in the atmosphere for maintaining a radiational balance between the earth and space it is of great interest to know whether this output of CO_2 has caused a significant increase of the total content of carbon dioxide in the atmosphere or whether most of it has been transferred into the oceans. Some twenty years ago CALLENDAR (1938) could show that most likely a noticeable increase of the CO_2 in the atmosphere had occurred and he has recently (CALLENDAR, 1958) indicated that this increase in 1955—56 amounted to about 10 % as compared with an output due to combustion of about 14 % of the total amount of CO_2 present in the atmosphere (cf. REVELLE and SÜESS, 1957). His conclusions have recently been supported by BRAY (1959) in a detailed statistical investigation. However, by studying the C^{14} distribution in the atmosphere and the sea and its variation in the atmosphere during the last 100 years as revealed by the ratio C^{14}/C^{12} in wood one has been able to show that the exchange time between the atmosphere and the ocean is about 5 years (CRAIG, 1957, 1958; REVELLE and SÜESS, 1957; ARNOLD and ANDERSON, 1957; RAFTER and FERGUSSON, 1958). It has then been concluded (REVELLE and SÜESS, l.c.) that most of the CO_2 due to combustion has been transferred into the ocean and that a net increase of CO_2 in the atmosphere of only

[1] The research reported in this paper was partly sponsored by the Office of Naval Research through the Woods Hole Oceanographic Institution. Contribution No. 1025 from the Woods Hole Oceanographic Institution.

a few percent has actually occurred. Callendar's deduction has therefore been rejected particularly since the CO_2 measurements from the 19th century are indeed very uncertain.

Towards the end of their paper Revelle and Süess point out, however, that the sea has a buffer mechanism acting in such a way that a 10 % increase of the CO_2-content of the atmosphere need merely be balanced by an increase of about 1 % of the total CO_2 content in sea water to reach a new equilibrium. The crude model of the sea they used assuming it to be one well-mixed reservoir of CO_2, did not permit them to study the effect of this process more in detail.

The low buffering capacity of the sea mentioned by Revelle and Süess is due to a change in the dissociation equilibrium between CO_2 and H_2CO_3 on one hand and HCO_3 and CO_3 ions on the other. An addition of CO_2 to the water will change the pH and thereby decrease the dissociation resulting in a larger portion of CO_2 and H_2CO_3 molecules. Since the pressure of CO_2 in the gas phase being in equilibrium with CO_2 dissolved in water is proportional to the number of CO_2 and H_2CO_3 molecules in the water, an increase of the partial pressure occurs which is much larger (about 12.5 times) than the increase of the *total content* of CO_2 in the water. The change of this equilibrium in the sea is almost instantaneous. However, in course of its circulation the ocean water gets in contact with solid $CaCO_3$ on the bottom of the sea whereby a change towards another equilibrium takes place. This latter process is extremely slow and may be disregarded when discussing changes due to fossil fuel combustion. It will, however, be indicated in section 2 how this equilibrium is of major interest when being concerned with processes with a time scale of several thousand years.

In discussing the consequences of such a shift in the dissociation equilibrium with respect to the exchange of CO_2 between the atmosphere and the sea and within the sea it is not sufficient to treat the ocean as one well-mixed reservoir. We shall instead first follow a suggestion by CRAIG (1957) and divide the ocean in two layers. The upper reservoir, in direct contact with the atmosphere, is the part of the ocean located above the thermocline and constitutes about 1/50 of the total sea. This part of the ocean is well mixed due to wind action and convection. The remaining part of the ocean, the deep sea, is also taken as a well-mixed water body in direct exchange with the mixed layer above. Certainly this latter assumption is a poor approximation to actual conditions but will, as we shall see, give internally consistant results. In the first instance we shall neglect the effect of living matter on the earth but some general remarks about the exchange of CO_2 between vegetation and the atmosphere will be given towards the end of the paper.

It is obvious that an addition of CO_2 to the atmosphere will only slightly change the CO_2 content of the sea but appreciably effect the CO_2 content of the atmosphere. It is possible to deduce a relation between the exchange coefficient for transfer from the atmosphere to the sea and the corresponding coefficient for the exchange between the deep sea and the mixed layer. It turns out that a 10 % increase of the CO_2 content of the atmosphere as a result of a total output due to combustion amounting to 13 % of the total CO_2 content of the atmosphere would result for a residence time of water in the deep sea of around 500 years. Only a considerably more rapid turn over of the ocean model yield appreciably lower values, while the rate of exchange between the atmosphere and the sea is much less important.

The change in the dissociation equilibrium in water resulting from a transfer of CO_2 to the sea also effects the C^{14} distribution in the three reservoirs and REVELLE's and SÜESS' (1957) considerations in this matter are thereby appreciably changed. It is clear that a large percentage change of the CO_2 in the atmosphere and a comparatively small percentage change in the sea will yield a C^{14}/C^{12} ratio in the sea which is considerably greater than that of the atmosphere. The distribution of C^{14} between these two reservoirs is therefore not in equilibrium any longer. A transfer of C^{14} from the sea to the atmosphere will result. A more detailed study of this secondary effect reveals that

a) the steady state considerations of CO_2 exchange between the atmosphere and the sea as given by CRAIG (1957, 1958) are somewhat modified and a likely residence time for CO_2 in the atmosphere is 5 years.

b) the Süess effect would be 3—5 % depending on the rate of overturning of the sea.

In view of the observed values of the Süess-effect being around 3 % in 1954 (before the hydrogen bomb tests) (cf. BROECKER and WALTON, 1959; DE VRIES, 1958) the values obtained in this analysis are somewhat too large if using a value for the residence of water in the deep sea of 500 years. One possible explanation of this discrepancy would be the neglect of the exchange of CO_2 between the atmosphere and the biosphere. The main difficulty met when trying to incorporate this effect is, that we actually do not know whether a net increase of the amount of CO_2 present in vegetation may have occurred due to a transfer from the atmosphere or whether the direct influences from man's activities have had an effect in the opposite direction. It is clear, however, that even if no net transfer of CO_2 from the atmosphere into living or dead matter on land has occurred these exchange processes will modify the estimate of the "Süess effect" obtained by merely considering the atmosphere and the sea.

2. The CO_2-system in the sea

The different components of CO_2 present in the sea are CO_2, H_2CO_3, HCO_3^- and CO_3^{-2}. As CO_2 is difficult to distinguish from H_2CO_3 it is customary to express the sum of these species as CO_2. The sea is also in contact with ample amounts of solid $CaCO_3$ which should be considered in equilibrium being attained over several "turnover times" of the sea itself. Another important item in the system is the carbonate alkalinity, denoted here by A which is the sum of those cations which balance the charges of HCO_3^- and CO_3^{-2}. The following average values for the concentrations of the different components will be used here:

$C_{CO_2} = 0.0133$ mmol $\times$ l^{-1} (sum of CO_2 and H_2CO_3)
$C_{HCO_3^-} = 1.90$ mmol $\times$ l^{-1}
$C_{CO_3^{-2}} = 0.235$ mmol $\times$ l^{-1}

The sum of all these species is denoted by ΣC_{CO_2} and becomes 2.148 mmol $\times$ l^{-1}. A is given in mval $\times$ l^{-1} and becomes, $A = C_{HCO_3^-} + 2\,C_{CO_3^{-2}} = 2.37$ mval $\times$ l^{-1}. Now the following relationships can be derived, namely

$$\Sigma C_{CO_2} = \left(1 + \frac{K_1}{C_{H^+}} + \frac{K_1 K_2}{C_{H^+}^2}\right) C_{CO_2} \tag{1}$$

$$A = \left(\frac{K_1}{C_{H^+}} + \frac{2K_1 K_2}{C_{H^+}^2}\right) C_{CO_2} \tag{2}$$

where K_1 and K_2 are the first and second dissociation constants of H_2CO_3 in sea water and C_{H^+} is the hydrogen ion concentration. It is convenient to have the average values of the fractions within the brackets. They are

$$\frac{K_1}{C_{H^+}} = 143 \qquad \frac{K_1 K_2}{C_{H^+}^2} = 18$$

As to calcium carbonate, its solubility product L_p can be written

$$C_{Ca^{+2}} \cdot C_{CO_3^{-2}} = L_p$$

or more conveniently

$$C_{Ca^{+2}} = L_p \frac{C_{H^+}^2}{K_1 K_2} \frac{1}{C_{CO_2}} \tag{3}$$

and in sea water $C_{Ca^{2+}} = 10$ mmol $\times$ l^{-1}.

Finally we have for the equilibrium between the atmospheric CO_2 and that in sea water

$$P_{CO_2} = \frac{1}{\alpha} C_{CO_2} \tag{4}$$

where α is a proportionality constant and P_{CO_2} is the partial pressure of CO_2 in the atmosphere.

The constants K_1, K_2, L_p and α are only functions of temperature and salinity and will be regarded as constants in the following. We may therefore consider relations between small variations in P_{CO_2}, C_{CO_2}, ΣC_{CO_2}, A, C_{H^+} and $C_{Ca^{2+}}$. Using the variational method applied on equations (1) to (4) one obtains

$$\frac{\delta \Sigma C_{CO_2}}{\Sigma C_{CO_2}} = \frac{\delta C_{CO_2}}{C_{CO_2}} + \frac{\frac{\partial}{\partial C_{H^+}}\left(1 + \frac{K_1}{C_{H^+}} + \frac{K_1 K_2}{C_{H^+}^2}\right)}{1 + \frac{K_1}{C_{H^+}} + \frac{K_1 K_2}{C_{H^+}^2}} \delta C_{H^+} \tag{5}$$

$$\frac{\delta A}{A} = \frac{\delta C_{CO_2}}{C_{CO_2}} + \frac{\frac{\partial}{\partial C_{H^+}}\left(\frac{K_1}{C_{H^+}} + \frac{2K_1 K_2}{C_{H^+}^2}\right)}{\frac{K_1}{C_{H^+}} + \frac{2K_1 K_2}{C_{H^+}^2}} \delta C_{H^+} \tag{6}$$

$$\frac{\delta C_{Ca^{+2}}}{C_{Ca^{+2}}} = \frac{2\,\delta C_{H^+}}{C_{H^+}} - \frac{\delta C_{CO_2}}{C_{CO_2}} \tag{7}$$

$$\frac{\delta P_{CO_2}}{P_{CO_2}} = \frac{\delta C_{CO_2}}{C_{CO_2}} \tag{8}$$

First we see that if P_{CO_2} varies and the hydrogen ion concentration were kept constant, the relative changes would be the same in the sea as in the atmosphere. As the total amount of CO_2 in the sea is about 50 times that in the air, practically all excess CO_2 delivered to the atmosphere would be taken up by the sea when equilibrium has been established. One cannot, however, assume that pH is uninfluenced by changes in the ΣC_{CO_2} of the sea. We may see if any condition can be imposed upon the alkalinity. Obviously this should be kept constant if we consider changes that takes place over a relatively short time interval, less than the "turnover time" of the sea, because A is really the concentration of cations that balance the charges of HCO_3^- and CO_3^{-2}. If $CaCO_3$ is excluded the sum of these charges must remain constant. And then we see that any change in the P_{CO_2} will also change C_{H^+}. From eq. (5), (6) and (8) we get by putting $\delta A = 0$

$$\frac{\delta P_{CO_2}}{P_{CO_2}} = \frac{\delta C_{CO_2}}{C_{CO_2}} = 12.5 \frac{\delta \Sigma C_{CO_2}}{\Sigma C_{CO_2}} \qquad (9)$$

using the numerical values listed earlier. This tells us that 1 percent change in the total CO_2 concentration in the sea would require 12.5 percent change in the atmospheric CO_2 to maintain equilibrium. If we consider only the "mixed layer" of the oceans, i.e. the surface layer which contains about as much CO_2 as the atmosphere less than 10 percent of the excess fossil CO_2 in the atmosphere should have been taken up by the mixed layer. It is therefore obvious that the mixed layer acts as a bottleneck in the transport of fossil CO_2 into the deep sea (cf. the following section).

It may be of interest also to consider the effect of the $CaCO_3$ on the bottom of the oceans; the effect this may have for the final equilibrium which is attained after a long time. Then alkalinity will change by $\delta A = 2\ \delta C_{Ca^{+2}}$ and with this condition using the whole system of equations and $C_{Ca^{+2}} = 10$ mmol $\times$ 1^{-1},

$$\frac{\delta P_{CO_2}}{P_{CO_2}} = \frac{\delta C_{CO_2}}{C_{CO_2}} = 2.36 \frac{\delta \Sigma C_{CO_2}}{\Sigma C_{CO_2}} \qquad (10)$$

which shows that the sea, given enough time, has an appreciable buffer capacity for atmospheric CO_2. However, in the case of eq. (10) part of the change of total CO_2 comes from dissolution or precipitation of $CaCO_3$ and this has obviously to be subtracted if we want to know how much of the excess of atmospheric CO_2 the sea ultimately can consume. The amount that dissolves or precipitates is obviously equal to $\delta C_{Ca^{+2}}$ and becomes

$$\delta C_{Ca^{+2}} = 0.444 \frac{\delta C_{CO_2}}{C_{CO_2}}$$

Expressed as a part of the total CO_2 it becomes

$$\frac{\delta C_{Ca^{+2}}}{\Sigma C_{CO_2}} = 0.206 \frac{\delta C_{CO_2}}{C_{CO_2}} \qquad (11)$$

Now, rewriting (9) we find

$$\frac{\delta \Sigma C_{CO_2}}{\Sigma C_{CO_2}} = 0.424 \frac{\delta C_{CO_2}}{C_{CO_2}}$$

The part of the increase in total CO_2 that has come from the atmosphere is therefore

$$\Delta \frac{\delta \Sigma C_{CO_2}}{\Sigma C_{CO_2}} = \frac{\delta \Sigma C_{CO_2}}{\Sigma C_{CO_2}} - \frac{\delta C_{Ca^{+2}}}{\Sigma C_{CO_2}} = 0.238 \frac{\delta C_{CO_2}}{C_{CO_2}} \qquad (12)$$

or

$$\frac{\delta P_{CO_2}}{P_{CO_2}} = \frac{\delta C_{CO_2}}{C_{CO_2}} = 4.20\, \Delta \left(\frac{\delta \Sigma C_{CO_2}}{\Sigma C_{CO_2}} \right) \qquad (13)$$

Thus, in equilibrium one percent increase in ΣC_{CO_2} obtained from the atmosphere would occur for a 4.2 percent increase in the atmospheric partial pressure of CO_2. In other words, any excess CO_2 put into the atmosphere will ultimately be distributed so that about $^{11}/_{12}$ of it goes into the sea (again assuming the sea contains, 50 times more CO_2 than the atmosphere) while about $^{1}/_{12}$ remains in the atmosphere. Of the part that goes into the sea, 87 percent has taken part in the reaction

$$CaCO_3\,(s) + H_2CO_3\,(aq) = Ca^{+2} + 2\,HCO_3^{-1}$$

The rest has been used to lower the pH of sea water by the reaction

$$H_2CO_3\,(aq) \rightarrow H^+ + HCO_3^-$$

If the turnover time of the sea is of the order of 1,000 years, several thousands of years would be required to reach equilibrium with the $CaCO_3$ at the bottom of the sea.

It should finally be noted that, in case atmospheric CO_2 was withdrawn by some process, this would result in precipitation of $CaCO_3$ in the sea.

3. The exchange of inactive carbon between the atmosphere and the sea

In order to see more clearly the effect of the shift in the dissociation equilibrium in the sea we shall first disregard the role played by the biosphere and merely consider the atmosphere and the sea, the latter composed of two reservoirs. The top one, the mixed layer, is confined to the layer above the thermocline and the lower one, the deep sea, consists of the remainder of the sea. Both these reservoirs as well as the atmosphere are considered to be well-mixed and the exchange between them takes place through first order exchange processes. Introduce the following notations:

N_i = the total amount of C^{12} and C^{13} in reservoir i in a state of equilibrium as before 1850.

N_i^* = the total amount of C^{14} in reservoir i in a state of equilibrium as before 1850.

N_i' = the amount of C^{12} and C^{13} in reservoir i present in the form of CO_2 or non-dissociated H_2CO_3 (only for the ocean) in a state of equilibrium as before 1850.

$N_i^{*\prime}$ = the amount of C^{14} in reservoir i present in the form of CO_2 or non-dissociated H_2CO_3 (only for the ocean) in a state of equilibrium as before 1850.

n^i, n_i^*, n_i', $n_i^{*\prime}$ indicate the deviations from the equilibrium values given above.

k_{i-j} = exchange coefficient for transfer of C^{12} and C^{13} from reservoir i to reservoir j.

k_{i-j}^* = exchange coefficient for transfer of C^{14} from reservoir i to reservoir j.

$\tau_{i-j} = 1/k_{i-j}$

$\tau_{i-j}^* = 1/k_{i-j}^*$

λ = decay constant for C^{14}

$\gamma(t)$ = release of C^{12} and C^{13} due to fossil fuel combustion as a function of time t.

Q = mean production of C^{14} in the atmosphere due to cosmic rays.

The indices a, m and d refer to the atmosphere, the mixed layer and the deep sea respectively. The nomenclature is in part very similar to that used by CRAIG (1957).

Considering now first conditions for inactive carbon we obtain the following equilibria

$$\left.\begin{aligned} -k_{a-m}N_a + k_{m-a}N_m' &= 0 \\ k_{a-m}N_a - k_{m-a}N_m' - k_{m-d}N_m + k_{d-m}N_d &= 0 \\ k_{m-d}N_m - k_{d-m}N_d &= 0 \end{aligned}\right\} \tag{14}$$

Notice here particularly that the transfer from the sea to the atmosphere is put proportional to N_m' and not to the total amount of carbon in the mixed layer, N_m. On the other hand the transfer from the mixed layer to the deep sea and *vice versa* is due to the motion of water and should therefore be proportional to the total amounts of carbon present in the two reservoirs, *i.e.* N_m and N_d respectively. It should be pointed out here that an exchange of carbon between various strata of the ocean also occurs through the motion of organisms and the settling of dead organic material and precipitated $CaCO_3$ which is gradually being dissolved. From a recent paper by ERIKSSON (1958) it can be estimated that this is about 1/3,000 of the total amount of CO_2 in the sea per year. Naturally it is compensated by an upward flux of dissolved CO_2. This flux is small compared to the advective flux from deep water which is about the same as the horizontal transfer of atmospheric CO_2 in Eriksson's model giving a residence time of ≈ 600 years. His paper suggests anyway that the ratio between advective flux and gravitational is about 5. From (14) we now get

$$\left.\begin{aligned} k_{m-a} &= \frac{N_a}{N_m'} k_{a-m} = \alpha k_{a-m} \\ k_{m-d} &= \frac{N_d}{N_m} k_{d-m} = \beta k_{d-m} \end{aligned}\right\} \tag{15}$$

Due to combustion a deviation from this equilibrium now has occurred, which is governed by the following set of equations

$$\left.\begin{aligned} \frac{dn_a}{dt} &= -k_{a-m}n_a + k_{m-a}n_m' + \gamma(t) \\ \frac{dn_m}{dt} &= k_{a-m}n_a - k_{m-a}n_m' - k_{m-d}n_m + k_{d-m}n_d \\ \frac{dn_d}{dt} &= k_{m-d}n_m - k_{d-m}n_d \end{aligned}\right\} \tag{16}$$

In the previous section we found that the following relation exists between n_m' and n_m (cf. eq. (9))

$$n_m' = 12.5 \frac{N_m'}{N_m} n_m = B_1 n_m \tag{17}$$

Introducing this expression for n_m' into (16) we obtain a system of three ordinary linear differential equations for the three dependant variables n_a, n_m and n_d. Eliminating two of the three variables we obtain

$$\frac{d^3n_i}{dt^3} + [(1 + B_1\alpha)k_{a-m} + (1 + \beta)k_{d-m}]\frac{d^2n_i}{dt^2} + + [1 + B_1\alpha + \beta]k_{a-m}k_{d-m}\frac{dn_i}{dt} = S_i \quad (18)$$

$$i = a,\ m,\ d$$

where

$$\left.\begin{aligned} S_a &= \gamma''(t) + [B_1\alpha k_{a-m} + (1+\beta)k_{d-m}]\gamma'(t) + \\ &\quad + B_1\alpha k_{a-m}k_{d-m}\gamma(t) \\ S_m &= k_{a-m}\gamma'(t) + k_{a-m}k_{d-m}\gamma(t) \\ S_d &= \beta k_{a-m}k_{d-m}\gamma(t) \end{aligned}\right\} \quad (19)$$

The general solution of (18) is

$$n_i = C_{1i}e^{\lambda_1 t} + C_{2i}e^{\lambda_2 t} + C_{3i}e^{\lambda_3 t} + P_i \quad (20)$$

where C_{1i}, C_{2i} and C_{3i} are integration constants, λ_1, λ_2 and λ_3 solutions to the algebraic equation

$$\lambda_3 + [(1 + B_1\alpha)k_{a-m} + (1+\beta)k_{d-m}]\lambda^2 + + [1 + B_1\alpha + \beta]k_{a-m}k_{d-m}\lambda = 0 \quad (21)$$

and P_i are particular solutions depending on the functions S_i. Assuming now that [CRAIG (1957)]

$$\left.\begin{aligned} N_m &= 1.2\ N_a \\ N_d &= 60\ N_a \end{aligned}\right\} \quad (22)$$

we obtain

$$\left.\begin{aligned} B_1\alpha &= 12.5\frac{N'_m}{N_m}\frac{N_a}{N'_m} = 10.4 \\ \beta &= \frac{N_d}{N_m} = 50 \end{aligned}\right\} \quad (23)$$

The values chosen for N_m and N_d are somewhat uncertain but as we shall see later, do not influence the results significantly. The solutions to eq. (21) then are, due regard taken to the fact that $k_{a-m} \gg k_{d-m}$ and thus $(1 + B_1\alpha)\cdot k_{a-m} + (1+\beta)k_{d-m} \gg (1 + B_1\alpha + \beta)k_{a-m}k_{d-m}$ where $\gg$ denotes about two orders of magnitude

$$\left.\begin{aligned} \lambda_1 &= 0 \\ \lambda_2 &= -\frac{(1 + B_1\alpha + B)k_{a-m}k_{d-m}}{(1 + B_1\alpha)k_{a-m} + (1+\beta)k_{d-m}} \\ \lambda_3 &= -[(1 + B_1\alpha)k_{a-m} + (1+\beta)k_{d-m}] \end{aligned}\right\} \quad (24)$$

To obtain the particular solutions we have to specify $\gamma(t)$. We shall assume that $\gamma(t)$ may be approximated by

$$\gamma(t) = \gamma_0 e^{rt} \quad (25)$$

where

$$\left.\begin{aligned} \gamma_0 &= 4.96\ N_a\ 10^{-4} \\ r &= 0.029\ \text{year}^{-1} \end{aligned}\right\} \quad (26)$$

which fits the values given by REVELLE and SÜESS (1957) for carbon production until today and also the estimated values to year 2010 with sufficient accuracy if $t=0$ at 1880 (see table 1).

Table 1. CO_2 added to the atmosphere by fossil fuel combustion and a comparison with an analytical expression

Decade	Average amount added per decate (% of N_a)		Cumulative total added (% of N_a)	
	measured or estimated	$\gamma(t)$	measured or estimated (since 1860)	$\int_0^t \gamma(t)dt$ (since 1880)
1880—89	0.54	0.57	1.13	0.57
1890—99	0.79	0.77	1.92	1.34
1900—09	1.27	1.03	3.19	2.37
1910—19	1.72	1.37	4.91	3.74
1920—29	2.00	1.83	6.91	5.57
1930—39	2.11	2.47	9.02	8.04
1940—49	2.71	3.17	11.73	11.21
1950—59	3.9	4.4	15.6	15.6
1960—69	5.4	5.8	21.0	21.4
1970—79	7.5	8.0	28.5	29.4
1980—89	10.5	10.4	39.0	39.8
1990—99	14.5	13.7	53.5	53.5
2000—09	20.0	19.0	73.5	72.5

Thus we obtain

$$\left.\begin{aligned} S_a &= \gamma_0[r^2 + \{B_1\alpha k_{a-m} + (1+\beta)k_{d-m}\}r + \\ &\quad + B_1\alpha k_{a-m}k_{d-m}]e^{rt} = \gamma_0 S_{a0}e^{rt} \\ S_m &= \gamma_0[k_{a-m}r + k_{a-m}k_{d-m}]e^{rt} = \gamma_0 S_{m0}e^{rt} \\ S_d &= \gamma_0\beta k_{a-m}k_{d-m}e^{rt} = \gamma_0 S_{d0}e^{rt} \end{aligned}\right\} \quad (27)$$

One then easily finds the particular solutions

$$P_i = \frac{\gamma_0}{r}\frac{S_{i0}}{S_{a0} + S_{m0} + S_{d0}}e^{rt} \quad (28)$$

$$i = a,\ m,\ d$$

In order to determine the three constants C_{ij} for each solution $n_i(t)$ we shall apply the initial conditions

$$n_a = n_m = n_d = 0$$

which yields

$$\left.\begin{aligned} &\frac{dn_a}{dt} = \gamma(t); \quad \frac{dn_m}{dt} = \frac{dn_d}{dt} = 0 \qquad t = 0 \\ &\frac{d^2 n_a}{dt^2} = \gamma'(t) - k_{a-m}\gamma(t) \\ &\frac{d^2 n_m}{dt^2} = k_{a-m}\gamma(t); \\ &\frac{d^2 n_d}{dt^2} = 0 \end{aligned}\right\} \quad (29)$$

These equations are obtained from the system (16) and also yield

$$n_a + n_m + n_d = \frac{\gamma_0}{r}(e^{rt} - 1) \quad (30)$$

As can easily be verified the final solutions of n_a, n_m and n_d will be independant of the exact initial conditions for $t \gg 200$ years if the values for τ_{a-m} and τ_{d-m} are of the order of 5 and 500 years respectively. It also follows that $\lambda_3 = -2$ years^{-1} and that thus the term containing exp $(\lambda_3 t)$ in (20) may be neglected for $t \gg 2$—3 years. With due regard taken to this latter fact we finally obtain

$$\left.\begin{aligned} n_a &= \frac{\gamma_0}{r}\left[\frac{S_{a0}}{S}(e^{rt} - 1) + \right. \\ &\qquad \left. + \frac{r}{\lambda_2}\left(1 - \frac{S_{a0}}{S}\right)(e^{\lambda_2 t} - 1)\right] \\ n_m &= \frac{\gamma_0}{r}\frac{S_{m0}}{S}\left[(e^{rt} - 1) - \frac{r}{\lambda_2}(e^{\lambda_2 t} - 1)\right] \\ n_d &= \frac{\gamma_0}{r}\frac{S_{d0}}{S}\left[(e^{rt} - 1) - \frac{r}{\lambda_2}(e^{\lambda_2 t} - 1)\right] \\ S &= S_{a0} + S_{m0} + S_{d0} \end{aligned}\right\} \quad (31)$$

From CRAIG'S (1957, 1958) investigation of the exchange time for carbon dioxide between the atmosphere and the sea and the exchange within the sea the best estimates of τ_{a-m} and τ_{d-m} at present are $\tau_{a-m} = 5$ years and $\tau_{d-m} = 500$—1,000 years. FERGUSSON and RAFTER (1958) give a value $\tau_{a-m} = 3$ years. Fig. 1 shows the amount to be expected in the atmosphere 1954, when the total fossil fuel combustion since the middle of the last century is estimated to have been 13.2 % of the previous content of the atmosphere, for values of τ_{a-m} and τ_{d-m} in the vicinity of those quoted above. It first of all shows that *the net increase in the atmosphere is almost independant of the precise rate of exchange between the atmosphere and the sea.* This depends on the fact that the top layer of the ocean only need to absorb a small amount of CO_2 from the atmosphere as compared to the quantities released to be in approximate balance. Its capacity is therefore too small to be of any major importance. The decisive factor is instead the rate of overturning of the deep sea. Thus even using a residence time of only 200 years for the deep sea water an 8—9 percent increase of CO_2 in the atmosphere must have taken place. For a value of $\tau_{d-m} = 500$ years an increase of the atmosphere's content of CO_2 of about 10 percent would have occurred in 1954. This value compares very favourably with the value of 10 percent given by CALLENDAR (1958) as the total increase until 1955 deduced from a careful survey of all available measurements.

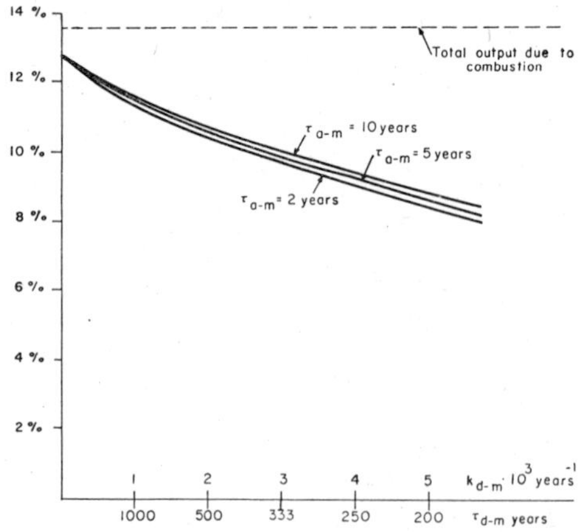

Fig. 1. Net increase of CO_2 in the atmosphere in 1954 due to release of fossil CO_2 according to UN-estimates as dependant on the rate of exchange between the atmosphere and the sea and the mixed layer and the deep sea.

The results obtained above are, however, dependant on our assumptions of the size of the three reservoirs, i.e. N_a, N_m and N_d. Of course, the total amount of CO_2 in the atmosphere, N_a is quite well known, but the division of the sea into two layers is somewhat arbitrary. It is of some interest to see how sensitive the solution is to a variation of N_m and N_d. Instead of chosin the values given in (22) we shall assume

$$\text{a)} \begin{cases} N_m = 0.8\ N_a \\ N_d = 60\ N_a \end{cases} \qquad \text{b)} \begin{cases} N_m = 2\ N_a \\ N_d = 59\ N_a \end{cases} \quad (32$$

We then obtain the values $n_a = 10.6\,\%$ and $n_a = 10.0\ \%$ respectively as compared with $n_a = 10.3\,\%$ previously, using $\tau_{a-m} = 5$ years and $\tau_{d-m} = 500$ years. Our solution is quite insensitive to the exact division of the ocean. However, the value of the total amount of carbon dioxide in the sea ($\approx 61\ N_a$) effects the solution more, but here we quite accurately know the actual amounts as just mentioned.

4. The exchange of radio-carbon between the atmosphere and the sea

REVELLE and SÜESS (1957) assume that the exchange of radio carbon between the atmosphere and the sea takes place independantly of changes in the distribution of inactive CO_2. If this were the case the decrease of the C^{14}/C^{12} ratio in the atmosphere since 1850, the Süess effect, would be a direct measure of the increase of the inactive CO_2 during the same time, since fossil fuel contains no C^{14}. As a matter of fact, they deduce an exchange coefficient for transfer of CO_2 from the atmosphere to the sea on this bases. As was indicated in the introduction this is not correct. The change of pH in the sea will shift the dissociation equilibrium also for the carbon dioxide containing C^{14}. We may assume an equilibrium rapidly being established and have

$$\frac{N_m^{*\prime}}{N_m^*} = \varkappa \frac{N_m'}{N_m} \tag{33}$$

where $\varkappa$ is dependant on the fractionation. If changes of N_m and N_m' occur as discussed in the previous section, we obtain by variation the following expression for the changes in N_m^* and $N_m^{*\prime}$

$$\frac{n_m^{*\prime}}{N_m^{*\prime}} - \frac{n_m^*}{N_m^*} = \frac{n_m'}{N_m} - \frac{n_m}{N_m} \tag{34}$$

Making use of (17) we obtain

$$\left.\begin{aligned} n_m^{*\prime} &= \frac{n_m^*}{N_m^*} N_m^{*\prime} + 11.5 \frac{n_m}{N_m} N_m^{*\prime} \\ &= B_2 n_m^* + B_3 n_m \end{aligned}\right\} \tag{35}$$

We see here clearly how a change of the total amount of CO_2 in the top layer of the ocean will influence the amount of radioactive carbon in the form of CO_2 and H_2CO_3 and therefore the partial pressure, which will mean that the equilibrium with the atmosphere is disturbed. Actually the amount of C^{14} in the form of undissociated CO_2 is much more influenced by changes in the *total* amount of CO_2 present in the water than by changes of the amount of *radioactive* carbon dioxide.

Corresponding to the system of equations in (16) we have the following set describing the transfer of radioactive carbon

$$\left.\begin{aligned} \frac{dn_a^*}{dt} &= -k_{a-m}^* n_a^* + k_{m-a}^* n_m^{*\prime} - \lambda n_a^* \\ \frac{dn_m^*}{dt} &= k_{a-m}^* n_a^* - k_{m-a}^* n_m^{*\prime} - \\ &\quad - k_{m-d} n_m^* + k_{d-m} n_d^* - \lambda n_m^* \\ \frac{dn_d^*}{dt} &= k_{m-d} n_m^* - k_{d-m} n_d^* - \lambda n_d^* \end{aligned}\right\} \tag{36}$$

Notice here that the exchange coefficients between the atmosphere and the sea are different from those used in equation (16) thereby taking into consideration the fractionation effect. Following CRAIG (1957) we have

$$\frac{k_{m-a}^*}{k_{a-m}^*} = \mu \frac{k_{m-a}}{k_{a-m}} = \mu \frac{N_a}{N_m'} \approx \frac{N_a}{N_m'} \tag{37}$$

where $\mu = 1/1.012 = 0.988$. The deviation of μ from unity will be completely irrelevant in the following discussion and we will therefore put $\mu = 1$ as indicated by the last expression in (37). We shall also put $k_{a-m}^* = k_{a-m}$ and thus neglect fractionation. For the exchange between the top layer of the ocean and the deep sea the exchange is the same as for inactive carbon with the assumption made that it is due to the motion of sea water only.

Introducing (35) into (36), taking into consideration (15) and (37) and rearranging terms we obtain

$$\left.\begin{aligned} \left(\frac{d}{dt} + k_{a-m} + \lambda\right) n_a^* - B_2 \alpha k_{a-m} n_m^* &= B_3 \alpha k_{a-m} n_m \\ - k_{a-m} n_a^* + \left(\frac{d}{dt} + B_2 \alpha k_{a-m} + \beta k_{d-m} + \lambda\right) n_m^* - k_{d-m} n_d^* &= -B_3 \alpha k_{a-m} n_m \\ - \beta k_{d-m} n_m^* + \left(\frac{d}{dt} + k_{d-m} + \lambda\right) n_d^* &= 0 \end{aligned}\right\} \tag{38}$$

We find thus that the changes of n_m appear as "driving forces" for the C^{14}-system. Knowing n_m as a function of time, we may calculate the changes that will occur in the distribution of radio carbon and thus also compute the Süess effect. The problem is implicit, however, since the distribution of n_m depends on k_{a-m} and k_{d-m} as shown in the previous section and our problem is therefore to find the particular pair of values that are in agreement with observed changes in the total amount of CO_2 in the atmosphere *and* the changes of the C^{14}/C^{12} ratio. Eliminating n_m^* and n_d^* from the equations (38) and in doing so taking account of the fact that $k_{a-m} \gg k_{d-m} \gg \lambda$ we obtain

$$\frac{d^3 n_a^*}{dt^3} + [(B_2\alpha + 1)k_{a-m} + (\beta + 1)k_{d-m}]\frac{d^2 n_a^*}{dt^2} + (1 + \beta + B_2\alpha)k_{a-m}k_{d-m}\left(\frac{dn_a^*}{dt} - n_a^*\lambda\right) =$$
$$= B_3\alpha k_{a-m}\left[\frac{d^2 n_m}{dt^2} + (\beta + 1)k_{d-m}\left(\frac{dn_m}{dt} + \lambda n_m\right)\right] \qquad (39)$$

Now $|n_m^{-1} dn_m/dt| \gg \lambda$ and we shall also assume that our solution n_a^* satisfies the same relation, which will be verified *a posteriori*. It means that the decay of C^{14} is unimportant for the discussion of the exchange between the atmosphere and the sea. We thus finally obtain

$$\frac{d^3 n_a^*}{dt^3} + [(B_2\alpha + 1)k_{a-m} + (\beta + 1)k_{d-m}]\frac{d^2 n_a^*}{dt^2} + (1 + \beta + B_2\alpha)\, k_{a-m}k_{d-m}\frac{dn_a^*}{dt} =$$
$$= B_3\alpha k_{a-m}\left[\frac{d^2 n_m}{dt^2} + (1 + \beta)k_{d-m}\frac{dn_m}{dt}\right] \qquad (40)$$

This equation is principally the same as eq. (18) and thus possesses a solution of the character given by (20) where now λ_1^*, λ_2^* and λ_3^* are solutions of an equation similar to (24). From the three equations (38) and with due regard to the expression for dn_m/dt given by eq. (16) we obtain the initial conditions

$$n_a^* = \frac{dn_a^*}{dt} = \frac{d^2 n_a^*}{dt^2} = 0 \qquad (41)$$

and similar expressions for n_m^* and n_d^* if we wish to study their variations. Introducing the expression for n_m given by equation (31) and solving for n_a^* we obtain with some simplifications similar to those done previously

$$\frac{n_a^*}{N_a^*} = Q_1\left[e^{rt} - 1 - \frac{r}{\lambda_2^*}(e^{\lambda_2^* t} - 1)\right] -$$
$$- Q_2\left[e^{\lambda_2 t} - 1 - \frac{\lambda_2}{\lambda_2^*}(e^{\lambda_2^* t} - 1)\right] \qquad (42)$$

where

$$\left.\begin{aligned} Q_1 &= \frac{[r + (1 + \beta)k_{d-m}]\, H}{r\,[r^2 + \{(B_2\alpha + 1)k_{a-m} + (1 + \beta)k_{d-m}\}\, r + (1 + \beta + B_2\alpha)k_{a-m}k_{d-m}]} \\ Q_2 &= \frac{[(1 + \beta)k_{d-m} + \lambda_2]\, H}{\lambda_2\,[\lambda_2^2 + \{(B_2\alpha + 1)\, k_{a-m} + (1 + \beta)\, k_{d-m}\}\, \lambda_2 + (1 + \beta + B_2\alpha)k_{a-m}k_{d-m}]} \end{aligned}\right\} \qquad (43)$$

having introduced the symbol H and λ_2^* according to

$$H = B_3\alpha\,\frac{\gamma_0}{r}\,\frac{k_{a-m}^2(r + k_{d-m})\, r}{r^2 + [(B_1\alpha + 1)k_{a-m} + (1 + \beta)k_{d-m}]\, r + (1 + \beta + B_1\alpha)\, k_{a-m}k_{d-m}} \qquad (44)$$

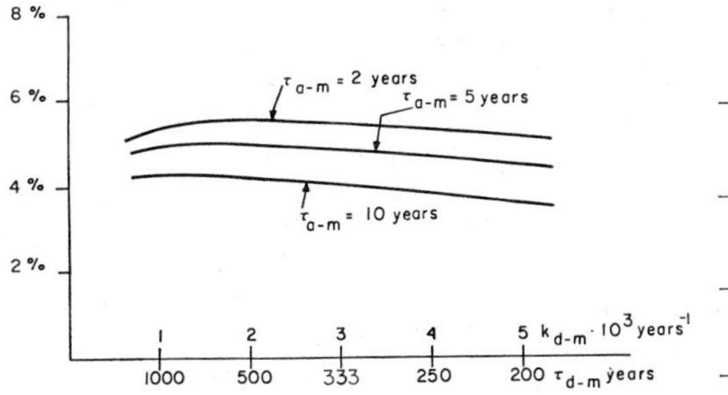

Fig. 2. The increase of C^{14} in the atmosphere in 1954 by a net transfer from the sea resulting from release of fossil CO_2 and a change of the dissociation equilibrium in the sea.

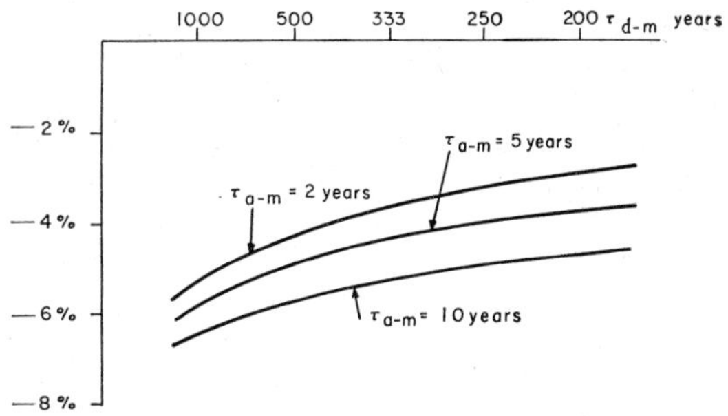

Fig. 3. The expected value of the Süess effect in 1954 for various rates of exchange between the atmosphere and the sea and within the sea.

$$\lambda_2^* = -\frac{(1+\beta+B_2\alpha)\,k_{a-m}\,k_{d-m}}{(1+B_2\alpha)\,k_{a-m}+(1+\beta)\,k_{d-m}} \qquad (45)$$

Figure 2 shows the values of n_a^* in 1954 when the total output of CO_2 into the atmosphere is estimated to have been 13.2 %. A more pronounced variation with the value of $\tau_{a-m}=k_{a-m}^{-1}$ is here obtained than was the case for n_a. This is easily understandable. The slower the exchange between the atmosphere and the sea takes place the less rapid is the response of the sea to changes of the CO_2 content of the atmosphere. If $\tau_{a-m}=0$ and $\tau_{d-m}=\infty$ obviously $12.5\times\left(\frac{n_m}{n_a}\right):\left(\frac{N_m}{N_a}\right)=1$ according to equation (17). Computing n_m from (31) and inserting we obtain here

$$12.5\cdot\frac{n_m}{n_a}\cdot\frac{N_a}{N_m}=\begin{Bmatrix}0.77\\0.73\\0.69\end{Bmatrix}\text{ for }\tau_{a-m}\begin{Bmatrix}2\text{ years}\\5\text{ years}\\10\text{ years}\end{Bmatrix} \qquad (46)$$

which values are almost independant of the value of τ_{d-m} in the range 200—1,000 years considered here. The changes of n_m are the "driving force" for changes in the C^{14} system and again the slower the exchange between the sea and the atmosphere is, the greater the lag of the C^{14} adjustment in the atmosphere relative to the sea becomes.

The results obtained from eq. (42) are again quite independant of the exact division of the ocean into two reservoirs. Making the computations with the values of N_a and N_m given in (32) yields values of n_a^* only a few tenths of a percent different from those shown in fig. 2.

By a comparison of the results given by eq. (31) and (42) we can compute the changes of the C^{14}/C^{12} ratio in the atmosphere, the "Süess effect". The result is shown in fig. 3. It is of special interest to compare these values with actually observed values. Süess' measurements give an average value of —1.7 % which may be considered representative for about 1946 (Revelle and Süess 1957). Broecker and Walton (1959) have found a value of —2.9 % for 1938, and a lower value of —1.8 % for 1954. The latter sample may, however, already have been influenced by the Castle tests in the Pacific early in 1954. Finally de Vries (1958) gives a value of —2.9 % for 1954. Summarizing these measurements a value of —2.5 to —3 % seems plausible for the Süess effect in 1954 before any appreciable amounts of C^{14} had been introduced into the atmosphere due to atomic bomb tests. More measurements from all over the world would, however, be desirable to determine this value more accurately. It is seen from fig. 3 that the computed value is somewhat larger particularly if the exchange between the three reservoirs is relatively slow.

Craig (1958) has given the value $\tau_{a-m}=5$ years as the most likely value for the exchange time between the atmosphere and the sea. It is obtained by studying the difference in the C^{14}/C^{12} ratio in the atmosphere and the sea with due regard taken to fractionation. It is furthermore assumed that the Süess effect is — 1.25 %, which seems to be an underestimate even if it is true that some of the values later reported perhaps are not truely representative. Chosing a value of — 3 % would yield a value of about 3 years. However, due to the fact that a net transfer of CO_2 from the atmosphere to the sea occurs at present $(N_a+n_a)\,(N_m+n_m)^{-1}$ is somewhat larger than would be the case in equilibrium. On the other hand a net transfer of C^{14} takes place from the sea to the atmosphere and therefore $(N_a^*+n_a^*)\,(N_m^*+n_m^*)^{-1}$ is smaller than in equilibrium. The deviations are larger the slower the

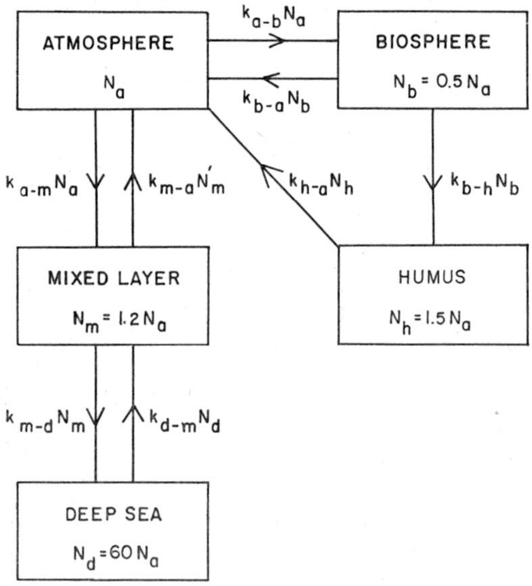

Fig. 4. Model of the CO_2 exchange between the deep sea, the mixed layer of the sea, the atmosphere, the biosphere and humus on land.

exchange between the atmosphere and the sea takes place. Thus the difference of the C^{14}/C^{12} ratio in the atmosphere and the sea (corrected for fractionation) should be larger in the equilibrium case than in the case where a net transfer occurs as indicated here.

It should be pointed out at this moment that similar deviations of the C^{13}/C^{12} ratios from the equilibrium values may occur if the net transfer of C^{13} and C^{12} are different. This is important since all C^{14} measurements are corrected for fractionation with the aid of the C^{13}/C^{12} ratio. Obviously such a procedure assumes equilibrium conditions. In the case of exchange between the atmosphere and the sea this need not be the case as we have shown above. It so happens, however, that the ratio C^{13}/C^{12} is almost the same in fossil fuel as in the atmosphere, the difference being only about 2 %. Thus no significant errors are therefore introduced in assuming equilibrium conditions.

With the model presented above one can now easily compute how large the deviations from equilibrium are which are due to the fact that a net transfer of both inactive and radioactive carbon occurs. The most likely value of the exchange time again becomes $\tau_{a-m} = 5$ years.

Measurements of C^{14} in the deep sea BROECKER (1957) and RAFTER and FERGUSSON (1958) in many cases indicate an age relative surface waters of 500 years or more and the interpretation of these values are not essentially influenced by considerations of the kind presented here. It is thus seen from fig. 3 that the computed value of the Süess effect should be around -5 % in comparison with the observed value of about -3 %. There may be many explanations for this discrepancy but first of all the accuracy of our model is not greater than it could be explained merely as due to this crudeness. Our assumption of a well-mixed deep sea is of course an unrealistic one and a more complete formulation of the problem in this respect seems very desirable. Secondly, we have completely neglected the effect of the biosphere on land. In view of the relatively small buffering effect of the sea the changes of the CO_2 (as well as $C^{14}O_2$) content of the atmosphere are here computed to be quite large. One may therefore very well expect that the biosphere also is influenced in some way (cf. ERIKSSON and WELANDER, 1956).

5. Estimates of the effect of CO_2 exchange between the atmosphere and the biosphere

The amount of carbon stored in the biosphere on land N_b is not very well known. Different estimates give values varying between 12 % (CRAIG, 1957) and about 85 % (ERIKSSON and WELANDER, 1956) of the amount present in the atmosphere. Estimates of dead organic matter, humus (N_h), also vary considerably, between values of 1.1 N_a to 1.7 N_a. For the following estimates we shall assume $N_b = 0.5\ N_a$ and $N_h = 1.5\ N_a$.

We may now extend our previous model of the CO_2-exchange in nature to the one depicted in fig. 4, which in case of equilibrium has been studied by CRAIG (1957). In complete anology with the previous analysis we obtain in the equilibrium case

$$\left.\begin{aligned} -k_{a-m}N_a + k_{m-a}N'_m - k_{a-b}N_a + {}& \\ + k_{b-a}N_b + k_{h-a}N_a &= 0 \\ k_{a-b}\,N_a - k_{b-a}N_b - k_{b-h}N_b &= 0 \\ -k_{h-a}\,N_h + k_{b-h}N_b &= 0 \\ k_{a-m}N_a - k_{m-a}N'_m - k_{m-d}N_m + {}& \\ + k_{d-m}N_d &= 0 \\ k_{m-d}N_d - k_{d-m}N_d &= 0 \end{aligned}\right\} \quad (47)$$

Again denoting the deviations from equilibrium due to fossil fuel combustion by n_i we obtain

$$\left.\begin{aligned}
&\frac{dn_a}{dt} + k_{a-m}n_a - k_{m-a}n'_m + k_{a-b}n_a - \\
&\qquad - k_{b-a}n_b - k_{h-a}n_h = \gamma(t) \\
&\frac{dn_b}{dt} - k_{a-b}n_a + k_{b-a}n_b + k_{b-h}n_b = 0 \\
&\frac{dn_h}{dt} + k_{h-a}n_h - k_{b-h}n_b = 0 \\
&\frac{dn_m}{dt} - k_{a-m}n_a + k_{m-a}n'_m + k_{m-d}n_m - \\
&\qquad - k_{d-m}n_d = 0 \\
&\frac{dn_d}{dt} - k_{m-d}n_m + k_{d-m}n_d = 0
\end{aligned}\right\} \quad (48)$$

It is hardly justified to carry through such a complete analysis here as presented previously in view of the fact that the assumptions made about the exchange processes between the atmosphere, biosphere and humus are more doubtful. An estimate shows, however, that $n_a \approx +7\%$ if we assume $\tau_{a-m}=5$ years, $\tau_{d-m}=500$ years, $\tau_{a-b}=30$ years and $\tau_{b-h}=30$ years compared with 10 % in the case of no net increased assimilation as a result of increased CO_2 content of the atmosphere.

Obviously the distribution of $C^{14}O_2$ between the various reservoirs also is influenced by an exchange with the biosphere and this would be the case even if no net increase of inactive CO_2 in the biosphere and in the humus has occurred. We can obtain a lower limit for the Süess effect if we assume an infinitely rapid adjustment of the C^{14} content between the four reservoirs, the atmosphere, the mixed layer of the sea, the biosphere and humus, i.e. the Suess effect is the same in all reservoirs and also considering that no C^{14} is supplied from the deep sea to these reservoirs. Since $N_m + N_a + N_b + N_h \approx 4\ N_a$ and since the exchange between the mixed layer and the deep sea is comparatively slow so that only a small part (0.02—0.04 N_a) of the fossil CO_2 released until 1954 ($\approx 0.13\ N_a$) has found its way into the deep sea we estimate that the Süess effect should be 2—2.5 %. As pointed out previously the observed Süess effect was about —3 % in 1954 which is in very good agreement with this estimate.

6. Forecast of the CO_2 changes in the atmosphere during the remainder of the 20th century

Certainly the estimates presented above are partly quite uncertain but it is of some interest to see what they imply with regard to future changes of the CO_2-content of the atmosphere. An upper limit is obtained if neglecting the exchange with the biosphere as done in section 4. A lower limit on the other hand is determined if an infinitely rapid exchange between the atmosphere and the biosphere takes place and obviously this would be equivalent to putting N_a equal to the sum of the CO_2 found in the atmosphere, the biosphere and the humus. Introducing the values for the various residence times as given in the previous section yields a forecast in between these two extremes. Fig. 5 shows the variations to be expected until year 2000 based on an output of CO_2 into the atmosphere as given by table 1. The most likely value for n_a at that time seems to be about + 25 %, it may possibly be larger but probably not exceed 40 %. These values are considerably larger than those estimated for example by REVELLE and SÜESS (1957). The implications with regard to the radiational equilibrium of the earth in such a case may be considerable but falls outside the scope of this paper.

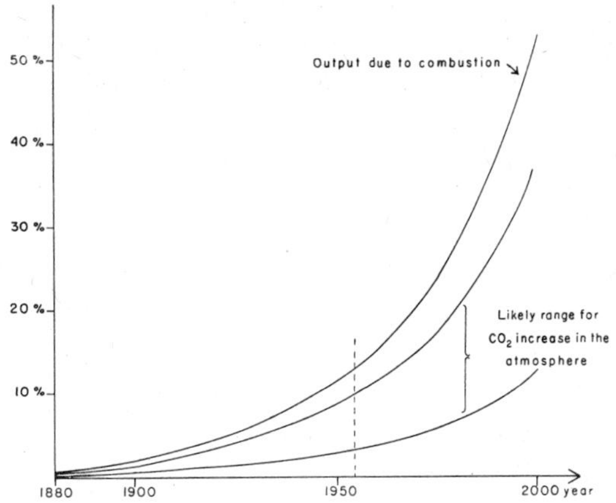

Fig. 5. Estimate of likely range for CO_2 increase in the atmosphere as a result of fossil fuel combustion according to UN estimates.

Fig. 5 also shows that the present increase of CO_2 in the atmosphere probably is 0.1—0.3 % per year. Recent measurements in regions far away from industrial areas such as Hawaii and the Antarctica (personal communication from Rakestraw) show remarkably constant values of the CO_2 content in the atmosphere throughout the year. It should therefore be possible within a few years to observe whether an increase occurs with this computed rate or not.

REFERENCES

ARNOLD, J. R. and ANDERSON, E. C., 1957: The distribution of carbon-14 in nature. *Tellus*, **9**, p. 28.

BRAY, J.R., 1959: An analysis of the possible recnt change in atmospheric carbon dioxide concentration. *Tellus,* **11** (in press).

BROECKER, W., 1957: Application of radiocarbon to oceanography and climate chronology. *Thesis Faculty of Pure Science, Columbia Univ.*

BROECKER, W. and WALTON, A., 1959: The geochemistry of C14 in the fresh water system. *Geochimica et Cosmochimica Acta* **16,** p. 15—38.

CALLENDAR, G. S., 1938: The artificial production of carbon dioxide and its influence on temperature. *Q. J. Roy. Met. Soc.*, **64**, p. 223.

CALLENDAR, G. S., 1958: On the amount of carbon dioxide in the atmosphere. *Tellus*, **10**, p. 243.

CRAIG, H., 1957: The natural distribution of radio carbon and the exchange time of carbon dioxide between atmosphere and sea. *Tellus*, **9**, p. 1.

CRAIG, H., 1958: A critical evaluation of radio carbon techniques for determining mixing rates in the oceans and the atmosphere. *Second United Nations International Conference for the Peaceful Uses of Atomic Energy,* Geneva (in press).

ERIKSSON, E., 1959: The circulation of some atmospheric constituents in the sea. *Rossby Memorial Volume.* Esselte, Stockholm, pp. 147—157.

ERIKSSON, E. and WELANDER, P., 1956: On a mathematical model of the carbon cycle in nature. *Tellus,* **8**, 155—175.

HARVEY, H. W., 1955: *The chemistry and fertility of sea waters.* Cambridge University Press.

RAFTER, T. A. and FERGUSSON, G. J., 1957: Recent increase in the C14 content of the atmosphere, biosphere and surface waters of the ocean. *N.Z. J. Science and Tech.*, B 38, p. 871.

RAFTER, T. A. and FERGUSSON, G. J., 1958: Atmospheric radio carbon as a tracer in geophysical circulation problems. *Second United Nations International Conference on the Peaceful Uses of Atomic Energy,* Geneva (in press).

REVELLE, R. and SÜESS, H., 1957: Carbon dioxide exchange between atmosphere and ocean and the question of an increase of atmospheric CO_2 during past decades. *Tellus*, **9**, p. 18.

(Manuscript received November 15, 1958)

Salinity and the Residence Time of Subtropical Oceanic Surface Water[1]

By R. B. MONTGOMERY[2]

Chesapeake Bay Institute, Johns Hopkins University, Baltimore 18, Md.

Abstract

The distribution of salinity over the ocean surface shows subtropical maxima of about 36.5 per mille, which exceeds the prevailing deep salinity (about 34.7 per mille) by a factor of 1 in 20. The thickness of the layer of high salinity is estimated as 200 m. The cause of the maxima is that evaporation locally exceeds precipitation, by about 1 m/yr. The implication of these values is that the residence time of the water in each region of high salinity is of the order of 10 years.

1. Qualitative considerations

The last few years have seen increased attention to the time of circulation in various oceanic circuits, to mixing time, and to the age of water since aeration at the sea surface. The present paper points out the fact that a time can be deduced from the degree to which the salinity of the subtropical ocean surface is increased by the local excess of evaporation over precipitation. WÜST (1920, 1954) has analyzed surface salinity in relation to the difference between evaporation and precipitation, but the significance of the observed magnitude of the salinity excess seems not to have been discussed. Clearly, the salinity excess reflects not only the evaporation-precipitation excess but also the sluggishness, or time, of the water movement. The time so obtained may be called *residence time* (see section 2).

Charts of surface salinity show a closed subtropical center of high salinity in each of four oceans—North Pacific, South Pacific, North Atlantic, South Indian—and a comparable center touching Brazil in the South Atlantic Ocean. (The North Indian Ocean is more peculiar and will not be considered.) Below the surface layer of high salinity and high temperature all water has lower salinity, lower temperature, and greater density. From each of the five separate centers a layer of high salinity extends equatorward beneath surface water of lower salinity and lower density.

The product of salinity excess, of density, and of depth of the layer of high salinity represents an excess of salt per unit area. This excess salt results from the evaporation of a certain thickness of sea water. This thickness would be achieved in a time that can be obtained from the rate of evaporation-precipitation difference. The resulting residence time is a measure of the mean duration of the water's residence in the region of excessive evaporation.

The mechanisms that tend to reduce the residence time by exchanging water with surrounding regions might be classified as horizontal and vertical mixing and horizontal convection. No attempt is made in the present paper to assess the relative contributions of these mechanisms. The actual conditions are complex, and it may be impossible to arrive at a clear interpretation of residence time.

It is seen that, regardless of how complex the circulation may be, and regardless of the precise interpretation of the result, a residence time can be computed from the following quantities, for all of which there are observations or estimates available: surface salinity, base salinity, thickness of layer of high salinity, excess of evaporation over precipitation.

---

[1] Contribution No. 37 from Chesapeake Bay Institute. This study was supported in part by the Office of Naval Research and by the National Science Foundation.

[2] Visitor at C.S.I.R.O. Division of Meteorological Physics, Melbourne, as Fulbright research scholar, 1958.

2. Assumed model

A rigorous formula for residence time can be derived by assuming a simplified model that retains some essential features of the natural conditions.

It is assumed that the subtropical oceanic surface layer behaves like a steady-state rigid reservoir filled with sea water that is kept homogeneous by mixing. The water in the reservoir has density ϱ and salinity s, and the depth of the reservoir is h, which is uniform. The rate of evaporation minus precipitation, dimensions length per time, is $E - P$, also uniform over the reservoir.

The outside water is assumed to have uniform salinity s_0. The water in the reservoir is renewed by inflow of outside water, the inflow balancing the sum of outflow and the much smaller evaporation-precipitation difference. The inflow is expressed in terms of the *renewal rate*, k, so defined that to mass M of sea water in the reservoir the mass $Mk\,\delta t$ of outside water is added in the short time δt. The time τ is now defined as the reciprocal of the renewal rate k. It is seen that the inflow in time τ equals, in mass, the contents of the reservoir. Furthermore, the average time that the inflowing molecules reside in the reservoir is τ, which, therefore, is called *residence time.*

If attention is focused on the particular molecules in the reservoir at any instant, the time τ is, as CRAIG (1957) has shown, the time for their concentration to decrease from unity to $1/e$ and is also the average over all these molecules of the time they will continue to reside in the reservoir. These molecules have already resided in the reservoir an equal average time, so their average total time of residence is 2τ. Thus, the time of residence is twice as great when averaged over the molecules resident at a given time as when averaged over the inflowing molecules.

For unit area of reservoir in time δt: The mass of sea water gained by inflow is $\varrho hk\,\delta t$, and the mass of salt gained is $s_0\varrho hk\,\delta t$. The mass of water lost across the sea surface is $\varrho_r(E-P)\delta t$, where ϱ_r is the density of pure water. The mass of sea water lost by outflow is

$$[\varrho hk - \varrho_r(E-P)]\,\delta t,$$

and the mass of salt lost by outflow is s times this expression.

The condition of salt balance requires that

$$s_0\varrho hk = s[\varrho hk - \varrho_r(E-P)].$$

Solution gives the formula for residence time,

$$\tau = \frac{1}{k} = \frac{\varrho}{\varrho_r}\,\frac{s-s_0}{s}\,\frac{h}{E-P},$$

in which the ratio of densities is practically unity.

3. Data and calculated residence time (Table 1)

Unlike the sharply defined conditions of the model, the natural conditions in the ocean are diffuse. How best to choose data poses problems; but precision is not sought, because the results are unavoidably rough. The present choice is admittedly arbitrary. Although, for surface salinity and evaporation-precipitation difference, mean values over a suitable subtropical area might be more suitable, maximum values are used, for simplicity, and this choice is partly justified because salinity excess and evaporation-precipitation difference occur as a ratio in the formula.

Surface salinity (s) is from SCHOTT's (1935; 1944) charts. The value used is that of the highest isohaline on each ocean.

The base salinity (s_0) adopted is the modal salinity for the entire volume of each ocean,

Table 1. Data and Calculated Residence Time

Ocean	s	s_0	$s-s_0$	h	$E-P$	$\tau = \frac{s-s_0}{s}\frac{h}{E-P}$
North Pacific.....	35.50 ‰	34.65 ‰	0.85 ‰	100 m	1.0 m/yr	2 yr
South Pacific......	36.50	34.65	1.85	230	1.0	12
North Atlantic....	37.25	34.95	2.30	375	1.0	23
South Atlantic....	37.25	34.65	2.60	190	1.5	9
South Indian......	36.00	34.75	1.25	170	1.0	6
averages..........	36.50	34.73	1.77	213	1.1	10

from COCHRANE (1958), POLLAK (1958), and MONTGOMERY (1958).

The layer thickness (h), like the base salinity, is subject to different interpretations depending on what mode of renewal is envisaged as dominant. One choice would be the depth of the nearly homogeneous surface layer; DEFANT's (1936, Abb. 64) chart of this depth over the Atlantic Ocean shows about 100 m at both subtropical salinity maxima. The values in Table 1, however, are the depths where, at the positions of the surface salinity maxima, the salinity has decreased to the average of s and s_0. The depths were determined from serial stations published in various sources.

Evaporation-precipitation difference ($E - P$) is from DIETRICH's (1957, Abb. 73) chart. The value used is that of the highest isopleth on each ocean. The chart represents an estimate based on various indirect sources of information.

4. Discussion

The mean value calculated for the residence time for all oceans is 10 years. The tentative interpretation of this result is that the mean time for a water particle to remain in the subtropical surface layer, without reaching high latitudes or the equatorial zone and without sinking to great depth, is roughly 10 years.

Some water of high salinity crosses the equator and, presumably, passes without much dilution from one high-salinity center to the opposite one. In particular, water of salinity exceeding 36.5 per mille is known to cross from the South Atlantic into the North Atlantic (DEFANT, 1936; DIETRICH, 1957, Abb. 197). The interpretation, therefore, must be relaxed to allow this partial leak between opposite high-salinity centers.

The variation in residence time computed for the different oceans represents, to considerable extent, the uncertainty of the results. It is unlikely, however, that the differences are due entirely to random error, and there is no reason to expect all five oceans to have equally sluggish subtropical water.

The exceptionally large computed time for the North Atlantic Ocean results from the exceptionally great layer thickness. This great thickness of the salty layer presumably results in part from inflow of salty South Atlantic water as already mentioned and from inflow of Mediterranean water. A residence time mentioned by SVERDRUP et al. (1942, p. 647) for the Mediterranean Sea is 75 years. The computed North Atlantic residence time must include some residence in the South Atlantic and in the Mediterranean. The residence time for the open North Atlantic itself can be expected not to differ much from the average value of 10 years.

The computed residence time of 2 years for the North Pacific center is so much below the others as to indicate a significant departure.

GILETTI and BAZAN (1957) obtain times of 5 years, 1 year, and 25 years relating to parts of the upper layers of the North Atlantic Ocean. These values are similar in order of magnitude to the present results.

CRAIG (1957) finds that the residence time of carbon in the oceanic mixed layer before transfer into the deep sea "is about 4 years" (p. 12) and "is most probably not more than 10 years, and almost certainly not more than 20 years" (p. 15). The downward flux of carbon is enhanced by the sinking of organic matter and may, therefore, be relatively much greater than the vertical flux of salt water. On the other hand, horizontal mixing and horizontal convection may be very effective in exchanging salt water between subtropics and lower latitudes, while the corresponding exchange of carbon may be negligible. (Exchange between subtropics and higher latitudes, where the deeper waters surface, must be important for both salt water and carbon.) It is seen that the mechanisms governing carbon are significantly different from those governing salinity, so the residence times need not be equal.

REFERENCES

COCHRANE, J. D., 1958: The frequency distribution of water characteristics in the Pacific Ocean. *Deep-Sea Res.*, **5**, 111—127 & plate.

CRAIG, HARMON, 1957: The natural distribution of radiocarbon and the exchange time of carbon dioxide between atmosphere and sea. *Tellus*, **9**, 1—17.

DEFANT, ALBERT, 1936: Die Troposphäre des Atlantischen Ozeans. Berlin, Verlag von Walter de Gruyter & Co., Wissenschaftliche Ergebnisse der Deutschen Atlantischen Expedition auf dem Forschungs- und Vermessungsschiff "Meteor" 1925—1927 herausgegeben von A. Defant, **6**, I Teil, Schichtung und Zirkulation des Atlantischen Ozeans, pp. 289—411 & plates.

DIETRICH, GÜNTER, 1957: *Allgemeine Meereskunde, eine Einführung in die Ozeanographie*. Berlin, Gebrüder Borntraeger, 492 pp. & plates.

GILETTI, B. J., and BAZAN, F., 1957: Near-surface ocean circulation from tritium measurements. Abstract. *Trans. Amer. geophys. Union*, **38**, 392.

MONTGOMERY, R. B., 1958: Water characteristics of Atlantic Ocean and of world ocean. *Deep-Sea Res.*, **5**, 134—148.

POLLAK, M. J., 1958: Frequency distribution of potential temperatures and salinities in the Indian Ocean. *Deep-Sea Res.*, **5**, 128—133.

SCHOTT, GERHARD, 1935: *Geographie des Indischen und Stillen Ozeans.* Hamburg, Verlag von C. Boysen, 413 pp. & plates.

— 1944: *Geographie des Atlantischen Ozeans.* 4. Auflage. Hamburg, Verlag von C. Boysen, 438 pp. & plates.

SVERDRUP, H. U., JOHNSON, M. W., and FLEMING, R. H., 1942: *The oceans, their physics, chemistry, and general biology.* New York, Prentice-Hall, 1087 pp. & 7 charts.

WÜST, GEORG, 1920: Die Verdunstung auf dem Meere. *Veröff. Inst. Meeresk. Univ. Berlin*, neue Folge, A, **6**, 95 pp.

— 1954: Gesetzmässige Wechselbeziehungen zwischen Ozean und Atmosphäre in der zonalen Verteilung von Oberflächensalzgehalt, Verdunstung und Niederschlag. *Archiv Meteor. Geophysik Bioklimat.*, Serie A, **7**, 305—328.

(Manuscript received April 11, 1958)

The Circulation of Some Atmospheric Constituents in the Sea[1]

By Erik Eriksson[2]
Department of Meteorology, The University of Chicago

Abstract

The meridional circulation of sea water causes corresponding meridional circulations of those atmospheric gases whose solubility in sea water are temperature dependant. The magnitudes of these atmospheric meridional circulations can be estimated from the poleward flux of water vapour and from oceanographic average data using a simple model of the meridional circulation of sea water. From available data the meridional carbon dioxide flux has been estimated to 2.5×10^{16} kg $\times$ year^{-1} which agrees roughly with the pressure differences sea water—air that have been measured. For fixed nitrogen available data give as result a net flux into the sea amounting to roughly 3 kg $\times$ ha^{-1} $\times$ year^{-1}, i.e. the same magnitude as in rain water.

It is shown that abrupt changes in the deep sea meridional circulation have but a small effect on the atmospheric carbon dioxide content and then only because of the gravitational transport of assimilated or precipitated carbon dioxide from the surface into the deep sea.

I. Introduction

Some years ago Buch (1939 a) pointed out that a general flow of carbon dioxide in the atmosphere must take place from equatorial regions to polar regions. He arrived at this conclusion from a close study of the physical properties of carbon dioxide in sea water, the solubility being rather temperature sensitive. Actually, this circulation if it takes place should not be unique for carbon dioxide but should be most obvious for this compound as it is very soluble in water compared to other gases.

One prerequisite for such a meridional transport is, of course, that there be a net transport of carbon dioxide in the sea from polar to equatorial regions either by mixing or by advection or by both. It is evident that either of these or both must exist, or else it would be impossible to relate the net evaporation in temperature and tropical regions to the surface salinity in the way Wüst (1954) has done. As net evaporation certainly represents a flow of water vapor from warm surface water regions to cold surface water regions and must be balanced by an equal net transport in the sea in the opposite direction, the same mechanism that transports the water must transport any other constituent. It therefore seems possible to use the net evaporation of the oceans to compute a transport function for the sea and then use this function for computing the atmospheric flux of other gaseous constituents in the atmosphere. In order to do this a relatively simple model of the sea will be used.

II. Theoretical approach

1. *A general model*

A remarkable feature of the sea is that the main mass of the water has an average temperature of around +3° C whereas a very thin layer between latitudes 40° N and 40° S has an average temperature of around +23° C. It seems therefore appropriate to divide the sea into three portions as outlined in fig. 1, one containing all warm surface waters, a second the rest of the surface waters, and a third containing the remaining part of the sea. The last reservoir is consequently completely isolated from direct communication

[1] This investigation was supported in part by research grants S-12 (C) and S-12 (C2) from the National Institutes of Health, PHS.

[2] On leave from the International Meteorological Institute in Stockholm, Sweden.

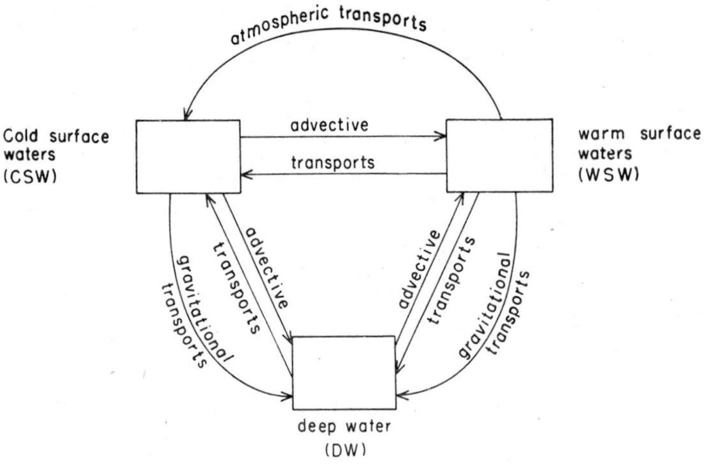

Fig. 1. General model of the circulation of atmospheric constituents in the sea.

with the atmosphere. Transports to and from this reservoir of atmospheric constituents can take place only by mixing and advection and in some cases by gravitational flow of particulate matter. As mixing can be regarded as a two-way advection it can be easily accounted for in the model as shown in fig. 1.

It is convenient to name the three reservoirs, the first being called Warm Surface Water, WSW, the second Cold Surface Water, CSW, and the third Deep Water, DW. Deep water is consequently used in a different sense than in oceanography.

Fig. 2 pictures the transport rates and directions in this general model. The advective transports are made proportional to the (factors k_i) amounts present in the reservoirs which, of course, is a mere definition, though useful as will appear later. The amounts are given by the symbols W', C', and D', used with primes throughout except for salt amounts where the primes will be dropped. The significance of this difference lies in the fact that the bulk sea salt has the simplest circulation in this model since both the atmospheric and the gravitational transports can be neglected.

It is seen that the total advective flow from each reservoir is split into two fractions, α being the fraction that goes in an anti-clockwise direction in the figure.

The atmospheric flux is given by the symbol F_a and for any specified constituent a superscript will be used like $F_a^{O_2}$ for the atmospheric transport of oxygen. The gravitational fluxes are given by the symbols βF_g and $(1 - \beta)_g F_g$ where β is the fraction of the total gravitational flux that originates in CSW. Superscripts are also to be employed here for any specific constituent.

Assuming steady state conditions for the circulation in fig. 2 the following equations are derived:

$$\alpha_1 k_1 C' - (1 - \alpha_2) k_2 D' + \beta F_g =$$
$$= \alpha_2 k_2 D' - (1 - \alpha_3) k_3 W' - (1 - \beta) F_g =$$
$$= \alpha_3 k_3 W' - (1 - \alpha_1) k_1 C' + F_a \qquad (1)$$

By elimination of C' or D' two useful expressions are arrived at:

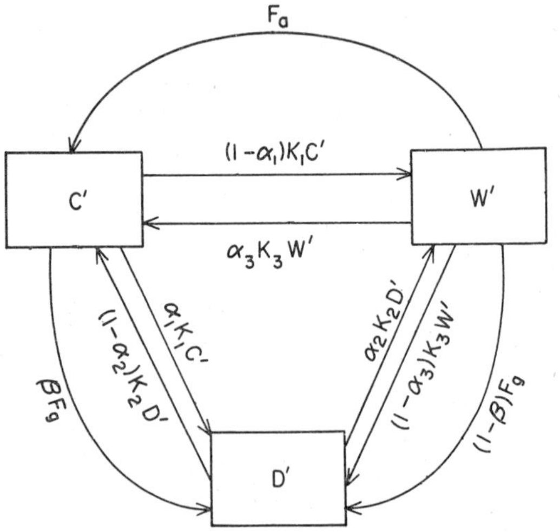

Fig. 2. Transport rates in the general model. W', C' and D' are amounts present in the reservoirs WSW, CSW and DW respectively. K_1, K_2 and K_3 are rate coefficients and α_1, α_2 and α_3 dimensionless constants giving the fractions of the total fluxes from the reservoirs which go in an anti-clockwise direction in the figure.

$$(\alpha_1\alpha_3 + 1 - \alpha_3)k_3W' = \\ = (\alpha_1\alpha_2 + 1 - \alpha_1)k_2D' - F_g + \alpha_1\beta F_g - \alpha_1 F_a \quad (2)$$

$$(\alpha_1\alpha_2 + 1 - \alpha_1)k_1C' = \\ = (\alpha_2\alpha_3 + 1 - \alpha_2)k_3W' - \alpha_2 F_g + (1 - \beta)F_g + F_a \quad (3)$$

These two equations will serve as a basis for further derivations.

2. *The flux of salt*

In the case of salt $F_a = F_g = 0$. Dropping the primes, one obtains

$$(\alpha_1\alpha_3 + 1 - \alpha_3)k_3W = \\ = (\alpha_1\alpha_2 + 1 - \alpha_1)k_2D = F_1 \quad (4)$$

$$(\alpha_1\alpha_2 + 1 - \alpha_1)k_1C = \\ = (\alpha_2\alpha_3 + 1 - \alpha_2)k_3W = F_2 \quad (5)$$

where F_1 and F_2 can be regarded as advective transport functions.

3. *The flux of water and the general case*

For water $F_g = 0$ and $F_a = E - P$ the net evaporation from WSW. Equations (2) and (3) give in this case:

$$(\alpha_1\alpha_3 + 1 - \alpha_3)k_3W' = \\ = (\alpha_1\alpha_2 + 1 - \alpha_1)k_2D' - \alpha_1(E - P) \quad (6)$$

$$(\alpha_1\alpha_2 + 1 - \alpha_1)k_1C' = \\ = (\alpha_2\alpha_3 + 1 - \alpha_2)k_3W' + E - P \quad (7)$$

Dividing through by equations (4) and (5) and rearranging gives the following expressions for the transport functions F_1 and F_2.

$$F_1 = \frac{\alpha_1(E - P)}{\left(\frac{D'}{D} - \frac{W'}{W}\right)_{H_2O}} \quad (8)$$

$$F_2 = \frac{E - P}{\left(\frac{C'}{C} - \frac{W'}{W}\right)_{H_2O}} \quad (9)$$

the subscript H_2O referring to the case when C', D', and W' stand for the water amounts in the reservoirs. It is obvious that the ratios $\frac{D'}{D}$, $\frac{W'}{W}$, and $\frac{C'}{C}$ can be interpreted as ratios of average mixing ratios of water and salt in the three reservoirs.

For any constituent A equations (2) and (3) can be rewritten using equations (4), (5), (8), and (9) to read

$$\alpha_1 F_a^A - \alpha_1\beta F_g^A + F_g^A = \alpha_1(E - P)Q_{D,W}^A \quad (10)$$

$$F_a^A - \alpha_2 F_g^A + (1 - \beta)F_g^A = (E - P)Q_{C,W}^A \quad (11)$$

where the symbol $Q_{D,W}^A$ stands for

$$\left(\frac{D'}{D} - \frac{W'}{W}\right)_A \bigg/ \left(\frac{D'}{D} - \frac{W'}{W}\right)_{H_2O}$$

and the symbol $Q_{C,W}^A$ stands for

$$\left(\frac{C'}{C} - \frac{W'}{W}\right)_A \bigg/ \left(\frac{C'}{C} - \frac{W'}{W}\right)_{H_2O}$$

These two equations show that in the case of a constituent that is completely conservative in DW ($F_g = 0$) the atmospheric flux is simply related to the net evaporation and is independent of the values of the α's. As to the gravitational transports F_g^A, they can be expressed by eliminating F_a^A from equations (10) and (11), and become:

$$F_g^A = \frac{\alpha_1(E - P)}{\alpha_1\alpha_2 + 1 - \alpha_1}[Q_{D,W}^A - Q_{C,W}^A] \quad (12)$$

which shows that they are strongly dependent upon the choice of the α's.

4. *The circulation of oxygen*

Oxygen is not conservative in DW as it is slowly consumed in the decomposition of organic material, carried down from the surface by gravitational forces. It is, however, possible to account for this consumption as a negative gravitational flux which obviously is related to the gravitational flux of carbon dioxide in organic matter. Assimilation of carbon dioxide takes place in the surface, with concomitant formation of molecular oxygen. If the decomposition of this organic matter took place in the surface, the amount of oxygen formed during the assimilation would be consumed. If, however, the assimilated carbon dioxide is separated from the oxygen formed and is carried down to deep water by gravitational forces, there will be an excess of oxygen on the surface. On a steady state basis there will be one oxygen molecule left in the surface layer for every oxygen molecule consumed in the deep water by decomposing organic matter. Therefore it will appear as if oxygen were brought from the deep water to the surface by some other mechanism than advectional flows. Obviously, this "negative gravitational flux" of oxygen from DW to the surface is related to the actual gravitational flux of assimilated carbon dioxide by means of the respiratory coefficient. From the study of the oxygen circulation we are consequently able to estimate the gravitational flux of carbon dioxide. This is actually of great advantage because oxygen data are far more abundant than carbon dioxide data.

The gravitational flux of oxygen is given by equation (12), and the atmospheric flux obtained by combining equations (11) and (12) becomes:

$$F_a^{O_2} = (E-P)\cdot \left[\frac{1-\alpha_1\beta}{\alpha_1\alpha_2+1-\alpha_1} Q_{C,W}^{O_2} - \frac{\alpha_1(1-\alpha_2-\beta)}{\alpha_1\alpha_2+1-\alpha_1} Q_{D,W}^{O_2}\right] \tag{13}$$

5. *The circulation of carbon dioxide*

Carbon dioxide has the most complicated circulation pattern in the present model as well as in nature. Apart from advectional transports there are two kinds of gravitational transports to consider. One of these has already been discussed, namely the downward flux of assimilated carbon dioxide in organic particulate matter. If R is the respiratory coefficient this flux is apparently $-RF_g^{O_2}$ and consequently $-\beta RF_g^{O_2}$ derives from CSW and $(1-\beta) RF_g^{O_2}$ from WSW.

The other gravitational flux is due to sinking particulate matter containing calcium carbonate. This process takes place from WSW and also causes a downward flux of alkalinity, when the calcium carbonate is redissolved in DW. For every equivalent of calcium released by dissolution of calcium carbonate 0.5 moles of carbon dioxide is set free.

The magnitude of this inorganic gravitational flux of carbon dioxide can thus be calculated from the gravitational flux of alkalinity. In the circulation of alkalinity $F_a^{alk} = 0$ and $\beta = 0$ as all the gravitational flux is supposed to come from the WSW. Using equation (10) under these circumstances gives:

$$F_g^{alk} = \alpha_1(E-P)Q_{D,W}^{alk} \tag{14}$$

and the corresponding flux of carbon dioxide is therefore 0.5 F_g^{alk}

The total gravitational flux to be accounted for becomes:

a) From CSW: $-\beta RF_g^{O_2}$

b) From WSW: $-(1-\beta)RF_g^{O_2} + 0.5 F_g^{alk}$

Equation (10) can be written

$$\alpha_1 F_a^A + \beta F_g^A + (1-\beta)F_g^A - \alpha_1\beta F_g^A = = \alpha_1(E-P)Q_{D,W}^A$$

so in the case of carbon dioxide

$$\alpha_1 F_a^{CO_2} - \beta RF_g^{O_2} + \alpha_1\beta RF_g^{O_2} - (1-\beta)RF_g^{O_2} + + 0.5\, F_g^{alk} = \alpha_1(E-P)Q_{D,W}^{CO_2}$$

or

$$F_a^{CO_2} = (E-P)Q_{D,W}^{CO_2} + \frac{(1-\alpha_1\beta)R}{\alpha_1} F_g^{O_2} - 0.5\, F_g^{alk}$$

Finally, using equations (12) and (14)

$$F_a^{CO_2} = (E-P)\left[Q_{D,W}^{CO_2} + \frac{(1-\alpha_2\beta)R}{\alpha_1\alpha_2+1-\alpha_1}\cdot (Q_{D,W}^{O_2} - Q_{C,W}^{O_2}) - 0{,}5\, Q_{D,W}^{alk}\right] \tag{15}$$

It should be noted that the effect of the constants α_1 and α_2 is limited to the second term in the brackets. As will appear later there are strong reasons to believe that α_1 is small while α_2 may be near unity. This will reduce the effect of these two constants very markedly.

6. *Other compounds*

Evidently, similar expressions can be set up for other compounds in the atmosphere that are known to circulate through the sea. As an example the flux of heavy water HDO could be computed if the average concentrations in WSW and DW were known. The flux of this compound would be completely independent of the choice of the α's. Rare gases very probably show a similar flux which should be easily computed if information existed on their average concentrations in WSW and DW. Carbon-14 offers an opportunity to compute the α's if data existed. In this case the decay of the isotope in DW could be accounted for by a non-advective flux of carbon-14 from DW to CSW and WSW in the same way as for oxygen because on a steady state basis one carbon-14 must enter the surface from the atmosphere for every carbon-14 disappearing in DW.

Another element of interest in atmospheric chemistry is fixed nitrogen. A computation of its circulation will be done later from existing data even though such a computation has only a tentative value. It has to be based upon the circulation of phosphorus within the sea and on certain estimates of the N/P ratio of sea water as a whole and of plankton, the latter representing the composition of WSW. The derivations of the appropriate expression are of no special interest, however, and will be omitted.

III. Calculations

1. *Data used*

All data used in the computations are assembled in table 1. Net evaporation is obtained from WÜST (1954) using his values for 5° zones between 40° N and 40° S in his table 1. This is the region where net evaporation is positive with some exceptions near the equator. From the same table the average salinity of WSW was obtained by weighting each 5° zone value according to the zonal area, again using the data between 40° N and 40° S. For CSW salinity the data in the same table were used with some modification. Apparently due to melting ice at very high latitudes—observations are mostly made during the summer months when melting is strong—the surface salinities become far too low. Salinity values from these areas were therefore estimated by extrapolation from the linear relation between surface salinity and net evaporation found by WÜST for the main area of the sea. Also in this case the average for CSW was obtained after proper weighing.

Table 1. Data used in the computations

	WSW	DSW	DW
Salinity $kg \cdot kg^{-1}$	0.03525	0.03405	0.03465
Oxygen $mmol \cdot l^{-1}$	0.22	0.29	0.17
Total carbon dioxide $mmol \cdot l^{-1}$	2.080	—	2.317
Carbonate alkalinity $mval \cdot l^{-1}$	2.245	—	2.376
Phosphorus $\mu g \cdot l^{-1}$	—	—	50
N/P	7.0	—	6.8
Net evaporation $kg \cdot year^{-1}$	7.3×10^{16}	—	—
Area cm^2	2.5×10^{18}	1.0×10^{18}	—

$\beta = 0.29 \quad \alpha_1 = 0.1 \quad \alpha_2 = 1.0 \quad R = 0.7$

C:P in organic matter in WSW = 100:2.4.

When concentration is expressed per litre no correction has been made for the effect of density in the computations.

Deep water salinity was estimated from the horizontal maps of the Atlantic published by WÜST & DEFANT (1936), from *Carnegie* data in the Pacific (SVERDRUP et al., 1944) and from three stations in the Indian Ocean listed by SVERDRUP et al. (1942, p. 746), properly weighed according to the volumes of these oceans.

The estimates of the average oxygen are not as good as those of the salinities, but as the relative differences are very large the accuracy obtained in the calculations is perhaps just as good as the accuracy when using the salinity estimates. For CSW a value of 6.5 ml. l^{-1} has been chosen. This is equivalent to 0.29 mmol. l^{-1}. The average for DW estimated from a table listed by SVERDRUP et al. (1942, p. 746) when weighed becomes about 0.18 mmol.l^{-1}. Considering, however, that intermediate waters are generally lower in oxygen than deep waters, a figure of 0.17 was chosen. For WSW, three north-south sections in the Atlantic published by WATTENBERG (1939b) give 0.217 mmol.l^{-1} for the surface between 40° N and 40° S. The average for all oceans must therefore be close to 0.22 mmol. l^{-1}.

Carbon dioxide and alkalinity averages were obtained entirely from the data[1] (BRUNEAU et al. 1953) which no doubt represent the most accurate and extensive modern set of data on the carbon dioxide system in the sea. The way the total carbon dioxide was computed from their data is the standard procedure described by HARVEY (1955) using tables prepared by BUCH (1951) and listed by Harvey. As the *Albatross* pH values were corrected for depth a recorrection to surface pressure had to be done. Carbonate alkalinity was obtained from the published total alkalinity using the corrections for ionized boric acid calculated by BUCH (1951) and given by HARVEY (loc. cit.).

The *Albatross* data are mainly from equatorial regions. This fact does not seriously affect the DW averages but may bias the WSW average for total carbon dioxide. A way of correcting this was, however, found by using Wattenberg's

[1] This refers to the Swedish Deep Sea Expedition with MS *Albatross*, 1947—48.

Meteor-data (WATTENBERG, 1933) on temperature and pH. Assuming a constant specific alkalinity the total carbon dioxide divided by the carbonate alkalinity can be expressed as a function of temperature and pH (the salinity influence being small). Values of this function are tabulated by HARVEY (l.c.) and were used for computing the total carbon dioxide from the *Albatross* data. It was found from Wattenberg's data that if this function was plotted against temperature a linear relation existed between 0° C and 27° C. As the average temperature for the surface *Albatross* data was 27.7° C while that for WSW is 23.3° C the linear relation mentioned above showed that the *Albatross* value had to be corrected by about 12 %; the correction being, of course, positive.

As to phosphorus the average for DW used is close to the average for the North Atlantic (cf. RILEY, 1951, p. 86). The N/P ratio for sea water has been estimated by COOPER (1938) and that for phytoplankton by FLEMING (1940).

It remains now to discuss some probable values of α_1 and α_2 which appear in the equations derived. In the model used DW represents almost entirely deep and bottom waters, the influence of intermediate waters being small. It is known that an appreciable part of the deep water is formed in a small area in the northwest Atlantic where it has a salinity close to 34.9 per mille, which is fairly high. Judging from the oxygen concentrations in the deep waters this North Atlantic deep water seems to move south, enter the Indian Ocean and then the Pacific, being gradually mixed with less saline waters which probably originate as high latitude bottom water. The apparent age of the North Atlantic deep water has been estimated to be about 600 years from recent carbon-14 measurements (BROECKER et al., 1957). This is, as a matter of fact, the age that could be expected from the salinity distribution of surface water in the North Atlantic and the net evaporation between the equator and 40° N in the Atlantic, assuming that no intermediate water is formed in the North Atlantic. If the age of 600 years is accepted this requires a sinking of about 1.4×10^{16} kg salt per year. In order to get the proper salinity in the model only half of this can come from CSW, the rest must come from WSW. Now, from the salinity data listed one would expect the total salinity flux from CSW to be about 7×10^{16} kg per year provided α_2 is around unity, i.e. neglecting mixing between DW and CSW (cf. equations 5 and 9). As the requirement seems to be that only one tenth of this should go into DW, α_1 should be close to 0.1. Thus only one tenth of the total flow from WSW to CSW returns via DW. The circulation is, in other words, rather superficial, taking part mainly in the upper few hundred meters.

In the calculation of the atmospheric fluxes the constants α_1 and α_2 enter in the factor $f = \dfrac{1 - \alpha_1\beta}{\alpha_1\alpha_2 + 1 - \alpha_1}$. The value of this factor for various likely combinations of α_1 and α_2 is given in table 2. It is seen that f on the whole is rather insensitive to varying values of α_1 and α_2.

Table 2. The factor $f = \dfrac{1 - \alpha_1\beta}{\alpha_1\alpha_2 + 1 - \alpha_1}$ for different combinations of α_1 and α_2

α_2	α_1			
	0.1	0.2	0.3	0.4
1.0	0.97	0.94	0.91	0.88
0.8	0.99	0.98	0.97	0.96
0.6	1.01	1.02	1.03	1.05
0.4	1.03	1.07	1.11	1.16

2. *The atmospheric flux of oxygen*

With the data given $Q^{O_2}_{C,W}$ becomes 2.2 and $Q^{O_2}_{D,W}$ — 2.7. Using equation (13) the atmospheric flux works out to 13.7×10^{16} mmol. year^{-1}. Converted into volume at STP it becomes 3.1×10^{12} m$^3 \cdot$ year^{-1}. Compared to the total amount in the atmosphere this is a very small quantity.

It is seen from equation (13) that if α_2 were less than unity the flux would be increased. This can be easily understood; in this case oxygen is carried into DW from CSW by mixing. The figure arrived at may therefore represent a minimum rate.

3. *The atmospheric flux of carbon dioxide*

Using a respiratory coefficient of 0.7 which is that to be expected when complete decomposition of plankton occurs, equation (15) gives for $F_a^{CO_2}$

$$F_a^{CO_2} = 7.3 \times 10^{16}(16.1 - 3.3 - 4.9) =$$
$$= 5.8 \times 10^{17} \text{ mmol} \cdot \text{year}^{-1}.$$

The maximum uncertainty in the middle term where α_1 and α_2 enters (for the limits given in table 2) is about 15 per cent. In absolute measure it is $\pm 0.4 \times 10^{17}$ mmol. year^{-1}, and is thus less than 10 per cent of the calculated flux.

Table 3. Calculated P_{CO_2} in surface sea water from Albatross data

Station No.	Lat.	Long.	$P_{CO_2} \times 10^4$	Station No.	Lat.	Long.	$P_{CO_2} \times 10^4$
	Atlantic				*Pacific (cont)*		
325	15° 53′ N	25° 27′ W	3.9	105	7° 38′ S	152° 53′ W	5.3
326	13° 37′ N	25° 55′ W	5.4	108	2° 01′ S	152° 16′ W	6.2
327	11° 12′ N	26° 24′ W	5.3	111	0° 02′ N	153° 07′ W	7.0
330	7° 53′ N	24° 43′ W	3.2	113	2° 06′ N	149° 49′ W	9.2
332	5° 45′ N	21° 43′ W	3.6	115	4° 04′ N	149° 42′ W	8.1
333	3° 48′ N	20° 32′ W	6.8	116	5° 47′ N	149° 42′ W	5.8
335	2° 06′ N	20° 07′ W	3.4	119	8° 43′ N	148° 36′ W	5.1
336	0° 43′ N	18° 52′ W	13.0	121	11° 25′ N	149° 33′ W	4.3
337	0° 03′ S	18° 13′ W	4.7	130	8° 40′ N	169° 28′ W	3.7
354	0° 06′ N	34° 91′ W	4.9	133	5° 00′ N	172° 02′ W	5.7
373	28° 05′ N	60° 49′ W	4.0				
400	43° 04′ N	19° 40′ W	3.2				
	Pacific				*Indian Ocean*		
55	2° 44′ S	92° 45′ W	6.5	200	11° 01′ S	88° 26′ E	5.3
58	1° 04′ N	93° 20′ W	5.7	202	8° 26′ S	88° 16′ E	3.9
59	2° 10′ N	95° 30′ W	6.6	204	6° 26′ S	88° 53′ E	4.4
60	3° 18′ N	97° 44′ W	5.6	205	4° 47′ S	88° 18′ E	4.5
62	4° 33′ N	100° 07′ W	6.8	206	2° 33′ S	88° 19′ E	4.8
63	5° 42′ N	101° 41′ W	3.9	207	0° 01′ S	88° 18′ E	4.2
65	6° 21′ N	103° 42′ W	5.0	208	1° 56′ N	88° 12′ E	4.7
67	7° 38′ N	106° 17′ W	3.9				
69	8° 22′ N	108° 00′ W	4.8				
70	9° 14′ N	109° 39′ W	4.5				
72	10° 35′ N	112° 05′ W	6.3				
74	11° 39′ N	114° 15′ W	6.9				
76	13° 20′ N	117° 58′ W	6.2				
77	14° 13′ N	120° 25′ W	6.4				
78	15° 40′ N	123° 21′ W	6.4				
80	17° 46′ N	126° 51′ W	4.6				

If converted into grams the atmospheric flux becomes

$$F_a^{CO_2} = 2.5 \times 10^{16} \text{ g} \cdot \text{year}^{-1}$$

It is possible to calculate the pressure head needed to drive this amount of carbon dioxide through the surfaces of WSW and CSW using the residence time (7 years) of atmospheric carbon dioxide estimated by CRAIG (1957). As the carbon dioxide content of the atmosphere is $0.46 \text{ g} \cdot \text{cm}^{-2}$ the exchange rate with the sea must be $\frac{0.43 \times 5.1}{7 \times 3.6} = 0{,}0931 \text{ g} \cdot \text{year}^{-1} \cdot \text{cm}^{-2}$. If the average pressure head for this exchange is 3.2×10^{-4} atm the rate of exchange becomes 291 $\text{g} \cdot \text{year}^{-1} \cdot \text{cm}^{-2} \cdot \text{atm}^{-1}$. The pressure head over the WSW surfaces then becomes 0.34×10^{-4} atm and that over the CSW surfaces 0.85×10^{-4} atm.

There are practically no comparisons made at low latitudes on the pressure of carbon dioxide in surface water and in the atmosphere. It is, however, possible to calculate the carbon dioxide pressure in the surface water samples from the Albatross cruise, again using a table prepared by BUCH (1951) and given by HARVEY (l.c.). Table 3 shows the calculated pressures for the three oceans. If is seen that the values are in general well above the normal atmospheric value. There is also a systematic variation revealed in the eastern Pacific where a minimum seems to exist around 7° N.

The Atlantic values can be compared to a

couple of determinations of atmospheric carbon dioxide on samples taken along a cruise from South America to Sweden by a passenger ship in the early part of 1957.[1] Surprisingly high values were encountered west of North Africa. One sample was taken on the equator on around 28° W and contained 3.64×10^{-4} atm of carbon dioxide. The position is not far from the *Albatross* station 354 the data of which give a partial pressure of carbon dioxide in the surface water of 4.9×10^{-4} atm. The second atmospheric value is from about 12° N and 24° W and amounts to 5.07×10^{-4} atm. The nearest *Albatross* station is 326 with a calculated partial pressure in the surface water of 5.4×10^{-4} atm. Even though the measurements are widely separated in time they show a pressure head in the water of the right order of magnitude.

WATTENBERG (1933) has calculated the partial pressures of carbon dioxide at the *Meteor*-stations. His surface values seem to be low when compared to the Swedish values. Actually, the atmospheric data mentioned above agree most excellently with Wattenberg's values calculated for 100 metres depth.

For high latitude the excellent work by BUCH (1939 a) in the North Atlantic and adjoining seas provides valuable information on the negative pressure head of carbon dioxide in cold surface waters. On two voyages between Europe and North America Buch made regular observations on the atmospheric carbon dioxide pressure and on the partial pressure in the surface water. The voyages took place along a common route for ocean liners that follows approximately an average isotherm of the surface water. Furthermore, it is quite near the 40° N parallel so one would not expect any spectacular effect. The average negative pressure head for the trip between Skagen and Boston in June 1935 is 0.45×10^{-4} atm and for the trip New York—Copenhagen in September 1935 is 0.21×10^{-4} atm. From still higher latitudes BUCH (1939 b) has data from a trip between North Norway and North Spitzbergen. The average pressure deficiency found on this trip is 0.45×10^{-4} atm. This is, however, in the branch of the Gulf Stream that penetrates into the Arctic Basin. He found that real cold sea water had the expected partial pressure of around 1.5×10^{-4} atm.

In Antarctic waters no direct comparison between the partial pressures of air and surface water has been made. WATTENBERG's (1933) data show fairly high partial pressures in the water but these data are, as pointed out before, not quite reliable. DEACON (1940) summarizes computed data on the partial pressure of carbon dioxide in Antarctic waters; they are also fairly high. It would be highly desirable to obtain more recent data on the carbon dioxide system in the sea from these latitudes.

4. *The nitrogen balance of the sea*

The role of the sea in the circulation of fixed nitrogen in nature is an old problem. The first investigator who seems to have made a serious effort to discuss this is probably SCHLOSING (1875) who made a very attractive picture of the circulation of fixed nitrogen in nature. Nitrogen in ammonia and nitrate was brought to the soil by precipitation where part of it was taken up by the plants and later returned to the soil and all was leached out from the soil as nitrate. This latter was carried by river waters to the sea where it was converted to ammonia. The physicochemical properties of sea water were, however, such that it could not retain ammonia which therefore escaped into the air, and was precipitated over land to close the cycle. Losses occurring in the soil due to denitrification were made up by inorganic fixation of nitrogen in the atmosphere by lightning discharges. This was a brave idea at a time when geochemistry was poorly known, and must have been very stimulating. His theory was hardly ever accepted as much evidence existed against it. When more reliable information was gathered on the nitrogen compounds in the sea it was seriously discredited, and nobody seems to have made any effort to make a more satisfactory picture of the circulation of nitrogen compounds in the sea on a similar basis as Schlosing's. Very recently, however, the question of the nitrogen balance in the sea has been taken up by EMERY et al. (1955). They have shown that if fixed nitrogen is added to the sea in precipitation at a rate of the same order of magnitude as over land there must be a process going on in sea water that removes this excess, keeping a balance in the nitrogen circulation of the sea. The problem as seen by them is thus viewed from a different angle; if ammonia is not given off from the sea denitrification must occur.

It may be of interest to see how the present model pictures the circulation of fixed nitrogen in the sea. The data given in table 1 are sufficient

[1] I am indebted to Mr S. Fonselius, Institute of Meteorology, Stockholm, Sweden, for making these data available.

for such a calculation when the carbon dioxide circulation is given, and if it is assumed that all, or, practically all nitrogen and phosphorus in the WSW is bound in organic living matter. The way to attack the problem is to calculate the total phosphorus concentration in WSW, basing it on a circulation that excludes any atmospheric flux of phosphorus but includes the gravitational flux by organic particulate matter. This can also be expressed as the flux of carbon dioxide in sinking organic matter times the concentration of phosphorus in this organic matter.

The $F_g^{CO_2}$ is given by $-0.7\, F_g^{O_2}$ and becomes

$$F_g^{CO_2} =$$

$$= -0{,}7(E-P)\frac{\alpha_1}{\alpha_1\alpha_2 + 1 - \alpha_1}(Q_{D,W}^{O_2} - Q_{C,W}^{O_2})$$

and that for phosphorus, using equation (10)

$$F_g^{P} = (E-P)\frac{\alpha_1}{1-\alpha_1\beta}Q_{D,W}^{P}$$

Now as $F_g^P = R_P F_g^{CO_2}$ where R_P is the P/CO_2 ratio in organic matter

$$Q_{D,W}^{P} = -\frac{0{,}7\, R_P(1-\alpha_1\beta)}{\alpha_1\alpha_2 + 1 - \alpha_1}[Q_{D,W}^{O_2} - Q_{C,W}^{O_2}]$$

which also shows that the influence of the α's is small. From $Q_{D,W}^P$ the ratio $\left(\frac{W'}{W}\right)_P$ in WSW can be calculated. Using the listed data one finds $\left(\frac{W'}{W}\right)_P = 75 \times 10^{-5}\, g \cdot kg^{-1}$ compared to $\left(\frac{D'}{D}\right)_P = 144 \times 10^{-5}\, g \cdot kg^{-1}$. It is thus seen that WSW is strongly depleted in phosphorus relative to DW, which, of course, is due to the gravitational transport and the fact that phosphorus is so strongly involved in the biological processes in the sea.

Now using the ratios of N/P given in table 1 the following ratios for fixed nitrogen are arrived at

$$\left(\frac{D'}{D}\right)_N = 980 \times 10^{-5}\, g \cdot kg^{-1}$$

$$\left(\frac{W'}{W}\right)_N = 525 \times 10^{-5}\, g \cdot kg^{-1}$$

For computing the atmospheric flux F_a^N equation (10) can be used, relating F_g^N to F_g^P by the N/P ratio in sinking organic matter which most probably consists of zooplankton with a N/P ratio of 7.4 (Fleming, 1940). Again it is noticed that the influence of the α's is small. The final computation gives $F_a^N = -7.7 \times 10^{13}\ g \cdot year^{-1}$ which means that this amount has to be added to WSW in order to keep a steady state. The fact that it has to be added is simply because the ratio of N/P used for WSW is larger than that for DW. If this ratio had been smaller, fixed nitrogen would have had to leave the WSW and go to the atmosphere. The only possible way it could leave the WSW is in the form of ammonia but the physico-chemical conditions in the sea together with the low ammonia concentrations observed do not favor such a process. It is actually much easier physically to account for an addition of fixed nitrogen to the sea surface by ammonia and nitrate in precipitation. If the amount that has to be added is converted into a different unit it can be expressed as $3.1\ kg \cdot ha^{-1} \cdot year^{-1}$ (1 ha equal to $10^4\ m^2$). This is surprisingly close to the amount that can be expected to be delivered by precipitation yearly. Of course, one should not exclude the possibility that some ammonia may leave the sea surface but it is probably quantitatively small compared to that in precipitation.

The calculations above are tentative in the sense that the N/P ratios used are far from accurate. But it is interesting that when used in this model they lead to the same question as raised by Emery et al. (l.c.), namely, how to dispose of the added nitrogen in the sea. It is probable that just as much is added to CSW per unit area, so about $10^{14}\ g \cdot year^{-1}$ has to be denitrified in the sea. Emery et al. shows that this denitrification hardly can be done in the bottom sediments alone so it has apparently to be done in the water, which being an aerated medium, is not a favorable location for such a process. The only possibility is then that there are organisms that can carry out denitrification inside their bodies. It may be possible that at least in some species denitrification occurs as a by-product in the normal reduction of nitrate to ammonia which has to be carried out in the assimilation of nitrate by plants. It has been shown recently by investigations on argon and nitrogen in a lake that denitrification must take place because the nitrogen-argon ratio was greater than the value one would calculate from the atmospheric ratio and the solubilities.[1]

[1] Personal communication by Prof. S. Oana, Chem. Institute, Nagoya University, Japan.

In these experiments the nitrogen was determined volumetrically so no distinction could be made between molecular nitrogen and another possible denitrification product, nitrous oxide, N_2O. Nitrous oxide has been shown to form in all soils (ARNOLD, 1954) and is present in the atmosphere in a comparatively high concentration (cf. GOODY 1954, p. 77). If this gas is formed in sea water it would be easy to establish whether or not denitrification takes place. If, however, molecular nitrogen is formed, it would be extremely difficult to establish this process.

While speculating, another interesting aspect of this problem should be discussed. Is the addition of fixed nitrogen from the atmosphere a process that has gone on for geologic times and has this process, coupled with a corresponding denitrification and the physical circulation of sea water, determined—by adaptation—the present N/P ratio in plankton? Stretching the imagination further, is it responsible for the present arrangement of nucleoproteins in plants and animals? It would not be unreasonable to believe. After all, fixation of molecular nitrogen in the atmosphere into chemically active compounds is a process that has been known for long time even though quantitative aspects of this process have been and are still lacking.

IV. Non-steady state conditions

When dealing with circulations in nature it is common to start with a steady state approach because of the enormous simplification of the problem achieved in this way. Of course, the validity of this approach can always be questioned but it is a general experience in natural sciences that it is possible to regard circulations as steady state phenomena and, if the effect of unsteady conditions is of interest, to treat these as small perturbations of the steady state.

In the present model, the data suggest a rather rapid superficial circulation of the sea between cold and warm regions and a sluggish deep water circulation. Fluctuations in the rapid part of the circulation can hardly have any noticable time lag effect on the atmospheric transports. The response of these would be almost momentary, i.e. their fluxes would follow the flux of water without any time lag. Consequently, one would not expect any noticeable variations in the atmospheric concentrations of carbon dioxide due to variations in the rate of the upper water circulation.

As to deep water, changes in its circulation rate cannot be expected to influence the atmospheric concentrations of gases that show a simple circulation path, i.e. that are only advectively transported. In fact, the effect of perturbations in this case would be even less, since rates of change of the deep water circulation most likely would never reach such magnitudes as rates of change of the upper water circulation. In the case of gases that can be transported by gravitational forces the effect upon the atmospheric concentration would be much more noticeable because the gravitational transport is at least formally independent of the advective transports. As an extreme example one can assume the deep sea circulation to behave like a square wave function. This case can be chosen because WORTHINGTON (1954) has recently postulated a discontinuous formation of deep water in the North Atlantic, the main bulk of the present deep water being formed during a few years of catastrophic cold in the early 19th century. What would happen if a short period of rapid circulation of deep water was followed by a long period of almost no motion? During the latter period organic particulate matter would sink down at a more or less constant rate, thereby increasing the total carbon dioxide content of deep water while depleting the atmosphere. The atmospheric content would show a slow decrease. Likewise the oxygen content of DW would decrease, and the phosphorus content of the surface water would be slowly depleted. If now a catastrophic formation of deep water should take place an equal volume of water that sinks must come up to the surface where it would lose its accumulated carbon dioxide rapidly, causing a rapid increase in the atmospheric carbon dioxide. Rapid increases in the atmospheric carbon dioxide content followed by slow decreases are therefore characteristics of such a mode of formation of deep water. REVELLE and SUESS (1957) have actually touched the effect of changes in the deep water circulation when they point out that a change in the organic matter content of the sea affects the atmospheric content of carbon dioxide. However, they do not consider specifically the gravitational transport as a means of increasing the organic matter content of the sea and think that it is the rate of decomposition in the sea which is important. This is highly unlikely to be the case. Once organic matter is brought to the surface and into a warmer environment it would rapidly decompose. It is only the rate at which it is brought to the surface either as organic or inorganic carbon dioxide and the rate at which it is brought down into deep water in sinking organic particulate matter that counts.

There are, however, some limits to the accumulation of carbon dioxide in the deep water by gravitational flux. The limiting factor of greatest importance is the phosphorus in the surface water. When this becomes depleted no further gravitational transport of organic carbon dioxide into the deep water can take place. At present there seems to be around 25 micrograms per litre of phosphorus in WSW as calculated from the oxygen distribution and the deep water phosphorus concentration. If this was carried into DW in assimilated organic matter it would decrease the carbon dioxide content in WSW by only 0.09 mmol $\cdot$ l^{-1}. This is only about 4 per cent of the carbon dioxide concentration in WSW. Further, as the amount of carbon dioxide in the surface above the thermocline is about equal to that in the atmosphere (cf. CRAIG, 1957), the total effect of decreasing the deep sea circulation to nil (including mixing) would be a decrease in the atmospheric carbon dioxide content of about 3.5 per cent. It is seen that even such a drastic change in the deep sea circulation would not have any pronounced effect upon the atmospheric carbon dioxide content. It is therefore highly unlikely that the relatively rapid increase in the atmospheric carbon dioxide during the last fifty years can be attributed to changes in the deep sea circulation.

The discussion above may seem to be highly speculative, but it can be concluded that fluctuations in the deep water circulation can affect the atmospheric carbon dioxide concentration only because of the gravitational transport of assimilated carbon dioxide from the surface to the deep water, and then only to a very limited extent.

REFERENCES

ARNOLD, P. W., 1954: Losses of nitrous oxide from soil. *J. Soil Sci.*, **5**, 116.

BROECKER, W. S., EWING, M., GERARD, R., HEEZEN, B. C., and KULP, J. L., 1957: Deep ocean circulation patterns in the Atlantic Ocean based on carbon-14 data. *Proc. UGGI-meeting*, Toronto 1957.

BRUNEAU, L., JERLOV, N. G., and KOCZY, F. F., 1953: Physical and chemical methods. *Rep. Swedish Deep-Sea Expedition.* 1947—48, **3**, 99.

BUCH, K., 1939 a: Beobachtungen über das Kohlensäureaustausch zwischen Atmosphäre und Meer im Nordatlantischen Ozean. *Acta. Acad. Åbo. Math. and Phys.*, **11**, No. 9.

— 1939 b: Kohlensäure im Atmosphäre und Meer an der Grenze zum Arcticum. *Ibid.*, **11**, No. 12.

— 1951: Das Kohlensäuregleichgewichtssystem im Meerwasser. *Havsforskningsinstitutets Skrifter*, Helsingfors No. 151.

COOPER, L. H. N., 1938. Redefinition of the anomaly of the nitrate-phosphate ratio. *J. Mar. Biol. Assn. U.K.* **23**, 179.

CRAIG, H., 1957: The natural distribution of radiocarbon and the exchange time of carbon dioxide between atmosphere and sea. *Tellus*, **9**, 1.

DEACON, G. E. R., 1940: Carbon dioxide in the Arctic and Antarctic seas. *Nature*, **145**, 250.

EMERY, K. O., WILSON, L. ORR., and RITTENBERG, S. C., 1955. Nutrient budgets in the ocean. *Essays in the natural sciences in honor of Captain Allan Hancock*, p. 299.

FLEMING, R. H., 1940: Composition of plankton. *Proc. 6th Pac. Sci. Congr.*, **3**, 535.

GOODY, R. M., 1954: *The physics of the atmosphere.* Cambr. University Press, p. 77.

HARVEY, H. W., 1955: *The chemistry and fertility of sea waters.* Camb. University Press.

REVELLE, R., and SUESS, H. E., 1957: Carbon dioxide exchange between atmosphere and ocean and the question of an increase of atmospheric CO_2 during the past decades. *Tellus*, **9**, 18.

RILEY, G. A., 1951: Oxygen, phosphate, and nitrate in the Atlantic Ocean. *Bull. Bingh. Oceanogr. Lab. Coll.*, **13**, 1.

SCHLOSING, T., 1875. Sur les lois des échanges d'ammoniaque entre les mers, l'atmosphère et les continents. *Compt. Rend.*, **81**, 81.

SVERDRUP, H. U., JOHNSON, M. W., and FLEMING, R. H., 1942: *The oceans.* Prentice-Hall Inc., New York.

SVERDRUP, H. U., FLEMING, J. A., SOULE, F. M., and ENNIS, C. C., 1944: *Observations and results in physical oceanography on the last cruise of Carnegie. Oceanography* I-A.

WATTENBERG, H., 1933: Das chemische Beobachtungsmaterial und seine Gewinnung. *Wiss. Erg. Atl. Exp. "Meteor"*. **8**.

— 1939 a: Die Verteilung des Sauerstoffs im Atlantischen Ozeans. *Ibid.*, **9**.

— 1939 b: Atlas zu: Die Verteilung des Sauerstoffs im Atlantischen Ozean. *Ibid.*, **9**. Atlas.

WORTHINGTON, L. V., 1954: A preliminary note on the time scale in North Atlantic circulation. *Deep-Sea Res.*, **1**, 244.

WÜST, G., and DEFANT, A., 1936. Atlas zur Schichtung und Zirkulation des Atlantischen Ozeans. *Wiss. Erg. Atl. Exp. "Meteor"*. **6**: Atlas.

WÜST, G., 1954: Gesetzmässige Wechselbeziehungen zwischen Ozean und Atmosphäre in der zonalen Verteilung von Oberflächensalzgehalt, Verdunstung und Niederschlag. *Arch. Met. Geophysik u. Bioklimatologie.* Ser. A, **7**, 307.

(Manuscript received December 19, 1957)

Meteorological Aspects of Oxidation Type Air Pollution

By M. Neiburger

Department of Meteorology, University of California, Los Angeles

Abstract

The replacement of coal by petroleum products as an energy source, instead of eliminating air pollution, has led to a new type of air pollution characterized by the presence of oxidizing substances, chiefly ozone, and the occurrence of eye irritation, damage to vegetation, and reduction to visibility. It has been shown that photochemical reactions involving hydrocarbons and nitrogen dioxide in concentrations of a few parts per million can produce all these manifestations.

The photochemical reactions require the combination of (1) sources of the reagents, (2) conditions which prevent their dispersal, and (3) adequate solar radiation. The tremendous concentrations of automobile traffic, the exhaust from which is estimated to contain seven per cent of the hydrocarbons put into the fuel tank, in all metropolitan centers in the U.S. constitute sources which are at least as large as industrial sources (refineries). However, only on the subtropical west coasts of continents do the meteorological conditions for accumulation of pollutants, namely persistent light winds and temperature inversions, occur consistently together with adequate solar radiation. The outstanding example of this combination is Los Angeles, California.

Studies of the relationship of air trajectories to the smog manifestations in Los Angeles are presented. These studies demonstrate the contribution of automobile exhaust as a principal source.

The traditional problems of air pollution have been concerned principally with the products of coal combustion, namely carbon soot and sulfur dioxide, and also the effluents from smelters and other industrial operations, which usually involve the same contaminants. In the United States, and to a lesser extent in the world as a whole, petroleum products have been playing an increasing role as the source of energy. In the United States (Figure 1) the use of petroleum products and natural gas has increased rapidly and they now exceed coal as an energy source, although not on a tonnage basis (Figure 2). Together with the more efficient use of coal, this might be expected to decrease the amount of air pollution, but in fact, air pollution problems have been increasing, or at least they have been receiving increased attention throughout the world.

The fact that pollution is not uniquely associated with coal burning economies is stressed by the fact that Los Angeles, California, where coal has not been used for many years, has replaced Pittsburgh, Pennsylvania, as the pollution capital of the United States, and is competing with London, England for the world title. It is now recognized that this new type of pollution, associated with a petroleum economy, is closely related to the consumption of gasoline by the tremendous number of automobiles in Los Angeles county—now over 2,700,000—and is coming to be felt in other cities where motor traffic reaches high enough levels.

Figure 3 shows the consumption of motor fuel in the United States during the past 25 years. The increase since World War II has been at a much higher rate than previously, with the present consumption almost three times the pre-war level. About 10 per cent of the country's total is consumed in California, and over one-half of that in Los Angeles county. The current consumption in Los Angeles is about 6,000,000 gallons a day.

The burning of gasoline in internal combustion motors is carried out at relatively low air-fuel ratios, in contrast to the burning of natural gas and fuel oil, the fuels used in the Los Angeles

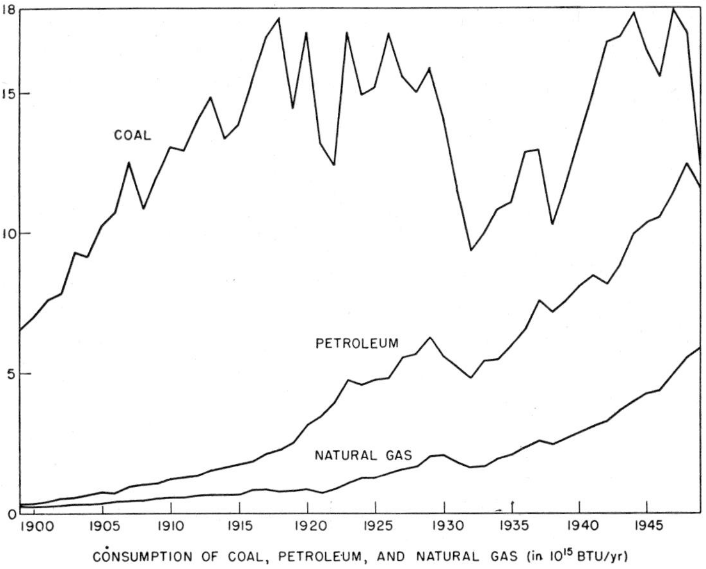

Fig. 1. Energy equivalent of coal, petroleum and natural gas consumed annually in the United States 1899—1949 (BTU/yr) (Data from American Petroleum Institute, "Petroleum Facts and Figures", 9th edition, 1950, 11th edition, 1953).

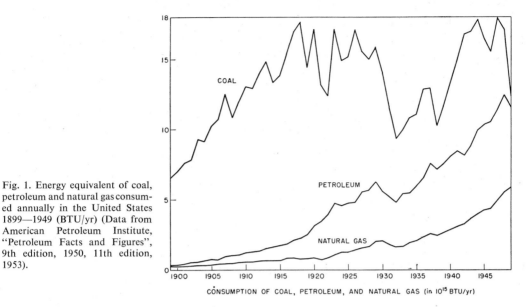

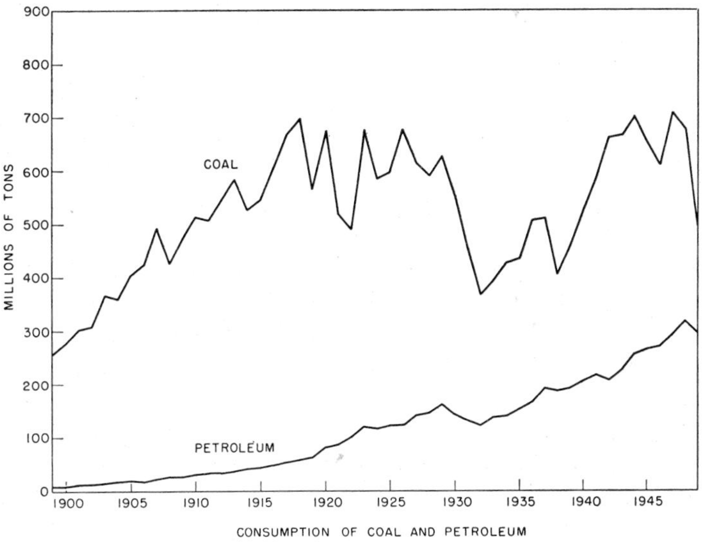

Fig. 2. Annual consumption of coal and petroleum in the United States 1899—1949 (ton/yr). (See Figure 1 for source of data.)

Basin for heat and power, in which an excess of air is normally present. The gasoline consumption in the Los Angeles Basin is roughly twice the amount of fuel oil burned.

That the use of petroleum and natural gas instead of coal as a fuel for heat and power should be expected to result in a decrease in the amount of pollution may be seen from Table 1. The particulates from boilers using oil total about one-tenth of those from boilers using coal, while from gas-burning boilers the amount is completely negligible. Sulfur dioxide, on the other hand, is given off in almost as large quantities from petroleum burning as from the burning of coal.

When eye irritation and plant damage first manifested themselves in Los Angeles sulfur dioxide was immediately suspected as the responsible agent, in spite of the fact that measured concentrations generally were much lower than the

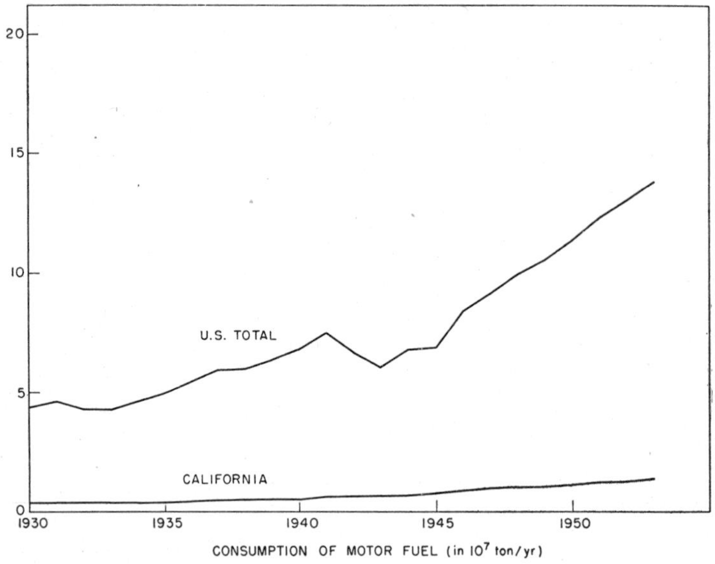

Fig. 3. Annual consumption of motor fuel in the United States 1930—1953. (See Figure 1 for source of data.)

thresholds for irritation and damage. The first step taken in control of atmospheric pollutants was the requirement that chemical plants and refineries reduce their emission of sulfur dioxide into the air. This resulted in a reduction by more than 50 per cent of the total sulfur dioxide emission in the Basin, but no noticeable reduction in the smog manifestations took place.

Table 1. Comparison of Contaminants from Combustion of Coal, Oil, and Natural Gas (Industrial Boilers) (in lbs/10^7 BTU)

	Coal[1]	*Oil*[2]	*Gas*[2]
Particulates			
Carbon smoke	10.6	1.26	
Fly ash (minerals) ..	3.5	0.31	
Sulfuric anhydride .	—	0.34	0.14
Phosphoric anhydride..........	—	0.02	
Gaseous Contaminants			
Sulfur dioxide	24.4	17.5	0.02
Sulfur trioxide	—	0.02	0
Nitrogen oxides	—	8.5	4.7
Aldehydes	—	0.3	0.5
Organic acids	—	0.2	0.02
Hydrocarbons......	—	0.1	—
Chlorides	2.4	—	—

[1] Data for coal from A. R. MEETHAM (1952).
[2] Data for oil and gas from C. V. KANTER, R. G. LUNCHE, and A. P. FUDURICH (1957).

Table 2 shows the measured concentrations of aerosol and vapor phase pollutants in the Los Angeles atmosphere, as measured in downtown Los Angeles in 1954, together with the intensities of smog manifestations. Since the meteorological conditions on smoggy days are unfavorable for dispersion of pollutants, the concentrations of all the contaminants are higher than on clear days. However, the maximum values of neither the oxides of sulfur nor the aldehydes were high enough to explain the eye irritation and plant damage.

Most striking is the concentration of oxidant. This name is given to the totality of oxidizing substances which are measured by the normal chemical means for testing for ozone (such as release of free iodine from a buffered solution of potassium iodide). It has been shown by other analytical procedures that a large proportion of the oxidant is ozone, but other oxidizing substances are present also. The presence of ozone in concentrations of almost one-half part per million was indeed surprising, since all previous reported values near the earth's surface were about one-twentieth part per million or less.

The explanation of eye irritation and plant damage came when HAAGEN-SMIT (1952) showed that these effects could be reproduced in the

Table 2. Pollutants and Smog Manifestations in Downtown, Los Angeles, 1954[1]

A. Gaseous pollutants pphm, August—November, 1954

Pollutant	Average	Maximum
Aldehydes	22	70
Carbon Monoxide	960	4,300
Hydrocarbon	36	160
Oxidant	13	42
Oxides of Nitrogen	16	30
Sulfur Dioxide	10	23

[1] Data from: RENZETTI, N. A., ED. (1955).

B. Particulate pollutants $\mu g/m^3$, October, 1954

Pollutant	Average	Range
Arsenic	0.01	0—0.03
Beryllium	0.0002	<0.0001—0.0007
Chloride (Cl^-)	1.92	0.21—3.10
Copper	0.50	0.22—1.18
Fluoride (F^-)	0.72	
Iron	5.0	2.4—8.4
Lead	7.5	3.1—13.8
Magnesium	6.9	0.6—13.6
Manganese	0.21	0.09—0.40
Nitrate (NO_3^-)	22.9	2.7—96.0
Organic Matter (Benzol extractable)	80.0	22.4—165.0
Phosphate (PO_4^{---})	1.43	0—4.23
Polycyclic Hydrocarbon	7.1	2.5—17.8
Potassium	3.7	1.5—6.6
Silver	< 0.001	0—0.0014
Sodium	5.2	1.5—8.5
Strontium	0.10	0—0.28
Sulfate (SO_4^{--})	38.9	1.0—154.5
Tin	0.01	<0.01—0.05
Titanium	0.23	0.06—0.55
Vanadium	0.034	0.022—0.060
pH of water extract	4.8	3.7—6.5

C. Smog Manifestations August—November, 1954

	Average	Maximum	Percentage of Days
Eye Irritation (Scale of 0—55)	19	38	27[1]
Damage to Vegetation (Scale of 0—10)	0.72	3.6	88[2]

[1] Percentage of days with Eye Irritation index greater than 25.
[2] Percentage of days with plant damage.

laboratory by the interaction of ozone with hydrocarbons occurring in gasoline. The presence of ozone was explained by his demonstration (HAAGEN-SMIT, 1953) that irradiation of mixtures of nitrogen dioxide and hydrocarbons produced ozone and plant damage. Subsequent tests have confirmed that irradiation of hydrocarbons and nitrogen dioxide in concentrations observed in the Los Angeles atmosphere result in the production of ozone, eye irritation, plant damage, and reduction of visibility.

The mechanisms of the photochemical reaction have not yet been identified precisely. Various sets of reactions have been proposed, one of which by H. S. JOHNSTON (1956) is as follows: Nitrogen dioxide, which forms rapidly by the oxidation of the nitric oxide formed during high temperature combustion either in stacks or in automobile engines, is dissociated by the absorption of sunlight, releasing oxygen atoms. Some of these oxygen atoms react with oxygen molecules to form ozone, while others react with hydrocarbons and water vapor to form OH ions and free radicals. The OH ions further react with other hydrocarbon molecules to form other free radicals and water. Interaction of the free radicals with oxygen and with hydrocarbons result in formation of organic peroxides and ozone, as well as other free radicals. The free radical chains continue to be propagated until there is a collision of two free radicals. The ozone reacts with the nitric oxide to form nitrogen dioxide once more.

The irradiation also produces a reduction of visibility. In Haagen-Smit's experiments using ozone and high hydrocarbon concentrations a visible cloud is produced in the flask. This matter has been studied in the Air Pollution Foundation's 500 cubic foot irradiation chamber at the Southern California laboratories of the Stanford Research Institute. DOYLE and RENZETTI (1957), using a photo-electric photometer and particle counter, found that the transmissivity is greatly reduced during radiation, with an increase in the number of particles less than 0.4 microns in equivalent diameter. GOETZ (1958), using a centrifugal aerosol spectrometer which separates particles down to 0.1 micron, showed that this increase of particles between 0.3 and 0.4 microns may be largely due to growth of pre-existing smaller ones, possibly by condensation of products of the photochemical reaction.

Thus all of the smog manifestations: eye irritation, reduced visibility, and plant damage can be attributed to the photochemical reaction products of nitrogen dioxide and hydrocarbons.

Initially the main source of the hydrocarbons was thought to be losses at the refineries during the production and storage of gasoline, while oxides of nitrogen are produced in all high temperature combustion, as we have seen in Table 1. The refineries in Los Angeles county have been required to install control measures which have reduced their hydrocarbon losses to the atmosphere from about 800 tons per day to 150 tons per day.

While these installations were in progress, it became increasingly recognized that an equal or larger source of hydrocarbons in the atmosphere is the automobile traffic, which uses internal combustion engines operating at air-fuel ratios which insure incomplete combustion. Table 3, taken from FAITH (1957), shows the constituents of auto exhaust under various operating conditions. During the deceleration phase of operation, which occurs as much as 20 per cent of the time in city stop-and-go driving, up to 60 per cent of the supplied fuel comes out of the exhaust in the form of unburned hydrocarbons. Averaged for all phases of city driving, about 7 per cent of the hydrocarbons in the fuel finds its way into the atmosphere. At the same time, an adequate supply of nitric oxide is put into the air during the acceleration and cruising phases to insure the availability of the reagents for the smog reaction.

That the oxidant is a result of photochemical reaction is confirmed by its diurnal variation. Figure 4 shows the diurnal variation on a typical smoggy day (August 30, 1955) as measured by release of iodine from a buffered solution of potassium iodide. The oxidant has a low value until sunrise, after which it increases rapidly to a maximum shortly before noon. In the afternoon it decreases rapidly but with some variation in rate, apparently due to advection of pollution. For comparison, the dotted curve in Figure 4 shows the average diurnal variation for the period July 15—November 15, 1955. Although the average for the entire period has a maximum of 25 parts per hundred million instead of the approximately 50 parts per hundred million on a day of intense smog, the general characteristics of the diurnal variation are the same.

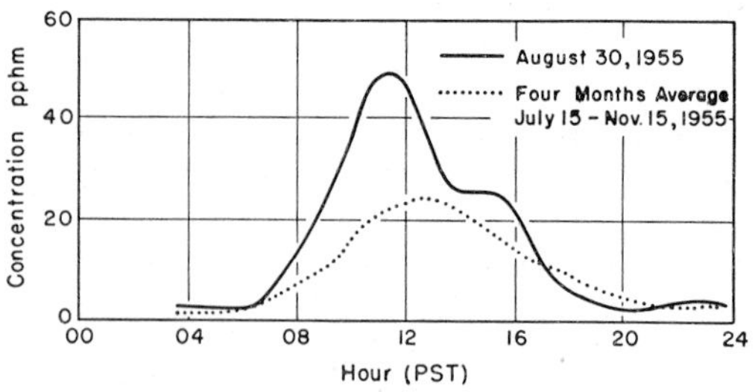

Fig. 4. Diurnal variation of oxidant on a typical smoggy day and average diurnal variation for July 15—November 15, 1955. (From RENZETTI and ROMANOVSKY, 1956.)

The diurnal variation of the oxides of nitrogen shows quite a different behavior. Except for a peak at about 8 a.m., apparently due to the morning rush hour automobile traffic, the values are low during the day and high during the night.

Table 3. Effect of Engine Operating Conditions on Composition of Auto Exhaust

	Idle	Acceleration	Cruising	Deceleration
Air-fuel ratio	11 : 1—12.5 : 1	11 : 1—13 : 1	13 : 1—15 : 1	11 : 1—12.5 : 1
Engine speed (rpm)	400—500	400—3,000	1,000—3,000	3,000—400
Air flow (cfm)	6—8	30—35	15—35	6—8
Cylinder vacuum (in. Hg)	16—20	0—7	7—19	20—25
Exhaust analysis:				
CO (%)[1]	4—6	0—6	1—4	2—4
NO (ppm)	10—50	1,000—4,000	1,000—3,000	10—50
Hydrocarbons (ppm)	500—1,000	50—500	200—300	4,000—12,000
Unburned fuel (per cent of supplied fuel)	4—6	2—4	2—4	20—60

[1] The concentrations of carbon-monoxide have been revised on the basis of later information provided by Dr. Faith.

We now turn to the more specifically meteorological aspects of this type of smog. It is clear that for smog which is produced by a photochemical reaction to occur in high concentrations it is necessary that the meteorological conditions favoring slow dispersion should occur together with intense sunshine. The conditions which deter the diffusion and advection of pollutants are (1) light winds and (2) temperature inversions. These occur generally under anticyclonic conditions at night and in winter. Thus most of the serious smog incidents of the traditional type have occurred during the winter. However, at least in high latitudes, solar radiation is reduced during the winter because of the low angle of the sun, and thus the other essential ingredient for oxidation type smog, namely intense sunshine, is absent. During the warm months of the year when the sun is sufficiently high to provide the necessary radiation, inversions are infrequent in most regions.

The exception is the subtropical west coasts of continents, where the inversions associated with the subtropical high pressure areas are present. These inversions are present both day and night throughout the warm season, and occasionally during the rest of the year. As an indication of the characteristics of the one over the North Pacific Ocean, Figure 5 shows a cross-section of average temperature conditions at various levels from San Francisco to Honolulu. The inversion is lowest at the coast, and slopes upward, first rapidly then more slowly, from about 400 meters at San Francisco to about 2,000 meters at Honolulu. Its thickness is not far from constant, but the temperature increase through the inversion is largest just off the coast, where it exceeds 8° C, and drops to about 2° C over Honolulu. Thus, all along the California coast, there is an intense inversion which acts as a lid on upward dispersion, with an average height of about 400 meters. When the inversion is below its average height smog is likely to be intense in areas of concentrated human activities, such as Los Angeles and San Francisco.

The presence of the inversion as a deterrent to the dispersion of contaminants is reinforced by characteristic light winds in the area. These winds may be characterized as a weak monsoon, i.e., seasonal flow from the cool ocean to the heated continent, on which a moderate land-sea breeze is superposed. Figure 6 shows the flow pattern in Los Angeles at the time of maximum sea breeze on a typical day. The streamlines show the flow of air eastward across the basin from the coast, with speeds ranging from 8 to 16 mph. Figure 7 shows the flow pattern at sunrise the following morning. This pattern is representative of the flow prevailing throughout the night, with velocities below 2 mph over most of the basin, and the flow generally down the mountains, across the basin and out over the coast. As a result of this diurnal variation, the trajectories followed by any air parcel consists of alternate

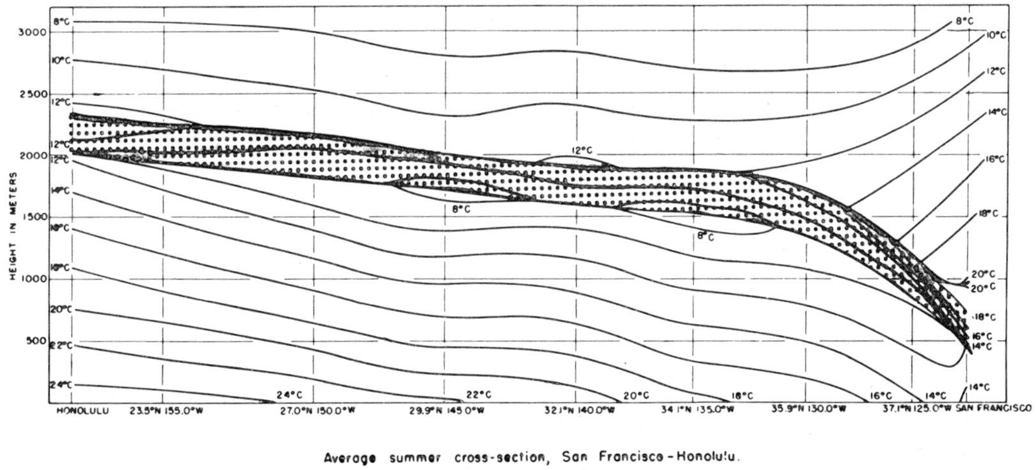

Fig. 5. Cross-section showing average temperature (°C) at various levels from San Francisco to Honolulu in summer. The inversion layer is outlined with heavy lines and shaded. This figure was prepared as part of a project sponsored by the United States Office of Naval Research at the University of California, Los Angeles.

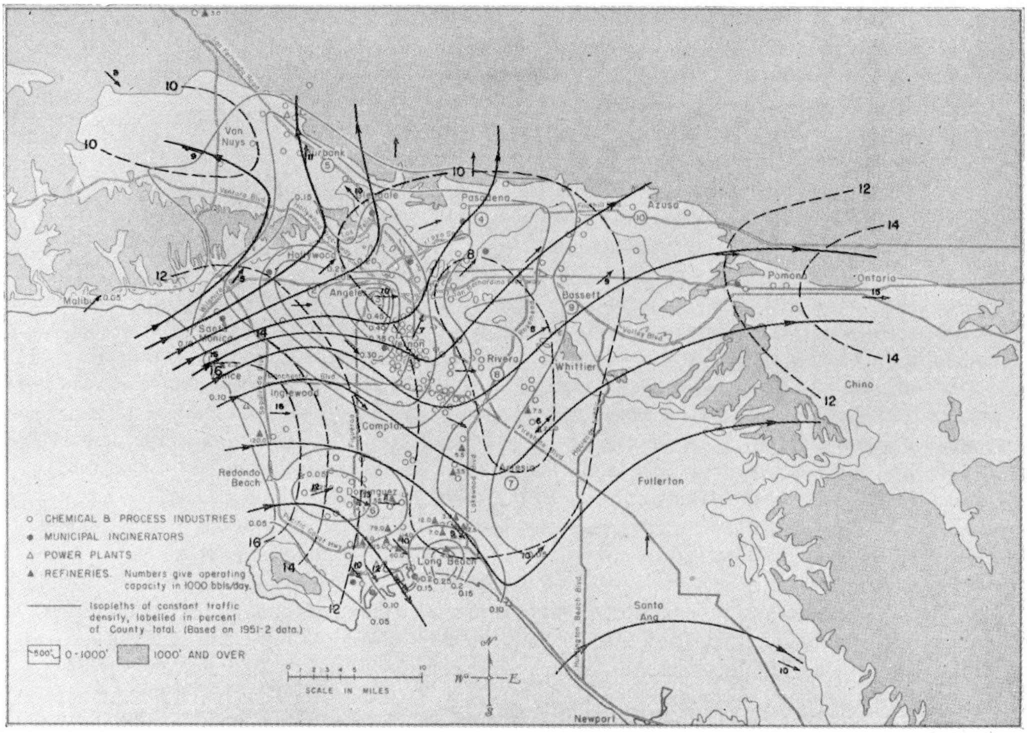

Fig. 6. Flow pattern in Los Angeles at 1430 September 21, 1954. (From NEIBURGER et al., 1956.)

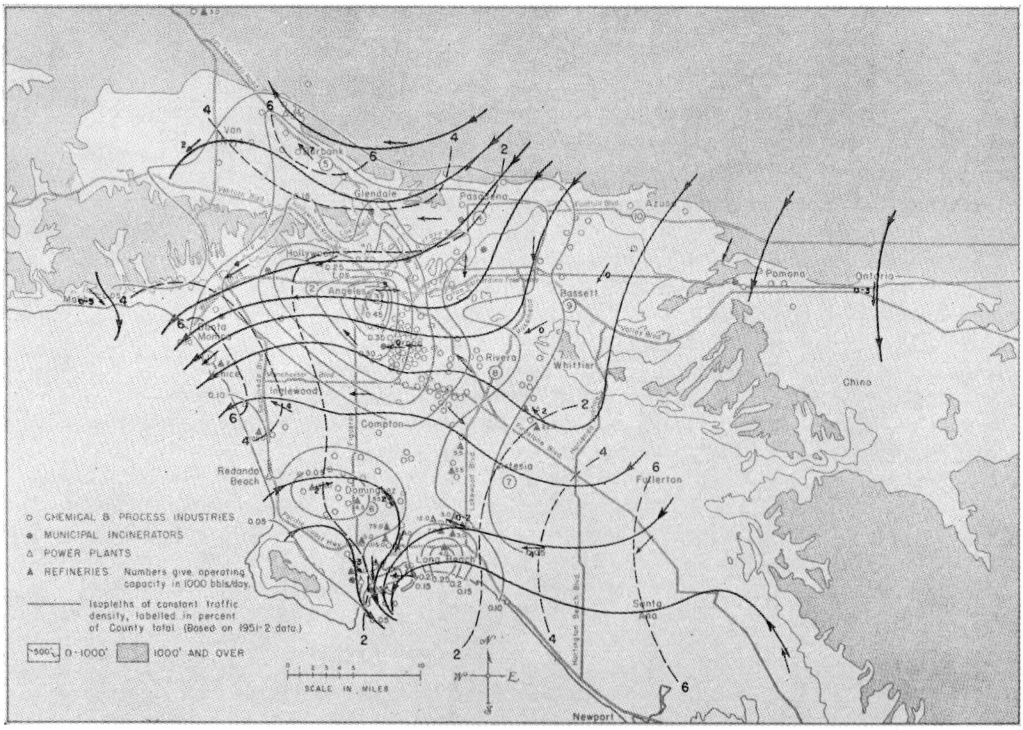

Fig. 7. Flow pattern in Los Angeles at 0630 September 22, 1954. (From NEIBURGER et al., 1956.)

large displacements landward during the day, followed by small displacements seaward at night. Figure 8 shows a trajectory of air arriving at Pasadena at noon September 23, 1954, with high values of oxidant and eye irritation. The air crossed the coast at about 9.30 a.m. the previous day, possibly after having moved offshore with the land breeze the night before. It moved inland to the vicinity east of Pasadena by nightfall, and then stagnated or drifted slowly back towards the ocean until the following morning, when it moved inland toward Pasadena again. During the afternoon it ascended the mountains north of Pasadena. It is during the period of stagnation or slow movement that the high concentrations of pollutants are assumed to have accumulated.

The background of Figures 6 and 7 shows the distribution of the principal industrial sources of pollution in Los Angeles county, and the isopleths of traffic density. These isopleths are expressed in per cent of the county total. By assuming that the unburned hydrocarbons escaping through the exhaust into the atmosphere is 7% of the total of 6 million gallons per day consumed in Los Angeles, it is found that the 0.1 per cent isopleth corresponds to about 1 ton per square mile per day of hydrocarbons, and if this diffuses rapidly up to an average inversion height of 400 meters, it represents an increase in concentration of 0.6 pphm per hour. Using this conversion it is possible to compute the amount of hydrocarbon which is added to the air parcel as it moves along its trajectory, assuming that the traffic density is uniform throughout the day and night. Figure 9 shows the results of such a computation for the trajectory on Figure 8. At the time the parcel reached Pasadena, when the hydrocarbon content was measured to be 31 pphm, the accumulated increase was computed to be 21 pphm. The discrepancy could be due to hydrocarbons present in the air when it crossed the coast, presumably because it had been over the Basin previously, or it could be due to the accumulation of hydrocarbons from other sources such as the Standard Oil Refinery at El Segundo (north of Redondo Beach) near which the trajectory passed. It also could be due to deviations from one or another of the assumptions. However the discrepancy is small enough to indicate auto traffic is a major source of the measured hydrocarbons.

Similar computations can be made for other components of the exhaust. For instance, the assumption that the exhaust averages 3% carbon monoxide results in an accumulation represented by the same curve referred to the scale on the right hand side of Figure 9. At noon, September 23, the accumulation totals about 700 pphm, compared with a measured value of 620 pphm. The discrepancy again may be due to errors in the computation, or to oxidation of some of the carbon monoxide.

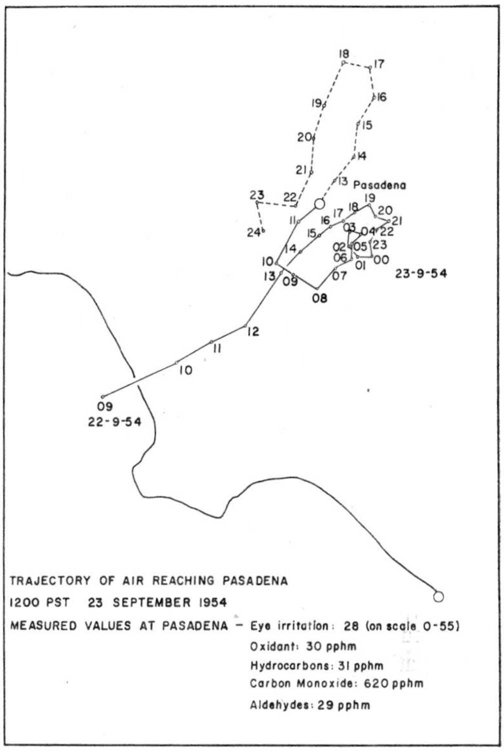

Fig. 8. Trajectory of air arriving at Pasadena at noon September 23, 1954 with high values of oxidant and eye irritation.

The values of the oxidant along the trajectory were obtained by drawing hourly maps of oxidant concentration on the basis of measurements made at 10 stations throughout the basin. The result is shown by the heavy line in Figure 9. It will be noted that the oxidant maximum on September 22 occurs at about 4 p.m. The reason it occurs so long after the maximum solar intensity is doubtless due to the fact that the hydrocarbons and oxides of nitrogen in the air parcel are increasing through this period. On the 23rd apparently the reagents are present in large enough quantities for the available radiation to be the limiting factor.

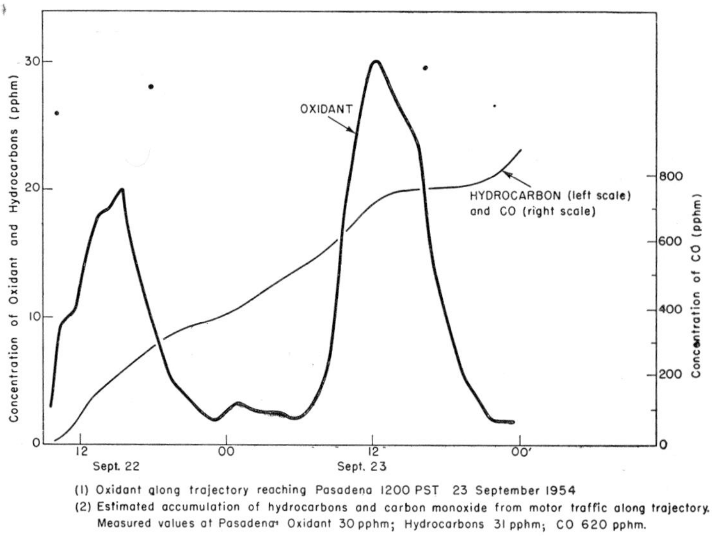

Fig. 9. Concentrations of hydrocarbons, carbon monoxide and oxidant in an air parcel moving along the trajectory shown in Figure 8. Hydrocarbons and carbonmonoxide computed assuming that traffic density is uniform through the day and night. Oxidant obtained from hourly maps of measured concentrations.

The question of the accuracy of trajectories computed from surface winds as representative of the path of pollutants through the basin was investigated (NEIBURGER, 1955) using fluorescent particles as tracers. Figure 10 shows the result of one such test. The closed curve represents the estimated location of the cloud of fluorescent particles which was emitted from the Compton Airport between 5 and 6 a.m., based on particle counts by samplers at the points indicated by small dots. The area of the fluorescent cloud increased approximately tenfold in the 7 hours during which it remained within the sampling network. Figure 11 shows a comparison of the movement of the centroid of the fluorescent cloud with the trajectories computed by several meteorologists. While there are considerable differences among the computed trajectories and between the computed trajectories and the observed ones, the general pattern of movement is represented fairly well in the sense that for the most part the computed positions fell within the fluorescent cloud even though not necessarily close to its centroid.

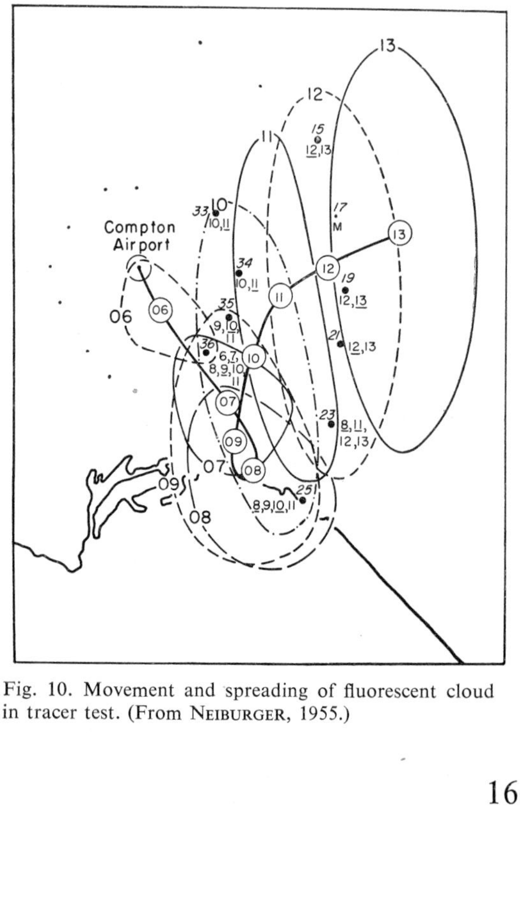

Fig. 10. Movement and spreading of fluorescent cloud in tracer test. (From NEIBURGER, 1955.)

With these limitations on the accuracy of computed trajectories in mind the question whether eye irritation and other smog manifestations could be attributed entirely to industrial sources was examined (NEIBURGER *et al.*, 1956). Trajectories were computed for the air reaching sampling stations at times of high measured values of pollutants and smog effects. Table 4 shows the frequency with which trajectories arriving with peak values of eye irritation (rated by panels on a scale of 0—50) passed near refineries of various capacities. It will be noted for instance that while all three cases in which eye irritation greater than 30 was reported in Pasadena passed near refineries, of the 11 with eye irritation between 20 and 29 only three passed within five miles of refineries. All of them passed over regions of high traffic density. Similar studies with respect to hydrocarbons, etc., lead to the conclusion that smog manifestations must at least in some cases be attributed to other sources than refineries, and confirm the implication of the automobile as a principal source.

As a final item of interest Figure 12 shows the average concentration of oxidant at three-hour intervals during the day in September 1954. The 0530 chart shows the representative distribution through the night, with values of about 2 pphm over most of the basin. Shortly after sunrise the amount increases, particularly in the central part of the coastal plain and in the San Gabriel Valley. The pattern during the morning, with highest values in the central part of the coastal plain and the San Gabriel Valley, is probably a reflection of the combined effects of (1) the distribution of residual pollutants from the previous day, when the sea breeze had cleared the western and southern portions of the basin and carried the pollutants north-eastward, (2) the distribution of insolation, with less in the coastal strip than farther inland, due to stratus cloud, and (3) the

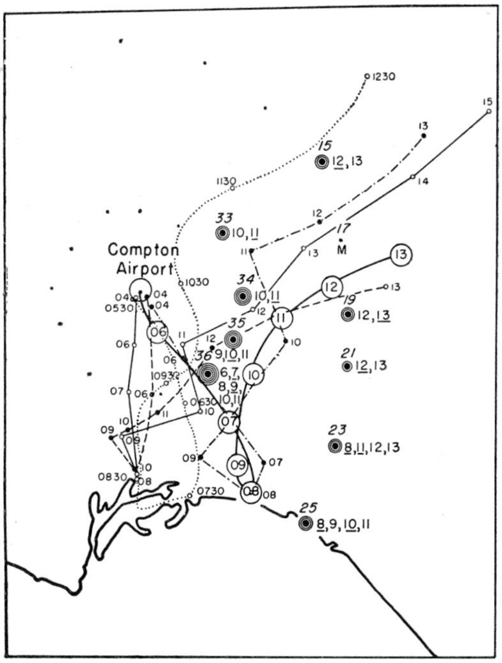

Fig. 11. Comparison of movement of centroid of fluorescent cloud with trajectories computed from surface winds. (From NEIBURGER, 1955.)

Table 4. Frequency with which Trajectories Arriving with Peak Values of Eye Irritation Passed Near Refineries[1]

Station	Peak value	Number of Cases	Number passing within 5 miles of refineries having capacity of > 50,000 bbls/day	10,000—50,000 bbls/day	< 10,000 bbls/day
Downtown Los Angeles	⩾ 30	5	3	0	0
	20—29	14	4	2	7
	< 20	6	1	1	4
Pasadena	⩾ 30	3	1	1	1
	20—29	11	2	1	0
	< 20	13	0	2	2
Burbank	⩾ 30	8	2	3	2
	20—29	11	4	0	6
	< 20	1	0	0	0
Artesia	20—29	7	6	0	1
	< 20	7	2	5	0

[1] Data from NEIBURGER, M., RENZETTI, N. A., and TICE, R. (1956).

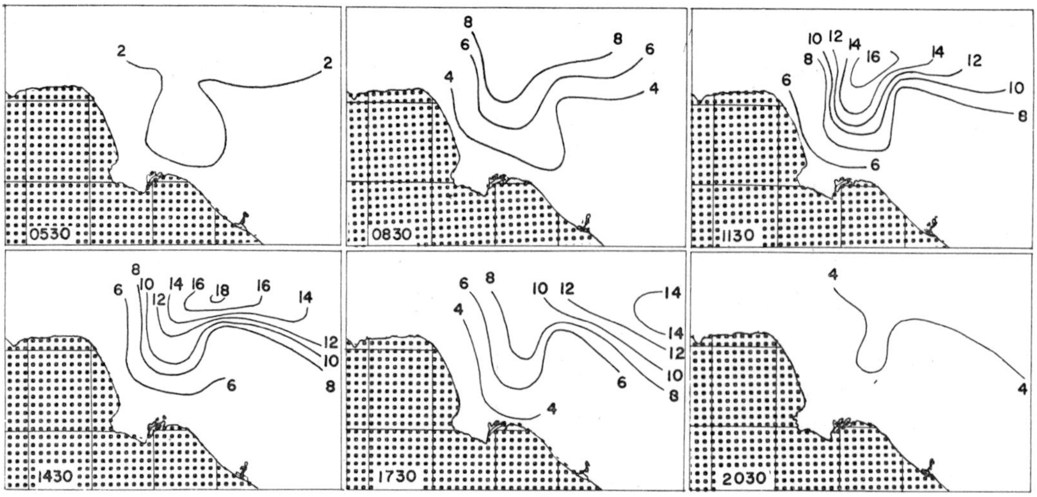

Fig. 12. Average concentration of oxidant at three-hour intervals in September, 1955.

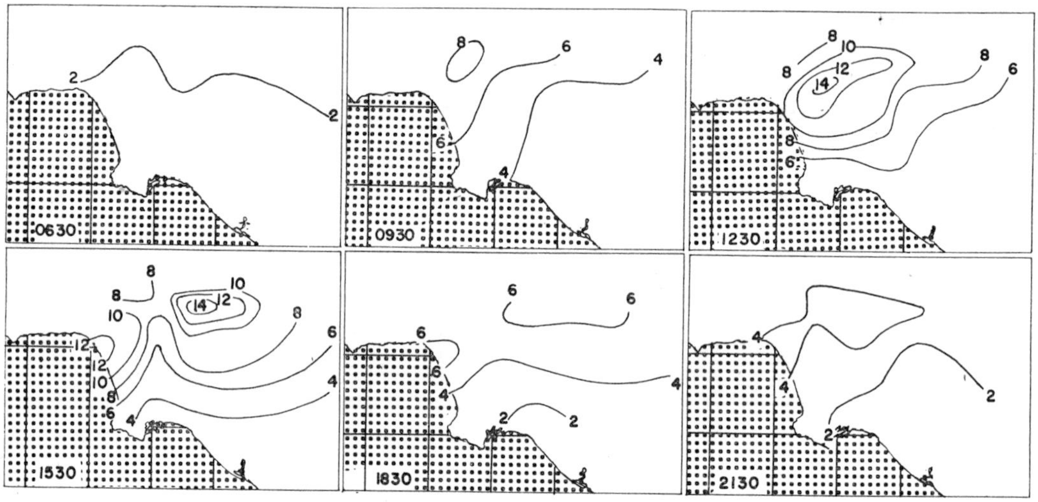

Fig. 13. Average concentration of oxidant at three-hour intervals in November, 1955.

contribution of new pollution due to the automobile traffic, which is concentrated in central Los Angeles.

As the afternoon progresses, the effect of advection due to the sea breeze becomes evident. The center of maximum concentration has moved eastward between 1130 and 1430, and continues moving eastward during the rest of the day. The highest concentration at the center occurs at about 1430, after which the effect of the decreasing insolation overcompensates the addition of pollutants.

As the fall season progresses the summer monsoon is gradually replaced by the winter one, in which the average effect is a drift of air seaward on which the land-sea breeze is superposed. November is a month during which there is alternation between periods when the sea breeze is stronger than the land breeze, and periods when the reverse is true. The average hourly oxidant concentration in November (Figure 13) reflects this by the splitting of the oxidant maximum into two centers, showing the effect in the average of the two types of days.

The magnitude of the maximum average concentration is somewhat smaller in November than in September. This may be due in part to the decrease in insolation and in part to the occurrence of days on which there was no inversion.

In the foregoing we have seen some of the manifestations and meteorological aspects of oxidation type smog. Because of the requirement for solar radiation to produce the photochemical reactions involved, it is primarily a warm season and lower latitude phenomenon. However, there have been already evidences that occasionally daytime inversions of sufficient persistence and strength occur in such cities as New York and Detroit for long enough periods to produce the characteristic eye irritation. To the extent that these conditions, i.e. daytime inversions and light winds, occur, oxidation type smog may be expected wherever automobile traffic is sufficiently concentrated, as long as automobile engines are operated at low air-fuel ratios without provision for control of their exhaust gases by completion of the oxidation or other measures. Work is proceeding on control devices, and it is to be hoped that we will not have to wait until the exhaustion of our petroleum resources to be rid of oxidation type smog.

REFERENCES

AMERICAN PETROLEUM INSTITUTE, 1950, 1953: *Petroleum Facts and Figures* 9th ed. 1950. 11th ed. 1953. New York.

DOYLE, G. J., and RENZETTI, N. A., 1957: The formation of aerosols by irradiation of dilute auto exhaust. Presented at American Chemical Society Meeting, New York, September 9, 1957.

FAITH, W. L., 1957: The Role of Motor Vehicle Exhaust in Smog Formation. *Journal of the Air Pollution Control Association*, **7**, 3, pp. 219—221.

GOETZ, A., 1958: The Particle Spectrometer. *Proceedings of the Semi-Annual Technical Conference of the Air Pollution Control Association, November 18—19,* 1957.

HAAGEN-SMIT, A. J., 1952: Chemistry and physiology of Los Angeles Smog. *Ind. Eng. Chem.* **44**, pp. 1342—6.

HAAGEN-SMIT, A. J., BRADLEY, C. E., and FOX, M. M., 1953: Ozone Formation in Photochemical Oxidation of Organic Substances. *Ind. Eng. Chem.* **45**, pp. 2086—9.

JOHNSTON, H. S., 1956: Photochemical Oxidation of Hydrocarbons. *Ind. Eng. Chem.*, **48**, pp. 1488—91.

KANTER, C. V., LUNCHE, R. G., and FUDURICH, A. P., 1957: Techniques of Testing for Air Contaminants from Combustion Sources. *Journal of the Air Pollution Control Association*, **6**, 4, pp. 191—199.

MEETHAM, A. R., 1952: *Atmospheric Pollution*, London.

NEIBURGER, M., 1955: Tracer Tests of Trajectories Computed from Observed Winds. *Air Pollution Foundation Report No. 7.* Los Angeles, California.

NEIBURGER, M., RENZETTI, N. A., and TICE, R., 1956: Wind Trajectory Studies of the Movement of Polluted Air in the Los Angeles Basin. *Air Pollution Foundation Report No. 13.* Los Angeles, California.

RENZETTI, N. A., ed., 1955: An Aerometric Survey of Los Angeles Basin, August—November 1954. *Air Pollution Foundation Report No. 9.* Los Angeles, California.

RENZETTI, N. A., and ROMANOVSKY, J. C., 1956: A Comparative Study of Oxidants and Ozone in Los Angeles Atmosphere. *A.M.A. Archives of Industrial Health.* **14**, pp. 458—467.

(Manuscript received March 7, 1958)

A Method for Calculation of Infrared Flux for Use in Numerical Models of Atmospheric Motion[1]

By LEWIS D. KAPLAN
Department of Meteorology, Massachusetts Institute of Technology, Cambridge, Massachusetts

Abstract

The pressure-scaling method to determine the flux of infrared radiation in the atmosphere is reviewed, and the assumptions inherent in the method are discussed from the point of view of use in studies of atmospheric motions.

A more accurate method, which enables the temperature dependence of the absorption coefficient and the exact line shape to be taken into account, is then outlined. A matrix can be constructed from which the infrared heating terms in the equations of motion can be introduced into numerical models of the atmosphere with a machine computation time equal to or less than the time required to make the hydrodynamic computations.

Introduction

This paper is in a large sense the culmination of work on a problem suggested to the author by Professor Rossby ten years ago. Professor Rossby had even then been interested in the effect of increased atmospheric carbon dioxide content on the secular change in surface temperature, and proposed that the author examine, among other things, the means then available for calculating radiative flux.

Professor Rossby's interest in atmospheric radiation was not new. It was at his suggestion and with his encouragement that PEKERIS (1932) wrote his summary of the early work in this field; and he had many discussions with Elsasser during the course of the work leading to the preparation of ELSASSER's (1942) famous monograph. Professor Rossby had also been instrumental in the introduction of the study of radiation into meteorological curricula in the United States.

The suggested carbon dioxide study has not yet been completed, because it soon became evident that the existing models were not realistic enough to describe many of the features of molecular spectra that are of fundamental importance for atmospheric radiation. For application to circulation studies there are even greater requirements of precision. This is because two differentiations of the transmission are required to obtain cooling rates, three differentiations to obtain radiatively induced stability changes, and four differentiations to obtain the three-dimensional changes in the field of available potential energy.

The standard methods of determining radiative flux divergence greatly simplify the calculation by scaling the absorbing gas concentration with some power of the pressure. Before presenting a more accurate method, the assumptions involved in pressure-scaling will be reviewed. The method of ELSASSER (1942) will be chosen as the prototype.

Pressure-Scaling

When the radiation transfer equation is integrated over mass of absorbing material m in the vertical, over solid angle, and over frequency ν, the following result is obtained for the net up-

[1] This paper represents in part results of research carried out at the Department of Meteorology, Imperial College, under an Institute for Advanced Study (Princeton) contract with the Office of Naval Research. The results were presented in a seminar at the International Meteorological Institute in Stockholm on July 30, 1957.

ward flux of radiation through a surface designated by the subscript r:

$$\uparrow(m_r) = \int_{T_\infty}^{T_G}\int_0^\infty \tau_\nu^*(m_r, m)\frac{d\pi B_\nu(T)}{dT}\,d\nu dT - \int_0^\infty \tau_\nu^*(m_r, m_\infty)\pi B_\nu(T_\infty)\,d\nu, \qquad (1)$$

where B_ν is the black-body radiation per unit area normal to the beam, per unit solid angle, per unit frequency interval, at the temperature $T(m)$; and

$$\tau_\nu^*(m_r, m) = 2\int_1^\infty e^{-x\sum_i \left|\int_{m_{ir}}^{m_i} k_{\nu i}\,du\right|} x^{-3}dx \qquad (2)$$

is the transmission of diffuse radiation in a plane-stratified atmosphere containing several gases, each having separate mass absorption coefficients $k_{\nu i}$. The subscript G refers to ground level, or cloud top if there is an undercast; the subscript ∞ refers to some arbitrary level, from above which practically no radiation reaches the level m_r. If there is an overcast, the subscript ∞ should refer to the cloud base and the second integral on the right hand side of equation (1) should be removed.

The difficulty in performing the integration in equation (1) lies in the very rapid fluctuation of the absorption coefficient $k_{\nu i}$ with frequency, since each band spectrum in the infrared consists of hundreds of lines. ELSASSER (1942), faced with the problem of developing a simple graphical integration method, simplified the integral by making the following assumptions:

1) Each individual spectral line has the Lorentz shape

$$k_{\nu ij} = \frac{S_{ij}}{\pi}\frac{\gamma_{ij}}{(\nu - \nu_{ij})^2 + \gamma_{ij}^2}, \qquad (3)$$

where $S_{ij} = \int_{-\infty}^{+\infty} k_{\nu ij}\,d(\nu - \nu_{ij})$ is the line intensity of the line centered at ν_{ij} and γ_{ij} its half-width at half height.

2) Only water vapor contributes to radiative flux divergence in the atmosphere; so the subscript i can be dropped.

3) The total absorption coefficient at a given frequency can be represented by the sum of absorption coefficients from an infinite series of equally spaced lines with equal intensities and half-widths of magnitude equal to the mean value for the strongest lines:

$$k_\nu = \sum_{-\infty}^{+\infty}\frac{S}{\pi}\frac{\gamma}{(\nu - nD)^2 + \gamma^2} = \frac{S(\nu)\sinh\beta(\nu)}{D(\nu)\left[\cosh\beta(\nu) - \cos\dfrac{2\pi\nu}{D(\nu)}\right]} \qquad (4)$$

where $D(\nu)$ is the mean line-spacing and

$$\beta(\nu) = \frac{2\pi\gamma(\nu)}{D(\nu)}. \qquad (5)$$

This replaces the subscript j with a smooth variation with frequency.

4) The major part of the transfer occurs in the wings of lines, where $(\nu - \nu_{ij}) \gg \gamma$.

5) S and γ are independent of temperature.

There were several other approximations, but they were unnecessary for the purpose.

The important approximations are the last two, as they permit a drastic reduction in the number of independent variables. The half-width γ is directly proportional to the collision frequency and therefore to the pressure. Approximations (4) and (5) thus result in a direct pressure dependence of the absorption coefficient[2] and its independence from temperature. Since k_ν and m only enter the transfer equation as a mutual product, the pressure dependence of the absorption coefficient can be taken into account by using transmission determined for some standard pressure p_s, and replacing the mixing-ratio with a scaled mixing-ratio through $dm^* = \frac{p}{p_s}dm$. The interior integral in equation (1) is then a function only of the reduced mass m^* and the temperature and can be evaluated once and for all, and used for a graphical evaluation of the net flux from the distribution with height of m^* and T.

If the pressure-scaling method is used, it is not necessary to calculate transmission at the standard pressure. Instead, laboratory measurements can be used, and have been used in the pressure-

[2] Due to a misinterpretation of some experimental results, Elsasser and others erroneously introduced a square-root pressure dependence (see KAPLAN (1952)).

scaling techniques of PLASS (1952) and others. In the actual construction of his radiation diagram Elsasser had also adjusted his originally calculated transmission to agree with emissivity measurements.

Unfortunately, the pressure-scaling method is inadequate for use in precisely those studies of atmospheric motion for which radiative heat transfer is most important. It has been shown (KAPLAN, 1954) that heating of the upper troposphere and lower stratosphere by the ground and warm lower-level air is most efficiently gained by the central portions of moderately weak lines. Most of these lines were omitted from Elsasser's schematic spectrum. Even if they had been included, however, their effective pressure-dependence would have been greatly exaggerated by pressure-scaling, since it is their central portions which are important, and assumption (4) is invalid. Moreover, their intensities are strongly temperature dependent, through the Maxwell-Boltzmann distribution:

$$S_{H_2O} = \frac{L e^{-\frac{1.4388\,\nu''}{T}}\left(1 - e^{-\frac{1.4388\,\nu}{T}}\right)}{T^{3/2} Q_v(T)} \tag{6}$$

and

$$S_{CO_2} = \frac{L e^{-\frac{1.4388\,\nu''}{T}}\left(1 - e^{-\frac{1.4388\,\nu}{T}}\right)}{T Q_v(T)} \tag{7}$$

where L is a constant proportional to the line-strength, Q_v the vibrational partition function, ν the line frequency, and ν'' the frequency corresponding to the energy level of the lower state. For the moderately weak lines of importance for heat transfer from below, the intensity at tropopause height is smaller, on the average, than that near the ground by about a factor of four for the mean tropospheric lapse-rate.[3] Thus, to calculate radiative flux accurately enough to determine perhaps even the order of magnitude of changes in stability, the exact line shape, the actual line distribution, and the temperature variation of the line intensities should be taken into account. A more realistic radiation model than one involving pressure-scaling is therefore desirable.

[3] Since the pressure also varies by about a factor of four from ground to tropopause, one might be tempted to propose that pressure-scaling automatically takes into account the temperature variation of the weak lines, for which the pressure variations are less important. The errors, however, would be a monotonic function of the stability and must at least be estimated from accurate calculations before use of scaling methods in determination of stability changes.

The Statistical Model

A straightforward integration of equation (1) is out of the question, even with the use of high-speed computers. On the other hand, major features of infrared band spectra, such as line-shapes and intensities and the pressure and temperature dependence of the absorption coefficients must be taken into account. GOODY (1952) noticed the apparent randomness of the line-position in the water vapor spectrum and showed that an assumption of complete randomness greatly simplifies the expression for the transmission. The author (KAPLAN, 1953 b) found that an assumption of randomness of line-positions gives a remarkable simplification of the transmission even if the actual lines in a given spectral interval are taken into account. In this case the transmission is, for a homogeneous path of mass per unit area m:

$$\tau = e^{-\frac{1}{D}\sum_j \int_{-\infty}^{+\infty}\left[1 - e^{-k_{\nu_j} m}\right] d(\nu - \nu_j)}, \tag{8}$$

where the summation is over all the lines in the interval D. For Lorentz lines, equation (8) becomes

$$\tau = e^{-\frac{2\pi}{D}\sum \gamma_j x_j e^{-x_j}[I_0(x_j) + I_1(x_j)]}, \tag{9}$$

where I_0 and I_1 are Bessel functions of imaginary argument and

$$x_j = \frac{S_j m}{2\pi\gamma_j} \tag{10}$$

The function $xe^{-x}[I_0(x)+I_1(x)]$ is tabulated (KAPLAN and EGGERS, 1956).

This model has been used to calculate ozone absorption in the central region of the 9.6 micron band. The results were used to determine band intensity and line-width, assuming no variation of the latter from line to line, by comparison with WALSHAW's (1957) measured values. In Fig. 1 the final calculated integrated absorption, obtained by adjusting the two unknowns to obtain best fit, is plotted against observed integrated absorption for which the ultraviolet absorption at 3021 Å was used to determine the mass. It is seen that the model gives an excellent fit to a forty-five degree straight line for a seven-fold

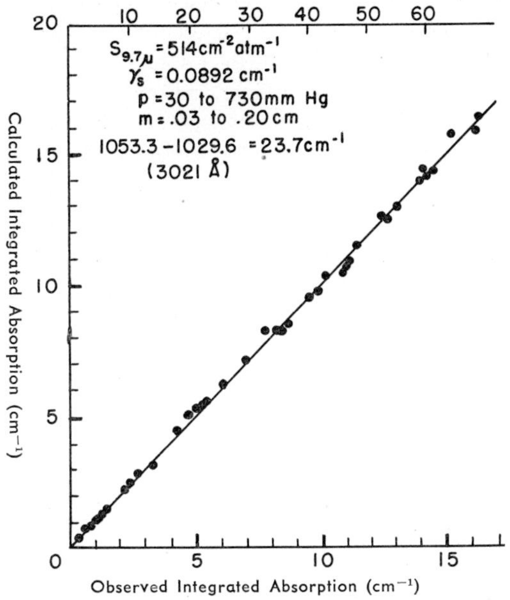

Fig. 1. Comparison of calculated integrated absorption by the central portion of 9.6 micron ozone band with Walshaw's measurements

variation in mass and a fourteen-fold variation in pressure. This is despite the regularities that occur in the ozone spectrum (KAPLAN, MIGEOTTE, and NEVEN, 1956). Since the water vapor spectrum is much more random in character, there is little doubt that the method is applicable to water vapor absorption.

The regularities in the carbon dioxide spectrum, however, are too marked to be neglected; and the appropriate model is a series of randomly overlapping Elsasser bands, for which the total transmission is represented by the product of individual sub-band transmissions (KAPLAN, 1953b). If the lines have the Lorentz shape, each sub-band has an absorption coefficient given by equation (4). For a homogeneous path:

$$\tau = \prod_j \frac{1}{D_j} \int_{-D_j/2}^{D_j/2} e^{-\frac{S_j m}{D_j} \frac{\sinh \beta_j}{\cosh \beta_j - \cos \frac{2\pi\nu}{D_j}}} d\nu$$

$$= \prod_j [1 - \sinh \beta_j \int_0^{y_j} e^{-t \cosh \beta_j} I_0(t)\, dt], \qquad (11)$$

where

$$y_j = \frac{S_j m}{D_j \sinh \beta_j}, \qquad (12)$$

The author (KAPLAN, 1953 a) has given a very rapidly convergent series for evaluating the right-hand term in the bracket of equation (11), and a partial tabulation. This model has been used successfully in an intensity analysis of the low-frequency wing of the 15 micron carbon dioxide band (KOSTKOWSKI and KAPLAN, 1957).

When bands of several gases overlap, the transmission is equal to the product of the transmissions of the individual gases (KAPLAN, 1953 b):

$$\tau = \tau_{H_2O}\, \tau_{CO_2}\, \tau_{O_3}. \qquad (13)$$

The Curtis-Godson Approximation

Equations (9) and (11) are valid, for water vapor and carbon dioxide, respectively, only over spectral intervals of the order of ten wavenumbers, and only for homogeneous paths. The analogous expressions for non-homogeneous paths are more complicated. Fortunately, homogeneous path transmission can be used to represent atmospheric transmission providing one carefully chooses a mean half-width. This was first proposed by CURTIS (1952) and later generalized and tested by GODSON (1955). The method of selecting the appropriate mean half-width is quite general, but will be illustrated here only for the case of an isolated Lorentz line.

Since the use of any value for the mean half-width in the denominator of equation (3) will give correct results for large absorption, a value $\bar{\gamma}$ will be chosen that gives the correct result to first order for small absorption:

$$\int_{-\infty}^{+\infty}\int \frac{S}{\pi} \frac{\gamma dm d\nu}{(\nu - \nu_0)^2 + \gamma^2} = \int_{-\infty}^{+\infty}\int \frac{S}{\pi} \frac{\gamma dm d\nu}{(\nu - \nu_0) + \bar{\gamma}^2}, \qquad (14)$$

where the inner integrals represent the exponent in the monochromatic transmission and therefore the first term in the Taylor expansion of the absorption. Equation (14) can be rewritten

$$\frac{1}{\pi} \int S dm \int_{-\infty}^{+\infty} \frac{dx}{x^2 + 1} = \frac{1}{\pi} \frac{\int S\gamma dm}{\bar{\gamma}} \int_{-\infty}^{+\infty} \frac{dx}{x^2 + 1}. \qquad (14')$$

The appropriate mean half-width is therefore

$$\bar{\gamma} = \frac{\int S\gamma dm}{\int S dm} \qquad (15)$$

or the half-width averaged with respect to frequency-integrated optical path. The inner integral on the right-hand side of equation (14) now becomes

$$\int \frac{S}{\pi} \frac{\gamma dm}{(\nu-\nu_0)^2+\bar{\gamma}^2} = \frac{\bar{\gamma}}{\pi} \frac{\int S dm}{(\nu-\nu_0)^2+\bar{\gamma}^2} \qquad (16)$$

which is exactly equivalent to the expression for the homogeneous path exponent with γ replaced by $\bar{\gamma}$ and Sm replaced by $\int Sdm$; and equations (9) and (11) can be used for water vapor and carbon dioxide, respectively, with the following new definitions:

$$x_j = \frac{\int S_j dm}{2\pi\bar{\gamma}_j}, \qquad (10')$$

$$y_j = \frac{\int S_j dm}{D_j \sinh \bar{\beta}_j}, \qquad (12')$$

and

$$\bar{\beta}_j = \frac{2\pi\bar{\gamma}_j}{D_j} \qquad (5')$$

where $\bar{\gamma}_j$ is given by equation (15).

Maximum errors due to the Curtis-Godson approximation can be specified within useful limits for heat transfer in the troposphere. For this purpose, we will examine the integrated absorption due to a single Lorentz line by the layer between the ground and a level at p atmospheres. We will assume, for simplicity, that $\gamma(p) = \gamma_s p$. The transmission then becomes (KAPLAN, 1954)

$$\tau_\nu = e^{\int_1^p \frac{2\eta p\, dp}{x^2+p^2}}, \qquad (17)$$

where

$$\eta = \frac{\alpha S}{2\pi\gamma_s \varrho_s g} \qquad (18)$$

and

$$x = \frac{\nu-\nu_0}{\gamma_s}. \qquad (19)$$

α is the fraction by volume of absorbing gas, ϱ_s the air density at the ground, g the acceleration of gravity, and ν_0 the line-center frequency. We will consider only the case of constant η, since the errors are greatly reduced if η decreases with height, as it normally does in the troposphere.

The maximum error in optical path occurs at the line-center, and is compensated by errors of opposite sign in the wings. In the transmission, however, the errors compensate only to first

Table I. Line-center transmission and integrated absorption between surfaces at one and p atmospheres, for single Lorentz line with $\eta = 1$.

p	$\tau_\nu(\nu_0)$			$\pi^{-1}\gamma_s^{-1}\int A_\nu d\nu$				
(atm.)	Exact	Curtis	% error	Exact	Div.	Curtis	Div.	% error
0	.0000	.0183	∞	1.0000		1.0476		
					.0100		.0262	162
.1	.0100	.0379	279	.9900		1.0214		
					.0300		.0418	118
.2	.0400	.0695	74	.9600		.9796		
					.0500		.0591	18
.3	.0900	.1160	28	.9100		.9205		
					.0700		.0744	6.3
.4	.1600	.1801	13	.8400		.8461		
					.0900		.0933	3.7
.5	.2500	.2336	5.4	.7500		.7528		
					.1100		.1117	1.5
.6	.3600	.3679	2.2	.6400		.6411		
					.1300		.1307	0.5
.7	.4900	.4937	0.8	.5100		.5104		
					.1500		.1504	0.3
.8	.6400	.6412	0.2	.3600		.3600		

order. For $\eta = 1$, the transmission at the line-center is

$$\tau_\nu(\nu_0) = p^2, \tag{20}$$

while the Curtis-Godson approximation gives

$$\tau_\nu(\nu_0) = e^{-4\frac{1-p}{1+p}}. \tag{20'}$$

These are compared in Table I. It is seen that radiative transfer over a wide variation in pressure can be quite accurately represented by the Curtis-Godson approximation even at the line-center. As the ratio of the end pressures becomes greater than two or three, however, the accuracy rapidly deteriorates. Table I also compares the integrated absorption, again with $\eta = 1$. The exact integrated absorption is

$$\int A_\nu d\nu = \int_{-\infty}^{+\infty} (1 - \tau_\nu) d(\nu - \nu_0) = $$
$$= \pi\gamma_s(1 - p^2), \tag{21}$$

while the Curtis-Godson approximation gives

$$\int A_\nu d\nu = 2\pi\gamma_s f\left(2\frac{1-p}{1+p}\right), \tag{21'}$$

where

$$f(x) = xe^{-x}[I_0(x) + I_1(x)]. \tag{22}$$

The integrated absorption in Table I is apart from the common factor $\pi\gamma_s$. The differences for the various 100 mb layers are also listed, as it is the flux-divergence in which we are particularly interested.

Table II gives the integrated absorption by the entire atmosphere for various values of η as determined by

$$\frac{\int A_\nu d\nu}{\pi\gamma_s} = \frac{2}{\sqrt{\pi}} \frac{\Gamma\left(\eta + \frac{1}{2}\right)}{\Gamma(\eta)} \tag{23}$$

for the exact case, and

$$\frac{\int A_\nu d\nu}{\pi\gamma_s} = 2f(2\eta) \tag{23'}$$

with the Curtis-Godson approximation. It is seen that the error has a sharp maximum for lines with η close to unity.

The magnitude of the errors in flux-divergence indicate, therefore, that the Curtis-Godson approximation is adequate for determination of infrared heating of the troposphere, at least in middle and high latitudes. Above the 200 mb level, some other method may have to be used for determination of heating from the ground and lower troposphere.

Table II. Integrated absorption between surfaces at one and zero atmospheres, for single Lorentz line, as function of η.

η	$\pi^{-1}\gamma_s^{-1}\int A_\nu d\nu$		
	Exact	Curtis	% error
.05	.0937	.0952	1.6
.1	.1766	.1818	2.9
.2	.3190	.3337	4.6
.5	.6366	.6737	5.8
1.0	1.0000	1.0476	4.8
1.5	1.2732	1.3195	3.6
2	1.5000	1.5430	2.9
5	2.4609	2.4910	1.2
10	3.5239	3.5457	0.6
20	5.0148	5.0304	0.3

The Atmospheric Model

Since the statistical model involves breaking the spectrum up into intervals of the order of 10 cm^{-1} the value $\bar{B}_k$ of B_ν at the center of each interval $\nu_k - \frac{\Delta\nu}{2}$ to $\nu_k + \frac{\Delta\nu}{2}$ can be used for the entire interval with negligible loss in accuracy. For computation purposes, equations (1) and (2) then become:

$$\uparrow(m_r) = \int_{p_\infty}^{p_G} \sum_k \tau_k^*(m_r, m)\Delta\nu \frac{d\pi\bar{B}_k(T)}{dT}\frac{dT}{dp}dp$$
$$- \sum_k \tau_k^*(m_r, m_\infty)\pi\bar{B}_k(T_\infty) \tag{1'}$$

and

$$\tau_k^*(m_r, m) = \int_1^\infty \prod_i \tau_{ki}\left(x\int_{m_r}^{m} S du, \bar{\gamma}\right)x^{-3}dx, \tag{2'}$$

where the product is over the absorbing gases.

For a given sounding, the integration with respect to pressure can be performed by standard numerical methods once the summation is obtained. The summation, however, involves hundreds of computations of the integrals $\int S dm$ and $\int S\gamma dm$; and it is desirable to have an efficient routine for their integration.

To obtain such a routine, we will assume that the sounding can be divided into layers in each of which the temperature is a linear function of height and the water vapor mixing-ratio an exponential function of pressure. Thus,

$$T = T_0 \left(\frac{p}{p_0}\right)^{\varkappa} \quad (24)$$

and

$$dm = \left(\frac{dm}{dp}\right)_0 \left(\frac{p}{p_0}\right)^{\lambda} dp, \quad (24)$$

where the subscript zero denotes a value at some level in the layer. We will further assume that the carbon dioxide concentration is constant (i.e. $\lambda = 0$), and that the half-widths vary according to the kinetic theory variation of collision frequency.

$$\gamma = \gamma_s \frac{p}{p_s} \sqrt{\frac{T_s}{T}}, \quad (26)$$

where the subscript s represents conditions for which γ_s has been determined. For water vapor,

$$Q_\nu(T) \cong 1; \quad (27)$$

and for the 15 micron carbon dioxide band,

$$\frac{1 - e^{-\frac{1.4388\,\nu}{T}}}{Q_\nu(T)} \cong 1 - 2e^{-\frac{960}{T}} - e^{-\frac{1.4388\,\nu}{T}} \cong$$

$$\cong 1 - 3e^{-\frac{960}{T}}. \quad (28)$$

From equations (6) and (7), and (24) to (28), the required integrals then become, for H_2O:

$$\int_{m_1}^{m_0} S dm = \frac{A_1}{\sqrt{T_0}} F\left(\frac{2\lambda - \varkappa + 2}{2\varkappa}, 1.4388\,\nu, 1\right) \quad (29)$$

and

$$\int_{m_1}^{m_0} S\gamma dm = A_2 F\left(\frac{\lambda - \varkappa + 2}{\varkappa}, 1.4388\,\nu, 1\right), \quad (30)$$

and, for CO_2:

$$\int_{m_1}^{m_0} S dm = A_1 F\left(\frac{1}{\varkappa}, 960, 3\right) \quad (31)$$

and

$$\int_{m_1}^{m_0} S\gamma dm = A_2 \sqrt{T_0}\, F\left(\frac{4 - \varkappa}{2\varkappa}, 960, 3\right), \quad (32)$$

where

$$A_1 = L \left(\frac{dm}{dp}\right)_0 \frac{p_0}{\varkappa T_0}, \quad (33)$$

$$A_2 = \frac{A_1 \sqrt{T_s}\, \gamma_s p_0}{p_s T_0}, \quad (34)$$

and

$$F(n, a, b) = E_n\left(\frac{1.4388\,\nu''}{T_0}\right) - bE_n\left(\frac{1.4388\,\nu'' + a}{T_0}\right) - \left(\frac{T_1}{T_0}\right)^{n-1} \cdot \left[E_n\left(\frac{1.4388\,\nu''}{T_1}\right) - bE_n\left(\frac{1.4388\,\nu'' + a}{T_1}\right)\right] \cdot (35)$$

$$E_n(x) = \int_1^\infty e^{-xt} t^{-n} dt \quad (36)$$

is the generalized exponential integral. It is tabulated[4] by PLACZEK (1954) for positive integral n and by KOTANI (1955) for negative integral n; and a general routine for evaluating it for any n is now being prepared for the IBM 704, and will be described elsewhere.

The basic spectral data for carbon dioxide are available (KAPLAN and EGGERS, 1956; KOSTKOWSKI and KAPLAN, 1957; MADDEN, 1956); and those for water vapor are now being normalized and prepared for publication.

The mathematical difficulties remaining for an accurate calculation of infrared flux are minor, the most serious one being the order of the integration and product in equation (2′). Clearly much computation time would be saved if the order could be reversed. Although this would lead to a systematic error, the effect on cooling rates would probably be small, since the only serious overlapping under tropospheric conditions is in a narrow spectral region on the low frequency side of the 15 micron carbon dioxide band. A further simplification can be made by scaling the concentration with a transmission-dependent factor to obtain the diffuse radiation

[4] A very useful tabulation by G. F. Miller is now in press as N.P.L. Mathematical Tables, Volume 3.

(see GODSON, 1953); but a routine that avoids this approximation would probably require less than double the computation time, and should at least be used in enough cases to check the accuracy of approximations.

Application to Numerical Models

The method described above for calculation of infrared flux makes possible, for the first time, the computation of radiative cooling rates of sufficient ascertainable accuracy for use in the calculation of radiatively-induced stability changes. It also can be used to determine the adequacy of simplifying approximations for which maximum errors cannot be specified within useful limits.

The method as described is obviously much too cumbersome for direct use in numerical atmospheric models. It is possible, however, to use it to form a matrix whose elements are radiative flux or cooling rates, and which only needs to be determined once for use in a specific model. In any model for which the flux at a constant-pressure surface can be represented by that due to a lapse-rate independent of height and an exponential variation of mixing-ratio with pressure, a four dimensional matrix can be available for each cloud distribution. The independent variables would be, for example, two temperatures and two mixing-ratios. For each calculation of cooling rate only a small part of the matrix need be taken into the permanent memory for interpolation.

A choice of $\pm^1/_9$, $\pm^2/_9$ and $\pm^3/_9$ for $\varkappa$ and integers for λ would make the order n of E_n integral or half-integral. It is then either tabulated or can be obtained by standard methods from tables of the error function and incomplete gamma function. Since the flux for $\varkappa = 0$ is easily calculated, a seven-point interpolation can be used.

It is not necessary, however, to restrict n to integral or half-integral values. If the matrix is fine enough for linear interpolation, the computation time required to make a radiative flux calculation at a grid point will be of the same order of magnitude as that required for the hydrodynamic calculation. The average time would be reduced if, as is most likely the case, radiative calculations need be made less frequently than hydrodynamic calculations.

Details of the preparation of the matrix and examples of the calculation of radiative flux for specific meteorological problems will appear in forthcoming papers.

REFERENCES

CURTIS, A. R., 1952: Discussion of Goody's "A statistical model for water-vapour absorption". *Quart. Jour. R.M.S*, **78**, p. 638.

ELSASSER, W. M., 1942: Heat transfer by infrared radiation in the atmosphere. *Harvard Meteor. Stud.* No. 6.

GODSON, W. L., 1953: Spectral models and the properties of transmission functions. *Proc. Toronto Meteor. Conference*, pp. 35—42.

— 1955: The computation of infrared transmission by atmospheric water vapor. *J. of Met.*, **12**, pp. 272—284.

GOODY, R. M., 1952: A statistical model for water-vapour absorption. *Quart. Jour. R.M.S.*, **78**, pp. 165—169.

KAPLAN, L. D., 1952: On the pressure dependence of radiative heat transfer in the atmosphere. *J. of Met.*, **9**, pp. 1—12.

— 1953 a: Regions of validity of various absorption-coefficient approximations. *J. of Met.*, **10**, pp. 100—104.

— 1953 b: A quasi-statistical approach to the calculation of atmospheric transmission. *Proc. Toronto Meteor. Conference*, pp. 43—48.

— 1954: Energy transfer by infrared bands. *J. of Met.*, **11**, pp. 16—19.

KAPLAN, L. D., MIGEOTTE, M. V., and NEVEN, L., 1956: 9.6-micron band of telluric ozone and its rotational analysis. *J. of Chem. Phys.*, 24, pp. 1183—1186.

KAPLAN, L. D., and EGGERS, D. F., 1956: Intensity and line-width of the 15-micron CO_2 band, determined by a curve-of-growth method. *J. of Chem. Phys.*, **25**, pp. 876—883.

KOSTKOWSKI, H. J., and KAPLAN, L. D., 1957: Absolute intensities of the 721 and 742 cm^{-1} bands of CO_2. *J. of Chem. Phys.*, **26**, pp. 1252—1253.

KOTANI, M. ET AL., 1955: *Table of molecular integrals.* Tokyo, Maruzen Co., Ltd.

MADDEN, R. P., 1956: Study of CO_2 absorption spectra between 15 and 18 microns. Ph. D. dissertation, Johns Hopkins University.

PEKERIS, C. L., 1932: The development and present state of the theory of the heat balance in the atmosphere. *Mass. Inst. of Technology Meteor. Course, Prof. Notes*, No. 5.

PLACZEK, G., 1954: The functions $E_n(x)=\int_1^\infty e^{-xu}u^{-n}du$, and appendices by G. Blanch and Math. Tables Project. *Nat. Bur. of Standards Applied Math. Series*, No. 37,pp. 57—111.

PLASS, G. N., 1952: A method for the determination of atmospheric transmission functions from laboratory absorption measurements. *J. Opt. Soc. of America*, **42**, pp. 677—683.

WALSHAW, C. D., 1957: Integrated absorption by the 9.6 μ band of ozone. *Quart. Jour. R.M.S*, **83**, pp. 315—321.

(Manuscript received April 30, 1958)

On the General Circulation of the Atmosphere

By JULE CHARNEY[1]

Massachusetts Institute of Technology, Cambridge, Mass.

Abstract

A model of the general circulation of the atmosphere is constructed in the following manner: The energy sources are determined on the assumption that the atmosphere is isothermal, transparent to solar radiation and "grey" to terrestrial radiation, and that the earth has zero heat capacity. Energy dissipation is provided for by a correspondingly simplified frictional mechanism. On the basis of these assumptions the steady, zonally symmetric circulation is calculated for a simple geometry. This circulation is found to be unstable with respect to asymmetric wave perturbations, and the form of the most unstable perturbation is calculated by solving numerically the small amplitude perturbation equations for a coarse grid. It is next assumed that the perturbation grows in amplitude while retaining its shape, modifying the zonal flow by the action of eddy stresses and eddy conduction of heat, until the rate at which it receives potential energy from the zonal flow just balances the rate at which it loses potential energy by radiative equalization of temperature and the rate at which it loses kinetic energy by the work of the Reynolds stresses on the zonal flow and by frictional dissipation. The mean zonal velocity and temperature profiles for this new equilibrium state are calculated from the momentum and heat equations as functions of the amplitude of the wave perturbation. The amplitude is then determined from the energy balance condition, and both the perturbation and the mean zonal flow are calculated. The resultant circulation is found to be similar to that obtained by Phillips (1956) in his well-known numerical experiment and to have about the same degree of verisimilitude. It is pointed out, however, that the fluctuating motion in the actual atmosphere is better described by a system consisting of two or more perturbation modes and a zonal flow in mutual interaction. The results of a barotropic numerical integration made some years ago in Princeton are presented as an example of the type of interaction that might be expected to occur.

1. Introduction

The outlines of a self-consistent theory of the general circulation of the atmosphere have been gradually emerging from the extensive work of recent years on the planetary motions of the atmosphere. The mechanisms of the formation of the large-scale migratory waves and vortices in the zonal flow and their roles in transferring momentum and heat have been greatly clarified, the dynamical necessity and importance of mean meridional circulations has been demonstrated, and attempts to model atmospheric circulations in the laboratory have met with considerable success. It is now the task of the dynamic meteorologist to combine the physical principles revealed by this work into a comprehensive mathematical theory from which the particular behavior of the earth's atmosphere may be deduced. The task is a formidable one and no simple solution can be foreseen. In this article a possible method of attack is set forth and is applied to a highly simplified physical situation.

The argument is based on the following set of principles, which may now be accepted with a certain degree of confidence: (1) The axially-symmetric convective circulation set up by solar heating on a uniform, rotating earth is unstable for asymmetric wave-like perturbations traveling in the zonal direction (CHARNEY, 1947; EADY, 1949; FJØRTOFT 1950). (2) These perturbations act as eddy elements distorting the mean zonal flow through the action of Reynolds stresses and eddy conduction of heat (JEFFRIES,

[1] This research was sponsored by the Office of Naval Research under contract Nonr — 1841 (18) with added support from the Geophysics Research Directorate, Air Force Cambridge Research Center.

1926; STARR et al, 1954, 1957; J. BJERKNES et al, 1955, 1957). (3) The zonal flow is ordinarily stable with respect to horizontal energy exchange processes so that the perturbations tend to transfer kinetic energy to the zonal flow through the work of the Reynolds stresses (KUO, 1951: CHARNEY, 1951). (4) The large-scale components of the flow are quasi-geostrophic except near the equator; hence one may use the geostrophic equations in their analysis (CHARNEY, 1948; ELIASSEN, 1949). These equations provide a simple means to compute mean zonal flow once the sources of momentum and heat are known (ELIASSEN, 1952). The method of computation is based on the principle that the changes in zonal momentum and density brought about by the real and eddy sources of momentum and heat must be such as to maintain a condition of geostrophic and hydrostatic balance. Since these changes are not usually compensating, meridional circulations are required to restore the balance.

The underlying problem of this article may be stated in purely hydrodynamical terms as follows: A distributed heat source decreasing in intensity from equator to pole produces a slow, axially-symmetric, convective circulation with a poleward temperature gradient and a zonal wind field increasing in westerly intensity with height. This flow is unstable for small-amplitude wave-like perturbations, which therefore grow to finite amplitude. It is required to calculate the mean properties of the final state of motion and also, if possible, the nature of the perturbations.

One may distinguish two possible classes of motion: (1) The secondary wave disturbances may themselves be stable and approach a constant-amplitude equilibrium state. (2) Several different disturbance modes may be excited by instability of the primary flow, by instability of the secondary disturbances, or by self-interaction of the secondary disturbances; these modes will appear as a regularly fluctuating state of motion or as a state approaching fully developed turbulence. Whereas the atmospheric circulation is better described by a fluctuating state of motion it may resemble the equilibrium state in important aspects. Both states have been produced in the laboratory, the equilibrium state by HYDE (1953) in a fluid confined to a rotating cylindrical annulus heated at the outer rim and cooled at the inner, and the fluctuating state by FULTZ (1951) in a rotating cylindrical pan of water heated at the rim. Apparently the constraint imposed by the inner boundary of the annulus prevents the occurrence of the multiple modes. In this article no attempt will be made to deal directly with the regularly fluctuating or turbulent regimes. However, some results which may have a bearing on the fluctuating state will be presented at its conclusion.

By confining attention to the steady-amplitude regime it becomes possible to introduce a number of simplifying approximations which greatly facilitate the mathematical analysis. We shall take into account only the non-linear interaction between the disturbance and the mean flow, disregarding self-interaction of the disturbance and the subsequent cascade of interactions. By the same token we shall permit changes in amplitude but no changes in the shape of the disturbance.

Within the limitations imposed by these approximations, one may envisage the process by which the finite-amplitude regime is established in the following way: Imagine a small wave disturbance superimposed on the steady symmetric flow produced by the symmetric heating. In the initial stages its interaction with the mean motion may be ignored. But as its amplitude grows, at first exponentially, it begins to distort the main flow, directly through the action of the Reynolds stresses and eddy conduction of heat, and indirectly through the action of the forced meridional circulations. At length the mean flow becomes so modified that the rate at which the perturbation receives energy from the mean flow is just balanced by the rate at which it loses potential energy through radiative temperature equalization and kinetic energy through the action of the Reynolds stresses and through frictional dissipation. The form of the disturbance is first calculated from the first-order instability theory; the modification of the mean flow as a function of an undetermined amplitude is then calculated by means of the quasi-geostrophic equations; and finally the amplitude is determined by making use of energy balance relationships.

The above second-order perturbation technique has been applied with good result by STUART (1958) to the calculation of two-dimensional, finite-amplitude disturbances of Poiseuille flow and of flow between rotating cylinders. W. MALKUS and VERONIS (1958) have applied a similar technique to the study of finite amplitude convection. A qualitative analysis of the general circulation of the atmosphere from much the same point of view as is adopted here has been given by EADY (1950).

2. Construction of the model

Most of the fluid dynamical elements that are deemed to be of importance are contained implicitly in a simplified mathematical model of the atmosphere developed by the writer and N. PHILLIPS (1953) as part of a numerical weather prediction program. The results of a numerical experiment involving fixed heat sources and a dissipation mechanism have been presented by PHILLIPS (1956). The success of this experiment in predicting several important features of the general circulation may be attributed, at least in part, to the inclusion of these elements, Hence, in the present treatment, the same model will be adopted, but with different mechanisms of heating and frictional dissipation.

The motion is referred to the *Rossby plane*, in which the kinematical effects of the earth's curvature are ignored but the dynamical effects are retained through the inclusion of the variability of the Coriolis parameter. The flow is assumed to be periodic in the zonal direction and to be bounded at the north and south by latitudinal vertical walls whose distance apart is the same as that between pole and equator. To have in mind a concrete physical picture one might think of the flow as occupying the annular region between two rotating concentric circular cylinders whose radii are so large compared to their distance apart that curvature effects may be ignored, except that this model would lack the stabilizing effect of the variable vertical component of the earth's vorticity (Coriolis parameter) on the zonal flow. The model is thus neither an accurate representation of atmospheric flow nor of flow in a cylindrical annulus, but as has been made abundantly clear by ROSSBY's work (cf. 1939) it is capable of shedding much light on natural planetary motions and on their laboratory analogues.

The continuously varying atmosphere is replaced by an atmosphere consisting essentially of two layers in each of which the horizontal velocities and pressure forces are independent of height. This is the simplest kind of model in which meteorologically relevant potential-to-kinetic energy conversions can take place. It is the natural extension of ROSSBY's barotropic model (1939) to a baroclinic atmosphere.

For easy reference Phillips' notation will be adopted:

x = cartesian distance coordinate to east
y = cartesian distance coordinate to north
p = pressure
t = time
Φ = latitude
(u, v, ω) = time rates of change of (x, y, p) following the motion
$\mathbf{V}$ = horizontal velocity vector
g = acceleration of gravity
ϕ = geopotential (= gz where z is height)
Ω = angular speed of earth's rotation
$\mathbf{k}$ = vertical unit vector
ζ = vertical vorticity component
f = Coriolis parameter = $2\Omega \sin \Phi$
f_0 = $2\,\Omega \sin \Phi_0$ (Φ_0 a mean latitude)
β = $(df/dy)_0 = 2\,\Omega \cos \Phi_0/a$
a = radius of earth
$2W$ = $\pi a/2$ = distance between walls = distance between pole and equator
A = lateral kinematic eddy-viscosity coefficient
τ = frictional stress acting at a horizontal surface
θ = potential temperature
T = temperature
α = specific volume
dQ/dt = non-adiabatic rate of heating per unit mass
∇ = horizontal gradient operator on an isobaric surface
c_p, c_v = specific heats of air at constant pressure and volume
R = $c_p - c_v$
ψ = ϕ/f_0 = geostrophic stream function

Pressure is the vertical coordinate and quantities at the isobaric levels 0, 250, 500, 750, and 1,000 mb are denoted by the subscripts 0, 1, 2, 3, and 4, respectively. The boundary conditions are $\omega = 0$ at $p = 0$ and, approximately, $\omega = 0$ at $p = p_4$.

The simplified equations of motion consist of the geostrophic vorticity equation at the levels 1 and 3, the continuity equations at the levels 1 and 3, and the geostrophic first law of thermodynamics at the level 2, in all of which equations vertical derivatives are expressed as centered finite differences. One obtains (cf. PHILLIPS, 1956) the vorticity equations,

$$(\partial/\partial t + \mathbf{V}_1 \cdot \nabla)(\zeta_1 + \beta y) - f_0\omega_2/p_2 = = A\nabla^2\zeta_1 - g\nabla \times \boldsymbol{\tau}_2 \cdot \mathbf{k}/p_2, \qquad (2.1)$$

$$(\partial/\partial t + \mathbf{V}_3 \cdot \nabla)(\zeta_3 + \beta y) + f_0\omega_2/p_2 = = A\nabla^2\zeta_3 + g\nabla \times (\boldsymbol{\tau}_2 - \boldsymbol{\tau}_4) \cdot \mathbf{k}/p_2, \qquad (2.2)$$

the continuity equations,

$$\omega_2/p_2 = \nabla \cdot \mathbf{V}_3 = -\nabla \cdot \mathbf{V}_1, \quad (2,3)$$

and the first law of thermodynamics,

$$f_0\omega_2/p_2 = \lambda^2 [(\partial/\partial t + \mathbf{V}\cdot\nabla)(\psi_1 - \psi_3) - (R/f_0c_p)dQ_2/dt], \quad (2.4)$$

where

$$\lambda^2 = \frac{f_0^2}{RT_2(\theta_1 - \theta_3)/\theta_2}, \quad (2.5)$$

and the velocity $\mathbf{V}$ and vorticity ζ appearing in eqs. 2.1, 2.2, and 2.4 are evaluated geostrophically from

$$\mathbf{V} = \nabla\psi \times \mathbf{k} \quad (2.6)$$

and

$$\zeta = \nabla \times \mathbf{V}\cdot\mathbf{k} = \nabla^2\psi \quad (2.7)$$

The quantity $\psi_1 - \psi_3$ in eq. 2.4 may be taken as proportional to the temperature at the level 2. This follows from the hydrostatic equation

$$\alpha_2 = -\left(\frac{\partial\Phi}{\partial p}\right)_2 \cong \frac{\phi_1 - \phi_3}{p_2} \quad (2.8)$$

and the equation of state

$$RT_2 = p_2\alpha_2 \cong p_2\left(\frac{\phi_1 - \phi_3}{p_2}\right) = f_0(\psi_1 - \psi_3). \quad (2.9)$$

It is thereby seen that, while eqs. 2.1, 2.2, and 2.4 govern the velocity components at the levels 1 and 3, they govern the temperature at only the level 2. The model does not permit the calculation of temperature variations in the vertical, and the numerical value of the stability parameter λ^2 defined by 2.5 must be prescribed as an empirical constant. A more sophisticated treatment would eliminate this empirical element from the theory by dealing with models containing three or more degrees of freedom in the vertical.

Phillips postulated a linearly-varying, geographically-fixed heat source

$$dQ_2/dt = -2H(y/W) \quad (2.10)$$

where H was determined from estimates of actual mean heat transports in the atmosphere, the origin of the y-coordinate being placed midway between the walls. In reality, of course, the atmosphere determined its own heat sources as a function primarily of its temperature distribution. We shall therefore replace the fixed heat source of Phillips' model by a very simple radiative transfer mechanism according to which the atmosphere is assumed to be isothermal, transparent to solar radiation and "grey" to terrestrial radiation, and the ground is assumed to have negligible heat capacity. For additional verisimilitude the albedo of the earth ε will be prescribed. Because of the extensive covering of the earth's surface by ocean it would be more realistic to assume zero heat capacity for the solid earth and infinite heat capacity (fixed surface temperatures) for the oceans. However, such an assumption would introduce complexities which should be avoided in a first treatment.

Let us assume that the sun is at equinox, then the flux of solar radiation at the outer limit of the atmosphere is approximately

$$S = \frac{S_0}{\pi}\cos\Phi,$$

where S_0 is the solar constant. Since the ground is assumed to have no heat capacity, the net radiative flux at the ground is zero. Hence by Kirchoff's Law

$$(1-\varepsilon)S + \nu\sigma T_2^4 - \sigma T_4^4 = 0,$$

where σ is Boltzmann's black-body constant and ν is the absorptivity of the atmosphere for long-wave radiation. The net heating of a column is therefore

$$\nu\sigma T_4^4 - 2\nu\sigma T_2^4 = \nu[(1-\varepsilon)S - (2-\nu)\sigma T_2^4],$$

and the heating per unit mass is

$$\frac{dQ_2}{dt} = \frac{g\nu(2-\nu)}{p_2}\left[\left(\frac{1-\varepsilon}{2-\nu}\right)S - \sigma T_2^4\right]. \quad (2.11)$$

This expression for dQ_2/dt is linearized as follows: Let $T_2{}^*$ be the radiative equilibrium temperature,

$$T_2^* = \left[\left(\frac{1-\varepsilon}{2-\nu}\right)\frac{S}{\sigma}\right]^{\frac{1}{4}} \cong T_R - \left(\frac{\partial T^*}{\partial\Phi}\frac{d\Phi}{dy}\right)_{y=0} = T_R\left(1 - \frac{y}{4a}\right), \quad (2.12)$$

where $T_R = T_2{}^*(0)$. Setting $\varepsilon = 0.4$ and $\nu = 0.8$ we get $T_R = 238°$ C which is sufficiently close to T_m the observed mean value of T_2 to permit one to equate the two. Eq. 2.11 therefore becomes

$$\frac{dQ_2}{dt} = \frac{gv(2-v)\sigma}{2p_2}[(T_2^*)^4 - T_2^4] =$$

$$\cong \frac{4gv(2-v)\,\sigma T_m^3(T_2^* - T_2)}{2p_2} \cong$$

$$\cong \frac{4gv(2-v)\sigma T_m^4}{2p_2}\left[1 - \frac{y}{4a} - \frac{f_0(\psi_1 - \psi_3)}{RT_m}\right] \quad (2.13)$$

which may be interpreted to state that the air is heated or cooled according as its temperature $f_0(\psi_1 - \psi_3)/R$ is below or above the radiative equilibrium temperature $T_2{}^* = T_m(1 - y/4a)$.

In Phillips' model frictional dissipation was assumed to take place by lateral diffusion of momentum by small-scale eddies and by surface friction. For simplicity he took the surface stress to be proportional to the first power of the surface wind; thus in eqs. 2.1 and 2.2 he set

$$\left.\begin{aligned} \nabla \times \boldsymbol{\tau}_2 \cdot \mathbf{k} &= 0, \\ \nabla \times \boldsymbol{\tau}_4 \cdot \mathbf{k} &= -p_2 k \zeta_4 / g, \end{aligned}\right\} \quad (2.14)$$

in which ζ_4 was obtained by extrapolation downward from levels 1 and 3:

$$\zeta_4 = \tfrac{3}{2}\zeta_3 - \tfrac{1}{2}\zeta_1.$$

The constant k was given the value 4×10^{-6} sec^{-1} corresponding to a mean anemometer-level wind of about 10 m sec^{-1}.

While there is good evidence for the surface dissipation mechanism postulated by Phillips, the data do not support even an order of magnitude choice of the eddy coefficient for lateral momentum diffusion. What evidence there is favors vertical diffusion of momentum by small-scale eddies as the primary dissipation mechanism in the free atmosphere. RIEHL (1951) and PALMÉN (1955 a, b) have obtained values which agree at least in order of magnitude. We shall therefore retain the surface friction postulated in Phillips' model but shall replace the horizontal small-scale eddy transport of momentum in the free atmosphere by a vertical transport. This is accomplished by setting A equal to zero in eqs. 2.1 and 2.2 and writing

$$\boldsymbol{\tau}_2 = \mu\left(\frac{\partial \mathbf{V}}{\partial z}\right)_2 \cong -\frac{\mu g}{\alpha_2}\left(\frac{\partial \mathbf{V}}{\partial p}\right)_2 \cong$$

$$\cong \frac{p_2}{g} k_i(\mathbf{V}_1 - \mathbf{V}_3) \quad (2.15)$$

where $k_i = \mu g^2/\alpha_2 p_2^2$. Accepting the value $\mu = 225$ gm cm^{-1} given by PALMÉN (1954 a) we obtain $k_i = \frac{1}{2} \times 10^{-6}$ sec^{-1}. Finally, we shall assume that ζ_4 is approximately equal to $\frac{1}{2}\zeta_3$ rather than to $\frac{3}{2}\zeta_3 - \frac{1}{2}\zeta_1$.

Phillips also postulates a lateral diffusion of heat by small-scale eddies, but since this effect, in addition to being quite hypothetical, can be shown to have negligible influence on the symmetric motion it will not be considered here.

3. Calculation of the mean zonal momentum

Let L be the spatial period of the motion and define the zonally averaged mean value of the quantity $G\ (x, y, t)$ by

$$\overline{G}(y,t) = \frac{1}{L}\int_0^L G(x,y,t)\,dx, \quad (3.1)$$

and its perturbation value by

$$G'(x,y,t) = G(x,y,t) - \overline{G}(y,t) \quad (3.2)$$

The momentum equations are then obtained by averaging eqs. 2.1 – 2.4 and utilizing 2.6 together with the boundary conditions $v\ (\pm W) = 0$. After an integration by parts one gets

$$\frac{\partial^2 \bar{u}}{\partial y \partial t} + f_0 \frac{\overline{\omega}_2}{p_2} = A\frac{\partial^3 \bar{u}_1}{\partial y^3} - \frac{\partial^2 M_1}{\partial y^2} - k_i \frac{\partial}{\partial y}(\bar{u}_1 - \bar{u}_3), \quad (3.3)$$

$$\frac{\partial^2 \bar{u}_3}{\partial y \partial t} - f_0 \frac{\overline{\omega}_2}{p_2} = A\frac{\partial^3 \bar{u}_3}{\partial y^3} - \frac{\partial^2 M_3}{\partial y^2} + k_i \frac{\partial}{\partial y}(\bar{u}_1 - \bar{u}_3) - k\frac{\partial \bar{u}_4}{\partial y}, \quad (3.4)$$

$$\frac{\overline{\omega}_2}{p_2} = \frac{\partial \bar{v}_3}{\partial y} = -\frac{\partial \bar{v}_1}{\partial y}, \quad (3.5)$$

$$f_0 \frac{\overline{\omega}_2}{p_2} = \lambda^2\left[\frac{\partial}{\partial t}(\bar{\psi}_1 - \bar{\psi}_3) - \frac{R}{f_0 c_p}\frac{d\overline{Q}_2}{dt} + \frac{\partial B}{\partial y}\right], \quad (3.6)$$

where

$$M = \overline{u'v'}, \quad B = \overline{v'(\psi_1' - \psi_3')}. \quad (3.7)$$

Integration of eqs. 3.3 and 3.4 with respect to y and use of 3.5 then gives

$$\frac{\partial \bar{u}_1}{\partial t} - f_0 \bar{v}_1 = A\frac{\partial^2 \bar{u}_1}{\partial y^2} - \frac{\partial M_1}{\partial y} - k_i(\bar{u}_1 - \bar{u}_3), \quad (3.8)$$

$$\frac{\partial \bar{u}_3}{\partial t} - f_0 \bar{v}_3 = A\frac{\partial^2 \bar{u}_3}{\partial y^2} - \frac{\partial M_3}{\partial y} + k_i(\bar{u}_1 - \bar{u}_3) - k\bar{u}_4, \quad (3.9)$$

in which the terms $-\partial M_1/\partial y$ and $-\partial M_3/\partial y$ represent the forces due to the Reynolds stresses M_1 and M_3. We note that the non-linear terms $\bar{v}_1\partial\bar{u}_1/\partial y$ and $\bar{v}_3\partial\bar{u}_3/\partial y$ are absent from the left sides of the above equations. This is because they are absent in the geostrophic approximation.

When the quantities M_1, M_3, and B are known, one may utilize eqs. 3.5, 3.6, 3.8, and 3.9 to calculate the mean zonal flow and the mean meridional circulation in the steady state ($\partial/\partial t = 0$). The axially – symmetric circulation in Phillips' model is readily found to be

$$\bar{u}_1 = \frac{U}{2}\left(1 - \frac{y^2}{W^2}\right) - \frac{U}{12}\left(1 - \frac{y^4}{W^4}\right),$$

$$\bar{u}_3 = \frac{\bar{u}_1}{3} - \frac{4}{3}\frac{U}{\delta^2}\left(1 - \frac{y^2}{W^2}\right) + \\ + \frac{8}{3}\frac{U}{\delta^4}\left(1 - \frac{\cosh \delta y/W}{\cosh \delta}\right),$$

$$\bar{v}_1 = -\bar{v}_3 = \frac{AU}{f_0 W^2}\left(1 - \frac{y^2}{W^2}\right),$$

where $U = \lambda^2 RHW^3/f_0 c_p A$ and $\delta^2 = 3kW^2/2A$. Phillips adopted the following values for the physical parameters:

$$\begin{aligned} f_0 &= 10^{-4}\ \text{sec}^{-1} \\ R &= 287\ \text{kj ton}^{-1}\ \text{deg}^{-1} \\ c_p &= 1004\ \text{kj ton}^{-1}\ \text{deg}^{-1} \\ A &= 10^5\ \text{m}^2\ \text{sec}^{-1} \\ k &= 4\times 10^{-6}\ \text{sec}^{-1} \\ H &= 2\times 10^{-3}\ \text{kj ton}^{-1}\ \text{sec}^{-1} \\ \lambda^2 &= 1.5\times 10^{-12}\ \text{m}^{-2} \end{aligned}$$

From these one gets $U = 10{,}760$ m sec^{-1} and $\delta^2 = 1{,}500$, which give max $\bar{u}_1 = 5U/12 = 4{,}480$ m sec^{-1} and max $\bar{u}_3 \cong$ max $u_1/3 = 1{,}490$ m sec^{-1}. These extremely large values were never attained in Phillips' experiment because the symmetric flow became unstable long before the steady state was reached. One asks, however, whether the symmetric flow is as unstable as is implied by Phillips' assumptions. This is unlikely, for the large values of $\bar{u}_1$ and $\bar{u}_3$ can be attributed both to the choice of an artificial lateral eddy-viscosity and to the fixing of the heat sources. The latter assumption implies that the heat transport across a latitude circle is the same before and after the appearance of eddy motions. Obviously this cannot be so, for the development of eddies through instability of the symmetric circulation increases the rate of depletion of the potential energy of the mean flow and hence increases the meridional heat transport. The heat transport across a latitude circle must therefore be smaller in the symmetric regime than in the eddying regime. The present model permits such changes in heat flow and has, moreover, a stronger internal frictional dissipation mechanism. Thus one finds that the steady state flow in the symmetric case is far weaker than is implied by Phillips' assumptions and is consequently less unstable.

In the case of steady state symmetric motion eqs. 2.13, 3.5 and 3.6 combine to give

$$f_0\frac{d\bar{v}_1}{dy} = f_0\Lambda\left[1 - \frac{y}{4a} - \frac{f_0(\bar{\psi}_1 - \bar{\psi}_3)}{RT_m}\right] - \lambda^2\frac{dB}{dy}, \tag{3.10}$$

where

$$\Lambda = 4\lambda^2 Rg\nu(2-\nu)\sigma T_m^4/f_0^2 c_p p_2 = \\ = 3.06\times 10^{-6}\ \text{sec}^{-1}, \tag{3.11}$$

and eqs. 3.8 and 3.9 become

$$-f_0\bar{v}_1 = -dM_1/dy - k_i(\bar{u}_1 - \bar{u}_3), \tag{3.12}$$

$$-f_0\bar{v}_3 = -dM_3/dy + k_i(\bar{u}_1 - \bar{u}_3) - k\bar{u}_3/2. \tag{3.13}$$

Addition of the latter two gives

$$0 = -d(M_1 + M_3)/dy - k\bar{u}_3/2, \tag{3.14}$$

which states that the convergence of momentum into a unit vertical column is exactly balanced by its flux through the ground due to surface friction. Internal friction leads merely to a redistribution of momentum, and the net transport of the earth's momentum vanishes because the net mass transport $\bar{v}_1 + \bar{v}_3$ vanishes.

Elimination of $\bar{v}_1$ between eqs. 3.10 and 3.12 gives the following equation for $\bar{\psi}_1 - \bar{\psi}_3$

$$f_0\Lambda\left[\frac{f_0(\bar{\psi}_1 - \bar{\psi}_3)}{RT_m} - \left(1 - \frac{y}{4a}\right)\right] = \\ = -\lambda^2\frac{dB}{dy} - \frac{d^2M_1}{dy^2} + k_i\frac{d^2}{dy^2}(\bar{\psi}_1 - \bar{\psi}_3), \tag{3.15}$$

subject to the boundary conditions

$$\frac{d\bar{\psi}_1}{dy}(\pm W) = \frac{d\bar{\psi}_3}{dy}(\pm W) = 0. \tag{3.16}$$

From the way in which the eq. 3.15 was derived it is possible to give a physical interpretation of its individual terms. The left-hand side represents the radiative heating due to the deviation of the temperature from its value at radiative equilibrium. The first term on the righthand side is the convergence of the eddy heat transport, and the second and third terms are the convergence of the heat transport due to the meridional motion produced by the eddy momentum flux. An increase in the eddy convergence of heat will tend to raise the temperature so that the radiative heat loss to space can compensate for the gain. The effect of the eddy momentum flux is more complex: An increase in the convergence of the eddy momentum flux must be accompanied by a southward meridional flow at high levels and a northward flow at low levels to compensate for the momentum change (eq. 3.12). Since entropy increases upward there is a corresponding southward heat transport. The second term in eq. 3.15 therefore represents the heating due to the meridional circulation produced by the large-scale eddy stresses. The last term is again an indirect heating effect due to the influence of internal friction on the meridional circulation.

The velocity $\bar{u}_3$ is given immediately by eq. 3.14, and $\bar{u}_1 - \bar{u}_3$ is determined by solving eq. 3.15 for $\bar{\psi}_1 - \bar{\psi}_3$, or else by solving

$$k_i \frac{d^2}{dy^2}(\bar{u}_1 - \bar{u}_3) - \frac{f_0^2 \Lambda}{RT_m}(\bar{u}_1 - \bar{u}_3) =$$

$$= -\lambda^2 \frac{d^2 B}{dy^2} - \frac{d^3 M_1}{dy^3} - \frac{\Lambda f_0}{4a}, \qquad (3.17)$$

which is obtained by differentiating eq. 3.15 with respect to y. The meridional velocity is then found by substitution in eq. 3.12.

The symmetric circulation is found by setting $M_1 = M_3 = B = 0$ in eqs. 3.14, 3.17 and 3.12. One obtains

$$\left.\begin{aligned} \bar{u}_3 &= 0, \\ \bar{u}_1 &= \frac{RT_m}{4af_0}\left(1 - \frac{\cosh \gamma y}{\cosh \gamma W}\right), \\ \bar{v}_1 &= k_i \bar{u}_1, \end{aligned}\right\} \qquad (3.18)$$

where

$$\gamma^2 = f_0^2 \Lambda / RT_m\, k_i = 90 \times 10^{-14} \mathrm{m}^{-2}. \quad (3.19)$$

The velocities $\bar{u}_1$ and $\bar{v}_1$ calculated from the above formulae are shown in Figs. 1 and 2 respectively. For comparison the corresponding curves for a

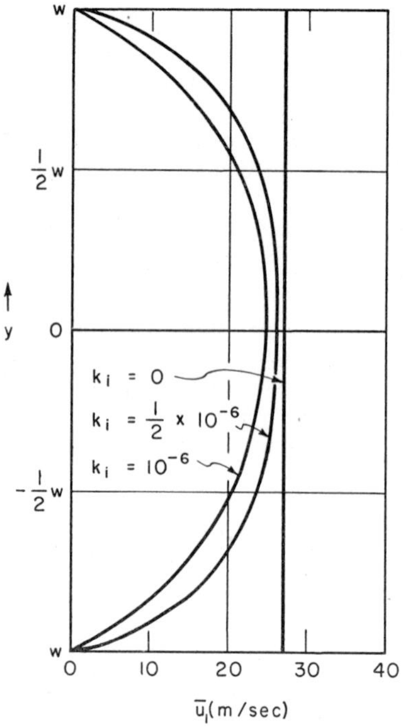

Fig. 1. The zonal velocity at level 1 mb in the steady symmetric regime for different values of the internal frictional coefficient k_i.

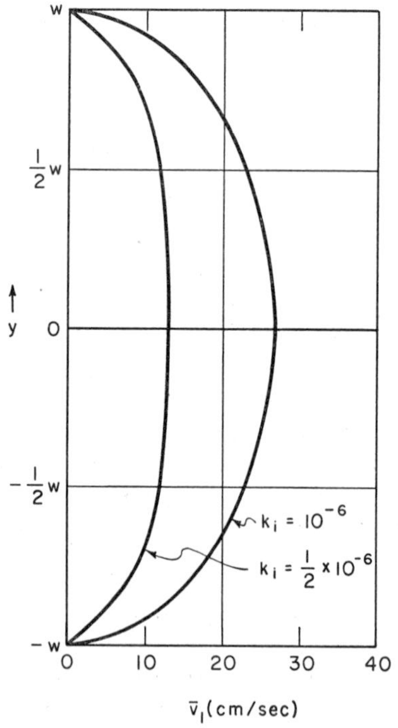

Fig. 2. The meridional velocity at level 1 in the steady symmetric regime for different values of the internal frictional coefficient k_i.

value of k_i twice as great as that computed from PALMÉN's (1955 a) data, and corresponding more to RIEHL's (loc. cit.), are also shown. It will be seen that the zonal velocities change little. We may therefore accept these velocities with greater confidence than is warranted by the accuracy k_i itself.

The case of vanishingly small friction is that of radiative equilibrium. From eq. 3.18 one obtaines $v_1 = 0$ and $\bar{u}_1 = RT_m/4af_0 = 26.8$ m sec^{-1} which is shown as a vertical line in Fig. 1.

The symmetric flow consists of a broad band of upper westerlies decreasing rapidly to zero at the northern and southern walls and a slow, thermally direct meridional circulation. This circulation is not very efficient in transporting heat: the pole-to-equator temperature difference at radiative equilibrium is $WT_m/2a$ or 93 °C and is reduced an amount $WT_m/2a\gamma$ or19 °C by the circulation.

4. The eddy motion

We shall now demonstrate that the symmetric flow which has just been established is unstable and shall calculate the form of the most unstable wave disturbance. Substituting

$$\psi = \bar{\psi} + \psi', \quad \mathbf{V} = \bar{\mathbf{V}} + \mathbf{v}', \quad \zeta = \bar{\zeta} + \zeta', \quad \omega = \bar{\omega} + \omega'$$

in eqs. 2.1, 2.2, 2.4, 2.13, 2.14 and 2.15, and recalling that $A = 0$ and $\zeta_4 = \frac{1}{2}\zeta_3$, we obtain

$$\left.\begin{array}{l} \nabla^2(\partial\psi_1'/\partial t) + \mathbf{V}_1'\cdot\nabla\zeta_1' + \bar{\mathbf{V}}_1\cdot\nabla\zeta_1' + \\ \quad + \mathbf{V}_1'\cdot\nabla\bar{\zeta}_1 - f_0\omega_2'/p_2 = -k_i(\zeta_1' - \zeta_3') \\ \nabla^2(\partial\psi_3'/\partial t) + \mathbf{V}_3'\cdot\nabla\zeta_3' + \bar{\mathbf{V}}_3\cdot\nabla\zeta_3' + \mathbf{v}_3'\cdot \\ \quad \cdot\nabla\bar{\zeta}_3 + f_0\omega_2'/p_2 = k_i(\zeta_1' - \zeta_3') - k\zeta_3'/2 \\ f_0\omega_2'/p_2 = \lambda^2[\partial(\psi_1' - \psi_3')/\partial t + \mathbf{V}_1'\cdot \\ \quad \cdot\nabla(\psi_1' - \psi_3') + \bar{\mathbf{v}}_1\cdot\nabla(\psi_1' - \psi_3') + \mathbf{V}_1'\cdot \\ \quad \cdot\nabla(\bar{\psi}_1 - \bar{\psi}) + (\Lambda f_0^2/RT_m\lambda^2)(\psi_1' - \psi_3')] \end{array}\right\} \quad (4.1)$$

If second order terms are ignored, and the heating and frictional terms are also ignored, in anticipation of the result that the time constants for heating and friction will be found to be large in comparison with the amplification time of an unstable disturbance, the following pair of equation are obtained by setting

$$\psi' = \Psi(y)exp[i\mu(x - ct)]:$$

$$\left.\begin{array}{l} (\bar{u}_1 - c)[d^2\Psi_1/dy^2 - \mu^2\Psi_1 - \\ \quad - \lambda^2(\Psi_1 - \Psi_3)] + [\beta - d^2\bar{u}_1/dy^2 + \\ \quad + \lambda^2(\bar{u}_1 - \bar{u}_3)]\Psi_1 = 0 \\ (\bar{u}_3 - c)[d^2\Psi_3/dy^2 - \mu^2\Psi_3 + \\ \quad + \lambda^2(\Psi_1 - \Psi_3)] + [\beta - d^2\bar{u}_3/dy^2 - \\ \quad - \lambda^2(\bar{u}_1 - \bar{u}_3)]\Psi_3 = 0 \end{array}\right\} \quad (4.2)$$

As it has not been possible to solve these equations exactly, we shall resort to finite-difference approximations. Noting first that $\bar{u}$ is symmetric about $y = 0$, we look for a symmetric solution for Ψ. The interval $-W \leq y \leq W$ is divided into four equal sub-intervals at $y = -W$, $-\frac{1}{2}W$, 0, $\frac{1}{2}W$, W, and the second derivatives appearing in eqs. 4.2 are expressed as centered finite incremental ratios at the points $y = 0$ and $y = \frac{1}{2}W$, thus

$$\frac{d^2\Psi_1}{dy^2}(0) \simeq \frac{\Psi_1(\frac{1}{2}W) - 2\Psi_1(0) + \Psi_1(-\frac{1}{2}W)}{(\frac{1}{2}W)^2} =$$

$$= \frac{8}{W^2}[\Psi_1(\tfrac{1}{2}W) - \Psi_1(0)],$$

$$\frac{d^2\Psi_1}{dy^2}(\tfrac{1}{2}W) \simeq \frac{\Psi_1(W) - 2\Psi_1(\frac{1}{2}W) + \Psi_1(0)}{(\frac{1}{2}W)^2} =$$

$$= \frac{4}{W^2}[\Psi_1(0) - 2\Psi_1(\tfrac{1}{2}W)],$$

and similarly for Ψ_3. In deriving the above equations we have made use of the conditions that $\Psi(\pm W) = 0$, which follow from the condition that the normal velocity $v' = \partial\psi_1/\partial x$ vanishes at each wall. Substitution in eqs. 4.2 gives four linear homogeneous equations in the four unknown quantities $\Psi_1(0)$, $\Psi_1(\frac{1}{2}W)$, $\Psi_3(0)$, $\Psi_3(\frac{1}{2}W)$. If these equations are to possess a non-zero solution, the determinant of their coefficients must vanish. This gives a biquadratic equadratic equation in c. The solutions with a positive imaginary part c_i lie on two distinct branches, $C_1(\mu)$ and $C_2(\mu)$,, of the function c, corresponding to two distinct unstable modes of motion. It may be seen from Table 1 that both modes have nearly the same maximum value of the amplification rate μc_i. It therefore appears likely that both will exist simultaneously. Since, however, the present method of analysis applies only to a single mode, a choice must be made, but it must be borne in mind that the necessity for such a choice places a definite limitation on

Table I

$\mu(m^{-1})$	$c_1(m\ \mathrm{sec}^{-1})$	$c_2(m/\mathrm{sec}^{-1})$	$\mu(c_i)_1$	$\mu(c_i)_2$
2.005×10^{-6}	8.636 ± 4.832	10.094 ± 5.695	—	—
1.563×10^{-6}	$7.429 \pm 3.062i$	8.323 ± 0.440	4.79	—
1.444×10^{-6}	$6.787 \pm 4.129i$	$7.871 \pm 3.142i$	5.96	4.54
1.337×10^{-6}	$6.048 \pm 4.898i$	$7.394 \pm 4.305i$	6.55	5.76
1.228×10^{-6}	$5.130 \pm 5.498i$	$6.814 \pm 5.246i$	6.75	6.44
1.114×10^{-6}	$3.949 \pm 5.848i$	$6.095 \pm 5.929i$	6.50	6.61
1.010×10^{-6}	$2.566 \pm 5.765i$	$5.322 \pm 6.364i$	5.82	6.42
0.891×10^{-6}	$0.54 \pm 4.67\ i$	$4.30 \pm 6.51\ i$	4.16	5.80
0.668×10^{-6}	-6.00 ± 9.30	$1.76 \pm 6.08\ i$	—	4.05
0	-84.1 ± 90.2	-5.7 ± 9.4	—	—

the present analysis and that a more general analysis would provide at least for the simultaneous interaction of both modes with the mean flow. We shall choose the branch $c_1(\mu)$ with

$$c = c_r + ic_i = 5.130 + 5.498\,i\ \mathrm{m\ sec^{-1}} \quad (4.3)$$

giving the maximum amplification rate μc_i. The corresponding wave length $L = 2\pi/\mu$ is 5,116 km. The e-folding time for a disturbance is thus $1/\mu c_i = 1.7$ days, which is small compared to the internal dissipation time $1/k_i = 23$ days, and, to a lesser extent, small compared to the surface dissipation time $2/k = 5.8$ days. From the third of eqs. 4.1 the relaxation time for radiational heating is found to be $RT_m\,\lambda^2 A f^2 = 38.8$ days. Thus the neglect of internal friction and heating in the perturbation equations is amply justified but the neglect of surface friction is only approximately so.

Inserting the value for c into the four linear homogeneous equations for the Ψ's, we obtain the following relations

$$\left.\begin{aligned} \Psi_1(\tfrac{1}{2}W) &= 1.437\,e^{35.3^\circ i}\,\Psi_1(0),\\ \Psi_3(0) &= 0.699\,e^{-62.4^\circ i}\,\Psi_1(0),\\ \Psi_3(\tfrac{1}{2}W) &= 0.869\,e^{-17.9^\circ i}\,\Psi_1(0). \end{aligned}\right\} \quad (4.4)$$

It may be seen that the wave in the streamlines at level 1 precedes the wave in the streamlines at level 3 by a phase angle which varies from 62.4° at $y = 0$ to $35.3^\circ - (-17.9^\circ) = 53.2^\circ$ at $y = \pm \frac{1}{2}W$ and that at each level there is a south-west to north-east tilt of the troughs and ridges south of $y = 0$ and a north-west to south-east tilt north of $y = 0$. From the quantities in 4.4 one may calculate the eddy momentum flux M and the eddy heat flux B defined by eqs. 3.7. A sample calculation will suffice to show how this is done. At any fixed time we may write

$$\left.\begin{aligned} &\psi_1'(x,0) = \Pi \sin \mu x, \quad \psi_1'(x, \tfrac{1}{2}W) = \\ &\qquad = 1.437\,\Pi \sin(\mu x + 35.3^\circ),\\ &\psi_3'(x,0) = 0.699\,\Pi \sin(\mu x - 64.3^\circ),\\ &\text{where } \Pi = \Psi_1(0). \end{aligned}\right\} \quad (4.5)$$

Then, if y-derivatives are expressed as centered differences, we have, for example,

$$M_1(\tfrac{1}{2}W) = \overline{u_1'(x, \tfrac{1}{2}W)\, v_1'(x, (\tfrac{1}{2}W)}$$

$$= -\frac{1}{L}\int_0^L \left[\frac{\psi_1'(x,W) - \psi_1'(x,0)}{W}\right] \cdot \frac{\partial \psi_1'}{\partial x}(x, \tfrac{1}{2}W)\,dx$$

$$= -0.719\,(\sin 35.3^\circ)\cdot(\mu/W)\Pi^2 = $$

$$= -0.416(\mu/W)\Pi^2.$$

Altogether we obtain

$$\left.\begin{aligned} M_1(0) &= M_1(W) = M_3(\mathrm{x}) = M_3(W) = 0,\\ M_1(\tfrac{1}{2}W) &= -0.416\,(\mu/W)\Pi^2,\\ M_3(\tfrac{1}{2}W) &= -0.213\,(\mu/W)\Pi^2,\\ B(0) &= 0.310\,\mu\Pi^2,\\ B(\tfrac{1}{2}W) &= 0.499\,\mu\Pi^2,\ B(W) = 0. \end{aligned}\right\} \quad (4.6)$$

For comparison the values Ψ calculated from $c = 6.095 + 5.929$ i, $\mu = 1.114 \times 10^{-6} m^{-1}$, $L =$

5,640 km, corresponding to the maximum μc_i for the second mode, are given below together with the calculated fluxes.

$$\left.\begin{aligned}
\Psi_1(\tfrac{1}{2}W) &= 0.356 e^{133.0^\circ i}\,\Psi_6(0)\\
\Psi_3(0) &= 0.687\, e^{-55.0^\circ i}\,\Psi_1(0),\\
\Psi_3(\tfrac{1}{2}W) &= 0.199\, e^{-87.1^\circ i}\,\Psi_1(0),\\
M_1(\tfrac{1}{2}W) &= -0.1303\,(\mu/W)\,\Pi^2,\\
M_3(\tfrac{1}{2}W) &= -\,0.0420\,(\mu/W)\,\Pi_2,\\
B(0) &= 0.2815\,\mu\Pi^2,\\
B(\tfrac{1}{2}W) &= 0.0255\,\mu\Pi^2.
\end{aligned}\right\} \quad (4.7)$$

We note that although the tilts of the troughs and ridges have the same sense the relative amplitudes and the eddy transports are very different from those previously calculated.

It now becomes possible to evaluate the new zonal velocity distribution produced by the Reynolds stresses and eddy conduction of heat. This is done by writing eqs. 3.14 and 3.17 in finite central difference form and solving for $u(0)$ and $u(\frac{1}{2}W)$, making use of the symmetry properties of M and B, and the fact that $dM/dy = 0$ at $y = \pm W$. We obtain

$$\left.\begin{aligned}
u_1(0) &= \bar{u}_1^*(0) + 0.069\,\mu^2\Pi^2\\
u_1(\tfrac{1}{2}W) &= \bar{u}_1^*(\tfrac{1}{2}W) - 0.221\,\mu^2\Pi^2,\\
\bar{u}_3(0) &= 0.022\,\mu^2\Pi^2,\\
\bar{u}_3(\tfrac{1}{2}W) &= 0,
\end{aligned}\right\} \quad (4.8)$$

where the asterisks denote the symmetric solution 3.18.

These expressions reduce to those for the undisturbed symmetric flow when Π is set equal to zero.

5. Determination of the amplitude

By hypothesis the disturbance will grow and modify the mean flow until the rate at which it receives potential energy from the mean flow just balances the rate at which it dissipates potential energy by radiative temperature equalization, does work on the mean flow by means of the Reynolds stresses and dissipates kinetic energy by friction.

The energy equations are obtained by eliminating the ω_2' term from the first two of eqs. 4.1 by means of the third, multiplying the first by ψ_1', the second by ψ_3', adding, and integrating over the rectangle $0 \leq x \leq L, -W \leq y \leq W$. This gives.

$$\begin{aligned}
\frac{d}{dt}\Big\{\frac{1}{2}\iint [(\nabla\psi_1')^2 + (\nabla\psi_3')^2]\,dxdy &+ \\
+\frac{1}{2}\lambda^2 \iint (\psi_1' - \psi_3')^2\,dxdy &= \\
= \lambda^2 \iint B(\bar{u}_1 - \bar{u}_3)\,dxdy &+ \\
+ \iint \left(\bar{u}_1 \frac{dM_1}{dy} + \bar{u}_3 \frac{dM_3}{dy}\right) dxdy &- \\
- \varkappa\lambda^2 \iint (\psi_1' - \psi_3')^2\,dxdy &- \\
- \frac{k}{2} \iint (\nabla\psi_3')^2\,dxdy &- \\
- k_i \iint [\nabla(\psi_1' - \psi_3')]^2\,dxdy, &\qquad (5.1)
\end{aligned}$$

where $\varkappa = \Lambda f_0^2/RT_m\lambda^2$. This equation may be given the following interpretation: The first term on the lefthand side represents the rate of change of perturbation kinetic energy and the second term the rate of change of perturbation potential energy; the first term on the right-hand side represents the rate of conversion of mean flow potential energy to perturbation potential energy, the second term the rate of conversion of mean flow kinetic energy to perturbation kinetic energy, the third term the rate of destruction of perturbation potential energy by radiative temperature equalization, the fourth the loss of perturbation kinetic energy through surface friction, and the fifth the loss of perturbation kinetic energy through internal friction. In Phillips' notation this equation may be written

$$\begin{aligned}
\frac{d}{dt}(K' + P') = \{\bar{P}\cdot P'\} - \{K'\cdot\bar{K}\} &- \\
- \{P'\cdot R\} - \{K'\cdot k\} - \{k'\cdot k_i\}, &\qquad (5.2)
\end{aligned}$$

where the terms are self-explanatory. The first two integrals on the right-hand side are evaluated by substituting the expressions 4.8 and approximating by finite sums, and the last three by proceeding first, as with the calculation of M and B, to obtain

$$\overline{(\psi_1' - \psi_3')^2} = \begin{cases} 0.40\,\Pi^2 \text{ at } y = 0,\\ 0.66\,\Pi^2 \text{ at } y = W/2;\end{cases}$$

$$\overline{(\nabla\psi_3')^2} = \begin{cases} 0.24\,\mu^2\Pi^2 \text{ at } y = 0,\\ (0.24/W^2 + 0.38\,\mu^2)\,\Pi^2 \text{ at } y = W/2;\end{cases}$$

$$\overline{[\nabla(\psi_1' - \psi_3')]^2} = \begin{cases} 0.42\,\mu^2\Pi^2 \text{ at } y = 0,\\ (0.42/W^2 + 0.66\,\mu^2)\,\Pi^2 \\ \qquad \text{at } y = W/2.\end{cases}$$

and then approximating the integrals by finite sums. We find

$$\left.\begin{aligned}
\{\bar{P}\cdot P'\} &= \frac{L\lambda^2 W^2}{\mu W}\,(16.0\,\mu^2\,\Pi^2 - \\
&\qquad\qquad - 0.103\,\mu^4\Pi^4),\\
\{K'\cdot\bar{K}\} &= \frac{2L}{\mu W}(5.41\,\mu^2\Pi^2 + \\
&\qquad\qquad + 0.0166\,\mu^4\Pi^4),\\
\{P'\cdot R\} &= \varkappa\lambda^2 LW(0.86\,\Pi^2),\\
\{K'\cdot k\} &= \tfrac{1}{2}\,k\,LW(0.51\,\mu^2\Pi^2),\\
\{K'\cdot k_i\} &= k_i LW(0.88\,\mu^2\Pi^2).
\end{aligned}\right\} \quad (5.3)$$

In accordance with our hypothesis that the flow approaches a constant amplitude state the above expressions are substituted in eq. 5.2 and the left-hand side is set equal to zero. Dividing through by the factor L we get the following equation for $\chi = \mu^2\Pi^2$:

$$\overset{\{\bar{P}\cdot P'\}}{96.93\,\chi - 0.624\,\chi^2} \;\overset{\{K'\cdot\bar{K}\}}{- 1.75\,\chi + 0.005\,\chi^2} \; - \overset{\{P'\cdot R\}}{1.29\,\chi} - \overset{\{K'\cdot k\}}{5.10\,\chi} - \overset{\{K'\cdot k_i\}}{2.20\,\chi} = 0. \quad (5.4)$$

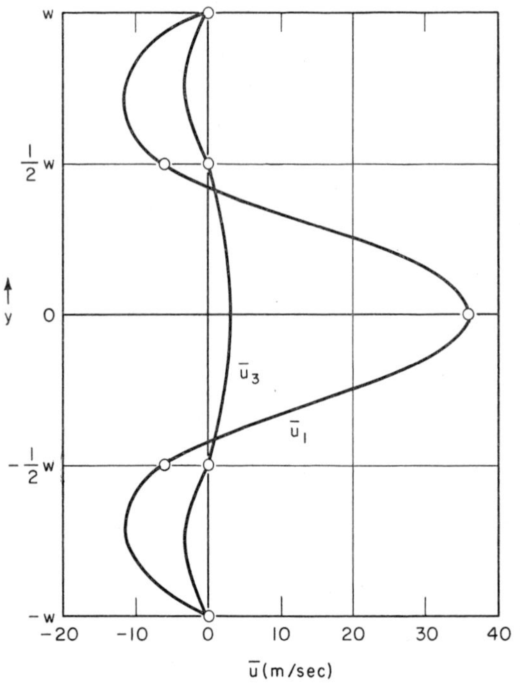

Fig. 3. The zonal velocities at levels 1 and 3 in the steady asymmetric regime.

Its solution, $\chi = 137.7$ m² sec⁻² enables to to calculate the perturbation stream functions (4.6) and the mean flow velocities (4.8).

Before discussing the results, some of the implications of eq. 5.4 are worth noting. The first and second order terms of the $\{\bar{P}\cdot P'\}$ conversion dominate the remaining first and second order terms respectively. This means that the energy equilibrium occurs primarily because the mean flow becomes so modified through eddy processes that its potential energy is no longer converted into perturbation potential energy; frictional and radiative dissipation and, surprisingly, the $\{K'\cdot\bar{K}\}$ conversion play very little role in bringing about the equilibrium. This is not to say that in the final equilibrium the various conversions are not of comparable magnitude. Thus, if the soliton of eq. 5.4 is substituted back in 5.4, the five energy conversions, in the order in which they appear, are found to be in the ratios (1.52) : (0.34) : (0.18) : 0.70) : 0.30).

It also follows that in the initial stages of the disturbance, when its amplitude is small, its growth is determined by the $\{\bar{P}\cdot P'\}$ conversion almost entirely, and, as anticipated, the frictional dissipations are small, amounting altogether to less than 10 per cent of the $\{\bar{P}\cdot P'\}$ conversion. However, before applying these results to the atmosphere one must take into account the considerable geometrical distortions and artificial constraints in the model. These may be expected to influence the ratio of $\{\bar{P}\cdot P'\}$ and $\{K'\cdot\bar{K}\}$ since this ratio depends directly upon the factor λ^2W^2, and $2W$ is unrealistically large for the north-south scale of a typical disturbance.

6. Discussion of results

The $\bar{u}_1$ and $\bar{u}_3$ profiles are shown in Fig. 3. By comparison with Fig. 1 we see that the eddy exchange process drastically modifies the symmetric profiles. In place of a broad band of westerlies at level 1 there is now a westerly jet in middle latitudes and weaker easterly jets near the walls; and at level 3, where before the zonal velocity was zero, there is now a band of westerlies at middle latitudes and easterlies to the north and south. The corresponding temperature profile is changed from one in which the temperature decreases uniformly from wall to wall to one in which the variation is concentrated in narrow bands at middle latitudes and near the walls. The total pole-to-equator temperature contrast is considerably reduced by the eddies: the temperature contrast under conditions of purely radiative equilibrium, is first reduced from 93° C to 74° C by the symmetric convective circulation, and then to 26° C by the eddy processes.

A comparison of Figs. 2 and 4 shows that the eddy motion decreases the intensity of the thermally direct meridional circulation slightly in middle latitudes and greatly near the walls. It may be seen from eqs. 3.12 and 3.17 that these effects are due both to the changes in $\bar{u}_1$—$\bar{u}_3$ brought about by the eddy heat transports and the convergence of the eddy flux of momentum. Much depends upon the fact that the computed eddy heat flux has a minimum at $y=0$.

The streamlines at the level 3 (750 mb) and the temperature at the level 2 (500 mb) are shown in Fig. 5. The patterns are seen to correspond to an extra-tropical cyclone in the early stages of development. They resemble the patterns computed by PHILLIPS (1956) at a relatively early stage after the onset of instability. In view, however, of the artificial geometrical constraints and the crude character of the approximations used, one can expect no more than a crude correspondence to actual atmospheric or laboratory situations. The most valid comparison would be with the results of a machine computation made for the same model. Such a test is planned for the future.

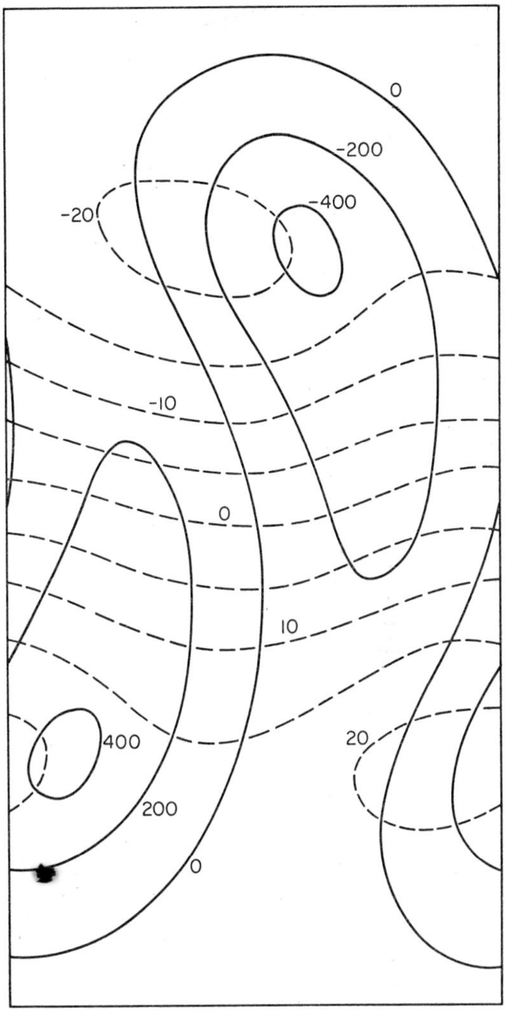

Fig. 5. Height contours (solid lines) at level 3 and isotherms at level 2. The height is measured in feet and the temperature in degrees centigrade.

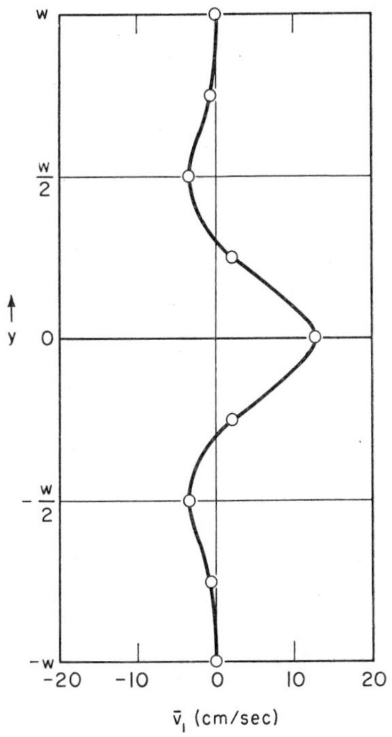

Fig. 4. The meridional velocity level 1 at in the steady asymmetric regime.

7. Critique and conclusion

The analysis in this article is subject to criticism on several points:

(1) It has been assumed that the symmetric circulation permits of only one unstable mode, which then grows to a finite steady amplitude. Such flows can be realized in the laboratory where the energy inputs may be controlled, but may not be realized in nature where the energy

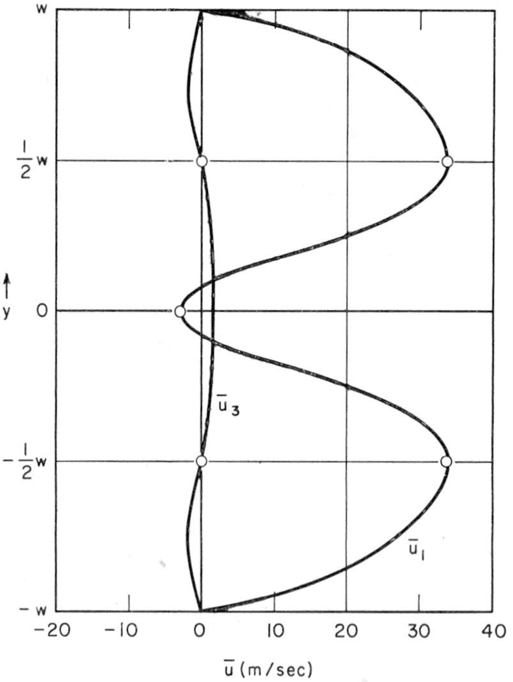

Fig. 6. The zonal velocities at levels 1 and 3 calculated for the second eigenmode.

inputs are unique. Indeed, the physical parameters in the atmosphere are such that the symmetric flow is probably unstable for more than one eigenmode. The meridional temperature gradient and the vertical shear of the zonal wind in the symmetric case are not very different from those obtained under conditions of radiative equilibrium where the zonal winds are uniform at each level. The stability problem in this case can easily be solved (cf. PHILLIPS 1951). The eigenfunctions are of the form

$$\psi \sim \exp\,[i\varkappa(x - ct)]\,\cos\,(n\pi y/2W). \quad (7.1)$$

where n is an odd integer, and the criterion for instability is

$$2 - 2\sqrt{1 - \frac{\beta^2}{\lambda^4(\bar{u}_1 - \bar{u}_3)^2}} < \frac{\mu^2}{\lambda^2} + \frac{n^2\pi^2}{4W^2\lambda^2} < 2 + 2\sqrt{1 - \frac{\beta^2}{\lambda^4(\bar{u}_1 - \bar{u}_3)^2}}.$$

Substituting the radiative equilibrium value of $\bar{u}_1 - \bar{u}_3$ we find that these inequalities are satisfied for $n = 3$ and 5 as well as for $n = 1$. In the case under discussion, a horizontal shear in the zonal winds acts to stabilize the motion, but does not prevent the occurrence of at least a second unstable eigenmode. Thus all four roots of the biquadratic equation described in section 4 are complex for a finite range of μ, and since these roots occur in conjugate pairs, there are at least two unstable modes. The simultaneous occurrence of several unstable modes gives rise to a fluctuating or aperiodic regime which cannot be treated by the methods developed in this paper. To overcome this difficulty a principle of selection has been used according to which the most unstable of the eigenmodes eventually dominates, but it is doubtful whether this principle can be rigorously justified.

The zonal and meridional velocity profiles based on the assumption that the second eigenmode, given by eqs. 4.7, predominates have been calculated and are shown in Figs. 6 and 7. It will be seen that these velocities are very different from those shown in Figs. 3 and 4. The difference is due primarily to the fact that the maximum eddy flux of heat now takes place at $y = 0$. As a consequence there is an eddy convergence of heat to the north of this latitude and a divergence to the south, with a rise in

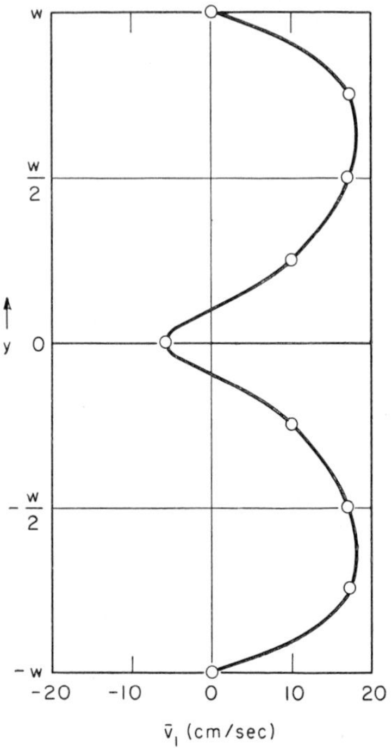

Fig. 7. The meridional velocity at level 1 calculated for the second eigenmode.

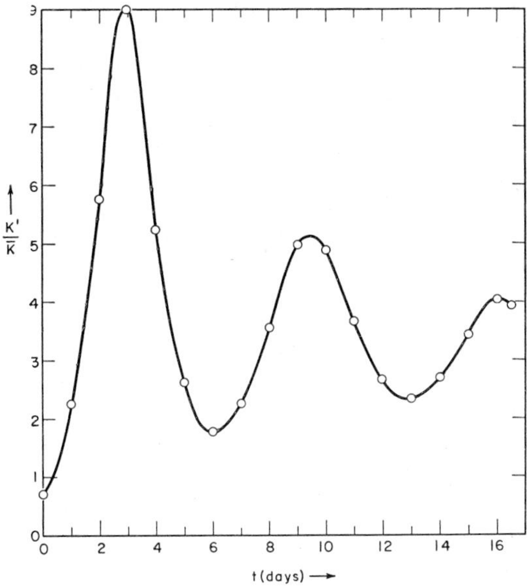

Fig. 8. The ratio of the perturbation kinetic energy. to the mean kinetic energy.

temperature to the north and a fall to the south to allow for radiative compensation. This produces a diminished thermal wind at middle latitudes and therefore a diminished zonal wind at upper levels. The actual zonal flow observed in the atmosphere, and, under certain circumstances, in laboratory models, can be described as a vacillation (to use the term employed by Hide, loc. cit.) between two extremes similar to the ones represented by Figs. 3 and 6. This suggests that the motion is more suitably described as a shuttling of energy between these modes and the mean flow. The logical extension of the present analysis should therefore include means for dealing with several disturbance modes.

Several years ago the author observed an analogous phenomenon in the interaction between a finite-amplitude wave disturbance and the zonal motion in two-dimensional barotropic flow. The initial mean flow was described by the stream function

$$\bar{\Psi} = -U \int \cos^6 my\,dy$$

or

$$\bar{u} = U \cos^6 my$$

where $m = \Pi/2W$, $W = 2\,775$ km, $U = 50$ m sec^{-1}. The initial perturbation had the form

$$\Psi' = (U/2\,l) \sin l \times \cos my$$

where $l = 2\Pi/L$ and $L = 7\,070$ km was chosen to give an initially large rate of amplification. The evolution of the flow was calculated numerically on the Institute for Advanced Study electronic computer by solving the following vorticity equation, governing two-dimensional, incompressible, viscous flow on the β-plane:

$$\frac{\partial \eta}{\partial t} + u\frac{\partial \eta}{\partial x} + v\frac{\partial \eta}{\partial y} = \nu \nabla^2 \eta, \qquad \eta = \nabla^2 \Psi + \beta y,$$

or

$$\nabla^2 \frac{\partial \Psi}{\partial t} = \frac{\partial(\nabla^2 \Psi + \beta y)}{\partial(x, y)}.$$

A small coefficient of viscosity $\nu = 2 \times 10^4$ m^2 sec^{-1} was introduced to prevent the occurence of large truncation errors associated with extreme gradients of vorticity. The flow was calculated for 16.5 days. The fluctuation in the ratio of the perturbation kinetic energy K' to the zonal kinetic energy $\bar{K}$ is shown in Fig. 8. It will be seen that this quantity executes a very regular damped oscillation with a period of between 6 and 6.5 days. During the 16.5 days the total kinetic energy decreased at the constant rate of 1.62 % of its initial value per day. However, calculations made with zero viscosity indicated that the damping of the oscillation was not a viscous effect. An examination of the actual form of the perturbation and of the zonal flow showed that the perturbation tended to vary between two extreme forms, associated with two extreme forms of the zonal velocity profile. It is not known whether the two perturbation modes can actually be approximated by eigenmodes of a suitably defined mean flow.

(2) The exaggeration of area in polar regions, the failure to provide for the rapid diminution of the Coriolis parameter towards the equator, and the artificial constraint of walls make comparison with the atmosphere in the vicinity of the walls almost meaningless. The geometric distortions are not difficult to overcome; one need only deal with motion on a sphere. But to extend the analysis to equatorial regions it may be necessary to replace the geostrophic approximation equations by the primitive equations or the balance equations. These equations would also enable one to take into account the transfer of relative momentum by the meridional circulations (vid. eqs. 3.8 and 3.9).

(3) Fixing the static stability, as in the present

model, produces a bias in favor of development, for a release of potential energy, i.e., a sinking of cold air and a rising of warm, implies an upward flow of heat which in turn increases the static stability and inhibits the development. A model which permits the static stability to vary is also necessary on general principles, for no theory of the general circulation of the atmosphere can be complete unless it accounts for the vertical temperature structure. A two-level, four-parameter model devised by LORENZ (1958), in which both the velocities and the temperatures are permitted to vary at each of two levels, seems particularly well suited for this purpose. The vertical temperature structure must be calculated as a combined effect of heat transport by radiation and heat transport by small- and large-scale convection.

(4) The radiative mechanism in the present model is effectively Newtonian conduction. This mechanism may be criticized as being too highly simplified for realistic application to the atmosphere. SIMPSON (1928) pointed out that an increase in surface temperature need not necessarily lead to an increase in back radiation to space, for the back radiation comes primarily from the tops of clouds and from high levels where the temperatures do not appear to respond readily to surface changes. Moreover, the effect of condensation and cloud have been excluded altogether in this paper although these effects are important in the actual atmosphere. For example, about one half of the heat transported in middle latitudes is in the form of latent heat of water vapor.

(5) While there is some justification for the frictional mechanism used in the model, one should, in principle, avoid wherever possible the use of obscure and unphysical austausch hypotheses. The physical importance of internal friction in the free atmosphere is in any case questionable. It is therefore desirable to calculate the circulation in the absence of internal friction. The symmetric circulation for zero internal friction is exactly the state of radiative-geostrophic equilibrium, with $\bar{u}_3 = 0$ and $\bar{u}_1 = 26.8$ m sec^{-1} (see Fig. 2). Since there is no horizontal shear of the zonal currents in this case the unstable streamline perturbations will be symmetric about the trough and ridge axes and the eddy stresses $\overline{u'v'}$ will vanish. The stream field will have the form 7.1, and the eddy flux of heat will be proportional to $\cos^2(n\pi y/2W)$. Taking $n = 1$ one finds from eq. 3.17 that the effect of the eddy heat transport will be to decrease $\bar{u}_1 - \bar{u}_3$ at $y = 0$ and to increase it at $y = \pm\frac{1}{2}W$. The zonal velocity at level 3 will remain zero, as follows from eq. 3.14. These zonal velocity profiles do not correspond well to observed profiles, but one should bear in mind that there are other effects which might well modify this picture. The meridional temperature gradient at radiative equilibrium on a spherical earth would not be uniform but would increase toward the poles. The thermal wind would not be constant, and there would be a tilt in the streamline trough and ridge axes and consequently a non-zero Reynolds stress, which would also contribute towards changes in the zonal velocities.

It is clear from the foregoing remarks that the theory presented in this article is but a crude first step towards the synthesis of a general circulation model. The approach, however, gives an insight into the nature of the processes at work and with suitable refinement and generalization should provide a means for analyzing more precise and realistic models.

8. Acknowledgment

I had the opportunity to discuss the contents of this paper with Professor Rossby shortly before his death. He was critical of the heat transfer mechanism in my model. But it was characteristic of him that his criticism was positive and enthusiastic. He had become convinced that the earth as a whole was capable of storing heat over long periods of time, and it was in his role as an innovator and proponent, not as an opponent, that he urged consideration for non Newtonian-conductive mechanisms which tend to preserve temperature anomalies. I should like to acknowledge my indebtedness to him, not merely for these discussions, but for all our other discussions to which he gave himself so unstintingly. Their influence will be found in this, as well as in almost all the others of my papers.

REFERENCES

Bjerknes, J., et al., 1955: Investigations of the general circulation of the atmosphere. *Final Report Gen. Circ. Proj., No. AF 19 (122)—48*, U.C.L.A., Dept. of Meteorology.

— 1957: Large scale synoptic processes. *Final Report Gen. Circ. Proj., No. AF (604)—1286*, U.C.L.A., Dept. of Meteorology.

Charney, J. G., 1947: The dynamics of long waves in a baroclinic westerly current. *J. Meteor.*, **4**, pp. 135—162.

— 1948: On the scale of atmospheric motions. *Geof. Publ.*, **17**, pp. 1—17.

— 1951: On baroclinic instability and the maintenance of the kinetic energy of the westerlies. *Procès-Verbaux Séances de l'Assoc. de Météor.*, Bruxelles, U.G.G.I., pp. 47—63.

— and Phillips, N., 1953: Numerical integration of the quasi-geostrophic equations for barotropic and simple baroclinic flows. *J. Meteor.*, **10**, pp. 71—99.

Eady, E. T., 1949: Long waves and cyclone waves. *Tellus*, **1**, pp. 33—52.

— 1950: The cause of the general circulation of the atmosphere. *Cent. Proc. R. Met. Soc.*, London, pp. 156—172.

Eliassen, A., 1949: The quasi-static equations of motion with pressure as independent variable. *Geof. Publ.*, **17**, pp. 1—44.

— 1952: Slow thermally or frictionally controlled meridional circulation in a circular vortex. *Astrophys. Norv.*, **5**, pp. 19—60.

Fjørtoft, R., 1950: Application of integral theorems in deriving criteria of stability for laminar flows and for the baroclinic circular vortex. *Geof. Publ.*, **17**, pp. 1—52.

Fultz, D., 1951: Experimental analogies to atmospheric motions. *Am. Meteor. Soc. Compendium of Meteorology*, Boston, A. Meteor. Soc., pp. 1235—1248.

Hide, R., 1953: Fluid motion in the earth's core and some experiments on thermal convection in a rotating liquid. *Fluid Models in Geophysics. Proc. First Symposium on Use of Models in Geophysics*, Johns Hopkins University, pp. 101—116.

Jeffries, H., 1926: On the dynamics of geostrophic winds. *Quart. J. Roy. Met. Soc.*, **52**, pp. 85—104.

Kuo, H.-L., 1951: Dynamical aspects of the general circulation and the stability of zonal flow. *Tellus*, **3**, pp. 268—284.

Lorenz, E. N., 1957: Static stability and atmospheric energy. *Scientific Report No. 9, Gen. Circ. Proj., No. AF 19(604)—1000*, M.I.T., Dept. of Meteorology, pp. 450—490.

Malkus, W. V. R., and Veronis, G., 1958: Finite amplitude cellular convection. *J. Fluid Mech.*, **4**, pp. 225—260.

Palmén, E., 1955 a: On the mean meridional circulation in low latitudes of the northern hemisphere in winter and the associated meridional and vertical flux of angular momentum. *Societas Scientiarum Fennica. Commentationes Physico-Mathematicae*, **XVII**, pp. 1—33.

— 1955 b: On the mean meridional drift of air in the frictional layer of the west-wind belts. *Quart. J. Roy. Met. Soc.*, **81**, pp. 459—461.

Phillips, N., 1951: A simple three-dimensional model for the study of large-scale extratropical flow patterns. *J. Meteor.*, **8**, pp. 381—394.

— 1956: The general circulation of the atmosphere: a numerical experiment. *Quart. J. Roy. Met. Soc.*, **82**, pp. 123—164.

Riehl, H., et al., 1951: The north-east trade of the Pacific Ocean. *Quart. J. Roy. Met. Soc.*, **77**, pp. 598—626.

Rossby, C.-G., 1939: Relation between variations in the intensity of the zonal circulation of the atmosphere and the displacements of the semi-permanent centers of action. *J. Marine Res.*, **2**, pp. 38—55.

Simpson, G. C., 1928: Further studies in terrestrial radiation. *Mem. Roy. Met. Soc.*, **3**, p. 23.

Starr, V. P., et al., 1954: Studies of the atmospheric general circulation, Part I. *Final Report Gen. Circ. Proj., AF 19(122)—153*, M.I.T., Dept. of Meteorology, 535 pp.

— 1957: Studies of the atmospheric general circulation, Part II. *Final Report Gen. Circ. Proj., AF 19(604)—1 000*, M.I.T., Dept. of Meteorology, 672 pp.

Stuart, J. T., 1958: On the non-linear mechanics of hydro-dynamic stability. *J. Fluid Mech.*, **4**, pp. 1—21.

(Manuscript received August 29, 1958)

Some Results Concerning the Distribution and Total Amount of Kinetic Energy in the Atmosphere as a Function of External Heat Sources and Ground Friction

By R. FJØRTOFT
Norwegian Meteorological Institute, Oslo

Abstract

In a long-term steady state of the atmosphere there is necessarily a positive correlation between potential temperature and vertical velocity whereby the work of gravity can balance frictional dissipation of kinetic energy. (By the phrase »work of gravity» it is meant only a certain component part of the total work of gravity, the latter of course being zero in a steady state. In this paper it is essentially the work exerted by gravity if only those components of vertical velocity are considered which are compensated in each horizontal plane.) The corresponding stabilization in the vertical is offset by a cooling in high levels relative to the lower levels. In a vertically stable atmosphere this will tend to decrease total variance of potential temperature. To keep this constant it is therefore necessary, in a gravitationally stable atmosphere, to have a horizontal distribution of heating whereby relatively warm regions are heated and cold regions cooled. We might formulate this in other words by introducing the total variance of the deviation of potential temperature from its horizontal mean. This variance is steadily decreased in a vertically stable atmosphere because of the warming by downward currents in the cold region and cooling by ascending currents in the warm region. The balance is maintained by the forementioned horizontal distribution of heating (LORENTZ 1955).

For motions satisfying approximately the thermal wind balance equation it is possible to eliminate vertical velocities in the integral expressing the work of gravity. It follows that this work, save for a positive proportionality factor, essentially equals the change which by advection alone would be caused in the square of the horizontal temperature gradients integrated over the total atmosphere. Since on the other hand the total square of potential temperature is unaffected by advection, it is necessary to have an advective flow of temperature amplitude, or variance, from horizontally larger to smaller scales. Since the large-scale temperature field, on which the smaller scale fields ultimately feed, essentially is a zonal one, we let this be represented by zonally averaged temperatures, while the corresponding eddy temperatures are used for the small-scale field. The total horizontal temperature variance is a sum of the pure large- and small scale parts. The advectively conditioned change in one of them, equals, with opposite sign, the corresponding change in the other, and is proportional to the meridional gradient of mean potential temperature and the eddy flux of potential temperature. The rate at which the eddy variance is increased by this large-scale turbulent mixing process determines also, when it is multiplied by the difference between the inverse of the squares of two wavelengths characterizing the typical scales of the mean and eddy field, the rate at which the integrated horizontal gradient squared is increased advectively, and thereby also the long-term effect of gravity forces. This is essentially used to balance dissipation in the eddy motion which is put proportional to surface eddy kinetic energy. Besides this balance condition we have two others. The one expresses that the advectively conditioned increase in eddy temperature variance is balanced, both by a damping due to heating, and the temperature effects of vertical motions. The other expresses that differential heating in meridional direction balances the drop, by advection, in amplitude of the mean temperature field.

Of these three balance conditions, the two first ones determine a relation between the meridional gradient of mean temperature, vertical stability, and the typical wavelengths of the mean and eddy temperature fields. It is concluded that (1) a lower limit for the meridional temperature gradient exists below which no eddy motion is possible in a long-term steady state, and (2) that an upper and lower limit for the characteristic wavelength of the eddy temperature field exist beyond which the meridional temperature gradient becomes so large that the third balance condition is violated, whereby instead the equatorial regions are cooled and the polar regions warmed. For wavelengths between these critical limits eddy solutions are possible with varying amounts of surface eddy and "mean" kinetic energy, and eddy and "mean" temperature variance, depending, essentially on the typical wavelength used, and on the numerical value of the parameters determining the intensity of the external heat sources. As a basic principle for picking out the solution which is considered most likely we take the wavelength for which the effect of gravity forces becomes a maximum in the eddy motion. In finding this wavelength it is at first assumed that vertical stability might be considered a quasi-constant. Next stability is considered to increase with increasing effect of the gravity forces which has the forementioned stabilizing influence in the vertical. It is shown that particular solutions exist for which the effect of gravity will increase with increasing meridional differential heating due to external sources. The corresponding increase in vertical stability will cause a shift of the typical wavelength towards higher values because of the way in which the critical wavelengths depend upon vertical stability. It is pointed out that this is an agreement with the results of rotating fluid experiments. Finally the theory is tested to some extent on atmospheric conditions.

Introduction

It is possible to define long-term steady states of the atmosphere. They constitute averages over periods long enough to make frictional dissipation of kinetic energy large as compared with the observed changes in energy, and further long enough to make the averages quasi-constant. A long-term steady state of a certain kind is solely a product of certain invariable properties of atmospheric air on the one hand, and on the other hand of certain external conditions, which may vary. It is clear that a long-term steady state of one kind cannot change to one of a different kind under constant external conditions. In this article we plan to discuss how the external parameters determine total kinetic energy together with its distribution between a surface and a thermal wind field, and between a zonally averaged field and the corresponding eddies, including the typical horizontal wavelength of the latter.

1. Derivation of some general integral relationships

For the meteorologically significant motions we may adopt a set of simplified equations:

$$\nabla \cdot Q\mathbf{v} = 0 \tag{1}$$

$$\frac{d\mathbf{v}}{dt} + 2\Omega \times \mathbf{v} - \mathbf{F} - \Theta \nabla \varphi = \text{laminar}^1 \tag{2}$$

$$\frac{d\Theta}{dt} = \frac{\Theta}{C_p T} \cdot q \equiv H. \tag{3}$$

[1] In this form the equation of motion applies sufficiently well to the lower, say, nine tenths of the mass of the atmosphere.

As boundary conditions we assume for vertical velocity:

$$\left.\begin{aligned} w &= 0 \text{ at the ground;} \\ Qw &= 0 \text{ at the top of the atmosphere.} \end{aligned}\right\} \tag{4}$$

The symbols above have the following meanings:

- Q = standard density depending upon z only
- φ = geopotential
- $\mathbf{F}$ = frictional force
- Θ = potential temperature divided by a constant average potential temperature in the atmosphere[2]
- q = supply of heat per unit time and mass[3]
- T = temperature
- $\mathbf{v}$ = velocity
- Ω = the earth's angular velocity

From eqs. (1)—(4) are obtained the following integral relationships:

$$\Delta \int \tfrac{1}{2}\, \mathbf{v}^2 dm = \int g\Theta w d\varkappa - \int \delta d\varkappa \tag{5}$$

$$\Delta \int (\tfrac{1}{2}\, \mathbf{v}^2 - \varphi\Theta)\, dm = -\int \varphi H d\varkappa - \int \delta d\varkappa \tag{6}$$

$$\Delta \int \Theta dm = \int H d\varkappa \qquad (7$$

$$\Delta \int \tfrac{1}{2}\, \Theta^2 dm = \int \Theta H d\varkappa$$

[2] Θ will be denoted potential temperature.
[3] H defined in (3) will be denoted as heating.

Here $\int dm = \int_V Q dV$ where V is the volume of the atmosphere, $\int d\varkappa \equiv \int_t \int dm dt$ where t is the length of the integration period, Δ indicates the corresponding increase of the quantity inquestion, and δ is the dissipation.

If t is sufficiently long, then $\int \delta d\varkappa$ will become increasingly large as compared to the left sides of eqs. (5) and (6), provided $\mathbf{v}^2$ is not identically zero, and $\Delta \int \frac{1}{2} \mathbf{v}^2 dm$, $\Delta \int \varphi \Theta dm$ keep bounded. Therefore, noting that $\int w d\varkappa = 0$, the mechanical energy equation (5) expresses the well known fact that in a long-term steady state a positive correlation must exist between vertical velocity and potential temperature to balance by gravity effects the frictional dissipation. The steady stabilization in the vertical which follows from this is offset on the other hand by a corresponding negative correlation between geopotential and heating as revealed by eqs. (6), (7) provided also $\Delta \int \Theta dm$ keeps bounded.

We now introduce averages Θ_0, H_0 over complete horizontal surfaces of Θ and H and the corresponding deviations ϑ and h. We have

$$\vartheta_0 = h_0 = 0. \tag{9}$$

We might then write eq. (3) as

$$\frac{\partial \Theta}{\partial t} = -\mathbf{v} \cdot \nabla \vartheta - w \frac{d\Theta_0}{dz} + H. \tag{3'}$$

We note that:

$$\int \vartheta \frac{\partial \Theta}{\partial t} d\varkappa = \Delta \int \tfrac{1}{2} \vartheta^2 dm$$

$$\int H \vartheta d\varkappa = \int h \vartheta d\varkappa$$

$$\int \vartheta \mathbf{v} \cdot \nabla \vartheta d\varkappa = 0$$

and

$$\int \vartheta w \frac{d\Theta_0}{dz} d\varkappa = \int \Theta w \frac{d\Theta_0}{dz} d\varkappa$$

Accordingly, by multiplying (3)′ with ϑ and integrating, we get:

$$\Delta \int \tfrac{1}{2} \vartheta^2 dm = \int \vartheta h d\varkappa - \int \frac{d\Theta_0}{dz} \Theta w d\varkappa \tag{10}$$

Defining an average value S of $\frac{d\Theta_0}{dz}$ by

$$\int \frac{d\Theta_0}{dz} \Theta w d\varkappa \equiv S \int \Theta w d\varkappa, \tag{11}$$

we get by a substitution for $\int \Theta w d\varkappa$ from eq. (5):

$$\Delta \int \left(\tfrac{1}{2} \vartheta^2 + \frac{S \mathbf{v}^2}{2g} \right) dm = -\frac{S}{g} \int \delta d\varkappa + \int \vartheta h d\varkappa. \tag{10'}$$

Again, for sufficiently long periods, the left side becomes small in comparison with the r.h.s.-term with the dissipation. Therefore, in a gravitationally stable atmosphere a positive correlation between ϑ and "differential" heating h is necessary to have a long-term balance (LORENTZ, 1955).

2. Energy balance conditions when gravity and rotational forces are in quasi-equilibrium

To simplify notation throughout the rest of this paper let now ∇ be the horizontal nabla operator and $\mathbf{v}$ a horizontal nondivergent velocity:

$$\mathbf{v} = -\nabla \psi \times \mathbf{k} \tag{12a}$$

$\mathbf{v}$ is further specified to give the whole rotational part of the horizontal velocity $\mathbf{v}_h$:

$$\mathbf{v}_h = \mathbf{v} + \nabla \alpha. \tag{12b}$$

The balance between gravity and Coriolis forces can be expressed by the thermal wind relationship

$$\frac{\partial \mathbf{v}}{\partial z} = -\frac{g \nabla \vartheta \times \mathbf{k}}{f_c}, \tag{13}$$

having for simplicity taken a constant average value f_c for the Coriolis parameter. Actually, the approximate validity of (13) also guarantees that

$$\mathbf{v} \approx \mathbf{v}_h \tag{14}$$

As one governing equation for $\mathbf{v}$ we have the equation for the vertical component of vorticity. Above the "friction layer" this can be written approximately as

$$\frac{\partial}{\partial t} \nabla^2 \psi = -\mathbf{v} \cdot \nabla (\nabla^2 \psi + f) + \frac{f_c}{Q} \frac{\partial Q w}{\partial z}. \tag{15}$$

We assume that ϑ, w, ψ, and Q take the values $\vartheta^{(0)}$, $w^{(0)}$, $\psi^{(0)}$, and $Q^{(0)}$ at the top of the "friction layer". The frictional inflow and outflow in the "friction layer" in areas with surface cyclonic and anticyclonic vorticities respectively, give rise to vertical velocities $w^{(0)}$ which may be put proportional to relative vorticity at the top of the "friction layer". This might be stated as:

$$\frac{f_c Q^{(0)} w^{(0)}}{\int_\varepsilon^\infty Q dz} = \nu \nabla^2 \psi^{(0)} \qquad \begin{pmatrix} \nu = \text{a quasi-constant} > 0 \\ \varepsilon = \text{height of "friction layer"} \end{pmatrix} \tag{16}$$

Eq. (15) implies that friction is neglected alltogether in the "free" atmosphere, while eq. (16) implies that it is taken account of in the "friction layer" in the particular way outlined by CHARNEY and ELIASSEN (1949). As a particular consequence of their method we have approximately

$$\int \delta d\varkappa = \nu \int \mathbf{v}^{2(0)} d\varkappa. \tag{17}$$

We assume now a two-parametric representation of $\mathbf{v}$ in the vertical:

$$\mathbf{v} = \hat{\mathbf{v}} - \frac{F(z) - \widehat{F(z)}}{f_c} \cdot g \nabla \vartheta^* \times \mathbf{k} \tag{18 a}$$

where $\hat{}$ and $*$ are defined by

$$\hat{\mathbf{v}} \equiv \int_\varepsilon^\infty \mathbf{v} Q dz \Big/ \int_\varepsilon^\infty Q dz; \quad \vartheta^* \equiv \int_0^\infty \vartheta Q dz \Big/ \int_0^\infty Q dz, \tag{18 b}$$

and F is a function of z which makes the model most applicable to the actual atmosphere.

As an approximation ϑ will in the following be replaced by ϑ^* in all equations where ϑ occurs. It then becomes unnecessary to distinguish in notation between ϑ and ϑ^*, i.e. we let

$$\vartheta = \vartheta^*. \tag{18 c}$$

We now write eq. (3)′ as:

$$\frac{\partial \Theta}{\partial t} = -J(\psi, \vartheta) - \nabla \alpha \cdot \nabla \vartheta - w \frac{\partial \Theta}{\partial z} + H, \tag{19}$$

where J denotes the ordinary Jacobian on a sphere. It is understood that $-J(\psi, \vartheta)$ represents the change in ϑ per unit time caused by advection of ϑ in the nondivergent field $\mathbf{v}$. We shall denote this by:

$$\left(\frac{\partial \vartheta}{\partial t}\right)_{\text{adv}} \equiv -J(\psi, \vartheta). \tag{20}$$

In view of (18) we might take for ψ the stream function in an arbitrary level.

Averaging eq. (15) vertically from $z = \varepsilon$ to $z = \infty$, using (18 b) together with the lower boundary condition (16) and the upper one $Qw = 0$, we get:

$$\frac{\partial \nabla^2 \hat{\psi}}{\partial t} = -J(\hat{\psi}, \nabla^2 \hat{\psi} + f) - nJ(\vartheta, \nabla^2 \vartheta) - \nu \nabla^2 \psi^{(0)} \tag{21 a}$$

$$n \equiv \frac{g^2 \widehat{(F - \hat{F})^2}}{f_c^2} \equiv \frac{g^2 d^2}{f_c^2}. \tag{21 b}$$

A multiplication of eq. (21 a) with $-Q\hat{\psi}$ together with a subsequent integration gives

$$\Delta \int \tfrac{1}{2} \hat{\mathbf{v}}^2 dm = n \int \nabla^2 \vartheta J(\psi, \vartheta) d\varkappa + \frac{gl\nu}{f_c} \int \vartheta \nabla^2 \psi^{(0)} d\varkappa - \nu \int \mathbf{v}^{2(0)} d\varkappa. \tag{22 a}$$

$$l \equiv \hat{F} - F(z = \varepsilon). \tag{22 b}$$

To get this we have utilized the relationships

$$\int \hat{\psi} J(\hat{\psi}, \nabla^2 \hat{\psi} + f) d\varkappa = 0.$$

and

$$\int \hat{\psi} J(\vartheta, \nabla^2 \vartheta) d\varkappa = \int \nabla^2 \vartheta J(\psi, \vartheta) d\varkappa.$$

By a comparison of eqs. (5) and (22), noting (17), we obtain in the long-term steady state:

$$g \int \vartheta w d\varkappa = n \int \nabla^2 \vartheta J(\psi, \vartheta) d\varkappa + \frac{gl\nu}{f_c} \int \vartheta \nabla^2 \psi^{(0)} d\varkappa \tag{23}$$

What in fact has been accomplished by the particular use of the balance condition (18) leading to eq. (22) is therefore an elimination of vertical velocity in the mechanical energy equation.

Of the two r.h.s. integrals in (23) the second one is easy to understand physically: It expresses how the frictional inflow in surface cyclones and frictional outflow in surface anticyclones will effect $\int g\vartheta w d\varkappa$ depending upon whether cyclones are warm and anticyclones cold, in which case $\int g\vartheta w d\varkappa$ will get a positive contribution, or whether cyclones are cold and anticyclones warm, in which case $\int g\vartheta w d\varkappa$ will get a negative contribution. In the atmosphere, however, an undertaken examination of observations seems to show that no definite correlation between ϑ and surface vorticity exists. At least it is certain that

$$\frac{gl}{f_c}\int \vartheta \nabla^2 \psi^{(0)} d\varkappa \ll \int \mathbf{v}^{2(0)} d\varkappa. \tag{24}$$

Using (20), we get:

$$\int \nabla^2 \vartheta J(\psi, \vartheta) d\varkappa = -\int_t \int \nabla^2 \vartheta \frac{\partial \vartheta}{\partial t_{\text{adv}}} dm dt =$$

$$= \Delta_{\text{adv}} \int \tfrac{1}{2} (\nabla \vartheta)^2 dm.$$

Eq. (22) might therefore be written:

$$\Delta \int \tfrac{1}{2} \hat{\mathbf{v}}^2 dm = n \Delta_{\text{adv}} \int \tfrac{1}{2} (\nabla \vartheta)^2 dm +$$

$$+ \frac{glv}{f_c} \int \vartheta \nabla^2 \psi^{(0)} d\varkappa - v \int \mathbf{v}^{2(0)} d\varkappa. \tag{22'}$$

In view of (24) it is therefore clear that in the long-term balanced atmosphere the dissipative loss of kinetic energy cannot be balanced without having $\Delta_{\text{adv}} \int \frac{1}{2} (\nabla \vartheta)^2 dm > 0$. Since on the other hand

$$\Delta_{\text{adv}} \int \tfrac{1}{2} \vartheta^2 dm = 0, \tag{25}$$

an advective flow of temperature amplitude must therefore take place from large to small horizontal scales (FJØRTOFT, 1955). Consequently, to keep the atmosphere in a long-term steady state it is necessary to have a non-advective large-scale source and a small-scale sink for $\int \vartheta^2 d\varkappa$.

Naturally, the above remarks lead us to consider the balance on different horizontal scales separately. In recognition of the fact that the large-scale component of the temperature field on which the smaller scale components feed, essentially is a zonal one, we are led to consider components $\bar{\vartheta}$ and ϑ' as representing the large- and small-scale fields, respectively, $\bar{\vartheta}$ denoting a zonal average and ϑ' the corresponding deviation, or eddy field. We have

$$\overline{\vartheta'} = \overline{\mathbf{v}'} = \overline{h'} = 0. \tag{26}$$

We might now derive an expression for $n\Delta_{\text{adv}} \cdot \int \frac{1}{2} (\nabla \vartheta)^2 dm$ in terms of the zonally averaged motion and the eddies. We then first note that eq. (25) might be written as

$$\Delta_{\text{adv}} \int \tfrac{1}{2} \bar{\vartheta}^2 dm + \Delta_{\text{adv}} \int \tfrac{1}{2} \vartheta'^2 dm = 0. \tag{25'}$$

Noting further that

$$\frac{d}{dt_{\text{adv}}} \int \tfrac{1}{2} \bar{\vartheta}^2 dm = \int \bar{\vartheta} \frac{\partial \bar{\vartheta}}{\partial t_{\text{adv}}} dm$$

we get by substitution for $\frac{\partial \bar{\vartheta}}{\partial t_{\text{adv}}}$ and integration:

$$\Delta_{\text{adv}} \int \tfrac{1}{2} \bar{\vartheta}^2 dm = \int \bar{\vartheta} (-\mathbf{v} \cdot \nabla \vartheta) d\varkappa =$$

$$= \int \frac{d\bar{\vartheta}}{dy} v' \vartheta' d\varkappa. \tag{27}$$

We may write

$$\int (\nabla \bar{\vartheta})^2 d\varkappa \equiv a_2 \int \bar{\vartheta}^2 d\varkappa \tag{28}$$

and

$$\int (\nabla \vartheta')^2 d\varkappa \equiv a_q \int \vartheta'^2 d\varkappa \tag{29}$$

where the quantities a_2 and a_q defined herefrom are inversely proportional to the squares of some lengths which are characteristic in the above sense for some average horizontal scales of the two fields.

If as a theoretical case $\bar{\vartheta}$ and ϑ' are represented each by a spherical harmonic, then a_2 and a_q are the corresponding "eigen" values defined from

$$\nabla^2 \bar{\vartheta} = -a_2 \bar{\vartheta}$$
$$\nabla^2 \vartheta' = -a_q \vartheta'.$$

The subscript 2 is chosen to indicate that in the atmosphere the second zonal harmonic, except in midsummer, is a good approximation to the zonally averaged temperature field.

In view of eqs. (25)′, (27), (28), and (29) we now get

$$n\Delta_{\text{adv}} \int \tfrac{1}{2} (\nabla \vartheta)^2 dm =$$

$$= -n(a_q - a_2) \int \frac{d\bar{\vartheta}}{dy} v' \vartheta' d\varkappa, \tag{30}$$

and by a substitution of this into eq. (22)′

$$\Delta\int \tfrac{1}{2}\hat{\mathbf{v}}^2 dm = -n(a_q - a_2)\int \frac{d\bar{\vartheta}}{dy} v'\vartheta' d\varkappa + \frac{glv}{f_c}\int \vartheta \nabla^2\psi^{(0)} d\varkappa - v\int \mathbf{v}^{2(0)} d\varkappa. \quad (31)$$

Noting that $-\int \hat{\bar{\psi}} \frac{\partial}{\partial t}\nabla^2 \hat{\bar{\psi}} d\varkappa = \Delta \int \tfrac{1}{2}\hat{\bar{\mathbf{v}}}^2 dm$ and $-\int \hat{\psi}' \frac{\partial}{\partial t} \nabla^2 \hat{\psi} d\varkappa = \Delta\int \tfrac{1}{2}\hat{\mathbf{v}}'^2 dm$, the corresponding equations for the mean and eddy motions are obtained by a substitution for $\frac{\partial}{\partial t}\nabla^2\hat{\psi}$ from eq. (21 a). We then obtain

$$\Delta\int \tfrac{1}{2}\hat{\bar{\mathbf{v}}}^2 dm = \frac{glv}{f_c}\int \bar{\vartheta}\nabla^2\bar{\psi}^{(0)} d\varkappa - v\int \bar{\mathbf{v}}^{2(0)} d\varkappa + B \quad (32\,\mathrm{a})$$

$$\Delta\int \tfrac{1}{2}\hat{\mathbf{v}}'^2 dm = -n(a_q - a_2)\int \frac{d\bar{\vartheta}}{dy} v'\vartheta' d\varkappa + \frac{glv}{f_c}\int \vartheta' \nabla^2\psi'^{(0)} d\varkappa - v\int \mathbf{v}'^{2(0)} d\varkappa - B \quad (32\,\mathrm{b})$$

where

$$B \equiv n\int \hat{\bar{\psi}} J(\vartheta', \nabla^2\vartheta') d\varkappa + \int \hat{\bar{\psi}} J(\hat{\psi}', \nabla^2\hat{\psi}') d\varkappa \quad (32\,\mathrm{c})$$

We shall now also derive separately for the mean and eddy motion the equations corresponding to eq. (10)′. Since

$$\int \bar{\vartheta}\frac{\partial\Theta}{\partial t} d\varkappa = \Delta\int \tfrac{1}{2}\bar{\vartheta}^2 dm \quad \text{and}$$

$$\int \vartheta' \frac{\partial\Theta}{\partial t} d\varkappa = \Delta\int \tfrac{1}{2}\vartheta'^2 dm,$$

we get by a substitution for $\frac{\partial\Theta}{\partial t}$ from eq. (19)

$$\Delta\int \tfrac{1}{2}\bar{\vartheta}^2 dm = -\int \bar{\vartheta} J(\psi, \vartheta) d\varkappa - \int \bar{\vartheta} w \frac{\partial\Theta}{\partial z} d\varkappa + \int \bar{\vartheta} h d\varkappa \quad (33\,\mathrm{a})$$

and

$$\Delta\int \tfrac{1}{2}\vartheta'^2 dm = -\int \vartheta' J(\psi, \vartheta) d\varkappa - \int \vartheta' w \frac{\partial\Theta}{\partial z} d\varkappa + \int \vartheta' h d\varkappa. \quad (33\,\mathrm{b})$$

The terms $\int \bar{\vartheta}\nabla\alpha \cdot \nabla\vartheta d\varkappa$ and $\int \vartheta' \nabla\alpha \cdot \nabla\vartheta d\varkappa$ drop out because of (1), (4), (12) and (18 c).

We assume further that as an approximation the overall stability S defined in (11) can be substituted as follows:

$$\int \bar{\vartheta} w \frac{\partial\Theta}{\partial z} d\varkappa = S\int \bar{\vartheta}\bar{w} d\varkappa \quad (34\,\mathrm{a})$$

and

$$\int \vartheta' w \frac{\partial\Theta}{\partial z} d\varkappa = S\int \vartheta' w' d\varkappa \quad (34\,\mathrm{b})$$

Here we can substitute for the r.h.s. the expressions which can be found from the mechanical energy equations valid for the mean and zonal motion, respectively. Using eqs. (12), (13), (15), and the equation corresponding to (15) in the "friction layer", we get

$$\Delta\int \tfrac{1}{2}\bar{\mathbf{v}}^2 dm = \int g\bar{\vartheta}\bar{w} d\varkappa - \int \delta_{\bar{\mathbf{v}}} d\varkappa + \{k_{\bar{\mathbf{v}}}, k_{\mathbf{v}'}\} \quad (35\,\mathrm{a})$$

and

$$\Delta\int \tfrac{1}{2}\mathbf{v}'^2 dm = \int g\vartheta' w' d\varkappa - \int \delta_{\mathbf{v}'} d\varkappa - \{k_{\bar{\mathbf{v}}}, k_{\mathbf{v}'}\} \quad (35\,\mathrm{b})$$

where $\{k_{\bar{\mathbf{v}}}, k_{\bar{\mathbf{v}}'}\}$, the partition term due to the particular "Reynolds stresses" related to the non-linear interaction between the zonally mean flow and the eddy motion, is given by

$$\{k_{\bar{\mathbf{v}}}, k_{\mathbf{v}'}\} = \int \bar{\psi} J(\psi', \nabla^2\psi') d\varkappa, \quad (36)$$

and where, corresponding to eq. (17),

$$\int \delta_{\bar{\mathbf{v}}} d\varkappa = v\int \bar{\mathbf{v}}^{2(0)} d\varkappa \quad (37\,\mathrm{a})$$

and

$$\int \delta_{\mathbf{v}'} d\varkappa = v\int \mathbf{v}'^{2(0)} d\varkappa. \quad (37\,\mathrm{b})$$

By an elimination of $\int g\bar{\vartheta}\bar{w} d\varkappa$ and $\int g\vartheta' w' d\varkappa$ between eqs. (33) and (35) we now get

$$\Delta\int \tfrac{1}{2}\left(\bar{\vartheta}^2 + \frac{S\bar{\mathbf{v}}^2}{g}\right) dm = \int \bar{\vartheta}\bar{h} d\varkappa + \int \frac{d\bar{\vartheta}}{dy} v'\vartheta' d\varkappa - \frac{S}{g}\left[v\int \bar{\mathbf{v}}^{2(0)} d\varkappa - \{k_{\bar{\mathbf{v}}}, k_{\mathbf{v}'}\}\right] \quad (38\,\mathrm{a})$$

and

$$\Delta\int\tfrac{1}{2}\left(\vartheta'^2+\frac{S\mathbf{v}'^2}{g}\right)dm=\int\vartheta' h' d\varkappa-$$

$$-\int\frac{d\bar{\vartheta}}{dy}v'\vartheta' d\varkappa-\frac{S}{g}\left[\nu\int\mathbf{v}'^{2(0)}d\varkappa+\{k_{\bar{\mathbf{v}}},k_{\mathbf{v}'}\}\right] \tag{38 b}$$

Finally, we shall now write down the expressions for $\int g\bar{\vartheta}\bar{w}d\varkappa$ and $\int g\vartheta' w' d\varkappa$ which are obtained by an elimination of $\int\delta_{\bar{\mathbf{v}}}d\varkappa$ and $\int\delta_{\mathbf{v}'}d\varkappa$ between eqs. (32) and (35):

$$\int g\bar{\vartheta}\bar{w}d\varkappa=\frac{gl\nu}{f_c}\int\bar{\vartheta}\nabla^2\bar{\psi}^{(0)}d\varkappa+$$

$$+B-\{k_{\bar{\mathbf{v}}},k_{\mathbf{v}'}\}+\Delta\int\tfrac{1}{2}\left(\bar{\mathbf{v}}^2-\bar{\hat{\mathbf{v}}}^2\right)dm \tag{39 a}$$

and

$$\int g\vartheta' w' d\varkappa=-n(a_q-a_2)\int\frac{d\bar{\vartheta}}{dy}v'\vartheta' d\varkappa+$$

$$+\frac{gl\nu}{f_c}\int\vartheta'\nabla^2\psi'^{(0)}d\varkappa-B+\{k_{\bar{\mathbf{v}}},k_{\mathbf{v}'}\}+$$

$$+\Delta\int\tfrac{1}{2}(\mathbf{v}'^2-\hat{\mathbf{v}}'^2)dm. \tag{39 b}$$

3. On some further simplifications of the problem

Confining ourselves to a study of the long-term steady state of the atmosphere, we may put the left hand sides of eqs. (32) and (38) equal to zero. In the resulting equations we shall now introduce some simplifications by suppressing certain terms which are small under atmospheric conditions due to the observed existence of the following relations between order of magnitudes of certain terms:

$$\{k_{\bar{\mathbf{v}}},k_{\mathbf{v}'}\}\text{ and }B=(10^{-1}\text{ to }10^{-2})\times$$

$$\times n\int\nabla^2\bar{\vartheta}J(\psi,\vartheta)d\varkappa=(10^{-1}\text{ to }10^{-2})\cdot$$

$$\cdot n(a_q-a_2)\int\frac{d\bar{\vartheta}}{dy}v'\vartheta' d\varkappa \tag{40 a}$$

and

$$\frac{gl\nu}{f_c}\int\vartheta'\nabla^2\psi'^{(0)}d\varkappa=$$

$$=\text{negligible compared to }n(a_q-a_2)\int\frac{d\bar{\vartheta}}{dy}v'\vartheta' d\varkappa. \tag{40 b}$$

In this paper we shall abstain from a thorough discussion of the reasons why these relationships are satisfied. Instead we shall mainly just take them as observational facts. This procedure is similar to that by which the thermal wind equation was introduced.

As we also intend to discuss how the solutions will depend upon a hypothetical variation of the scale characteristics and some external parameters, as for instance the intensity of external heat sources, we shall further assume that the balance equation (13) together with the relations (40) above remain true under these variations. In this connection it would of course be important to know what the conditions are for having the thermal wind equation and the relations (40) satisfied. With respect to the former one it is known from independent investigations that when the Richardson number

$$g\frac{d\Theta}{dz}\Big/\left(\frac{d\mathbf{v}}{dz}\right)^2\gg 1, \tag{41}$$

then this is a necessary and sufficient condition for a quasibalance between gravity and Coriolis forces. If now by applying among others the thermal wind equation, results could be derived which would show that (41) was violated when the external parameters where passing some critical values, we would then have arrived at an inconsistency. This result, however, would also have been a very valuable one since it would have determined conditions for a total change in the character of the motion.

With respect to the assumptions made in (40) we shall confine ourselves to a few general remarks. We then first note that while $\{k_{\bar{\mathbf{v}}},k_{\mathbf{v}'}\}$ and B must be exactly zero if each of the eddy fields ψ' and ϑ' is represented by just a single spherical harmonic, this on the other hand does not necessarily nullify the term $n(a_q-a_2)\cdot\int\frac{d\bar{\vartheta}}{dy}v'\vartheta' d\varkappa$. That $\{k_{\bar{\mathbf{v}}},k_{\mathbf{v}'}\}$ and B vanish in this case is seen by substituting $\nabla^2\psi'=-a\psi'$ and $\nabla^2\vartheta'=-b\vartheta'$ in the expressions (36) and (32 c) for $\{k_{\bar{\mathbf{v}}},k_{\mathbf{v}'}\}$ and B. To obtain $\{k_{\bar{\mathbf{v}}},k_{\mathbf{v}'}\}$ and B different from zero, at least two spherical harmonics with different "eigen"-values must therefore be used to represent ψ', $\hat{\psi}'$, and ϑ'. Suppose now that $\psi'=\psi_r'+\psi_s'$, $\hat{\psi}'=\hat{\psi}_r'+\hat{\psi}_s'$, and $\vartheta'=\vartheta_r'+\vartheta_s'$ with $\nabla^2\psi_r'=-a_r\psi_r'$, $\nabla^2\psi_s'=-a_s\psi_s'$, and the similar relations for $\hat{\psi}'$ and ϑ', we obtain for instance for $\{k_{\bar{\mathbf{v}}},k_{\mathbf{v}'}\}$:

$$-\{k_{\bar{v}}, k_{v'}\} = (a_r - a_s)\int \frac{d\bar{\psi}}{dy} v_r' \psi_s' d\varkappa \qquad (42)$$

If this expression shall not vanish identically it is necessary that 1) $a_r \neq a_s$, and 2) that ψ_r' and ψ_s' have the same wavelengths in zonal direction. These conditions together imply that v_r' and ψ_s' must have different wavenumbers in meridional direction. This gives a tendency for $\int \frac{d\bar{\psi}}{dy} v_r' \psi_s' d\varkappa$ to become small because of interference, provided $\bar{\psi}$ is a more slowly varying function with latitude than ψ_r' and ψ_s' are. This interference is not necessarily present in the integral $\int \frac{d\bar{\vartheta}}{dy} v' \vartheta' d\varkappa$ which tends to get a maximum value when v' and ϑ' have similar meridional scales. It is believed that what has been mentioned above together with the conditions making $\bar{\psi}$ and $\sqrt{n}\bar{\vartheta}$, ψ' and $\sqrt{n}\vartheta'$ of the same order of magnitude are essentially the reasons why the assumption (40 a) holds in the atmosphere.

With respect to (40 b) we note that in order to make $\int \frac{d\bar{\vartheta}}{dy} v' \vartheta' d\varkappa$, which equals $\int \frac{d\bar{\vartheta}}{dy} v'^{(0)} \vartheta' d\varkappa$, large, then the zonal phases of $\psi'^{(0)}$ and ϑ' must be essentially different, while on the other hand a marked tendency for coinciding zonal phases of $\psi'^{(0)}$ and ϑ' is necessary to make $\int \vartheta' \nabla^2 \psi'^{(0)} d\varkappa$ large. Because of this it is justified to some extent to study the effects from these terms as separate cases such that besides (40 b) we could also have looked into the theoretical case, in which

$$-n(a_q - a_2)\int \frac{d\bar{\vartheta}}{dy} v' \vartheta' d\varkappa \ll \frac{glv}{f_c}\int \vartheta' \nabla^2 \psi'^{(0)} d\varkappa.$$

We shall, however, abstain from this in the present article. For reasons which will appear clearly later we shall confine ourselves to scales such that

$$\frac{Sn(a_q - a_2)}{g} < 1.$$

Using this, it follows from (40 a):

$$\frac{S}{g}\{k_{\bar{v}}, k_{v'}\} \text{ and } \frac{SB}{g} \leq (10^{-1} \text{ to } 10^{-2}) \times \int \frac{d\bar{\vartheta}}{dy} v' \vartheta' d\varkappa \qquad (43)$$

Using (43) in eq. (38 b) and (40) in eq. (32 b) these equations are simplified to:

$$-\int \frac{d\bar{\vartheta}}{dy} v' \vartheta' d\varkappa + \int \vartheta' h' d\varkappa = \frac{Sv}{g}\int \mathbf{v}'^{2(0)} d\varkappa \qquad (44)$$

and

$$-n(a_q - a_2)\int \frac{d\bar{\vartheta}}{dy} v' \vartheta' d\varkappa = v\int \mathbf{v}'^{2(0)} d\varkappa. \qquad (45)$$

We shall now eliminate $v\int \bar{\mathbf{v}}^{2(0)} d\varkappa$ in eq. (38 a) by means of eq. (32 a). We then first write

$$\frac{glv}{f_c}\int \bar{\vartheta} \nabla^2 \bar{\psi}^{(0)} d\varkappa = -\frac{glv}{f_c}\int \nabla\bar{\vartheta} \cdot \nabla\bar{\psi}^{(0)} d\varkappa \equiv$$

$$\equiv -\frac{glv}{f_c}\sigma \sqrt{\int (\nabla\bar{\vartheta})^2 d\varkappa \cdot \int \bar{\mathbf{v}}^{2(0)} d\varkappa},$$

where σ is the correlation coefficient between $\nabla\bar{\vartheta}$ and $\nabla\bar{\psi}^{(0)}$. Substituting this in (32) we get:

$$v\int \bar{\mathbf{v}}^{2(0)} d\varkappa + \frac{glv\sigma}{f_c}\sqrt{\int (\nabla\bar{\vartheta})^2 d\varkappa} \cdot \sqrt{\int \bar{\mathbf{v}}^{2(0)} d\varkappa} - B = 0$$

Correspondingly, two solutions are always possible for $v\int \bar{\mathbf{v}}^{2(0)} d\varkappa$, one of which is

$$v\int \bar{\mathbf{v}}^{2(0)} d\varkappa = O_{1B}, \qquad (46\text{ a})$$

where O_{1B} is a term whose order of magnitude is at most equal to B, and the second is

$$v\int \bar{\mathbf{v}}^{2(0)} d\varkappa = \frac{g^2 l^2 v \sigma^2}{f_c^2}\int (\nabla\bar{\vartheta})^2 d\varkappa + O_{2B}, \qquad (46\text{ b})$$

where O_{2B} is a term of order of magnitude equal to B.

It is now seen by comparing eq. (46 a) with eq. (45) in connection with (40 a) that the solution (46 a) corresponds to a case where the dissipation in the zonal mean motion is negligible in comparison with the dissipation in the eddy motion, while the second solution in (46 b) is one where the dissipation in the zonal mean motion might be considerable. Substituting from (46 a) or (46 b) in eq. (38 a), using (43), we obtain

$$0 = \int \bar{\vartheta}\bar{h} d\varkappa + \int \frac{d\bar{\vartheta}}{dy} v' \vartheta' d\varkappa - \frac{\alpha S g l^2 \sigma^2 v}{f_c^2}\int (\nabla\bar{\vartheta})^2 d\varkappa; \quad \alpha = 0 \text{ or } 1, \qquad (47)$$

where

$$\alpha = 0 \text{ corresponds to } \int \bar{\mathbf{v}}^{2(0)} d\varkappa = $$

$$= (10^{-1} \text{ to } 10^{-2}) \cdot \int \mathbf{v}'^{2(0)} d\varkappa. \tag{48}$$

4. Adoption of a simplified law of heating

To advance further in a theoretical discussion it is now necessary to fix the laws of heating. It is outside the scope of this article to enter into a general discussion of all the processes by which the atmosphere is heated. Instead only a few general remarks will be offered. First of all it should be noted that having used the thermal wind equation we have restricted ourselves to consider components of motion with wavelengths larger than, say, approximately 2,000—3,000 km. In the preceding equations $\mathbf{v}$ and ϑ must therefore be considered as correspondingly smoothed quantities. If $\mathbf{v}''$ and ϑ'' denote the corresponding "turbulent" quantities we have to include a "turbulent" diffusion term $-\frac{1}{Q}\nabla_3 \cdot Q\vartheta''\mathbf{v}''$.[1] In accordance with this we may write

$$H = H_d + H_c - \frac{1}{Q}\nabla_3 \cdot Q\vartheta''\mathbf{v}''$$

having also distinguished between heating due to latent heat (H_c) and heating due to radiation and molecular diffusion (H_d). It will be assumed as a first approximation that all condensed water is falling out as precipitation so that H_c may be taken as positive.

We are interested in heating only in so far as it influences the total horizontal variance of ϑ as expressed by the integral $\int \vartheta h d\varkappa$ of eq. (10). More particularly we are interested in how it influences the large-scale part of the variance (assumed as zonal) as expressed by the integral $\int \bar{\vartheta}\bar{h} d\varkappa$ of eq. (38 a), and on the other hand the eddy variance $\int \vartheta'^2 d\varkappa$ as expressed by the integral $\int \vartheta' h' d\varkappa$ of eq. (38 b). Thereafter we are also interested in the vertical distribution of H as it enters in the integral $\int \varphi H_0 d\varkappa$ of eq. (6). Having considered as a first approximation ϑ as a vertical average with respect to mass, it follows that h might be considered as such an average, as well. Assuming that $\frac{1}{Q}\nabla_3 \cdot Q\vartheta''\mathbf{v}'' \approx \frac{1}{Q}\frac{\partial}{\partial z} Q\vartheta'' w''$, and noting that $Q\vartheta'' w'' = 0$ at the ground and at the top of the atmosphere, it is clear that turbulent diffusion can only redistribute heat in the vertical, thus having zero contribution to the heating of complete vertical columns. Indirectly, however, the vertical eddy diffusion is of great importance for the other processes by which vertical columns of air are heated or cooled.

The external source of horizontal differential heating of the atmosphere + the earth is the radiation coming in from the sun and absorbed in the atmosphere and the earth. Averaged over all seasons this radiation warms the equatorial regions more than it warms the polar regions. Only a minor part of this differential heating is balanced by transport processes in the oceans and a much smaller part in the crust of the earth. By reemission from the earth to the atmosphere and by release of latent heat by condensation this differential heating is mainly used for a differential heating of the *atmosphere*. Actually, however, the differential heating is less than it would be with only the external sources acting, the main reason for this being that the equatorial regions with their higher temperature radiate more energy than the polar regions. In the atmosphere $\int \bar{\vartheta}\bar{h} d\varkappa > 0$. However, due to the way the outgoing radiation depends upon ϑ we must assume that $\int \bar{\vartheta}\bar{h} d\varkappa$ will ultimately become negative if the temperature contrasts between equatorial and polar regions surpass some critical values assuming that, simultaneously, other factors of importance for the differential heating undergo a comparatively small change.

An additional reason for focussing the attention upon the dependence of the differential heating upon temperature rather than upon amounts of clouds, water vapour and so on is the clearcut dependence of ϑ upon the motion, for which we have the equation (3). For we are interested not so much in differential heating itself as in the interaction between motion and differential heating. The large-scale horizontal mixing as expressed by $\frac{\partial v'\vartheta'}{\partial y}$ smooths the meridional temperature contrasts and is thereby influencing the conditions for horizontal differential heating. Indeed, the heating of equatorial regions and

[1] For the same reason the dissipation term $\int \delta d\varkappa$ occurring in earlier equations must be written as

$$\int \delta d\varkappa = -\int \mathbf{v} \cdot \frac{1}{Q}\nabla_3 \cdot Q\mathbf{v}''\mathbf{v}'' d\varkappa + \int (\delta_{\mathbf{v}})_{\text{mol}} d\varkappa$$

where a "turbulent" dissipation term has been added to the molecular dissipation in the smoothed motion.

the cooling of polar regions might be looked upon as a result of this mixing which keeps the meridional temperature contrasts sufficiently low to allow for a residual differential heating due to external sources.

We might state more explicitly what has now been said by assuming for the vertical average of heating, H^*, a functional relationship:

$$H^* = F(\Theta_e^* - \Theta^*) \tag{49}$$

Here Θ_e^* represents a vertical average of an equilibrium potential temperature such that

$$H^* = 0 \text{ when } \Theta^* = \Theta_e^*$$

Besides, F is a monotonically increasing function of $\Theta_e^* - \Theta^*$. Expanding F in powers of $\Theta_e^* - \Theta^*$ and taking as a first approximation just the linear term we obtain

$$H^* = r(\Theta_e^* - \Theta^*); \quad r = \text{const} > 0$$

For h we get correspondingly

$$\left.\begin{array}{l} h = r(\vartheta_e - \vartheta) \\ (\vartheta_e \equiv \Theta_e^* - \Theta_{e0}^*) \end{array}\right\} \tag{50}$$

In terms of this relationship we have

$$\int \bar{\vartheta}\bar{h}\,d\varkappa = r\int(\bar{\vartheta}\bar{\vartheta}_e - \bar{\vartheta}^2)\,d\varkappa \tag{51}$$

and

$$\int \vartheta' h'\,d\alpha = r\int(\vartheta'\vartheta_e' - \vartheta'^2)\,d\varkappa. \tag{52}$$

To the extent to which it is permissible to use (50) as the heating law, we might now by means of (51) formulate quantitatively, what was stated qualitatively earlier. Introducing the correlation σ_1 between $\bar{\vartheta}$ and $\bar{\vartheta}_e$ we get

$$\int \bar{\vartheta}\bar{h}\,d\varkappa = r\left(\sigma_1\sqrt{\int \bar{\vartheta}_e^2\,d\varkappa}\cdot\sqrt{\int \bar{\vartheta}^2 d\varkappa} - \int \bar{\vartheta}^2 d\varkappa\right) \tag{51$'$}$$

Hence, for positive σ_1,

$$\int \bar{\vartheta}\bar{h}\,d\varkappa \gtrless 0 \text{ according as} \int \bar{\vartheta}^2 d\varkappa \lessgtr \sigma_1^2 \int \bar{\vartheta}_e^2\,d\varkappa. \tag{53}$$

We shall see that this result, namely that sufficiently large values of $\int \bar{\vartheta}^2 d\varkappa$ lead to a reversal of the sign of $\int \bar{\vartheta}\bar{h}\,d\varkappa$, is in a specifiic way of importance for the theoretical discussion later on.

Of importance in a different way is what the heating law (49), or more approximately the law (52), implies with respect to $\int \vartheta' h'\,d\varkappa$. We then first note that because of the distribution of oceans and continents the field ϑ_e cannot possibly have an exact zonal character. Taking account of this we could conveniently define eddies $\vartheta^{(\,)}$ and $h^{(\,)}$ relative to mean quantities which are taken along the isolines of ϑ_e instead of zonal circles. By definition we would then have $\vartheta_e^{(\,)} = 0$, and using (50) we would then obtain $\int \vartheta^{(\,)} h^{(\,)} d\varkappa = -r\int \vartheta^{(\,)2} d\varkappa$. When we idealize by taking instead means along zonal circles we must at the same time assume that $\vartheta_e' = 0$ to be sure that we maintain this damping influence from differential heating on the eddy variance $\int \vartheta'^2 d\varkappa$. We then get

$$\int \vartheta' h'\,d\varkappa = -r\int \vartheta'^2 d\varkappa. \tag{52$'$}$$

The application to the atmosphere of a heating law as (49) might be an oversimplification. This is particularly so because of the role of condensation in large-scale phenomena. The individual cooling leading to condensation in saturated air is mainly brought about by ascending motions such that

$$H_c = (w + w'')\gamma \text{ when } w + w'' > 0$$

and

$$H_c = 0 \text{ when } w + w'' \leq 0.$$

Here γ is the moistadiabatic lapserate in terms of Θ, and $w + w''$ is the vertical velocity written as the sum of the large-scale vertical velocity w, and a "turbulent" vertical velocity w'' representing all scales less than 2,000—3,000 km. If now further w is written as $w = \bar{w} + w'$ we obtain as an expression for the contribution from condensation heat to the changes in the variances $\int \bar{\vartheta}^2 d\varkappa$ and $\int \vartheta'^2 d\varkappa$:

$$\int \bar{\vartheta} H_c\,d\varkappa = \int_1 \gamma\bar{\vartheta}(\bar{w} + w' + w'')\,d\varkappa$$

and

$$\int \vartheta' H_c\,d\varkappa = \int_1 \gamma\vartheta'(\bar{w} + w' + w'')\,d\varkappa.$$

Here $\int_1$ indicates that the integration is carried out where $\bar{w} + w' + w'' > 0$ and the air saturated at the same time.

Obviously, the relative magnitudes of $\bar{w}$, w', and w'' must now be important for the precise way in which condensation heat effects the large-scale variances of ϑ. In the atmosphere we certainly have $|w'| \gg |\bar{w}|$ and $|w''| \gg |w'|$. Therefore, if the mesoscale- and convection phenomena connected with the vertical velocities w'' are correlated with for instance ϑ' this might overshadow the large-scale influence of condensation due to the correlation (positive) between ϑ' and w'. In the atmosphere condensation in convective currents mainly occurs where $\vartheta' < 0$. This is due to the destabilizing influence from the generally warmer ground. It is therefore difficult to anticipate without closer examinations the influence of H_c on $\int \vartheta'^2 d\varkappa$. In a *theoretical* atmosphere, however, the overall stability might conceivably be so large that convective phenomena are sufficiently suppressed to guarantee that $|w'| \gg |w''|$. In such an atmosphere we would have $\int \vartheta' H_c d\varkappa = \int \vartheta' h_c d\varkappa = \int_1 \gamma \vartheta' w' d\varkappa$ which, from continuity reasons mainly, approximately equals $\frac{1}{2} \int \gamma \vartheta' w' d\varkappa$.

Substituting $h = h_d + h_c$ in eq. (33 b) we therefore get for such a *theoretical* atmosphere:

$$\Delta \int \tfrac{1}{2} \vartheta'^2 dm = - \int \vartheta' J(\psi, \vartheta)\, d\varkappa - \int \left(\frac{d\Theta}{dz} - \frac{\gamma}{2} \right) \vartheta' w' d\varkappa + \int h_d' \vartheta' d\varkappa.$$

Writing here

$$\int \left(\frac{d\Theta}{dz} - \frac{\gamma}{2} \right) \vartheta' w' d\varkappa = \left(S - \tfrac{1}{2} \gamma_{\text{const}} \right) \int \vartheta' w' d\varkappa,$$

where γ_{const} is some average value of γ, it is seen that derivations like the ones that led to eq. (38 b) now instead will give

$$- \int \frac{d\bar{\vartheta}}{dy} v' \vartheta' d\varkappa + \int \vartheta' h_d' d\varkappa = = \frac{S - \frac{1}{2}\gamma_{\text{const}}}{g} \left[\nu \int \mathbf{v}'^{2(0)} d\varkappa - \{ k_{\bar{\mathbf{v}}}, k_{\mathbf{v}'} \} \right] \tag{54}$$

Here, in the second l.h.s. integral we could for h_d' which does not depend upon condensation, more safely use the temperature dependence law (49), or its approximate form (50). Simultaneously, however, condensation would imply an effective reduction in the overall vertical stability, from S to approximately $S - \frac{1}{2}\gamma_{\text{const}}$. As long as $S - \frac{1}{2}\gamma_{\text{const}}$ keeps a positive sign this would, however, not change the quality of the results which are going to be derived. In the actual atmosphere where condensation, besides reducing S, also damps the large-scale eddy variance $\int \vartheta'^2 d\varkappa$ as a result of small-scale convective currents, it is probably wisest, for lack of better knowledge, not to take condensation into account at all in its possible influence upon the eddy variance $\int \vartheta'^2 d\varkappa$.

Postponing the discussion of the vertical distribution of H until section 6, we shall now proceed with a discussion of eqs. (44), (45), and (47).

5. Discussion of eqs. (44), (45), and (47)

We first note that it is possible to write

$$- \int \frac{d\bar{\vartheta}}{dy} v'^{(0)} \vartheta' d\varkappa = = \sigma_2 \sqrt{\frac{\int (\nabla \bar{\vartheta})^2 d\varkappa}{\int d\varkappa}} \cdot \sqrt{\int \mathbf{v}'^{2(0)} d\varkappa \cdot \int \vartheta'^2 d\varkappa}, \tag{55}$$

where σ_2 is a proportionality factor which is a function of the "kinematics", but not of the integral quantities under the square root signs. In particular σ_2 might be a function of the scale characteristic a_q of the ϑ'-field. However, it is important to note that σ_2 is bounded, i.e.

$$|\sigma_2| \leq |\sigma_2|_{\max} < 1. \tag{56}$$

If we next substitute for $\int (\nabla \bar{\vartheta})^2 d\varkappa$ from (28) we might also write (55) as

$$- \int \frac{d\bar{\vartheta}}{dy} v'^{(0)} \vartheta' d\varkappa = \sigma_2 \sqrt{a_2} \sqrt{\frac{\int \bar{\vartheta}^2 d\varkappa}{\int d\varkappa}} \cdot \sqrt{\int \mathbf{v}'^{2(0)} d\varkappa \int \vartheta'^2 d\varkappa} \tag{57}$$

We shall now introduce some new notations defined from:

$$\int \bar{\vartheta}^2 d\varkappa \equiv \bar{\vartheta}_A^2 \int d\varkappa$$

$$\int \vartheta_e^2 d\varkappa \equiv \vartheta_{eA}^2 \int d\varkappa$$

$$\int \mathbf{v}'^{2(0)} d\varkappa \equiv \mathbf{v}_A'^{2(0)} \int d\varkappa \equiv x^2 \int d\varkappa$$

and

$$\int \vartheta'^2 d\varkappa \equiv \vartheta_A'^2 \int d\varkappa \equiv y^2 \int d\varkappa.$$

Using (52)', (57) and the notations above, then eqs. (44), (45) might after a division by $\int d\varkappa$, be written as:

$$\sigma_2 \sqrt{a_2}\, \bar{\vartheta}_A x y - r y^2 = \frac{S \nu x^2}{g} \tag{58}$$

$$u\sigma_2\sqrt{a_2}\,\overline{\vartheta}_A xy = \frac{S\nu x^2}{g}. \qquad (59)$$

Here u is a dimensionless number given by

$$u \equiv \frac{Sn(a_q - a_2)}{g} = \frac{gSd^2}{f_c^2}(a_q - a_2) \qquad (60)$$

having substituted the expression defining n in (21 b). It will be assumed that

$$S > 0 \qquad (61)$$

Eq. (47) might now with a substitution from eq. (51)′ for $\int \overline{\vartheta}\,\overline{h}\,d\varkappa$ and from (59) for $\int \frac{d\overline{\vartheta}}{dy} v'\vartheta' d\varkappa$, be written as

$$\frac{S\nu x^2}{g} = ru\left(\sigma_1 \vartheta_{eA}\overline{\vartheta}_A - \overline{\vartheta}_A^2\right) - \frac{\alpha S g l^2 \nu \sigma^2 a_2 u}{f_c^2}\overline{\vartheta}_A^2; \quad \alpha = 0 \text{ or } 1, \qquad (62)$$

where σ and σ_1 are the correlation coefficients defined on pp. 201 and 203, respectively.

From (59) we get

$$y = \frac{S\nu x}{g\sigma_2\sqrt{a_2}\,\overline{\vartheta}_A u}, \qquad (63)$$

which by substitution in (57) gives:

$$\frac{S\nu x^2}{g}\left(\frac{1}{u} - \frac{Sr\nu}{g a_2 \sigma_2^2 u^2 \overline{\vartheta}_A^2} - 1\right) = 0.$$

Consequently, to obtain solutions for x and y which are not both zero, the following relation between u and $\overline{\vartheta}_A^2$ must exist:

$$\frac{1}{u} - \frac{Sr\nu}{g a_2 \sigma_2^2 u^2 \overline{\vartheta}_A^2} - 1 = 0,$$

or

$$\overline{\vartheta}_A^2 = \frac{r\nu S}{g a_2 \sigma_2^2 (1-u)u}. \qquad (64)$$

Since now $u(1-u)_{max} = \frac{1}{4}$, we obtain now as a lower limit to the values of $\overline{\vartheta}_A$ for which an eddy motion is possible:

$$(\overline{\vartheta}_A^2)_{min} = \frac{4r\nu S}{g a_2 \sigma_{2\,max}^2} > \frac{4r\nu S}{g a_2} \qquad (65)$$

This result is similar to Rayleighs result for ordinary convection. It is understood that the existence of a lower limit to the values of $\overline{\vartheta}_A$ compatible with the existence of eddy motion is a consequence of dissipation ($\nu > 0$) and of the damping of eddy variance of ϑ' ($r > 0$), as well.

A further result which is immediately clear from (64) and (61) is that one and zero are absolute limits to u. Actually, these limits will be closer together since u cannot assume values arbitrarily close to 1 or 0 without making $\overline{\vartheta}_A^2$ increasingly large, and thereby violating the condition that $\overline{\vartheta}_A^2$ in consequence of (62) and (61) is bounded upwards to the value above which $\int \overline{\vartheta}\,\overline{h}\,d\varkappa$ becomes negative. Using (60) we therefore get

$$a_2 + \frac{f_c^2 u_{max}}{gSd^2} > a_q > a_2 + \frac{f_c^2 u_{min}}{gSd^2};$$

$$u_{max} < 1 \text{ and } u_{min} > 0. \qquad (66)$$

Quite generally we might find how x^2 depends upon u and the other parameters by substituting in eq. (62) for $\overline{\vartheta}_A$ the expression in (64). This gives

$$\nu \mathrm{v}_A'^{2(0)} = \frac{gru}{S}\cdot \left(\sigma_1 \vartheta_{eA}\sqrt{\frac{r\nu S}{g a_2 \sigma_2^2 u(1-u)}} - \frac{r\nu S}{g a_2 \sigma_2^2 u(1-u)}\right) - \frac{\alpha g r \nu^2 S \sigma^2 l^2}{\sigma_2^2 f_c^2 (1-u)}; \quad \alpha = 0 \text{ or } 1. \qquad (67)$$

For given ϑ_{eA} there is accordingly a whole set of non-zero eddy solutions depending upon which value of u is taken between the permitted limits, and depending upon whether the value zero or one is taken for α. Some principle is therefore needed if we want to pick out just the solution which we think is most likely to exist. By hypothesis we shall assume this principle to be equivalent with a maximization of the total effect of the driving forces that maintain the eddy motion against dissipation. It should be stressed that we are not maximizing the effect of the forces which are maintaining the *total* motion against dissipation, but only the eddy part of it. The underlying reason for this is that we are considering, as the very essential thing in our problem, the dynamic processes according to which an axialsymmetric motion under quite general conditions is breaking up, due to a fundamental instability, into a non-symmetric eddy motion. The adoption of the above maximization principle should then analogously imply that any non-symmetric solution of the long-term steady state problem cannot possibly exist as a stable motion except when the effect of the driving forces has a maximum. It should be mentioned that nothing has been proved theoretically to show that such a principle exists, even approximately. As possible supporting evidence for its correctness we can therefore at this stage only use the conclusions which might be drawn from it. For a satisfactory discussion of this problem it will be necessary to consider the conditions for long-term balance on each of a number of eddy spectral components, which exist *simultaneously*, and not only one at a time. (A maximization principle similar to the one above has earlier been used by MALKUS (1954) and KUO (1957).

The effect of the driving forces in the eddy motion equals the effect of the dissipative forces in the eddy motion, and is therefore given by the expression on the right hand side of eq. (67). To maximize this it is first of all clear that the zero value must be taken for α. In view of (48) this is the case in which the surface kinetic energy of the zonal mean motion is negligible in comparison with the one of the eddy motion which agrees with the actual conditions in the atmosphere.

With $\alpha = 0$ in (67) this becomes:

$$\nu \mathbf{v}_A'^{2(0)} = \frac{gru}{S} \cdot \left(\sigma_1 \vartheta_{eA} \sqrt{\frac{r\nu S}{ga_2\sigma_2^2 u(1-u)}} - \frac{r\nu S}{ga_2\sigma_2^2 u(1-u)}\right). \quad (68)$$

From this is now obtained the upper and lower limits for u beyond which no eddy motion is possible. These values are:

$$u_{\max} = \tfrac{1}{2} + \tfrac{1}{2}\sqrt{1 - \frac{4r\nu S}{ga_2\sigma_2^2\sigma_1^2\vartheta_{eA}^2}} \quad (69\,\text{a})$$

and

$$u_{\min} = \tfrac{1}{2} - \tfrac{1}{2}\sqrt{1 - \frac{4r\nu S}{ga_2\sigma_2^2\sigma_1^2\vartheta_{eA}^2}} \quad (69\,\text{b})$$

By a substitution of this into (66) we get the corresponding expressions for the upper and lower limits for a_q. It is seen from (69) that ϑ_{eA}^2 must fulfill a relation analogous to the one for $\overline{\vartheta}_A^2$ in eq. (65), namely:

$$(\vartheta_{eA}^2)_{\min} = \frac{4r\nu S}{ga_2\sigma_{2\max}^2\sigma_1^2} > \frac{4r\nu S}{ga_2\sigma_1^2} \quad (70)$$

As σ_1^2 is at most equal to one, $(\vartheta_{eA}^2)_{\min}$ is equal to or greater than $(\overline{\vartheta}_A^2)_{\min}$.

Let now u_M denote the value of u for which $\nu \mathbf{v}_A'^{2(0)}$ assumes its maximum value. Under the assumptions that S does not depend upon u, and σ_2 might be considered a virtual constant, we find for u_M and the corresponding values of a_q, $\overline{\vartheta}_A$, $\mathbf{v}_A'^{2(0)}$ and $\vartheta_A'^2$:

$$u_M = \frac{1}{1 + \dfrac{4r\nu S}{a_2 g\sigma_2^2\sigma_1^2\vartheta_{eA}^2}} \quad (71\,\text{a})$$

$$a_q \equiv \frac{(\nabla\vartheta')^2{}_A}{\vartheta_A'^2} = a_2 + \frac{f_c^2 u_M}{gSd^2} \quad (71\,\text{b})$$

$$\overline{\vartheta}_A = \frac{\sigma_1\vartheta_{eA}}{2u_M} \quad (72)$$

$$\mathbf{v}_A'^{2(0)} = \frac{gr\left(1 - \dfrac{1}{2u_M}\right)\sigma_1^2\vartheta_{eA}^2}{2\nu S} \quad (73)$$

$$\vartheta_A'^2 = \frac{(1-u_M)\left(1 - \dfrac{1}{2u_M}\right)\sigma_1^2\vartheta_{eA}^2}{2u_M} \quad (74)$$

If we add (48),

$$\overline{\mathbf{v}}_A^{2(0)} = (10^{-1} \text{ to } 10^{-2}) \times \mathbf{v}_A'^{2(0)} \quad (75)$$

we have here in eqs. (71)—(75) the expressions which are assumed to characterize in the above respect the eddy and mean zonal motion in a long-term steady state as a function of some external parameters and some internal physical properties of the fluid. For an application of this to the atmosphere we return in section 7.

6. The case with a vertical stability depending upon the motion

In the preceding section S was considered as independent of u when the particular $u = u_M$ was found that maximized $\nu \mathbf{v}_A'^{2(0)}$. This must, however, be considered only as a first approximation. In view of (5), (17) and (48) we have in fact approximately:

$$\int g\Theta w d\varkappa = \nu \int \mathbf{v}'^{2(0)} d\varkappa \tag{76}$$

On p. 196 we remarked that the positive correlation between Θ and w implies a stabilization of the atmosphere in the vertical which is offset on the other hand in the long-term balance by the proper vertical distribution of heating as expressed by eq. (6). This becomes now

$$-\int \varphi H_0 d\varkappa = \nu \int \mathbf{v}'^{2(0)} d\varkappa. \tag{77}$$

Let us now for instance assume that $\int \mathbf{v}^{2'(0)} d\varkappa$ is increased by varying the parameters upon which $\int \mathbf{v}'^{2(0)} d\varkappa$ depends. According to (76) there is then an increased tendency for the stabilization in the vertical. The corresponding decrease in $\int \varphi H_0 d\varkappa$ must then be thought of as being brought about by a real increase in vertical stability according to which the upper layers have become relatively warmer and therefore are being cooled at a higher rate than before relative to the lower layers.

We might express this by writing a simplified law for the horizontally averaged heating H_0:

$$H_0 = k[(\Theta_0 - \Theta_{0e}) - (\Theta_0^* - \Theta_{0e}^*)] \tag{78}$$

$$(k = \text{const} > 0).$$

It is seen that this law also takes account of eq. (7). Θ_{0e}, that represents some equilibrium vertical distribution of Θ_0, will together with Θ_0 be assumed to depend linearly upon z. Substituting from (78) into (77) we then get

$$gk(S - S_e)\int (z - z^*)^2 d\varkappa = \nu \int \mathbf{v}'^{2(0)} d\varkappa \tag{79}$$

with

$$S = \frac{d\Theta_0}{dz}; \qquad S_e \equiv \frac{d\Theta_{0e}}{dz}$$

Hence

$$S = S_e + \frac{\nu \mathbf{v}_A'^{2(0)}}{gk\{(z - z^*)^2\}^*}. \tag{80}$$

The relation (66) might also be interpreted as determining the intervals in which a_q must lie for different vertical stabilities S given by (80). It might therefore be concluded that if as a consequence of a change in the important parameters a balanced motion is reestablished in which $\mathbf{v}_A'^{2(0)}$ has increased sufficiently, then simultaneously the characteristic scale must have increased, as well.

To see whether $\mathbf{v}_A'^{2(0)}$ really can be increased arbitrarily or not by a variation of the important external parameters, we must return to eqs. (58), (59) and (62), substituting there the expression (80) for S. With the notation t defined by

$$t \equiv n(a_q - a_2) = \frac{g^2 d^2 (a_q - a_2)}{f_c^2}, \tag{81}$$

these equations might then be written:

$$\sigma_2 \sqrt{a_2}\,\overline{\vartheta}_A xy - ry^2 = \frac{S_e \nu x^2}{g} + \frac{\nu^2 \varkappa^4}{kg^2\{(z - z^*)^2\}^*} \tag{82}$$

$$t\sigma_2 \sqrt{a_2}\,\overline{\vartheta}_A xy = \nu x^2 \tag{83}$$

$$rt(\sigma_1 \vartheta_{eA} \overline{\vartheta}_A - \overline{\vartheta}_A^2) = \nu x^2, \tag{84}$$

having again put $\alpha = 0$ in eq. (62) for the reasons mentioned on p. 206. Eliminating y between eqs. (83) and (82) and introducing

$$\omega \equiv t\overline{\vartheta}_A, \tag{85}$$

we get:

$$kg^2\{(z - z^*)^2\}^* \left(\frac{\overline{\vartheta}_A}{\omega} - \frac{r\nu}{\omega^2 \sigma_2^2 a_2} - \frac{S_e}{g}\right) = \nu x^2 \tag{86}$$

Further, introducing ω from (85), we might write (84) as:

$$r\omega \left(\frac{\sigma_1 \vartheta_{eA}}{\overline{\vartheta}_A} - 1\right) \overline{\vartheta}_A = \nu x^2 \tag{84'}$$

It is seen that for large values of $\sigma_1 \vartheta_{eA}$ eqs. (86) and (84)' will be satisfied, as a particular solution, when

$$\sigma_1 \vartheta_{eA} = \text{const}_1 \overline{\vartheta}_A$$

and

$$\omega = \text{const}_2,$$

provided that

$$\frac{kg^2\{(z - z^*)^2\}^*}{\text{const}_2} = r\,\text{const}_2\,(\text{const}_1 - 1).$$

In this case, we get

$$\begin{aligned} \nu x^2 = \nu \mathbf{v}_A'^{2(0)} &= r\,\text{const}_2\,(\text{const}_1 - 1)\overline{\vartheta}_A \\ &= r\,\text{const} \cdot \sigma_1 \vartheta_{eA}. \end{aligned} \tag{87}$$

Comparing this with (73) it is understood that

with a vertical stability depending upon the motion in accordance with (80), $\mathbf{v}_A^{\prime 2(0)}$ will have a linear instead of a quadratic dependence upon $\sigma_1 \vartheta_{eA}$ for large values of $\sigma_1 \vartheta_{eA}$.

Eq. (87) above demonstrates that it is possible by increasing $\sigma_1 \vartheta_{eA}$ to find a set of long-term steady solutions with increasing values of $\nu \mathbf{v}_A^{\prime 2(0)}$. However, there is again for any value of $\sigma_1 \vartheta_{eA}$ a choice among a set of different possible solutions. In particular it is for instance always possible, however large the value of $\sigma_1 \vartheta_{eA}$ may be, to have the solutions with negligible amounts of $\mathbf{v}_A^{\prime 2(0)}$ which correspond to values of a_q close to the upper limit emerging from (66) if S is there approximated by S_e. If, however, the maximization principle is used, then the particular solution studied above shows that a sufficiently increased external differential heating will cause an increase in $\mathbf{v}_A^{\prime 2(0)}$ and the characteristic scale, as well. It is remarkable that this is exactly what is found in rotating tank experiments with differential heating (FULTZ, 1956). If no other explanation can be offered for the change towards greater typical wavelengths which is observed in these experiments when the differential heating is increased, we might take this as good evidence for the hypothesis that the fluid adopts itself to the types of motion in which the effect of the driving forces in the eddy motion becomes large, if not a maximum.

With regard to a possible explanation of this, following the remark on p. 206, one may now make this comment: On the one hand it is natural to assume that the eddy motions of any possible scale have an *a priori* equal chance to develop. On the other hand, however, having once been formed an arbitrary one of these will influence the remaining ones in a manner which varies markedly with the scale of the disturbance first considered. Now, actually, the one with the maximum effect of the driving forces reduces the possibilities for the other components to exist much more than *vice versa*. This is primarily so because of the manner in which vertical stability is coupled with the motion as revealed by several of the earlier formulae.

With this we are closing the theoretical discussion in the belief that some major results related to our problem have been exposed. It is of course possible to carry the discussion further in more detail, for instance in close connection with the observed phenomena in rotating tank experiments. It would be of particular interest to find how the Richardsons number varies with varying external parameters since this would illuminate the conditions under which such motions are possible when rotation and gravity forces are in equilibrium as expressed by the thermal wind relationship. This would, however, lead us beyond the scope of this article.

7. Testing of theoretical results by a comparison with motions in the atmosphere

In the atmosphere the overall stability is significantly greater in winter than in summer. This agrees qualitatively with the contents of relation (80), since $\mathbf{v}_A^{\prime 2(0)}$ is greater in winter than in summer. We are then assuming that we can apply the integrals of the preceding sections to an hemisphere even if they strictly only apply to the total atmosphere. Approximately they will, however, also be applicable to parts of the atmosphere if these are not too small, provided ϑ and h are taken as deviations from horizontal averages over the corresponding areas. Since S_e is difficult to determine directly from the laws of heating, we shall instead try to find its probable value by using the observed winter and summer values of S and $\mathbf{v}_A^{\prime 2(0)}$ in connection with (80). Considering S_e and k as approximate yearly constants we get

$$S_e = \frac{S_s(\mathbf{v}_A^{\prime 2(0)})_w - S_w(\mathbf{v}_A^{\prime 2(0)})_s}{(\mathbf{v}_A^{\prime 2(0)})_w - (\mathbf{v}_A^{\prime 2(0)})_s}. \tag{88}$$

We compute S from

$$S = \int_F \int_0^\infty \frac{\partial \Theta}{\partial z} Q dz dF \Big/ \int_F \int_0^\infty Q dz dF$$

where Q is a standard density given by $Q = \text{const}\, e^{-\frac{z}{D}}$, and F is the horizontal area covered by the integration. This gives

$$S = \frac{1}{F \cdot T_{\text{const}}} \int \left[\frac{g}{c_p} + \frac{1}{D}(T^* - T_{1000}) \right] dF$$

where T_{const} is an average T, and T_{1000} is the temperature in the 1,000 mb surface.

Using the northern hemisphere data for $\overline{T}$ published by MINTZ (1955), we have tabulated below (Table I) the winter and summer values of

$$\frac{g}{c_p} + \frac{1}{D}(\overline{T}^* - \overline{T}_{1000}) = \frac{g}{c_p} + \left(\frac{\partial \overline{T}}{\partial z}\right)^*$$

Table I.

$10 \sin \Phi$	2—3	3—4	4—5	5—6	6—7	7—8	8—9	9—10	$10^3 T_{\text{const}} S$
$10^3 \left(\frac{g}{c_p} + \left(\frac{\partial T}{\partial z}\right)\right)$ °/m	5.0	5.1	5.2	5.3	5.6	5.9	6.2	6.7	5.6 (July—Aug. 49)
»	6.0	6.2	6.4	6.7	7.0	7.6	7.8	8.2	7.0 (Jan.—Febr. 49)

as function of 10 sin Φ, where Φ is latitude. The corresponding values of S are given at the right end of the table, taking D = 7,200 m.

For the corresponding values of $\mathbf{v}_A'^{2(0)}$ we have used:

Table II
(North of 20° N)

	Jan.—Febr. 49	July—Aug. 49
$\mathbf{v}_A^{2(0)}$	109 m² sec⁻²	40 m² sec⁻²

The winter value is found from data given by Pisharoty (1955 a), while the summer value is found by the author.

By a substitution of the above values of S and $\mathbf{v}_A'^{2(0)}$ in (88), using $\mathbf{v}_A'^{2(0)} \approx \mathbf{v}_A{}^{2(0)}$, we get:

$$T_{\text{const}} S_e = 4.8 \; 10^{-3} \; °/\text{m}.$$

Comparing this value of $T_{\text{const}} S_e$ with the ones for $T_{\text{const}} S$ it is understood that the dynamics contributes significantly to the vertical stability of the atmosphere.

The difference between the winter and summer values of vertical stability might also be illuminated by the table below where the Δ indicates a temperature difference between winter and summer (Table III).

By the adoption of relation (80) we have anticipated that the difference in averaged vertical stability in winter and summer is mainly due to the large-scale dynamical influences, or more precisely the difference in differential heating which favours larger values of $\int \Theta w d\varkappa$ during the winter than during the summer. Table III shows in particular that it is impossible in any discussion of the causes for the climatic changes in lower levels not to take into account the changes in vertical stability, which are caused by the large-scale dynamics.

Although significant, the large-scale dynamical contribution to S is relatively small in the atmosphere. As a first approximation we might therefore test the theory on the atmospheric conditions by using the results expressed in eqs. (71)—(75) which were based on the assumption of constant S. In these formulae σ_2 is an unknown parameter characterizing the kinematics. Further, r and ϑ_{eA} are relatively little known from the heating laws. We shall therefore use the established formulae, partly in a diagnostic, and partly in a prognistic way. We then first note that eq. (74) in view of (72) also might be written

$$\vartheta_A'^2 = (1 - u_M)(2u_M - 1)\bar{\vartheta}_A^2 \qquad (74)'$$

Using this in (71) b) we obtain further

$$(\nabla \vartheta')^2{}_A = \frac{f_c^2 u_M (1 - u_M)(2u_M - 1)\bar{\vartheta}_A^2}{gSd^2} + $$
$$+ (1 - u_M)(2u_M - 1) a_2 \bar{\vartheta}_A^2. \qquad (89)$$

Noting (18 a) and the definition of d^2 in eq. (21 b) we obtain

$$\frac{g^2 d^2}{f_c^2} (\nabla \vartheta')_A^2 = \widehat{(\mathbf{v}' - \hat{\mathbf{v}}')_A^2}$$

and

$$\frac{g^2 d^2}{f_c^2} a_2 \bar{\vartheta}_A^2 = \frac{g^2 d^2}{f_c^2} (\nabla \bar{\vartheta})_A^2 = \widehat{(\bar{\mathbf{v}} - \hat{\bar{\mathbf{v}}})_A^2},$$

Table III

Φ°N	80	70	60	50	40	30
$\Delta T_{850\,\text{mb}}$°	— 22.5	— 23.5	— 21.6	— 19.5	— 17.1	— 12.3
$\Delta T_{300\,\text{mb}}$°	— 14.7	— 13.7	— 12.0	— 12.2	— 13.3	— 10.4

which, when combined with (89) gives

$$\widehat{(\mathbf{v}' - \hat{\mathbf{v}}')^2_A} = \frac{gu_M(1-u_M)(2u_M-1)\overline{\vartheta}^2_A}{S} + \\ + (1-u_M)(2u_M-1)\widehat{(\bar{\mathbf{v}} - \hat{\bar{\mathbf{v}}})^2_A}. \qquad (89)'$$

Finally, eq. (73) might in view of (51)′ and (72) be written

$$\mathbf{v}'^{2(0)}_A = \frac{gu_M}{\nu S} \cdot \frac{\int \bar{\vartheta}\bar{h}\,d\varkappa}{\int d\varkappa} \qquad (73)'$$

A diagnostic value of u_M may be obtained by solving (74)′ above using a value for $\vartheta'^2_A/\overline{\vartheta}^2_A$ taken from analyzed maps for the period Jan.—Feb. 1949. This value was found to be

$$(\vartheta'^2_A/\overline{\vartheta}^2_A)_{\text{obs}} \approx \tfrac{1}{11} \text{ (Jan.—Febr. 49)}$$

Rejecting the smaller root of

$$(1-u_M)(2u_M-1) = \tfrac{1}{11},$$

since this one does not make $\mathbf{v}'^{2(0)}_A$ so large as does the other root, we obtain

$$(u_M)_{\text{diagn.}} = 0.88 \qquad (90)$$

Below are the approximate values for $\overline{T}^*$ averaged over Jan.—Febr. 1949 as obtained from the publication of MINTZ (1955):

Table IV
(Jan.—Febr. 49)

10 sin Φ	0—1	1—2	2—3	3—4	4—5	5—6	6—7	7—8	8—9	9—10
$\overline{T}^*$ °A	259	258	256	255	252	249	246	243	238	232

Let Q_{AE} denote the total radiation balance for the system atmosphere-earth for the months January—February and averaged along zonal circles. According to BAUER and PHILLIPS, (1935), the values of Q_{AE} measured in 10^3 cal cm^{-2} min^{-1} as function of latitude are approximately:

Table V.
(Jan.—Febr.)

10 sin Φ	0—1	1—2	2—3	3—4	4—5	5—6	6—7	7—8	8—9	9—10	
Q_{AE}	58	50	26	0	—30	—66	—100	—137	—162	—194	10^{-3} cal cm^{-2}min^{-1}

Applying (73)′ and (89) to the northern hemisphere, we obtain as a first approximation, neglecting certain terms which presumably are small,

$$(\mathbf{v}'^{2(0)}_A)_{\text{Theor.}} = \frac{gu_M 7 \cdot 10^{-8}}{\nu S T^2_{\text{const}}} \cdot \\ \cdot \left(\tfrac{1}{10} \sum_1^{10} \overline{T}^* Q_{AE} - \tfrac{1}{100} \left(\sum_1^{10} \overline{T}^* \right) \left(\sum_1^{10} Q_{AE} \right) \right)$$

and

$$\widehat{(\mathbf{v}' - \hat{\mathbf{v}}')^2_A}_{\text{Theor.}} = \frac{gu_M(1-u_M)(2u_M-1)}{S T^2_{\text{const}}} \cdot \\ \cdot \left(\tfrac{1}{10} \sum_1^{10} \overline{T}^{*2} - \tfrac{1}{100} \left(\sum_1^{10} \overline{T}^* \right)^2 \right) + \\ + \text{a negligible term.}$$

Substituting here $T_{\text{const}} = 250°\ A$ and the values above for S, u_M, $\overline{T}^*$, and Q_{AE}, and further the value $\nu = 2 \cdot 10^{-6}$ sec^{-1} used for instance by PISHAROTY (1955 a), we get:

$$(\mathbf{v}'^{2(0)}_A)_{\text{Theor}} = 126 \text{ m}^2 \text{ sec}^{-2} \text{ (Jan.—Febr. 49)}$$

and

$$\widehat{(\mathbf{v}' - \hat{\mathbf{v}}')^2_A}_{\text{Theor}} = 34 \text{ m}^2 \text{ sec}^{-2}.$$

As we do not for the moment have the corresponding observed value of the latter quantity, we shall make use of the known fact that total eddy kinetic energy might be obtained from

$$\mathbf{v}'^2_A = \mathbf{v}'^{2(0)}_A + (3 \text{ to } 4) \times \widehat{(\mathbf{v}' - \hat{\mathbf{v}}')^2_A}$$

We get therefore

$$(\mathbf{v}_A'^2)_{\text{Theor,}} = (126 + (3 \text{ to } 4) \cdot 34)\ \text{m}^2\,\text{sec}^{-2} =$$
$$= (228 \text{ to } 262)\ \text{m}^2\,\text{sec}^{-2}.$$

In comparison we have according to PISHAROTY (1955 b), as an average north of 20° N,

$$(\mathbf{v}_A'^2)_{\text{obs.}} = 212\ \text{m}^2\,\text{sec}^{-2}\ \text{(Jan.—Febr. 49)},$$

and the earlier quoted value

$$(\mathbf{v}_A'^{2(0)})_{\text{obs.}} = 109\ \text{m}^2\,\text{sec}^{-2}.\ \text{(Jan.—Febr. 49)}.$$

In view of the fact that $\mathbf{v}_A^{2(0)} = \mathbf{v}_A'^{2(0)} + \varepsilon$ where $\varepsilon = (10^{-1} \text{ to } 10^{-2})\ \mathbf{v}_A'^{2(0)}$, it is understood that both theoretical values are in good agreement with the observed ones. In conclusion we dare therefore say that the above test seems to show that the theory, including in particular the maximization principle, is essentially correct even if we allow for considerable tolerance due to uncertainties of different kinds.

Acknowledgements

I am indebted to Mr. P. Thrane and Mr. J. Nordø for valuable assistance and discussions.

REFERENCES

BAUR, F. and PHILLIPS, H., 1934: Der Wärmehaushalt der Lufthülle der Nordhalbkugel im Januar und Juli zur Zeit der Äquinoktien und Solstitien. *Gerlands Beitr. Geophys.*, **42**, 160—207, und **45**, 82—132.

CHARNEY, J. G. and ELIASSEN, A., 1949: A numerical method for predicting the perturbations of the middle westerlies. *Tellus*, **1**, 38—54.

FJØRTOFT, R., 1955: On the use of space-smoothing in physical weather forecasting. *Tellus*, **7**, 462—480.

FULZ, D., 1956: Studies in experimental hydrodynamics applied to large-scale meteorological phenomena. *Hydrodynamics Laboratory. Dept. of Met. University of Chicago. Final Report. Part I. Contract AF 19 (122)—160.*

KUO, H. L., 1957: Application of energy integrals to finite amplitude thermal convection. *M.I.T. Dept. of Met. General Circulation Project. Final Report. Contract No. AF 19 (604)—1000*, 343—354.

LORENTZ, E. N., 1955: Available potential energy in the atmosphere. *Tellus*, **7**, 157—167.

MALKUS, W. V. R., 1954: Discrete transitions in turbulent convection. *Proc. Roy. Soc. A.*, **225** (1161), 185—195.

MINTZ, Y., 1955: Final computation of the mean geostrophic poleward flux of angular momentum and of sensible heat in the winter and summer of 1949. *Dept. of Met. U.C.L.A., Los Angeles. Final Report. General Circulation Project. No. AF 19 (122)—48.* Article V, 7.

PISHAROTY, P. R., 1955 a: The kinetic energy of the atmosphere. *Dept. of Met., U.C.L.A., Los Angeles. Final Report. General Circulation Project. No. AF 19 (122)—48.* Article XIV, 14.

—1955 b: The kinetic energy of the atmosphere. *Dept. of Met., U.C.L.A., Los Angeles. Final Report. General Circulation Project. No. AF 19 (122)—48.* Article XIV, fig. 5.

(Manuscript received October 4, 1958)

On the Maintenance of Kinetic Energy in the Atmosphere

By E. PALMÉN
Academy of Finland

Abstract

An attempt is made to compute or estimate the conversion between potential and kinetic energy in the Northern Hemisphere during the cold season. The conversion in the Trade-wind belt is computed from the work done by the mean meridional pressure forces acting upon the mean Hadley circulation, thus neglecting the conversions due to different types of disturbances of the mean flow. A tentative budget, considering only this part of the energy cycle and including the corresponding mean frictional dissipation of kinetic energy, is presented. The total net generation of 22×10^{10} kj sec^{-1}, according to previous computation by Palmén, Riehl and Vuorela, is in fair agreement with the mean northward eddy flux of kinetic energy according to Pisharoty.

In middle latitudes conversions of potential energy into kinetic energy occur essentially in connection with disturbances of different types, corresponding to conversion of "available eddy potential energy" into "eddy kinetic energy" according to a scheme presented by Starr and Lorenz. Using as an example the release of kinetic energy in cyclone "Hazel" at the time when this was transformed into an extratropical cyclone, an estimate of the total conversion between potential and kinetic energy in middle and high latitudes is attempted using estimates of total frictional dissipation and the values for the influx of kinetic energy from the south. The results are necessarily extremely approximate, and the whole reasoning is in many respects rather speculative.

1. Fundamental equations

The change of horizontal kinetic energy in a fixed volume V of the atmosphere is expressed by the equation

$$\frac{\partial}{\partial t}\int_V \varrho k dV = -\int_V \nabla\cdot(\varrho \mathbf{v} k)dV - \int_V \frac{\partial(\varrho w k)}{\partial z}dV - \int_V \mathbf{v}\cdot\nabla p dV - \int_V \varrho\mathbf{v}\cdot\mathbf{F}dV. \quad (1)$$

Here ϱ is the density of air, k the horizontal kinetic energy per unit mass, $\mathbf{v}$ the horizontal wind vector, w the vertical wind component, $-\nabla p$ the horizontal pressure gradient and F the horizontal frictional force per unit mass.

In the following we select the volume V so that it is bounded from the outside atmosphere by a vertical surface S extending from the ground to the upper limit of the atmosphere, from the pressure $p = p_0$ to $p = 0$. The area of intersection between S and a constant isobaric surface is denoted by A and the length of its periphery by L. Both A and L are considered independent of height or pressure. Eq. (1) can then be written:

$$\frac{\partial}{\partial t}\int_V \varrho k dV = -\frac{1}{g}\int_0^{p_0}\int_L k v_n dL\, dp - \frac{1}{g}\int_0^{p_0}\int_A \mathbf{v}\cdot\nabla\phi dA dp - \int_0^{\infty}\int_A \varrho\mathbf{v}\cdot\mathbf{F}dA dz, \quad (2)$$

where g is the acceleration of gravity, v_n the wind component normal to S, and Φ the geopotential of the arbitrary isobaric surface.

The first term on the right in Eq. (2) represents the outflow of kinetic energy through the vertical boundary S, the second term denotes the work done by the horizontal pressure forces inside V, and the third term represents the dissipating influence of friction. The work term can be transformed into

$$\frac{1}{g}\int_0^{p_0}\int_A \phi \nabla \cdot \mathbf{v} dA dp - \frac{1}{g}\int_0^{p_0}\int_L \phi v_n dL dp. \quad (3)$$

It should be held in mind that the above expression vanishes identically for geostrophic winds (VAN MIEGHEM, 1956). If we express the horizontal wind vector as the sum of the geostrophic wind, $\mathbf{v}_g$, and the ageostrophic wind, $\mathbf{v}_a$, we get

$$\mathbf{v} \cdot \nabla \phi = \mathbf{v}_a \cdot \nabla \phi = \nabla \cdot (\phi \mathbf{v}_a) - \phi \nabla \cdot \mathbf{v}_a. \quad (4)$$

Eq. (2) therefore can be written in the form:

$$\frac{\partial}{\partial t}\int_V \varrho k dV =$$

$$= -\frac{1}{g}\int_0^{p_0}\int_L k v_n dL dp - \frac{1}{g}\int_0^{p_0}\int_L \phi v_{na} dL dp +$$

$$+\frac{1}{g}\int_0^{p_0}\int_A \phi \nabla \cdot \mathbf{v}_a dA dp - \int_0^{\infty}\int_A \varrho \mathbf{v} \cdot \mathbf{F} dA dz, \quad (5)$$

where v_{an} now denotes the horizontal ageostrophic wind component normal to S. The first two right-hand terms represent energy fluxes through the boundary of volume V. A comparison of the magnitude of both fluxes is difficult since the first term contains the total normal wind, but the second term only the ageostrophic part of the normal wind.

If we make use of the hydrostatic equation, $\frac{\partial \phi}{\partial p} = -\alpha$, where α is the specific volume, and by ω denote $\frac{dp}{dt}$ we get:

$$\int_0^{p_0}\int_A \phi \nabla \cdot \mathbf{v} dA dp =$$

$$= -\int_0^{p_0}\int_A \phi \frac{\partial \omega}{\partial p} dA dp = -\int_0^{p_0}\int_A \alpha \omega dA dp. \quad (6)$$

Since $\nabla \cdot \mathbf{v}_a \approx \nabla \cdot \mathbf{v}$ Eq. (5) can be written in the form:

$$\frac{\partial}{\partial t}\int_V \varrho k dV =$$

$$= -\frac{1}{g}\int_0^{p^0}\int_L k v_n dL dp - \frac{1}{g}\int_0^{p_0}\int_L \phi v_{na} dL dp -$$

$$-\frac{R}{g}\int_0^{p_0}\int_A \frac{T\omega}{p} dA dp - \int_0^{\infty}\int_A \varrho \mathbf{v} \cdot \mathbf{F} dA dz, \quad (7)$$

where R is the gas constant and T the absolute temperature. Here the third right-hand term represents the conversion between potential and kinetic energy. For a closed system, e.g. the whole atmosphere, the flux terms disappear, and the increase of kinetic energy equals the conversion of potential energy into kinetic energy diminished by the frictional dissipation of kinetic energy (e.g. WHITE and SALTZMAN, 1956).

For a closed system the change of kinetic energy can be computed either from the work terms in Eq. (1) and (2) or from the conversion terms in Eq. (5), (6) and (7). For open systems it seems most practical to use the work terms, since the flux of potential energy could be difficult to evaluate.[1] It should especially be pointed out that the local change of kinetic energy hardly can be computed, or even estimated, from the local change of potential energy between consecutive synoptic times. For such a computation it would be necessary to consider radiation, condensation etc. further to compute advection of internal and potential energy very exactly. Since the atmospheric kinetic energy always represents a very small quantity compared with the internal and potential energy even very small errors in the local change of the latter quantities would result in extremely large relative errors in the computed change of kinetic energy (LORENZ, 1955). A synoptic study by SPAR (1950) also showed that no success can be expected from such computations.

In real atmospheric processes an increase of kinetic energy through conversion of potential energy into kinetic energy does not necessarily mean that the potential energy actually decreases

[1] The absolute values of both terms in expression (3) often are much larger than the whole expression. The terms therefore should not, without great care, be treated separately.

even when radiational processes and advection of potential energy are disregarded. The vertical circulation associated with conversion between potential and kinetic energy very commonly is accompanied by liberation of latent heat, thus adding a heat source as a result of the conversion process. As a typical example of this type of atmospheric processes tropical cyclones could be mentioned. During the formation of a tropical cyclone kinetic, potential and internal energy increase simultaneously (PALMÉN and RIEHL, 1957). Extratropical cyclones which undoubtedly derive a large part of their kinetic energy from their available potential energy also are influenced by liberation of latent heat as a result of the vertical solenoidial circulations; this new heat source counteracts the decrease of potential energy. Consequently, an intensifying cyclonic disturbance may act as a source region of both kinetic and potential + internal energy.

2. General atmospheric circulation

The general atmospheric circulation can be defined in different ways. It could be defined as the mean three-dimensional air movement as a function of longitude, latitude and height for sufficiently long time periods. Considering the strong seasonal variations of atmospheric conditions it is convenient to treat the general circulation for different seasons separately. In a more general form the general circulation could be defined as the mean three-dimensional flow as a function of latitude and height only. In this case the zonal, meridional and vertical components of wind have been averaged over time and longitude.

In the following we shall disregard the variation with time and consider $\bar{u}$, $\bar{v}$ and $\bar{w}$ as the mean zonal, meridional and vertical wind components at a given latitude and height averaged over time for the selected time period. The mean horizontal kinetic energy, $\bar{k}$, for a selected latitude and height is then given by:

$$\bar{k} = \frac{1}{2}\left(\bar{u}^2 + \bar{v}^2\right) + \frac{1}{2}\left(\overline{u'^2} + \overline{v'^2}\right) = k_m + k_e \quad (8)$$

where $'$ denotes the local deviation from the mean value along a given parallel circle. In the above equation k_m can be defined as the kinetic energy of the mean horizontal motion (including the meridional component) and k_e the kinetic energy of the "eddy motion".

The total mean flux of kinetic energy through the latitude φ is per unit length of the parallel determined by

$$\frac{1}{g}\int_0^{p_0} \overline{kv}\, dp = \frac{1}{g}\int_0^{p_0} \left(\bar{k}\bar{v}_a + \overline{k'v_a'} + \overline{k'v_g'}\right) dp \quad (9)$$

About the value of the product $\overline{k'v_a'}$ very little is known. It is probably in most cases small compared with the product $\overline{k'v_g'}$ and will therefore be disregarded. Since $\bar{v}_a = \bar{v}$ the flux can be written in the form

$$\frac{1}{g}\int_0^{p_0} \left(\bar{k}\bar{v} + \overline{k'v_g'}\right) dp. \quad (10)$$

In computation of the existing kinetic energy, k, geostrophic winds represent a satisfactory approximation polewards from a belt around the Equator, but for low latitudes the real winds should be used.

The work done per unit area by the horizontal pressure forces can be expressed by

$$-\int_0^{\infty}\left[\bar{v}\,\frac{\overline{\partial p}}{\partial y} + \overline{u'\left(\frac{\partial p}{\partial x}\right)'} + \overline{v'\left(\frac{\partial p}{\partial y}\right)'}\right] dz =$$

$$= \frac{f}{g}\int_0^{p_0} \left(\bar{v}\bar{u}_g - \overline{u_a'v_g'} + \overline{v_a'u_g'}\right) dp, \quad (11)$$

where f denotes the Coriolis parameter. The first term under the integral represents the work done by the mean meridional pressure gradient on the air moving at the mean meridional velocity $\bar{v}$. Since the mass transport integrated over height approximately vanishes for longer time periods a positive work is done if $\bar{v}$ and $\bar{u}_g$ are positively correlated. Due to the mean meridional temperature field in the troposphere such a positive correlation exists if the mean meridional movement is directed polewards in the upper troposphere and equatorwards in the lower troposphere. This mean meridional motion must be associated with ascent of warmer air in low latitudes and descent of colder air in higher latitudes. It can be defined as a direct mean circulation, whereas the opposite type of circulation is defined as an indirect or reversed circulation.

The two last terms of the integrand in expression (11) represent the work done by the horizontal pressure forces due to variations in wind and pressure gradient along the parallel circle. Those terms are difficult to evaluate on global scale because they contain the deviations from the mean ageostrophic wind components. Only for selected areas with a dense network of good wind stations could an estimate of these contributions succeed.

The dissipation of kinetic energy per unit area due to friction can be expressed by

$$\overline{\tau_{x0}u_0} + \overline{\tau_{y0}v_0} + \int_0^\infty \overline{\left[\mu\left(\frac{\partial u}{\partial z}\right)^2 + \mu\left(\frac{\partial v}{\partial z}\right)^2\right]} dz \quad (12)$$

Here τ_{x0}, τ_{y0} are the zonal and meridional components of the surface drag, u_0, v_0 the wind components at ground (anemometer level), and μ denotes the coefficient of eddy viscocity in the atmosphere. The surface drag can be computed in different ways. If c_0 denotes the total wind velocity at anemometer height the dissipation due to friction at the ground can be expressed by

$$\overline{\varkappa\varrho_0 c_0^3} = \overline{\varkappa\varrho_0 c_0^2} \cdot \overline{c_0} + \overline{(\varkappa\varrho_0 c_0^2)' c_0}, \quad (13)$$

where $\varkappa$ is the drag coefficient, if we assume the surface drag to be proportional to the square of the wind velocity. The first term to the right can be evaluated on a global scale using mean values presented by PRIESTLEY (1951). The second term, representing the influence of the variations of wind along different parallel circles, is more difficult to compute. Further, there exists another type of dissipation associated with the "mountain effect" (MINTZ, 1955) which also is hard to estimate. Consequently, the total frictional dissipation at the ground cannot yet, even approximately, be computed. The additional dissipation due to eddy friction in the atmosphere is even more difficult to estimate. The total frictional dissipation could, however, in some special cases be estimated from Eq. (2) if all other terms could be computed.

3. Budget of kinetic energy in the northern Trade-wind belt

An attempt to compute the conversion of potential energy into kinetic energy as a result of the mean "Hadley circulation" between Equator and 30° N was recently made by PALMÉN, RIEHL and VUORELA (1957) for the winter months December 1950—1951 and January—February 1951—1952. For these six winter months the total mean mass circulation in the whole Hadley

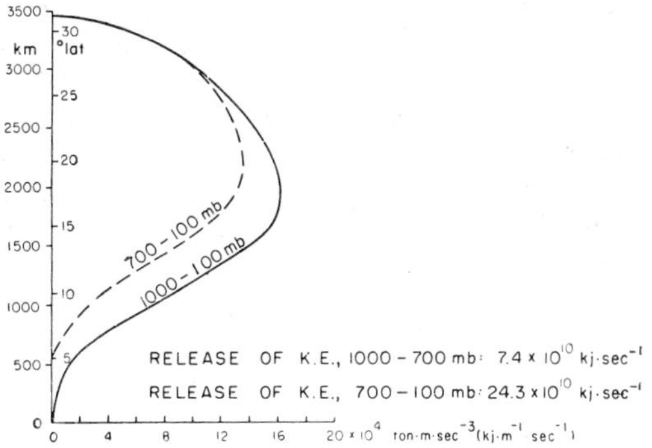

Fig. 1. Production of kinetic energy per unit length of the meridian by the mean meridional Hadley-type circulation for the time December—February according to Palmén, Riehl and Vuorela for the layer 1000—100 mb (solid curve) and for 700—100 mb (dashed curve).

cell was computed as about 260×10^6 tons per second. In this mean meridional circulation the essential southward mass transport occurs in the layer between the ground and 700 mb, with maximum intensity around 950 mb, and the essential northward transport in the layer between 350 and 100 mb, with maximum intensity around 200 mb, whereas the layer 700—350 mb represents a neutral region with practically no mean meridional mass transport. The meridional mass circulation is most intense between the latitudes 10—15° N.

This new computation, founded on the wind observations from 47 different stations, thus gave a somewhat stronger mean mass circulation than a previous less complete determination by PALMÉN (1955). With aid of the mean meridional mass flow at different levels the work done by the mean meridional pressure forces per unit length or the meridian, δW, was computed from the simple formula

$$\delta W = \frac{2\pi a f \cos\varphi}{g} \int_{10\,\mathrm{cb}}^{100\,\mathrm{cb}} \bar{v}\bar{u}_g \, dp, \quad (14)$$

where a is the earth's radius. The result is presented in Fig. 1 with the contribution of the layer 1,000—700 mb given separately. The integrated work for the whole Hadley cell between Equator and 30° N up to 100 mb amounts to 31.3×10^{10} kilojoules per second, the contribution of the lower layer 1,000—700 mb being 7.4×10^{10} kj sec^{-1}.

The flux of kinetic energy through different latitudes was computed from Expr. (10) using PISHAROTY's (1954) values for the mean distribution of k with height and his values of the eddy geostrophic flux of kinetic energy. Since Pisharoty's computation of the geostrophic eddy flux extended southwards only to the latitude 20° N his values wore extrapolated to the Equator assuming no flux across this southernmost latitude. Hence our flux values are very approximate for the southern part of the Hadley cell. It should also be mentioned that Pisharoty limited his computation to the layer 1,000—150 mb. Since high values of k are observed above 150 mb it is probable that his values therefore are somewhat underestimated.

As already mentioned, only a part of the ground friction could be computed, at least approximately, from the formula (13). The mean surface drag according to PRIESTLEY (1951) and PALMÉN (1955) multiplied by the mean surface wind represents the part of frictional dissipation presented in Fig. 2 from which then the dissipation for different zones was computed. For the whole region 0—30° N PALMÉN, RIEHL and VUORELA (1957) had computed this part of the surface dissipation to 3.7×10^{10} kj sec^{-1}.

In Table 1 the results of the above computations of production, flux and dissipation of kinetic energy are presented. The first three columns give the two fluxes in expression (10) and their sum for the whole length of the different latitudinal circles. The fourth column represents the divergence of the total flux for belts of 10° of latitude, the fifth column gives the generation of kinetic

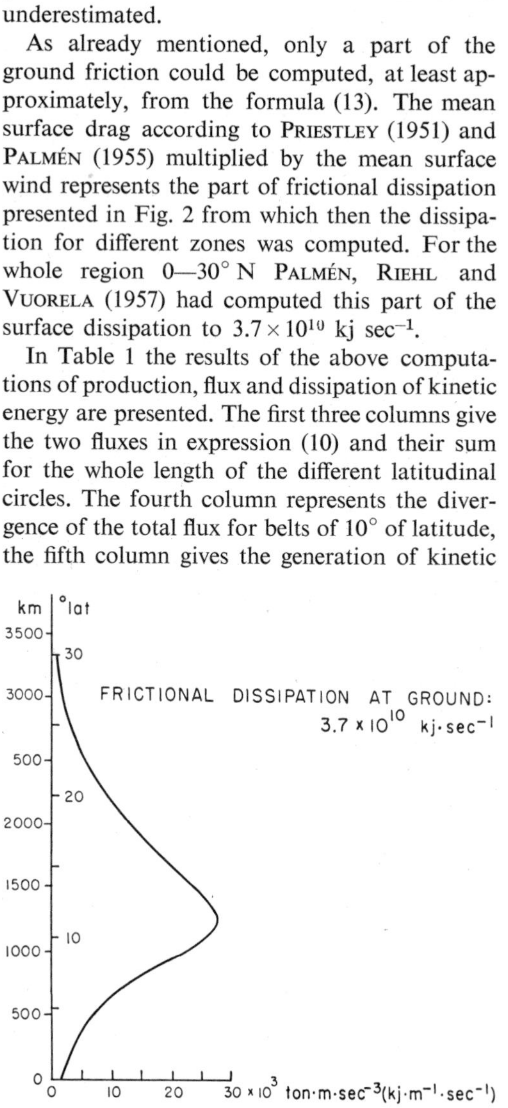

Fig. 2. Frictional dissipation of kinetic energy at ground per unit length of the meridian according to the first right-hand term in Eq. (13).

energy for the same belts according to Fig. 1, and the sixth column the difference between generation and flux divergence. These latter values should then represent the total dissipation due to friction according to Eq. (2) if the local change of kinetic energy is assumed to be zero. Column seven gives the part of frictional dissipation of kinetic energy due to ground friction computed from Fig. 2, and the last column, representing the differences between the values in column 6 and 7, is the frictional dissipation not considered in Fig. 2.

The greatest weakness in the above tentative budget lays in the neglection of the eddy terms in Eq. (11) and (13), and further on in the very crude estimate of the frictional dissipation. The negative value in the last column for the zone 0—10° N, indicates how unsatisfactory our determination is. On the other hand, the total value, 5.2×10^{10} kj sec^{-1}, for the whole belt 0—30° N does not appear too unrealistic compared with the total value of the frictional dissipation at ground. A part of it is confined to the frictional layer which in most earlier investigations has been included in the ground friction (BRUNT, 1939, PISHAROTY, 1954). Hence the total frictional dissipation in the free atmosphere actually would be somewhat lower than the dissipation in the frictional layer (ground—1 km approximately), in agreement with an assumption made by BRUNT (1939). If we assume that all the kinetic energy generated below the 700-mb again is dissipated by friction, since very little is transported across the horizontal and vertical boundaries, the total dissipation needed according to Fig. 1 would be about 7.4×10^{10} kj sec^{-1}. To the value 3.7×10^{10} we should then have to add 3.7×10^{10} representing the dissipation in the atmosphere up to 700 mb and in addition the contribution of the second term in Eq. (13).[1]

From the second term in expression (12) we can again separate the part of the frictional dissipation which is associated with the mean circulation. We then get for this part of the dissipation per unit area the expression

$$\int_0^\infty \bar{\mu} \left[\left(\frac{\partial \bar{u}}{\partial z} \right)^2 + \left(\frac{\partial \bar{v}}{\partial z} \right)^2 \right] dz. \qquad (15)$$

[1] In the Trade-wind zone, as a whole, there is a slight upward net transport of kinetic energy from the layer 1000—700 mb, probably partly compensated by a downward flux due of stresses in the free atmosphere.

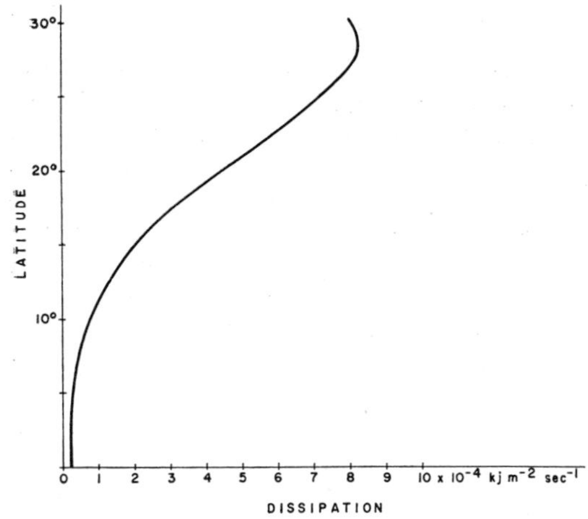

Fig. 3. Mean frictional dissipation per m² of the earth's surface computed from the vertical shear of the mean zonal wind assuming the coefficient of eddy viscosity to be 100 g cm^{-1} sec^{-1}.

In evaluating this expression we consider μ as constant with height and disregard the second relatively small term in the integrand. The vertical shear of the zonal mean wind $\bar{u}$ was determined primarily by use of the same data as those used for the computation of the generation of kinetic energy. For a constant value for μ of 100 g cm^{-1} sec^{-1} the result of the computation for the layer 1—12 km is presented in Fig. 3, from which the frictional dissipation in the whole belt Equator — 30° N was graphically computed to 4×10^{10} kj sec^{-1}. This value is in good agreement with the value of the last column in Fig. 1.

It must naturally be stressed that not too much emphasis should be put on this agreement. The assumption of a constant coefficient of eddy friction with the value 100 g cm^{-1} sec^{-1} has not been supported by any observations. The coefficient could be either larger or smaller, and certainly it is not independent of height. The above estimates were only made to show that the values in the two last columns of Table 1 are not quite absurd.

Since the generation of kinetic energy due to eddies of different types was not considered here, but, on the other hand, the poleward flux through latitude 30° essentially is an eddy flux the whole tentative budget in Table 1 seems questionable. The additional kinetic energy undoubtedly produced by different kinds of disturbances should also be considered. However, the eddy dissipation was also disregarded in our budget. The question then arises whether most of the kinetic energy released in tropical disturbances also is dissipated there due to friction. At least in tropical cyclones this seems to be true (PALMÉN and RIEHL, 1957); in a characteristic tropical cyclone the generation and dissipation of kinetic energy is of the order of magnitude 1.5×10^{10} kj sec^{-1}.

Summarizing the results we can conclude that the mean Hadley circulation is essential for the maintenance of the kinetic energy in the tropical zone and especially for the maintenance of the intense subtropical jet stream on the northern border of the mean circulation cell. The kinetic energy produced by this large-scale mean vertical circulation is only partly consumed by the ground friction and the internal friction in the free atmosphere, and the rest is exported northwards essentially as a large-scale eddy flux. In this respect the budget of kinetic energy in its essential features shows the same characteristics as the budget of angular momentum.

Table 1. Tentative budget of kinetic energy between Equator and 30° N for December—February. Unit: 10^{10} kj sec^{-1}

Latitude	Flux of kin. energy			Divergence of flux	Generation	Gener.-flux	Ground friction	Remaining dissip.
	$\overline{kv}$	$\overline{kv_g}$	$\overline{kv}$					
30° N......	2.1	20.3	22.4					
				8.7	12.9	4.2	0.5	3.7
20°.........	5.9	7.8	13.7					
				11.6	15.5	3.9	2.1	1.8
10°.........	0.6	1.5	2.1					
				2.1	2.9	0.8	1.1	—0.3
0°..........	0.0	0.0	0.0					
0—30° N...				22.4	31.3	8.9	3.7	5.2

4. Budget of kinetic energy in middle latitudes

The conversion between potential and kinetic energy can, according to Eq. (6) be written in the form (See also WHITE and SALTZMAN, 1956):

$$\frac{1}{g}\int_0^{p_0}\int_A \alpha\omega dA\, dp =$$

$$-\frac{A}{g}\int_0^{p_0}\{[\alpha][\overline{\omega}] + [\alpha''\overline{\omega}''] +]\overline{\alpha'\omega'}]\}\, dp. \quad (16)$$

Here [ ] denotes a mean value along a meridian, and ″ denotes the local deviation from the same mean value, all at a given isobaric surface. The first term under the integral, representing the mean areal values of α and ω can here be disregarded. The second term represents the conversion due to mean vertical circulations in the meridional plane. As already was shown this term is of essential importance in low latitudes. The third term in Eq. (16) represents the conversion between eddy potential available energy (LORENZ, 1955) and eddy kinetic energy. In

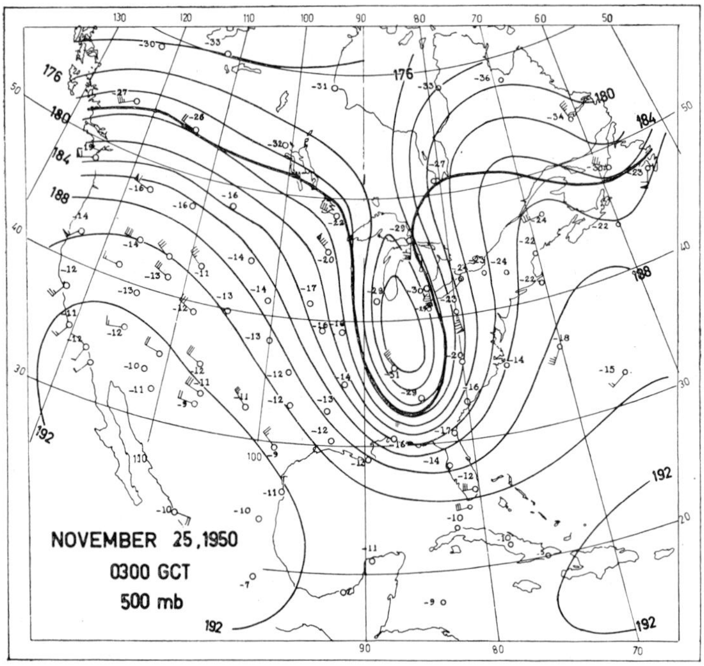

Fig. 4a

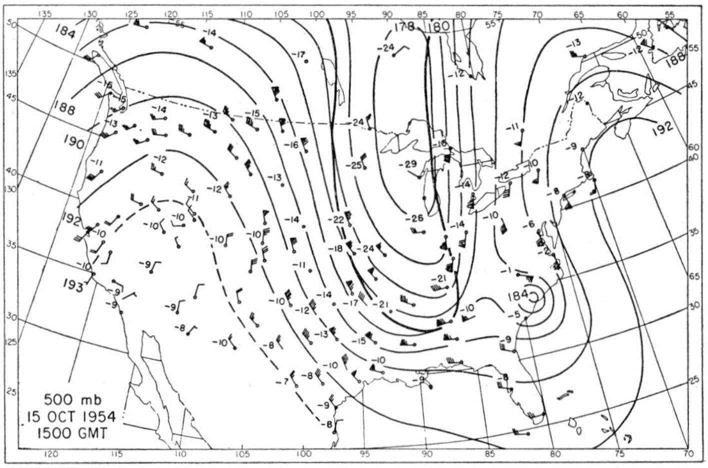

Fig. 4b

Fig. 4. Charts for the 500 mb surface November 25, 1950, 0300 GCT and October 15, 1954, 1500 GCT showing two cases of very strong development on the east coast of the United States. The heavy lines separate the cold tongues from the surrounding warmer air masses.

middle latitudes this last term obviously is the most important one.

A realistic description of this last conversion process has recently been presented by STARR (1954) and LORENZ (1955). According to them the available mean potential energy maintained by radiation and large-scale advective processes cannot directly be converted into mean kinetic energy through mean meridional circulations because of the stabilizing influence of the earth's rotation. The available mean potential energy has first to be transformed into "eddy available potential energy", a transformation that results in formations of tongues of cold and warm air masses. Cold tongues then in the middle and upper troposphere form cold troughs and warm tongues warm ridges. This new mass distribution favours vertical circulation processes, primarily in zonal planes, with sinking cold air and ascending warm air. In these processes considerable kinetic energy is released according to Eq. (6) or (7) due to the negative correlation between α and ω.

Some years ago ROSSBY (1949) made an attempt to explain theoretically this sinking of cold air masses expelled from their polar source region. Synoptic studies e.g. by PHILLIPS (1949) and by PALMÉN and NEWTON (1953) have shown that general mass subsidence really occurs in such cold tongues in connection with cyclone development; and distribution of precipitation, in addition, indicates that the corresponding ascent of warm air essentially occurs on the western and northern side of the warm tongues. Hence, the region between a western cold trough and an eastern warm ridge in the middle troposphere represent the principal region of conversion of available eddy potential energy into eddy kinetic energy.

The famous storms over the eastern parts of the U.S. on November 25, 1950 and October 15, 1954 ("Hazel") show clearly this process of conversion. In both cases (Fig. 4) pronounced tongues of cold air masses surrounded by warmer air extended far southwards. These cold tongues were subsiding, and the cold masses were spreading out meridionally and zonally at low levels, whereas the warm air to the east was ascending producing very intense precipitation.

In Fig. 5 the frontal contours of the cold air mass on November 25, (1950) 0300 GCT are presented, and in the same figure the principal precipitation area is marked by shading. As can be seen the shaded area extends as a long and relatively narrow band in a north—south direction on the eastern slope of the frontal surface indicating vertical direct circulations in zonal planes. The vertical mass transport and the mean

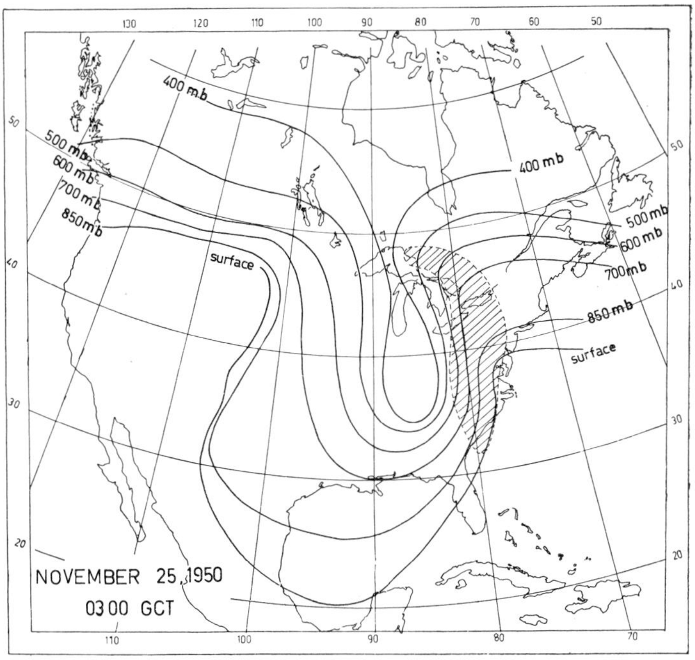

Fig. 5. Frontal contours for different isobaric surfaces on November 25, 1950, 0300 GCT and the corresponding precipitation area (shaded).

vertical velocity in the cold air south of latitude 45° N was computed assuming conservation of mass according to the principle developed by PALMÉN and NEWTON (1951). The result for the time period November 24, 1500—25, 1500 GCT is shown in Table 2. At the 500-mb level the mean downward velocity of about 5 cm sec^{-1} was found. Judging from the precipitation intensity east of the cold air mass, the maximum upward motion in the warm air must have reached values of up to at least 20 cm sec^{-1} at the same level for periods of several hours. In connection with this very intense direct solenoidal circulation, essentially in zonal planes one of the severest East-coast storms in recent years developed.

Table 2. Mean downward mass transport and vertical velocity in the cold air south of latitude 45° N around the synoptic time Nov. 25, 0300 GCT, 1950

Pressure mb	Area of cold air, km²	Downward mass transport, tons/day	Vertical velocity, cm/see
350	0.3×10^6	0.3×10^{12}	— 2.5
400	0.5	1.0	— 4.0
500	1.0	2.9	— 4.8
600	1.6	4.7	— 4.2
700	2.4	6.1	— 3.1
800	4.0	6.3	— 1.7
900	5.8	4.4	— 0.7
1000	6.6	0.0	0.0

The second storm "Hazel" shows generally the same thermal structure and pattern of vertical circulation. "Hazel", however, originally started as a tropical hurricane, but was at the time discussed here rapidly transformed into a typical extratropical storm of great intensity. The center of the original tropical cyclone can still be seen on the 500-mb chart in Fig. 4.

The total precipitation during the 24 hour period October 15, 0600 to October 16, 0600 GCT in Fig. 6 shows a similar elongated south—north area as was characteristic of the November case. In the same figure the position of the front between the warm masses in the east and the cold masses in the west at the synoptic time October 15, 1500 GCT is marked by a heavy line. The extreme temperature contrasts between the two principal masses appears very clearly from the vertical cross section approximately along latitude 40° N (Fig. 7). An attempt was made (PALMÉN, 1956) to compute the divergence field and the vertical velocity at the corresponding synoptic time from the wind data at different levels. The result showed that the rain area was characterized by very strong ascending motion reaching a maximum value around 500—400 mb, whereas the cold air to the west of the frontal boundary was subsiding. Fig. 8 shows the distribution of vertical velocity at the 500-mb level

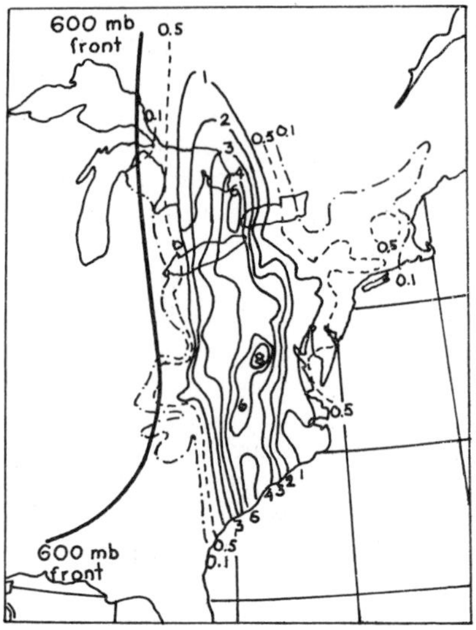

Fig. 6. Total precipitation (in inches) during the 24 hour period beginning October 15, 0600 GCT, showing the relation between the principal rain area and the front at the 600-mb surface.

along the parallel of the cross section in the previous figure, and in the same figure the corresponding temperature distribution is marked. The peak of the ascending motion, between 35 and 40 cm sec^{-1}, was determined by considering the precipitation intensity. Both curves in Fig. 8 show a pronounced positive correlation between temperature and vertical velocity, indicating strong conversion of potential energy into kinetic energy or intense direct solenoidal circulation essentially in zonal planes.

The work done by the horizontal pressure forces was determined from the second right-hand term of Eq. (2) and the conversion of potential energy into kinetic energy was computed from the third right-hand term in Eq. (7). Both computations were performed for the same area $A = 370 \times 10^{10}$ m². For the synoptic time October 15, 1500 GCT the computation gave as result 18.9×10^{10} and 19.7×10^{10} kj sec^{-1},

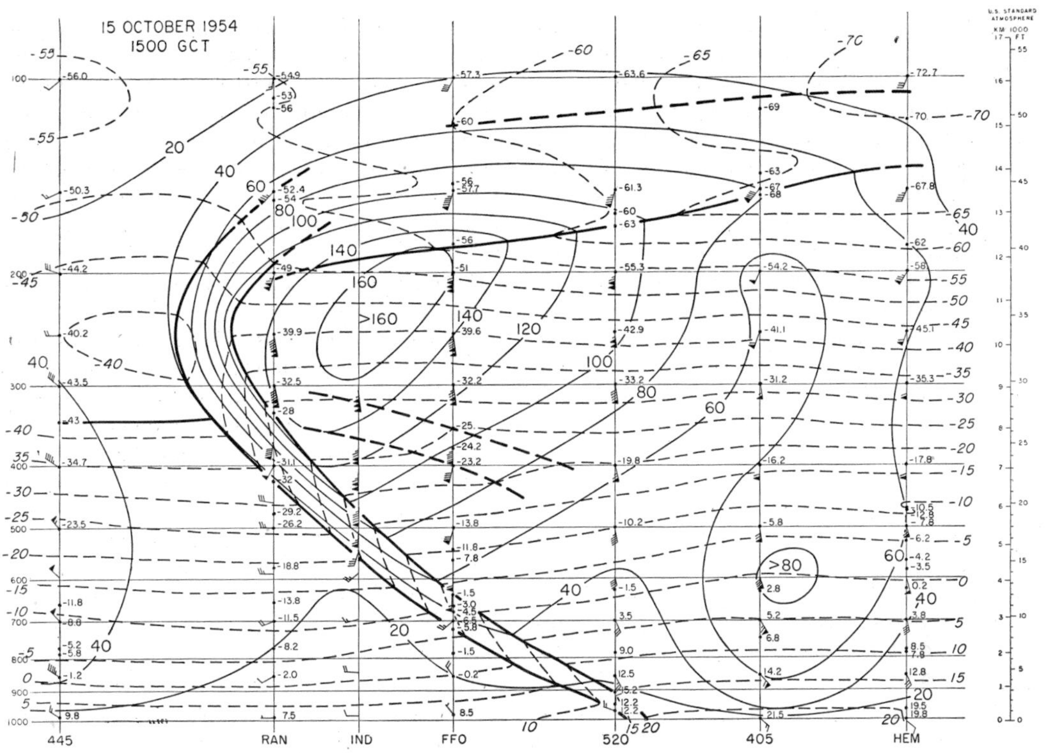

Fig. 7. Zonal vertical cross section along latitude 40° N through the intense cold front on October 15, 1954, 1500 GCT. Frontal boundaries, tropopauses, isotherms, and isotachs are marked in the section.

respectively.[1] For the same region the dissipation of kinetic energy due to friction at the ground was estimated to a small part of the above values, or to about 10^{10} kj sec^{-1}, and the total dissipation due to friction at the ground and in the free atmosphere to about 2×10^{10} kj sec^{-1}. It should, however, be stressed that those estimates were very rough and extremely approximate. At the same time the net outflux of kinetic energy from the area in question was computed to 18.7×10^{10} kj sec^{-1}, showing, according to Eq. 2, a slight local decrease in kinetic energy. These results show that the region of the extratropical cyclone "Hazel" furnished the surrounding atmosphere with very large amounts of kinetic energy produced by direct solenoidal circulations.

[1] The computation was performed between 1000 and 200 mb. The additional contribution of the layers above 200 mb could not be estimated. However, it seems probable that the stratorsphere somewhat suppresses the release of kinetic energy transforming a part of it again in potential energy in connection with the formation of a pronounced tropopause funnel with its characteristic high stratospheric temperature.

The case of "Hazel" was a very extreme one. Because of the large temperature contrasts and the unusually intense vertical velocities associated with very strong liberation of latent heat the

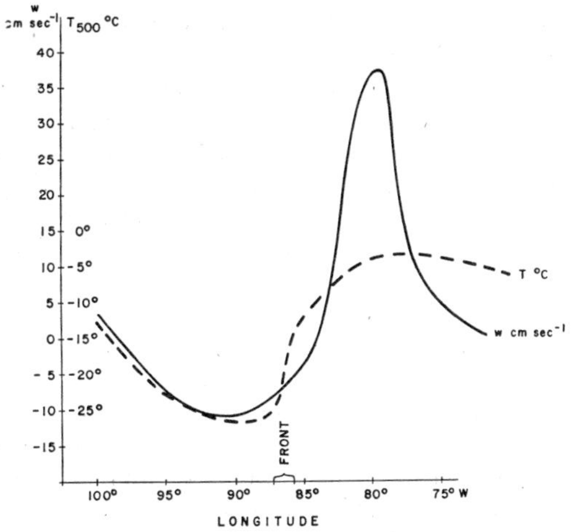

Fig. 8. Distribution of mean vertical velocity and temperature along the zone 35—40° N at 500 mb computed from the field of divergence and the precipitation intensity at the synoptic time October 15, 1500 GCT.

energy conversion in this case must have been considerably stronger than in more regular extratropical disturbances. Per unit area the release of kinetic energy was about 5 times the average release of kinetic energy in tropical cyclones. From the precipitation the liberation of latent heat was estimated to 156×10^{10} kj sec^{-1} in mechanical units. The release of kinetic energy thus was about 12 per cent of this value, whereas in tropical cyclones, which derive their energy only from this source, the corresponding figure is 2—3 per cent. It therefore seems permissible to assume that the largest part of the kinetic energy in extratropical cyclones is formed through conversion of preexisting available potential energy, but that the heat source associated with the liberation of latent heat in the warm limb of ascending air should not be considered unimportant in maintaining the solenoid field against the destructive influence of the vertical circulation.

It may be of interest to use the above computation of the energy conversion to achieve some ideas of the total budget of kinetic energy in middle latitudes north of 30° N. The following estimates, valid for the colder season, are necessarily very crude, and I hesitate very much to present them at all.

The total area of the cap north of latitude 30° N is about 35 times larger than the area A considered in cyclone "Hazel". Over this later area A the total production of kinetic energy amounted to about 19×10^{10} kj sec^{-1} if friction was disregarded. This is almost the same value as the net import of kinetic energy from the south through the entire parallel of 30° N (Table 1). It is probable that a part of this imported kinetic energy again is transformed into available potential energy as a result of the weak mean meridional circulation of reversed type postulated by Rossby (1941) and computed later by Mintz and Lang (1955). This reconversion was by Pisharoty (1954) estimated to $5—10 \times 10^{10}$ kj sec^{-1}.

For a complete budget we need an estimate of the total frictional dissipation of kinetic energy. Such an estimate was made by Brunt already in 1926 (Brunt, 1939). He estimated the dissipation to 3×10^{-3} kilowatts or kj sec^{-1} per m^2 for the layer up to 1 km and to 2×10^{-3} kj sec^{-1} for the layer 1—10 km representing a total frictional dissipation in the troposphere of about 5×10^{-3} kj sec^{-1} m^{-2}. According to Pisharoty the mean kinetic energy of the whole cap north of 30° N was for the period January—February 1949 about 240×10^{15} kj. Assuming the total area of the cap to be 127×10^{12} m^2 the total dissipation due to friction would amount to 63.5×10^{10} kj sec^{-1} using Brunt's values. If the same rate of dissipation were maintained for 3.8×10^5 seconds or about 4.4 days the total kinetic energy would be destroyed in that time.[1]

Brunt, and after him several other meteorologists, assumed that the above value of the mean frictional dissipation of kinetic energy was too large. This assumption does not seem to be obvious. First, there must always be a tendency to underestimate the mean friction when mean wind conditions are used. Second, in most estimates of the frictional dissipation the "mountain effect", referred to earlier, has been disregarded. It therefore is quite possible that the mean frictional dissipation, at least in winter time, could be larger than 5×10^{-3} kj sec^{-1} m^{-2}.

Assuming the net import from the south to be 20×10^{10} kj sec^{-1}, the total conversion of potential energy into kinetic energy in middle and high latitudes would amount to 45×10^{10} kj sec^{-1} during the northern winter. If we further assume that a mean meridional circulation of the reversed type reduces kinetic energy at a rate of $5—10 \times 10^{10}$ kj sec^{-1} the conversion of eddy potential energy into kinetic energy should be of the order of magnitude $50—55 \times 10^{10}$ kj sec^{-1}. Hence, only about 3 active extratropical disturbances of the same intensity as "Hazel" would suffice in producing the kinetic energy necessary for the maintenance of the total kinetic energy of the whole cap.[2]

Since the area used for the energy computation in the case "Hazel" was only about $^1/_{35}$ of the area of the whole cap one has to conclude from the above reasoning that every region of strong conversion of potential energy into kinetic energy must be surrounded by areas of at least moderate or weak reconversion of the exported kinetic energy into potential energy. This conclusion still holds if we consider the development

[1] In his original paper Brunt estimated this time to only 1 $^1/_6$ days. The low value for the time of decay depended upon the small value of the mean kinetic energy used by Brunt.

[2] The estimates of the frictional dissipation in middle latitudes should not directly be compared with the values in Table 1 for the tropical zone. In this latter zone the additional dissipation and production of kinetic energy in disturbances were neglected.

in "Hazel" to be strong compared with averaged cyclones. We can visualize the process of conversion and reconversion considering the velocity variations in the "polar-front jet". On circumpolar charts regions of strengthening and weakening of the jet always alternate. In the case of "Hazel" e.g. the velocity maximum in the jet core increased by 60—70 knots over the area discussed previously. The increase resulted in a very strong net export of kinetic energy out from the region. The charts also showed that the jet in this case had reached its maximum velocity when leaving the region and weakened later. This velocity decrease could not entirely be explained as a result of internal friction. Much more important for the deceleration of the jet must a cross-isobaric flow from lower to higher pressure have been connected with vertical reversed circulations. Hence, a large part of the kinetic energy exported out from the "Hazel" region was again reconverted into potential energy and only a smaller part was dissipated by internal friction.

Recently RIEHL and FULTZ (1957) have thrown new light on the question of the interpretation of the reversed mean meridional circulation in middle latitude. Using results of "dish-pan" experiments they were able to show that the indirect mean circulation in "middle latitudes" of this dish-pan was the result of the zonal averaging due to the circumstance that the strongest downward motion essentially occurs in the southern parts of the cold tongues of fluid, whereas ascending motion characterizes northern parts of the warm tongues. If, however, the averaging of vertical velocities was performed in the same experiments with reference to the upper "jet stream" they got a mean ascending motion of warmer water to the right of the jet and mean descending motion of colder water to the left.

Applied on the atmosphere an averaging with reference to the polar-front jet would probably give the same result. Since the high-tropospheric northern jet, on the average, is situated vertically above the polar-front zone around the 500-mb level the result would correspond to mean ascending movement of warm air to the right (looking in the direction of the general air motion) and mean descending motion of cold air to the left of the polar front at that level. The maintenance of the northern or polar-front jet could then also be considered as the result of a mean vertical circulation just as the subtropical jet was maintained by the Hadley circulation. Between the average latitude of the polar-front jet (around 50° N in winter) and the average latitude of the subtropical jet (about 28° N) there would probably still be place for the weak middle latitude reversed circulation as postulated by ROSSBY (1941). The very strong meandering of the polar-front jet associated with rapid deformations and cutting-off processes makes, however, every averaging according to the principles used by Riehl and Fultz in interpreting some of the experiments with rotating fluids very difficult. Even if such an averaging would succeed, the conversion between potential and kinetic energy would still show very strong variations along the jet stream, and regions of direct and indirect solenoidal circulations would alternate. Similar alternations also occur in the tropical zone Equator — 30°. Since these however are much less pronounced and the subtropical jet is much better fixed geographically, the mean Hadley circulation can be approximately determined by mean of simple zonal averaging.

REFERENCES

BRUNT, D., 1939: *Physical and dynamical meteorology*, Cambridge, p. 285.

LORENZ, E. N., 1955: Available potential energy and the maintenance of the general circulation. *Tellus*, **7**, p. 157.

MINTZ, Y., 1955: The total energy budget in the atmosphere. *Final Report*, *Gener. Circ. Proj.* No AF 19/122/-48, Dept. of Meteor., Univ. of Calif. No. 13.

MINTZ, Y., and LANG, J., 1955: A model of the mean meridional circulation. *Final Report*, *Gen. Circ. Proj.* Dept. of Meteor., Univ. of Calif. No AF 19/122/—48.

PALMÉN, E., 1955: On the mean meridional circulation in low latitudes of the Northern Hemisphere in winter and the associated meridional and vertical flux of angular momentum. *Soc. Scient. Fennica, Comm. Phys. Math.*, **17**, 8.

PALMÉN, E., 1956: Vertical circulation and release of kinetic energy during the development of hurricane Hazel into a extratropical storm. *Univ. of Chicago, Dept. of Meteor. Scient. Rep.* No. 14, Contr. No AF 19/604/—1293.

PALMÉN, E., and NEWTON, C. W., 1951: On the three-dimensional motions in an outbreak of polar air. *J. of Meteor.*, **8**, p. 25.

— 1953: On the dynamics of cold air outbreaks in the westerlies. *Univ. of Chicago, Dept. of Meteor., Final Report*, Proj. Nr 082003, Office of Naval Research.

PALMÉN, E., and RIEHL, H., 1957: Budget of angular momentum and kinetic energy in tropical cyclones. *J. of Meteor.*, **14**, p. 150.

PALMÉN, E., RIEHL, H., and VUORELA, L., 1957: On the meridional circulation and release of kinetic energy in the tropics. *Univ. of Chicago, Dept. Meteor. Proj.* No. 082—120, Office of Naval Research.

PHILLIPS, N. A., 1949: The work done on the surrounding atmosphere by subsiding cold air masses. *J. of Meteor.* **6**, p. 193.

PISHAROTY, P. R., 1954: The kinetic energy of the atmosphere. *Final Report Gen. Circ. Proj.* No AF 19/122/-48.

PRIESTLEY, C. H. B., 1951: A survey of the stress between the ocean and the atmosphere. *Union Géod. et Géophys., Symposium sur la circulation générale des océans et de l'atmosphère*, p. 64.

RIEHL, H., and FULTZ, D., 1957: Jet streams and long waves in a steady rotating disphan experiment, Part II: General circulation mechanism. *Scient. Report* No 2, Contr. No N60ri—02036 and No AF 19/604/-1292, Univ. of Chicago, Dept. of Meteor.

ROSSBY, C.-G., 1941: The scientific basis of modern meteorology. Climate and Man, *Yearbook of Agriculture*, p. 599.

— 1949: On the mechanism for the release of potential energy in the atmosphere. *J. of Meteor.*, **6**, p. 163.

SPAR, J., 1950: Synoptic studies of the potential energy in cyclones. *J. of Meteor.*, **7**, p. 48.

STARR, V. P., 1954: Commentaries concerning research on the general circulation. *Tellus*, **6**, p. 268.

VAN MIEGHEM, J., 1956: Réflexions sur le transport et la production du moment et de l'énergie cinétiques dans l'atmosphère et sur l'existence de circulations méridiennes moyennes. *Beitr. Physik der Freien Atmosphäre.* **29**, p. 55.

WHITE, R. M., and SALTZMAN, B., 1956: On conversion between potential and kinetic energy in the atmosphere. *Tellus* **8**, p. 357.

(Manuscript received May 1, 1958)

Explication dynamique de la circulation générale de l'atmosphère sur la base des idées de Rossby

Par PAUL QUENEY

Professeur à la Faculté des Sciences de Paris

Abstract

Rossby was the first to suggest that, owing to earth's curvature, the Reynolds' stresses due to large-scale meridional exchanges (operated by the perturbations superimposed on the general circulation) are quite different in nature from the molecular-viscous stresses, and that instead of damping the air motions they can create or maintain such winds as the jet streams. If the assumption is made that the exchanges are mainly due to the tropical perturbations, then a very simple dynamical theory can be built accounting for all the characteristic properties of the general tropospheric circulation (meridional as well as zonal circulation), and summarizing as follows:

i) The tropical perturbations are permanently producing in the upper troposphere a system of Reynolds' stresses which in the average are directed eastward at middle latitudes and westward at low latitudes. The first consequence is the production of the observed zonal winds.

ii) Under the effect of the unbalanced geostrophic force applied to them, these winds are deflected anticyclonally, therefore they converge toward subtropical latitudes and diverge above polar fronts, and this in turn explains the tricellular meridional circulation which in each hemisphere accounts for the general distribution of rainfall and deserts.

iii) As a result of this meridional circulation the isotherms are concentrated horizontally above subtropical latitudes, also in the polar fronts during winter, and finally this concentration probably explains the jet streams.

This theory may be considered as revolutionary, but it is apparently the only possible one: a purely thermal theory would lead to an unacceptable meridional circulation, and the assumption (made by Rossby) of exchanges mainly due to polar-front perturbations makes impossible any explanation of the belt of westerlies.

1. Introduction

Dans toutes les théories de la circulation générale qui furent proposées antérieurement à 1933 on supposait celle-ci entièrement entretenue par l'excès d'échauffement des régions équatoriales: c'étaient donc des théories essentiellement thermiques. Elles supposaient en outre que la circulation générale était un mouvement d'évolution très lente (consistant à peu près uniquement en une variation annuelle) et que c'était elle qui opérait le transport méridien vers les pôles de l'excès de chaleur et d'humidité des régions équatoriales. Cependant pour les raisons qui seront précisées plus loin ces théories ne peuvent plus être admises aujourd'hui.

Dès 1921 le développement de la théorie norvégienne des cyclones avait conduit divers météorologistes à la conclusion que les échanges méridiens de chaleur et d'humidité devaient être opérés non par la circulation générale elle-même, laquelle est le plus souvent du type zonal, mais bien par l'ensemble des perturbations de grande échelle qui lui sont superposées et que l'on peut en effet considérer comme formant une vaste turbulence horizontale, ou *macroturbulence*. Lorsqu'il eût ensuite été prouvé que l'intensité de cette turbulence avait bien l'ordre de grandeur nécessaire, ce point de vue fut universellement admis: une partie importante du problème de la circulation générale se trouvait donc résolue.

Or puisqu'on admettait qu'à très grande échelle les phénomènes de diffusion et de conduction calorifique sont dus à la macroturbulence, il devenait nécessaire d'admettre en même temps que les forces de Reynolds qu'elle crée devaient jouer en rôle essentiel dans l'entretien de la circulation générale, tout au moins dans la troposphère. Mais jusqu'à Rossby il ne vint à l'idée de personne que ces forces pouvaient être de nature très différente de celles de la viscosité moléculaire, donc on admettait qu'elles ne pouvaient qu'amortir les vents et non les créer ou les intensifier. On peut donc affirmer que c'est bien le petit article que publia Rossby en 1947 sur l'effet dynamique de la macroturbulence (STAFF MEMBERS, METEOROLOGY DEPARTMENT, UNIVERSITY OF CHICAGO, 1947) qui marqua l'avènement d'une ère nouvelle en météorologie dynamique, celle où le véritable mécanisme des grands mouvements de l'atmosphère a commencé à être élucidé.

2. Impossibilité d'une théorie purement thermique

Lorsqu'on s'en tient à la troposphère, le problème fondamental à résoudre est l'explication des vents d'Ouest des latitudes moyennes et des vents d'Est équatoriaux. Or puisque ces vents ont leur vitesse la plus grande dans la troposphère supérieure, si on admet que les forces de Reynolds ne peuvent agir que comme facteur d'amortissement on ne peut évidemment expliquer les vents d'Ouest que par une force de Coriolis dirigée vers l'Est, ce qui nécessite une composante méridienne du vent dirigée vers le pôle dans la troposphère supérieure, et de même les vents d'Est ne peuvent être expliqués que par une composante méridienne dirigée vers l'équateur dans la zone équatoriale. Or cela conduit inévitablement à une circulation méridienne du type représenté sur la fig. 1, comportant des vents descendants à l'équateur et vers la latitude de 60°, et des vents ascendants aux latitudes subtropicales, c'est-à-dire juste l'inverse de ce que l'on doit admettre pour rendre compte de la répartition générale des précipitations à la surface du globe. Donc une théorie purement thermique est en contradiction absolue avec les faits d'observation les mieux établis.

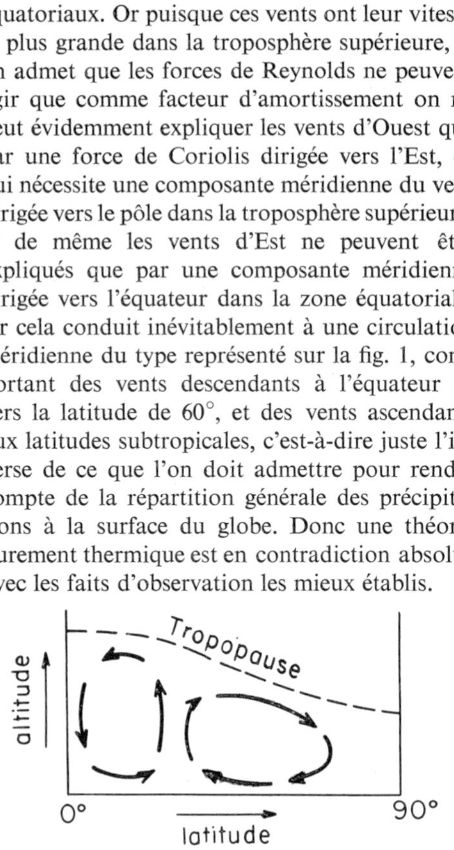

Fig. 1

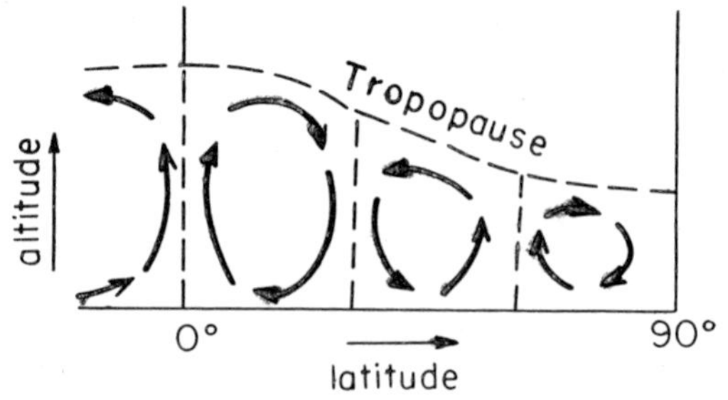

Fig. 2

3. Circulation méridienne et phénomènes associés

Le schéma de circulation méridienne que l'on doit admettre dans la troposphère pour rendre compte à la fois des pluies équatoriales, des pluies tempérées et des déserts subtropicaux est celui indiqué sur la fig. 2. Il comporte dans chaque hémisphère trois cellules: une cellule équatoriale (ou cellule de Hadley), une cellule tempérée et une cellule polaire, la première étant d'ailleurs nettement prédominante en étendue. La frontière commune aux deux cellules équatoriales est le front intertropical, et de même dans chaque hémisphère la surface séparant la cellule polaire de la cellule tempérée n'est autre que le front polaire, mais on voit qu'il existe en outre un troisième front analogue entre la cellule tempérée et la cellule équatoriale: c'est ce que nous appelons le front tropical.

En réalité cette circulation et ces fronts n'existent qu'en moyenne, mais on retrouve néanmoins très nettement les régions d'ascendance ou de descente et les régions de convergence ou de divergence horizontale qui leur correspondent, sur les cartes synoptiques hémisphériques lorsque la circulation générale est du type zonal, c'est-à-dire lorsque les jet-streams sont peu ondulés :

1° Le front intertropical se manifeste par la zone de convergence des alizés, par l'ascendance générale de l'air équatorial et par la divergence des contre-alizés dans la troposphère supérieure, laquelle est bien établie.

2° Chaque front polaire se manifeste de même par la convergence, dans la troposphère inférieure, de l'«air tropical» vers l'«air polaire», qui est nette surtout en hiver et se traduit alors par une forte concentration des isothermes horizontales à tous les niveaux de la troposphère (conformément à la théorie norvégienne classique). Cette concentration d'isothermes entraîne à son tour une forte pente des surfaces isobares dans la troposphère supérieure (conformément à l'équation hydrostatique), et par suite une forte concentration de la vitesse des vents d'Ouest à cet endroit : d'où l'explication de la branche polaire du jet-stream, laquelle est en effet particulièrement intense en hiver et presque toujours localisée aux mêmes latitudes que le front polaire. Par contre en été le front polaire est peu intense et rejeté à des latitudes élevées, d'où une concentration d'isothermes peu marquée et une branche polaire du jet-stream généralement inexistante.

3° Chaque front tropical se manifeste de même par la divergence entre les alizés et l'air tropical, et par une convergence dans la troposphère supérieure entraînant une seconde concentration des isothermes horizontales, donc de la vitesse des vents d'Ouest, mais contrairement à ce qui se passe pour le front polaire cette concentration existe en toutes saisons, et c'est cela qui est sans aucun doute la raison de la permanence de la branche tropicale du jet-stream. Ainsi en hiver le jet-stream comporte le plus souvent deux branches (une branche polaire et une branche tropicale, pouvant d'ailleurs confluer comme conséquence des ondulations des lignes de courant), alors qu'en été seule la branche tropicale existe de façon nette. A chaque branche il correspond en générale un courant de perturbations cycloniques. On voit donc que la circulation méridienne permet d'expliquer la concentration des vents d'Ouest de la troposphère supérieure sous la forme de jet-streams; toutefois elle ne permet évidemment pas d'expliquer les vents d'Ouest eux-mêmes, ni les vents d'Est équatoriaux.

4. Répartition des forces de Reynolds

Le schéma de la fig. 2 indique que dans la troposphère supérieure la composante méridienne du vent général est dirigée vers le pôle dans chaque cellule équatoriale, vers l'équateur dans chaque cellule tempérée, et de nouveau vers le pôle dans chaque cellule polaire. En conséquence la force géostrophique qui en résulte est dirigée vers l'Est aux basses latitudes et aux latitudes élevées, et vers l'Ouest aux latitudes moyennes. Elle tend donc à ralentir aussi bien les vents d'Est équatoriaux que les vents d'Ouest des latitudes moyennes, et par conséquent l'entretien de la circulation générale exige certainement une force de Reynolds dirigée vers l'Ouest dans les régions équatoriales, et vers l'Est dans les zones tempérées, cette force étant en outre au moins égale à la force géostrophique résultant du mouvement méridien (lequel se monte en moyenne à quelques m/sec).

Inversement si on suppose l'existence d'une telle force de Reynolds répartie comme nous venons de l'indiquer et possédant une intensité suffisante, on peut expliquer non seulement l'entretien de la composante zonale de la circulation générale, mais en outre celui de la circulation méridienne et même prouver la nécessité de cette circulation méridienne.

En effet une force de Reynolds dirigée vers l'Ouest dans la zone équatoriale tend d'abord à créer des vents d'Est, mais comme la force géostrophique due à ces derniers est dirigée vers le pôle et ne peut pas être équilibrée par la force horizontale de pression qui a la même direction, il en résulte nécessairement aussi une composante méridienne du vent dirigée vers le pôle. De même dans la zone tempérée une force de Reynolds dirigée vers l'Est tend à créer des vents d'Ouest, et si sa grandeur est suffisante la force géostrophique due à ceux-ci est supérieure à la force horizontale de pression qui a la même direction, donc l'air doit se déplacer vers l'équateur. Donc par la seule action des forces de Reynolds il s'établit dans la troposphère supérieure un mouvement méridien qui est divergent au-dessus de l'équateur, convergent aux latitudes subtropicales, et de nouveau divergent au-dessus des fronts polaires, d'où nécessairement une circulation méridienne du type de la fig. 2.

Or nous avons vu que cette circulation méridienne explique à son tour les jet-streams. Donc en définitive tout revient à découvrir le mécanisme qui crée les forces de Reynolds avec la répartition indiquée ci-dessus.

5. Explication des forces de Reynolds comme effet dynamique des perturbations de la troposphère supérieure équatoriale

Dans son article de 1947 Rossby montra clairement pour la première fois que l'effet statistique d'une turbulence horizontale de grande échelle est très différent de celui d'une turbulence de petite échelle. On peut en effet admettre que ce dernier est en gros très analogue à celui de l'agitation moléculaire, les molécules étant ici remplacées par des éléments fluides transportant avec eux la quantité de mouvement prise en un point du fluide, puis la cédant au fluide environnant auquel il se mélange en un autre point: d'où une tendance à l'uniformisation de la quantité de mouvement, se traduisant par des forces de Reynolds ayant les mêmes propriétés que les forces de viscosité moléculaires, donc se comportant en général comme facteur d'amortissement. Dans le cas d'une turbulence horizontale de grande échelle, par contre, on ne peut plus admettre la conservation de la quantitté de mouvement pour chaque élément turbulent, cela en raison de la courbure terrestre qui ne peut plus être négligée. Ce qui se conserve en première approximation, c'est la composante verticale du tourbillon absolu, du moins si on admet que la divergence horizontale de l'air est négligeable, et c'est en se basant sur ce résultat classique que Rossby a pu suggérer que *l'effet dynamique de la macroturbulence doit être une tendance à l'uniformisation de ce tourbillon vertical à chaque niveau.* Ensuite il en a déduit qu'il pouvait en résulter des vents de très grande vitesse, comparable ou même supérieure à celle des jet-streams. Cependant cette loi ne permet pas en réalité d'obtenir l'expression des forces de Reynolds, et d'ailleurs il est bien douteux que l'uniformisation du tourbillon puisse être effectivement réalisée par la macroturbulence : en effet au moment du mélange d'un élément turbulent avec l'air environnant, lequel nécessite des forces de Reynolds dues à une turbulence d'échelle inférieure, il n'y a pas du tout conservation du tourbillon vertical.

En fait Rossby appliqua la loi en question avec l'idée préconçue que la macroturbulence était à peu près exclusivement constituée par les perturbations des fronts polaires ou par les perturbations de plus grande échelle des zones tempérées, et il montra ainsi que la concentration des vents d'Ouest en jet-streams pouvait être expliquée par le seul effet dynamique de cette turbulence. Mais par contre il ne put pas expliquer les vents d'Ouest eux-mêmes, et la raison de cet échec est évidente : si la macroturbulence crée des vents d'Ouest à certaines latitudes elle crée nécessairement en même temps, par compensation, des vents d'Est à d'autres latitudes, puisque le moment angulaire total de l'atmosphère doit demeurer constant à chaque niveau lorsqu'on néglige l'effet du frottement du sol. Donc si l'on veut expliquer à la fois les vents d'Est équatoriaux et les vents d'Ouest des zones tempérées il faut faire appel à une macroturbulence opérant des échanges entre l'équateur et les latitudes moyennes dans la troposphère supérieure, ce qui n'est évidemment pas le cas pour les perturbations des fronts polaires.

Or l'existence à peu près permanente de perturbations de grande échelle dans la troposphère supérieure tropicale fut signalée par Rossby luimême en 1938 dans un article qu'il publia en collaboration avec J. NAMIAS (ROSSBY, NAMIAS, 1938), et où il montra notamment que ce sont ces perturbations qui occasionnent vraisemblablement les orages d'été aux Etats-Unis. D'autre part dès 1931 il avait été montré par J. DUBIEF (1935) que des perturbations bien organisées s'observent fréquemment sur le Sahara français, leur trajectoire étant très analogue à celle des cyclones tropicaux (elles se déplacent d'abord vers l'Ouest, puis dévient vers le Nord et ensuite vers l'Est), et cela suggère aussi l'existence d'autres perturbations dans la troposphère supérieure, dont l'effet ne se ferait sentir au niveau du sol que lorsque la troposphère inférieure est suffisamment instable. Enfin les cyclones tropicaux eux-mêmes semblent bien être déclenchés par des perturbations se développant elles aussi en altitude et à de basses latitudes.

Donc l'ensemble de tous ces faits d'observation peut être considéré comme une preuve de l'existence d'une classe bien définie de perturbations localisées dans la troposphère supérieure tropicale ou équatoriale, et s'y développant d'une façon pratiquement permanente. En conséquence c'est à elles qu'il y a lieu de faire appel pour expliquer les échanges méridiens entre les cellules équatoriales et les cellules tempérées, ces échanges se traduisant à leur tour par des forces de Reynolds expliquant l'entretien de la circulation générale.

Dans son article de 1938 Rossby avait montré que les perturbations de la troposphère supérieure comportaient essentiellement chacune deux courants s'affrontant de façon assez analogue à ce qui se passe dans une perturbation de front polaire (fig. 3) : d'une part un courant humide dirigé vers le pôle et s'incurvant progressivement vers l'Est dans le sens anticyclonique, et d'autre part un courant sec dirigé vers l'équa-

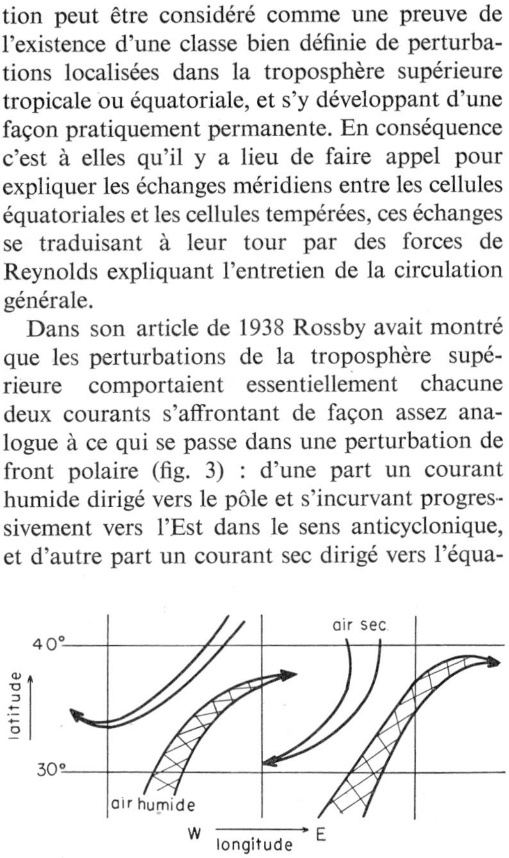

Fig. 3

teur et s'incurvant lui aussi dans le sens anticyclonique, donc vers l'Ouest (c'est seulement audessous des courants humides que se produisent les orages d'été). Or chacun de ces courants se mélangeant progressivement à l'air environnant il en résulte bien un échange à grande échelle entre les régions équatoriales et les zones tempérées, et on voit en outre clairement quel doit être l'effet dynamique de cet échange : manifestement les courants humides tendent à accélérer l'air des latitudes moyennes vers l'Est, les courants secs tendant au contraire à accélérer l'air des basses latitudes vers l'Ouest, et par conséquent l'effet global est un système de forces de Reynolds ayant justement la répartition voulue pour la création simultanée de vents d'Est équatoriaux et de vents d'Ouest tempérés. Naturellement il y aurait lieu de chercher à préciser davantage la répartition de ces forces, mais cette première constatation nous suffira, et en conséquence nous admettrons que c'est bien l'effet dynamique moyen des perturbations tropicales de la troposphère supérieure qui est responsable de l'entretien de la circulation générale (nous voyons qu'il n'est pas besoin pour cela de faire appel à la conservation du tourbillon vertical dans les perturbations).

6. Conclusion

En somme nous arrivons à un schéma d'ensemble qui paraît parfaitement capable d'expliquer toutes les propriétés essentielles de la circulation générale d'une façon remarquablement simple, et qui peut se résumer ainsi :

1° La macroturbulence constituée par les perturbations tropicales de la troposphère supérieure crée constamment des forces de Reynolds approximativement zonales, dirigées vers l'Ouest aux basses latitudes et vers l'Est aux latitudes moyennes, ce qui signifie qu'elles opèrent un transport continuel vers les pôles de l'excès de quantité de mouvement zonal des régions équatoriales (il s'agit d'une quantité de mouvement absolu).

2° Sous l'effet de ces forces il apparaît simultanément dans la troposphère supérieure des vents d'Est aux basses latitudes et des vents d'Ouest dans les zones tempérées, mais comme ces vents doivent être en équilibre géostrophique approximatif aux latitudes supérieures à 20° environ il en résulte l'apparition d'un vent méridien dirigé vers le pôle aux basses latitudes et vers l'équateur aux latitudes moyennes, d'où la circulation méridienne de la fig. 2 (toutefois pour expliquer la cellule polaire il est nécessaire de faire intervenir l'effet des forces de Reynolds dues aux perturbations des fronts polaires, mais ce n'est là en somme qu'un effet secondaire, n'existant d'ailleurs probablement qu'en hiver).

3° Cette circulation méridienne à son tour produit une concentration des isothermes horizontales expliquant la concentration des vents d'Ouest en jet-streams, ainsi que nous l'avons indiqué ci-dessus.

Si on admet cette théorie on voit ainsi que la circulation générale est entièrement créée et entretenue par l'action dynamique de la macroturbulence constituée par les perturbations de la troposphère supérieure, et que par conséquent c'est celle-ci qui fournit l'énergie nécessaire à cet entretien. Naturellement cette énergie est en fin de compte fournie par des facteurs thermiques, mais c'est à l'échelle des perturbations et non à celle de la circulation générale que s'opère la transformation de l'énergie calorifique en énergie mécanique (toutefois il est probable qu'une certaine contribution à cette transformation est apportée par la circulation méridienne des deux cellules équatoriales et des deux cellules polaires, alors que dans les cellules tempérées il y a au contraire transformation d'énergie mécanique en chaleur).

On voit aussi que la circulation générale observée est la seule qui peut s'établir avec la répartition supposée de la macroturbulence, et que c'est en définitive la courbure de la Terre et sa rotation qui déterminent les propriétés caractéristiques de cette circulation, notamment l'existence des trois cellules méridiennes dans chaque hémisphère entraînant la répartition générale des précipitations en trois grandes zones séparées par deux zones de déserts.

BIBLIOGRAPHIE

Staff Members, Meteorology Department, University of Chicago, 1947: On the General Circulation of the Atmosphere in Middle Latitudes.— *Bull. Amer. Met. Soc.*, **28**, 6.

Rossby, C.-G., and Namias, J., 1938: Fluid Mechanics Applied to the Study of Atmospheric Circulation. *Papers in Physical Oceanography and Meteorology*, **VII**, No. 1.

Dubief, J., et Queney, P., 1935: Les Grands Traits du Climat du Sahara Algérien. *La Météorologie*, série II, **11**.

(Manuscript recived Marsh 28, 1958)

On the Selective Rôle of the Motion Systems in the Atmospheric General Circulation

By J. VAN MIEGHEM, P. DEFRISE and J. VAN ISACKER
Royal Meteorological Institute of Belgium, Brussels

Abstract

Harmonic analysis of the altitude and temperature fields at the 500 mb level along latitudes 50 and 55° N has been performed. Spectra of several quantities connected with the general circulation are used to investigate the relative rôle of different scales of motion systems. These quantities are: the kinetic energy of the geostrophic motion and its meridional and zonal components; the flux of sensible heat and west momentum; the available energy and the baroclinicity. In each case, the respective contributions of the quasi-stationary waves and of the moving waves are distinguished.

1. Introduction

Recent studies SHEPPARD, 1953, 1954; VAN MIEGHEM, 1955; (DEFRISE et al., 1956; VAN ISACKER et al., 1956) have emphasized the important fact that atmospheric motion systems do not all play the same rôle in the general circulation processes: the importance of their respective contributions to the main features of the planetary flow pattern and to the thermal and mechanical processes maintaining the zonal circulation depends largely on the space and time scales of the motion system envisaged. The particular rôle of each scale of motion in the atmospheric general circulation may be demonstrated by the harmonic analysis along latitude circles of appropriate meteorological parameters, such as the height z of standard isobaric surfaces, the absolute air temperature T, the zonal and meridional geostrophic wind components u and v, and derived functions such as the kinetic energies $\frac{1}{2}u^2, \frac{1}{2}v^2, \frac{1}{2}(u^2+v^2)$, the available energy $\frac{1}{2}g\left(\frac{\Gamma-\gamma_e}{T_e}\right)^{-1} \cdot \left(\frac{T^*}{T_e}\right)^2$ for conversion into kinetic energy (LORENZ 1955; VAN MIEGHEM, 1956), the meridional transport of sensible heat c_pTv and west momentum uv. As usual, c_p designates the specific heat of dry air at constant pressure, g the acceleration due to gravity, $T_e(z)$ the absolute air temperature at hydrostatic equilibrium, T^* the temperature fluctuation in isobaric surfaces with respect to T_e ($T = T_e + T^*$), γ_e the temperature lapse rate $-\frac{dT_e}{dz}$ and Γ the dry adiabatic lapse rate g/c_p.

Longitude λ,[1] latitude φ, pressure p being chosen as independent space variables, the meteorological parameters envisaged are functions of λ, φ, p and time t.

The method used consists essentially of expanding in Fourier series, as a function of longitude λ, the meteorological parameters z, T, u, v at given pressure levels and properly chosen latitudes.

2. Zonal averages, period means and grid points

The average values most commonly used in general circulation studies are the zonal averages *or* the space-time averages for a latitude circle and a certain time interval, which in most cases is supposed to be large with respect to the local life time of the motion systems, i.e., the atmospheric disturbances as revealed by the upper-air weather maps.

The zonal average $[X]$ of an arbitrary meteorological parameter $X(\lambda, \varphi, p, t)$ is defined by the well known formula

$$[X] = \frac{1}{2\pi}\int_0^{2\pi} X(\lambda, \varphi, p, t) \cdot \delta\lambda \qquad (2.1)$$

[1] We have adopted here a variable λ varying eastwards from 0 to 2π.

and the period mean value, in the same way, by

$$\overline{X} = \frac{1}{t_2 - t_1} \int_{t_1}^{t_2} X(\lambda, \varphi, p, t) \cdot \delta t. \qquad (2.2)$$

The mean value of X for a period of N days will be written $\overline{X}^N$. Finally, the average value for a given time interval and latitude circle will be determined by the arithmetic mean value

$$\overline{[X]}^N = \frac{1}{N} \sum_{i=1}^{N} [X]_i \qquad (2.3)$$

of the N instantaneous values $[X]_i$ of $[X]$ in the time interval considered; these instantaneous values are in fact values deduced from the daily upper-air charts.

In order to be able to compute numerical values of quantities derived from the meteorological parameters, the latitude circles have been subdivided into $2m$ equal arcs. Any of these arcs is represented by the longitude interval (λ_k, λ_{k+1}) where $\lambda_k = k \cdot \frac{\pi}{m}$, $(k = 0, 1, \ldots, 2m-1)$. The longitude of the mid-point of the arc (λ_k, λ_{k+1}) is $\lambda_{k+1/2} = \left(k + \frac{1}{2}\right) \frac{\pi}{m}$.

Writing X_k instead of $X(\lambda_k, \varphi, p, t)$, we have

$$[X] = \frac{1}{2\pi} \int_0^{2\pi} X \cdot \delta\lambda \cong \frac{1}{2m} \sum_{k=0}^{2m-1} X_k, \qquad (2.1\,\text{a})$$

at pressure level p, latitude φ and time t.

3. Fourier analysis

Considering an arbitrary meteorological parameter $X(\lambda, \varphi, p, t)$ and assuming that at time t, latitude φ and pressure p, the real function of longitude $X(\lambda)$ may be represented by a Fourier series, we may write

$$X(\lambda) = \sum_{-\infty}^{+\infty} \xi_n \cdot e^{in\lambda}, \qquad (3.1)$$

where ξ_n are the Fourier coefficients of X at time t, latitude φ and pressure p. It is well known that

$$\xi_n = \xi_n' - i\xi_n'' = \frac{1}{2\pi} \int_0^{2\pi} X(\lambda) e^{-in\lambda}\, \delta\lambda \cong$$

$$\cong \frac{1}{2m} \sum_{k=0}^{2m-1} X_k e^{-ik\frac{n\pi}{m}}, \qquad (3.2)$$

where ξ_n' and $-\xi_n''$ are the real and imaginary parts of the complex Fourier coefficient ξ_n. The function $X(\lambda)$ being real, the following conditions are fulfilled,

$$\xi_0 = \xi_0', \; \xi_0'' = 0, \; \xi_n' = \xi_{-n}', \; \xi_n'' = -\xi_{-n}''. \qquad (3.3)$$

Obviously, we have

$$X(\lambda) = \xi_0' + 2 \sum_1^{\infty} (\xi_n' \cos n\lambda + \xi_n'' \sin n\lambda) =$$

$$= A_0 + \sum_1^{\infty} A_n \cos(n\lambda - \psi_n), \qquad (3.1\,\text{a})$$

where

$$A_n = 2 \left| \sqrt{(\xi_n')^2 + (\xi_n'')^2} \right|$$

denotes the amplitude of the nth harmonic and where the corresponding phase angle ψ_n is determined by the formula

$$\text{tg}\, \psi_n = \xi_n'' / \xi_n'.$$

It should be noted that ξ_0, ξ_0' and A_0 are equal and real ($\xi_0' = \xi_0 = A_0$).

The advantages of the use of Fourier analysis in general circulation investigations will appear from the following remarks.

The parameter n in the above recalled classical formulae represents the zonal wave number, that is to say the number of motion systems or atmospheric disturbances distributed zonally around the earth. Therefore it allows the introduction of scale considerations. It is a well established fact that, as a consequence of these disturbances, the streamlines do not follow a zonal course along the latitude circles but meander several times north and south. The distance between two successive bends in the streamlines is an appropriate measure of the zonal dimension of the atmospheric disturbances; this distance is the wave length $L = \frac{2\pi}{n} a \cos \varphi$ (a is the earth's radius), estimated along the latitude circle φ.

The amplitude A_n of the nth harmonic defines the contribution of the atmospheric disturbances of wave length $\frac{2\pi}{n} a \cos \varphi$ to the meteorological parameter X, while the corresponding phase angle ψ_n defines the zonal distribution of this contribution. The pattern of the longitudinal distribution of X in the pressure surfaces, at time t, is such that this distribution presents "ridges" at longitudes $\lambda = \frac{\psi_n + 2k\pi}{n}$ and "troughs" at longitudes $\lambda = \dfrac{\psi_n + (2k+1)\pi}{n}$, ($k = 0, 1, \ldots, n-1$).

As a rule, only a few harmonics are needed in order to describe adequately an arbitrary meteorological parameter $X(\lambda)$; generally, the ten or twelve first harmonics suffice (GRAHAM, 1955; DEFRISE et al., 1956; VAN ISACKER, VAN MIEGHEM 1956). A smaller number of harmonics, namely the first five or six, provides a good representation of the monthly mean value $\overline{X}^{30}(\lambda)$ (GRAHAM, 1955) and also of the corresponding seasonal and yearly means (SALTZMAN, PEIXOTO, 1957). A still smaller number of harmonics, namely the first three, represent with a high approximation the corresponding monthly *normal* value (GRAHAM, 1955). Thus the long waves ($n = 1, 2, 3$) contribute mainly to the permanent basic features of the X-field, the shorter waves to the day-to-day changes in this field. Therefore, the shorter waves may be identified with the moving disturbances. Moreover the differences between the first three (or four) harmonics of the instantaneous (daily) values of X and the corresponding monthly *normal* values of X correspond to more or less persisting anomalies in the X-field, which in turn correspond to characteristic anomalies in the weather systems (GRAHAM, 1955).

The value of the Fourier coefficient ξ_0 or A_0 is the average value of X along the latitude circle φ, at pressure p and time t,

$$[X] = \frac{1}{2\pi}\int_0^{2\pi} X(\lambda)\,\delta\lambda = \xi_0 \cong \frac{1}{2m}\sum_{k=0}^{2m-1} X_k, \quad (3.4)$$

by virtue of (2.1), (2.1 a) and (3.2).

The amplitude A_1 of the first harmonic is a measure of the *eccentricity* of the instantaneous circumpolar distribution of X in the pressure surface p, at latitude φ and time t. When $A_1 = 0$, the geographic pole is the centre of this distribution, but when $A_1 \neq 0$, its centre is located at a point the position of which, with respect to the geographical pole, is determined by the amplitude A_1 and the phase angle ψ_1 of the wave $n = 1$.

The second harmonic indicates the *ellipticity* of the instantaneous circumpolar distribution of X in the same pressure surface at the same latitude and time. The intensity and orientation of the flattening of the planetary distribution of X are determined by the amplitude A_2 and the phase angle ψ_2 of the wave $n = 2$.

The following harmonics ($n = 3, 4, 5, \ldots$) characterize the true *wave-like pattern* of the circumpolar distribution of X.

Finally let us consider two arbitrary meteorological parameters X and Y, functions of λ, φ, p and t. Substituting (3.1) in the integral expression of $[XY]$ and taking into account the identity

$$\int_0^{2\pi} e^{i(n+n')}\,\delta\lambda \equiv 0, \quad \text{when } n + n' \neq 0,$$

we obtain

$$[XY] = \frac{1}{2\pi}\int_0^{2\pi} X(\lambda)\,Y(\lambda)\,\delta\lambda =$$

$$= \frac{1}{2\pi}\sum_n\sum_{n'} \xi_n \eta_{n'} \int_0^{2\pi} e^{i(n+n')}\delta\lambda =$$

$$= \sum_{-\infty}^{+\infty} \xi_n \eta_{-n} = \xi_0\eta_0 + \sum_1^{\infty}(\xi_n\eta_{-n} + \xi_{-n}\eta_n) =$$

$$= \xi_0'\eta_0' + 2\sum_1^{\infty}(\xi_n'\eta_n' + \xi_n''\eta_n'') \quad (3.5)$$

where $\xi_n = \xi_n' - i\xi_n''$ and $\eta_n = \eta_n' - i\eta_n''$ are the Fourier coefficients of X and Y along the latitude circle φ, at pressure p and time t.

The term

$$\xi_n\eta_{-n} + \xi_{-n}\eta_n \quad \text{or} \quad 2(\xi_n'\eta_n' + \xi_n''\eta_n'')$$

represents the contribution of the disturbance of wave number n to the zonal average value $[XY]$ of the product XY of the two meteorological parameters envisaged (VAN ISACKER, VAN MIEGHEM, 1956).

4. Geostrophic assumption

In the absence of an adequate network of radio or radar wind stations, the geostrophic hypothesis must necessarily be introduced. Considering the latitude circles φ and $\varphi^x (\varphi^x > \varphi)$, we may then write, as a first approximation, the following relations at the point of longitude $\lambda_{k+1/2}$, on the latitude circle $\dfrac{\varphi + \varphi^x}{2}$, at the pressure level p (VAN ISACKER, VAN MIEGHEM, 1956, see fig. 1),

$$\left.\begin{aligned} u_{k+1/2} &\cong \frac{g}{2f\Delta y}(z_k - z_k^x + z_{k+1} - z_{k+1}^x) \\ v_{k+1/2} &\cong \frac{g}{2f\Delta x}(z_{k+1} - z_k + z_{k+1}^x - z_k^x) \\ T_{k+1/2} &\cong \frac{1}{4}(T_k + T_{k+1} + T_k^x + T_{k+1}^x) \end{aligned}\right\} \quad (4.1)$$

where (z_k, T_k) and (z_k^x, T_k^x) designate at longitude λ_k the values of (z, T) on the latitude circles φ and φ^x respectively, where

$$\Delta x = \frac{\pi}{m}\, a \cos \frac{\varphi + \varphi^x}{2}, \quad \Delta y = \frac{\pi}{m}\, a$$

and

$$f = 2\omega \sin \frac{\varphi + \varphi^x}{2},$$

ω being the angular velocity of the earth and $\varphi^x = \varphi + \dfrac{\pi}{m}$.

The values z_k, z_k^x and T_k, T_k^x, of z and T at the standard pressure levels along given latitude circles φ and φ^x may be taken directly from the upper-air charts.

If ξ_n and Θ_n are the Fourier coefficients of the height z and the absolute air temperature T respectively, at pressure p, both parameters being considered at time t, as functions of longitude λ along the latitude circle φ, we have, (3.2),

$$\zeta_n \cong \frac{1}{2m} \sum_{0}^{2m-1} z_k e^{-ik\frac{n\pi}{m}} \quad \text{and}$$

$$\Theta_n \cong \frac{1}{2m} \sum_{0}^{2m-1} T_k e^{-ik\frac{n\pi}{m}}.$$

Substituting now the Fourier series

$$z_k = \sum_{-\infty}^{+\infty} \zeta_n e^{ik\frac{n\pi}{m}} \quad \text{and}$$

$$T_k = \sum_{-\infty}^{+\infty} \Theta_n e^{ik\frac{n\pi}{m}} \quad (k = 0, 1, \ldots, 2m-1)$$

in (4.1), we immediately obtain

$$\left.\begin{aligned} u_{k+1/2} &= \sum_{-\infty}^{+\infty} \alpha_n e^{ik\frac{n\pi}{m}}, \\ v_{k+1/2} &= \sum_{-\infty}^{+\infty} \beta_n e^{ik\frac{n\pi}{m}}, \\ T_{k+1/2} &= \sum_{-\infty}^{+\infty} \gamma_n e^{ik\frac{n\pi}{m}}, \end{aligned}\right\} \quad (4.2)$$

where the Fourier coefficients α_n, β_n, γ_n may be expressed as follows (VAN ISACKER, VAN MIEGHEM, 1956):

$$\left.\begin{aligned} \alpha_n &= \frac{g}{2f\Delta y} (\zeta_n - \zeta_n^x) \left(1 + e^{i\frac{n\pi}{m}}\right) \\ \beta_n &= \frac{-g}{2f\Delta x} (\zeta_n + \zeta_n^x) \left(1 - e^{i\frac{n\pi}{m}}\right) \\ \gamma_n &= \frac{\Theta_n + \Theta_n^x}{4} \left(1 + e^{i\frac{n\pi}{m}}\right) \end{aligned}\right\} \quad (4.3)$$

By virtue of (3.4), we have

$$\alpha_0 = [u], \quad \beta_0 = [v] = 0, \quad \gamma_0 = [T].$$

It should be noted that $\beta_0 = 0$ is a consequence of the geostrophic hypothesis.

5. Data and computations

The spot values of z and T at the 500 mb level have been extracted from the Synoptic Weather Maps, Daily Series (U.S. Weather Bureau), once a day (15 h GMT) for the following periods:
1st period: November 1st, 1950 till February 28th, 1951, at latitude 50° N; values taken for longitudes which are multiples of 10°, ($\varphi = 50°$ N, $m = 18$);
2nd period: January 1st till April 30th, 1953, at latitudes 50° N and 55° N; values taken for longitudes which are multiples of 5°, ($\varphi = 50°$ N, $\varphi^x = 55°$ N, $m = 36$).

These values have been introduced in the formulae of sections 3, 4 and the computations

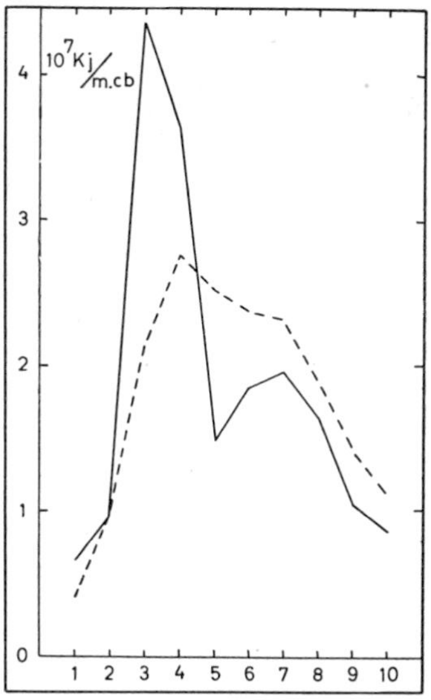

Fig. 1. Spectrum of the kinetic energy $\overline{E}_M^{60}$ of the meridional motion.
Dashed line: January—February 1951;
Solid line: January—February 1953.

were made with IBM punched cards, at the *Centre National de Calcul Mécanique* (Brussels).

Basic parameters are z[1] and T. Derived parameters are for the first period E_M, A, τ_H and for the second period E_M, E_Z, E, A, τ_H, τ_M (see sections 6 to 11).

Some results relating to the first period have already been reported (DEFRISE et al., 1956; VAN ISACKER, VAN MIEGHEM, 1956).

6. Spectrum of the kinetic energy of the geostrophic meridional motion

The kinetic energy E_M of the geostrophic meridional motion in a zonal ring of 1 centibar vertical thickness and 1 m meridional width, at pressure level p, along the latitude circle $\frac{\varphi + \varphi^x}{2}$ assumes the form

$$E_M = \frac{\pi a}{g} \cos \frac{\varphi + \varphi^x}{2} [v^2] = \sum_1^{\infty} (E_M)_n, \quad (6.1)$$

where, by virtue of (3.5) and (4.3),

$$(E_M)_n = \frac{2\pi a}{g} \cos \frac{\varphi + \varphi^x}{2} \beta_n \beta_{-n} = \\ = \frac{g m^2}{\pi f^2 a \cos \frac{\varphi + \varphi^x}{2}} \cdot \\ \cdot [(\zeta'_n + \zeta'^x_n)^2 + (\zeta''_n + \zeta''^x_n)^2] \left(1 - \cos \frac{n\pi}{m}\right) \quad (6.2)$$

represents the contribution of disturbances of wave number n to the kinetic energy E_M.

Figure 1 represents $\overline{E}_M^{60}$ (in kj m^{-1} cb^{-1}) for the periods of January—February 1951 and 1953. There is a marked maximum for either $n = 4$ (1951) or $n = 3$ (1953), and a secondary maximum for $n = 7$. But these two maxima are of different natures, as it is demonstrated by figure 2 (related to the period January—April 1953), in which $\overline{E}_M^{120}$ is broken down into two parts:

1) the contribution of the quasi-stationary waves with slowly fluctuating phase angles and amplitudes, obtained by taking the 10-day mean maps (running means), shows a very pronounced maximum for $n = 3$;

[1] We neglect the distinction between the altitude z and the geopotential expressed in geopotential meters.

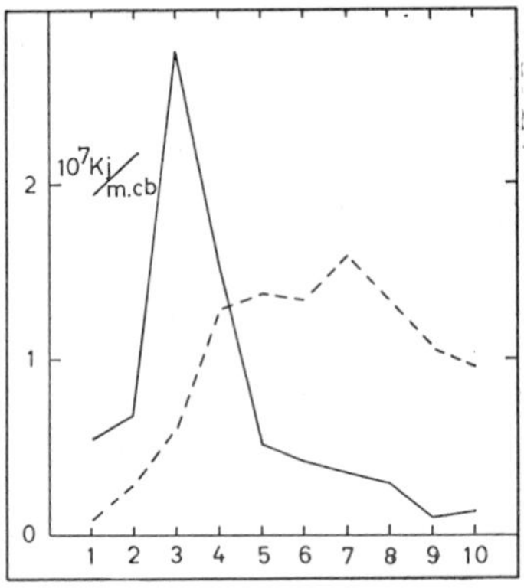

Fig. 2. Partition of the kinetic energy of the meridional motion $\overline{E}_M^{120}$ for the period January—April 1953.

Dashed line: contribution of the moving waves;
Solid line: contribution of the quasi-stationary waves.

2) the contribution of the moving waves with changing phase angles, obtained by subtracting 10 day-mean maps from instantaneous maps, shows a maximum for $n = 7$, with an important contribution for every $n \geq 4$.

For the whole of the first period (November 1950—February 1951), similar results had been obtained with the difference that the contribution of the quasi-stationary waves revealed a maximum not only for $n = 3$ but also for $n = 5$ (DEFRISE et al., 1956; see fig. 2).

In any case, the contribution of the very long waves $n = 1, 2$ (associated with the eccentricity and ellipticity of the circumpolar vortex) is very small, while the contribution of the shorter waves $n = 6$ to 10 is much more important. However, the contribution of these short waves decreases considerably when 5 or 10 day-mean values are substituted for the daily values; when monthly mean values are envisaged the influence of the shorter waves in the spectral distribution of E_M is even less and in the case of seasonal mean values this influence practically disappears (SALTZMAN, PEIXOTO, 1957).

All these results are to be compared with those obtained by R. M. WHITE and D. S. COOLEY (1956) and suggest that there are two types of atmospheric disturbances, namely:

1) quasi-stationary and persisting waves (5,000 to 6,500 km at latitude 50° N) which are presumably associated with the geographical distribution of continents and seas, with the orographic features of the earth's surface and with the distribution of heat sources and sinks;

2) shorter moving and transient waves (2,500 to 4,300 km at latitude 50° N) which are probably due to the baroclinic instability of the atmosphere.

7. Spectrum of the kinetic energy of the geostrophic zonal motion

The kinetic energy E_Z of the geostrophic zonal motion in a zonal ring of 1 centibar vertical thickness and 1 m meridional width, at pressure level p, along the latitude circle $\frac{\varphi + \varphi^x}{2}$ assumes the form

$$E_Z = \frac{\pi a}{g} \cos \frac{\varphi + \varphi^x}{2} [u^2] =$$

$$= \frac{\pi a}{g} \cos \frac{\varphi + \varphi^x}{2} \alpha_0^2 + \sum_1^\infty (E_Z)_n, \quad (7.1)$$

where, by virtue of (3.5) and (4.3),

$$(E_Z)_n = \frac{2\pi a}{g} \cos \frac{\varphi + \varphi^x}{2} \alpha_n \alpha_{-n} =$$

$$= \frac{gm^2}{\pi a f^2} \cos \frac{\varphi + \varphi^x}{2} [(\zeta'_n - \zeta'^x_n)^2 + (\zeta''_n - \zeta''^x_n)^2] \cdot$$

$$\cdot \left(1 + \cos \frac{n\pi}{m}\right) \quad (7.2)$$

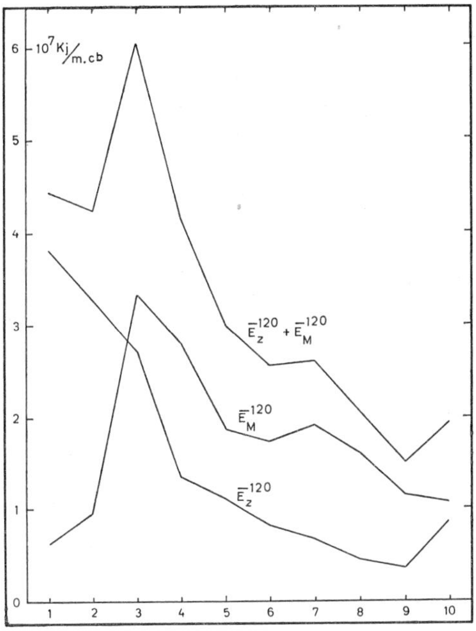

Fig. 3. Spectrum of the kinetic energy of the zonal and meridional geostrophic motions and of the geostrophic motion ($\overline{E}_Z^{120}$, $\overline{E}_M^{102}$, and $\overline{E}_Z^{120} + \overline{E}_M^{120}$, for the period January—April 1953.

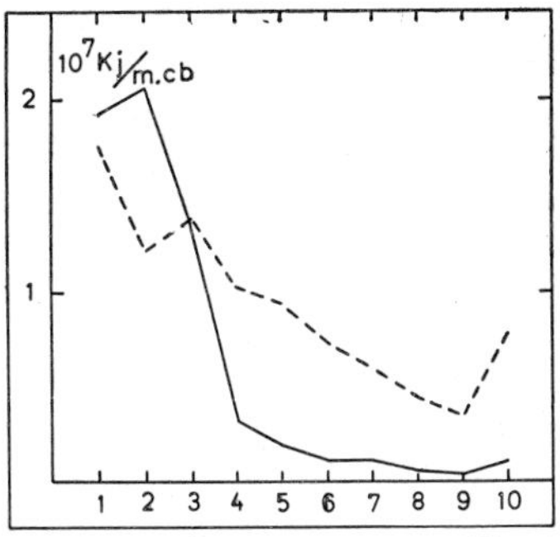

Fig. 4. Partition of the kinetic energy $\overline{E}_Z^{120}$ of the zonal motion for the period January—April 1953.
Dashed line: contribution of the moving waves;
Solid line: contribution of the quasi-stationary waves.

represents the contribution of wave number n to the kinetic energy E_Z and where

$$\alpha_0^2 = \frac{g^2 m^2}{\pi^2 a^2 f^2} (\zeta_0 - \zeta_0^x)^2.$$

Figure 3 shows that, for the period January—April 1953, $(\overline{E}_Z^{120})_n$ and $(\overline{E}_M^{120})_n$ are approximately equal for $n = 3$, that $(\overline{E}_Z^{120})_n$ is markedly superior for $n = 1, 2$ while the contrary is true for $n \geqslant 4$. Thus the theory of isotropic turbulence can hardly be applied to the large-scale horizontal motions in the atmosphere.

Moreover it appears that the spectral distribution of $\overline{E}_Z^{120}$ does not present peak values as was the case for the spectral distribution of $\overline{E}_M^{120}$.

In figure 4 appear, for $\overline{E}_Z^{120}$, the respective contributions of the long quasi-stationary waves and of the moving waves, following the same procedure as for figure 2 (cf. section 6); the differences between figures 2 and 4 are striking. Fig. 4 demonstrates clearly the existence of a third type of atmospheric disturbances, namely long moving waves ($n = 1, 2, 3$) (possibly oscillating zonally about a mean position) or/and long quasi-stationary waves ($n = 1, 2, 3$) with fluctuating amplitudes, probably associated with the latitudinal displacements and the wave-like structure of the subtropical jet stream.

The spectral analysis also revealed the fact that the contribution to E_Z of the quasi-stationary waves (related to 10 day-means) is important for $n = 1, 2, 3$ and practically negligible for $n \geqslant 4$.

8. Spectrum of the kinetic energy of the geostrophic motion

The kinetic energy E of the geostrophic motion

$$E = E_Z + E_M$$

in a zonal ring of 1 centibar vertical thickness and 1 m meridional width, at pressure level p, along the latitude circle $\frac{\varphi + \varphi^x}{2}$, may be expanded in the following way

$$E = \frac{\pi a}{g} \cos\frac{\varphi + \varphi^x}{2} [u]^2 + \sum_1^\infty [(E_Z)_n + (E_M)_n],$$

where $(E_Z)_n$ and $(E_M)_n$ are defined in (7.2) and (6.2).

The spectral distribution of the kinetic energy of the geostrophic motion for the period January—April 1953 is shown on figure 3.

Figure 5 brings out the distinction between the long quasi-stationary waves and the moving waves (cf. section 6); it is rather similar to figure 2 (for E_M). However, there are long and short moving waves, the long ones contributing materially only to the kinetic energy of the zonal motion (cf. section 7).

Figure 6 shows a marked maximum for $n = 3$, which subsists after the averaging processes, while because of these processes the contribution for $n \geqslant 5$ becomes very small.

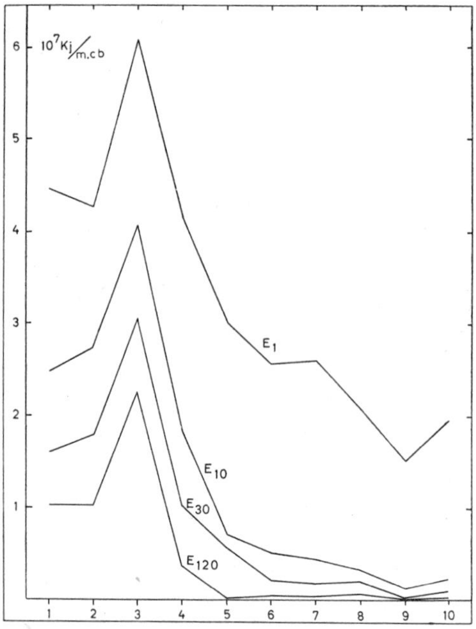

Fig. 6. Influence of the averaging processes on the spectral distribution of the mean kinetic energy of the geostrophic motion for the period January—April 1953.
E_1 or $\overline{E}^{120}$: mean kinetic energy computed from the daily maps;
E_{10}: mean kinetic energy computed from the 10-day mean maps (running means);
E_{30}: mean kinetic energy computed from the four monthly mean maps;
E_{120}: mean kinetic energy computed from the mean map for the whole period.

9. Spectrum of the available energy

The available energy A (expressed in kj m^{-1} cb^{-1}) of a zonal ring of 1 centibar thickness, at pressure level p, and of 1 m meridional width along the latitude circle $\frac{\varphi + \varphi^x}{2}$, has the following form

$$A = \frac{\pi a \cos \frac{\varphi + \varphi^x}{2}}{T_e(\Gamma - \gamma_e)} [T^{*2}] \tag{9.1}$$

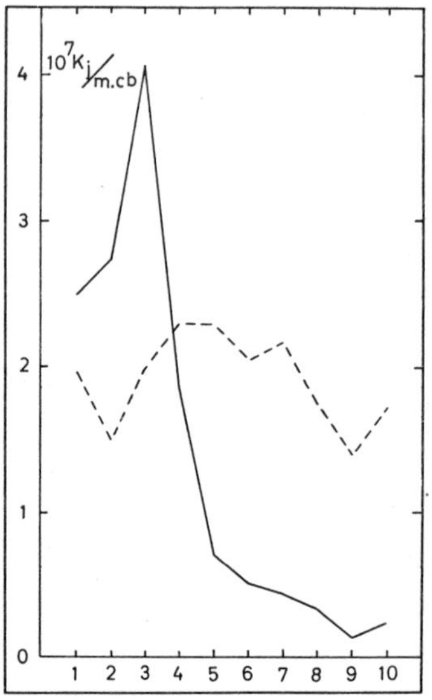

Fig. 5. Partition of the kinetic energy $\overline{E}^{120}$ for the period January—April 1953.
Dashed line: contribution of the moving waves;
Solid line: contribution of the quasi-stationary waves.

If we assume $T_e = [T] = \gamma_0$, the Fourier coefficients of T^* are

$$\gamma_0^* = 0, \quad \gamma_n^* = \gamma_n, \quad \gamma_{-n}^* = \gamma_{-n},$$

whence, (3.5),

$$[T^{*2}] = 2 \sum_1^\infty \gamma_n^* \gamma_{-n}^* = 2 \sum_1^\infty \gamma_n \gamma_{-n}.$$

Substituting (4.3) in (9.2) and (9.2) in (9.1), we obtain

$$A = \sum_1^\infty A_n,$$

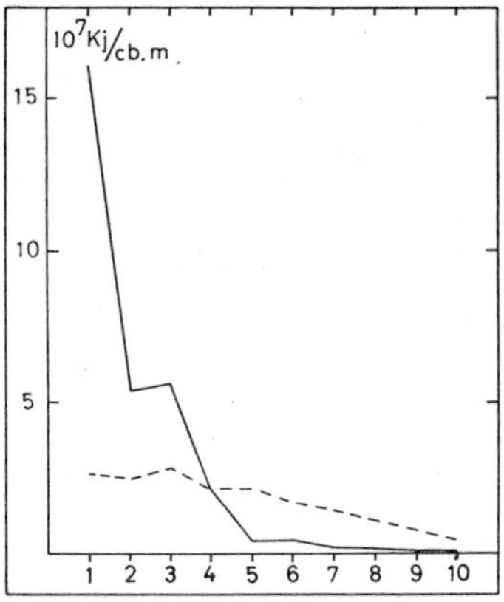

Fig. 7. Partition of the available energy $\overline{A}^{120}$ for the period January—April 1953.
Dashed line: contribution of the moving waves;
Solid line: contribution of the quasi-stationary waves.

where

$$A_n = \frac{2\pi a \cos \frac{\varphi + \varphi^x}{2}}{T_e(\Gamma - \gamma_e)} \gamma_n \gamma_{-n} =$$

$$= \frac{\pi a \cos \frac{\varphi + \varphi^x}{2}}{4\, T_e(\Gamma - \gamma_e)} [(\Theta'_n + \Theta'^x_n)^2 + (\Theta''_n + \Theta''^x_n)^2] \cdot \left(1 + \cos \frac{n\pi}{m}\right)$$

represents the contribution of wave number n to the available energy A of the zonal ring envisaged.

Figure 7 demonstrates the usual breakdown into long quasi-stationary waves and moving waves (cf. section 6): for the former, the contributions $\overline{A}_n^{120}$ for $n = 1, 2, 3$ (particularly for $n = 1$) clearly dominate; for the latter, $\overline{A}_n^{120}$ decreases slowly when n increases. There is an analogy between figures 4 and 7.

As in the case of $\overline{E}_z^{120}$, long and short moving waves contribute to the available energy $\overline{A}_n^{120}$ (cf. section 7).

10. Spectrum of the meridional eddy flux of sensible heat

The meridional eddy flux of sensible heat τ_H (expressed in kj sec^{-1} cb^{-1}) through a vertical strip of 1 centibar thickness, at pressure level p, extending over all longitudes along the latitude circle $\frac{\varphi + \varphi^x}{2}$, assumes the form

$$\tau_H = \frac{2\pi c_p}{g} a \cos \frac{\varphi + \varphi^x}{2} [Tv] = \sum_1^\infty (\tau_H)_n,$$

where, by virtue of (3.5) and (4.3),

$$(\tau_H)_n = \frac{2\pi a \cos \frac{\varphi + \varphi^x}{2}}{g} c_p(\beta_n \gamma_{-n} + \beta_{-n}\gamma_n) =$$

$$= \frac{m}{f} c_p [(\Theta'_n + \Theta'^x_n)(\zeta''_n + \zeta''^x_n) - (\Theta''_n + \Theta''^x_n)(\zeta'_n + \zeta'^x_n)] \sin \frac{n\pi}{m}$$

represents the contribution of wave number n to the meridional eddy flux τ_H of sensible heat.

The spectral analysis revealed the following facts:

1) the disturbances responsible for the major part of the meridional eddy transport of sensible heat have a wave length larger than 4,000 km ($n = 1$ to 6);
2) the time averaging process has only a very slight influence on the flux due to the long waves but reduces considerably the flux of the shorter waves;
3) as shown by figure 8 and following the same procedure as for fig. 2, the stationary waves bring a negligible contribution to τ_H when $n \geqslant 5$ (when $n \geqslant 6$ for the first period November 1950—February 1951 (DEFRISE et al., 1956; cf. fig. 3), while the contribution of the moving waves is important for n between 4 and 8.

11. Spectrum of the meridional eddy flux of west momentum

The meridional eddy flux of west momentum τ_M (expressed in ton m sec^{-2} cb^{-1}) through a

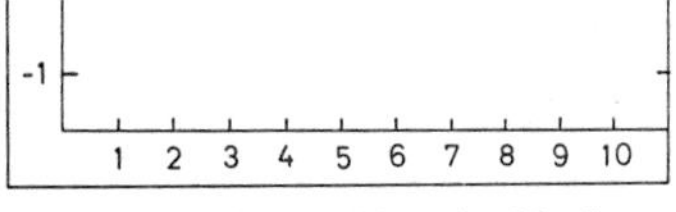

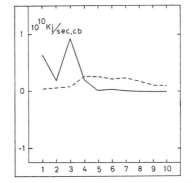

Fig. 8. Partition of the meridional eddy flux of sensible heat for the period January—April 1953.
Dashed line: contribution of the moving waves;
Solid line: contribution of the quasi-stationary waves.

vertical strip, 1 centibar in height, at pressure level p, extending over all longitudes along the latitude circle $\frac{\varphi + \varphi^x}{2}$ asumes the form

$$\tau_M = \frac{2\pi a \cos \frac{\varphi + \varphi^x}{2}}{g} [uv] = \sum_1^\infty (\tau_M)_n,$$

where, by virtue of (3.5) and (4.3),

$$(\tau_M)_n = \frac{2\pi}{g} a \cos \frac{\varphi + \varphi^x}{2} (\alpha_n \beta_{-n} + \alpha_{-n} \beta_n) =$$

$$= \frac{4m^2}{a\pi f^2} g (\zeta'_n \zeta''^x_n - \zeta'^x_n \zeta''_n) \sin \frac{n\pi}{m}$$

represents the contribution of wave number n to the meridional eddy flux τ_M of west momentum.

With regard to figure 9, we would add only the following remarks: the flux of the moving waves is generally negative (from North to South); as for the stationary waves, there is a significant negative flux for $n = 2$, an important positive flux for $n = 1$ and 3, while all fluxes for $n \geqslant 5$ are negligible.

Consequently, for the period January—April 1953, the troughs and ridges of the moving waves have generally a westward meridional tilt and the long stationary waves often an eastward one.

Our computations have shown that the monthly mean meridional eddy flux of west momentum at the 500 mb level is negative for January, March and April and strongly positive for February.

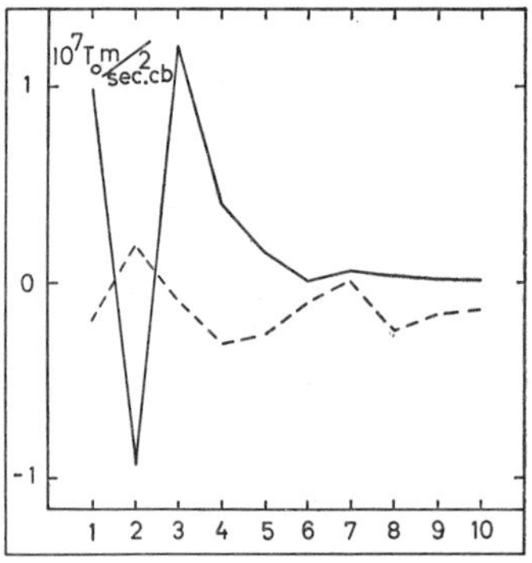

Fig. 9. Partition of the meridional eddy flux of west momentum for the period January—April 1953.
Dashed line: contribution of the moving waves;
Solid line: contribution of the quasi-stationary waves.

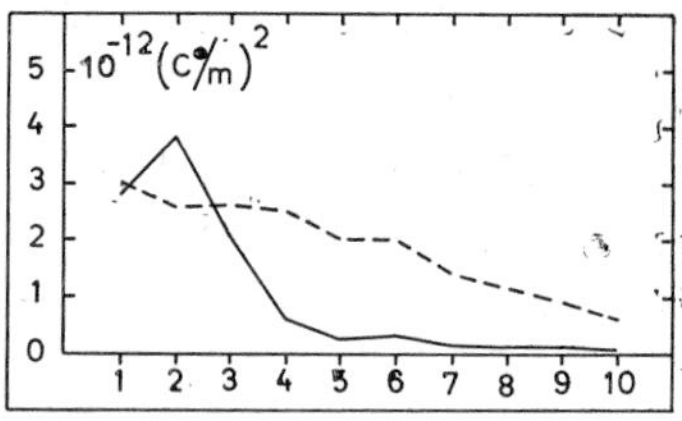

Fig. 10. Partition of the baroclinicity for the period January—April 1953.
Dashed line: contribution of the moving waves;
Solid line: contribution of the quasi-stationary waves.

12. Baroclinicity

The baroclinicity is evaluated by $\overline{\left[\left(\frac{\partial T}{\partial y}\right)^2\right]}^{120}$, for the period January—April 1953, $\frac{\partial T}{\partial y}$ being the differential of T along the meridian.

Figure 10 shows the spectral analysis for the stationary waves and for the moving waves respectively (cf. section 6 and 7), and needs no further comment.

13. Complementary remarks and further plans

It was of course only possible to reproduce here a selection of graphical representations resulting from our study; a few others are to be found in articles by DEFRISE et al., 1956; VAN ISACKER, VAN MIEGHEM, 1956. Some complementary remarks might be added.

Most meteorological parameters envisaged in the course of this study show very important fluctuations with time, which are often of the same order of magnitude as the mean value itself, or even larger. In addition, very few marked regularities or correlations appear at first sight.

Significant differences occur not only from month to month but also from year to year for the same month (particularly as regard the quasi-stationary waves).

It seems therefore desirable to extend the same or similar investigations to longer periods and for more than two latitude circles. We are now proceeding with such an extension for the months of January and February 1946 to 1952, for thirteen latitude circles at 500 mb. But other pressure levels also should be investigated, especially those where the meridional eddy transport of the meteorological quantities generally envisaged (angular momentum, enthalpy, kinetic energy, available energy, etc.) is maximum.

REFERENCES

DEFRISE, P., VAN ISACKER, J., et VAN MIEGHEM, J., 1956: Analyse harmonique le long du parallèle de 50° N et au niveau de 500 mb de quelques grandeurs météorologiques. *Miscelanea Geofisica, Serv. Meteor. de Angola*, 146—154.

GRAHAM, R. D., 1955: An empirical study of planetary waves by means of harmonic analysis. *J. of Meteor.*, **12**, 298—307.

LA SEUR, N. E., 1954: On the asymmetry of the middle latitude circumpolar current. *J. of Meteor.* **11**, 43—57.

LORENZ, N. E., 1955: Available potential energy and the maintenance of the general circulation. *Tellus*, **7**, 157—167.

SALTZMAN, B. and PEIXOTO, J. P., 1957: Harmonic analysis of the mean northern hemisphere wind field for the year 1950. *Quart. J. Roy. Met. Soc.*, **83**, 360—364.

SHEPPARD, P. A., 1953: Momentum flux and meridional motion in the general circulation. *Proc. Toronto Meteor. Conf. 1953*, 103—108.

SHEPPARD, P. A,. 1954: The vertical transfer of momentum in the general circulation. *Arch. Meteor. Geoph. Biokl.*, A.**7**, 114—124.

VAN ISACKER, J. en VAN MIEGHEM, J., 1956: De selectieve rol van de atmosferische storingen in de algemene luchtcirculatie. *Med. Kon. Vl. Acad. van België, Kl. Wet.*, Jg XVIII-1, 3—18.

VAN MIEGHEM, J., 1955: Réflexions sur le transport et la production du moment et de l'énergie cinétiques dans l'atmosphère et sur l'existence de circulations méridiennes moyennes. *Beitr. Phys. Atm.*, **29**, 55—82.

— 1956: The energy available in the atmosphere for conversion into kinetic energy. *Beitr. Phys. Atm.* **29**, 129—142.

WHITE, R. M., and COOLEY, D. S., 1956: Kinetic energy spectrum of meridional motion in the mid-troposphere. *J. of Meteor.* **13**, 67—69.

(Manuscript received July 7, 1958)

Persistence of Mid-Tropospheric Circulations Between Adjacent Months and Seasons

By Jerome Namias

U.S. Weather Bureau, Washington D.C.

Abstract

A series of analyzed mean 700 mb maps for months and seasons dating from 1932 has been used to compute fields of autocorrelation between adjacent months and seasons. While these maps embrace only the area extending from the western Pacific to Europe, they suggest regional and seasonal differences in persistence which appear to be statistically significant. Since areas of high correlation have approximately the scale of the centers of action, their explanation has a central bearing on the problem of climatic fluctuations. There seems to be some suggestion that areas of greatest persistence are linked with the sub-tropical upper level anticyclones, perhaps through reservoirs for anomalous heating or cooling provided by the underlying surface. Two cases of persistence, one involving heavy spring rains over Texas and another drought over the eastern seaboard of the United States, are described. These may indicate feed-back brought about by abnormally moist or dry soil.

Finally, it is suggested that certain highly abnormal forms of the general circulation, such as a contracted circumpolar vortex in summer and an expanded circumpolar vortex in winter, are inherently stable from a hydrodynamic standpoint.

Perhaps the most fascinating aspect of the subject of climatic fluctuations is the frequent tendency of anomalous regimes to persist from month to month, from season to season, and even from year to year. No one has been able to offer a satisfactory explanation of this persistence, and therefore predictions of climatic anomalies for periods this long have enjoyed little success. Because of the immense complexity of the problem, "probably the world's second most difficult", in the words of the late great John von Neumann, information furnished by nature herself in the form of lag correlations might throw some light on potentially profitable avenues for research.

Work of this nature has been reported in meteorological literature from time to time since the turn of the century, and the only novel element of this report is the use of mid-tropospheric data extending over a large portion of the northern hemisphere. In view of the fact that fluctuations in the position and intensity of the sea level centers of action were first physically explained by Rossby (1939) through the medium of planetary waves in mid-troposphere, perhaps newly gathered statistics may throw new light on large-scale and long period persistence.

The source of data for lag correlations comprises some twenty-five years of seasonally averaged maps of 700 mb height covering North America, the eastern North Pacific, and the North Atlantic and their derived departures from normal. Because of changing upper air networks, analytical procedures, etc., such a map series is obviously not of uniform reliability with respect to area and period—a fact which usually accounts for much of the frustration encountered in research on long-range problems. Nevertheless, the data are believed good enough for the coarse indications cited below, since departures from normal on seasonal maps are surprisingly large when one considers the observed day to day variability. An idea of this great variability of long period means is provided in Fig. 1 where the standard deviations of daily latitudinal mean sea level pressures computed from daily hemi-

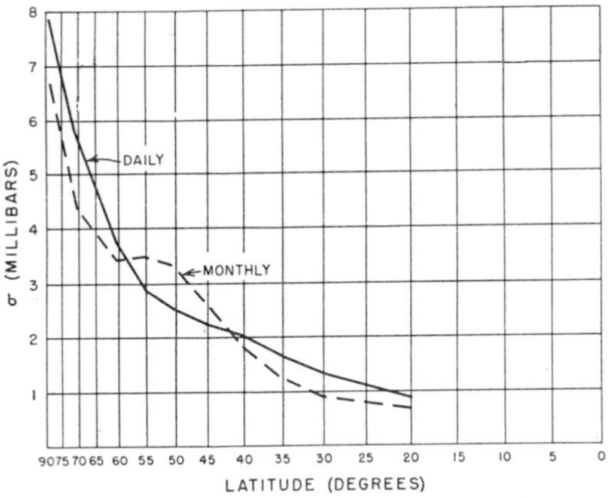

Fig. 1. Standard deviation of mean sea-level pressure along latitudes for daily (solid) and monthly mean (dashed) values for the Januarys from 1899 to 1939.

spheric maps of 40 Januarys are compared with the standard deviations derived from the 40 mean monthly January maps of the same period.

Seasonal lag correlations for a lattice of points 20 degrees of longitude apart at ten-degree latitudes from 20° N to 70° N have been computed and analyzed in the form of isopleths for the four seasons (Fig. 2). The values appear to group themselves into fairly large scale fields of the order of the centers of action. A preliminary study indicates that a closer grid of points would not materially influence the broad scale patterns.

While atmospheric inertial effects (so dominant in day-to-day changes) may conceivably be important over periods possibly as long as two weeks or a month, it is unlikely that they can account for such persistence as suggested in Fig. 2. Apparently there are regional differences in persistence, for a probability analysis of the coefficients indicates that those in the shaded areas are statistically significant beyond the 5% level.

From Fig. 2 it seems that persistence is related to latitude, and a stratification of this sort (Fig. 3) is highly suggestive of a real dependence. In seeking an explanation of this dependence the possibility arises that persistence may be partly related to the form of the general circulation itself. Thus, greatest seasonal persistence may lie in the sub-tropical anticyclone belt, because here surface winds are light and abnormalities in surface temperature, if they exert an effect on the

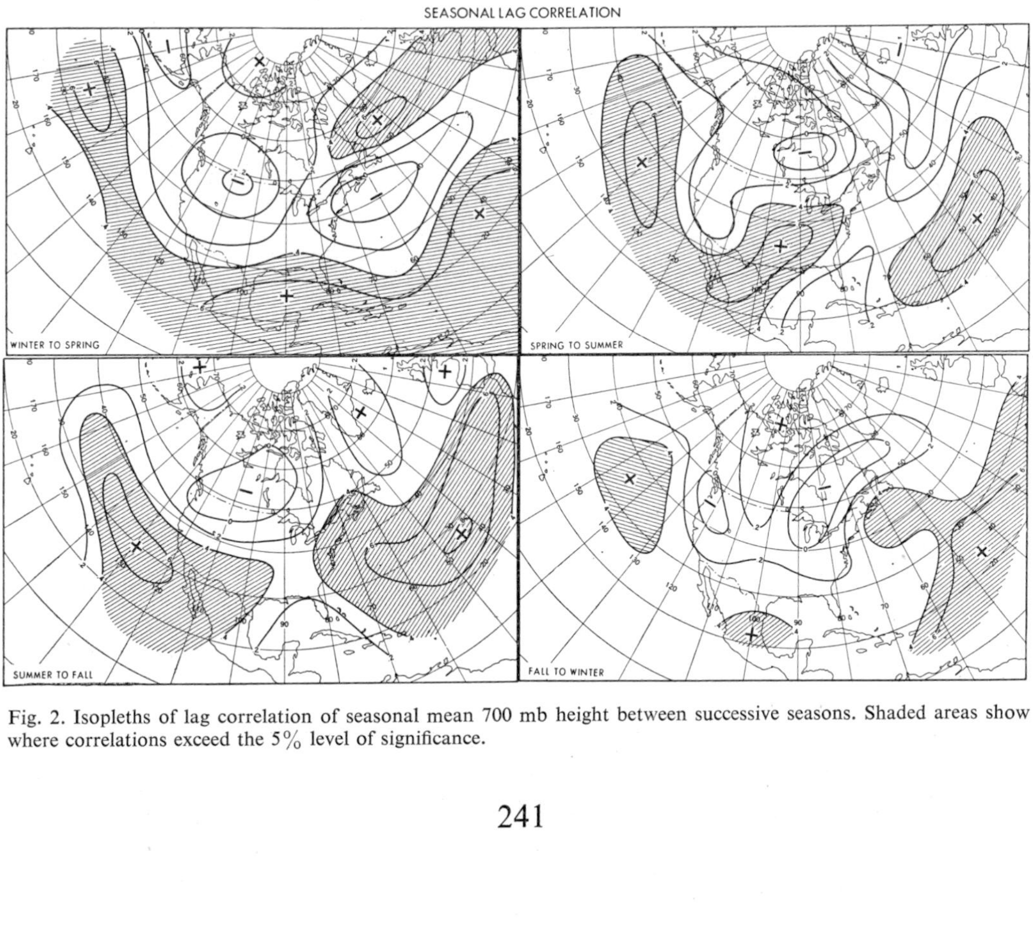

Fig. 2. Isopleths of lag correlation of seasonal mean 700 mb height between successive seasons. Shaded areas show where correlations exceed the 5% level of significance.

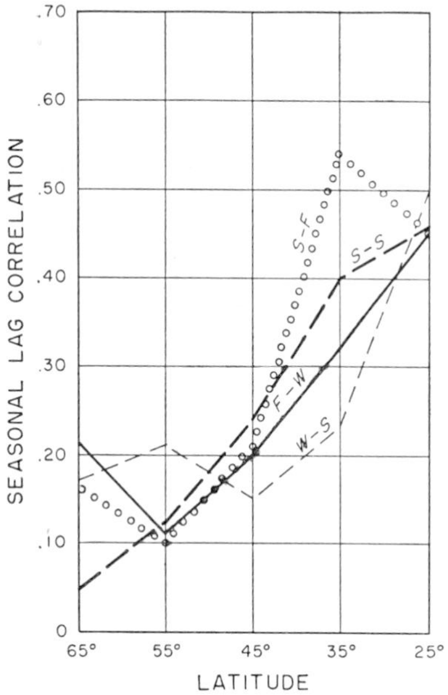

Fig. 3. Latitudinal averages of correlations mapped in Fig. 2.

upper level patterns, could have a long period of time to influence the overlying air circulation. At any rate the normal profiles of 700 mb height (Fig. 4) are very similar in form to the persistence profiles, and one obtains the impression that the Hadley cell once established is a rather stable feature of the general circulation.

Another indication of the dependence of persistence upon the sub-tropical anticyclones arises in connection with the emergence from spring to summer of a center of maximum persistence over the Southern Plains of the United States—precisely the area into which the continental upper level anticyclone normally settles as spring goes into summer.

Then again, the band of high lag correlation during the warmer half-year (summer—fall and spring—summer) appears to shift southward in winter, just as the sub-tropical high-pressure belt.

The conclusion that the sub-tropical areas are more persistent than others has indeed been suggested by LANDSBERG et al. (1943) who studied lag correlation with the help of historical monthly mean sea level maps for the period 1899—1939, using tetrachoric correlations.

In addition to the indication of a dependence of seasonal persistence on latitude possibly through the sub-tropical anticyclones, there is a suggestion that persistence is more pronounced over oceans than land areas. Claims of this nature have frequently been made (BERLAGE, 1957). Again, if the sub-tropical anticyclones are the major seats of this persistence, one might anticipate an oceanic—land difference between the North Atlantic and North Pacific with North America, because of the greater domination of southern portions of the oceans by these circulations. In order to test this hypothesis, possible latitudinal effects were removed by expressing each correlation as a deviation from its latitudinal average. These departures were then averaged over 21 oceanic points and 14 land points. For each of the interseasonal persistences (winter—spring, spring—summer, etc.) the averages over the ocean were higher than those over land, and the differences were significant at the 5 % level for spring to fall and fall to winter, almost significant at this level for winter to spring but not so for spring to summer. Here again, one presumably finds some persistence-enhancing influence of the warm season upper level anticyclone over the United States. Combining all four interseasonal values the difference between ocean and land comes out significant beyond the 1 % level.

To sum up, there are statistical indications that at mid-tropospheric levels persistence of mean seasonal flow patterns is higher at low than at high latitudes, that greater persistence may be linked with the sub-tropical anticyclones, and (perhaps for this reason) is higher over the adjacent oceans than over North America—except in summer when a great sub-tropical upper level anticyclone frequently exists over southern United States.

The physical reasons for such indications are naturally highly complex. A number of hy-

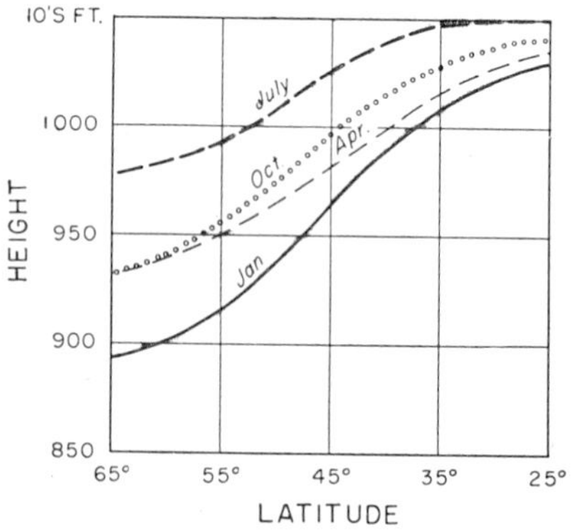

Fig. 4. Normal monthly profiles of 700 mb height.

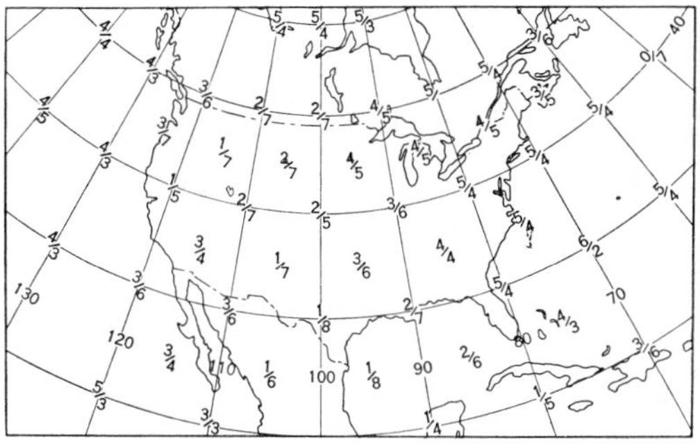

Fig. 5. Number of two-week periods from February through mid-June 1957 when empirically derived statistical predictions of 700 mb height were too high (lower figure) and too low (upper figure).

potheses to account for persistence have been advanced in past years. These range from possible extra-terrestrial effects to abnormal surface conditions as might be established through conservative factors like snow cover, ocean temperatures, etc. Whatever the ultimate cause, it is highly probable that the manifestation of abnormality becomes reflected in patterns of the general circulation. For this reason it is reasonable that certain parts of the general circulation of the order of the surface centers of action or of their associated upper level ridges and troughs, might be systematically forced into somewhat abnormal shapes or positions and these in turn would alter the large scale circulation in other areas. In other words, the forced perturbations would be due not only to the normal climatological influences exerted by mountains, coast lines, etc., but also to abnormal surface conditions. Because of the inter-dependence of circulation between remote areas of the globe, it has not yet been possible to determine which portions of the general circulation of a given month or season are "forced" and which are resonant or responsive.

In the course of routine long-range (30-day) forecasting work there are times when it seems like certain parts of the atmospheric circulation are remarkably persistent even though neighboring large-scale features are changing. One of the more recent and striking occurrences of this kind was during the spring of 1957 over the Texas area of the United States. Here, after several years of drought, the spring of 1957 was characterized by floods and severe storms including tornadoes. Indeed, the persistently bad weather there was the occasion for a separate detailed report (GILMAN, KLEIN and others, 1958).

One of the interesting characteristics of this period was the tendency for a mid-tropospheric pressure anomaly (negative) to persist over the afflicted area to a much higher degree than elsewhere over the country or over adjacent ocean areas. This circumstance is indicated in Fig. 5 where are shown the number of periods from February through mid-June when a predicted two-week average computed using normal autocorrelation of day to day heights was too low (upper figure) or too high (lower figure). The small ratios over the Texas area and along the Rockies compared to elsewhere may suggest that some geographically fixed influence may have been operating during this lengthy period, although it is always possible that such areas are the chance result of a peculiar combination of atmospheric conditions.

Accepting for the moment that the influence is geographically fixed, one might inquire what might have fixed it. Here one can speculate ad infinitum, but until dynamic computational methods are developed it will be impossible to test the validity of any hypothesis. The author submits that when such dynamic models are available, it might be possible to test the idea that in such cases as the Texas regime, the early spring heavy rains and the resulting moist soil may have served as a cooling reservoir by using for vaporization some of the heat normally associated with the spring to summer building of the upper level anticyclone in that area. The only reasons for such an assumption are that (1) early spring rainfall over this area was in many places the highest on record, amounting in some areas to more than 32 inches, and (2) dew points during late spring averaged considerably above normal, the increase in dew point from day to day as air masses were advected into this area seemed outstandingly rapid to experienced forecasters.

The possibility that heavy spring rains might influence subsequent summer temperatures was tested for the tri-state area—Arkansas, Oklahoma, and Texas. In order to do this the total seasonal precipitation and temperature records for this area were grouped into terciles and a contingency table (Table I) prepared.

Apparently there is a tendency for warm summers to follow dry springs and cool summers, wet springs. The "a priori hypothesis", namely that a negative relationship exists between these two

Table I. Summer temperature following spring precipitation over the southern plains of USA

		Subsequent summer temperature			
		Below normal	Near normal	Above normal	Total
Spring precipitation	Light	4	9	8	21
	Moderate	8	4	10	22
	Heavy	9	9	3	21
	Total	21	22	21	

variables, withstood a chi-square test, indicating a probability of 0.954 that such a relationship exists. However, these results may merely reflect another causal factor influencing both spring rain and summer temperature.

Another suggestion of the influence of soil moisture or dryness arose during the summer of 1957 over Eastern United States. This was a summer of severe drought over much of the area east of the Appalachians (McGuire and Palmer,

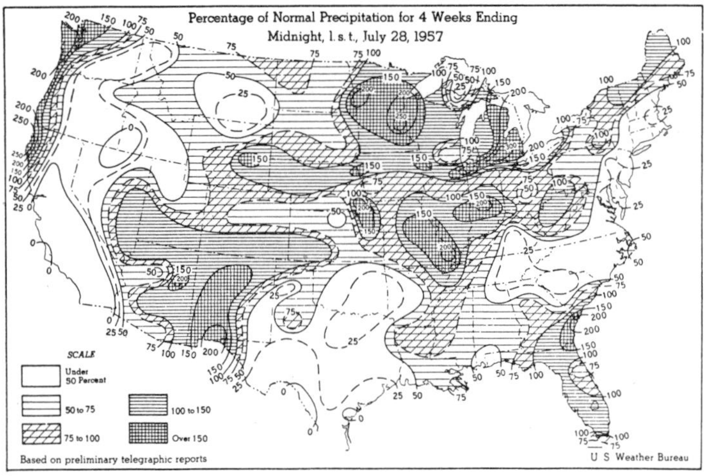

Fig. 6. Percentage of normal prepitation for July 1—28, 1957.

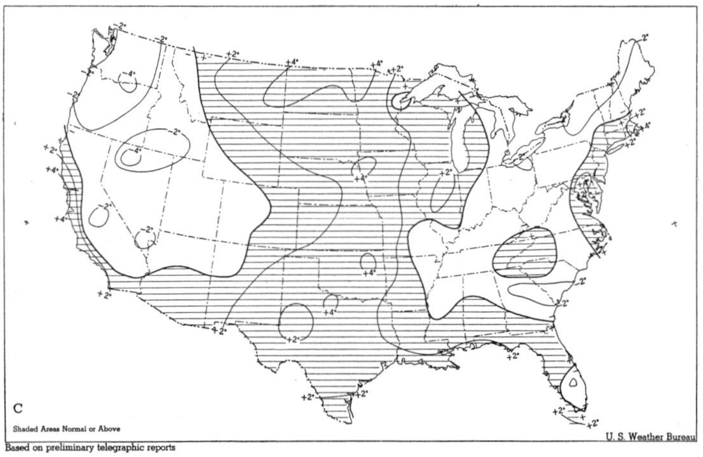

Fig. 7. Departure of average July 1957 temperature from normal (°F).

1957). A characteristic rainfall map (for July 1957) is produced in Fig. 6. The July temperature departures from normal are shown in Fig. 7. The corresponding 700 mb mean circulation and its anomaly are shown in Fig. 8. An objective (or subjective) estimate (MARTIN, HAWKINS, 1950), of the temperature anomaly expected to accompany this chart indicates uniformly cool temperatures (much below normal in fact) over the entire Northeast in response to the deep upper level trough along the east coast. Yet, appreciably, *above* normal values were reported over much of the area (Fig. 7). Note that these are precisely over the area of great precipitation deficiency.

Of course, this does not prove that the greater warmth than expected from the flow pattern was due to the dry soil, for it may only reflect the well-known negative correlation between precipitation and temperature observed over many continental areas during summer. That is, the lack of cloud frequently accompanying dry weather permits greater insolation. Yet, the marked deviation of temperatures in the above normal area from objective estimates derived from many summers of past data suggests that perhaps some reservoir of heat may have existed in the dry soil or, more probably that the dry soil acted somewhat like a desert, permitting higher daytime maxima which play the major role in determining mean temperatures over the Northeast in summer. The dryness developed not only in July but especially in June—a month very deficient in rainfall in the same area.

When one examines persistence on a month-to-month basis, it appears to have a distinct annual variation. This is perhaps most easily illustrated with the help of a graph (Fig. 9) showing the persistence between adjacent months

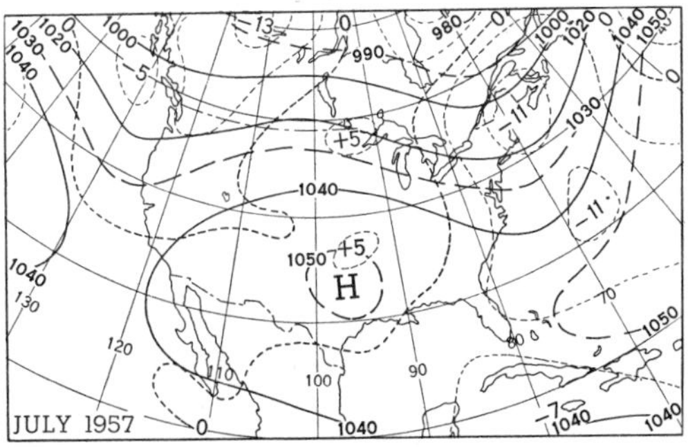

Fig. 8. Mean 700 mb contours (labeled in tens of feet) for July 1957 and isoplets of departure from normal (broken).

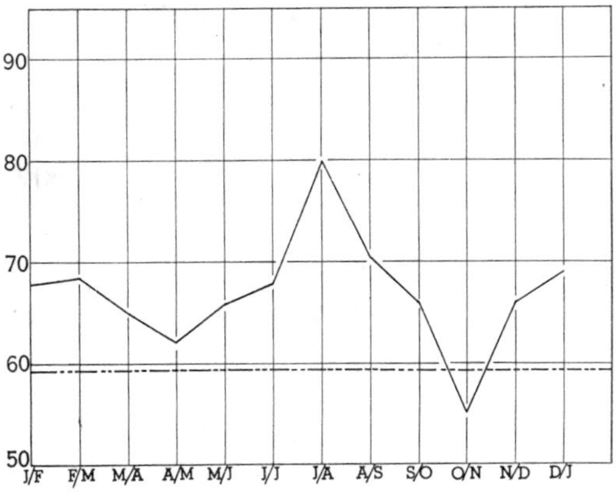

Fig. 9. Percentage of the United States in which the temperature anomaly did not change by more than 1 class (out of five possible) between consecutive months during the period March 1942 through 1957.

taken from an earlier study (NAMIAS, 1952) but with additional data added. This graph may be shown to be quite similar to one showing the course of persistence of month-to-month mid-tropospheric circulation patterns. The periods of least persistence during spring and fall were ascribed to the normal changeability at those times of year when land and water areas reverse their thermal roles and when the prevailing westerlies (measurably the zonal index) are most varying—thereby easily introducing instabilities in the planetary quasi-stationary wave trains. The period of great persistence during summer was ascribed to the sluggishness of the circulation and its small normal changeability, while the winter persistence was also ascribed to small changeability in normal zonal westerlies. There was some suggestion of a dependence of persistence upon zonal index in the sense of greater persistence with low than high index, greater atmospheric sluggishness perhaps encouraging surface constraints to operate more effectively. No attempt has been made to study persistence during any one season as a function of the type of circulation pattern. Partly, this stratification has not been introduced because of woefully inadequate data. Yet it seems very reasonable that certain mean patterns would be expected to be stable at a certain time of year while others would be highly transitory.

In the course of 30-day forecasting at least two types of patterns have arisen which appear to be rather stable, and, therefore, should be radically altered only with caution. These are: (1) the summertime pattern in which mid-tropo-

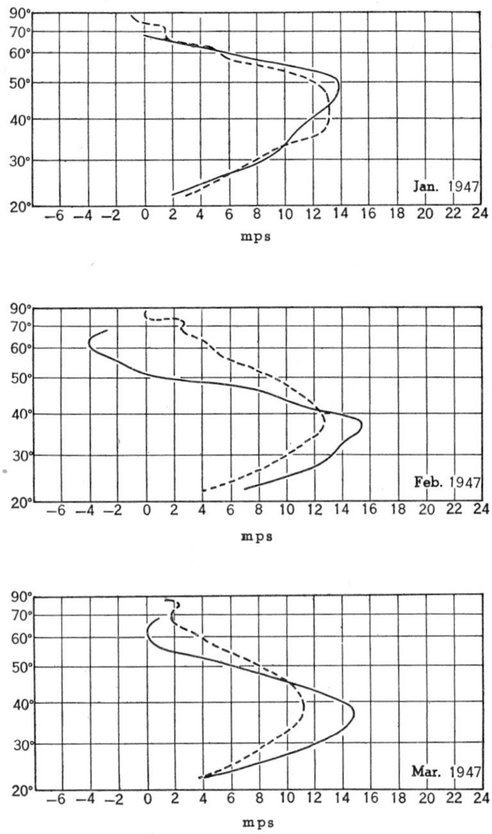

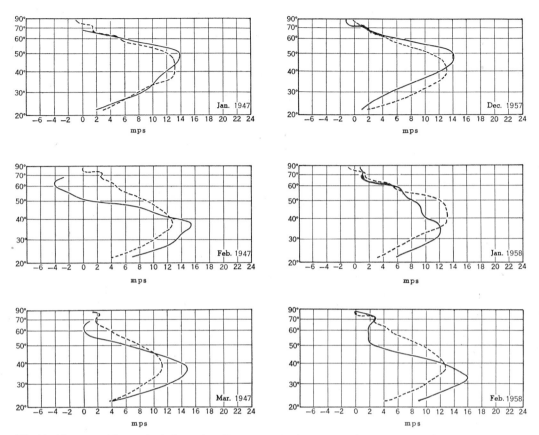

Fig. 10. Mean monthly zonal wind speed profiles at 700 mbs. for the area 0° westward to 180°. Broken lines show normals.

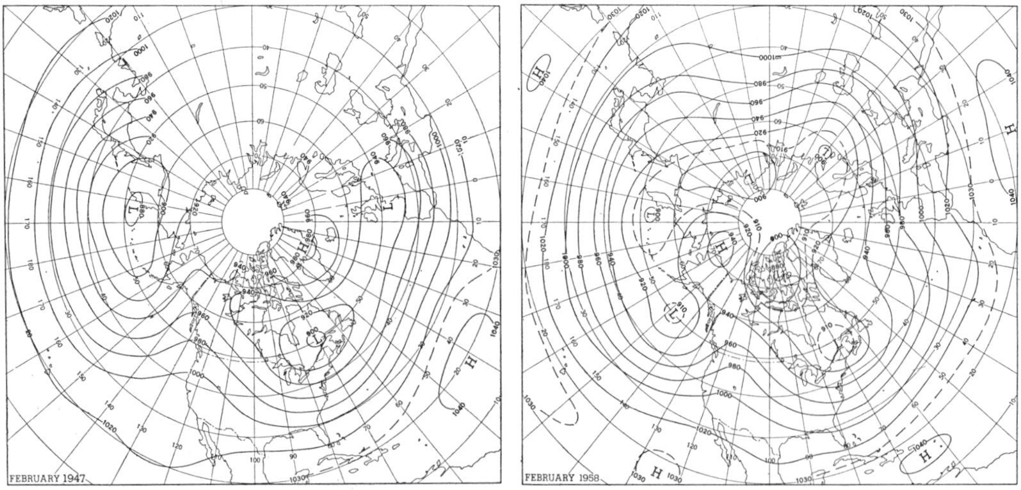

Fig. 11. Mean monthly 700 mb contours (labeled in tens of feet) for February 1947 and February 1958.

spheric westerlies are displaced well north of normal with sub-tropical highs similarly displaced and (2) the wintertime pattern wherein the westerlies are displaced far south of normal.

An example of the latter type is illustrated by the wind speed profiles for February and March 1947 and also for January and February 1958 (Fig. 10). These months were characterized by strong westerlies farther south than normal and by remarkably similar mid-tropospheric flow patterns and temperature anomalies (Figs. 11 and 12) over the United States. However, it is noteworthy that the character of the wind speed profile alone does not completely specify the phase of all planetary waves, since the European flow pattern differed materially in 1947 and 1958 (Fig. 11).

The stability of such anomalous regimes poses several questions for the dynamic meteorologist. Obviously, the atmosphere is readily doing the job required to transport momentum, heat and energy in spite of the great abnormalities, and one must conclude that the general circulation has a number of stable modes by means of which to operate. This fact, long recognized by people engaged in extended forecasting, has now been discovered in experiments with differentially heated rotating dishpans.

Another point of similarity between the regimes of 1947 and 1958 was that each far southward displacement of the westerlies was preceded by an extensive period during which the westerlies were stronger and farther *north* than normal (Fig. 10). This sequence lends support to a hypothesis of major index cycles suggested by the author (NAMIAS, 1950) in which the extent of "containment" of polar air preceding the year's primary index cycle determines the intensity and duration of the subsequent low index phase.

Therefore, evidence seems to be accumulating that in seeking the reason for long-period persistence, one must not only examine further anomalous surface conditions perhaps brought about by preceding circulations and weather, but also the inherent hydrodynamic stability of different

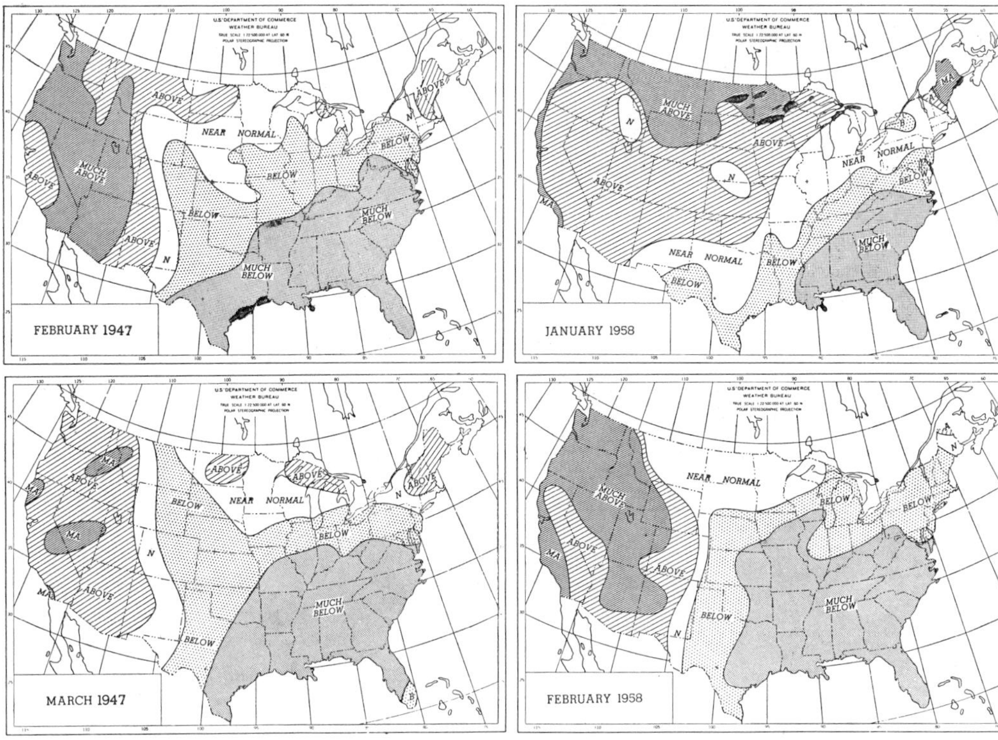

Fig. 12. Mean monthly temperature anomalies expressed in five classes.

mean flow patterns at certain times of the year. Needless to say, further information on these matters would pay great economic dividends in terms of long-range weather forecasting.

Acknowledgement

The author wishes to express thanks to Mr. I. Enger for his assistance in connection with statistical tests employed.

REFERENCES

ROSSBY, C.-G., and Collaborators, 1939: Relation between variations in the intensity of the zonal circulation of the atmosphere and the displacements of the semi-permanent centers of action. *J. Marine Res.*, **2**, pp. 38—55.

LANDSBERG, H., GEORGE, M. C., and APPEL, F. W., 1943: Studies on pressure, temperature, and precipitation persistence. A series of unpublished reports by the Military Climatology Project, Univ. of Chicago Inst. Meteor.

BERLAGE, H. P., 1957: Fluctuations of the general atmospheric circulation of more than one year, their nature and prognostic value. *Koninklijk Nederlands Meteorologisch Instituut.* No. 102—69.

GILMAN, C. S., KLEIN, W. H., and others, 1958: Rainfall and floods of April, May and June 1957 in the South-central States. *U.S. Wea. Bur. Tech. Paper*, No. 33.

MCGUIRE, J. K., and PALMER, W. C., 1957: The 1957 drought in the eastern United States. *Mon. Wea. Rev.*, **85**, No. 9, pp. 305—314.

MARTIN, D. E., and HAWKINS, H. F., JR., 1950: Forecasting the weather: the relationship of temperature and precipitation over the United States to the circulation aloft. *Weatherwise*, **3**, pp. 16—19, 40—43, 65—67, 89—92, 113—116, 138—141.

NAMIAS, J., 1952: The annual course of month-to-month persistence in climatic anomalies. *Bull. Amer. Meteor. Soc.*, **32**, pp. 279—285.

— 1950: The index cycle and its role in the general circulation. *J. Meteor.* **7**, pp. 130—139.

(Manuscript received March 18, 1958)

The Abrupt Change of Circulation over the Northern Hemisphere during June and October

By YEH TU-CHENG, DAO SHIH-YEN and LI MEI-TS'UN
Institute of Geophysics and Meteorology,
Academia Sinica, Peking

Abstract

In this paper we have shown that there is an abrupt change of the upper-air circulation over the Northern Hemisphere in June and October. In June this change is characterized by a sudden northward shift of the westerlies and easterlies. Associated with this a marked change in the upper flow pattern takes place followed by the establishment of the typical summer circulation. In October the abrupt change is characterized by a sudden southward shift of the westerlies and easterlies. This is also accompanied by a marked change in the upper flow pattern, after which the typical upper winter circulation is established.

The onset of the summer circulation is associated with the outburst of the SW monsoon in India and of Mai-yü in China and Japan and a rapid northward displacement of the inter-tropical convergence zone (ICZ). The onset of the winter circulation is followed by the retreat of the SW monsoon and the ICZ. The synoptic sequence of these developments is described.

In middle and high latitudes the synoptic weather processes are quite different in summer and winter. In each of these seasons the weather development follows a certain definite synoptic sequence. It would be helpful to the forecaster to know the characteristic beginning of such a natural synoptic season.

YIN (1949) once studied the onset of the monsoonal season in 1946 over Burma and India. He related the onset of the monsoon to the "retreat" of the westerly jet stream to the north of the Himalayas. The time of the occurrence of this event was at the beginning of June. YEH (1950) studied the displacement of this westerly jet in 1946 and pointed out that the typical winter upper circulation began when it had been established to the south of the Himalayas. The time of its occurrence was in the middle of October. Later YEH, KAO and LIU (1951) investigated the same problem in more detail and related some weather developments over Eastern Asia to the displacement of this jet. Recently DAO and CHEN (1957) studied the change of circulation from May to June still further. Figs. 1—3 are taken from their paper. All these studies indicate that there is a very abrupt change of the circulation both in June and in the middle of October over Eastern Asia.

SUTCLIFFE and BANNON (1954), in analyzing the upper-air winds over the Mediterranean—Middle East Asia, also found a sudden change of the wind conditions in this region in the beginning of June. In comparing Sutcliffe's and Bannon's work with the studies mentioned above, we may infer that the abrupt change of the upper air circulation is not only peculiar to Asia. It may very well be a world-wide phenomenon.

These studies also suggest that as far as certain gross features of the upper-air circulation are concerned there may only be two fundamental natural seasons during the year, namely summer and winter. In summer there is a definite type of the structure of the zonal circulation, while in winter another type prevails. The change from one to the other is very abrupt. This does, however, not imply that spring and autumn do not exist at all. Indeed, there are certain definite characteristic patterns that can be taken as spring and autumn. Actually YEH and CHU (1955) have studied the character of these transitional

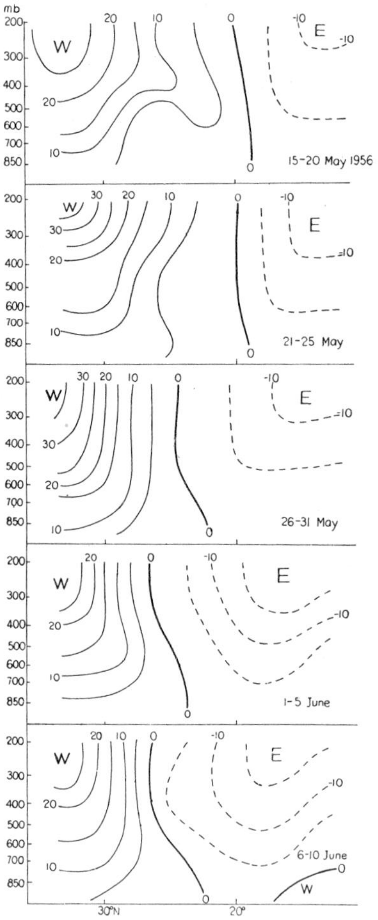

Fig. 1. 5-day mean cross-sections of the observed zonal wind (maps) along 45° E from May to June, 1956.

seasons over Eastern Asia. As far as the structure of the upper circulation is concerned, however, there are only two fundamental seasons during the year, the transitional periods between them being negligibly short.

In this paper we shall devote ourselves to the study of the above mentioned sudden changes of the upper circulation over the whole Northern Hemisphere and some phenomena associated with them. Over Asia data for five years are used and for North America four. Due to lack of data only two years have been studied in the Pacific Ocean. Since 1956 is common to all the regions we shall use this year as an illustration in this paper. However, it should be pointed out that the other years are quite similar. Indeed, in certain regions the phenomena discussed are even more pronounced in other years.

I. The sudden change of the structure of the upper westerlies

Since all the previous studies mentioned above indicate that the structure of the upper zonal circulation is a good indicator for the change of season, we shall start this study by investigating the variations of the structure of the westerlies along different longitudes over the Northern Hemisphere. We shall begin with the onset of the summer zonal circulation.

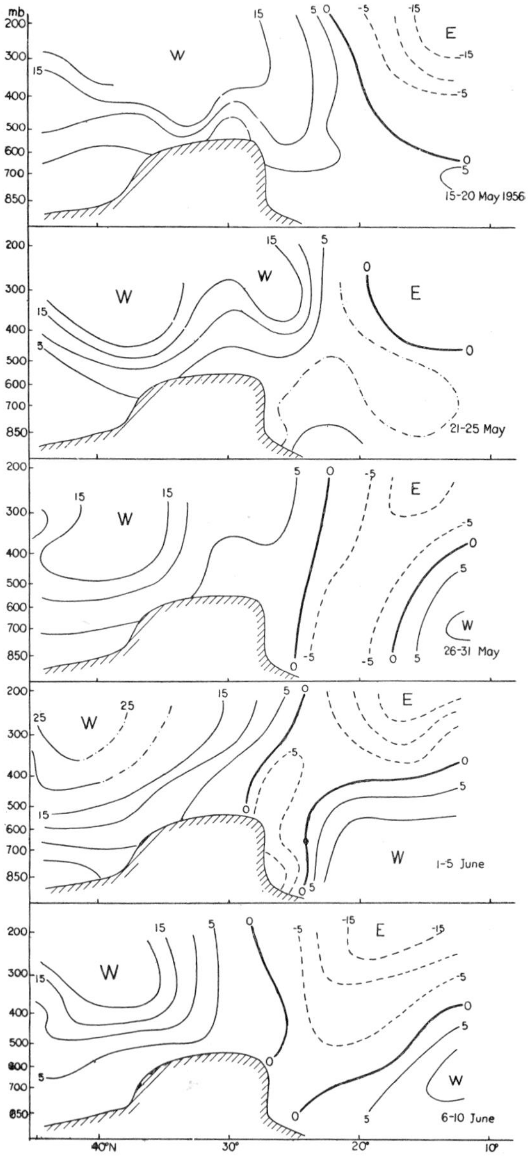

Fig. 2. 5-day mean cross-sections of the observed zonal wind (maps) along 90° E from May to June, 1956.

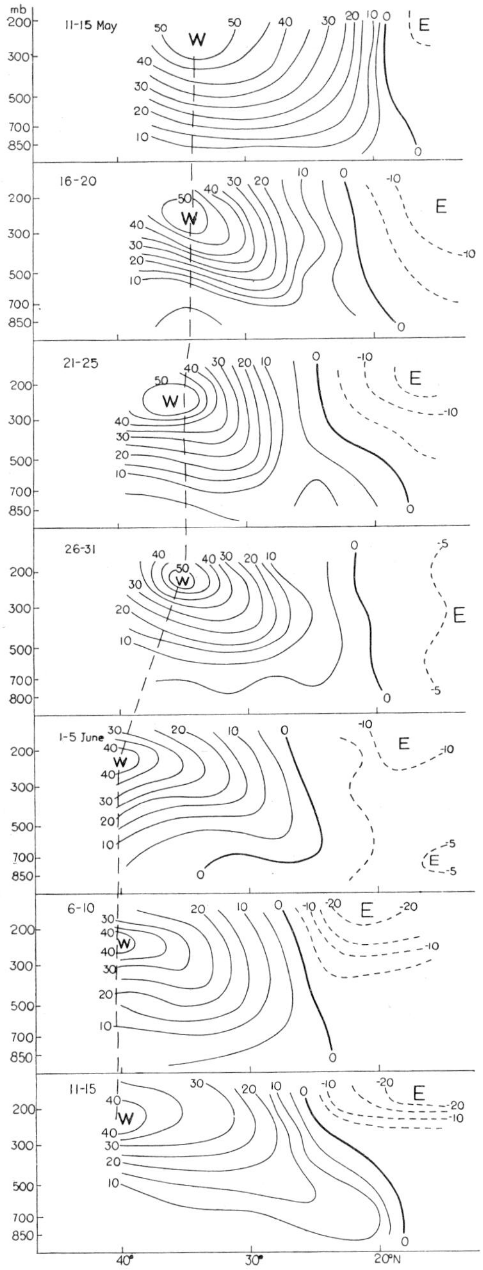

Fig. 3. 5-day mean cross-sections of the observed zonal wind (maps) along 125° E from May to June, 1956.

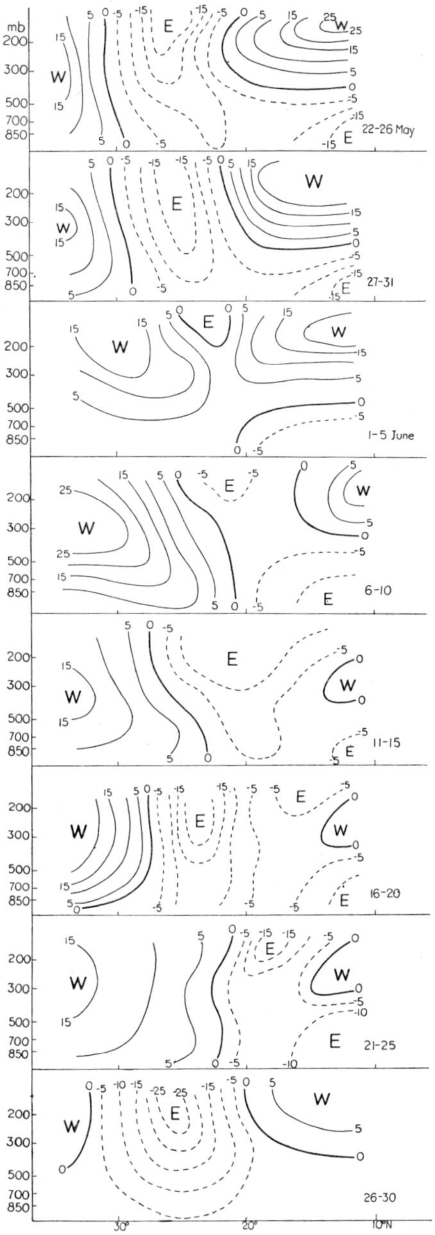

Fig. 4. 5-day mean cross-sections of the observed zonal wind (maps) along 165° E from May to June, 1956.

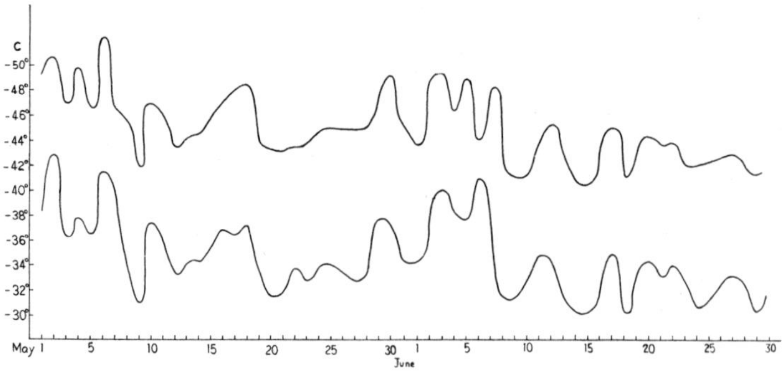

Fig. 5. Temperature var iations at 250 mb and 300 mb over stationary ship 25 V in the Pacific from May to June, 1956.

1. *The onset of summer circulation*

Along 45° E, 90° E, 125° E, 165° E, 100° W (not shown in this paper) and 80° W respectively we have analyzed the 5-day mean cross-sections for the observed west wind component from May to July. In all these cross-sections we found a similar variation, i.e. a sudden northward shift of the westerly jet stream and of the easterlies. The time of occurrence of this abrupt shift is almost the same over all Asia, namely at the end of May or in the beginning of June, but it is about two to three weeks later over North America.

In Fig. 1 we find that the line of separation between the easterlies and westerlies is located to the south of 20° N before the end of May, 1956 at longitude 45° E. In the last five days of this month it suddenly shifts northward to about 26° N. At this time an easterly jet appears at Aden and the westerly jet also moves northward.

Along 90° E (Fig. 2) we find two branches of strong westerlies before the end of May. One branch is to the north (called the northern jet) and the other is just to the south of the Himalayas (called the southern jet). These two jets over Asia have been studied extensively (STAFF MEMBERS OF INSTITUTE OF GEOPHYSICS AND METEOROLOGY, ACADEMIA SINICA, 1957; HSIEH and CHEN, 1951 and others). The separation between easterlies and westerlies is far to the south of Tibet at this time. In the last five days of May the southern branch of strong westerlies suddenly disappears and the easterlies advance to the southern rim of the Himalayas. At the same time we see that the SW monsoon rushes northward. In the beginning of June it has already reached the Himalayas which is its northernmost position.

Further downstream we have a cross-section along 125° E (Fig. 3). The explanation of this figure is self-evident. The sudden northward shift of the westerly jet and the advance of the easterlies occurs in the beginning of June.

Before proceeding further we shall point out that the coincidence of the time of disappearance

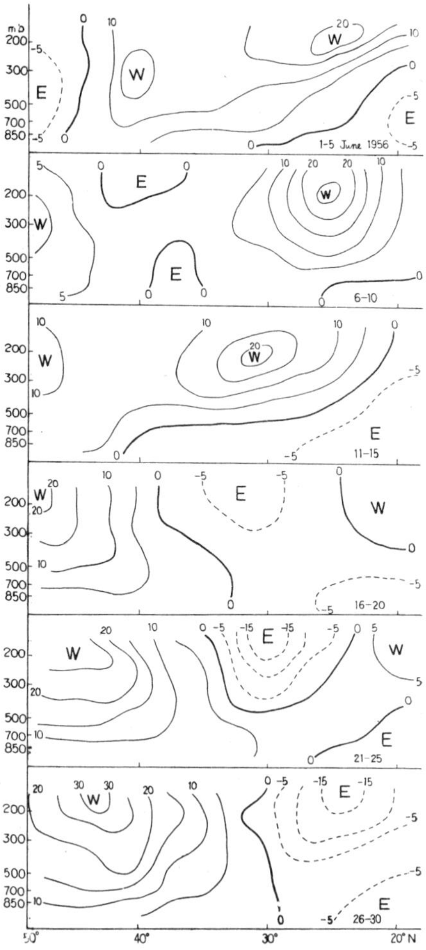

Fig. 6. 5-day mean cross-sections of the observed zonal wind (maps) along 80° W from May to June, 1956.

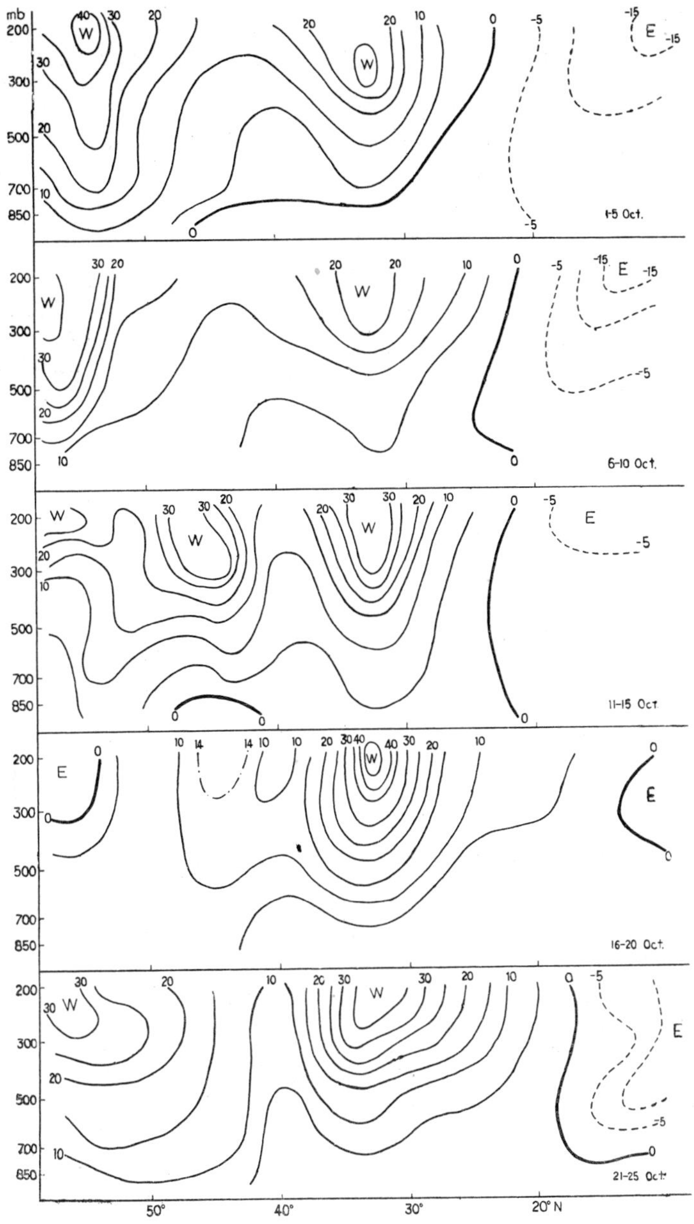

Fig. 7. 5-day mean cross-sections of the observed zonal wind (maps) along 45° E during October, 1956.

or retreat of the southern jet and that of the outburst of the SW monsoon is not peculiar to 1956 and 1946 (YIN, 1949), but is common to all years in our study. The dates of the onset of the SW monsoon determined by the Indian Meteorological Department[1] from rainfall records agree quite well with ours. The onset of Mai-Yü is also associated with the disappearance of the southern jet. (Mai-Yü is an important rainfall period in China and Japan. For an explanation see STAFF MEMBERS 1957.) This association has been pointed out by YEH and KOO (1955) and has been studied by DAO and CHEN (1957) and DAO (1958). A detailed description of the synoptic sequence for the onset of the SW monsoon and Mai-Yü in 1956 will be given in this report (cf. sec. III).

[1] Published in *Indian Journal of Meteorology and Geophysics.*

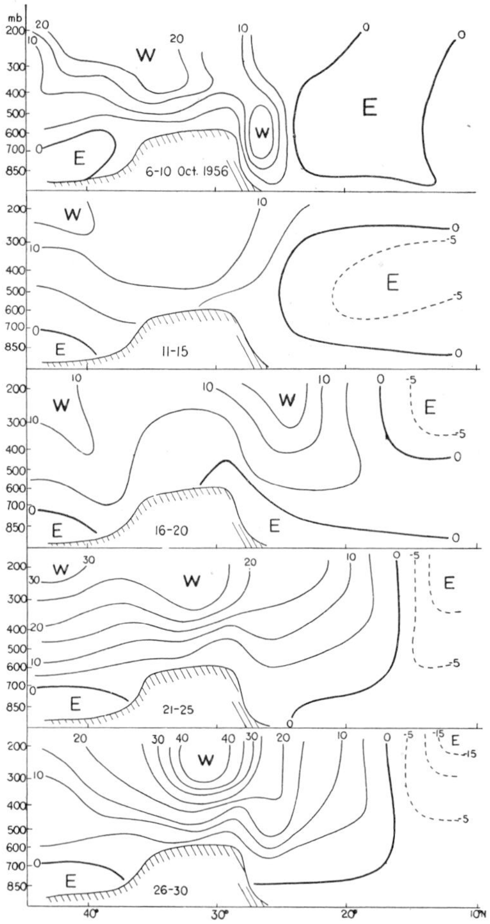

Fig. 8. 5-day mean cross-sections of the observed zonal wind (maps) along 90° E during October, 1956.

Fig. 4 is a cross-section roughly along 165° E and shows the situation over the Pacific Ocean. This cross-section only extends to latitude 33° N. Due to scarcity of rawin stations in the Pacific this is the only cross-section we could construct in this region. We see here that a branch of the westerlies exists in the upper troposphere at low latitudes all the time. This branch of the westerlies does not belong to the main westerlies in middle and high latitudes but is associated with a cyclonic vortex usually found over this part of the Pacific. Fixing our attention to this branch of westerlies we see that its intensity greatly decreases during the period 6—10 June. Hereafter its intensity never recovers. At the end of June we also find a quick retreat of the middle latitude westerlies. From Fig. 4 it is difficult to decide which one of these is the abrupt change which can be considered to characterize the onset of the summer circulation over the Pacific. In order to determine this we reproduce the temperature variations at 250 mb and 300 mb at the ship station 25 V (the northernmost station of this cross-section) from April through June, 1956 (Fig. 5). We see here that there is an abrupt increase of temperature around 8 June. Before that day the temperature oscillates around −46° C and afterwards around −42° C. This indicates that it is proper to set the date of abrupt change of the circulation over the Pacific to take place during the 5-day period 6—10 June. This is supported by a study of the change of circulation pattern which is given below.

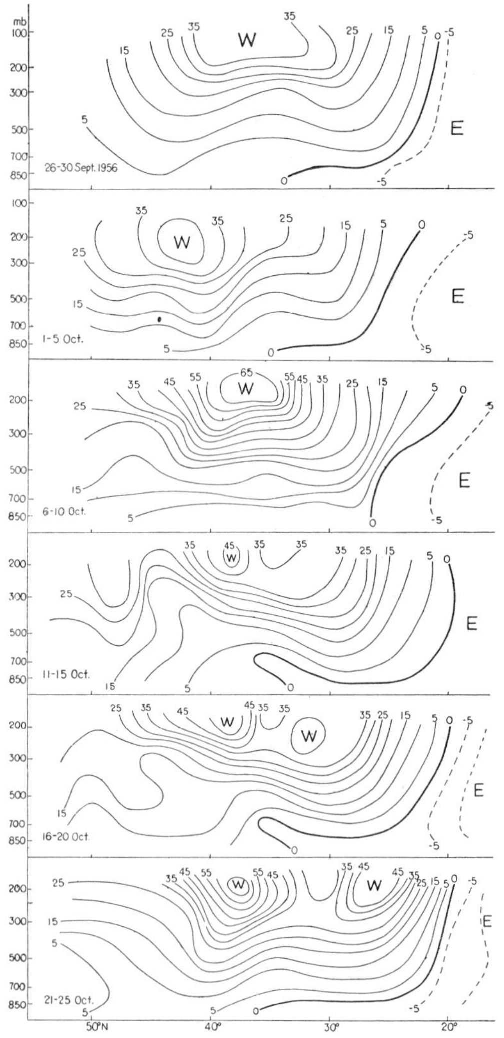

Fig. 9. 5-day mean cross-sections of the observed zonal wind (maps) along 125° E during October, 1956.

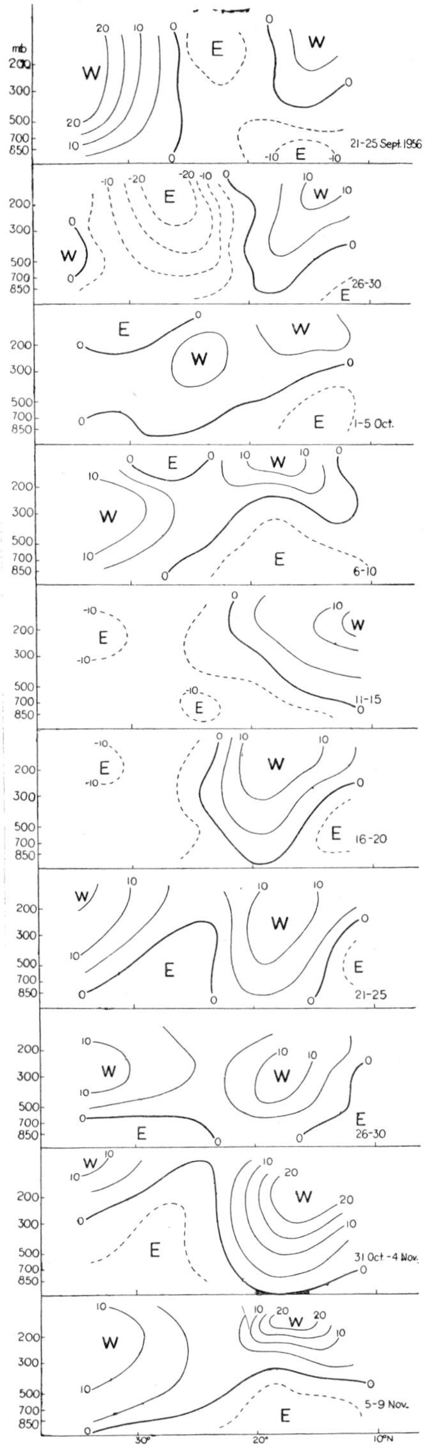

Fig. 10. 5-day mean cross-sections of the observed zonal wind (maps) along 165° E during October, 1956.

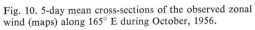

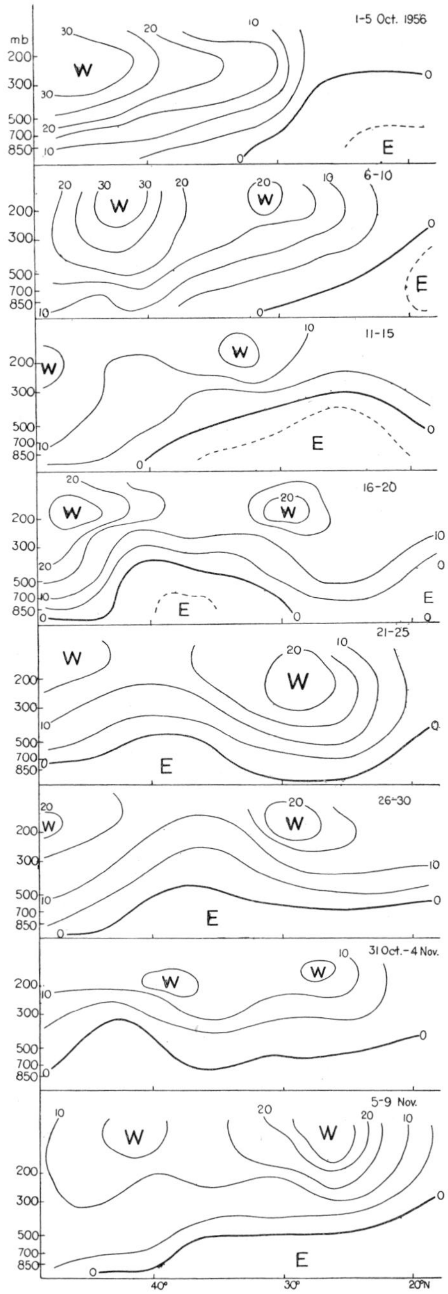

Fig. 11. 5-day mean cross-sections of the observed zonal wind (maps) along 80° W during October, 1956.

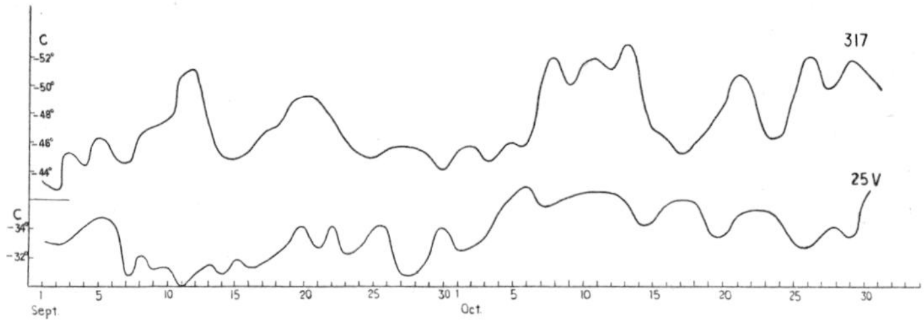

Fig. 12. Temperature variations a 250 mb over stationary ship 25 V in Pacific and at 300 mb over 317 in North America from September to October, 1956.

Fig. 6 shows conditions over North America. This figure clearly indicates that there is a strong westerly jet stream near 30° N before the middle of June, 1956 which is the normal winter position. After the middle of June this jet disappears rapidly and the easterlies develop.

From this series of cross-sections along different longitudes we may safely say that there is a sudden change of the upper air westerlies just before summer begins. If we may characterize the summer circulation by its normal structure of zonal circulation, we may state that the onset of the summer circulation is fairly abrupt. This change first occurs in the interior of Asia and successively later and later further downstream. The time difference between the change over Asia and that over North America is 2—3 weeks. It should be pointed out that no cross-section could be made over the Atlantic due to scarcity of upper air stations. The situation over this region is therefore not clear. However, a cross-section along the European coast has been made, but no such abrupt change could be found.

2. *The onset of winter circulation*

In the middle of October another sudden change of the upper air circulation takes place with a reverse sequence of events. This development is characterized by a southward advance of the westerlies and a retreat of the easterlies. Before this time the westerly jet is in its normal summer position, while after this time it has shifted to its normal winter position. Over Asia the change in middle October is of equal abruptness as that at the end of May or in the beginning of June. But over North America the change in October is usually less pronounced than the one in June.

Figs. 7—9 show the three Asiatic cross-sections respectively along 45° E, 90° E, and 125° E for October 1956. At longitude 45° E (Fig. 7) we see a westerly jet near 33° N all the time. The location of this jet is based on only one station, namely Baghdad. The upper wind over this station is all the time very strong (not only in October, but in

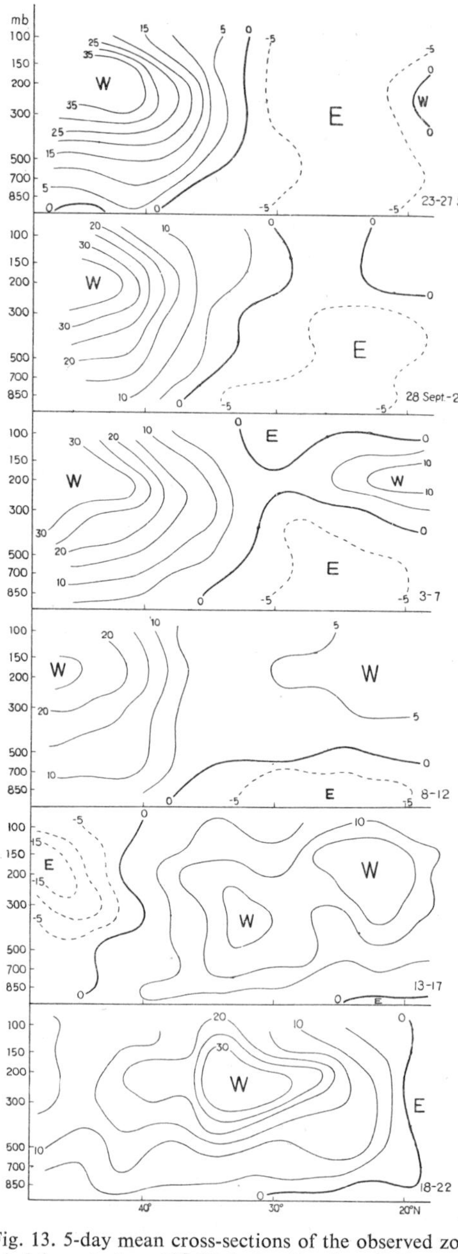

Fig. 13. 5-day mean cross-sections of the observed zonal wind (maps) along 80° W during October, 1955.

September as well) as compared with the surrounding stations. Its accuracy is doubtful. Disregarding this doubtful jet we see that the southern limit of the westerlies suddenly advances southward in the middle of October. The same is found at longitude 90° E (Fig. 8). Simultaneously the retreat of the SW monsoon occurs, the synoptic sequence of which is given in the later part of this paper. At longitude 125° E (Fig. 9) the double structure of the westerly jet is suddenly established in the middle of October. This is the normal feature of the winter circulation in this area.

Fig. 10 is the cross-section along 165° E for the corresponding period. We see again the low latitude westerlies as in June. In addition to these westerlies we find that before 16—20 October the upper westerlies only temporarily reach the station 131 (Marcus Island near 24° N) and that the easterlies prevail even to the north of 25° N. After 16—20 October, however, the easterlies do not appear in the high troposphere to the north of 25° N. This date may be assumed to be the time of transition from summer to winter circulation over the Pacific.

From the cross-section for North America (Fig. 11) it seems that we should set 21—25 October to be the date of transition from summer to winter type of the structure of the westerlies, because from this time on the main jet stream appears at lower latitudes (near 30° N) instead of at higher latitudes (near 40° N).

The above determined date for transition from summer to winter zonal circulation over the Pacific and North America corresponds quite well to that over Asia. If we, however, examine the temperature variations in the upper troposphere over the ship station 25 V over the Pacific and over the station 317 in North America, we find a different date, as shown by Fig. 12. It indicates a rapid decrease of temperature around 6 October for both regions. This date is more than one week earlier than that determined from the wind field. We shall return to this observation later.

We have already pointed out that we have chosen 1956 for discussion because in this year we have data for all regions and not because the changes are particularly well developed. Since the change over North America is not quite clear in 1956, we shall present conditions for another year as an illustration. Fig. 13 shows the change of zonal circulation along 80° W in October, 1955. It is seen that before 3—7 October the easterlies prevail at all latitudes south of 30° N, while after that time a westerly jet stream quickly appears and the easterlies never come back in latitudes north of 20° N.

From this series of cross-sections we conclude that the transition from the summer to the winter type of upper zonal circulation is also very abrupt. For the years under investigation the time of the transition over Asia is fairly accurately determined around the middle of October. Over North America it is subject to larger variations. In 1949 it seems to have taken place as early as in the later part of September. The time of occurrence over Asia is not only more persistent, the change is also sharper than that over North America.

II. The change of flow pattern in the middle troposphere

According to Rossby's (1939) theory the wavelength of the perturbations in the westerlies is more or less a reflection of the strength of the basic current. The westerlies are stronger in winter than in summer. Therefore the summer and winter flow pattern should be different. Actually the average number of long waves in summer is four and in winter three (in middle and high latitudes). It is interesting to investigate when and how the transition from summer to winter and back occurs. In the foregoing discussions we have seen that the westerlies in middle latitudes change abruptly in intensity in June and October. We should therefore also expect a change in the flow pattern during these periods. To show this we have prepared Fig. 14 for the June case and Fig. 15 for the October case. In these figures we have plotted the 5-day mean 500 mb height averaged between 50° N and 70° N for the June case and between 40° N and 60° N for the October case as a function of longitude. Fig. 14 shows the variations of the upper flow pattern from May through June. There are several outstanding features in this figure. Firstly, before 21—25 May there are three main ridges: one over middle Europe, the second over the Western Pacific and the third over the western part of North America. This is the time before the abrupt change of the upper zonal circulation took place. There are four main ridges after 10 June at which time the onset of the summer circulation in the upper troposphere has nearly been completed over the Northern Hemisphere. This is the average summer wave number. In the time between 26 May and 10 June the ridge and trough pattern is more or less chaotic. The

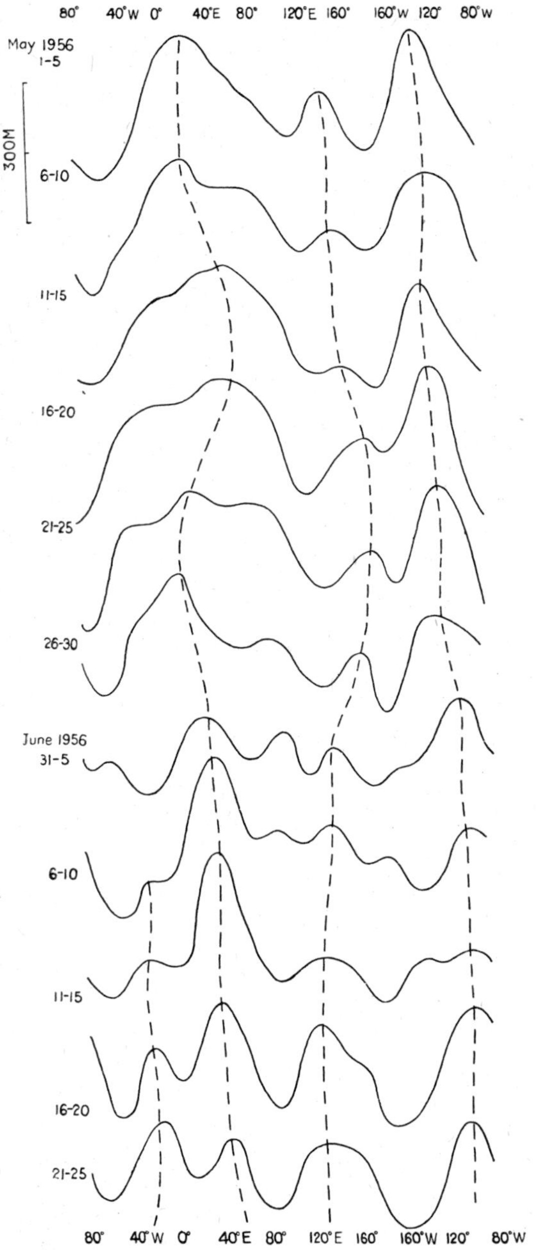

Fig. 14. The variation of average 5-day mean height of 500 mb between 50° N and 70° N against longitude from May to June, 1956. Vertical dashed lines give the position of the major ridges.

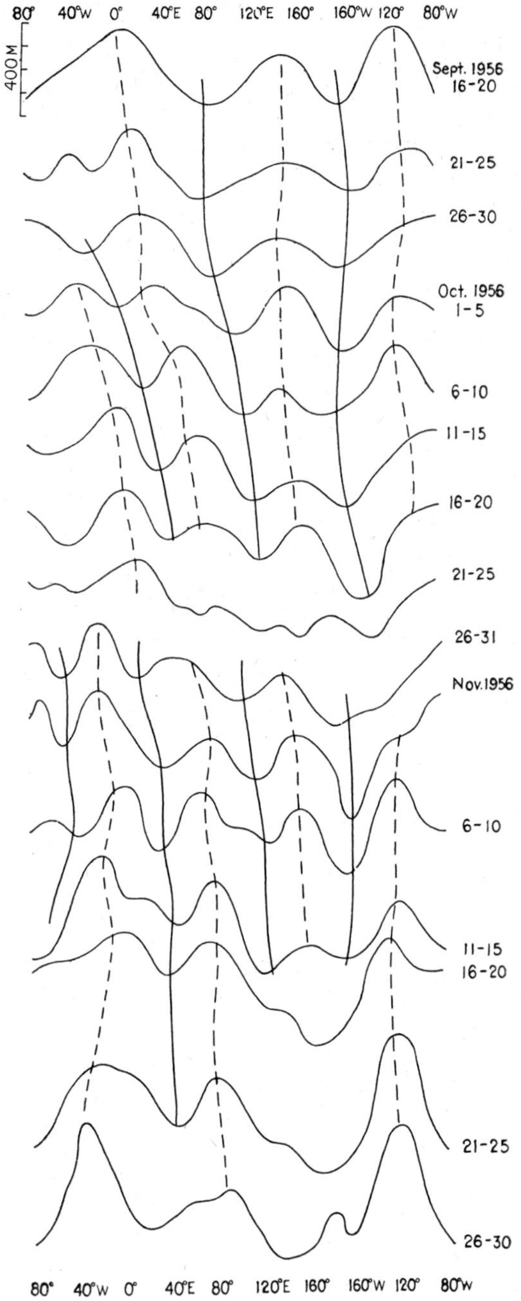

Fig. 15. The variation of average 5-day mean height of 500 mb between 40° N and 60° N against longitude from September to October, 1956. Vertical dashed lines give the position of the major ridges.

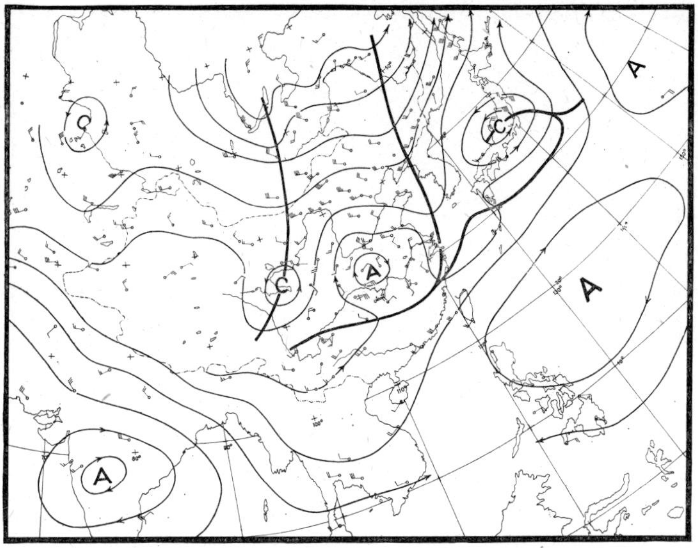

Fig. 16 a. 3 km stream line chart for 18 May, 1956. Thick lines indicate intertropical convergence zone and troughs.

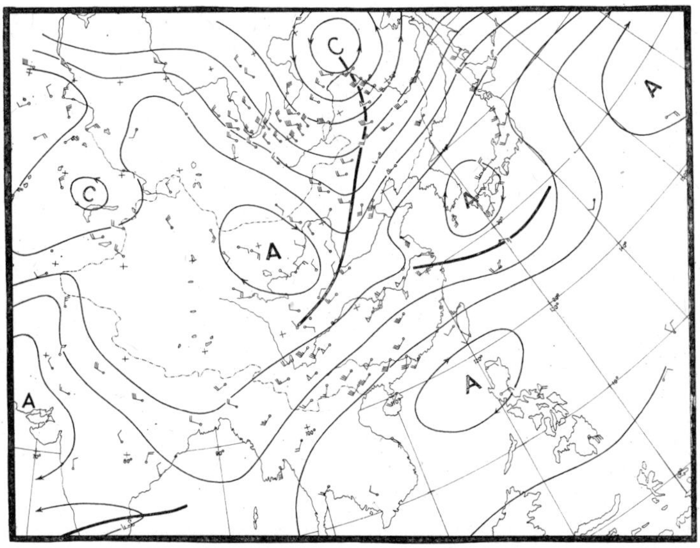

Fig. 16 b. 3 km stream line chart for 20 May, 1956.

second feature in Fig. 14 worth mentioning is the appearance of a trough in the vicinity of the Tibetean Plateau after 10 June. This is a typical summer feature. In winter a ridge is located in this area. Thirdly we observe a big change in the position of other ridges and troughs during the change of the structure of the westerlies.

Fig. 15 illustrates the variation of the upper-air flow pattern from the middle of September through November, 1956. It is seen that before the middle of October and after 26 October the wave pattern is clearcut. In the time between, on the other hand, the wave pattern is quite chaotic. Indeed, in the period 21—25 October it is difficult to trace the long waves in our figure. It is at this time that the structure of the upper westerlies in middle latitudes shows the large changes. Besides this, several other features may also be mentioned. Firstly, as was already pointed out in the foregoing paragraph, a trough is found in the range of longitudes of the Tibetean Plateau before 6 October which is a summer feature.

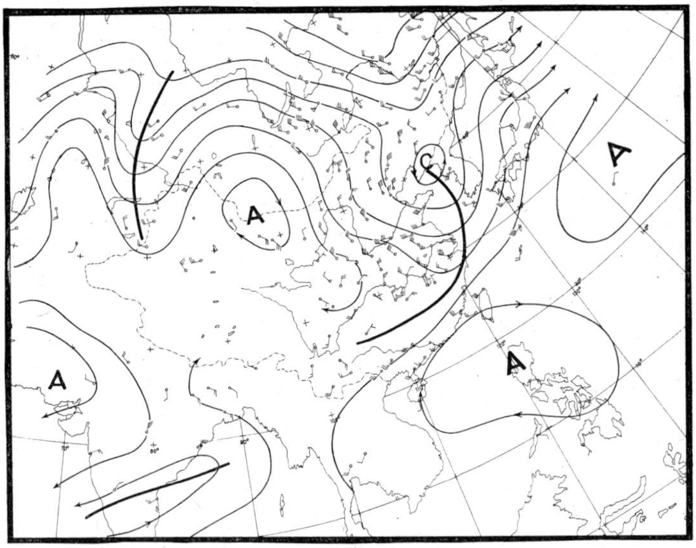

Fig. 16 c. 3 km stream line chart for 24 May, 1956.

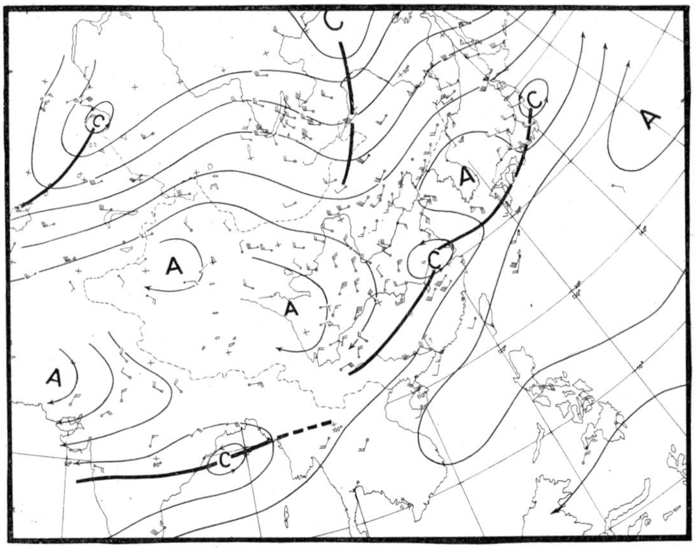

Fig. 16 d. 3 km stream line chart for 28 May, 1956.

After that time the trough gradually moves out from this region, and after the most chaotic period a ridge builds up which is a normal winter feature. Secondly, the European Coast ridge and its accompanied White Sea trough are being established after the chaotic period. By 21—25 October they are clear in shape and more or less fixed in their preferred positions. The Asiatic Coast trough starts to move into its winter position from 11—15 October and becomes more or less fixed there after 26—30 October. All these facts indicate that there is a marked change in the flow pattern after the middle of October. This change accompanies the abrupt shift of the upper zonal circulation.

III. The synoptic development over South Asia during the transition periods

1. *The onset of the SW monsoon and Mai-yü*

To investigate the synoptic development over South Asia associated with the abrupt change of

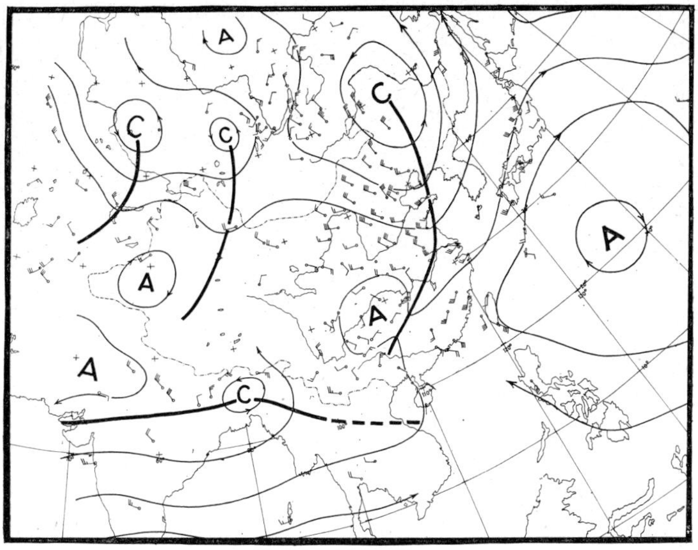

Fig. 16 e. 3 km stream line chart for 4 June, 1956.

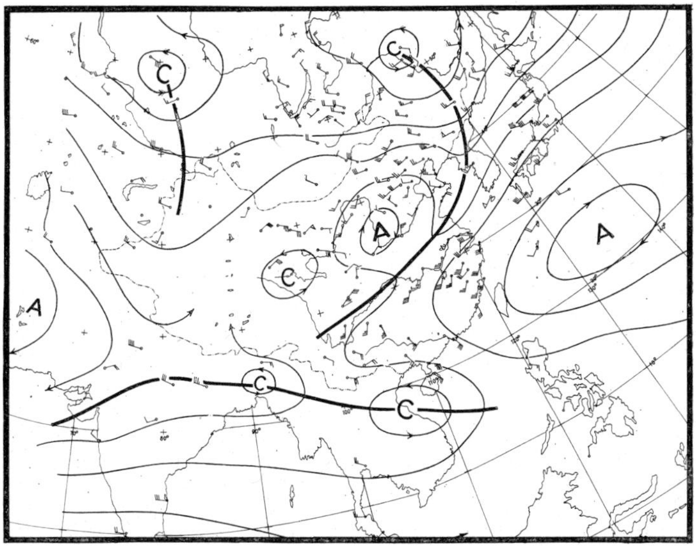

Fig. 16 f. 3 km stream line chart for 6 June, 1956.

the upper air circulation in June we have analyzed the 3-km level stream line charts in May and June, 1956. Figs. 16 a—g illustrate the sequence of events during this development from 18 May to 8 June. On and before 18 May an anticyclone is found over Indo-Pakistan. To the north of this anticyclone to the Himalayas the westerlies prevail. This may be considered to represent the typical flow pattern over this region before the outburst of the SW monsoon. In China, between 25° N and 30° N, a shear line is running in the west-east direction. This is the result of troughs aloft moving out from central Asia into China and Japan, becoming more and more tilted. This is a low level phenomenon. At the surface this shear line corresponds to the polar front. At 500 mb it becomes very indistinct. Rainfall in China during this period is mainly concentrated in a narrow belt along this shear line between 25° N and 30° N.

Beginning this day the anticyclone over Indo-Pakistan starts to shift northward and the SW monsoon and its associated intertropical convergence zone (hereafter abbreviated as ICZ) advances into India. From 20 May (Fig. 16 b) the SW monsoon begins to appear at the Malabar Coast to the south of 12° N. By 28 May (Fig. 16d) it has reached 20° N at the west coast and is firmly established here.

From 24 May (Fig. 16 c) the SW monsoon starts to advance northward also in the Bay of Bengal. This branch, however, does not move rapidly northward until a strong cyclonic development takes place over the Bay of Bengal on 28 May (Fig. 16 d). This cyclone moves to East Pakistan and North-East India. Following it the SW monsoon also invades this region. Therefore by the end of May the SW monsoon is also firmly established over East Pakistan and North-East India.

It is worth mentioning that by the time of the quick northward advance of the SW monsoon over the Bay of Bengal the ICZ also has its quickest northward motion. This is right at the time of the retreat (or disappearance) of the jet along the southern periphery of the Himalayas (see Figs. 2—3). After 4 June (Fig. 16 e) ICZ steadily oscillates near 25° N over India.

During this period the stream line pattern over China also changes considerably. The east-west shear line, originally oscillating between 25° N and 30° N (Fig. 16 a), reaches latitudes between 30° N and 35° N at the beginning of June (Fig. 16 d—e) after several discontinuous movements. This is the time when Mai-yü starts in China and Japan.

If we compare the first two charts (Figs. 16a—b) with the last two (Figs. 16f—g) in this series we find a considerable difference. Besides the change in position of ICZ over India and of the shear line in China, the upper westerlies over northern Indo-Pakistan never reappear after the end of May and the subtropical ridge over southern China and the western Pacific also shows a considerable northward movement in this period.

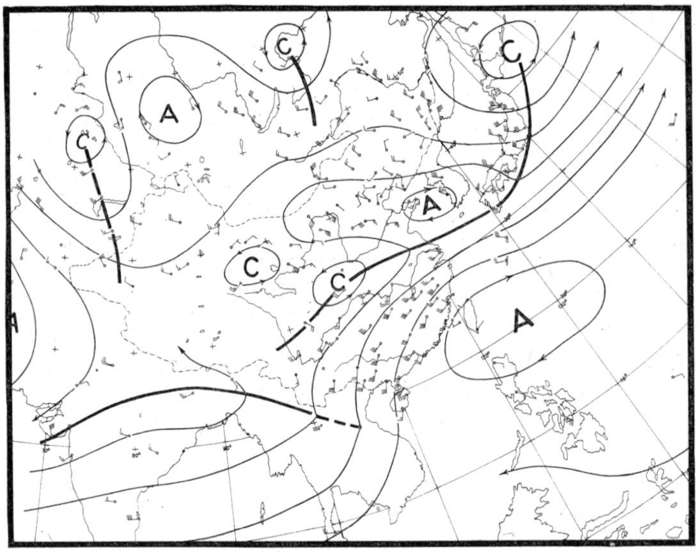

Fig. 16 g. 3 km stream line chart for 8 June, 1956.

The date of the outburst of the SW monsoon given in this paper agrees very well with that obtained by the Indian Meteorological Department[1] from rainfall records and the date of the onset of Mai-yü given here also agrees with that obtained by the Japanese Meteorological Agency[2] using other methods. Analyses for other years show a similar development.

[1] Published in *Indian Journal of Meteorology and Geophysics.*

[2] Published in *Geophysical Review*, June 1956, No. 682.

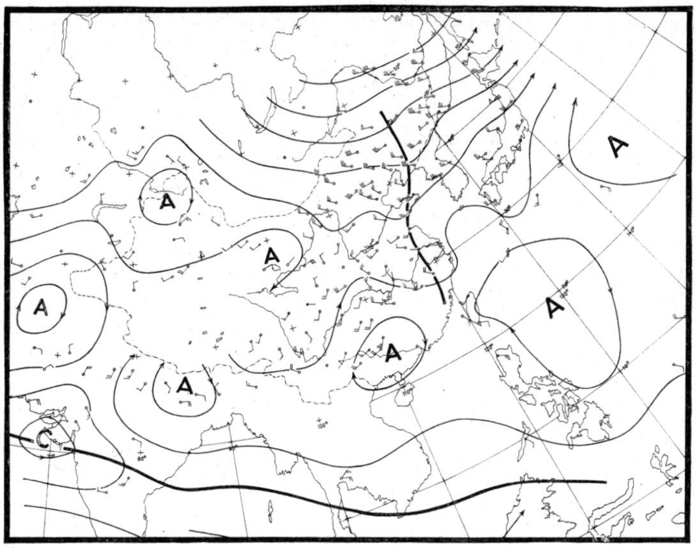

Fig. 17 a. 3 km stream line chart for 12 October, 1956. Thick lines indicate the intertropical convergence zone and troughs.

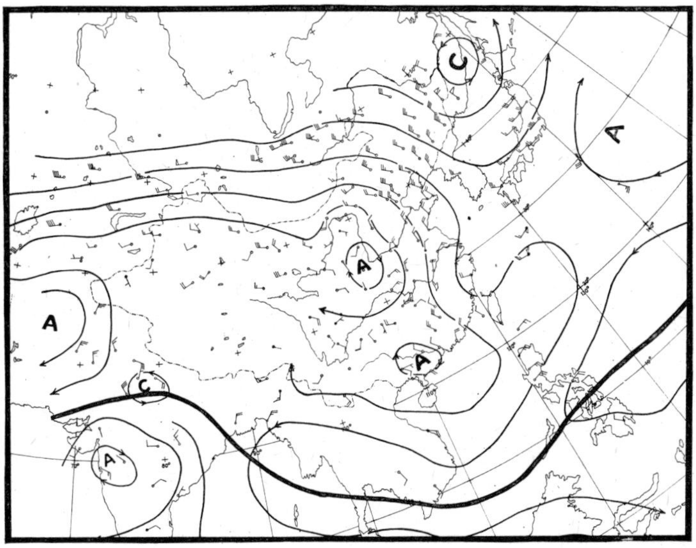

Fig. 17 b. 3 km stream line chart for 14 October, 1956.

2. *The retreat of the SW monsoon and ICZ*

As in May and June there is also a definite sequence of synoptic changes in the lower troposphere over Indo-Pakistan during the onset of the winter type of upper circulation in the middle of October. No marked change in the low level flow pattern associated with this change is, however, observed in China. The weather at low levels over China already changes markedly in September (YEH and CHU, 1955). During the middle of September the circulation near the surface fairly suddenly changes from a cyclonic type to an anticyclonic type. Then anticyclones frequently invade China from the north and the rainfall decreases considerably from this time on. This is the time of clear autumn weather in China. The polar front runs further to the north. THOMPSON (1951) pointed out that on the average the polar front arrives in Hongkong around the middle of October, as was also the case in 1956. The surface front passed Hongkong on 12 October of this year (Fig. 17 a).

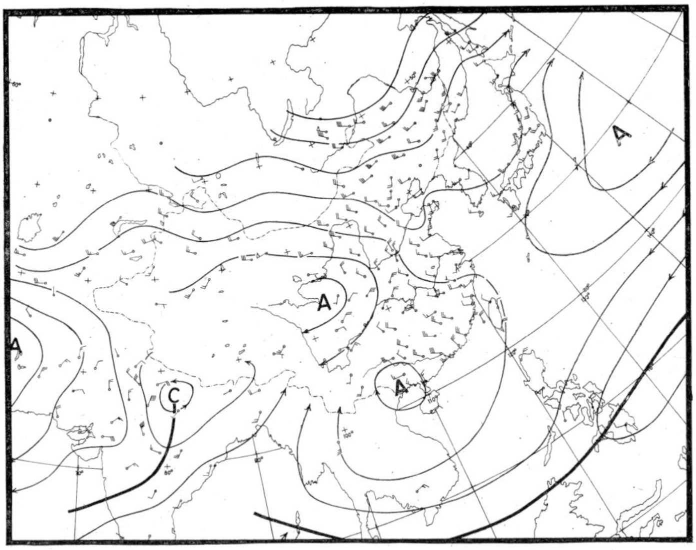

Fig. 17 c. 3 km stream line chart for 16 October, 1956.

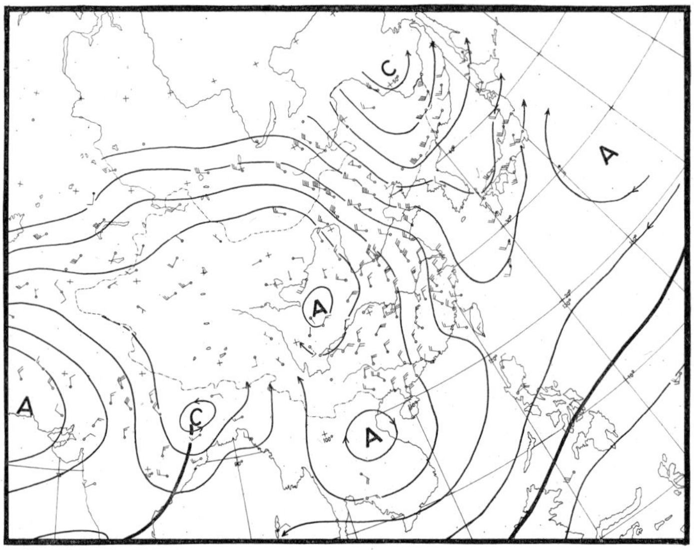

Fig. 17 d. 3 km stream line chart for 18 October, 1956.

On this day (12 October, Fig. 17 a) the circulation pattern over Indo-Pakistan is still of a typical monsoonal type. The ICZ runs from central India through the Bay of Bengal to the South China Sea. On 10 October (figure not shown) a cyclone had formed over the Arabian Sea off the coast of Bombay. This cyclone invades the continent on 12 October and by 14 October (Fig. 17 b) it has already reached the mountainous region of NW India. It is now in the stage of decay. Due to the influence of this cyclone the intensity of the SW monsoon along the west coast and in NW India greatly intensifies on 14 October (Fig. 17 b). After this day there is an upper westerly disturbance which moves from western Asia to India along the southern periphery of the Himalayas. Following this westerly disturbance the dry continental air from the north-west invades India and the ICZ rapidly retreats southward. By 16 October (Fig. 17 c) the summer monsoon has already shifted along the west coast to the south of 20° N. With eastward movement of the westerly disturbance the summer monsoon over the NE part of the subcontinent also retreats. By 18 October (Fig. 17 d) the SW monsoon still prevails only in a small section. From 20 October (Fig. 17 e) no trace of the summer monsoon can be detected over India. The north-westerlies of a winter type now dominate.

It should be pointed out that the appearance of the westerly disturbance is related to the sudden displacement of the westerlies to the south of the Himalayas in the middle of October (Fig. 8). In summer this type of westerly disturbances is very unusual. It can only reach India under an upper westerly steering current. PISHAROTY and DESAI (1956) once pointed out that the retreat of the summer monsoon is related to a westerly disturbance. The case of 1956 agrees with this.

From this series of maps we also notice the rapid retreat of ICZ not only over India but also over the South China Sea. Comparing the first and the last maps of this series (17 a and e) we find a remarkable change in the position of ICZ.

From the above analysis it is seen that the onset and retreat of the Indian summer monsoon and ICZ is an integral part of the seasonal change of the general circulation over the Northern Hemisphere.

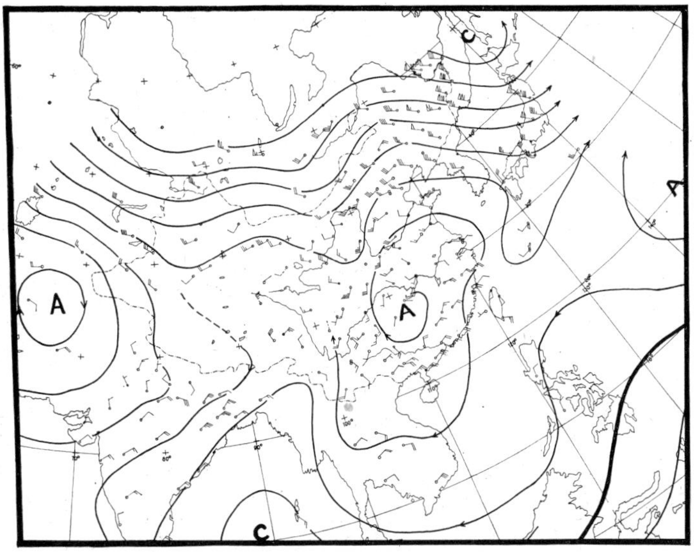

Fig. 17 e. 3 km stream line chart for 20 October, 1956.

IV. Concluding remarks

The foregoing discussions are not only based on the changes in 1956, but during several years. Therefore we may conclude that the phenomena described in this paper are fairly well established, though in some years they may not be too clear. If we accept this, it follows that as far as the upper circulation is concerned there are only two natural seasons during the year, summer and winter. The transitional periods between them are negligibly short. The winter is considerably longer, but since our analysis does not cover the whole year, we can not exclude the possibility that there are other rapid changes of the upper air circulation. The seasonal variations of the general circulation would then occur in a series of jumps.

Associated with the jump from one type of upper air circulation to another a definite synoptic sequence of weather processes in the lower troposphere occurs at least over Asia. With the onset of the summer upper air circulation the outburst of the SW monsoon occurs over India, ICZ moves in over south Asia and Mai-yü begins over China and Japan. SUDA and ASAKURA (1955) also studied the relation between the SW monsoon over India and Mai-yü over Japan. With the onset of winter upper air circulation

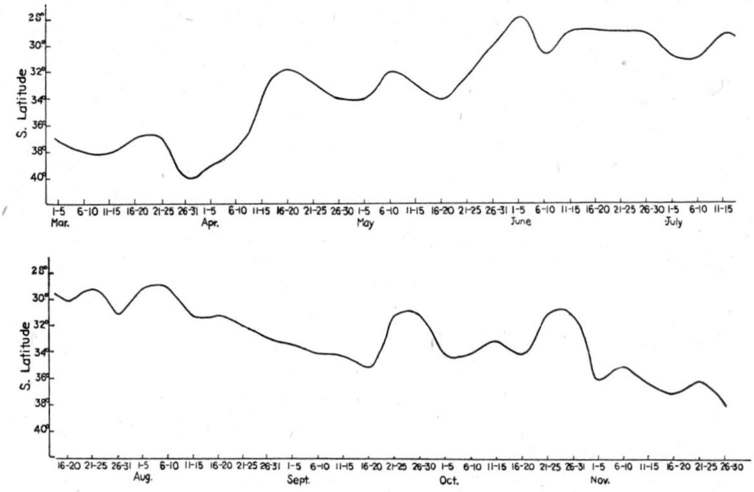

Fig. 18. The variation of the 3-year (1932—1934) average latitudinal position of the subtropical ridge over South Pacific in the range 120° E—150° W.

the SW monsoon over India and ICZ retreat from their northerly positions over Asia. It is the authors' guess that the occurrence of "Indian summer" in North America and the "old-women summer" in Europe may also be related to the change of the upper air circulation in October. It is worthwhile to study further the synoptic processes in the lower troposphere in other regions than south Asia during these transition periods and search for the link between the upper and lower circulation.

Concerning the cause of these abrupt changes we shall only propose the following reasons as a conjecture: From winter to summer the inclination of the sun over the Northern Hemisphere gradually increases. With this increase the temperature contrast between the equator and pole gradually decreases. When it has decreased to a certain value, a certain type of "instability" in the atmosphere appears and the abrupt change of the upper air circulation takes place. From summer to winter the "reversed" sequence of events would occur. Since the temperature and velocity fields are not independent of each other, a sudden change of the temperature field would also follow such a change of the circulation.

If the above conjecture has any reality at all, we should find similar abrupt transitions over the Southern Hemisphere. Unfortunately we do not have upper air data over this part of the world. Therefore we cannot undertake a similar analysis for the Southern Hemisphere. According to Radok and Grant (1957), however, the seasonal advance or retreat of the upper westerlies over the South Pacific is also fairly abrupt. If we content ourselves with the surface situation we can study the seasonal shift of the subtropical ridge which is the separation between surface easterlies and westerlies. We have three years (1932—34) surface charts from the Southern Pacific at our disposal. We have averaged the latitudes of the subtropical ridge in the range of longitudes 125° E—150° W, computed 5-day mean values and finally a three-year average. Fig. 18 shows the average position thus obtained from March through November. From this curve we see two sudden jumps southward in the position of the average subtropical ridge. The first jump occurs in the middle of April and the second in the later part of May. At both instances the subtropical ridge shifts poleward by 4—6 degrees of latitude. This is a fairly large shift. It is also interesting to note that the time of the second jump roughly corresponds to the sudden transition in June over the Northern Hemisphere. No correspondence to the October case in the Northern Hemisphere is found in Fig. 18. We should note that Fig. 18 shows surface conditions, and we should therefore not infer that nothing like the changes occurring in the Northern Hemisphere in October takes place in the Southern Hemisphere. We shall leave this question until we have ample upper air winds over the Southern Hemisphere.

To answer conclusively the above conjecture we wish to propose the following model experiment: In a rotating half sphere or two coaxial cylinders, as used by FULTZ (1949, 1951), LONG (1952) and others (HIDE, 1953), we heat differently the inner and outer part, then gradually decrease or increase the heating difference and observe whether we get the abrupt transitions of the circulation as observed in the atmosphere.

REFERENCES

DAO, SHIH-YEN, and CHEN, LUNG-SHUN, 1957: The structure of the general circulation over the continent of Asia in summer. *Acta Meteorologica Sinica*, **28**, 234—246 (in Chinese).

DAO, SHIH-YEN, 1958: An investigation of Mai-yü in China. To be published in *Acta Meteorologica Sinica* (in Chinese).

FULTZ, D., 1949: Preliminary report on experiments with thermally produced lateral mixing in a rotating hemispherical shell of liquid. *J. Meteor.* **6**, 17—33.

— 1951: Experimental analogies to atmospheric motion. *Compendium of Meteorology*, Amer. Meteor. Soc., 1235—1248.

HIDE, R., 1953: Some experiments on thermal convection in a rotating fluid. Quart. *J. Roy. Meteor. Soc.*, **79**, 161.

HSIEH, YI-PING and CHEN, YÜ-CHAU, 1951: On the wind and temperature fields over Western Pacific and Eastern Asia in winter. *J. Chinese Geophy. Soc.*, **2**, 279—298.

LONG, E. R., 1952: The flow of a liquid past a barrier in a rotating spherical shell. *J. Meteor.*, **9**, 187—199.

PISHAROTY, P. R., and DESAI, B. N., 1956: Western disturbance and Indian weather. *Ind. J. Meteor. and Geophy.*, **7**, 333—338.

RADOK, U., and GRANT, A. M., 1957: Variations in the high tropospheric mean flow over Australia and New Zealand. *J. Meteor.*, **14**, 141—149.

ROSSBY, C. G., and Collaborators, 1939: Relation between variations in the intensity of zonal circulation of the atmosphere and the displacements of semi-permanent centers of action. *J. Marine Res.*, **2**, 38—55.

STAFF MEMBERS OF INSTITUTE OF GEOPHYSICS AND METEOROLOGY, ACADEMIA SINICA, 1957: On the general circulation over Eastern Asia. *Tellus*, **9**, 432—446; **10**, 58—75; 299—312.

SUDA, K., and ASAKURA, A., 1955: A study in the unusual "Baiu" season in 1954 by means of northern hemispherical upper-air mean charts. *J. Meteor. Soc. Japan*, **33**, 233—244.

SUTCLIFFE, R. C., and BANNON, J. K., 1954: Seasonal changes in upper-air conditions in the Mediterranean —Middle East Asia. *Sci. Proc. International Association of Meteorology*, Rome, 1954, 322—334.

THOMPSON, B. W., 1951: An essay on the general circulation of the atmosphere over South-east Asia and the West Pacific. *Quart. J. Roy. Meteor. Soc.*, **77**, 569—597.

YEH, TU-CHENG, 1950: The circulation of high troposphere over China in the winter of 1945—46. *Tellus*, **2**, 173—183.

YEH, TU-CHENG, KAO, YU-HSIE, and LIU, KWANG-NAN, 1951: A study of the onset and retreat of the jet stream over Southern Asia and SW United States of America in 1945—46. *J. Chinese Geophy. Soc.*, **2**, 255—278.

YEH, TU-CHENG, and CHU, PAO-CHEN, 1955: The onset of transitional seasons of the Far East from the view-point of general circulation. *Acta Meteorologica Sinica*, **26**, 71—88 (in Chinese).

YEH, TU-CHENG, and KOO, CHEN-CHAO, 1955: On the influence of Tibetan Plateau on the circulation over Eastern Asia and the weather in China. *Scientia*, 29—33 (in Chinese).

YIN, M. T., 1949: A synoptic-aerological study of the onset of the summer monsoon over India and Burma. *J. Meteor.*, **6**, 393—400.

(Manuscript received January 10, 1958)

A Method of Solving the Nonlinear Differential Equations of Atmospheric Tides with Applications to an Atmosphere of Constant Temperature

By C. L. Pekeris and Z. Alterman

Department of Applied Mathematics, The Weizmann Institute, Rehovot, Israel.

Abstract

The purpose of this investigation is to develop a method of including the quadratic terms of the differential equations in the theory of atmospheric tides. The method is illustrated by applying it to the problem of determining the effect of the quadratic terms on the free period of oscillation of an atmosphere of constant temperature. In order not to encumber the exposition of the method by the complexity of the calculations, a simplification is introduced by treating a mode of semi-diurnal oscillation which is independent of longitude. The effect of the quadratic terms on the free period turns out to be small. This was to be expected, since in an atmosphere of constant temperature the energy-density of oscillation decreases exponentially with height, the wave-energy in a column above the level where the quadratic terms become equal to the retained linear terms being only of the order of 10^{-4} of the wave energy in the whole atmospheric column. The bearing of this result on the effect of the quadratic terms on the oscillation of an atmosphere in which the temperature increases with height in the region where the quadratic terms are dominant is discussed.

1. Introduction

The recent soundings of the atmosphere made with the aid of V-2 rockets (Best, Havens, La Gow, 1947) have verified a prediction made by the senior author in 1936 (Pekeris, 1936, 1937) that the temperature of the atmosphere between the levels of about 60 km to about 80 km must decrease with height, in order to account for the observed features of the semidiurnal tide in the atmosphere. These soundings have, however, also shown that between the 80 km and the 120 km levels the temperature rises again, as against a constant temperature which was assumed in the tidal theory. In attempting subsequently to ascertain whether a rising temperature in the region of the E-layer can be reconciled with the resonance theory of atmospheric tides a difficulty has been encountered in the fact that in the E-layer region the quadratic terms of the tidal equations are no longer negligibly small, but become equal to and eventually exceed the retained linear terms. If the temperature distribution in the E-layer were to have an effect on the period of free oscillation of the atmosphere then a treatment of the atmospheric tides in those regions must also incorporate the quadratic terms of the tidal equations.

This investigation was undertaken for the purpose of first developing a method of including the quadratic terms in the tidal theory. The complexity introduced by the quadratic terms is so great that it was thought prudent to apply the method first to a relatively simple model atmosphere in order to single out the principal effects and to systematize the treatment. The temperature of the atmosphere was, accordingly, assumed to be constant. Another simplification was introduced by treating a mode in which the oscillation is independent of longitude. In the actual atmospheric tides the principal term is dependent on longitude, being in fact a function of *local* time. We have chosen the simpler mode in order to reduce complications which are not germane to our main object, which is to exhibit in a concrete case the application of the method for the treatment of the effect of the quadratic terms.

2. The Tidal Differential Equations in the "Long Wave" Approximation

We adopt a system of spherical coordinates, with ϑ, φ and z denoting respectively colatitude, East longitude and height above ground. The corresponding velocity components are u, v, w. Let further p, ϱ and Ω denote pressure, density and the tidal potential. Let further

$$s = (1/\varrho), \qquad t = \tau/\sigma \tag{1}$$

where t denotes the time and σ is a constant of the dimensions of frequency, which is identical with the frequency of the tidal potential in case of forced oscillations. In case of free oscillations σ denotes the frequency of free oscillations. The equations of motion are

$$\sigma\frac{\partial u}{\partial\tau}+\frac{u}{a}\frac{\partial u}{\partial\vartheta}+\frac{v}{a\sin\vartheta}\frac{\partial u}{\partial\varphi}+w\frac{\partial u}{\partial z}-2\omega v\cos\vartheta-\frac{v^2}{a}\cot\vartheta=-\frac{s}{a}\frac{\partial p}{\partial\vartheta}-\frac{1}{a}\frac{\partial\Omega}{\partial\vartheta}, \tag{2}$$

$$\sigma\frac{\partial v}{\partial\tau}+\frac{u}{a}\frac{\partial v}{\partial\vartheta}+\frac{v}{a\sin\vartheta}\frac{\partial v}{\partial\varphi}+w\frac{\partial v}{\partial z}+2\omega u\cos\vartheta+2\frac{vu}{a}\cot\vartheta=-\frac{s}{a\sin\vartheta}\frac{\partial p}{\partial\varphi}-\frac{1}{a\sin\vartheta}\frac{\partial\Omega}{\partial\varphi}, \tag{3}$$

$$s\frac{\partial p}{\partial z}+g=0. \tag{4}$$

Here a denotes the radius of the earth, ω the angular rotation of the earth, and equation (4) results from the 'long wave' approximation and the neglect of the term $\varrho(\partial\Omega/\partial z)$. The terms in ω in equations (2) and (3) arise from the 'coriolis' force. With the divergence χ given by

$$\chi=\frac{\partial w}{\partial z}+\frac{1}{a\sin\vartheta}\frac{\partial}{\partial\vartheta}(u\sin\vartheta)+\frac{1}{a\sin\vartheta}\frac{\partial v}{\partial\varphi}, \tag{5}$$

the equation of continuity becomes

$$\sigma\frac{\partial s}{\partial\tau}+\frac{u}{a}\frac{\partial s}{\partial\vartheta}+\frac{v}{a\sin\vartheta}\frac{\partial s}{\partial\varphi}+w\frac{\partial s}{\partial z}=s\chi. \tag{6}$$

The condition of adiabatic change of pressure of a particle undergoing oscillations yields the relation

$$\sigma\frac{\partial p}{\partial\tau}+\frac{u}{a}\frac{\partial p}{\partial\vartheta}+\frac{v}{a\sin\vartheta}\frac{\partial p}{\partial\varphi}+w\frac{\partial p}{\partial z}=-\gamma p\chi, \tag{7}$$

where γ denotes the ratio of the specific heats for air, and is taken to have a value of 1.40 in the following. The above equations of motion are exact, except for the 'long wave' approximation incorporated in equation (4), and a second order term including w in (2) and (3).

In the standard linearized tidal theory one neglects all terms in the above equations which are not linear in the variables u, v, w and in the time-dependent parts s_1 and p_1 of the variables s and p. This simplification is justified as long as $p_1(z, t)$ is small in comparison with the undisturbed pressure $p_0(z)$, or when the velocities u, v and w are small in comparison with the local velocity of sound. The above condition is met in the observed tidal oscillations at levels below about 100 km. Above 130 km, however, the neglected quadratic terms are larger, and grow increasingly larger with height, than the linear terms retained in the linearized theory.

3. Method of Solution

The method of solution consists in expanding the dynamic variables in series proceeding according to powers of the amplitude of oscillation, the first terms in each series being proportional to the first power of the amplitude. This first approximation is the solution of the linearized equations in case of the problems of free oscillations. In the case of forced oscillations, the first approximation is not the solution of the linearized equations for *forced* oscillations, but is identical with the solution of the linearized equations for *free* oscillations. The effect of the forcing term (tidal potential) enters in this scheme only in the second approximation in which the quadratic terms of the first approximation are included. The terms in the series which are proportional to the third power of the amplitude include the effect of the coupling between terms of the first approximation and the second approximation.

Accordingly we set

$$u=\alpha u_1+\alpha^2u_2+\alpha^3u_3+\ldots, \tag{8}$$

$$v=\alpha v_1+\alpha^2v_2+\alpha^3v_3\ldots, \tag{9}$$

$$w=\alpha w_1+\alpha^2w_2+\alpha^3w_3\ldots, \tag{10}$$

$$\chi=\alpha\chi_1+\alpha^2\chi_2+\alpha^3\chi_3+\ldots, \tag{11}$$

Here, α is a dimensionless parameter which is proportional to the amplitude. The terms after the first in (8), (9), (10) and (11) arise from the quadratic terms in the differential equations. In the above and subsequent three equations we write out all the terms in the expansions which actually have to be worked out in order to determine the effect of the quadratic terms of the differential equations. We also put

$$p = p_0(z)+\alpha p_1+\alpha^2 p_2+\alpha^3 p_3+\ \ldots, \qquad (12)$$

$$s = s_0(z)+\alpha s_1+\alpha^2 s_2+\alpha^3 s_3+\ \ldots., \qquad (13)$$

where the first terms represent the undisturbed values. An essential step in the method is to put

$$\sigma = \sigma_0+\alpha\sigma_1+\alpha^2\sigma_2+\ \ldots. \qquad (14)$$

In the case of forced oscillations, σ is the *given* value of the frequency of the tidal potential. σ_0 will turn out to be the frequency of *free oscillation* of the atmosphere (in the linear approximation), whose thermal structure is given. The amplitude of the tidal potential enters first linearly in σ_1, and it also appears quadratically in σ_2. The last two terms can also be computed by solving the tidal equations. *Equation* (14) *then represents the amplification curve, or the 'resonance' curve, giving the variation of amplitude of oscillation with the frequency of the exciting tidal potential.*

In the case of free oscillations σ in (14) is not given, but denotes the frequency of the free oscillation which is to be determined by solving the non-linear tidal equations. σ_0 is then the approximation to σ resulting from the linearized theory; σ_1 and σ_2 then give the changes in the free period which arise from the quadratic terms in the differential equations.

In conformity with the scheme described above we write for the tidal potential Ω

$$\Omega = \alpha^2 A(\vartheta)\cos(\tau+n\varphi)\,, \qquad (15)$$

where n is an integer.[1]

4. Terms in α

If we substitute the expansions (8) to (14) into the tidal equations (2) to (7) we obtain from the terms proportional to α

$$\sigma_0\frac{\partial u_1}{\partial\tau} - 2\omega v_1\cos\vartheta + \frac{s_0}{a}\frac{\partial p_1}{\partial\vartheta} = 0\,, \qquad (16)$$

$$\sigma_0\frac{\partial v_1}{\partial\tau} + 2\omega u_1\cos\vartheta + \frac{s_0}{a\sin\vartheta}\frac{\partial p_1}{\partial\varphi} = 0\,, \qquad (17)$$

$$s_1 - \frac{s_0^2}{g}\frac{\partial p_1}{\partial z} = 0\,, \qquad (18)$$

$$\chi_1 = \frac{\partial w_1}{\partial z} + \frac{1}{a\sin\vartheta}\frac{\partial}{\partial\vartheta}(u_1\sin\vartheta) + \frac{1}{a\sin\vartheta}\frac{\partial v_1}{\partial\varphi}, \qquad (19)$$

$$\sigma_0\frac{\partial s_1}{\partial\tau} + w_1\frac{\partial s_0}{\partial z} - s_0\chi_1 = 0\,, \qquad (20)$$

$$\sigma_0\frac{\partial p_1}{\partial\tau} + w_1\frac{\partial p_0}{\partial z} + \gamma p_0\chi_1 = 0\,. \qquad (21)$$

These are the linearized equations of free oscillation whose solution is (PEKERIS, 1937)

$$\chi_1 = \sigma_0 F(z)\psi_1(\vartheta)\sin\Phi,\ \Phi = \tau + n\varphi\,, \qquad (22)$$

$$s_1 = s_0\left\{\left[\gamma - 1 - \frac{\gamma^2 g h_1}{c^2} + \frac{\dot{c}^2}{g} - \frac{\dot{c}^2}{c^2}\gamma h_1\right]F + \left(\gamma h_1 + \frac{\dot{c}^2 h_1}{g}\right)\dot{F}\right\}\psi_1(\vartheta)\cos\Phi\,, \qquad (23)$$

$$p_1 = (h_1/s_0)\,(\gamma g F - c^2\dot{F})\psi_1(\vartheta)\cos\Phi\,, \qquad (24)$$

$$g w_1 = \sigma_0\left[(c^2 - \gamma g h_1)F + h_1 c^2\dot{F}\right]\psi_1(\vartheta)\sin\Phi\,, \qquad (25)$$

$$u_1 = \frac{\sigma_0 h_1(-\gamma g F + c^2\dot{F})\sin\Phi}{4a\omega^2(f^2 - \cos^2\vartheta)}\left(\frac{\partial\psi_1}{\partial\vartheta} + \frac{n}{f}\cot\vartheta\,\psi_1\right), \qquad (26)$$

$$v_1 = \frac{\sigma_0 h_1(-\gamma g F + c^2\dot{F})\cos\Phi}{4a\omega^2(f^2 - \cos^2\vartheta)}\left(\frac{\cos\vartheta}{f}\frac{\partial\psi_1}{\partial\vartheta} + \frac{n\psi_1}{\sin\vartheta}\right), \qquad (27)$$

with

$$f = (\sigma_0/2\omega). \qquad (28)$$

Here c denotes the velocity of sound at any level, and is a function of the temperature T only

$$c^2(z) = \gamma R T(z)\,. \qquad (29)$$

h_1 is the first proper value and $\psi_1(\vartheta)$ is that corresponding solution of the differential equation

$$\frac{1}{\sin\vartheta}\frac{\partial}{\partial\vartheta}\left[\frac{\sin\vartheta}{f^2-\cos^2\vartheta}\left(\frac{\partial\psi}{\partial\vartheta} + \frac{n}{f}\cot\vartheta\,\psi\right)\right] - \frac{1}{(f^2-\cos^2\vartheta)}\left[\frac{n}{f}\cot\vartheta\frac{\partial\psi}{\partial\vartheta} + \frac{n^2\psi}{\sin^2\vartheta}\right] + \frac{4a^2\omega^2}{gh}\psi = 0 \qquad (30)$$

which, by (26), yields a vanishing value of u_1 at the poles. $F(z)$ is the solution of the equation

$$c^2\frac{d^2F}{dz^2} + \left(\frac{dc^2}{dz} - \gamma g\right)\frac{dF}{dz} + \frac{F}{h_1}\left[\frac{dc^2}{dz} + g(\gamma-1)\right] = 0\,, \qquad (31)$$

[1] In the previous paper on this subject by the senior author (PEKERIS, 1937) we wrote s in place of n, but in this paper s has already been used to signify $(1/\varrho)$.

which makes w_1, as given by (25), vanish at the ground, and which satisfies an appropriate boundary condition at $z = \infty$.

The procedure of solving the coupled boundary-value systems (30) and (31) is first to determine the value of h_1 from equation (31). With h_1 thus determined, and n given, one *determines the proper value of f from equation (30)*. This is the reverse procedure from the usual one, when f is given by the frequency of tidal potential, and h_1 is determined from (30). Finally, one determines σ_0 from (28).

In expressing the solution in (22) to (27) in terms of the first mode $\psi_1(\vartheta)$ of (30) only, rather than by a series in the ψ's, we have anticipated the fact that $A(\vartheta)$ in (15) is essentially represented by $\psi_1(\vartheta)$ only. This is a good approximation, since $P_2^2(\vartheta)$, to which $A(\vartheta)$ is proportional, is given by (PEKERIS, 1937)

$$P^2{}_2(\vartheta) = 0.940\psi_1(\vartheta) + .046\psi_2(\vartheta) + \ldots . \quad (32)$$

5. Terms in α^2

By annulling the coefficients of α^2 when the expansions (8) to (14) are substituted into the tidal differential equations (2) to (7), we obtain the differential equations for the second-order terms:

$$\sigma_0 \frac{\partial u_2}{\partial \tau} - 2\omega v_2 \cos\vartheta + \frac{s_0}{a}\frac{\partial p_2}{\partial \vartheta} = B_2\,, \quad (33)$$

$$\sigma_0 \frac{\partial v_2}{\partial \tau} + 2\omega u_2 \cos\vartheta + \frac{s_0}{a \sin\vartheta}\frac{\partial p_2}{\partial \varphi} = C_2\,, \quad (34)$$

$$s_2 - \frac{s_0^2}{g}\frac{\partial p_2}{\partial z} = s_0 Z_2\,, \quad (35)$$

$$\chi_2 = \frac{\partial w_2}{\partial z} + \frac{1}{a\sin\vartheta}\frac{\partial}{\partial\vartheta}(u_2 \sin\vartheta) + \frac{1}{a\sin\vartheta}\frac{\partial v_2}{\partial\varphi}\,, \quad (36)$$

$$\sigma_0 \frac{\partial s_2}{\partial \tau} + w_2 \frac{\partial s_0}{\partial z} - s_0 \chi_2 = s_0 D_2\,, \quad (37)$$

$$\sigma_0 \frac{\partial p_2}{\partial \tau} - \frac{g w_2}{s_0} + \gamma p_0 \chi_2 = p_0 E_2\,. \quad (38)$$

Here the operators on the left hand sides coincide with operators on the left hand sides of equations (16) to (21). The right hand sides arise from the quadratic terms and from the tidal potential.

$$B_2 = -\sigma_1 \frac{\partial u_1}{\partial \tau} - \frac{1}{a}\dot{A}\cos\Phi - \frac{u_1}{a}\frac{\partial u_1}{\partial\vartheta} - \frac{v_1}{a\sin\vartheta}\frac{\partial u_1}{\partial\varphi} - w_1 \frac{\partial u_1}{\partial z} - \frac{s_1}{a}\frac{\partial p_1}{\partial\vartheta} + \frac{v_1^2}{a}\cot\vartheta\,, \quad (39)$$

$$C_2 = -\sigma_1 \frac{\partial v_1}{\partial \tau} + \frac{An}{a\sin\vartheta}\sin\Phi - \frac{u_1}{a}\frac{\partial v_1}{\partial\vartheta} - \frac{v_1}{a\sin\vartheta}\frac{\partial v_1}{\partial\varphi} - w_1\frac{\partial v_1}{\partial z} - \frac{s_1}{a\sin\vartheta}\frac{\partial p_1}{\partial\varphi} - \frac{2v_1 u_1}{a}\cot\vartheta\,, \quad (40)$$

$$Z_2 = \frac{s_1}{g}\frac{\partial p_1}{\partial z}\,, \quad (41)$$

$$s_0 D_2 = -\sigma_1 \frac{\partial s_1}{\partial\tau} - \frac{u_1}{a}\frac{\partial s_1}{\partial\vartheta} - \frac{v_1}{a\sin\vartheta}\frac{\partial s_1}{\partial\varphi} - w_1\frac{\partial s_1}{\partial z} + s_1\chi_1\,, \quad (42)$$

$$p_0 E_2 = -\sigma_1 \frac{\partial p_1}{\partial\tau} - \frac{u_1}{a}\frac{\partial p_1}{\partial\vartheta} - \frac{v_1}{a\sin\vartheta}\frac{\partial p_1}{\partial\varphi} - w_1\frac{\partial p_1}{\partial z} - \gamma p_1\chi_1\,. \quad (43)$$

In the solution of the non-homogeneous equations (33) to (38) we follow the same procedure as the one used in solving the homogeneous system (16) to (21). This consists in eliminating the variables u_2, v_2, w_2, p_2 and s_2 until one arrives at a differential equation for χ_2, similar to (31). From equations (33) and (34) we solve for u_2 and v_2

$$\sigma_0^2 \frac{\partial^2 u_2}{\partial\tau^2} + 4\omega^2\cos^2\vartheta\, u_2 = -\frac{2\omega\cos\vartheta\, s_0}{a\sin\vartheta}\frac{\partial p_2}{\partial\varphi} - \frac{\sigma_0 s_0}{a}\frac{\partial^2 p_2}{\partial\vartheta\partial\tau} + \sigma_0\frac{\partial B_2}{\partial\tau} + 2\omega\cos\vartheta\, C_2\,, \quad (44)$$

$$\sigma_0^2 \frac{\partial^2 v_2}{\partial\tau^2} + 4\omega^2\cos^2\vartheta\, v_2 = \frac{2\omega\cos\vartheta\, s_0}{a}\frac{\partial p_2}{\partial\vartheta} - \frac{\sigma_0 s_0}{a\sin\vartheta}\frac{\partial^2 p_2}{\partial\varphi\partial\tau} - 2\omega\cos\vartheta\, B_2 + \sigma_0\frac{\partial C_2}{\partial\tau}\,. \quad (45)$$

The right hand sides of equations (33) to (38) contain trigonometric terms in the fundamental Φ as well as in the first harmonic $2\,\Phi$ and terms independent of Φ. We shall evidently have to obtain the solution of each separately. In the sequel it will be understood that the equations refer to each harmonic separately. We shall designate the particular harmonic involved by writing

$$\frac{\partial^2 u_2}{\partial \tau^2} = -\varepsilon^2 u_2 \,, \quad \frac{\partial^2 v_2}{\partial \tau^2} = -\varepsilon^2 v_2 \,, \qquad (46)$$

where ε takes on the value 1 for the fundamental, 2 for the first harmonic and 0 for the terms which are independent of Φ.

Eliminating s_2 between equations (35) and (37) we get

$$\frac{\sigma_0 s_0}{g}\frac{\partial^2 p_2}{\partial \tau \partial z} = -\frac{w_2}{s_0}\frac{\partial s_0}{\partial z} + \chi_2 + D_2 - \sigma_0 \frac{\partial Z_2}{\partial \tau} \,. \qquad (47)$$

By combining (47) with (38) we now obtain

$$\frac{\partial w_2}{\partial z} = \frac{c^2}{g}\frac{\partial \chi_2}{\partial z} - (\gamma - 1)\chi_2 + r_2 \,, \qquad (48)$$

where

$$r_2 = D_2 - \sigma_0 \frac{\partial Z_2}{\partial \tau} + E_2 - \frac{c^2}{\gamma g}\frac{\partial E_2}{\partial z} \,. \qquad (49)$$

We shall now develop w_2, χ_2 and p_2 into series of the proper functions Ψ_i of the differential equation

$$\frac{1}{\sin\vartheta}\frac{\partial}{\partial\vartheta}\left[\frac{\sin\vartheta}{(f^2\varepsilon^2 - \cos^2\vartheta)}\left(\frac{\partial \Psi_i}{\partial\vartheta} + \frac{n}{f}\cot\vartheta\,\Psi_i\right)\right] - \frac{1}{(f^2\varepsilon^2 - \cos^2\vartheta)}\left(\frac{n}{f}\cot\vartheta\frac{\partial\Psi_i}{\partial\vartheta} + \frac{n^2\varepsilon^2}{\sin^2\vartheta}\Psi_i\right) + \frac{4\omega^2 a^2}{g h_i}\Psi_i = 0 \,, \qquad (50)$$

where the h_i are determined by the condition that u_2, as given by

$$u_2 = \frac{1}{4\omega^2(f^2\varepsilon^2 - \cos^2\vartheta)}\left(\frac{\cot\vartheta}{af}\sigma_0 s_0 \frac{\partial p_2}{\partial\varphi} + \frac{\sigma_0 s_0}{a}\frac{\partial^2 p_2}{\partial\vartheta\partial\tau} - \sigma_0\frac{\partial B_2}{\partial\tau} - 2\omega\cos\vartheta\, C_2\right), \qquad (51)$$

shall vanish at the poles. When $\varepsilon = 1$, equation (50) reduces to (30), and the first two proper values h_i and functions Ψ_i are known (PEKERIS, 1937). In our application we also need to determine the h_i and Ψ_i for the case $\varepsilon = 2$. We thus put

$$p_2 = \sum_{i=1}^{\infty} p_{2i}\Psi_i(\vartheta), \quad w_2 = \sum w_{2i}\Psi_i, \quad \chi_2 = \sum \chi_{2i}\Psi_i \,, \qquad (52)$$

where, of course,

$$p_{2i} = \int_0^\pi p_2 \Psi_i \sin\vartheta\, d\vartheta \Big/ \int_0^\pi \Psi_i^2 \sin\vartheta\, d\vartheta \,. \qquad (53)$$

Writing now

$$T_2 = \left\{ -\frac{1}{4a\omega^2\sin\vartheta}\frac{\partial}{\partial\vartheta}\left[\frac{\sin\vartheta}{(f^2\varepsilon^2 - \cos^2\vartheta)}\left(2\omega\cos\vartheta\, C_2 + \sigma_0\frac{\partial B_2}{\partial\tau}\right)\right] + \frac{n\left(2\omega\cos\vartheta\frac{\partial B_2}{\partial\tau} + \sigma_0\varepsilon^2 C_2\right)}{4a\omega^2\sin\vartheta(f^2\varepsilon^2 - \cos^2\vartheta)}\right\} \qquad (54)$$

we get from (36), (45), (51), (50) and (38)

$$\chi_{2i} - \frac{\partial w_{2i}}{\partial z} = -\frac{\sigma_0 s_0}{g h_i}\frac{\partial p_{2i}}{\partial\tau} + T_{2i} = T_{2i} + \frac{1}{h_i}\left(-w_{2i} + \frac{c^2}{g}\chi_{2i} - \frac{c^2}{\gamma g}E_{2i}\right). \qquad (55)$$

When combined with (48) this yields

$$w_{2i} = L_i\chi_{2i} + h_i r_{2i} + h_i T_{2i} - \frac{c^2}{\gamma g}E_{2i} \,, \qquad (56)$$

where

$$L_i \equiv \left[h_i\frac{c^2}{g}\frac{\partial}{\partial z} + \left(\frac{c^2}{g} - \gamma h_i\right)\right]. \qquad (57)$$

On eliminating now w_{2i} between (55) and (56) we obtain

$$M_i\chi_{2i} = -\frac{\partial}{\partial z}(r_{2i} + T_{2i}) + \left(\frac{1}{\gamma g h_i}\right)\left[\gamma g r_{2i} + \frac{dc^2}{dz}E_{2i} + c^2\frac{\partial E_{2i}}{\partial z}\right], \qquad (58)$$

where

$$M_i \equiv \left\{\frac{c^2}{g}\frac{\partial^2}{\partial z^2} + \left(\frac{1}{g}\frac{dc^2}{dz} - \gamma\right)\frac{\partial}{\partial z} + \frac{1}{g h_i}\left[\frac{dc^2}{dz} + g(\gamma - 1)\right]\right\}. \qquad (59)$$

Equation (58) is to be solved under the conditions that

a) it meets the same boundary condition at $z = \infty$ as was imposed on the solution of (31), and that

b) it makes w_{2i} as given by (56), vanish at the ground.

Having obtained a particular solution of (58) we can add to it a term $K\chi_{2i}^{(0)}$, where

$$M_i \chi_{2i}^{(0)} = 0 \,. \tag{60}$$

The coefficient K is determined from the boundary condition at the ground

$$w_{2i}(0) = 0 \,. \tag{61}$$

Without the added term $K\chi_{2i}^{(0)}$ the condition (61) could not be satisfied. An exception occurs in case $\varepsilon = 1$, $i = 1$, for then $\chi_{2i}^{(0)}$ is identical with the solution $f(z)$ of (31), for which $L_i\chi_{2i}^{(0)}$ vanishes at the ground. Equation (61) then imposes the condition

$$h_1 r_{21}(0) + h_1 T_{21}(0) - \frac{c^2(0)}{\gamma g} E_{21}(0) = 0 \,. \tag{62}$$

The relation takes the form

$$\sigma_1 + GA = 0 \tag{63}$$

where G is a constant and A is the amplitude of the tidal potential defined in (15). Up to α-terms, our resonance curve is therefore given by

$$\sigma = \sigma_0 - \alpha GA \tag{64}$$

In case of free oscillations σ_1 is zero. The terms with $\varepsilon = 0$ can be obtained by taking the limit $h_i \to \infty$ in (56) to (59) because this yields a solution of constant Ψ in (50).

σ_2 is obtained from the solution of the α^3 terms. The procedure in solving the latter system is the same as the one used for the α^2 terms. Equations (33) to (38) retain their form except for the change of subscript 2 to 3. The right hand sides of equations (39) to (43) are of course different. Equations (44) to (59) retain their form, except for the change of subscript. Again, for the case $\varepsilon = 1$, $i = 1$, σ_2 is determined from a relation corresponding to (62). Details of the procedure will be illustrated in the following sections.

6. Applications to an Atmosphere of Constant Temperature

Since the method described above of dealing with the quadratic terms of the tidal equations is very laborious, we shall illustrate the details of its application by determining the effect of the quadratic terms on the free period of oscillation of a relatively simple model atmosphere. In addition to the assumption of a constant temperature, we shall introduce another simplification by treating a semidiurnal mode in which the oscillation does not depend on longitude. Thus

$$n = 0,\ c^2 = \gamma g H = \text{constant} \,. \tag{65}$$

The appropriate solution of equation (31) is

$$F(z) = e^{\lambda z},\ \lambda = (\gamma - 1)/\gamma H = (2/7H) \,. \tag{66}$$

In order for w_1 to vanish at the ground, we must have by (25)

$$h_1 = \gamma H = \gamma RT/g \,. \tag{67}$$

We shall assume that the temperature of the atmosphere is such that on the linear theory the period of the first mode is precisely equal to 12 solar hours. The required value of H will turn out to be 6.335 km. With

$$\sigma_0 = 2\omega,\ f = 1 \,, \tag{68}$$

the appropriate solutions of (30) are

$$\psi_i(\vartheta) = \cos(i\pi y),\quad y = \cos\vartheta \,, \tag{69}$$

$$h_i = \frac{4a^2\omega^2}{g\pi^2 i^2},\ i = 1,\ 2, \ldots \tag{70}$$

For $i = 1$, this gives the value of H quoted above.

The solution of the linearized tidal equations (16) to (21) is then

$$\chi_1 = \sigma_0 e^{\lambda z}\cos(\pi y)\sin\tau \,, \tag{71}$$

$$s_1 = -s_0 e^{z\lambda}\cos(\pi y)\cos\tau \,, \tag{72}$$

$$p_1 = \gamma p_0 e^{\lambda z}\cos(\pi y)\cos\tau \,, \tag{73}$$

$$u_1 = \frac{a\sigma_0}{\pi\sin\vartheta} e^{\lambda z}\sin(\pi y)\sin\tau \,, \tag{74}$$

$$v_1 = -\frac{a\sigma_0}{\pi}\cot\vartheta\, e^{\lambda z}\sin(\pi y)\cos\tau \,, \tag{75}$$

$$w_1 = 0 \tag{76}$$

An estimate of the order of magnitude of α can now be made by assuming that αp_1 is about 1 mm at $z = 0$. Since αp_1 is equal to $\alpha\gamma p_0$, by (73), it follows that α is of the order of 10^{-3}.

Substituting into equations (39) to (43) we get

$$B_2 = \frac{a\sigma_0^2}{\pi^2} e^{2\lambda z} \left\{ \left[\frac{y\sin^2(\pi y)}{\sin^3\vartheta} + \frac{\pi\sin(\pi y)\cos(\pi y)}{\sin\vartheta} \right] \sin^2\tau + \left[\frac{y^3\sin^2\pi y}{\sin^3\vartheta} + \pi\sin\vartheta\sin(\pi y)\cos(\pi y) \right] \cos^2\tau \right\}, \tag{77}$$

$$C_2 = \frac{a\sigma_0^2}{2\pi^2} e^{2\lambda z} \left[\frac{\sin^2(\pi y)}{\sin^3 \vartheta} - \frac{2\cos^2\vartheta \sin^2(\pi y)}{\sin^3 \vartheta} + \right.$$
$$\left. + \frac{\pi \cos\vartheta}{\sin\vartheta} \sin(\pi y)\cos(\pi y) \right] \sin(2\tau), \quad (78)$$

$$D_2 = -\frac{\sigma_0}{2} e^{2\lambda z} \sin(2\tau), \quad (79)$$

$$E_2 = \frac{\gamma\sigma_0}{4} e^{2\lambda z} [(1-\gamma) - (1+\gamma)\cos(2\pi y)] \sin(2\tau), \quad (80)$$

$$Z_2 = e^{2\lambda z} \cos^2(\pi y) \cos^2 \tau \quad (81)$$

Here we have anticipated the result that in case of *free oscillations σ_1 must be zero.*

On putting $n = 0$, $\varepsilon = 2$ in (50), it takes on the form

$$\frac{d}{dy}\left[\frac{(1-y^2)}{(4-y^2)}\frac{d\Psi_i}{dy}\right] + \beta_i \Psi_i = 0, \quad \beta_i = \frac{4\omega^2 a^2}{g h_i}. \quad (82)$$

We have solved for the first three proper functions of (82), using Hough's method (HOUGH, 1897). These are, in non-normalized form,

$$\Psi_1(y) = P_2(y) - .067994 P_4(y) + .001340 P_6(y) - - .0000125 P_8(y) \quad (83)$$

$$\beta_1 = 1.676959, \quad h_1 = 8.2396H, \quad (84)$$

$$\Psi_2(y) = .037820 P_2(y) + P_4(y) - .109850 P_6(y) + + .004438 P_8(y) - .000096 P_{10}(y), \quad (85)$$

$$\beta_2 = 5.692772, \quad h_2 = 2.427191H, \quad (86)$$

$$\Psi_3(y) = .002376 P_2(y) + .076242 P_4(y) + P_6(y) - - .148527 P_8(y) + .008937 P_{10}(y) - .000304 P_{12}(y), \quad (87)$$

$$\beta_3 = 11.995856, \quad h_3 = 1.151852H. \quad (88)$$

After considerable transformations, equation (58) can be put in the form

$$h_i \gamma H \ddot{\chi}_{2i} - \gamma h_i \dot{\chi}_{2i} + (\gamma-1)\chi_{2i} =$$
$$= -(1/2)\lambda h_i \sigma_0 (\gamma-1) e^{2\lambda z} \int_{-1}^{1} [(\gamma-2) + + \gamma\cos(2\pi y)] \Psi_i(y) dy$$
$$(-1/4)\sigma_0 (2+\gamma)(\gamma-1) e^{2\lambda z} \int_{-1}^{1} \cos(2\pi y) \Psi_i(y) dy -$$
$$- (1/2)\sigma_0(\gamma-1) e^{2\lambda z} \int_{-1}^{1} \frac{y^2 \sin^2(\pi y)}{\sin^2\vartheta} \Psi_i(y) dy. \quad (89)$$

Here, the Ψ_i must be normalized. It is seen that only the transforms of cos $(2\pi y)$ and of $[y^2 \sin^2 (\pi y)/\sin^2 \vartheta]$ are required. Similarly, equation (56) takes the form

$$w_{2i} = \gamma H h_i \dot{\chi}_{2i} - \gamma h_i \chi_{2i} + \gamma H \chi_{2i} -$$
$$- (1/4)\sigma_0 \gamma H e^{2\lambda z} \int_{-1}^{1} [(1-\gamma) - (1+\gamma)\cos(2\pi y)] \cdot$$
$$\cdot \Psi_i(y) dy + (1/4)\sigma_0 h_i (\gamma-1) e^{2\lambda z} \int_{-1}^{1} [-2 + \gamma +$$
$$+ \gamma\cos(2\pi y)] \Psi_i(y) dy +$$
$$+ .35\sigma_0 H e^{2\lambda z} \int_{-1}^{1} \frac{y^2\sin^2(\pi y)}{\sin^2\vartheta} \Psi_i(y) dy. \quad (90)$$

In deriving equations (89) and (90) use was made of the relation, resulting from (82)

$$\int_{-1}^{1} \frac{dQ}{dy}\left[\left(\frac{1-y^2}{4-y^2}\right)\frac{d\Psi_i}{dy}\right] dy = \beta_i \int_{-1}^{1} Q(y)\Psi_i(y) dy, \quad (91)$$

where $Q(y)$ is any function such that $(1-y^2)Q(y)$ vanishes at $y = \pm 1$. After having determined the transforms of cos $(2\pi y)$ and of $[y^2 \sin^2 (\pi y)/ /\sin^2 \vartheta]$, one has on the right-hand side of (89) simply a term $Ae^{2\lambda z}$, with the constant A known. The solution of (89) is then

$$\chi_{2i} = [Ae^{2\lambda z}/(h_i \gamma H 4\lambda^2 - \gamma h_i 2\lambda + \gamma - 1)] + Ke^{\lambda_i z}, \quad (92)$$

$$\lambda_i = (1/2H)(1 - \sqrt{1 - 4H(\gamma-1)/\gamma h_i}). \quad (93)$$

The constant K is now determined by making $w_{2i}(0)$ in (90) vanish. The solution thus obtained is

$$\chi_2 = -(1/4)\sigma_0(\gamma-1)e^{2\lambda z} + \{.15891 e^{2\lambda z} -$$
$$- .011795 \exp(.035970 z/H)\} \sigma_0 \Psi_1(y) +$$
$$+ \{1.98079 e^{2\lambda z} - .767309 \exp(.136289 z/H)\} \sigma_0 \cdot$$
$$\cdot \Psi_2(y) + \{113.46857 e^{2\lambda z}$$
$$+ 155.39744 \exp(.455816 z/H)\} \sigma_0 \Psi_3(y). \quad (94)$$

It is seen that the third mode is by far the dominating one. It appears that the forcing term on the right-hand side of (89) is close to resonance with the complementary solution. This is manifested by a nearly vanishing value of the denominator in (92). It was ascertained that the higher modes are again out of resonance. *Hence we can reprecent χ_2 by third mode only.*

As a result of this experience we can save a lot of numerical work in solving (58) for the more complicated case, where $n = 2$, by first trying out whether any of the modes show resonance with the solution of (60). In case near resonance exists, it is likely that the solution for χ_2 can be approximated by the resonating mode only.

With χ_2 and w_2 determined, p_2 can be solved for from equation (38). Then s_2 follows from (35), u_2 from (51) and v_2 from (45). We thus obtain for the solution of the second order terms

$$u_2 = -\frac{a\sigma_0}{\gamma\pi^2(4-\gamma^2)} f_1(z) \frac{\partial\Psi_3}{\partial\vartheta} \sin(2\tau), \quad (95)$$

$$v_2 = -\frac{a\sigma_0 \cos\vartheta}{2\gamma\pi^2(4-\gamma^2)} f_1(z) \frac{\partial\Psi_3}{\partial\vartheta} \cos(2\tau), \quad (96)$$

$$w_2 = H\sigma_0 f_2(z) \Psi_3(y) \sin(2\tau), \quad (97)$$

$$p_2 = (1/2) p_0 f_1(z) \psi_3(y) \cos(2\tau), \quad (98)$$

$$s_2 = -s_0 f_3(z) \Psi_3(y) \cos(2\tau), \quad (99)$$

$$\chi_2 = \sigma_0 f_4(z) \Psi_3(y) \sin(2\tau), \quad (100)$$

where

$$f_1(z) = (76.63758\, e^{2\lambda z} + 217.55642\, e^{\delta z}), \quad (101)$$

$$f_2(z) = 81.18811\, (e^{2\lambda z} + e^{\delta z}), \quad (102)$$

$$f_3(z) = (16.14023\, e^{2\lambda z} + 37.10467\, e^{\delta z}), \quad \delta = (.455816/H), \quad (103)$$

$$f_4(z) = (113.4686\, e^{2\lambda z} + 155.3974\, e^{\delta z}). \quad (104)$$

We can now proceed with the solution of the terms in α^3. This we must do since in our problem of free oscillations the effect of the quadratic terms appears first through σ_2, and the latter can be determined only from the α^3 terms. When the first harmonic terms in (95) to (100) are multiplied by the fundamental terms in (71) to (75), through the quadratic terms in the tidal equations, there result terms in the fundamental and in the second harmonic (3τ). Since σ_2 appears only in the fundamental terms we shall treat these only.

As was pointed out before, in treating the cubic terms equations (33) to (38) retain the same form except for a change of subscript 2 to 3 throughout. The content of the right hand sides is of course different. Thus

$$B_3 = -\sigma_2 \frac{\partial u_1}{\partial\tau} - \frac{u_1}{a}\frac{\partial u_2}{\partial\vartheta} - \frac{u_2}{a}\frac{\partial u_1}{\partial\vartheta} - w_2 \frac{\partial u_1}{\partial z} - \frac{s_1}{a}\frac{\partial p_2}{\partial\vartheta} - \frac{s_2}{a}\frac{\partial p_1}{\partial\vartheta}. \quad (105)$$

We shall omit here the intermediate steps leading to the equation

$$M_i \chi_{3i} = -\frac{\partial}{\partial z}(r_{3i} + T_{3i}) + \frac{1}{\gamma g h_i}\left[\gamma g r_{3i} + \frac{\partial}{\partial z}(c^2 E_{3i})\right], \quad (106)$$

which is the equivalent of (58). For the purpose of determining σ_2 we need to treat only the case

$$i = 1, \quad h_1 = \gamma H, \quad \Psi_1 = \cos(\pi y). \quad (107)$$

The differential equation (106) takes the form

$$\gamma H^2 \ddot{\chi}_{31} - \gamma H \dot{\chi}_{31} + (2/7)\chi_{31} = \sigma_0 \sin\tau\,[.8898\, e^{\lambda z}(\sigma_2/\sigma_0) + 2.34128\, e^{3\lambda z} - 5.39533\, e^{\nu z}]. \quad (108)$$

$$\nu = (.741531/H), \quad (109)$$

The solution of (108) is

$$\chi_{31} = \sigma_0 \sin\tau\,[-1.4830\, e^{\lambda z}(z/H)(\sigma_2/\sigma_0) + 20.4862\, e^{3\lambda z} - 310.323\, e^{\nu z}]. \quad (110)$$

Here we have not added the complementary solution $\chi_{31}^{(0)}$ because the operator $L_1\chi_{31}^{(0)}$ where L_1 is defined in (57), vanishes identically at the ground. The condition of the vanishing of w_3 at the ground

$$[\gamma^2 H \dot{\chi}_{31} + (\gamma - \gamma^2)\chi_{31} + \gamma r_{31} + \gamma T_{31} - E_{31}] = 0. \quad \text{at } z = 0 \quad (111)$$

takes the form

$$w_{31}(0) = \sigma_0 H \sin\tau\,[-7.2668(\sigma_2/\sigma_0) - 403.9890] \quad (112)$$

Hence

$$\sigma_2 = -55.59\sigma_0 \quad (113)$$

The free period of oscillation of our atmosphere is therefore given by

$$\sigma = 2\omega(1 - 55.59\,\alpha^2 + \ldots). \quad (114)$$

Since, as was pointed out before, for an amplitude of the pressure oscillation at the surface of

1 mm, α is of the order 10^{-3}, it follows that the correction to the free period due to the quadratic terms in the tidal equations is only of the order of 10^{-4}.

7. Discussion of Results

The results obtained above, that for an atmosphere of constant temperature the quadratic terms of the tidal equations have little effect on the period of free oscillation for the mode considered is most likely also valid for the mode of the semi-diurnal solar tide, where $n = 2$. The reason for this is that in an atmosphere of constant temperature the energy-density of wave motion decreases exponentially with height, in spite of the fact that the amplitude of the velocities of oscillation *increase* exponentially with height. The wave energy in a column extending above the level of about 140 km where the quadratic terms of the differential equations become equal to the retained linear terms, is only about 3×10^{-5} of the wave energy in the whole atmospheric column.

One should therefore not infer that the quadratic terms will have little effect on the free period of atmospheres in which the wave energy has a different distribution with height. In particular, an atmosphere in which the temperature increases with height in the region where the quadratic terms are dominant, would be expected to be affected differently, because in such an atmosphere the wave energy density actually *increases* with height. If, on the basis of the linear theory one finds that in the top of the atmosphere where the quadratic terms are dominant there is included a considerable fraction of the total wave energy in an atmospheric column, then the effect of the quadratic terms should be examined. The purpose of such a study would be, not to obtain a more accurate description of the nature of the oscillation at great heights, but rather to determine the effect of the quadratic terms on the amplification by resonance. This latter problem could be solved with sufficient accuracy by the method given in this paper.

One result of this investigation is that the terms in the *solution* of the non-linear equations which arise from the quadratic terms in the differential equations become comparable with the terms in the *linear solution* at about the same height as where the quadratic terms in the *differential equations* become comparable to the linear terms in the *differential equations*. This implies that in the E-layer and above the linearized solution becomes a poor approximation to the actula tides.

REFERENCES

BEST, N., HAVENS, R. and LAGOW, H., 1947: Pressure and Temperature of the Atmosphere to 120 km. *Phys. Rev.*, **71**, 915—916.

HOUGH, S., 1897: On the Application of Harmonic Analysis to the Dynamic Theory of the Tides. *Phil. Trans. Roy. Soc.*, **189**, 201—257,

PEKERIS, C. L., 1936: Atmospheric Oscillations. *Nature*, **138**, 642—643

PEKERIS, C. L., 1937: Atmospheric Oscillations. *Proc. Roy. Soc.*, **158**, 650—671.

(Manuscript received April 8, 1958)

On the Formation of Fronts in the Atmosphere

By Arnt Eliassen

University of Oslo

Abstract

Whereas large-scale horizontal deformation fields can satisfactorily explain the formation of relatively broad frontal zones, it is doubtful whether they suffice to produce sharp fronts. The frontogenetic effect of transverse circulations produced by the combined effect of surface friction and released heat of condensation is studied theoretically, and it is found that these effects may cause a diffuse frontal zone to develop into a sharp front within a time of about one day. It is suggested that a similar mechanism may perhaps explain the formation of the eye of tropical cyclones.

1. Introduction

The remarkable sharpness of atmospheric fronts represents one of the classical problems of dynamic meteorology. As revealed by synoptic charts, and in particular by continuous recordings from stations during frontal passages, typical fronts near the surface appear as narrow zones of transition whose horizontal width is of the order 10 km, with a horizontal wind shear of the order 10^{-3} sec^{-1} and a horizontal temperature gradient about 100 times the normal meridional gradient in middle latitudes. How are these discontinuities formed, and how are they maintained against the dissolving influence of turbulent diffusion? The meteorological literature gives an, at least partial answer to the first question, but hardly any to the second.

The classical theory of frontogenesis, first put forward by Bergeron (1928), and futher developed by Petterssen (1936), states that a front is formed as a kinematic result of temperature advection in a pre-existing, large-scale horizontal deformation field, where air particles from widely separated sources are brought into close proximity. Such horizontal deformation fields, in turn, are a necessary attribute to fields of motion that contain large-scale horizontal eddies, i.e. to the *Rossby regime* of planetary motion. If Bergeron's explanation is correct, one might therefore say that fronts are simply a necessary feature of the Rossby regime type of motion.

The typical rate of contraction (or dilatation) of large-scale horizontal deformation fields is of the order (12 hours)$^{-1}$. Assuming adiabatic changes, a ten-fold increase of the temperature gradient would therefore require a little more than a day (12 hours × ln 10). There is thus no reason to doubt that such horizontal deformation fields will result in the establishment of frontal zones, with a temperature change of the order 10° C over a horizontal distance of a few hundred kilometers. This is also supported by synoptic evidence and has been widely accepted.

To establish a real *front*, however, something like a hundred-fold increase in the temperature gradient is necessary; this would require between two and three days, assuming the same rate of contraction. Further delay of the frontogenetic process is to be expected as a result of non-adiabatic temperature changes.

It is not likely that the formation of fronts should depend upon such a pronounced persistence of the large-scale deformation fields. We are thus lead to assume that the role of the horizontal deformation field is to *initiate* the frontogenesis by the formation of a frontal zone, whereas the final *completion* of the frontogenetic process, and the subsequent *maintenance* of the sharpt front is accomplished by another mechanism.

Carl-Gustaf Rossby was always highly interested in the causes of the discontinuous features of atmospheric motions, such as fronts, jet streams, and the sharp shear lines which sometimes appear in the upper troposphere. As early as in 1924, he wrote a paper on frontogenesis where he suggested, among other possible explanations, that the deformation properties of a transverse field of motion, in vertical planes normal to the isotherms, might be important for the formation of sharp temperature contrasts (ROSSBY 1924). Such vertical deformation fields were also discussed by BERGERON (1928), and more recently, the role of vertical motions for the formation of fronts has been stressed by J. BJERKNES (1950), NEWTON (1954) and SAWYER (1956).

It is the aim of the present paper to investigate the possible frontogenetic effect of such vertical deformation fields. It should be emphasized, however, that it is not sufficient just to postulate a three-dimensional field of motion that produces the desired frontal concentration; to arrive at a valid explanation, the frontogenetic vertical deformation field must be derived from dynamical principles. KLEINSCHMIDT (1957) has emphasized the importance of friction and heat of condensation for the ascending motion along warm fronts. We shall find that the vertical circulations produced by these agencies are of vital importance for the formations of fronts.

2. The transverse circulation associated with the thermal concentration produced by horizontal deformation fields

The modern theory of large scale motions, which is utilized in the numerical prediction techniques, is based upon a partitioning of the velocity field into two partial fields. The one is a horizontal, non-divergent and quasi-geostrophic field of motion which can be used as an approximation to the true wind. The second partial field is three-dimensional and non-geostrophic, with zero vertical vorticity; it is much weaker than the first field and its kinetic energy is generally so small that its inertia can be ignored. We shall refer to the first of these partial fields as the *horizontal circulatory motion*, and to the second as the *vertical circulation*.

The horizontal circulatory motion causes the fields of temperature and vorticity to change by horizontal advection. The changes thus produced are generally not compatible with maintenance of approximate geostrophic balance between the vertical wind shear and the isobaric temperature gradient. The same is also true for changes of wind and temperature caused by friction and heat sources. A geostrophic balance, present at some initial instant, would soon be destroyed if the changes were due only to advection by the horizontal circulatory motion, or to the operation of friction and heat sources. When approximate geostrophic balance is nevertheless present almost everywhere and at all times, this must be because the additional wind and temperature changes produced by the vertical circulation serve to preserve the balance. If the factors which disturb the balance are known, then the requirement that geostrophic balance shall be preserved suffices to determine the vertical circulation uniquely, provided the atmosphere is statically and dynamically stable.

We shall now apply the quasi-geostrophic theory outlined above to the frontogenetic process. We assume, with Bergeron, that the horizontal circulatory motion produces a pronounced deformation within a certain region, and that within the same region a baroclinic zone exists, with the isotherms running more or less parallel to the axis of dilatation.

Advection of temperature by the horizontal circulatory motion causes the isobaric temperature gradient to increase. To maintain approximate geostrophic balance, a simultaneous increase of the vertical wind shear in the direction of the isotherms must take place. It is noteworthy that there is no general tendency for the vorticity advection in a deformation field to be distributed so as to produce such a change in the wind field. A vertical circulation is therefore necessary in order to maintain approximate geostrophic balance.

The determination of the vertical circulation requires elaborate calculations, and we shall here be content with a qualitative discussion of its main properties. It is clear that in order to increase the vertical wind shear in the baroclinic zone, the vertical circulation must have the general character of a transverse circulation in vertical planes normal to the isotherms. Moreover, the circulation must be in the thermodynamically direct sense. We thus arrive at the general picture of the transverse streamline pattern shown schematically in Fig. 1. There is one circulation cell in the troposphere, with ascending motion on the warm air side and descending motion on the cold air side. Another direct cell, circulating in the opposite sense, must exist in the lower stratosphere where the isobaric tem-

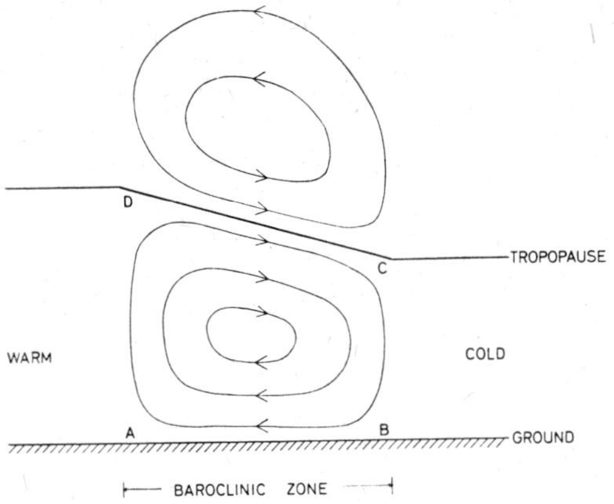

Fig. 1. Schematic streamline pattern of transverse circulation associated with an increase of baroclinicity caused by horizontal deformation.

perature gradient is reversed. It should be noted that the transverse particle displacements along these streamlines will only amount to a small fraction of a complete revolution.

It follows from the vorticity theorem (in its complete form) that these transverse circulations must produce cyclonic vorticity in the surroundings of the point C in the diagram, and anticyclonic vorticity in the surroundings of D. Hence, the west wind will increase at the tropopause level. This is precisely the mechanism for formation of jet streams proposed by NAMIAS and CLAPP (1949) under the name "confluence theory".

At low levels, cyclonic vorticity is produced near the point A and anticyclonic vorticity near the point B. Thus, a decrease of the surface westerlies must result within the baroclinic zone.

Besides producing changes in the wind field, the vertical circulations will also cause temperature changes. In the troposphere, the vertical motions indicated on Fig. 1 must cause a local temperature rise on the cold air side of the baroclinic zone, and a temperature drop on the warm air side, thus counteracting the formation of the temperature contrast and slowing down the frontogenetic process. More locally, however, the vertical circulation will cause a strengthening of the horizontal temperature gradient in regions where there is horizontal convergence, i.e. in the vicinity of the points A and C in the diagram. These are the same regions where cyclonic vorticity is being formed. One might therefore expect the surface front to form at the southern fringe of the baroclinic zone; this agrees with the well-known fact that the warm air south of a surface front is usually remarkably barotropic, whereas the cold air north of the surface front is considerably baroclinic.

The frontogenetic effect of this type of vertical circulation has been studied by SAWYER (1956).

3. Theory of forced transverse circulations in a straight baroclinic current

So far, we have only discussed those vertical circulations which are necessary to preserve geostrophic balance against the disturbing effect of a horizontal deformation field; this presents a truly three-dimensional problem. The geostrophic balance is also disturbed by other factors, however, such as surface friction and liberated latent heat in the ascending currents. These disturbances require additional vertical circulations in order for the balance to be maintained. These additional vertical circulations can probably be studied with useful approximation by assuming that the horizontal deformation field has ceased to exist, and that the horizontal circulatory motion is just a straight parallel, baroclinic current along parallel isobars and isotherms. This case will now be studied in some detail.

For the sake of simplicity, we shall ignore the earth's curvature and the variation of the Coriolis parameter; furthermore, we shall assume that the isotherms run east-west, so that we can use the words zonal, meridional, west, south, etc. to indicate directions relative to the isotherms.

We choose the x-axis eastwards and the y-axis northwards. Let f denote Coriolis parameter, g acceleration of gravity, H scale height, T temperature, Θ potential temperature, ϱ density, p pressure with $p_0 = 1{,}000$ mb, and $\zeta = H \ln (p_0/p)$ a vertical pressure coordinate. The velocity component in the direction of x, which represents the horizontal circulatory motion, will be denoted by u. The vertical circulation is a transverse motion in the $y\zeta$-plane, defined by the velocity component v in the direction of y, and $w = D\zeta/Dt$, which measures vertical velocity relative to the isobaric surfaces. All fields are assumed independent of x, so that the problem becomes a two-dimensional one.

As a measure of the zonal momentum, we shall take the quantity

$$m = f(u - fy). \qquad (3.1)$$

In the absence of friction, m is seen to be an individual constant, and we have

$$\frac{\partial m}{\partial t} + v\frac{\partial m}{\partial y} + w\frac{\partial m}{\partial \zeta} = \frac{Dm}{Dt} = 0. \quad (3.2)$$

Here $\frac{\partial}{\partial t}$ and $\frac{\partial}{\partial y}$ are taken at constant pressure. Equation (3.2) will be assumed to hold in the free atmosphere outside a shallow friction layer near the ground.

As a measure of entropy we take the quantity

$$s = g \ln \Theta. \quad (3.3)$$

This quantity will change individually when heat sources are present; thus we have

$$\frac{\partial s}{\partial t} + v\frac{\partial s}{\partial y} + w\frac{\partial s}{\partial \zeta} = \frac{Ds}{Dt} = E, \quad (3.4)$$

where E is proportional to the rate of heating.

The transverse velocity components v and w must satisfy the continuity equation, which should properly be written

$$\frac{\partial v}{\partial y} + \frac{\partial w}{\partial \zeta} - \frac{w}{H} = 0. \quad (3.5)$$

For the sake of simplicity, we shall here leave out the last term. This has the effect of distorting the transverse circulation pattern, but is not believed to be serious when the results are applied only to the lower troposphere.

Thus we write

$$v = -\frac{\partial \psi}{\partial \zeta}, \quad w = \frac{\partial \psi}{\partial y}, \quad (3.6)$$

where ψ is a stream function for the transverse motion. These expressions may be substituted for v and w in equations (3.2) and (3.4).

The equation expressing geostrophic balance is, with a slight approximation

$$\frac{\partial m}{\partial \zeta} + \frac{\partial s}{\partial y} = 0. \quad (3.7)$$

When this balance is assumed to persist at all times, we also have

$$\frac{\partial}{\partial y}\frac{\partial s}{\partial t} + \frac{\partial}{\partial \zeta}\frac{\partial m}{\partial t} = 0. \quad (3.8)$$

The equation for the transverse motion necessary to maintain this balance is obtained by eliminating $\partial s/\partial t$ and $\partial m/\partial t$ between (3.2), (3.4) and (3.8). This gives

$$\frac{\partial}{\partial y}\left(A\frac{\partial \psi}{\partial y} + B\frac{\partial \psi}{\partial \zeta}\right) + \frac{\partial}{\partial \zeta}\left(B\frac{\partial \psi}{\partial y} + C\frac{\partial \psi}{\partial \zeta}\right) = \frac{\partial E}{\partial y} \quad (3.9)$$

where

$A = \frac{\partial s}{\partial \zeta}$ measures dry static stability,

$B = -\frac{\partial s}{\partial y} = \frac{\partial m}{\partial \zeta}$ measures baroclinicity, and

$C = -\frac{\partial m}{\partial y}$ measures inertial stability. These coefficients all have the dimension of a frequency squared.

Equation (3.9) is of the elliptic type when the current is stable for transversal oscillations; i.e. when

$$A + C > 0, \quad \delta^2 = AC - B^2 > 0; \quad (3.10)$$

this is assumed here to be the case. When E is known everywhere, and ψ is known on the boundary, equation (3.9) defines ψ uniquely.

The discriminant δ^2 can be written in either of the following forms

$$\delta^2 = \frac{\partial s}{dy}\frac{\partial m}{\partial \zeta} - \frac{\partial s}{\partial \zeta}\frac{\partial m}{\partial y} = A\left(-\frac{\partial m}{\partial y}\right)_s = C\left(\frac{\partial s}{\partial \zeta}\right)_m. \quad (3.11)$$

Here the subscript s denotes that the derivative is taken at constant s, i.e. along the isentropes; and likewise the subscript m denotes derivative along the equimomentum lines (m = constant). As shown by the first of these expressions, δ^2 is the Jacobian determinant of s and m, and can therefore be represented as the inverse of the cross-sectional area of the sm-solenoids. It follows from the continuity equation that these areas are conserved individually in regions where there are no sources of heat and momentum. In such regions we therefore have

$$\frac{D\delta^2}{Dt} = 0. \quad (3.12)$$

The theory outlined above is a specialisation of the theory for quasi-static forced meridional circulations in a circular vortex, given in a previous paper (ELIASSEN 1952).

4. Transverse motions produced by surface friction

The following considerations are based upon the common hypothesis that the force of turbulent friction is significant only in a shallow friction layer next to the ground whereas above this layer, the motion can be regarded as frictionless. According to this hypothesis, the shearing stress at the ground is balanced primarily by the Coriolis force associated with an ageostrophic mass flux within the friction layer.

The theory for transverse motions in a baroclinic, parallel current, outlined in the preceding section, is applicable only to the free atmosphere above the friction layer. Within the friction layer, the northward mass flux M (in the direction of y) is given by

$$M = \frac{\tau}{f}, \qquad (4.1)$$

where τ is the zonal component of the surface stress.

We shall assume that τ can be expressed with sufficient accuracy as a function of the zonal wind velocity u_h at the top of the friction layer ($\zeta = h$); and this function will be assumed to be monotoneously increasing. The exact form of this relationship will not be a matter of decisive importance; a relation of the form

$$\tau = \gamma \varrho_h |u_h| u_h, \qquad (4.2)$$

where ϱ_h is a standard density at $\zeta = h$, and with $\gamma = 0.002$ is rather plausible and should at least give the right order of magnitude.

Continuity of mass requires, at the top of the friction layer, a vertical mass flux

$$\varrho_h w_h = -\frac{dM}{dy} = -\frac{1}{f}\frac{d\tau}{dy}. \qquad (4.3)$$

Since τ is assumed to vary monotoneously with u_h, it follows that the motion is directed upwards in regions where the horizontal shear at the top of the friction layer is cyclonic, and vice versa.

These vertical motions at $\zeta = h$ require, again for reasons of mass continuity, transverse motions in the free atmosphere above the friction layer. The meridional mass flux in the free atmosphere thus produced can be assumed equal to $-M$, so that the total meridional mass flux above the ground is zero. This transverse motion in the free atmosphere will cause the fields of zonal wind and temperature to change, by advection of

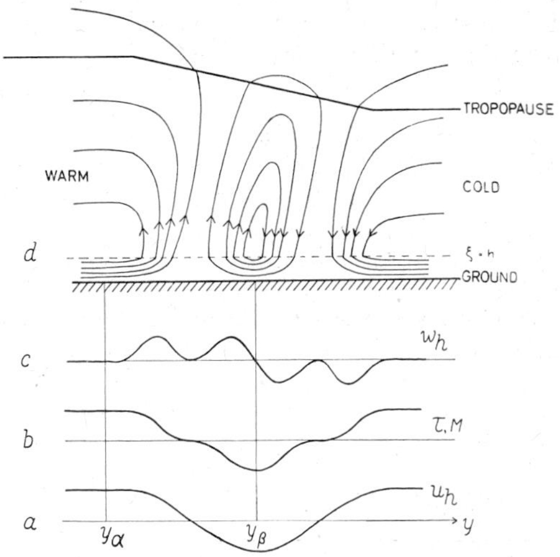

Fig. 2. a: Hypothetic meridional profile of zonal wind (u_h) at the top of the friction layer; b: corresponding profile of zonal surface stress (τ), or meridional mass transport within the friction layer (M); c: frictionally produced vertical motion (w_h) at the top of the friction layer; d: streamlines of frictionally produced transverse circulation.

momentum and entropy. Thus, in a field of surface westerlies, a transverse motion towards the south is set up in the free atmosphere, causing a decay of the westerly flow. This effect has been discussed by CHARNEY and ELIASSEN (1949).

Now consider a frontal zone formed by a horizontal deformation field, and suppose that the surface wind is originally westerly everywhere. As a result of the vertical circulations discussed in section 2, the surface westerlies within the baroclinic zone will be reduced, and may even be turned into easterlies. The resulting profile of u_h is shown schematically in Fig. 2, curve *a*. The corresponding distribution of τ, according to equation (4.2), is shown by curve *b*; on account of (4.1), this curve will also represent the distribution of M. Curve *c* shows the distribution of w_h according to (4.3).

The stream function for the transverse motion in the free atmosphere, produced by this distribution of w_h, must satisfy equation (3.9) with $E = 0$ (no heat sources) and with the condition $\partial\psi/\partial y = w_h$ at the boundary $\zeta = h$. The solution of this boundary value problem could be obtained by numerical integration. The main characteristics of the solution can be inferred from a slightly generalized potential theory, however, without much calculation. If A, B and C are constants, then the motion produced in the infinite $y\zeta$-plane by a point source of mass of unit strength, located in the point y_0, ζ_0, is given by the multi-valued stream function

$$\psi = \frac{1}{2\pi} \operatorname{arctg} \frac{C(y-y_0) - B(\zeta-\zeta_0)}{\delta(\zeta-\zeta_0)}. \quad (4.4)$$

As in the corresponding Laplacian problem, the stream lines are straight lines through the point source. The solution to our problem may now be obtained as a superposition of the fields of a number of such point sources of mass, located at the level $\zeta = h$, whose strengths (positive or negative) correspond to the distribution of w_h. The construction of the streamlines is thus a simple matter if the coefficients A, B and C are constants. In reality they are not; this causes a distortion of the streamline pattern, but will probably not change its main characteristics.

On the basis of these considerations, a qualitative picture of the frictionally produced streamline pattern has been drawn as shown in the upper part of Fig. 2. We conclude from this picture that the ascending motion at $\zeta = h$ within the zone of cyclonic shear will continue as an upward flow through a considerable part of the troposphere. The mass flux in this ascending current is equal to the influx of mass in the friction layer, and is thus

$$M_\alpha - M_\beta = \frac{1}{f}(\tau_\alpha - \tau_\beta)$$
$$= \frac{\gamma\varrho_h}{f}(|u_{h\alpha}| u_{h\alpha} - |u_{h\beta}| u_{h\beta}). \quad (4.5)$$

Here the subscript α refers to the point south of the ascending current where u_h has its maximum value, and the subscript β refers to the point on the northern side where u_h is a minimum (see Fig. 2).

We may assume that practically all water vapour contained in the air is condensed in the ascending current. The amount of condensation heat liberated per unit time is then

$$Q_1 = L(\mu_\alpha M_\alpha - \mu_\beta M_\beta)$$
$$= \frac{\gamma\varrho_h L}{f}(\mu_\alpha |u_{h\alpha}| u_{h\alpha} - \mu_\beta |u_{h\beta}| u_{h\beta}), \quad (4.6)$$

where μ denotes specific humidity in the friction layer, and L is the latent heat of condensation.

5. Transverse circulation driven by the heat of condensation released in the frontal cloud

Strictly speaking, released condensation heat should not be treated as a heat source, but as a change in the compressibility of the air. This would imply a discontinuous variation of the coefficients of the differential equation (3.9), their values depending upon the solution. In view of the mathematical difficulties connected with such a method, it has been found preferable to consider the heat condensation as a heat source in an otherwise dry-adiabatic atmosphere. The dependence of this heat source upon the motion can be accounted for by means of an iterative procedure in the following manner: The condensation heat Q_1 released in the frictionally produced updraft (equation 4.6) will be distributed over an area where the condensation takes place, causing the "dry entropy" s to increase individually at a rate E_1; this heating causes in turn a transverse motion ψ_1. The ascending currents defined by ψ_1 will cause additional condensation, and hence a new distribution of heat sources E_2, which again produce a transverse motion ψ_2, and so on. This simple superposition will be correct if it can be assumed that the heat sources E_1, E_2, E_3 etc. have similar distributions in space, differing only in having different amplitude factors. Clearly, these amplitude factors must form a geometrical series; therefore, if we can determine

$$k = \frac{E_2}{E_1}, \quad (5.1)$$

then the total heat source can be obtained from

$$E = E_1 + E_2 + E_3 + \ldots = \frac{E_1}{1-k} \quad (5.2)$$

provided $k < 1$. The stream functions ψ_1, ψ_2, ψ_3 must then also have similar spatial distributions and form a geometric series, so that the stream function for the total transverse motion produced by the heat source E is

$$\psi = \psi_1 + \psi_2 + \psi_3 + \ldots = \frac{\psi_1}{1-k}. \quad (5.3)$$

We shall now derive a simple analytic solution of (3.9), which represents the transverse motion produced by a heat source uniformly distributed over an elliptical area in the $y\zeta$-plane. Admittedly, the released condensation heat does not have such a distribution, and our solution is therefore nothing more than a crude approximation. It should be noted, however, that the exact distribution of the heating is important only in the immediate surroundings of the heat source, whereas at greater distances a system of heat sources will nearly have the effect of a single point source. Our solution is therefore perhaps not in all respects unrealistic.

We assume A, B and C to be constants, and introduce instead of y the horizontal coordinate

$$\eta = y - \frac{B}{C}\zeta. \tag{5.4}$$

The slanting lines η = constant are the lines of constant momentum. In the skew coordinates η, ζ, equation (3.9) assumes the form

$$\frac{\delta^2}{C}\frac{\partial^2\psi}{\partial\eta^2} + C\frac{\partial^2\psi}{\partial\zeta^2} = \frac{\partial E}{\partial\eta}. \tag{5.5}$$

Now suppose E has the constant value E_1 inside an ellipse of area σ, whose equation is

$$C\eta^2 + \frac{\delta^2}{C}(\zeta - \zeta_0)^2 = \frac{\delta}{\pi}\sigma, \tag{5.6}$$

and that E vanishes everywhere in the infinite plane outside this ellipse. The solution of (5.5) for this distribution of heat sources is

$$\psi_1' = \begin{cases} \dfrac{E_1\sigma}{2\pi\delta}\dfrac{C\eta}{C\eta^2 + \dfrac{\delta^2}{C}(\zeta-\zeta_0)^2} & \text{outside the ellipse} \\[2ex] \dfrac{E_1\sigma}{2\pi\delta}\dfrac{C\eta}{\dfrac{\delta}{\pi}\sigma} & \text{inside the ellipse.} \end{cases} \tag{5.7}$$

The solution is a linear transformation of the well-known Laplacian solution representing the field of motion inside and outside a cylinder that moves through an ideal, incompressible fluid. The proof will therefore be omitted.

The streamline pattern defined by (5.7) is shown in Fig. 3. Inside the ellipse (5.6) the motion is a parallel, uniform flow ascending in the direction of the sloping equimomentum lines; the vertical velocity here is

$$w_1' = \frac{\partial\psi_1'}{\partial\eta} = \frac{E_1 C}{2\delta^2}. \tag{5.8}$$

Outside the heat source, the streamline pattern represents a distorted field of a dipole.

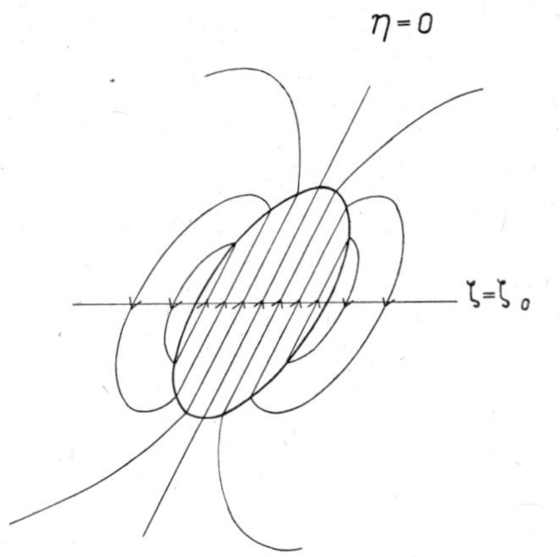

Fig. 3. Transverse motion produced by a hypothetic elliptical heat source in a baroclinic atmosphere of infinite extent.

This solution does not satisfy the boundary condition at the ground. To achieve this, we add the field ψ_1'' of a similar heat source of strength $-E_1\sigma$ (i.e. a cold source) centered in the point $0, -\zeta_0$:

$$\psi_1'' = -\frac{E_1\sigma}{2\pi\delta}\frac{C\delta}{C\eta^2 + \dfrac{\delta^2}{C}(\zeta+\zeta_0)^2}. \tag{5.9}$$

The combined field

$$\psi_1 = \psi_1' + \psi_1'' \tag{5.10}$$

is shown in Fig. 4. The line $\zeta = 0$ is a streamline and may be identified with the ground (or, strictly with the top of the friction layer). The cold source in the point $0, -\zeta_0$ is situated outside the boundary and is thus purely fictitious.

The field of motion inside the elliptical heat source is now no longer quite uniform. As a mean value of the rate of ascent in the heat source we may take the vertical velocity in the central point $0, \zeta_0$, which is found to be

$$w_1 = \left(\frac{\partial\psi_1}{\partial\eta}\right)_{\substack{\eta=0\\ \zeta=\zeta_0}} = \frac{E_1 C}{2\delta^2}\left(1 - \frac{\sigma C}{4\pi\delta\zeta_0^2}\right)$$

$$= \frac{E_1 C}{2\,\delta^2}\left(1 - \frac{c^2}{4\,\zeta_0^2}\right), \tag{5.11}$$

where c is the vertical half-depth of the ellipse (5.6). We may assume that c is much smaller than $2\zeta_0$, so that $w_1 \approx w'_1$, approximately.

Recalling the definition of E (equation 3.4),

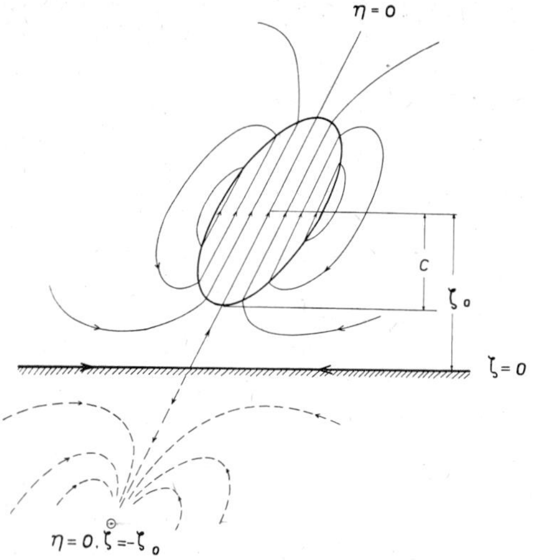

Fig. 4. Transverse motion produced by an elliptical heat source near the earth's surface.

the heat source E_2 due to release of condensation heat in the ascending current w_1 is

$$E_2 = w_1 \left(\frac{\partial s}{\partial \zeta}\right)_{\text{moistadiabatic}} = \frac{E_1 C}{2\,\delta^2}\left(\frac{\partial s}{\partial \zeta}\right)_{\text{moistadiabatic}} \tag{5.12}$$

Substituting here the last expression (3.11) for δ^2, the ratio k defined by (5.1) becomes

$$k = \frac{1}{2}\frac{\left(\frac{\partial s}{\partial \zeta}\right)_{\text{moistadiabatic}}}{\left(\frac{\partial s}{\partial \zeta}\right)_m} = \frac{1}{2}\frac{\left(\frac{\partial \Theta}{\partial \zeta}\right)_{\text{moistadiabatic}}}{\left(\frac{\partial \Theta}{\partial \zeta}\right)_m} \tag{5.13}$$

It is seen from this expression that if the temperature distribution along the lines m = constant is nearly dry-adiabatic, k will be greater than one, and our iteration procedure breaks down. On the other hand, k becomes small if the temperature distribution along the equimomentum lines is very stable. Generally, however, this temperature distribution is not far from moist-adiabatic, so that k is about ½. Adopting the value $k = \frac{1}{2}$, we obtain from (5.2) and (5.3)

$$E = 2E_1, \quad \psi = 2\psi_1 = 2\psi_1' + 2\psi_1'', \tag{5.14}$$

where E_1 is the condensation heating due to the frictionally driven ascent. The total heat supplied to the air per unit time from the heat source E_1 is

$$Q_1 = \int\int \frac{c_p T}{\Theta}\left(\frac{D\Theta}{Dt}\right)_1 \varrho\, d\eta\, d\zeta$$

$$\approx \frac{c_p}{R} H \int\int E_1 \varrho\, d\eta\, d\zeta \approx \frac{c_p}{R} H \varrho\, E_1 \sigma, \tag{5.15}$$

ignoring the variation of ϱ with height. Thus the strength of the heat source ($E_1\sigma$) can be expressed in terms of Q_1, which is given by (4.6).

6. Frontogenetic effect of the transverse circulation

As seen from Fig. 4, the transverse circulation produced by the released condensation heat has the character of a vertical deformation field where air near the ground is brought to converge from both sides towards the line $\eta = 0$. The isentropic and equimomentum lines are carried along with the air motion; a crowding of these lines must therefore take place, and a zone of intense gradients of zonal wind and temperature is thus formed in the vicinity of $\eta = 0$. We shall try to estimate the speed of such a development.

At $\zeta = 0$ the transverse motion is purely horizontal; the velocity is obtained from (5.14), (5.7) and (5.9),

$$v = \frac{D\eta}{Dt} = -\left(\frac{\partial \psi}{\partial \zeta}\right)_{\zeta=0} = -2\left(\frac{\partial \psi_1}{\partial \zeta}\right)_{\zeta=0}$$

$$= -4\left(\frac{\partial \psi_1'}{\partial \zeta}\right)_{\zeta=0}$$

$$= -\frac{4}{\pi}\frac{R}{c_p}\frac{Q_1}{H\varrho}\frac{\delta C^2 \eta \zeta_0}{(C^2\eta^2 + \delta^2\zeta_0^2)^2}. \tag{6.1}$$

We have here substituted the expression for $E_1\sigma$ obtained from (5.15). Equation (6.1) can be used to determine the coordinate η of an individual particle as a function of time, if it is known how the parameters Q_1, δ and C change with time as the frontal concentration proceeds.

The variation of Q_1 with time can be inferred from (4.6). The maximum west wind $u_{h\alpha}$ south of the front will increase as a result of the motion towards the north ($v>0$ when $\eta<0$); and the minimum west wind $u_{h\beta}$ north of the front will decrease due to the motion towards the south ($v<0$ when $\eta>0$), assuming conservation of momentum. Hence, Q_1 must increase. This increase is easily estimated; for the sake of simplicity, however, we prefer to consider Q_1 as a constant, remembering that the speed of the frontogenetic process is thereby underestimated.

As for δ, it was shown previously (equation 3.12) that this parameter is conserved individually outside the heat source. Its variation inside the heat source is not so easily determined; we shall assume, however, that this parameter does not vary significantly with time.

It remains to consider the variation of $C = -\partial m/\partial\eta$. This parameter will clearly increase significantly with time in the region below the heat source, and later also within the heat source, as a result of the advection of the equimomentum lines. Above the heat source, C is seen to decrease for the same reason. Our assumption that C is a spatial constant will therefore not be valid in the later stages of the development of the front. It is nevertheless plausible that (6.1) is applicable to the region below the heat source, with a value of C which is representative for this region. If $\eta(t)$ is the coordinate of a particle at $\zeta = 0$, we may assume the representative value of C to vary in inverse proportion to $\eta(t)$, i.e. we may write

$$C(t) = C_0 \frac{\eta_0}{\eta(t)}, \qquad (6.2)$$

where C_0 and η_0 are the initial values at the time $t = 0$. Substitution into (6.1) gives

$$\frac{D\eta}{Dt} = -\frac{\eta_0^2}{2t^*\eta}, \qquad (6.3)$$

where t^* is the constant

$$t^* = \frac{\pi}{8} \frac{c_p}{R} \frac{H\varrho}{Q_1} \left[1 + \left(\frac{C_0}{\delta}\frac{\eta_0}{\zeta_0}\right)^2\right]^2 \left(\frac{\delta}{C_0}\right)^2 \delta\zeta_0^3. \qquad (6.4)$$

Integration of (6.3) gives finally

$$\eta = \eta_0 \sqrt{1 - \frac{t}{t^*}}. \qquad (6.5)$$

This formula predicts the formation of an infinitely sharp front within a finite time, since η becomes zero when $t = t^*$. (The expression "infinitely sharp" must of course not be taken literally, since the sharpness will always be limited by turbulent diffusion). According to our theory, the front is thus not the asymptotic result of a gradual process, but is formed by a catastrophic development. The wind shear and the temperature contrast are formed simultaneously, since the lines of constant momentum and the lines of constant entropy will both be carried towards the point $\eta = 0$.

To obtain an estimate of the time scale of the process, we insert typical numerical values into (6.4) and (4.6). With the values

$$\gamma = 0{,}002,\ L = 2.5\times10^6\ \mathrm{m^2\,sec^{-2}},\ f = 10^{-4}\ \mathrm{sec^{-1}},$$

$$\mu_\alpha = 0.010,\ \mu_\beta = 0.005,\ u_{h\alpha} = -u_{h\beta} = 7\ \mathrm{m\,sec^{-1}},$$

$$\varrho = \varrho_h,\ H = 8{,}000\ \mathrm{m},\ C_0 = 10^{-3}\ \mathrm{sec^{-2}},\ \delta = 10^{-6}\mathrm{sec^{-2}},$$

$$\eta_0 = 10^5\ \mathrm{m},\ \zeta_0 = 2.5\times10^3\ \mathrm{m},\ \text{we obtain}$$

$$t^* = 17\ \text{hours}.$$

This value must of course be considered as nothing more than an indication of the order of magnitude.

7. Discussion

The result of the preceding section rests on a number of assumptions of varying credibility. Some of these questionable points will be commented on below.

(a) The assumption of straight and parallel isobars and isotherms is clearly restrictive; in reality, frontogenesis will usually take place under more general conditions. It is quite likely, however, that the combined effect of friction and heat of condensation would be operative also in more general fields of flow, and produce frontogenesis in much the same way. Such cases could conceivably be studied by using numerical integration techniques.

(b) SHEPPARD, CHARNOCK and FRANCIS (1952) have questioned the idea that friction should be negligible in the free atmosphere above a shallow friction layer, and have found strong evidence that a significant shearing stress exists throughout the troposphere in regions of pronounced baroclinicity. Their findings call for a revision of our equation (4.1). Thus the northward mass transport in the lowest layers in zones of surface westerlies must be much weaker than predicted by (4.1) and may even be lacking. In return, however, we get a much stronger southward mass flux in the zone of surface easterlies, so that the total frictionally produced import of mass towards the front assumed above (equation 4.5) will probably not be seriously in error.

(c) Formula (4.6) for the released heat of condensation might perhaps be criticized as an overestimate, because it does not account for the fact that part of the condensed water will not precipitate, but remain in the air and eventually re-evaporate. It should be remembered, however, that the additional cold sources thus produced will be located chiefly in the descending branches of the transverse circulation. The effect of cold sources thus located will be to intensify the transverse circulations, so that the frontogenetic process is speeded up.

(d) The weakest point in our theory is probably the use of solutions of equation (3.9) of the form (5.7), based on spatially constant coefficients A, B and C, whereas in reality the distribution of these coefficients becomes extremely non-uniform as the frontal concentration develops. It is difficult to judge what effect such crudeness of method has had upon our result; clearly, we cannot expect equation (6.5) to represent reality very well in the later stages of the development, as t approaches t^*.

In spite of all approximations involved, our result seems to justify the belief that the combined effect of friction and condensation heat may cause a diffuse frontal zone to develop into a very sharp front within a relatively short time. In any case there can hardly be any question that the mechanism discussed represents a frontogenetic effect of great significance.

It is particularly important to note that this frontogenetic mechanism does not depend upon a coincidental juxtaposition between the frontogenetic transverse field of motion and the front itself; the two are bound together, the frontal cloud representing the linkage between them. The process is therefore self-maintaining and irreversible: once started, it must go on at an accelerating speed until the frontogenesis is completed. From then on, the process must still continue, but now in a quasi-stationary manner, serving to maintain the front against the dissolving agencies of friction and diffusion.

8. Remarks on the growth of tropical cyclones

It is generally accepted that friction and released heat of condensation are essential factors in the dynamics of tropical cyclones. It is therefore tempting to try to apply the method used in the present paper to the growth of tropical storms. Some remarks on this subject are given below.

Clearly, the combined effect of friction and condensation heat cannot initiate the tropical storm; not until a surface low has been formed by some other process can the friction-condensation effect start to operate. The same is true with regard to the frontogenetic process, which is initiated by the horizontal deformation field.

The frictionally controlled vertical motion at the top of the friction layer in a symmetrical, circular low pressure area can be estimated by means of the method applied in section 4. Using cylinder coordinates, we now obtain instead of equation (4.3):

$$\varrho_h w_k = \frac{1}{fr}\frac{d}{dr}(r\tau), \tag{8.1}$$

where r measures distance from the center and τ is the frictional stress at the ground in the direction of the geostrophic wind. If τ varies in proportion to the *square* of the geostrophic wind, as indicated by (4.2), this formula predicts the ascending motion to have a maximum at some distance from the center, decreasing to zero in the center itself. The heat of condensation released by this frictional ascent is thus distributed in a ring around the center. From the theory of thermally produced meridional circulations in a circular vortex (ELIASSEN, 1952), it can be inferred that such a ring-shaped heat source must give rise to a meridional circulation with an ascending branch running through the heat source and with two descending branches, one outside the heat source, and another in the central region. The descending branch in the central region must overcompensate the weak frictional updrafts in a certain surrounding of the center. This process may have some bearing on the formation of the eye of the cyclone. It is also seen that the meridional circulation produced by the released condensation heat within the ringshaped cloud will produce a pronounced radial convergence at low levels. Air from the outside as well as from the inside will converge towards the eye boundary; here a circular "front" must therefore develop through a process very similar to that discussed in section 6 above.

Acknowledgements

The author has had the opportunity to discuss the origin of fronts with Professor J. G. Charney, and wishes to thank him for his encouragement, without which this study would not have been undertaken. The author's warmest thanks are also due to Professor E. Høiland for his valuable criticism and advice.

REFERENCES

BERGERON, T. 1928: Über die dreidimensional verknüpfende Wetteranalyse. *Geof. Publ.* **5**, No. 6.

BJERKNES, J., 1951: Extratropical cyclones, *Compendium of Meteorology, A.M.S.*, Boston, p. 577.

CHARNEY, J. G., and ELIASSEN, A., 1949: A numerical method for predicting the perturbations of the middle latitude westerlies. *Tellus* **1**, No. 2.

ELIASSEN, A., 1952: Slow thermally or frictionally controlled meridional circulations in a circular vortex. *Astrophysica Norvegica*, **5**, No. 2.

KLEINSCHMIDT, E., 1957, in Eliassen, A. and Kleinschmidt, E.: Dynamic meteorology. *Handbuch der Physik*, Springer-Verlag, **48**, p. 135.

NAMIAS, J., and CLAPP, P. F., 1949: Confluence theory of the high tropospheric jet stream. *J. Meteor.* **6**, p. 330.

NEWTON, C. W., 1954: Frontogenesis and frontolysis as a three-dimensional process. *J. Meteor.* **11**, p. 449.

PETTERSSEN, S., 1936: Contribution to the theory of frontogenesis. *Geof. Publ.* **11**, No. 6.

ROSSBY, C. G., 1924: On the origin of travelling discontinuities in the atmosphere. *Geografiska Annaler*, **6**, p 180.

SAWYER, J. S., 1956: The vertical circulation at meteorological fronts and its relation to frontogenesis. *Proc. Roy. Soc. A*, **234**, p. 346.

SHEPPARD, P. A., CHARNOCK, H. and FRANCIS, J. R. D., 1952: Observations of the westerlies over the sea. *Quart. J. R. Meteor. Soc.* **78**, p. 563.

(Manuscript received April 1, 1958)

Synoptic Comparisons of Jet Stream and Gulf Stream Systems

By C. W. Newton

The University of Chicago[1]

Abstract

Comparisons are made between typical examples of oceanic and atmospheric current structures. These indicate that the lateral dimensions of the Gulf Stream are about 1/25 those of the jet stream; the shapes of the current profiles are almost identical, with equivalent lateral shears. In the vertical, the dimensions are nearly in the ratio 1 : 10, which also characterizes meander sizes.

Striking similarities are found between thermal structures in the two systems. In both, variations from pronounced frontal concentrations to more gentle and broad barocline structures are observed over short distances or time intervals. Frontal slopes are equal, as are the vertical shears observed within frontal layers.

Marked axial variations of speed, and of lateral and vertical gradients of current speed and temperature, are present in both systems. Ageostrophic motions are prominent. Some comments are made on possible interpretations of these variations, in regard to transverse circulations and to inertia oscillations in the current systems.

1. Introduction

The striking similarity between atmospheric and oceanic current systems has been emphasized continuously throughout the remarkable series of investigations carried out by C.-G. Rossby over a number of years. Although some kind of superficial resemblance was generally recognized, Rossby perceived that this similarity between "apparently unrelated current systems ..... [suggests] that the factors controlling the shape and behaviour of jets must be fairly independent of their driving mechanism, and derivable from quite general dynamic principles" (Rossby, 1951).

Thus the principle of lateral mixing, which he introduced (Rossby, 1936) to account for basic features of the Gulf Stream, was employed by him (Rossby, 1947) to explain the atmospheric jet stream. Further extensions using lateral mixing concepts met with remarkable success in quantitatively accounting for the broadscale features of the oceanic current systems (Stommel, 1948; Munk and Carrier, 1950).

At first sight, it appears strange that these theories, which are essentially barotropic, can account for baroclinic phenomena, the jets. In regard to the atmosphere, Rossby (1949) observes that, "Lateral mixing within the polar cap north of the velocity maximum (jet stream) not only would equalize the vorticity but would likewise tend to destroy the horizontal temperature gradients in the zone of mixing and to concentrate the temperature contrasts between high and low latitudes on the southern boundary of the mixing zone, i.e., under the jet stream. This zone of concentrated temperature contrast would take on the character of a frontal zone. Thus the fronts in the free atmosphere and the jet stream would simply be different manifestations of one and the same process."

The idea of simultaneous generation of current maxima and of baroclinity, through such a mixing process, goes a long way toward resolving an apparent conflict, namely the concurrence of high values of kinetic and potential energy, which is hard to understand if one considers kinetic energy to be derivable directly from circulations in which potential energy is released. At the same time, Rossby's theory suggests a way in which the kinetic energy released by such overturnings in synoptic disturbances (Palmén, 1951)

[1] Published as a contribution to a research project on structure of current systems, sponsored by the U.S. Office of Naval Research, under Contract NR 082-161 with The University of Chicago. Most of the investigations reviewed are the result of work done under ONR support at a number of institutions.

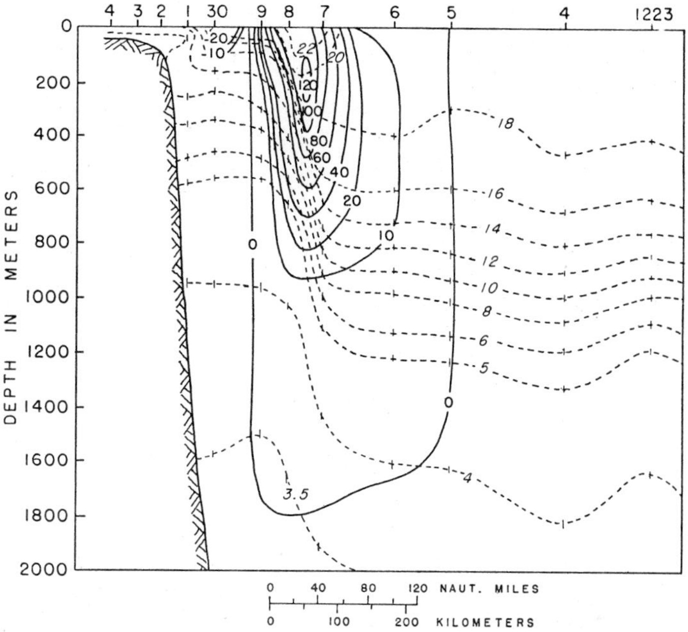

Fig. 1. A section through the Gulf Stream off Chesapeake Bay. Dashed lines, isotherms, deg C; solid lines, isotachs, cm/sec. Hydrographic stations shown at top. (Composite of figs. 5 and 27 in ISELIN, 1936.)

may be concentrated into an organized zone of strong current rather than haphazardly distributed eddies.

As ROSSBY himself (1951) points out, the mixing theory which accounts for the large-scale features cannot account satisfactorily for smaller details. Among such details, which are significant for processes on the scale of cyclones, are multiple jet systems, jets flanked by zones in which the vorticity is higher than the earth's polar vorticity, and jets with marked velocity and vorticity variations along the current direction.

This paper is an attempt to bring together some examples showing the remarkable similarity of the *details* as well as the broad-scale features of oceanic and atmospheric jets. I am conscious that the oceanographers particularly are well aware of most or all of the similarities to be shown. However, I feel that some purpose is served by collecting some comparative data in the hope that this will stimulate attempts to study the current systems on a parallel rather than independent basis.

2. General structure

The more obvious likenesses of the thermal and current structures of Gulf Stream and jet stream are seen by comparing fig. 1 (ISELIN, 1936) and fig. 2 (PALMÉN and NAGLER, 1948). The features shown are somewhat smoothed out, in fig. 1 because the hydrographic stations are fairly far apart in distance and time, and in fig. 2 because that section is a composite made by use of all observations within a longitudinal sector of 70 degrees rather than a single line of stations.

In both cases, most of the total available temperature difference between air or water masses is concentrated within a relatively narrow zone, this zone being in fig. 1 about 100 km wide and in fig. 2 about 1,000 km wide. To a certain extent, the concentration of vertical stability between the 6C and 16C isotherms in fig. 1 is matched by a similar stability between the 290K and 310K isentropes in fig. 2.

If the part of fig. 2 below the level of maximum wind (250 mb) is compared with fig. 1, it is seen that in both cases the greatest current speed coincides nearly with the location where the baroclinity, averaged through the whole depth of the medium, is greatest.[2]

Later examples will show that in individual instances some important features of both the current and temperature fields undergo pro-

[2] ISELIN (1936) notes that because of a very close correlation between temperature and salinity, inspection of the temperature field alone is enough to give a good estimate of the density distribution in the Gulf Stream region.

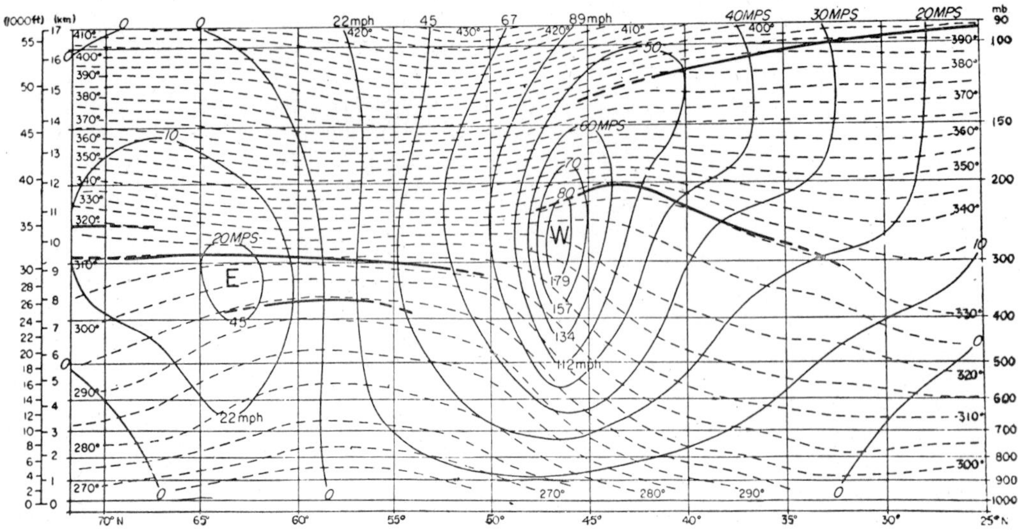

Fig. 2. Mean cross section for 0300 GCT 30 November 1946, showing average distribution of geostrophic west wind (solid lines, m/sec and mi/hr) and potential temperature (dashed lines, deg K), in a case with an approximately straight westerly jet stream. Heavy lines are tropopauses. (PALMÉN and NAGLER, 1948.)

nounced changes in structure with time and also along the direction of the current.

Characteristic dimensions and horizontal shear. The most striking features of the velocity fields in figs. 1 and 2 are the pronounced vertical and horizontal shears. Horizontal profiles of current speed near the level of maximum current are shown in fig. 3 (VON ARX, 1952) and fig. 4 (PALMÉN and NAGLER, 1948).

The frequent current measurements in fig. 3 bring out the high degree of concentration of the current. Taking the "width" as the distance between the points on either side where the velocity drops off to half maximum speed, this is for the Gulf Stream about 35 km, and for the jet stream example in fig. 4 about 800 km, giving a ratio of 1:20 or 1:25 for the lateral dimensions. In fig. 3, the average horizontal shear over most of the cyclonic side is 1 m sec^{-1} in 10 km (10^{-4} sec^{-1}) while the maximum shear in fig. 4 is about twice that value.

In both cases, the strongest anticyclonic shear

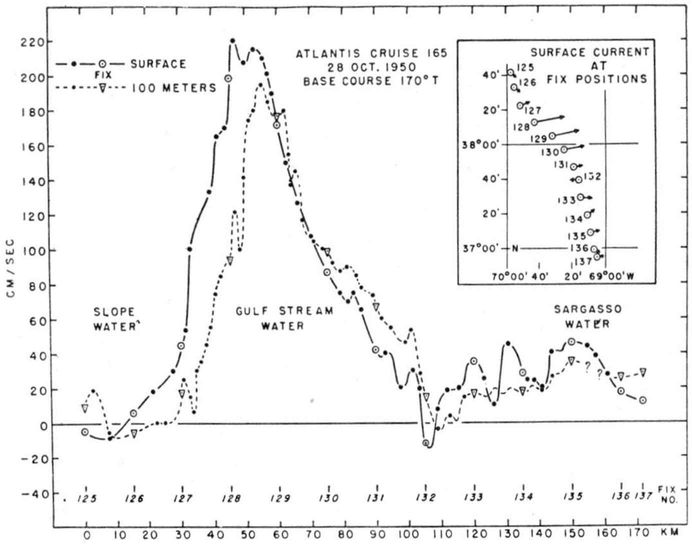

Fig. 3. Velocity profiles across the Gulf Stream, resulting from simultaneous measurements at surface and 100-meter levels with the geomagnetic electrokinetograph. Indicated surface speeds are 23 per cent less than average of navigational measurements of current speed. (VON ARX, 1952.)

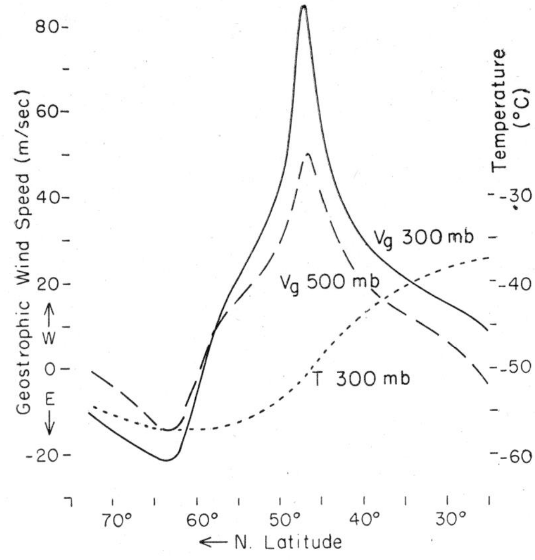

Fig. 4. Geostrophic wind speed profiles at the 300-mb and 500-mb levels, and the 300-mb temperature profile, for the case shown in fig. 2. (PALMÉN and NAGLER, 1948.)

averaged to the half-width limit is 0.8 to 0.9×10^{-4} sec^{-1}. This and numerous other examples establish that in both the Gulf Stream and the jet stream, the maximum anticyclonic shear tends to reach about the value of the Coriolis parameter (PALMÉN, 1948; ROSSBY, 1947; HAURWITZ and PANOFSKY, 1950), while the greatest cyclonic shear near the current maxima tends to exceed that value. BERGGREN (1953) and VUORELA (1953) show examples wherein the cyclonic shear (from measured winds) reaches 5×10^{-4} sec^{-1}, while VON ARX (1952) indicates that extreme values of this magnitude are found in the Gulf Stream also (average values being 1 to 3×10^{-4} sec^{-1}).

Characteristic maximum velocities are around 3 m sec^{-1} in the Gulf Stream, and 75 m sec^{-1} in the jet stream. Thus the maximum speeds in the two systems are characteristically in a ratio of about 1 : 25, while the geometrical shapes and horizontal shears are very much the same.

The depth below maximum current level at which the current speed drops off to one half the value at that level, may be taken as a measure of the vertical dimension. Comparison of figs. 1 and 2 shows that this depth is about 5 to 6 km in the case of the jet stream, and about 1/10 that value in the Gulf Stream. In the presence of fronts, as shown by later examples, this velocity decay with depth is much more pronounced.

Multiple current systems. — CRESSMAN (1950), PHILLIPS (1950), and others have shown that more than one jet stream is usually to be found crossing a given meridian. Their data and that of MCINTYRE and LEE (1953) suggest that, statistically, the individual jet streams tend to move southward with time. Moreover, Cressman has shown that the mean strength of the jet averaged around the hemisphere tends to be strongest near latitude 30°, suggesting that such southward-moving jets increase in speed as they approach that latitude. This is in agreement with ROSSBY's (1947) lateral mixing theory, since that theory would suggest stronger westerlies the more the polar cap, in which the mixing of vorticity takes place, is expanded. Largely due to the fact that wave patterns at different latitudes are not likely to be everywhere in phase (NAMIAS and CLAPP, 1944), the jet streams may in some locations be found quite close together.

Figure 5 illustrates such a case (the corresponding 300-mb chart is shown in a later section as fig. 16c). This example may be compared with fig. 6, taken from a paper by WORTHINGTON (1954), showing multiple currents in the Gulf Stream system. Although it cannot be conclusively proven (see arguments in Worthington's paper) that multiple currents as shown were present simultaneously, the structure of the computed velocity field in fig. 6 is quite similar to

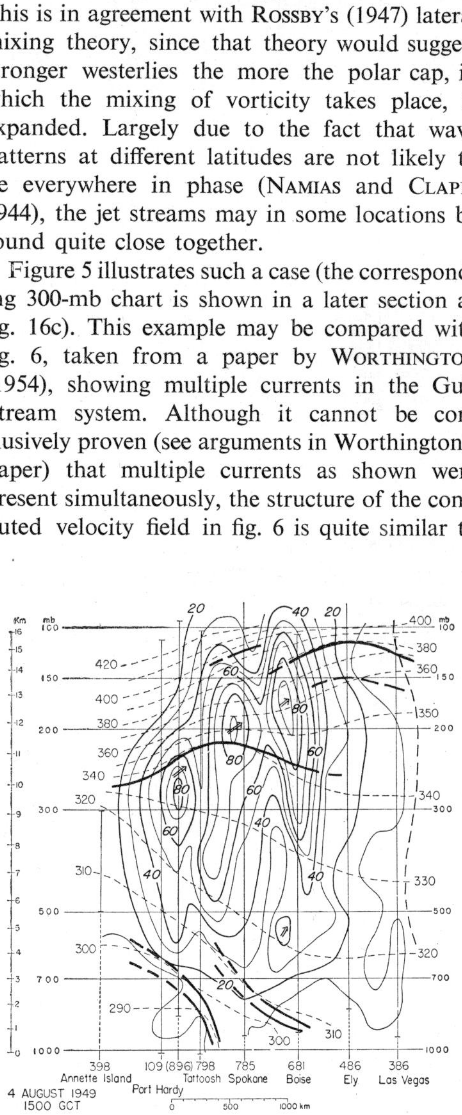

Fig. 5. Cross section through multiple jet streams on 4 August 1949, through southwesterly current over western North America shown in fig. 16c. (NEWTON and CARSON, 1953.)

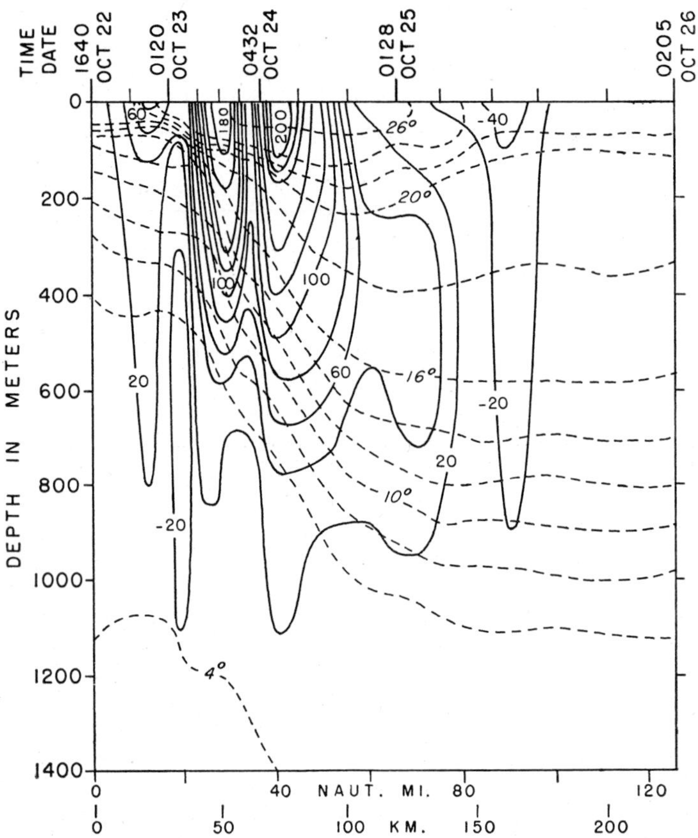

Fig. 6. Section through the Gulf Stream SSE of Cape Cod, near 38° N, 69° W. Dashed lines, isotherms, deg C; solid lines, geostrophic current speeds, cm/sec. Tick marks at top show hydrographic stations. (Composite of figs. 4 and 10 in WORTHINGTON, 1954.)

that in fig. 5, where actual wind observations support the analysis.

In fig. 5, a summertime example, the weak frontal layers seen in lower levels do not contribute significantly to the total solenoid field. When a strong front is present, it is frequently found that one jet may be closely associated with it, while another more or less parallel jet may be observed imbedded entirely within the warm air and not significantly associated with any front.

The characters of the individual current maxima in figs. 5 and 6 are essentially the same as shown earlier for single jets, the shears on the flanks being again of the order of the Coriolis parameter. About a 1 : 20 ratio is found for the lateral separations of the current maxima, this being roughly 500 km in fig. 5, and 25 km in fig. 6.

An interpretation by FUGLISTER (1951) suggests that multiple Gulf Stream maxima tend to appear in the open ocean east of Hatteras, where the main stream tends to become weaker than in the Florida current portion south of Hatteras. A tendency of the same sort is noted in individual synoptic cases of the jet stream. Where the jet stream is strong, there is a tendency for a single jet to dominate a region of, say, the size of the United States, while in the case of weak jets there may be several minor velocity streaks in such a region (see examples by RIEHL and TEWELES, 1953).

3. Waves on current systems

Wave disturbances in the atmosphere (example in fig. 10) range from a length of 2,000 km or less for "short" waves to a characteristic length of 5,000 to 7,000 km or more for "long" waves. In the Florida current portion where the Gulf Stream hugs the continental shelf, the characteristic length of waves on the current is about 220 km, according to a survey reported by O'HARE, CARLSON, and TAMBLYN (1954). In the oceanic portion farther east, the available observations (FUGLISTER and WORTHINGTON, 1951) indicate wave lengths of 350 km or longer.

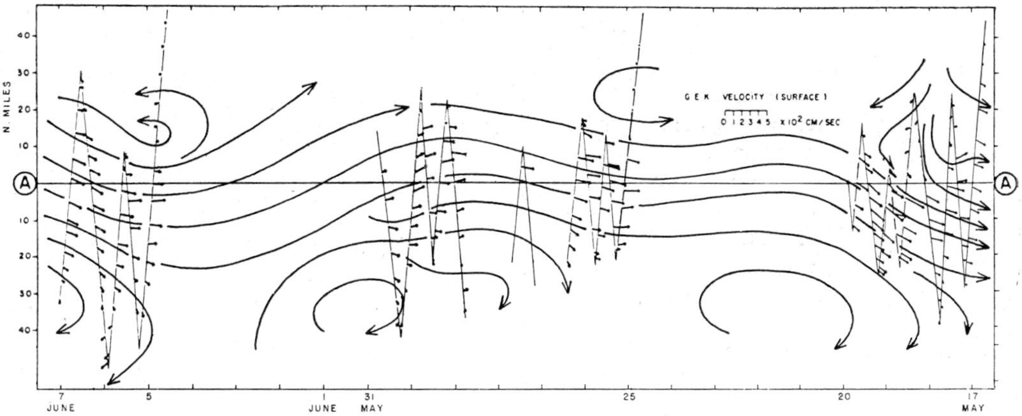

Fig. 7. Space-time section showing surface current observations from repeated sailings across Gulf Stream off Onslow Bay (SW of Hatteras), in May and June 1953. A—A indicates mean location of Gulf Stream. (After VON ARX, BUMPUS, and RICHARDSON, 1955; streamlines added.)

If these lengths are compared with the atmospheric *long* waves, a ratio around 1: 25 is found. This being the same ratio as observed for current widths, it appears that Gulf Stream waves bear a closer *geometrical* resemblance to atmospheric *long waves* than to the more transient short waves.

This conclusion appears to follow from the periodicity at a given location, also. In fig. 7 (VON ARX, BUMPUS, and RICHARDSON, 1955) is shown a series of observations made by the Woods Hole research vessel *Caryn*, which sailed back and forth across the Florida current along a fixed line during the 21-day period shown. Although varying interpretations of the "streamlines" are possible, it seems clear that the time taken for passage of a complete wave was between 9 and 14 days. Since atmospheric long waves, on the average, occupy a longitudinal sector of about 70° to 90° and move with average speeds of around 8° longitude per day, their periodicity (when it can be defined) is comparable to that of Gulf Stream waves. On the other hand, if the period of Gulf Stream waves is compared with that of atmospheric *short* waves (1 to 3 days), it is necessary to conclude, in agreement with ISELIN (1950), that, "The sort of changes that take place in one day in the atmospheric jets require a week or more in the Gulf Stream". Such a comparison is in fact justified if one considers the dynamical behaviour rather than simply the geometrical similarity of the current systems.

Current observations with the geomagnetic electrokinetograph (GEK) (VON ARX, 1951), carried out during a multiple ship survey, indicate that large values of cyclonic shear are associated with cyclonically curved portions of meanders in the Gulf Stream. Variations of relative vorticity in the surface current are of the order of the Coriolis parameter or larger. The waves concerned have much shorter lengths than do atmospheric waves, and the latitudinal variation of the Coriolis parameter contributes only an insignificant part to the vorticity variation in an individual wave disturbance. Since in a long Rossby wave the variations of relative and of the earth's vorticity are approximately equal and opposite in sign, it is evident that the Gulf Stream waves, although geometrically similar to long waves, are dynamically more analogous to very short atmospheric waves.

In fig. 7, the abscissa is time and the corresponding space dimension is unknown; it would be desirable to check on the probable dimensions of the waves, by application of some formula for the phase velocity. HAURWITZ and PANOFSKY (1950) have derived a wave formula applicable to Gulf Stream waves of restricted current width, which according to VON ARX (1951) gives computed phase velocities in good agreement with those observed during the multiple ship survey. Since particular solutions of their general formula are not conveniently available to the writer, a computation has been made using a form of PETTERSSEN's (1952) formula for jet stream waves:

$$C = U\left[1 + \left(\frac{L}{2\pi B}\right)^2\right]^{-1} \qquad (1)$$

This is a simplified form in which the assumption has been made that the horizontal variation of divergence is small; furthermore, a term involving variation of the Coriolis parameter has been dropped in accord with the earlier discussion. In (1), C is the wave speed, U the maximum speed at the current axis at a trough or ridge line, L the existing wave length (for a sinusoidal current), and B the "half width", or mean distance from the axis of the current to the points on either side where the current drops off to one half the maximum value.

Using several profiles constructed from data for some of the traverses in fig. 7, a mean value for B is taken to be 14 km, and U to be 3.4 m sec^{-1}. The wave length can be written $L = C\tau$, where τ is the wave period. As noted above, this is uncertain, but somewhere between 9 and 14 days. Solutions of (1) for the speed and wave length for these two cases are given in Table 1.

Table 1. Wave length and phase velocity of Florida current meanders using Petterssen's wave formula

τ	L	C
9 days	265 km	0.34 m sec^{-1}
14 days	305 km	0.25 m sec^{-1}

The speed C is seen to be in the neighborhood of 1/10 the maximum current speed. The second value (22 km or 12 mi/day) agrees well with the speed (11 mi/day) cited by FUGLISTER and WORTHINGTON (1951) observed in the multiple ship survey of 1950, for Gulf Stream waves just after they leave the continental shelf.

The wave lengths resulting from application of the wave formula (1) are intermediate between the typical wave length (220 km) reported by O'HARE *et al.* (1954) for the Florida current southwest of Hatteras, and the considerably larger

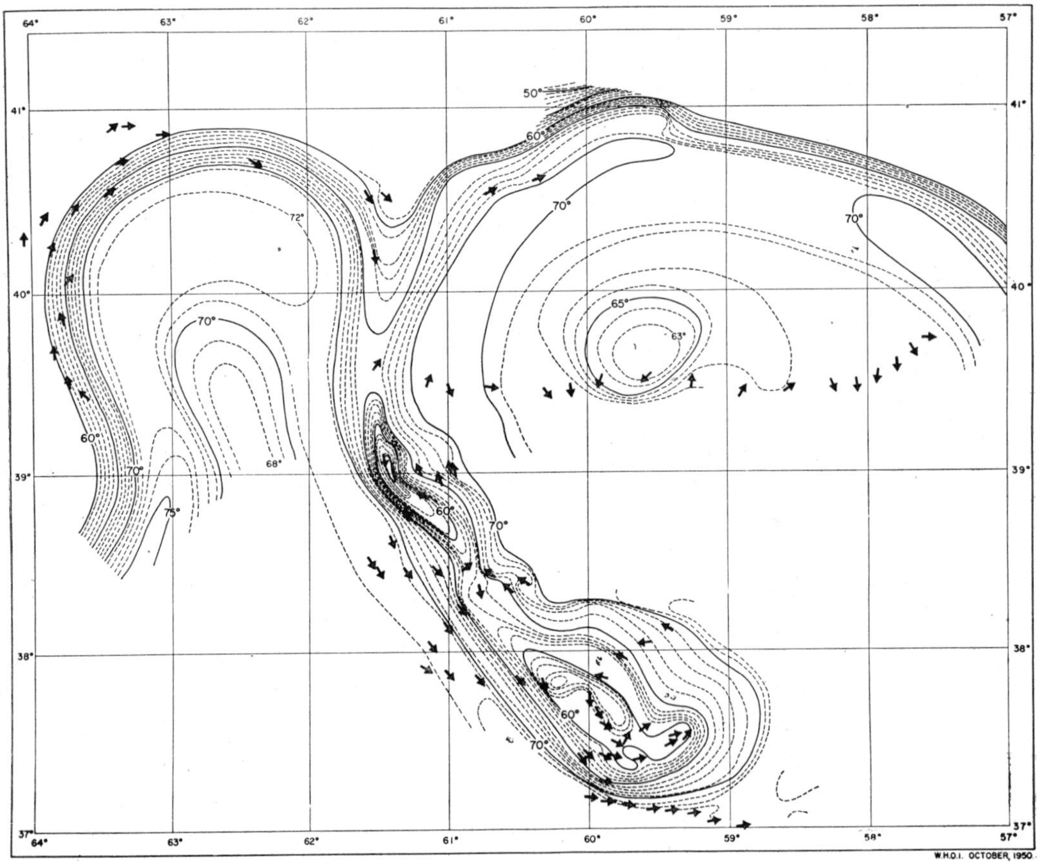

Fig. 8. A large meander in the Gulf Stream, 17 June 1950. Mean temperature, deg F, in the upper 200-meter layer. Current directions from GEK. (FUGLISTER and WORTHINGTON, 1951.)

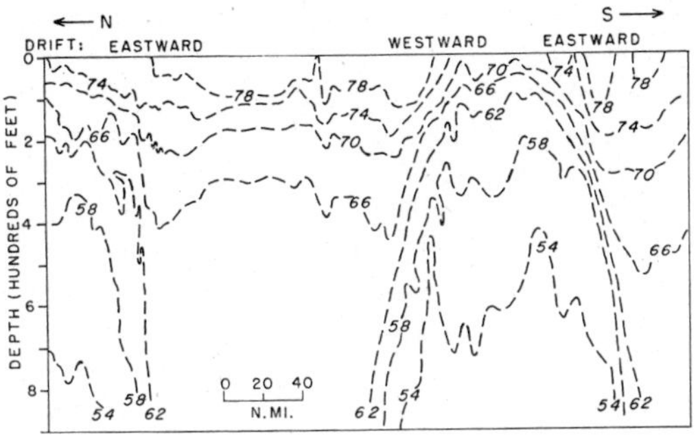

Fig. 9. Cross section through a cyclonic eddy of the type shown in fig. 8, observed in May 1946 near 38° N, 67° W. Isotherms in deg F. (ISELIN and FUGLISTER, 1948.)

wave lengths in the open ocean farther east. It should be noted, however, that in the form (1) the variations of horizontal divergence along streamlines have been neglected. Evidence given by VON ARX (1951) indicates that appreciable variations of divergence do occur, of the same kind that occur in the upper part of the troposphere, suggesting that the wave lengths computed above may be too long. Moreover, there is some uncertainty in a correction factor applied to the measured values of U, which may contribute in the same direction.

Available evidence is fragmentary, but definitely suggests[3] that Gulf Stream meanders become longer and slower-moving after the Stream leaves the continental shelf (note that in equation (1), increased wave length implies slower phase velocity, if stream speed and profile remain the same). Consequently, it may be concluded that more waves pass a given location in the Florida current portion than in the open ocean portion; this implies that some of the small meanders perish while others grow. There is, however, the possibility that, as in the atmosphere, the current system in the open ocean contains two scales of waves, one having large amplitude and length and another with smaller amplitude and length, which travel through the large disturbances and are difficult to discern with clarity because of their feeble amplitude when superimposed on major disturbances.

Structure of large-scale meanders. — ISELIN and FUGLISTER (1948) have drawn attention to the large cyclonic and anticyclonic eddies in the Gulf Stream region, and have suggested that these phenomena are parallel in nature to those

[3] See summary of Gulf Stream positions from various surveys, fig. 4 in FUGLISTER and WORTHINGTON (1951); also FORD and MILLER (1952).

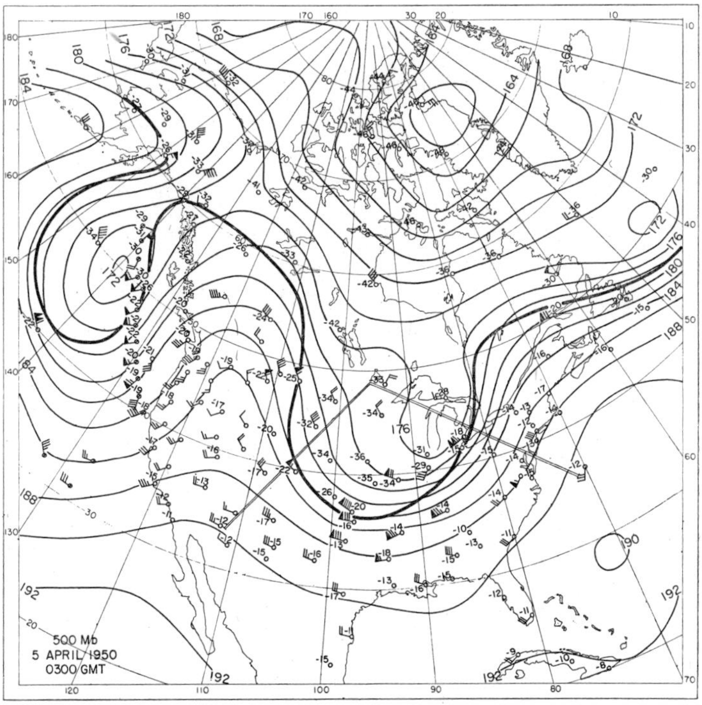

Fig. 10. 500-mb chart, 0300 GCT 5 April 1950. Heavy line, warm boundary of polar front; thin lines, isobaric contours (hundreds of feet). At stations, temperature (deg C) and wind (full barb, 10 knots; triangular flag, 50 knots). (PALMÉN and NEWTON, 1951.)

observed in the region of strong westerlies in the upper atmosphere.

Rossby (1951), exploring this comparison further, has demonstrated some striking similarities between large-scale meanders in atmosphere and ocean. In particular, he has indicated that the formation of large meanders tends to occur where the basic current velocity decreases downstream (characteristic in general for the Gulf Stream region east of Hatteras, and for regions upstream from "blocks" in the atmosphere). In such a region, according to Rossby, increase in amplitude of wave disturbances results from a longitudinal crowding and lateral expansion of the current system, with which is associated a decrease of phase velocity downstream.

Figure 8 shows a Gulf Stream meander (located 15° longitude east of Cape Hatteras) at an advanced stage of development. A somewhat similar perturbation on the polar front is seen in fig. 10, off the West Coast.[4] The histories of the development processes are quite analogous in the two cases, the elongated pendants of cold water or air having originated by growth in amplitude of disturbances on the Gulf Stream and the polar front respectively (Palmén, 1949; The University of Chicago, 1947; Hsieh, 1949). In fig. 10, the cold air in the western disturbance is in the process of becoming cut off (at 500 mb) from the main body of polar air to the north. Daily synoptic charts given by Fuglister and Worthington (1951) show that such a seclusion from the main cold water mass also occurred shortly afterward in the meander shown in fig. 8.

The overall dimensions of the disturbances in fig. 10 are roughly five to ten times those in fig. 8. In the sense that these disturbances are among the largest found in the two current systems, they are comparable. As shown earlier, however, waves of this scale on the Gulf Stream system must be regarded as dynamically analogous to "short waves", while those in fig. 10 are in the scale of "long wave" disturbances in the atmosphere.

Figure 9 shows a cross section through a cut-off cold water mass of the same type as in fig. 8, which was observed on an earlier cruise (Iselin and Fuglister, 1948). The cold dome on the right corresponds to a cyclonic eddy 60 mi wide, which extended 200 mi east-west; on the left side of the section the temperature concentration evidently corresponds to the main current of the Gulf Stream from which the eddy had become detached. A section along the 60th meridian in fig. 8 would probably be similar to fig. 9. Figure 11 shows a cross section through the eastern wave trough in fig. 10, which had not yet reached as advanced a stage of development as the trough further west, but could otherwise be considered comparable.

The most striking feature of both fig. 9 and fig. 11 (where the part below about 300 mb should be compared) is the remarkable horizontal

[4] An atmospheric meander strikingly similar to fig. 8 has been investigated by Palmén and Nagler (1949; see their fig. 19). Large oceanic current perturbations are also found in the Kuroshio (Uda, 1949).

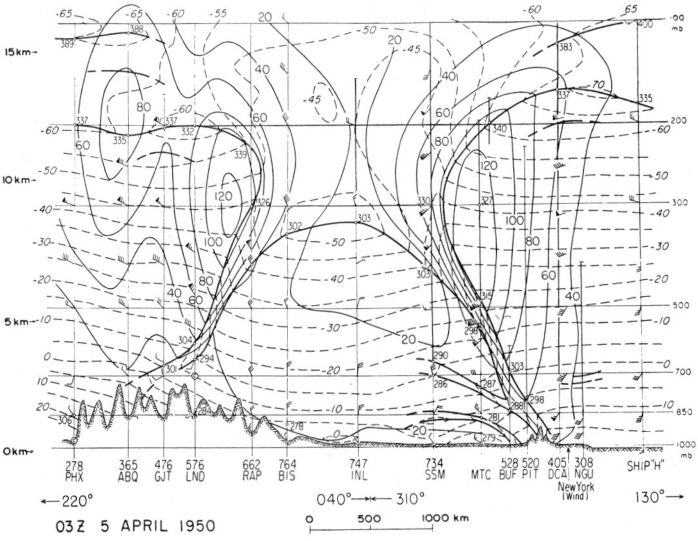

Fig. 11. Vertical cross section through eastern cold tongue in fig. 10. Left half is nearly normal to northwesterly flow on west side of trough; right half across southwesterly flow east of trough, along double lines in fig. 10. Heavy lines, frontal boundaries and tropopauses; dashed lines, isotherms; thin solid lines, isotachs (knots); wind symbols plotted as through north were at top of section. (Newton, 1958.)

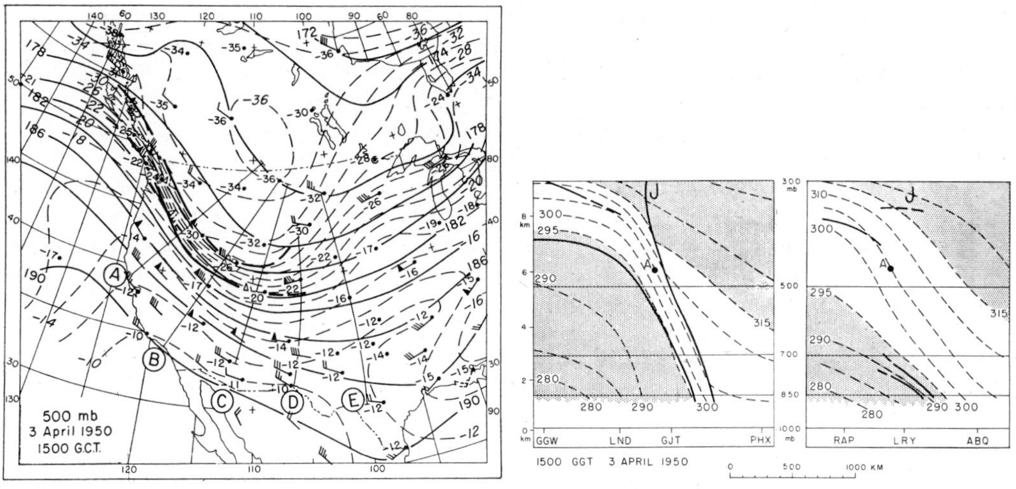

a b c

Fig. 12. (a) 500-mb chart, 1500 GCT 3 April 1950. Heavy lines indicate distinct boundaries of frontal layer; (b) section along line C; (c) section along lire D. Dashed lin:s are isentropes (deg K); stippled where potential temperature is greater than 315 K or less than 295 K. (NEWTON, 1954.)

concentration of isotherms, much more pronounced than in the sections shown earlier. Practically all of the available temperature contrast, about 7—8° C in fig. 9 and 10—15° C in fig. 11, is confined to the frontal zones bounding the cold domes.

The widths of the frontal zones are evidently about 15 km and 200 km respectively, roughly in the ratio 1 : 10 or 1 : 15 (about the same ratio as for the large-scale meander sizes). In the examples shown, the slopes of the frontal surfaces are in each case about 1 : 100; numerous other sections are also available which show that frontal slopes are on the average about the same for oceanic and atmospheric systems. This being the case, the vertical dimensions through the frontal layer are in about the same ratio as are the horizontal dimensions, corresponding nearly to the ratio 1 : 10 found earlier to be characteristic for the "depths" of the current systems.

The cold domes in figs. 9 and 11 were relatively symmetrical at the times shown. In fig. 8 there is evidence of asymmetry, with stronger horizontal temperature gradients and surface currents on the southwest than on the east side of the

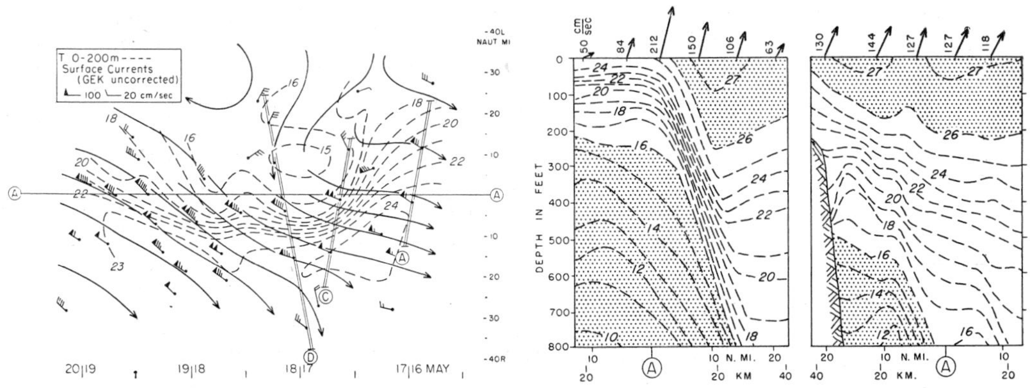

a b c

Fig. 13. (a) Mean isotherms for upper 200-meter layer (dashed, deg C), and surface streamlines, for right-hand group of observations in fig. 7; (b) section along line C; (c) section along line A; stippled where warmer than 26 C or colder than 16 C; GEK (uncorrected) surface currents at top. (After VON ARX, BUMPUS and RICHARDSON, 1955; chart (a) is writer's interpretation from their data.)

cold tongue. Such an asymmetry is characteristic of the developing stages of atmospheric troughs, and was strongly evident one day before the time of fig. 11.[5]

4. Variations in thermal structure

In connection with the examples shown earlier, it was noted that marked variations in thermal structure are to be found in different locations along the jet stream and the Gulf Stream. Figures 12 and 13 illustrate such variations, and bring out the astonishing similarities which can be found between atmospheric and oceanic systems.

The situation shown in fig. 13a (constructed from data given by VON ARX *et al.*, 1954) corresponds to the group of observations on the extreme right of fig. 7. Comparison with fig. 12a shows that the horizontal variations of temperature are very similar in the two cases, even in regard to the isotherm-streamline relationship.

Fig. 13a was constructed from successive sections along one traverse, and some caution must be observed in interpreting it in all aspects as a space map of the thermal field. However, it is probably admissible to regard the sections in parts *b* and *c* of figs. 12 and 13 as analogous in showing the very rapid variations to be found at a given time in locations relatively close together.

In the upstream sections (figs. 12b and 13b), both the vertical and horizontal gradients of temperature are highly concentrated in the frontal layer, while in the downstream sections the gradients become quite spread out. This variation is reflected in the velocity profiles also, which are sharply peaked in the upstream sections.

Structure of velocity fields. — Figures 14 and 15 illustrate the variations of the velocity field that accompany variations in thermal structure of this kind (the upstream sections are taken in somewhat different locations than in figs. 12b and 13b).

In fig. 14 the isotachs were analyzed with help from observed as well as geostrophic winds at all levels. In fig. 15 the surface velocity profile was constructed from GEK measurements given by VON ARX *et al.* (1954). Comparison of GEK velocities with navigational calculations of drift indicated that GEK speeds were too low, by a factor whose median value for the whole set of observations was 1.46. This factor (which varies) was here used as a constant multiplier for all surface current measurements. Below the surface, the current was computed by subtracting, from the observed surface current, a vertical shear computed from the geostrophic current equation.[6]

[5] For a discussion of the development of this trough from the standpoint of variations of frontal structure, see NEWTON (1958).

[6] In the latter operation, since subsurface salinities were not available, special tables for the Onslow Bay Section, given by STOMMEL (1947), were used in calculating dynamic height anomalies from the temperature field. In the uppermost strata, some loss of accuracy is expected (namely the computed vertical shear is too large) since the T—S correlation there is not so pronounced as in lower depths. Estimates of the probable error from this source, based on Stommel's tables, are no more than ten to twenty per cent of the total computed geostrophic current variations.

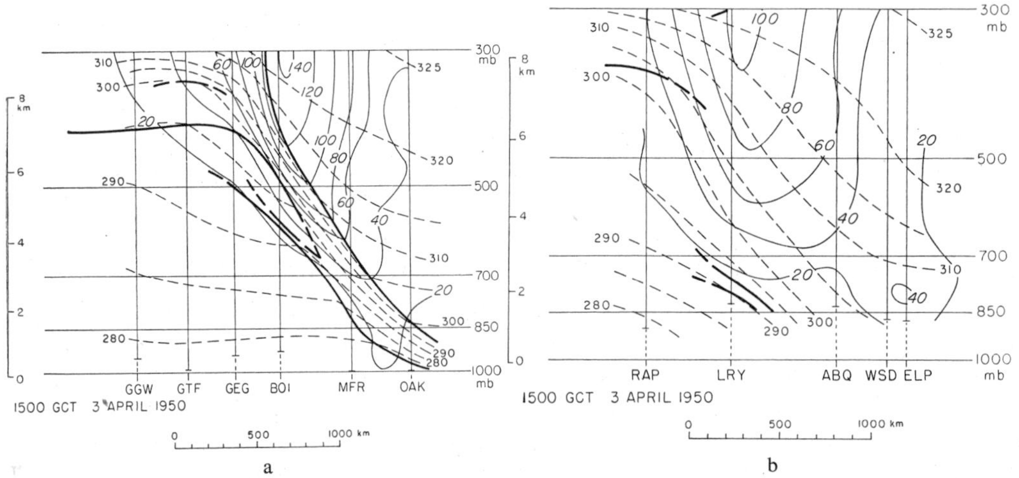

Fig. 14. Cross sections along (a) line A and (b) line D, in fig. 12 a. Solid thin lines, isotachs (knots); dashed lines, potential temperature (deg K); heavy lines, frontal boundaries or tropopause.

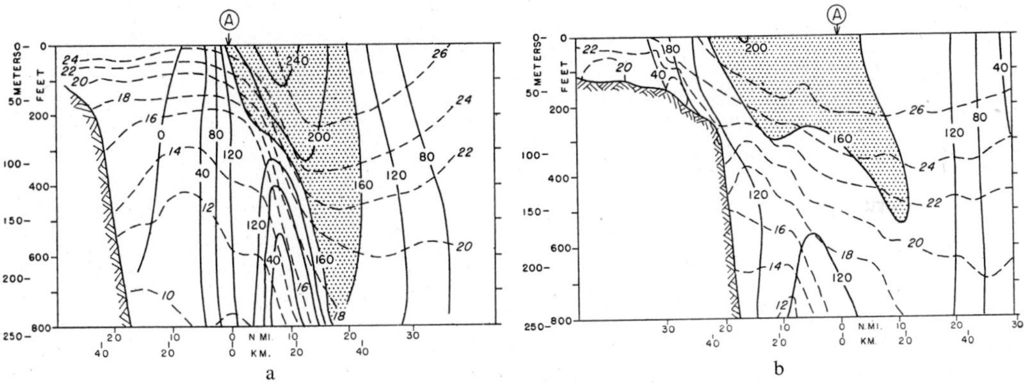

Fig. 15. Sections along (a) line D and (b) line A, in fig. 13 a. Dashed lines, isotherms (deg C); solid lines, isotachs (cm/sec). (Currents computed from data given by von Arx *et al.*, 1955; see text.)

The velocity sections show, for both current systems, that the currents are much more clearly defined, below as well as at the level of maximum speed, in the presence of fronts than in their absence. Within the frontal layer, both figs. 14a and 15a indicate cyclonic shear with values between 1 and 2 m/sec in 10 km horizontal distance (up to twice the Coriolis parameter). The frontal slopes are nearly equal (1 : 85 in fig. 12b and 1 : 70 in fig. 13b), and the vertical shears within the frontal layers are almost equal, with values between 1 and 2 m/sec in 100 m vertical distance.[7]

Thus structurally the oceanic and atmospheric frontal zones are amazingly alike. The only significant difference is that in fig. 15a, there appears a narrow region just inside the cold water mass where there is very little decay of current velocity below 100 m depth. Whether this feature of the geostrophic current calculation (which results in a double current structure at lower levels not evident in fig. 14a) is real, is open to doubt. The indicated structure appears on all of the nine sections embodied in fig. 13a, for which such subsurface calculations were made, and in about the same degree. As a possible argument against the reality of the secondary maximum, it is noteworthy that its right flank is dynamically unstable, having an anticyclonic geostrophic shear exceeding the value of the Coriolis parameter.

Transverse circulations in frontal zones. — As seen from figs. 14 and 15, the most pronounced variations in kinematic and thermal structures are to be found on the cyclonic sides of the current systems. In the atmospheric case, where both space and time variations can be observed readily, it is found that frontal zones of the sort shown in fig. 12a tend to move bodily along with the wind, but at a slower speed than the average wind in higher levels.

This being the case, the air in the upper troposphere overtakes such a frontal zone on the upstream side and blows out of it on the downstream ("exit") end. The structural variations imply that an individual mass of air in the upper troposphere, on entering or leaving the frontal layer, undergoes a marked increase or decrease of both horizontal and vertical shear, and horizontal and vertical potential temperature gradient (see points "A" in figs. 12b and 12c).

Synoptic evidence shows that lateral confluence of the streamlines can partly account for concentration of the fields in the horizontal (Namias and Clapp, 1949). That this mechanism is of consequence in the oceans also, is shown by Pillsbury's (1890) observations which indicate appreciable lateral confluence during periods when the Gulf Stream in the Florida Straits is most concentrated.

Computations taking into account the detailed structure (Miller, 1948; Newton and Carson, 1953; Reed and Sanders, 1953; Newton, 1954) show, however, that in the middle troposphere the observed degree of individual frontogenesis can only be accounted for by calling into play certain additional transverse circulations. Vertical shear and stability are intensified by vertical variations of the horizontal cross-stream circulation in a direct sense about the solenoids, which

[7] It should be noted that the oceanic sections show only the upper 250 m of the barocline layer, which as shown by figs. 1 and 6 extends to three to four times that depth.

are kinetic energy-producing (VAN MIEGHEM, 1950). Horizontal temperature gradients and wind shear, on the other hand, are intensified by differential vertical motions in an indirect solenoidal sense; that is, descent of the warm air relative to the cold, with consequent differential vertical transport of momentum and heat into a horizontal surface. This last process is in agreement with the types of vertical circulation postulated by ROSSBY (1936; 1947) as necessary to create compatibility between velocity and mass fields. Upwelling of cold water on the left flank of the Gulf Stream, thought by some oceanographers to play a role in its behaviour, would contribute to frontogenesis in the same way (see, e.g., UDA, 1949).

Transverse motions of these kinds, although appreciable, act in opposite sense in "entrance" and "exit" of a frontal zone. Considering that several distinct frontal segments may be found around the hemisphere, the average meridional circulation would, of course, only appear as a residual which is small compared to the transverse circulations observed locally. These may in a way be regarded as an "embroidery", although an apparently essential one, on a mean circulation scheme of the type embodied in Rossby's planetary jet stream theory. Likewise, fluctuations in Gulf Stream structure could be regarded in the same way.

The variations illustrated in fig. 13 b, c are the most pronounced ones that occurred in the 21-day period of the cruise summarized in fig. 7. Weaker variations of the same sort were, however, observed from section to section throughout the series of observations. From inspection of the twenty-seven sections presented in the paper by VON ARX *et al.* (1955), it appears that complete cyclic variations from weak to strong to weak thermal concentrations at the 100- to 200-meter levels occupied between three and four days.

It appears quite reasonable to suppose that these local variations can be interpreted in the same way as in the atmosphere, namely as moving streaks of strong and weak portions of the Gulf Stream front. Aerial reconnaissance of the Gulf Stream, by VON ARX and RICHARDSON (1954), indeed suggests that this is so. Visual evidence

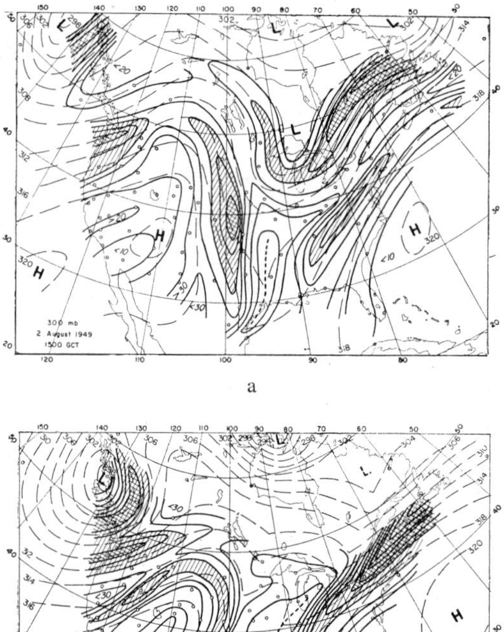

a

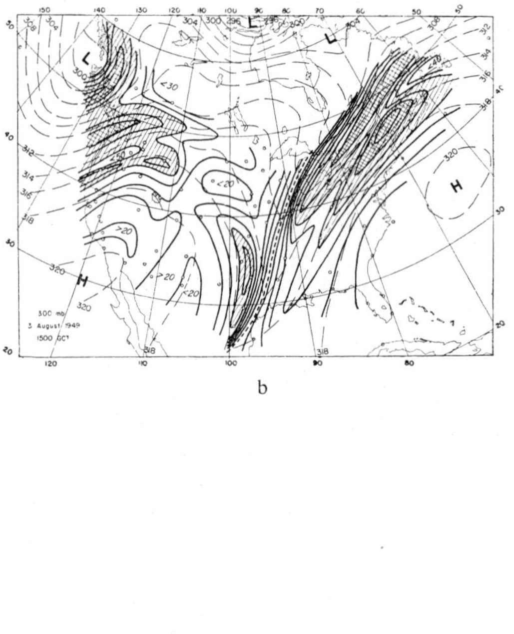

b

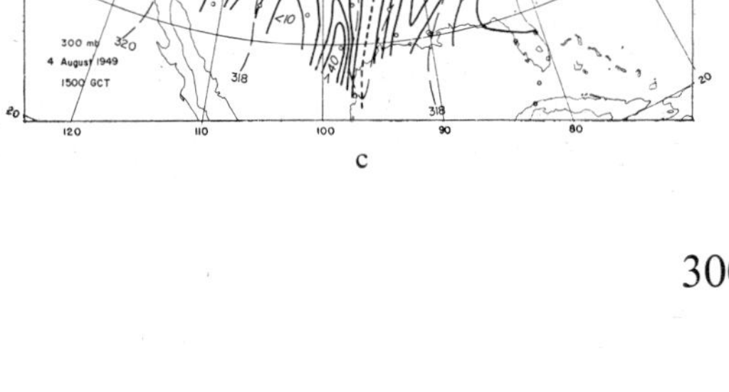

c

Fig. 16. 300-mb charts for (a) 1500 GCT 2 August; (b) 1500 GCT 3 August; (c) 1500 GCT 4 August 1949. Dashed lines, height contours; solid lines, isotachs at 10-knot intervals; hatched where wind speed over 50 knots, cross-hatched over 70 knots. (NEWTON and CARSON, 1953.)

and radiometer measurements show the presence of distinct overlapping segments of the surface frontal outcrop with individual lengths 100 to 300 km. VON ARX *et al.* state, "It is conceivable that each filament in the structure of the Gulf Stream may be in some way related to a day's discharge of water from the Gulf of Mexico . . . [which] in turn may be related to the tidal sequence . . ." More evidence is required to decide firmly whether the visible streaks have daily, or somewhat longer local periods as suggested above.

5. Velocity variations along the current

There is a general tendency for well developed fronts to be associated with strong jets, so that frontal variations of the kind discussed above will often be connected with velocity variations along the current direction.

Such velocity variations are not, however, always associated with distinct frontal variations. Figure 16 shows a series of summertime 300-mb charts, characterized not only by parallel multiple currents but by strong axial speed variations. In the upper troposphere, individual speed maxima of the kind shown here move slower than the wind in their neighborhood, so that the air near the jet axis undergoes strong acceleration and deceleration in passing through them. Thus ageostrophic (or agradient) motions are important in the jet stream region.

Figure 17 shows an interpretation of the surface velocity data given by VON ARX *et al.* (1954). It should be observed that the streamline pattern is apparently associated with fairly large and slow-moving wave disturbances (fig. 7), whose local time scale is entirely different from that of the speed variations shown. Thus fig. 17 is some sort of hybrid space-time chart.

Several distinct speed maxima are present in fig. 17a, whose local period appears to be in the neighborhood of a day. PILLSBURY (1890) showed that variations of Gulf Stream transport, having a period of a lunar day, occur as a result of tidal fluctuations of sea level in the Gulf of MEXICO.

As noted earlier, the major variations in frontal strength seem to have a period of three to four days, different from that of the speed maxima. The conclusion to be drawn is that the field of mass distribution does not vary in the same manner as the surface velocity field (although averaged over periods of days this may be so), so that the current must have important

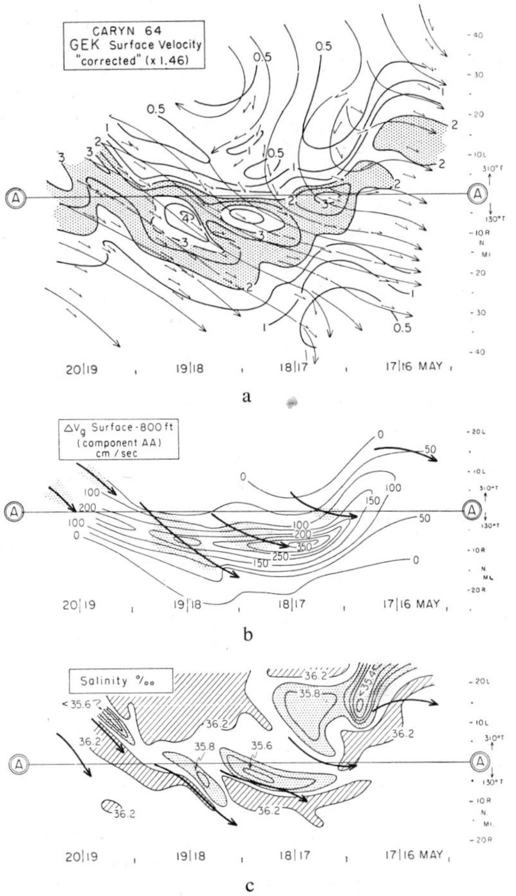

Fig. 17. (a) Surface streamlines (thin lines) and isotachs (heavy lines, m/sec.) for observations in Gulf Stream summarized in fig. 13 a. Measured current directions indicated by small arrows. (b) Geostrophic current variation from surface down to 800-foot depth (cm/sec). Heavy arrows, axes of surface current maxima; stippling shows areas where surface current speed exceeded 300 cm/sec. (c) Surface salinity and surface current axes; stippled where salinity is less than 36.0 ‰. (Analyzed from data given by VON ARX *et al.*, 1954.)

ageostrophic fluctuations. This is brought out graphically by fig. 17b, in which the local speed maxima are superimposed on the field of computed geostrophic current difference from surface down to 250 m depth. The mean thermal field appears to be relatively unaffected by the daily current fluctuations, although at the surface (fig. 17c) streaks of fresh and saline water are closely correlated with the more clearly defined speed maxima.

Laterally bounded jets. — The presence of the Gulf Stream as a concentrated current is essentially connected with the intimate presence of a

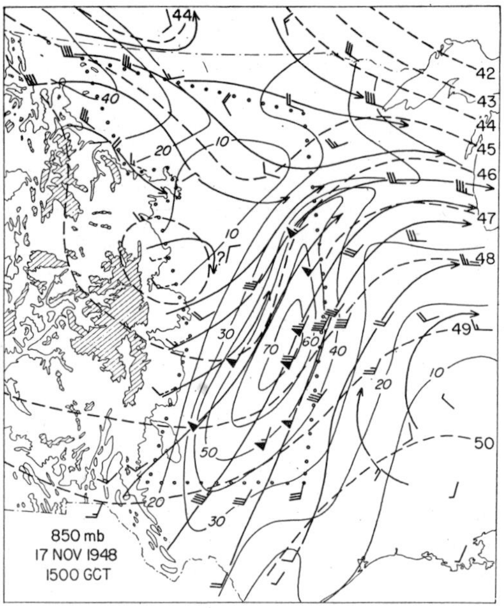

Fig. 18. 850-mb chart, 1500 GCT 17 November 1948. Solid lines with arrowheads are streamlines; thinner solid lines are isotachs (knots); dashed lines, contours of 850-mb surface (hundreds of feet). Wind observations: full barb, 10 knots; triangle, 50 knots. Mountain contours shown for 8000-foot (hatched inside) and 5000-foot levels. Isobaric surface intersects terrain near the latter. (NEWTON, 1956.)

lateral land boundary over much of its length (ROSSBY, 1936; STOMMEL, 1948). In the Florida Straits section, tide-gauge records indicate that accelerations of the current are closely connected with a downward slope of the free surface, along the current direction (MONTGOMERY, 1941; STOMMEL, 1953).

A partial analogy is afforded by the low-level jet streams typically found near 850 mb (1,500 m/sea level), which in North America reach their strongest development just east of the Rocky Mountains. An example is shown in fig. 18. Although due to changing synoptic situations such jets are transient phenomena, they may persist for days at a time.

In a situation of this kind, the air motions are constrained to lie more or less in isentropic surfaces, which intersect the land surface sloping upward toward the west. A consequence is that when the isobaric contours are oriented normal to the mountain contours as in fig. 18, the air tends to flow parallel to the physical boundary imposed by the land contours on the west, and air motions cut strongly across the isobaric contours.

In this case (wherein the isotach pattern was changing slowly) the height drop along the current axis, between the 30- and 70-knot isotachs upstream from the wind-speed maximum, is seen from the figure to be about 170 ft. This is almost exactly the amount of potential energy change required to account for the observed increase of kinetic energy downstream along the streamline.

Computations of the factors in circulation change for this case (NEWTON, 1956) indicate that a major source for the high vorticity on the left side of the jet was a torque due to lateral differences in frictional stress. These arise because accelerations of the air on the west boundary are strongly retarded by friction, while more or less free acceleration is allowed in the jet axis, which averages 1 km above the terrain and is thus not so strongly affected by surface friction.

Ageostrophic motions and inertia oscillations. — In the case of fluid motions in a uniform unchanging pressure field, it can be shown that any initially imposed ageostrophic motion will remain unchanged in magnitude but will undergo a cyclical variation in direction with time, whose period (the time between successive maxima or minima in particle speed) is ½ day cscΦ, the same as that of an inertia circle.

The notion of such an inertia oscillation is apt in the case of the Florida current, because the tidal variations in the Gulf of Mexico initiate impulses which must be strongly ageostrophic. Furthermore, these impulses, whose period is a lunar day, are imposed at a latitude (Florida Straits, 30° N) where the inertia period is also one day. It is heuristically attractive to suppose that this coincidence of the natural periods of the initiating impulse and of the resulting oscillations should favor their maintenance some distance after leaving their source.

BLACKADAR (1957) has shown that an inertia oscillation exists in the atmospheric boundary layer, which is initiated by diurnal variations in frictional coupling (and thus in the ageostrophic wind) between air and earth's surface. Such an oscillation has significant effects on diurnal variations of wind direction and speed over a wide area. Another manifestation possibly connected with inertia oscillations is found if one considers the time variations of wind velocity as air blows through an isotach pattern of the type shown in fig. 18.

In fig. 18 an average speed for the air in the general neighborhood of the jet may be taken as around 50 kt. Traveling at this average speed, about 22 hr would be required for an air particle to pass from the upstream region of weak wind speed, through the velocity maximum, to the downstream speed minimum, a distance of about 2,000 km. It seems significant that this time is very close to the inertia period for those latitudes, suggesting that the restricted length of the velocity streak is related to the inertia period, which is a natural period for the total acceleration and deceleration.

In the upper troposphere, some sort of relationship of this general nature is suggested by a crude proportionality (fig. 16) between lengths of jet velocity streaks and the wind speed; but this is obviously not so simple as suggested by the example above.

If such a streak moves with speed c, and the distance between wind speed maxima or minima is L, the period of a complete acceleration-deceleration cycle is $T = L/(\bar{v} - c)$, where $\bar{v}$ is the average current speed. Applying this to the jet streaks in fig. 16, it is found that T is somewhat longer than the inertia period of 0.7 to 0.9 day. However, it can be shown that if the pressure-gradient field (or the geostrophic wind $\mathbf{V}_g$) is not uniform but changes along with the real wind, the "inertia" period is longer than the half pendulum day. For example, if $d\mathbf{V}_g/dt = \frac{1}{2} \cdot (d\mathbf{V}/dt)$, the period of oscillation at latitude 30° would be two days instead of one. Such a tendency is apparent in the atmosphere.

This analogy with the Gulf Stream streaks can hardly be regarded as very concrete; however, it does suggest a possible approach to explaining the presence and dimensions of the axial velocity variations characterizing the current systems. The suggestion proposed here is in general accord with a principle outlined by ROSSBY (1951), although not all the details are clear. Rossby showed that with a prescribed volume transport in a current system, abstraction of momentum in certain layers of the system (such as by friction at a boundary) must lead to a concentration and intensification of the current in other layers. The necessary accelerations must be accounted for by height (or pressure) variations along the direction of flow. In the case of a circumpolar jet (for example) these axial variations cannot exist all around the hemisphere but must be accompanied by alternate axial variations of the opposite kind. Thus, Rossby concludes, a current system on which a velocity perturbation is imposed would consist of alternate velocity streaks of restricted length.

Acknowledgement

This paper was begun several years ago at the suggestion of Professor C.-G. Rossby. The opportunity I have had to share in his boundless scientific vision, enthusiasm, and integrity, and equally his personal nobility, generosity, and wisdom, is something for which I will always be profoundly grateful.

In addition to numerous stimulating conversations with Professor Rossby on the subject matter of this paper, I take pleasure in acknowledging very helpful discussions with Messrs. W. S. von Arx, C. O'D. Iselin, F. C. Fuglister, H. Stommel, and L. V. Worthington, during a stay at Woods Hole Oceanographic Institution in the summer of 1953.

REFERENCES

BERGGREN, R., 1953: On frontal analysis in the higher troposphere and the lower stratosphere. *Arkiv för Geofysik* (Stockholm), **2**, 13—58.

BLACKADAR, A. K., 1957: Boundary layer wind maxima and their significance for the growth of nocturnal inversions. *Bull. Amer. Metor. Soc.*, **38**, 283—290.

CRESSMAN, G. P., 1950: Variations in the structure of the upper westerlies. *J. Meteor.*, **7**, 39—47.

FORD, W. L., and MILLER, A. R., 1952: The surface layer of the Gulf Stream and adjacent waters. *J. Mar. Res.*, **11**, 267—280.

FUGLISTER, F. C., 1951: Multiple currents in the Gulf Stream system. *Tellus*, **3**, 230—233.

FUGLISTER, F. C., and WORTHINGTON, L. V., 1951: Some results of a multiple ship survey of the Gulf Stream. *Tellus*, **3**, 1—14.

HAURWITZ, B., and PANOFSKY, H. A., 1950: Stability and meandering of the Gulf Stream. *Trans. Amer. Geophys. Un.*, **31**, 723—731.

HSIEH, Y.-P., 1949: An investigation of a selected cold vortex over North America. *J. Meteor.*, **6**, 401—410.

ISELIN, C. O'D., 1936: A study of the circulation of the western North Atlantic. *Pap. Phys. Ocean. and Meteor.*, **4**, No. 4 (101 pp).

ISELIN, C. O'D., and FUGLISTER, F. C., 1948: Some recent developments in the study of the Gulf Stream. *J. Mar. Res.*, **7**, 317—329.

ISELIN, C. O'D., 1950: Some common characteristics of the Gulf Stream and the atmospheric jet stream. *Trans., New York Acad. Sci., Ser. II*, **13**, 84—86.

MCINTYRE, D. P., and LEE, R., 1953: Jet streams in middle and high latitudes. *Proc. Toronto Meteor. Conf., Roy. Meteor. Soc.*, 172—181.

MILLER, J. E., 1948: On the concept of frontogenesis. *J. Meteor.*, **5**, 169—171.

MONTGOMERY, R. B., 1941: Sea level difference between Key West and Miami, Florida. *J. Mar. Res.*, **4**, 32—37.

MUNK, W., and CARRIER, G. F., 1950: The wind-driven circulation in ocean basins of various shapes. *Tellus*, **2**, 158—167.

NAMIAS, J., and CLAPP, P. F., 1944: Studies of the motion and development of long waves in the westerlies. *J. Meteor.*, **1**, 57—77.

NAMIAS, J., and CLAPP, P. F., 1949: Confluence theory of the high-tropospheric jet stream. *J. Meteor.*, **6**, 330—336.

NEWTON, C. W., and CARSON, J. E., 1953: Structure of wind field and variations of vorticity in a summer situation. *Tellus*, **5**, 321—339.

NEWTON, C. W., 1954: Frontogenesis and frontolysis as a three-dimensional process. *J. Meteor.*, **11**, 449—461.

— 1956: Mechanisms of circulation change during a lee cyclogenesis. *J. Meteor.*, **13**, 528—539.

— 1958: Variations in frontal structure of upper level troughs. *Geophysica, Palmén 60th Anniv. Vol.* (Helsinki), **6**, 357—375.

O'HARE, J. E., CARLSON, Q. H., and TAMBLYN, W. E., 1954: Some results of a tanker survey of the Gulf Stream. *Trans. Amer. Geophys. Un.*, **35**, 420—430.

PALMÉN, E., 1948: On the distribution of temperature and wind in the upper westerlies. *J. Meteor.*, **5**, 20—27.

PALMÉN, E., and NAGLER, K. M., 1948: An analysis of the wind and temperature distribution in the free atmosphere over North America in a case of approximately westerly flow. *J. Meteor.*, **5**, 58—64.

PALMÉN, E., 1949: On the origin and structure of high-level cyclones south of the maximum westerlies. *Tellus*, **1**, No. 1, 22—31.

PALMÉN, E., and NAGLER, K. M., 1949: The formation and structure of a large-scale disturbance in the westerlies. *J. Meteor.*, **6**, 227—242.

PALMÉN, E., 1951: The rôle of atmospheric disburbances in the general circulation. *Quart. J. Roy. Meteor. Soc.*, **77**, 337—354.

PETTERSSEN, S., 1952: On the propagation and growth of jet stream waves. *Quart. J. Roy. Meteor. Soc.*, **78**, 337—353.

PHILLIPS, N. A., 1950: The behaviour of jet streams over eastern North America during January and February 1948. *Tellus*, **2**, 116—124.

PILLSBURY, J. E., 1890: Gulf Stream investigations and results. *U.S. Coast and Geod. Surv., Ann. Rep. 1890, Appendix 10*, 461—620.

REED, R. J., and SANDERS, F., 1953: An investigation of the development of a mid-tropospheric frontal zone and its associated vorticity field. *J. Meteor.*, **10**, 338—349.

RIEHL, H., and TEWELES, S., 1953: A further study on the relation between the jet stream and cyclone formation. *Tellus*, **5**, 66—79.

ROSSBY, C.-G., 1936: Dynamics of steady ocean currents in the light of experimental fluid mechanics. *Pap. Phys. Ocean. and Meteor.*, **5**, No. 1 (43 pp.).

— 1947: On the distribution of angular velocity in gaseous envelopes under the influence of large-scale horizontal mixing processes. *Bull. Amer. Meteor. Soc.*, **28**, 53—68.

— 1949: On the nature of the general circulation of the lower atmosphere. In: *The atmospheres of the earth and planets* (Ed., G. P. Kuiper). Chicago, Univ. Chicago Press (pp. 16—48).

— 1951: On the vertical and horizontal concentration of momentum in air and ocean currents. *Tellus*, **3**, 15—27.

— 1951: A comparison of current patterns in the atmosphere and in the ocean basins. *Un. Geod. et. Geophys. Int., 9th Gen. Assy., Assoc. de Météor.*, Brussels, 9—31.

STOMMEL, H., 1947: Note on the use of the T—S correlation for dynamic height anomaly computations. *J. Mar. Res.*, **6**, 85—92.

— 1948: The westward intensification of wind-driven ocean currents. *Trans. Amer. Geophys. Un.*, **29**, 202—209.

— 1953: Examples of the possible role of inertia and stratification in the dynamics of the Gulf Stream system. *J. Mar. Res.*, **12**, 184—195.

UDA, M., 1949: On the correlated fluctuation of the Kuroshio current and the cold water mass. *Oceanogr. Mag.*, (Tokyo), **1**, 1—12.

UNIVERSITY OF CHICAGO, Department of Meteorology, 1947: On the general circulation of the atmosphere in middle latitudes. *Bull. Amer. Meteor. Soc.*, **28**, 255—280.

VAN MIEGHEM, J., 1950: Sur la circulation transversale associée à un courant atmosphérique. *Tellus*, **2**, 52—55.

VON ARX, W. S., 1952: Notes on the surface velocity profile and horizontal shear across the width of the Gulf Stream *Tellus*, **4**, 211—214.

VON ARX, W. S., BUMPUS, D. F., and RICHARDSON, W. S., 1955: On the fine structure of the Gulf Stream front. *Deep Sea Res.*, **3**, 46—65.

VUORELA, L. A., 1953: On the air flow connected with the invasion of upper tropical air over northwestern Europe. *Geophysica* (Helsinki), **4**, 105—130.

WORTHINGTON, L. V., 1954: Three detailed cross-sections of the Gulf Stream. *Tellus*, **6**, 116—123.

(Manuscript received July 8, 1958)

On Hydrodynamic Instability Caused by an Approach of Subtropical and Polarfront Jet Stream in Northern Latitudes before the Onset of Strong Cyclogenesis

By Friedrich Defant[1]

International Institute of Meteorology in Stockholm

Abstract

Recent investigations of the General Circulation of the atmosphere (Fr. Defant, 1953 to 1958 b) have shown the importance of strong northward advances of the subtropical atmosphere (subtropical impulses), appearing in connection with sudden northward meandering behaviour of the subtropical jet stream, for the generation of large anticyclonic vortices (blocking anticyclones) over the mid-latitude belt. These processes had strong effect on the form of the polarfront jet, which assumes a more zonal form in northern latitudes (zonal circulation type, high index).

The approach of subtropical and polarfront jet in northern latitudes and the simultaneous approach of subtropical and polar atmosphere results in a rather complicated vertical temperature structure of the total atmosphere. Nearly all of the meridional temperature contrast of tropospheric layers is concentrated at the strongly inclined polarfront, while in the higher atmosphere a steeply inclined part of the tropopause (opposite inclination relative to that of the polarfront) assumes a frontlike character separating relatively warm stratospheric polar air in the north from extremely cold air occurring in the higher parts of the subtropical troposphere in the south.

This special kind of vertical structure of the total atmosphere in combination with double windmaxima (polarfront and subtropical jet) was observed to explode during a short time of some hours and at the same time unusual strong cyclogenesis occurred, especially at the northeastern edges of the extensive blocking anticyclones. As a result of the formation of large cyclones drastic changes in the form of polarfront jet occurred or, what is the same, the type of circulation changed drastically (from a zonal into a strongly meandering form of polarfront jet, from high to low index circulation).

A combined synoptic-theoretical study of the hydrodynamic equilibrium of these special atmospheric systems by means of a detailed vertical cross section south of Iceland before the onset of strong cyclogenesis on Jan. 8, 1956, 0300Z is the content of this paper. The principal results are the following:

(1) It is demonstrated that the atmospheric system under consideration is hydrodynamically unstable in three special regions: (a) in the middle and upper part of the polarfront and just below the lower boundary of the polarfront, (b) just south of the main core of the polarfront jet and most important (c) in an upper layer between the maximum wind and the tropopause.

(2) This is even true if the stratification of the atmosphere is assumed to be statically stable and no anticyclonic curvature of the flow is taken into account. In case of no such restrictions the hydrodynamic equilibrium of the system would be even more unstable.

(3) A computation of the Richardson Number Ri shows that regions with $Ri < 1$ are exactly consistent with the three regions of hydrodynamic instability and agree well with the observed regions of severe turbulence near to the polarfront jet core, especially with respect to the upper instability region just below the tropopause.

(4) Important aspects for drastic changes in the character (zonal or meridional) of the polarfront jet circulation, for strong cyclogenesis resp. are outlined.

[1] Tit. Prof. and Docent at the University of Innsbruck, Austria. Leiter der Wetterdienststelle Innsbruck der Zentralanstalt für Meteorologie und Geodynamik, Wien, for the time with the International Institute of Meteorology.

This article is part of investigations on the General circulation of the atmosphere, with special emphasis on upper atmospheric layers, Air Research and Development Command USAF, Contract AF 61 (514)—963, through the European Office, ARDC.

1. The purpose of investigation

More recent investigations of the General Circulation of the Atmosphere, (FR. DEFANT, 1953, 1954 a, b, 1955; FR. DEFANT and H. TABA 1957 a, 1957 b, 1958 a, 1958 b), by means of a complete study of the total radiosonde ascents of the Northern Hemisphere, by a classification of the radiosondes with respect to the position of the main cores of the westerlies (polarfront—and subtropical jet stream) and by use of hemispheric tropopause maps have led to a rather deep insight into the three-dimensional mechanism of motions of the total atmospheric circulation.

Especially could be shown that the atmospheric space with reference to the position of the main cores of the westerlies can be divided into three subspaces with astonishingly conservative vertical temperature structure in the tropo- and stratosphere and in each case characteristic height and form of the tropopause ((a) Polar space north of the position of the polarfront jet and of the sloping polarfront (b) middle space continuing southward until the position of the subtropical jet, normally near the 30° parallel, (c) subtropical—tropical space south of the position of the subtropical jet).

By these investigations sudden northward displacements of the subtropical—tropical space, referred to under (c), were shown to appear in connection with a rapid northward meandering behaviour of the subtropical jet stream (subtropical impulses). Such phenomena led to the generation of strong anticyclonic "blocks" of large extension over the mid-latitude belt, whereby inside the lower and middle troposphere an advection of pure subtropical air began. Meanwhile extremely cold air was advected in the vicinity and above the rather high situated tropopause (always higher than 200 mb).

Evidently this evolution caused an approach of subtropical and polarfront jet in northern latitudes, whereby the space with a middle tropopause and a middle temperature structure in the vertical, referred to under (b), is gradually narrowed between the spaces with purely polar and subtropical conditions. In special cases the middle space disappeared completely. Thereby strong temperature differences (c. 15° C) in the total troposphere were generated between polar and subtropical air concentrated at the polarfront (strong baroclinicity, rapid increase of wind with height inside the frontal boundaries). Above the level of maximum wind a strong decline of the tropopause towards north is observed (from 180 mb down to c. 350 mb, 12.5 to 8 km). It was mentioned that the steeply inclined tropopause possesses the character of an upper front with opposite inclination relative to the inclination of the polarfront and separates the cold temperatures of the higher tropospheric parts of the anticyclone in the south from relatively warm temperatures of the polar stratosphere. Once such a system has been formed a double baroclinicity is established vertically above each other. One can hardly observe a stronger concentration of the normal meridional temperature gradient in the troposphere combined with the opposite concentration of stratospheric meridional differences in temperature. Such systems therefore represent a special store of potential energy.

In such cases it was observed that a rapid and strong cyclogenesis appeared at those places where the above described conditions in the vertical structure of the atmosphere were present; (especially at the north-eastern edge of such subtropical impulse regions, where the anticyclonic curvature of the air trajectories is rather pronounced).

For such an atmospheric structure no hydrodynamic equilibrium seems to exist and due to instability it gives rise to a sudden overturn of the total atmospheric stratification combined with strong cyclogenesis. Furthermore it has been realised that marked changes in the type of the General Circulation follow this explosionlike cyclogenesis.

I therefore set the aim before me to carry on an investigation of hydrodynamic instability of these complicated and interesting atmospheric systems, especially *the locations of possible hydrodynamic instability* seems to be of much interest.

2. The observational basis

During the period January 3 to 7, 1956 such an advance of the subtropical atmosphere from the south-east coast of the United States took place in northeastern direction towards Iceland in connection with a northward displacement of the subtropical jet and the formation of an extensive and strong anticyclone. On January 7 and 8, 1956 the above mentioned critical conditions were present in the region southwest of Iceland. After 0900Z on January 8 a relatively weak low pressure center (1,023 mb) situated at the southern tip of Greenland developed along the northern border of the extensive Anticyclone (center of high pressure in the Mid-Atlantic

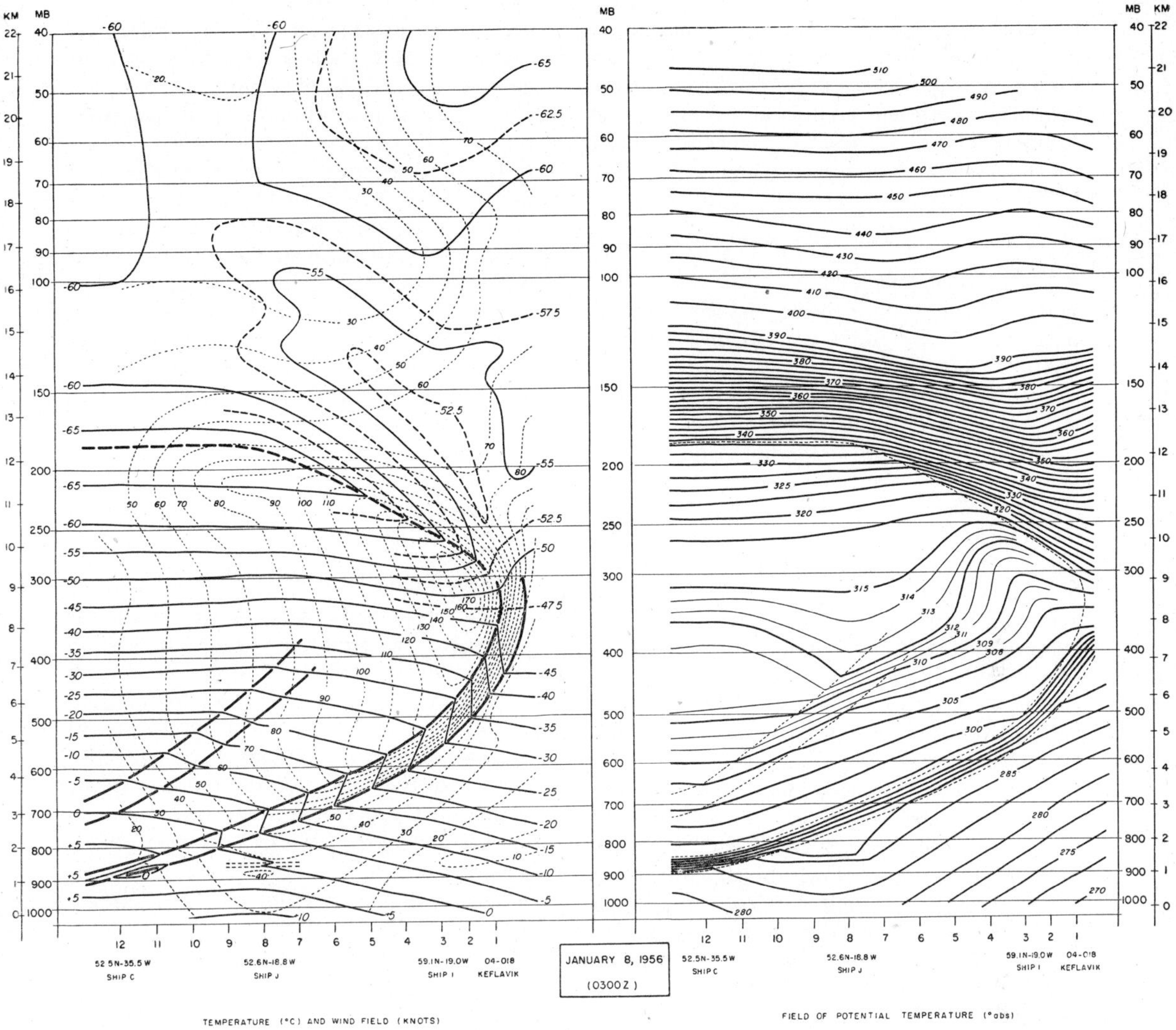

Fig. 1. Vertical cross section from Keflavik (Iceland) in southwestlery direction to the Atlantic weather ship 52° N, 35° W.

Picture to the left: Field of actual temperature in °C and of actual wind in knots. Heavy full lines: frontal boundaries of polarfront, resp. secondary front between middle and subtropical air. Heavy dashed lines: tropopause. Thin full lines: Isotherms. Thin dashed lines: lines of equal wind speed.

Picture to the right: Field of potential temperature in °C abs. Heavy full lines: Isentropes for each 2.5° C interval. Thin full lines: intermediate isentropes in some parts for each 1° interval. Thin dashed lines: Frontal boundaries of polarfront and secondary front. Tropopause.

Please note marks below the pictures, which denote the location of vertical lines used for the computations. (1 to 12.)

(50° N, 40° W)) during a few hours into a hurricane-like vortex with 962 mb pressure in its center; (61 mb pressure fall in the center in 24 hours or 2.5 mb/h, for some time even 4.5 mb/h). To study the vertical structure of the atmosphere 6 hours before the onset of this rapid cyclogenesis I have chosen the radiosondes of 0300Z on January 8 and I have constructed a vertical cross section in a south-southwesterly direction from Iceland to the weather ship 52° N 35° W. The general character of the flow made it possible to project two additional Atlantic weather ships (59° N 19° W and 52° N 18° W) carefully into the cross section. Fig. 1 (picture to the left) presents the field of actual temperature in °C and that of actual windspeed in knots and the picture to the right of Fig. 1 the corresponding field of potential temperature in °C (abs), which has been constructed from the previous field of actual temperature in a refined way.

The principle features of this cross section are the following:

Field of actual temperature:

Below the tropopause (heavy dashed line) the polarfront (heavy full lines), which from low layers in the left (SW) slopes with increasing steepness upwards to the right (NE), separates the pure polar air in the north and below from the much warmer air in the south and above. However, in this latter region one can locate another surface of discontinuity, which separates the moderately warm air (middle air) just above the polarfront from the pure tropical air in the higher troposphere. While in the polar region below the polarfront and in the middle region between the polarfront and this secondary surface of separation a rather uniform decline of the isothermal layers from left to right (SSW to NNE) exists, the isothermal surfaces in the tropical region are almost horizontal.

The meridional temperature gradient is strongest between the boundaries of the polarfront, but much weaker between those of the secondary front. An equalisation of meridional temperature differences can be found near to the 330 mb level (8.5 km) (about the isotherm of — 48° C).

Near to the rather high subtropical tropopause (about 180 mb or 12.5 km) we observe cold tropopause temperatures (—67° C), in contrast to the much warmer temperatures (about — 52° C) of the polar stratosphere. A steeply inclined part of the tropopause at the right side of the picture possesses therefore the character of an upper front.

Field of actual wind:

The field of motion shows a strong polarfront jet (170 knots), which in a characteristic way is concentrated into the angle between the upper part of the polarfront and the lower part of the opposite inclined tropopause. Just below the rather high tropopause, the subtropical jet (or a branch of it) is shown in bulges of the 90 and 80 knot lines. It is important to observe that the maximum wind in all parts of the cross section (turning of the lines of equal wind speed in vertical direction) appears somewhat below the tropopause. This could always be seen when one plots vertical wind profiles and vertical temperature distributions of soundings near to a jet core. Therefore a small layer remains between the level of maximum wind and that of the tropopause.

In the stratosphere a general decrease of wind with height can be noticed. This is especially true just above the sloping part of the tropopause in connection with the upper reversed horizontal temperature gradient.

In the upper right part of the picture between 80 and 40 mb there is again an increase of wind with height until another wind maximum of about 70 knots is reached. In these very high stratospheric layers rather cold temperatures appear, which in my opinion are due to an upper inflow of cold air from the subtropical—tropical stratosphere. But this phenomenon shall not be discussed further here.

Field of potential temperature:

The field of potential temperature shows the troposphere and stratosphere by the vertical separation of the isentropic surfaces (variable static stability in the vertical). But also the polarfront and the secondary front between the warmer air masses are shown by a packing of the inclined isentropic surfaces. For the latter one it is less pronounced. On the other hand there exist two regions with a rather marked separation of the isentropes, (a) inside the tropical warm air (nearly constant potential temperature with height and (b) just south of the polarfront jet maximum, where the isentropic surfaces are rather far apart from each other and strongly inclined (strong upward vaulting).

In the stratosphere the isentropic surfaces are approximately horizontal with the exception of the region above the inclined part of the tropopause. There the isentropes decline strongly from south to north. I shall restrict myself to this description of the most important features of such an atmospheric structure and ask for those locations in this vertical cross section, where hydrodynamic instability possibly may occur, because an answer to this question may allow a rather deep insight into the mechanism, which leads to sudden and extremely strong cyclogenesis.

3. Theoretical fundaments for an investigation of hydrodynamic instability

After an extensive study of existing literature on stability in the atmosphere it appeared to me that the theoretical work done by VAN MIEGHEM (1945, 1948, 1950, 1951) was most suitable. In these papers VAN MIEGHEM deals with a geostrophic basic current (straight or curved) the velocity of which does not change in the direction of the flow (longitudinal direction), but is assumed to be variable in the direction normal to the current, respectively in vertical direction towards zenith (transversal directions). This geostrophic basic flow in which allowance is made for windshear in transverse direction (normal to the current and in vertical direction) is subjected to transversal disturbances and VAN MIEGHEM has derived a criterion, which allows to determine the state of hydrodynamic equilibrium in a plane normal to the direction of the current (*YZ*-plane).

This criterion for the state of hydrodynamic equilibrium contains the following parameters: (a) the vertical stability of atmospheric stratification, (b) the horizontal transverse windshear and (c) the vertical windshear, whereby (b) appears in the expression for the inertial stability in absence of Archimedian buoyant forces and (c) in the expression for the so-called baroclinicity of the stratification. This criterion includes therefore all the possible forms of stability and is therefore most suitable for an investigation of hydrodynamic stability in the above presented cross section, because on a synoptic scale the horizontal pressure gradient, the Coriolis force, the centrifugal force, as well as vertical forces must be considered. Therefore no criterion considering only one of these factors can be used, but only a total criterion for the stability respectively instability of "hydrodynamic equilibrium". We refer the motion of the air to a right-handed rectangular Cartesian coordinate system $0xyz$, in rest relative to the earth, having the $0x$-axis directed parallel to the geostrophic current $\mathbf{u}$, the $0y$-axis normal to the $0x$-axis and the $0z$-axis toward the zenith above point 0. In this system the velocity components of the geostrophic current $\mathbf{u}$ are defined by $u_x \equiv u(y, z)$, $u_y \equiv \equiv u_z = 0$.

The potential temperature, the pressure as well as the geopotential are assumed to be functions of y and z only ($\Theta \equiv \Theta(y, z)$, $P \equiv P(y, z)$; $\Phi \equiv \Phi(y, z)$). If φ is the latitude of point 0 and α the angle between the vector $\mathbf{u}$ and the $W-E$ direction, the components of earth rotation $\boldsymbol{\omega}$ are given by $\omega_x = \omega \cos\varphi \sin\alpha$, $\omega_y = \omega \cos\varphi \cos\alpha$, $\omega_z = \omega \sin\varphi$ Then the following two equations characterise a state of hydrodynamic equilibrium of the geostrophic current: (1) geostrophic balance of all the forces acting in the transverse horizontal direction and (2) quasi-hydrostatic equilibrium of all forces acting in the vertical direction.

$$2\omega \sin\varphi \cdot u(y, z) = -\Theta \frac{\partial \Pi}{\partial y} = -S \frac{\partial P}{\partial y} \quad (1)$$

$$-2\omega \cos\varphi \cos\alpha \cdot u(y, z) =$$

$$= -\Theta \frac{\partial \Pi}{\partial z} - \frac{\partial \Phi}{\partial z} = -S \frac{\partial P}{\partial z} - g, \quad (2)$$

whereby $\Pi \equiv c_p(P/1000)^{R/c_P}$ and $S(y, z) = 1/\varrho$ denotes the specific volume S of the air and ϱ the density.

By differentiating (1) with respect to $-z$ and (2) with respect to y and subsequent addition *the equilibrium condition of Marqules* is obtained showing that the total transverse gradient of velocity is proportional to the number N of isobaric-isosteric solenoids per unit transverse area:

$$2\omega \sin\varphi \cdot \left(\frac{\partial u}{\partial z}\right) + 2\omega \cos\varphi \cos\alpha \cdot \left(\frac{\partial u}{\partial y}\right) =$$

$$= \frac{1}{\varrho^2}\left(\frac{\partial P}{\partial y}\frac{\partial \varrho}{\partial z} - \frac{\partial P}{\partial z}\frac{\partial \varrho}{\partial y}\right) \equiv N \quad (3)$$

This kind of geostrophic equilibrium inside the flow shall now be disturbed in such a way that a certain transverse impulse of disturbance (acting in the transverse plane in any direction) is applied to a certain air particle at the time $t = t_0$ and at the same time is taken away from it. Its resulting motion around the equilibrium characterised by (1), (2) and (3) is then studied. If the so disturbed air particle after performing a typical diminishing disturbance motion returns to its geostrophic equilibrium position or if it moves with increasing distance away from the equilibrium, the geostrophic motion of the air is said to be hydrodynamically stable or unstable for transverse disturbances.

Denoting with $\mathbf{v}(v_x, v_y, v_z)$ the velocity vector of the disturbance motion of the particle relative to $\mathbf{u}$ and with $\mathbf{V}(V_x, V_y, V_z)$ that of the same motion relative to the earth, the motion of the disturbed particle around its geostrophic equilibrium is then characterised by:

$$\frac{dV_z}{dt} + 2\omega_y V_z - 2\omega_z V_y = 0 \qquad (4\,a)$$

$$\frac{dV_y}{dt} + 2\omega_z V_x - 2\omega_x V_z = -\Theta_0 \frac{\partial \Pi}{\partial y} \qquad (4\,b)$$

$$\frac{dV_z}{dt} + 2\omega_x V_y - 2\omega_y V_x = -\Theta_0 \frac{\partial \Pi}{\partial z} - \frac{\partial \Phi}{\partial z} \qquad (4\,c)$$

whereby $V_x = \frac{dx}{dt} = u + v_x$, $V_y = \frac{dy}{dt} = v_y$, $V_z = \frac{dz}{dt} = v_z$ and Θ_0 the potential temperature of the disturbed particle at 0. The following boundary conditions are valid (v_y^0 and v_z^0 are the transverse components of the initially applied disturbance motion):

$$\text{For } t = t^0 \left\{ \begin{array}{l} x = y = z \equiv 0 \\ \text{and} \\ V_x = u_0 = u(0,0),\ V_y = v_y^0,\ V_z = V_z^0 \end{array} \right. \qquad (5)$$

From (4a) one gets by integration easily an expression for the longitudinal component v_x of the disturbance motion, which is only depending on the windshear in the y and z directions and on the transverse displacements of the particle. If we know the latter, than v_x is uniquely determined. The transverse motion can be investigated by (4b) and (4c) and one obtains:

$$\frac{dv_x}{dt} - 2\,\omega_x \cdot v_z = \psi_z; \quad \frac{dv_z}{dt} + 2\omega_x \cdot v_y = \psi_y \qquad (6)$$

whereby ψ_y and ψ_z are the components of a transverse acting force, which the surrounding medium exerts on the unit mass of the disturbed particle. This transverse force $\boldsymbol{\psi}$ is given by:

$$\boldsymbol{\psi} = (\Theta - \Theta_0) \nabla \Pi - 2\omega \times \mathbf{v}_x \qquad (7)$$

and is therefore composed of a first term which is perpendicular to the isobaric surfaces and represents the buoyant force of Archimedes in the absence of a geostrophic current and the second term is a pure inertia force due to the earth rotation.

The components ψ_y and ψ_z of this force can be determined if v_x is known and by replacing Θ by $\Theta_0 + (\partial\Theta/\partial y)_0 \cdot y + (\partial\Theta/\partial z)_0 \cdot z$

$$\psi_y = -a_{yy}^0 \cdot y - a_{yz}^0 \cdot z; \quad \psi_z = -a_{zy}^0 \cdot y - a_{zz}^0 \cdot z \qquad (8)$$

The coefficients in (8) are:

$$\left.\begin{array}{l} a_{yy} = f\left(f - \frac{\partial u}{\partial y}\right) - \frac{\partial \Pi}{\partial y}\frac{\partial \Theta}{\partial y} \\ a_{yz} = -f\left(f^* + \frac{\partial u}{\partial z}\right) - \frac{\partial \Pi}{\partial y}\frac{\partial \Theta}{\partial z} \\ a_{zy} = -f^*\left(f - \frac{\partial u}{\partial y}\right) - \frac{\partial \Pi}{\partial z}\frac{\partial \Theta}{\partial y} \\ a_{zz} = f^*\left(f^* + \frac{\partial u}{\partial z}\right) - \frac{\partial \Pi}{\partial z}\frac{\partial \Theta}{\partial z} \end{array}\right\} \qquad (9)$$

whereby $f = 2\omega_z = 2\omega \sin\varphi$ and $f^* = 2\omega_y = 2\omega \cos\varphi \cos\alpha$ and according to (3) a symmetry relation $a_{yz} \equiv a_{zy}$ holds.

From (9) it is rather obvious, that the transverse force acting on the particle depends on the physical and dynamical state of the atmosphere at the time of application of the impulse ($t = t_0$) and on the transverse components of displacement (y and z) of the particle. If the components of the applied force act in the same sense as the displacements (both of equal sign), then the displaced particle departs increasingly from its equilibrium and in the case of unequal sense of direction (different sign) the particle starts to oscillate around the equlibrium and approaches equilibrium state after some time.

Therefore it is shown that an expression of the form:

$$-\psi_y \cdot y - \psi_z \cdot z \gtreqless 0 \left\{ \begin{array}{l} \text{stable} \\ \text{indifferent hydrodynamic equilibrium} \\ \text{unstable} \end{array} \right. \qquad (10)$$

is the criterion for hydrodynamic stability, indifference or instability of the geostrophic basic current subjected to transverse disturbances. By introducing (8) into (10) one obtains the known quadratic form of KLEINSCHMIDT

$$Q = a_{yy}^0 \cdot y^2 + 2a_{yz}^0 \cdot yz + a_{zz}^0 \cdot z^2 \gtreqless 0 \left\{ \begin{array}{l} \text{stable} \\ \text{indifferent} \\ \text{unstable} \end{array} \right. \qquad (11)$$

the sign of which decides on the character of hydrodynamic stability of geostrophic motion.

VAN MIEGHEM (1951, p. 437) also shows that a corresponding quadratic form in case of isentropic displacements can be derived, because the form Q is independent on the transverse direction, in which the disturbed particle is displaced.

Because the sign of the quadratic form decides about the state of hydrodynamic equilibrium and because this sign is uniquely determined by the sign of its discriminant $a = (a^0_{yz})^2 - a^0_{yy} \cdot a^0_{zz}$ and in addition by the sign of one of the coefficients of the quadratic terms of Q(f.i. a^0_{zz}), it is necessary to investigate the signs of a and a^0_{zz}.

For middle and higher latitudes, for which the above presented cross section is valid, the two horizontal components ω_x and ω_y of $\boldsymbol{\omega}$ are rather small (for the polar region practically zero). For mid-latitudes one may safely neglect all the terms in the dynamic equations, which contain ω cos φ. Then the coefficients of the quadratic form (expressions (9)) reduce to:

$$\left.\begin{aligned} a_{yy} &= f\left[f - \Theta\frac{\partial}{\partial y}\left(\frac{u}{\Theta}\right)\right] \cong \\ &\cong f\left(f - \frac{\partial u}{\partial y}\right) \approx 10^{-8}\ \text{sec}^{-2} \\ a_{yz} &= -f\Theta\frac{\partial}{\partial z}\left(\frac{u}{\Theta}\right) \cong \\ &\cong -f\frac{\partial u}{\partial z} \approx 10^{-7} \text{ to } 10^{-6}\ \text{sec}^{-2} \\ a_{zy} &= \frac{g}{\Theta}\frac{\partial \Theta}{\partial y} \approx 10^{-7} \text{ to } 10^{-6}\ \text{sec}^{-2} \\ a_{zz} &= \frac{g}{\Theta}\frac{\partial \Theta}{\partial z} \approx 10^{-4}\ \text{sec}^{-2} \end{aligned}\right\} \quad (12)$$

The symmetry relation $a_{yz} \equiv a_{zy}$ yields the thermal wind relationship:

$$f\frac{\partial u}{\partial z} = -\frac{g}{\Theta}\frac{\partial \Theta}{\partial y} \equiv N \qquad (13)$$

In that case the baroclinicity N is according to (3) proportional to the vertical wind shear $\left(f\frac{\partial u}{\partial z}\right)$. With help of (12) the discriminant a of the quadratic form and a_{zz} can easily be approximated by the expressions:

$$\begin{aligned} a &= (a_{yz})^2 - a_{yy}a_{zz} \cong \\ &\cong \frac{fg}{\Theta}\frac{\partial \Theta}{\partial z}\left(\frac{\delta u}{\delta y} - f\right) \text{ and } a_{zz} = \frac{g}{\Theta}\frac{\partial \Theta}{\partial z} \end{aligned} \qquad (14)$$

whereby the operator

$$\frac{\delta u}{\delta y} \equiv \frac{\partial u}{\partial y} - \left(\frac{\partial \Theta/\partial y}{\partial \Theta/\partial z}\right)\frac{\partial u}{\partial z} \qquad (15)$$

denotes the isentropic wind shear along the transverse isentropic y-axis.

Because a vertical displacement of the displaced particle is related to a_{zz} in the quadratic form Q, we easily understand that the state of hydrodynamic equilibrium in each point for vertical displacement is decided by the classical criterion: $\frac{\partial \Theta}{\partial z} > 0$ (stable), $\frac{\partial \Theta}{\partial z} = 0$ (indifferent), $\frac{\partial \Theta}{\partial z} < 0$ (unstable) and one defines therefore the "static stability":

$$\nu_s^2 \equiv \frac{g}{\Theta}\frac{\partial \Theta}{\partial z} \equiv g\frac{\gamma_a - \gamma}{T} \approx 10^{-4}\ \text{sec}^{-2} \qquad (16)$$

whereby γ denotes the vertical, γ_a the adiabatic temperature gradient and T the absolute air temperature. Because $\partial\Theta/\partial z$ generally is positive for middle and higher latitudes (vertical stability), one realizes from (14) that the sign of the discriminant a or the state of hydrodynamic equilibrium is solely decided upon by $\left(\frac{\delta u}{\delta y} - f\right) \gtreqless 0$. Therefore the hydrodynamic stability of geostrophic motion depends on whether

the shear of the wind $\frac{\delta u}{\delta y} \gtreqless f$ (Coriolis parameter) in isentropic surfaces

(17)

In the absence of Archimedian buoyant forces, Q reduces to $f\left(f - \frac{\partial u}{\partial y}\right) \cdot y^2$ and therefore the pure inertial stability depends on the criterion: $\partial u/\partial y \gtreqless f$. We define accordingly the "inertial stability" by:

$$\nu_i^2 \equiv f\left(f - \frac{\partial u}{\partial y}\right) \approx 10^{-8}\ \text{sec}^{-2} \qquad (18)$$

By the use of (12) and (13) one obtains from condition (15) a total criterion for the state of hydrodynamic equilibrium:

$$\left[f\frac{\partial u}{\partial z}\right]^2 \gtreqless \left[f\left(f - \frac{\partial u}{\partial y}\right)\right]\left[\frac{g}{\Theta}\frac{\partial \Theta}{\partial z}\right] \quad \text{or}$$

$$N^2 \gtreqless \nu_i^2 \cdot \nu_s^2 \qquad (19)$$

In deriving this criterion it was assumed that the stratification of the atmosphere remains vertically stable ($\partial\Theta/\partial z$ or $\nu_s^2 > 0$).

The inequality (19) suggests the introduction of hydrodynamic stability:

$$v_d^2 \equiv f\left(f - \frac{\delta u}{\delta y}\right) \cong v_i^2 - \frac{N^2}{v_s^2} = \frac{v_i^2 \cdot v_s^2 - N^2}{v_s^2} \quad (19\,a)$$

We see from (19a) that the hydrodynamic stability is always less than the inertial stability (v_i^2).

4. Numerical evaluation of formula (19) for the vertical cross section (Fig. 1)

a) *Determination of* $\partial\Theta/\partial z$, $\partial u/\partial y$ and $\partial u/\partial z$

In the vertical cross section I have chosen 12 vertical lines extending from 1,000 mb upwards to 40 mb (see notation underneath Fig. 1) and vertical distributions of Θ and u have been drawn scrupulously exact for each of these vertical lines. For the determination of $\partial\Theta/\partial z$ and $\partial u/\partial z$ a finite number of vertical intervals have to be chosen, but because of linear interpolation in these intervals difficulties appeared at places where the vertical distribution of Θ and u show marked changes, which could only be avoided by making the intervals smaller and smaller. But then one has to read the values of Θ and u with more and more accuracy to secure an exact determination of $\partial\Theta/\partial z$ and $\partial u/\partial z$.

I have gone around these difficulties by placing a mirror exactly vertical to the plotted curves. Then I oriented the mirror for any number of points of the curves in such a way, that the course of the curve was reflected in the mirror without any kink. By drawing the orientation of the mirror for each point and measuring the angle between the vertical through the point and the mirror orientation one is able by simple calculation to arrive at values of $\partial\Theta/\partial z$ and $\partial u/\partial z$ for each point with a rather good accuracy. The adjustment of the mirror is quite sensible and can be made very accurate. This method has the advantage compared with each kind of finite difference method that the measurement can be made as dense as possible for as many points at critical places like frontal discontinuities, rapid shear, tropopause a. s. o.

In addition quite a number of horizontal surfaces have been chosen and for each of those u has been plotted as a function of y. The horizontal distance between the vertical lines in the cross section have been exactly computed for the curved surface of the earth. The same mirror method was applied to these curves to obtain values of $\partial u/\partial y$ for all heights in the cross section.

An example for this determination of the first order derivatives of Θ and u with respect to z is shown in Fig. 2. The picture contains vertical distributions of Θ and u along the line 2 exactly through the polar front jet core. The thin lines normal to these curves show the orientation of the mirror for a number of curve points. The dashed curves show the differentiated vertical distributions of $\partial\Theta/\partial z$ and $\partial u/\partial z$.

After having obtained the distributions of static stability $g/\Theta(\partial\Theta/\partial z)$ and of vertical and horizontal wind shear ($\partial u/\partial z$ and $\partial u/\partial y$) for all the vertical lines of the cross section, the total distributions of these quantities for the total region of the cross section were drawn and numerical values of the different terms were tabulated for each vertical line in vertical steps of 10 mb.

b) *The distribution of the static stability*

Fig. 3 (left hand picture) shows the distribution of static stability in the cross section. Large values of v_s^2 appear between the boundaries of the polar front (ca. 5 to 6×10^{-4} sec^{-2}, only in the inversion-like part at the left side ca. 10×10^{-4}) and in the stratospheric part of the section above the tropopause (ca. 6 to 7×10^{-4} sec^{-2}). But also in the higher parts of the stratosphere relatively high values appear (2.5 to 4). In the polar area below the polar front and in the middle area just above it, lower values of the static stability were found (0.7 to 1.5). The secondary frontal layer shows again slightly higher values (ca. 2) and above it a tongue of rather low values in the static stability (only 0.2 to 0.5), ascending from lower levels at the left to higher tropospheric levels at the right, indicates the region of inflow of the tropical air. Extremely low values appear in the region just south of the polar front jet core and here the critical point of static indifference is nearly reached.

Rather strong gradients in the lines of equal static stability appear at the tropopause, especially in its declining part, while for a part of the tropopause farther south (in the middle of the picture), where the subtropical jet was realized, this gradient seems to be weakened. To the right picture of Fig. 3 I will refer later on in section 7.

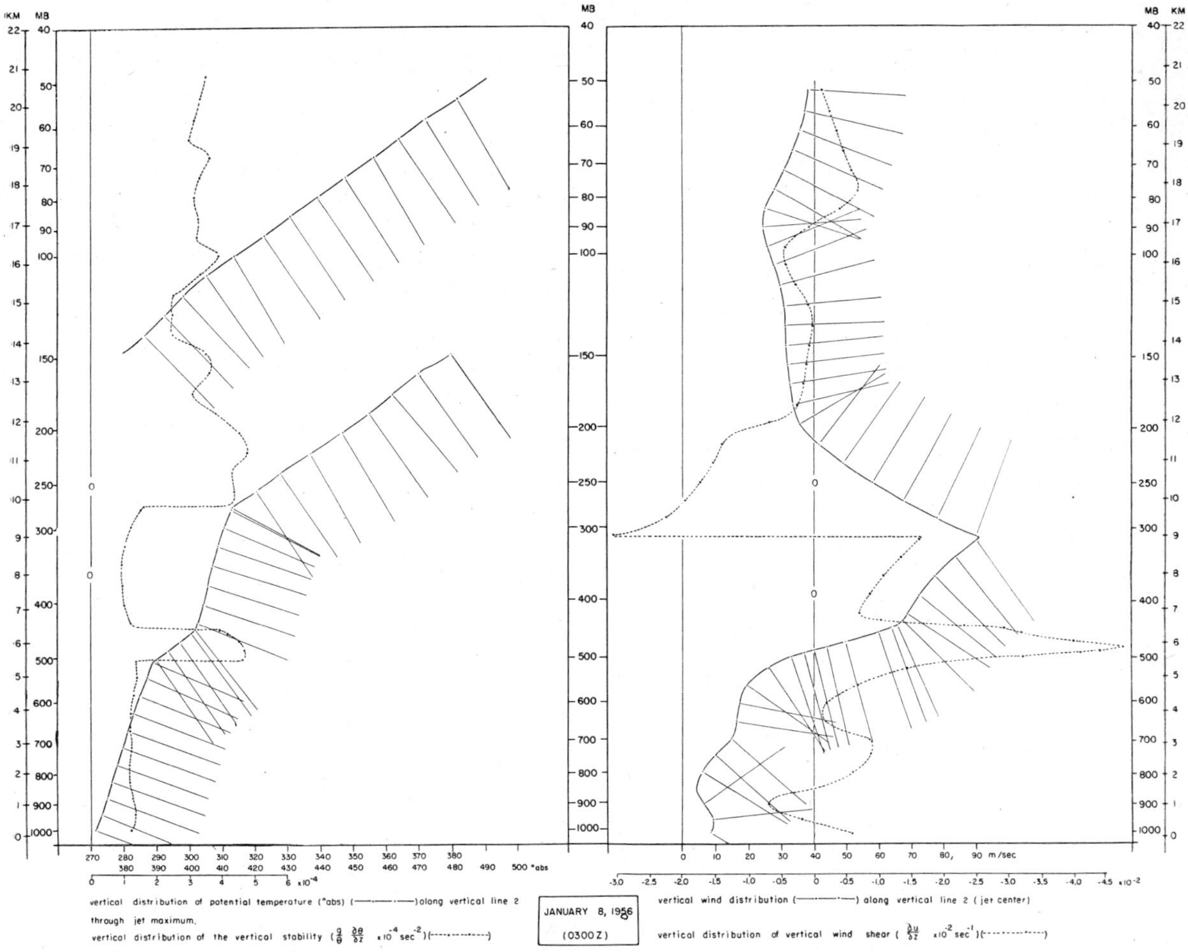

Fig. 2. Vertical distributions of potential temperature Θ and of wind speed u along line 2 of the cross section Fig. 1 and vertical distributions of $g/\Theta\ (\partial\Theta/\partial z)$ and $\partial u/\partial z$. (Thin lines for a number of points of the vertical distributions of Θ and u indicate the direction normal to the curves measured by the mirror.)

c) *The distribution of vertical and horizontal wind shear*

The distribution of vertical wind shear in the section is presented in Fig. 4 (picture to the left). Here it shows, that with the exception of small regions, everywhere wind increase with height (positive vertical wind shear) occurs upwards to the level of maximum wind. Two regions with rather strong wind increase with height stand out clearly (more steeply inclined upper part of the polar front, 5×10^{-2} sec^{-1} and an area just below the tropopause in the middle of the section, 1.7×10^{-2} sec^{-1}). Above the maximum wind (above the zero line) wind decrease with height occurs, which is strongest just above the maximum wind (ca. — 3×10^{-2} sec^{-1}). Only in the very high layers (upper right side of the picture) there appears again wind increase with height.

The distribution of the horizontal wind shear in the section is presented in Fig. 4 (picture to the right). Here a regularity is shown insofar, as north of the zero line (maximum wind in the horizontal) negative values of $\partial u/\partial y$ and south of it positive values of $\partial u/\partial y$ are present. The negative ones reach maximum values of four times the Coriolis parameter (-4×10^{-4} sec^{-1}), while the positive ones just south of the core of polar front jet only amount to 0.8 the Coriolis parameter. According to formula (18) the condition $\partial u/\partial y < f$ is everywhere fulfilled in the sec-

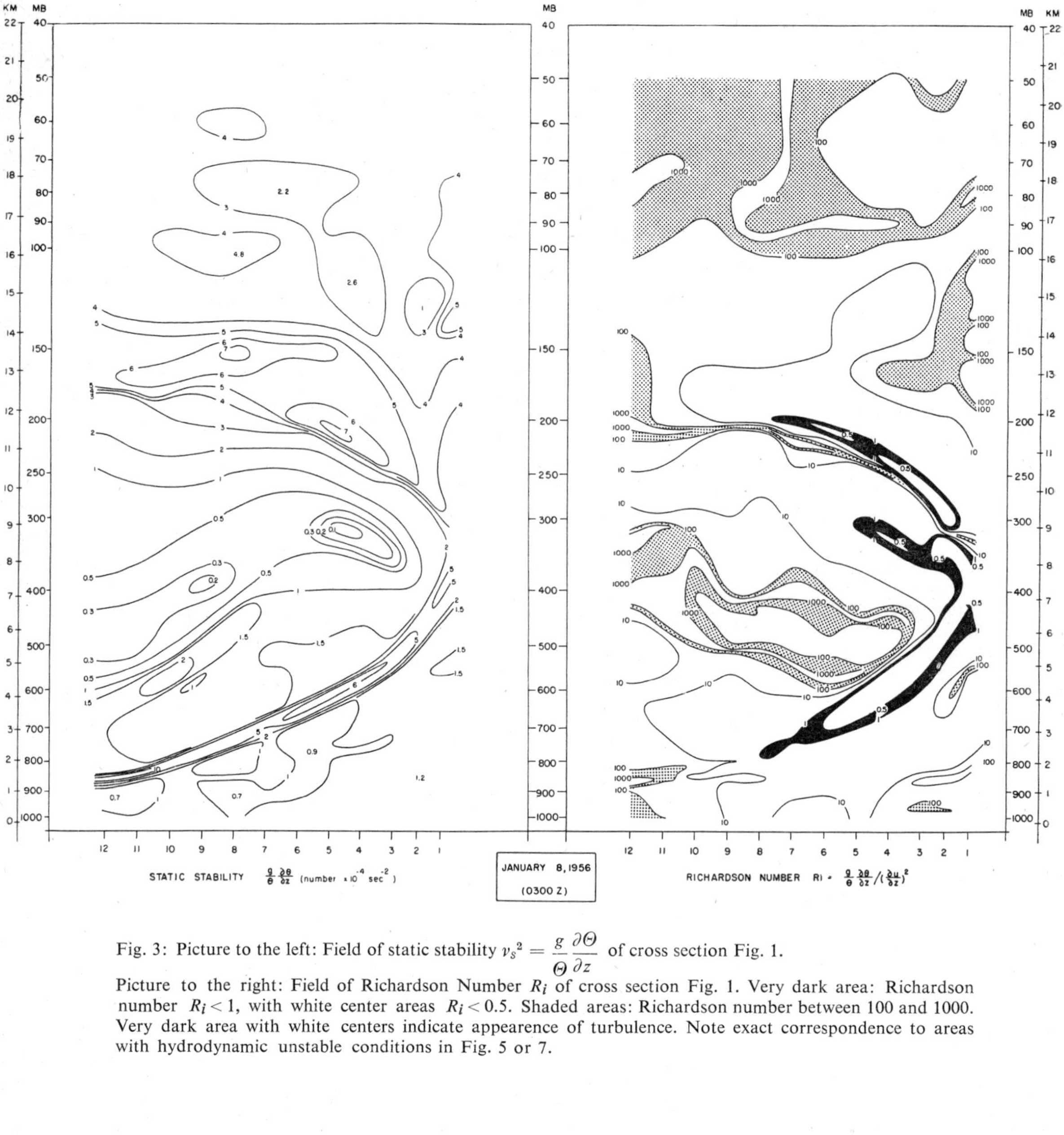

Fig. 3: Picture to the left: Field of static stability $v_s^2 = \dfrac{g}{\Theta}\dfrac{\partial\Theta}{\partial z}$ of cross section Fig. 1.

Picture to the right: Field of Richardson Number R_i of cross section Fig. 1. Very dark area: Richardson number $R_i < 1$, with white center areas $R_i < 0.5$. Shaded areas: Richardson number between 100 and 1000. Very dark area with white centers indicate appearence of turbulence. Note exact correspondence to areas with hydrodynamic unstable conditions in Fig. 5 or 7.

tion and the flow is therefore everywhere inertially stable. But this does not mean that the motion is hydrodynamically stable in all parts of the section, as we will see later on.

Systematically different and reversed is the distribution of values $\partial u/\partial y$ in the stratosphere. Here a region of positive horizontal wind shear is observed in the north and a region of rather weak negative shear in the south.

5. Computational evaluation of formula (19) (criterion for the state of hydrodynamic stability)

The tabulation of values $g/\Theta(\partial\Theta/\partial z)$, $\partial u/\partial z$, $\partial u/\partial y$ for each of the 12 vertical lines in the cross section and for vertical steps of 10 mb from 1,000 mb up to 40 mb allows now a detailed computation of the individual terms of formula (19). The exact latitude of each vertical line in the cross section and corresponding values of the

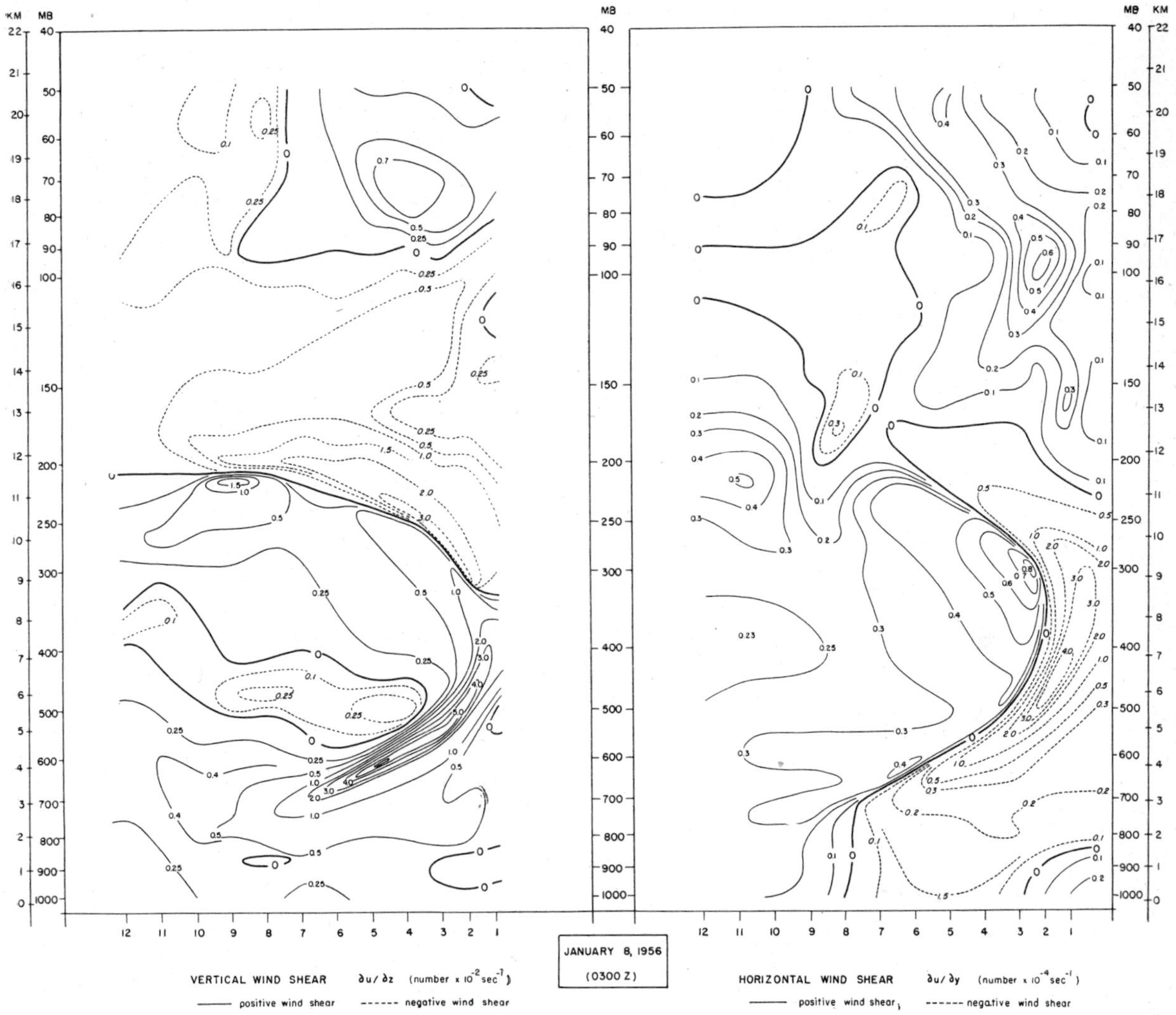

Fig. 4. Picture to the left: Field of vertical wind shear $\partial u/\partial z$ of cross section Fig. 1. Picture to the right: Field of horizontal wind shear $\partial u/\partial y$ of cross section Fig. 1.

Coriolis parameter were determined. Therefore a variation of the Coriolis parameter with latitude from line to line was introduced. Fig. 5 presents the result of a comparison between the magnitude of the terms $\left(f\,\frac{\partial u}{\partial z}\right)^2 \equiv N^2$ (baroclinicity) and $\left[f\left(f-\frac{\partial u}{\partial y}\right)\right]\left[\frac{g}{\Theta}\,\frac{\partial \Theta}{\partial z}\right] \equiv v_i^2 \cdot v_s^2$ (product of inertial and static stability) in form of vertical distributions for each of the 12 vertical lines. If the baroclinicity surpasses the product between inertial and static stability ($N^2 > v_i^2 \cdot v_s^2$), the atmosphere is hydrodynamically unstable at this place (dark areas in the vertical distributions of Fig. 5), in the opposite case ($v_i^2 \cdot v_s^2 > N^2$) hydrodynamic stability occurs (white areas in the vertical distributions). The magnitude of the difference in value between N^2 and ($v_i^2 \cdot v_s^2$) is given in units of 10^{-12} sec^{-4}. The height or position of the tropopause, of the polar front, respectively the secondary front are indicated by T and F in each of the vertical distribution in Fig. 5 for orientation of the reader.

An inspection of the positions of the dark areas in Fig. 5, which indicate the location of

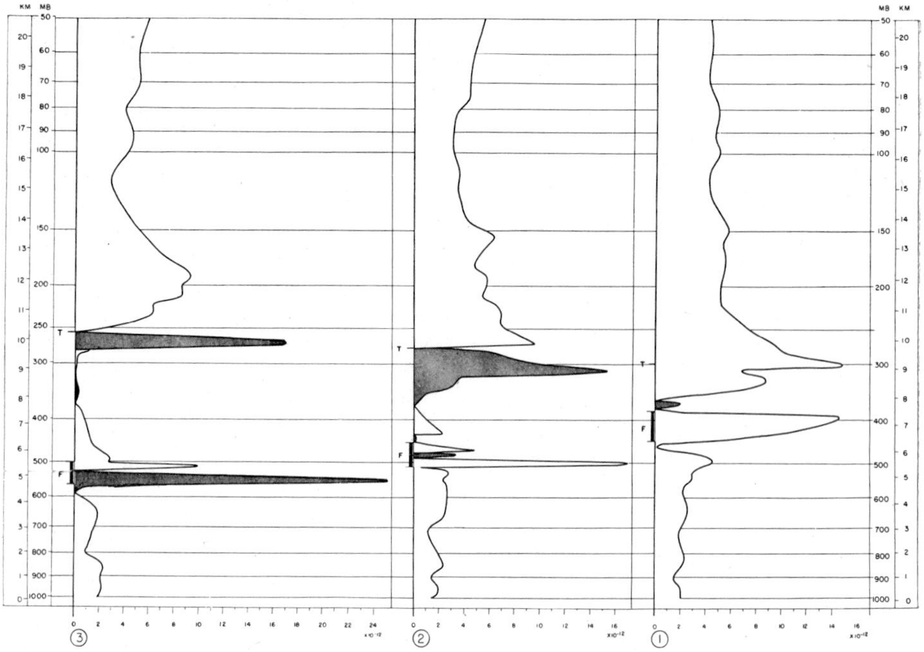

Fig. 5.

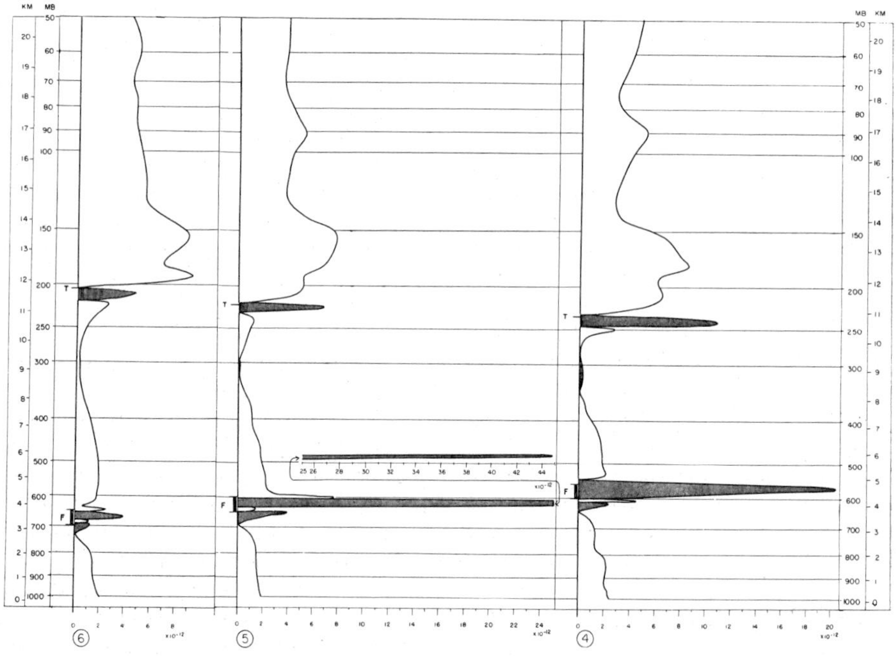

Fig. 5.

hydrodynamically unstable layers in the cross section, shows mainly three such places:

1 and 1 a) At the polar front, especially in its middle and upper steeply inclined part and in addition just below the lower boundary of the polar front. In the lower part of the front having the character of a quasi-horizontal inversion the strong static stability suppresses hydrodynamic

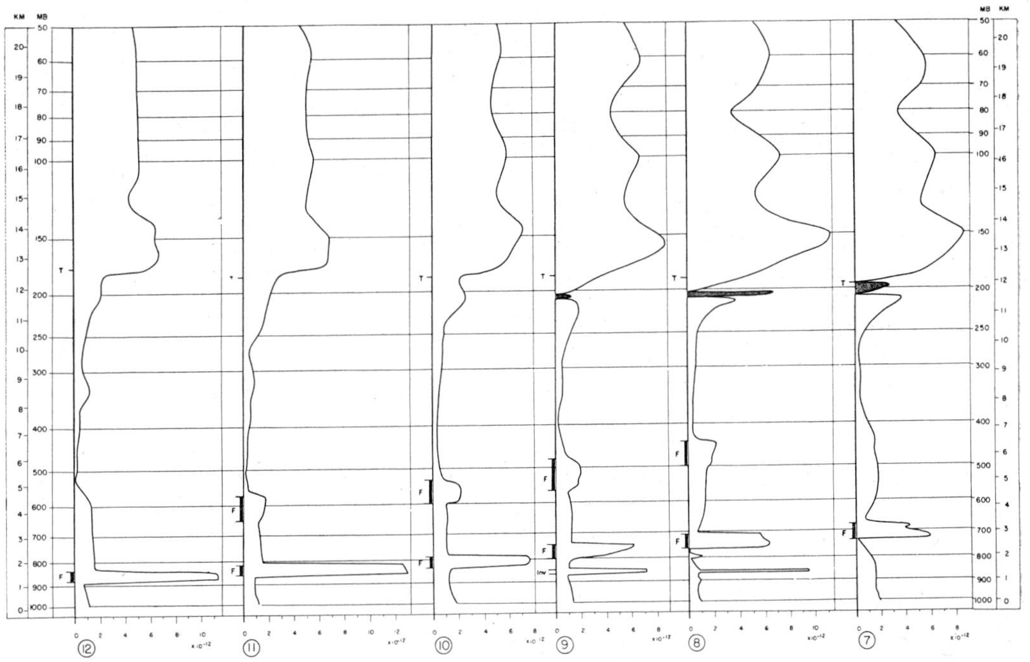

Fig. 5. Vertical distributions of hydrodynamic equilibrium according to formula (19) $N^2 \gtreqless \nu_i^2 \cdot \nu_s^2$ for each vertical line (1 to 12) of cross section Fig. 1. Dark areas show regions of hydrodynamic instability ($N^2 > \nu_i^2\ \nu_s^2$). White areas show regions with hydrodynamic stability ($N^2 < \nu_i^2\ \nu_s^2$). Black marks at each line indicate location of polarfront (F) and secondary front (F) and Tropopause (T).

instability. But also in the uppermost part of the polar front (quasi-vertical part, see line 1) there is only little instability to be seen just above the front, while inside the frontal boundaries stability prevails. There is already a partial hydrodynamic instability inside the frontal boundaries in the lines 2 and 3 and it becomes rather pronounced in the lines 4 and 5. It diminishes in line 6 and from there on until line 12 the polar front is hydrodynamically stable. However, it may be pointed out that in the lower part of the polar front hydrodynamic stability is solely caused by the strong static stability due to the quasi-horizontal inversion-like shape of the front near to the earth surface. If the front would keep its inclination down to the surface, as it is often the case, the total frontal zone may become hydrodynamically unstable. In addition there is hydrodynamic instability just below the lower boundary of the polar front.

2) In a region just below the 300 mb level in the lines 2, 3, 4 and 5. The magnitude of the values, however, is rather small. This region is situated little south and below the main core of the polar front jet.

3) And finally one realizes a further region just below the tropopause, where again pronounced hydrodynamic instability occurs. This third region shows the most pronounced values in line 2 (line through the polar front jet core) and joins here with region 2. It can clearly be found in the lines 3 to 9, but the values decrease in magnitude. Only in the line 8 (line through the subtropical jet core) we notice again an increase of the values.

In all the other parts of the section hydrodynamic stability prevails, which is of varying intensity, most pronounced just above the tropopause, but also in the higher stratosphere. The lower part of the polar front and the secondary front are hydrodynamically stable.

Fig. 6 presents the total vertical field of values ($N^2 \gtrless \nu_i^2 \cdot \nu_s^2$) in the cross section to give the reader an impression about the distribution of hydrodynamic equilibrium according to formula (19). However, it appeared also necessary to present in Fig. 7 the corresponding field of the hydrodynamic stability $\nu_d^2 = (\nu_i^2 \cdot \nu_s^2 - N^2)/\nu_s^2$ according to (19a), because ν_d (see discussion in the beginning of section 7) turns out to be the

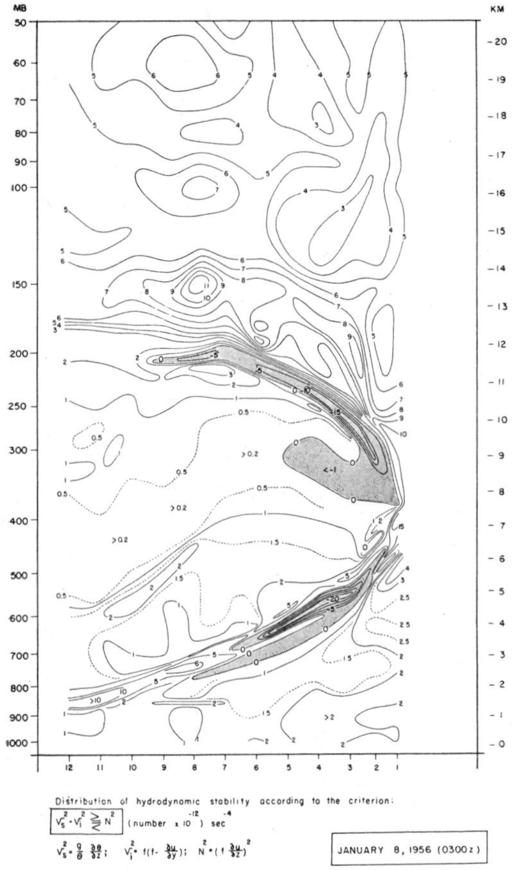

Fig. 6. Field of hydrodynamic equilibrium according to formula (19) $(\nu_i^2\ \nu_s^2) \gtreqless N^2$, Shaded area indicates regions with hydrodynamic instability.

frequency of inertial oscillations in isentropic surfaces in case ν_d is real and is also the parameter $\sqrt{-\nu_d^2}$ of hyperbolic trajectories in case ν_d is imaginary (hydrodynamic instability). Values of ν_d^2 in the different instability regions are strictly comparable in magnitude with each other and indicate therefore the effectiveness of deviations from the equilibrium state, which is not the case for the difference values between N^2 and $\nu_i^2 \cdot \nu_s^2$. The dark areas in Fig. 6 and 7 show the location of the instability regions, mentioned above. An explanation for the appearance of hydrodynamic instability in these special regions can easily be offered. This is done with help of Table 1 giving values ν_s^2, ν_i^2, $(\nu_i^2 \cdot \nu_s^2)$, N^2, $(\nu_i^2 \cdot \nu_s^2 - - N^2)$, and ν_d^2 for a number of points along the central parts of each unstable region (each point can be identified by its height in mb and by the number of the vertical line in the cross section.

To begin with region 1, the strong baroclinicity in the middle and upper part of the polar front (large values $\left(f\dfrac{\partial u}{\partial z}\right)^2$ or N^2, strong vertical and positive wind shear) gives rise to hydrodynamic instability inspite of the pronounced static stability ν_s^2 (see region 1 in Table I). In the region 1a the vertical and positive wind shear is already rather large just below the lower boundary of the polar front and the vertical stability ν_s^2 is small, so that N^2 is again $> (\nu_i^2 \cdot \nu_s^2)$.

In region 2 just south and very little below the

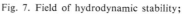

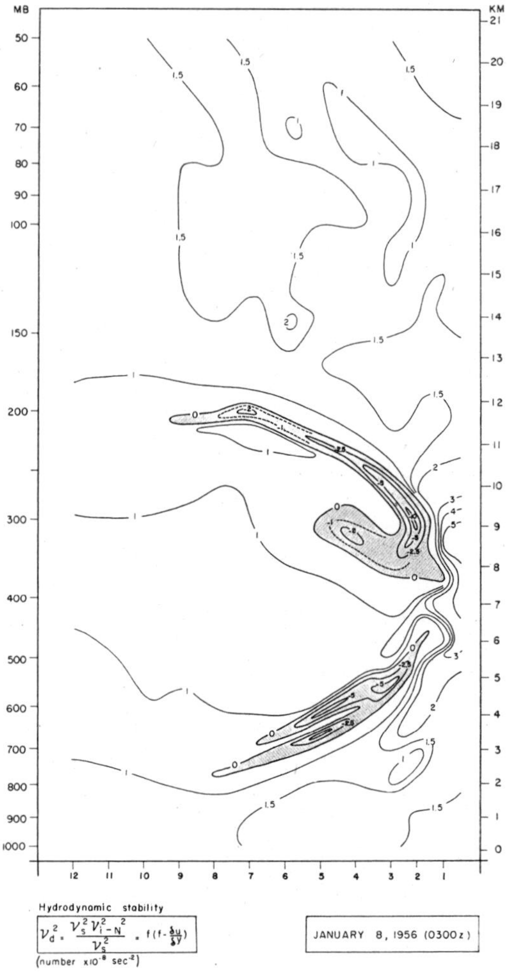

Fig. 7. Field of hydrodynamic stability;

$$\nu_d{}^2 = \frac{(\nu_i{}^2 \nu_s{}^2 - N^2)}{\nu_s{}^2} = f(f - \delta u/\delta y)$$

region with hydrodynamic instability = shaded
regions with hydrodynamic stability = unshaded

polar front jet core a much weaker baroclinicity (weaker vertical wind shear) is sufficient to create hydrodynamic instability at this place, because there the static stability is rather small and the inertial stability v_i^2 is also smaller (see region 2 in Table I). In both of these places one has always expected the appearance of hydrodynamic instability (see in this connection VAN MIEGHEM (1951, p. 440), PALMÉN (1951), ROSSBY (1947), J. BJERKNES (1951) and many others). But surprisingly new and so far not mentioned in literature is the appearance of hydrodynamic instability in the region 3 just below the tropopause (more exact in the space between the maximum wind and the tropopause) in such situations, for which the cross section is representative. Here the extremely strong decrease of the wind with height (negative vertical wind shear) is responsible for the generation of large values of N^2 (strong baroclinicity of reversed kind, strongly declining isentropic surfaces towards the north). The static stability (v_s^2) becomes only large above the tropopause and also the inertial stability (v_i^2) does not reach too large values in this region. Therefore also here the condition $N^2 > (v_i^2 \cdot v_s^2)$ is rather strongly fulfilled. (See region 3 in Table I.)

From this follows the proposition: If such high situated and reversed baroclinicity is generated in the atmosphere, which is only created by an approach of the main cores of the westerlies, an additional region or vertical layer, in which hydrodynamic instability may occur, is added to the other two regions in the close vicinity of the polar front jet stream and therefore a vertically rather deep layer of the atmosphere may become hydrodynamically unstable. But also the statically stable stratification may become unstable. According to VAN MIEGHEM (1951, p. 439) this should always occur after the threshold of hydrodynamic stability in isentropic surfaces has been reached, at least nearly simultaneous. Because the observations show strong cyclogenesis just at these places, the additional upper region of hydrodynamic instability must be basic for the generation of cyclogenesis.

Continuing with the hydrodynamic stable regions in Fig. 6 or 7, we refer the reader to Table II, where again the basic quantities are presented for the central parts of the subtropical air above the secondary front, of the middle air between secondary and polar front, and of the polar air below the polar front. It is easily to be seen from Table II that in the middle and polar air the hydrodynamic equilibrium is stable. However, in the region of inflow of subtropical air (see Table II, upper part) the weak static stability v_s^2 leads to rather small values of $(v_i^2 \cdot v_s^2)$ and due to the extremely weak baroclinicity (almost barotropic stratification, little wind increase with height) only a weak hydrodynamic stability is secured. A somewhat greater vertical wind shear in this region or a vertical indifference would immediately cause hydrodynamic instability. Therefore from the stable regions the region with tropical air is the least stable one. To the stable regions in the troposphere (Table II) the total stratosphere has to be added, in which also hydrodynamic stability is secured, because the static stability dominates above all the other terms, especially in the stratospheric part just above the tropopause.

6. Critical remarks to the above given determination of the locations of hydrodynamic instability in the cross section

Some critical remarks to the above presented method of determination of hydrodynamic instability in the polar front jet region seem to be necessary (points (a) to (c)):

(a) Terms of the form $+\dfrac{fu}{\Theta}\dfrac{\partial\Theta}{\partial y}$ and $+\dfrac{fu}{\Theta}\dfrac{\partial\Theta}{\partial z}$ have been neglected during the simplification of the expressions (9) for a_{yy} and a_{yz} (see formula (12). But for a consideration of these terms it can easily be shown that the final expression (19) would change into:

$$\left(f\frac{\partial u}{\partial z}\right)^2 \underline{-f^2\frac{1}{\Theta}\frac{\partial\Theta}{\partial z}u\frac{\partial u}{\partial z}} \gtreqless \left[f\left(f-\frac{\partial u}{\partial z}\right)\right]\left[\frac{g}{\Theta}\frac{\partial\Theta}{\partial z}\right] \tag{20}$$

and therefore an additional term (underlined) appears at the left hand side of (20). The magnitude of this term, however, amounts even for the most extreme values of its parts to only 10% of $\left(f\dfrac{\partial u}{\partial z}\right)^2$. As a first approximation this term can therefore be neglected. It would solely cause a decrease of the values of hydrodynamic instability at the polar front (positive $\partial u/\partial z$) and increase the ones in the upper instability zone, where $\partial u/\partial z$ is negative. It would therefore

REGIONS WITH HYDRODYNAMIC INSTABILITY

		line 2	line 3	line 4	line 5	line 6	line 7	line 8	line 9	magnitude of ν_s^2, ν_i^2, N^2
Region 3 Between wind maximum and Tropopause	Height in mb	310	268	240	224	210	197	203	208	
	ν_s^2 10^{-4} sec^{-2}	1.17	1.72	2.40	1.84	2.64	4.08	3.44	2.87	middle to large ν_s^2
	ν_i^2 10^{-8} sec^{-2}	2.71	2.11	2.34	1.62	1.45	1.34	1.51	1.45	middle ν_i^2
	$\nu_i^2 \cdot \nu_s^2$ 10^{-12} sec^{-4}	3.17	3.64	5.62	2.98	3.83	5.50	5.21	4.17	
	N^2 10^{-12} sec^{-4}	15.80	20.00	19.20	9.75	8.05	8.37	11.90	5.24	very large N^2
	$\nu_i^2 \cdot \nu_s^2 - N^2$ 10^{-12} sec^{-4}	-12.60	-16.40	-13.58	-6.77	-4.22	-2.87	-6.71	-1.07	
	ν_d^2 10^{-8} sec^{-2}	-10.80	-9.50	-5.66	-3.68	-1.60	-0.70	-1.95	-0.37	very unstable
Region 2 Just south of Polarfront Jet-core	Height in mb		345	318	310					
	ν_s^2 10^{-4} sec^{-2}		0.18	0.10	0.12					very small ν_s^2
	ν_i^2 10^{-8} sec^{-2}		0.94	1.01	1.07					small to middle ν_i^2
	$\nu_i^2 \cdot \nu_s^2$ 10^{-12} sec^{-4}		0.17	0.10	0.13					
	N^2 10^{-12} sec^{-4}		0.42	0.37	0.21					small N^2
	$\nu_i^2 \cdot \nu_s^2 - N^2$ 10^{-12} sec^{-4}		-0.25	-0.27	-0.08					
	ν_d^2 10^{-8} sec^{-2}		-1.39	-2.72	-0.68					weak unstable
Region I Upper and middle part of Polarfront	Height in mb	482	550	570	617	660				
	ν_s^2 10^{-4} sec^{-2}	4.66	5.20	6.10	5.98	6.08				very large ν_s^2
	ν_i^2 10^{-8} sec^{-2}	7.16	4.48	3.06	2.60	1.94				middle to large ν_i^2
	$\nu_i^2 \cdot \nu_s^2$ 10^{-12} sec^{-4}	33.30	23.27	18.76	15.55	11.81				
	N^2 10^{-12} sec^{-4}	38.40	48.32	39.16	59.80	15.78				extremely large N^2
	$\nu_i^2 \cdot \nu_s^2 - N^2$ 10^{-12} sec^{-4}	-5.10	-25.05	-20.40	-44.35	3.97				
	ν_d^2 10^{-8} sec^{-2}	-1.00	-4.80	-3.35	-7.38	-0.65				very unstable
Ia Just beneath the lower boundary of Polarfront in the polar air	Height in mb			620	650	695				
	ν_s^2 10^{-4} sec^{-2}			1.12	0.54	0.71				small to middle ν_s^2
	ν_i^2 10^{-8} sec^{-2}			2.64	2.45	1.91				middle ν_i^2
	$\nu_i^2 \cdot \nu_s^2$ 10^{-12} sec^{-4}			2.90	1.32	1.35				
	N^2 10^{-12} sec^{-4}			5.35	5.26	2.90				large N^2
	$\nu_i^2 \cdot \nu_s^2 - N^2$ 10^{-12} sec^{-4}			-2.45	-3.94	-1.55				
	ν_d^2 10^{-8} sec^{-2}			-2.22	-7.29	-2.18				unstable

Table I.

slightly benefit to the hydrodynamic instability appearing just below the tropopause.

(b) A more important objection could be raised against the above computation because of the curvature of the flow and because of using the actual wind velocity (approximately the gradient wind) instead of the geostrophic wind u_g for which the formula (19) holds.

First of all it must be pointed out that the radius of curvature of the flow R_y (more accurately the curvature of the trajectories of the air particles in this flow) can be approximated by the radius of curvature R_{is} of the isobars and terms containing R_z, the distance between the center of the earth and the point under consideration, can be neglected because of their small magnitude. The curvature R_y of the flow on January 8, 0300z was determined from horizontal maps with an order of magnitude of 3,000 to 5,000 km (3 to 5×10^8 cm). So the flow was approximately a straight flow and the influence of curvature remained in first approximation small. This was not true for the afternoon of January 8 and for January 9, but we are here solely concerned with January 8, 0300z. Also for the case of curved flow VAN MIEGHEM (1948, 1951, p. 446—447) has given a similar theoretical treatment and the corresponding criterion for hydrodynamic instability is:

$$\frac{\delta u}{\delta y} \gtrless f + \frac{u}{R_y}, \tag{21}$$

whereby $\delta u/\delta y$ is again the wind shear in isentropic surfaces and R_y is the radius of curvature of the isobars ($R_y > 0$ or < 0 means cyclonic or anticyclonic curvature). We may identify u in this formula as the gradient wind and just this formula should have been used for the computation. However, because of the fact that the radius of curvature cannot be determined exactly for each point in the cross section and only a certain order of magnitude can be estimated, I used only $\delta u/\delta y > f$ thereby neglecting the influence of the additional term u/R_y. In doing so it was assumed that the quantity $u/R_y f$ is small compared with 1. An estimation of the magnitude of the term $u/R_y f$ for different wind velocities u and different R_y given in percent of 1 results in:

REGIONS WITH HYDRODYNAMIC STABILITY

										magnitude of ν_s^2 ν_i^2 N^2 and character of hydrdyn. stability
		line 6	line 7	line 8	line 9	line 10	line 11	line 12		
Central part of Subtropical air	Height in mb	320	340	360	390	410	430	450		
	ν_s^2 10^{-4} sec^{-2}	0.46	0.33	0.31	0.20	0.30	0.30	0.20		very small ν_s^2
	ν_i^2 10^{-8} sec^{-2}	1.11	1.18	1.19	1.19	1.14	1.11	1.08		middle ν_i^2
	$\nu_i^2 \cdot \nu_s^2$ 10^{-12} sec^{-4}	0.51	0.39	0.37	0.24	0.34	0.33	0.22		
	N^2 10^{-12} sec^{-4}	0.17	0.03	0.01	0.00	0.00	0.00	0.02		extremely small N^2
	$\nu_i^2 \cdot \nu_s^2 - N^2$ 10^{-12} sec^{-4}	+ 0.34	+ 0.36	+ 0.36	+ 0.24	+ 0.34	+ 0.33	+ 0.20		
	ν_d^2 10^{-8} sec^{-2}	+ 0.74	+ 1.09	+ 1.16	+ 1.20	+ 1.13	+ 1.10	+ 1.00		slightly stable
		line 5	line 6	line 7	line 8	line 9	line 10	line 11	line 12	
Central part of Middle air	Height in mb	450	500	550	600	640	680	720	750	
	ν_s^2 10^{-4} sec^{-2}	1.33	1.49	1.50	1.30	1.30	1.30	1.40		middle ν_s^2
	ν_i^2 10^{-8} sec^{-2}	1.20	1.23	1.18	1.14	1.12	1.09	1.04		middle ν_i^2
	$\nu_i^2 \cdot \nu_s^2$ 10^{-12} sec^{-4}	1.59	1.83	1.77	1.48	1.46	1.41	1.46		
	N^2 10^{-12} sec^{-4}	0.00	0.03	0.01	0.18	0.24	0.30	0.18		very small N^2
	$\nu_i^2 \cdot \nu_s^2 - N^2$ 10^{-12} sec^{-4}	+ 1.59	+ 1.80	+ 1.76	+ 1.30	+ 1.22	+ 1.11	+ 1.28		
	ν_d^2 10^{-8} sec^{-2}	+ 1.18	+ 1.21	+ 1.17	+ 1.00	+ 1.94	+ 0.85	+ 0.91		stable
		line 2	line 3	line 4	line 5	line 6	line 7	line 8	line 9	
Central part of Polar air	Height in mb	720	760	800	830	860	880	900	910	
	ν_s^2 10^{-4} sec^{-2}	1.25	1.12	1.20	1.00	0.92	1.08	0.62	1.02	middle ν_s^2
	ν_i^2 10^{-8} sec^{-2}	2.01	1.94	1.91	1.86	1.82	1.69	1.52	1.26	middle ν_i^2
	$\nu_i^2 \cdot \nu_s^2$ 10^{-12} sec^{-4}	2.51	2.18	2.29	1.86	1.67	1.83	0.94	1.28	
	N^2 10^{-12} sec^{-4}	1.38	1.08	0.46	0.36	0.23	0.27	0.13	0.21	small N^2
	$\nu_i^2 \cdot \nu_s^2 - N^2$ 10^{-12} sec^{-4}	+ 1.13	+ 1.10	+ 1.83	+ 1.50	+ 1.44	+ 1.56	+ 0.81	+ 1.07	
	ν_d^2 10^{-8} sec^{-2}	+ 0.91	+ 0.98	+ 1.52	+ 1.50	+ 1.57	+ 1.44	+ 1.31	+ 1.05	stable

Table II.

u (10^2 cm/sec.)	Radius of curvature R_y (10^8 cm) 1	2	3	4	5
10	8	4	3	2	2
30	24	12	8	6	5
50	40	20	14	10	8
70	56	28	19	14	11
90	72	36	24	18	14

The table shows that this term becomes small for small wind velocities and for small curvature (large R_y) and is large for higher wind velocities and strong curvature (small R_y). However, what is most important in the anticyclonic case in which we are interested this term always reduces the right side (because R_y is negative) and thereby favors hydrodynamic instability.

On the other hand in computing $\delta u/\delta y$ one has to make use of the thermal wind relationship, which only holds for the geostrophic wind. In case of gradient wind another kind of thermal wind relation containing the effect of curvature has to be used, which reduces the left side of the criterion and thus hinders instability. Both effects counteract each other. But in any case for weak curvature of the order of magnitude of 3 to 5×10^8 cm both influences are anyway not very effective, which indicates that the computation performed is nearly correct.

Speaking in general solely *the locations* of possible appearance of hydrodynamic instability are of interest whereas the magnitude of instability is of less interest. Even if no instability zones would result, but solely weak zones of hydrodynamic stability relative to the more stable surroundings, it would have the meaning that these places are the ones for which the hydrodynamic equilibrium is most sensitive and disturbances of the flow may originate.

(c) Finally I want to raise the question, if the position of the region with hydrodynamically unstable conditions between the boundaries of the polar front is correct or not. Because of the upgliding process above and along the front cloud formation and even condensation occur. For moist air the isentropic shear of the wind should not be computed along the dry isentropic surfaces, but rather along the wet bulb isentropic ones. The latter are more inclined than the first ones, and therefore the shear must be stronger along the wet isentropic surfaces. As a consequence the resulting values of hydrodynamic instability would also increase. The region of instability may shift somewhat to the upper limit of the front or even to the space little above it. But in case of condensation also the vertical stability may be upset $\left(\frac{\partial \Theta}{\partial z} \lesseqgtr 0\right)$ and then the above applied formula does not hold anymore, because for its derivation the assumption of a statically stable stratification was made $\left(\frac{\partial \Theta}{\partial z} > 0\right)$ These condensation questions seem unimportant for the upper region of hydrodynamic instability just below the tropopause. In each case it may be noticed that anticyclonic curvature of the flow and the consideration of moisture content and condensation favors the appearance of hydrodynamic instability and therefore makes my result even more effective.

7. The distribution of the Richardson number in the cross section

As a criterion for the appearance of turbulence in stratified fluids F. L. RICHARDSON (1925) has introduced a dimensionless number:

$$R_i = \frac{g}{\Theta} \frac{\partial \Theta}{\partial z} \Big/ \left(\frac{\partial u}{\partial z}\right)^2 \equiv f^2 \frac{v_s^2}{N^2} \qquad (22)$$

He has concluded that a certain critical limiting number R_i^* exists and if the values of R_i in a region of a stratified fluid are smaller than the critical number R_i^* the flow is subjected to increasing turbulent motions. Such a fluid should then undergo a gradual destruction of its stratification. The numerical value of this critical Richardson number has to be estimated with different values for atmospheric flow, but seems to occupy the range between 0.25 and 1. According to (22) the Richardson number is direct proportional to the static stability (v_s^2) and inversely proportional to the square of baroclinicity (N^2), and will therefore mainly be influenced by the latter one.

The distribution of the Richardson number in the cross section has been determined and it is presented in Fig. 3, picture to the right. It shows immediately that regions with R_i-numbers smaller than 1 and such with R_i-numbers smaller than 0.5 (black areas with white center areas) appear in Fig. 3 in the middle and upper part of the polar front, in the region just south of the polar jet core and in the region just below the tropopause; therefore exactly in correspondence with the 3 regions of hydrodynamically unstable conditions.

In the other regions of the cross section mostly rather large R_i-numbers of > 10, partly even $> 1{,}000$ to ∞ can be noticed. This indicates that no turbulence can develop in these regions. This is true for the middle part of the troposphere, because there the vertical wind shear is so small that in spite of small values of the static stability (v_s^2) rather large R_i-numbers are created. Also in the higher part of the stratosphere areas with large R_i-numbers $> 1{,}000$ are present.

The region of possible turbulence, therefore, restricts itself to the regions with hydrodynamically unstable conditions, which is rather plausible. If one compares this turbulence region in Fig. 3 with the observed regions of strong turbulence (56 cases, BANNON (1952), RIEHL and co-workers (1953)) relative to the jet axis (see Fig. 8) the agreement is extraordinarily good. Especially also below the high situated tropopause south of the jet axis there is quite an evidence for turbulence according to this investigation. Because clouds are rare in this upper region, one would observe clear air-turbulence especially towards the subtropical jet away from the location of polar front jet (towards south).

8. Possible conclusions concerning large-scale developments in the general circulation

Theoretical investigation on the nature of the disturbance motions (VAN MIEGHEM) which the basic geostrophic current performs under influence of transversal disturbances show that such motions mainly consist of two types of periodic inertial motions on elliptical trajectories if the flow during the time of disturbance retains its static and hydrodynamic stability, (v_s^2 and $v_d^2 > 0$). The one type possesses a real circular frequency v_s and is therefore connected with the stability of hydrostatic equilibrium in vertical direction z, while the other type has a circular real frequency v_d and is related to the stability of hydrodynamic equilibrium in isentropic surfaces. It appears that the first type is of short period $\left(\tau_s = \frac{2\pi}{v_s} \approx 10 \text{ minutes, because } v_s \approx 10^{-2} \text{ sec}^{-1}\right)$, while the second type has a rather long period $\left(\tau_d = \frac{2\pi}{v_d} \approx 17.5 \text{ hours, because } v_d \approx 10^{-4} \text{ sec}^{-1}\right)$.

Therefore the isentropic inertial motion connected with the stability of hydrodynamic equilibrium seems to be of much more importance. Because of $v_d = f\,[1-1/f(\delta u/\delta y)]^{1/2}$ the period of this motion becomes $\tau_d \cong \tau_0 \cdot [1 - 1/f\,(\delta u/\delta y)]^{-1/2}$ whereby τ_0 denotes the pure inertial period $\frac{2\pi}{f} = \frac{\pi}{\omega \sin \varphi} = \frac{1}{2}$ (Foucault Pendulum day).

However when stability does not prevail and static, as well as hydrodynamic, instability occurs (v_s and $v_d < 0$), then the disturbance motion grows exponentially in time and takes place on hyperbolic trajectories of the parameters $\sqrt{-v_s^2}$, respectively $\sqrt{-v_d^2}$.

These fundamental theoretical results also are approximately valid when the flow is not geostrophic, but an arbitrarily directed and described flow (VAN MIEGHEM 1951, pp. 449—452).

After these remarks we are able to draw some rather remarkable conclusions concerning the origin of certain large-scale developments in the general character of the total atmospheric circulation, which always appear again in synoptic world-wide investigations:

(a) Let us discuss first the case of a northward motion of the subtropical jet and its approach to the polar front jet in northern latitudes (FR. DEFANT and H. TABA, 1957 b). To the origin of such northward shifts of the subtropical jet we devote the section (c), following later. If the main cores of the westerlies approach each other, then rather different parts of the atmosphere come in contact, the vertical temperature structure of which is either purely subtropical or polar. Strong contrasts are therefore generated in a narrow latitudinal interval and there the vertical structure of the atmosphere is so, as it was pictured in Fig. 1 and described above. A rather northward displaced polar front jet of quasi-zonal form and a strongly meandering subtropical jet are then typical for the existing zonal circulation type (earlier also called High Index Type). But this situation seems not likely in hydrodynamic equilibrium as we have seen. Due to the threefold appearance of hydrodynamic instability in

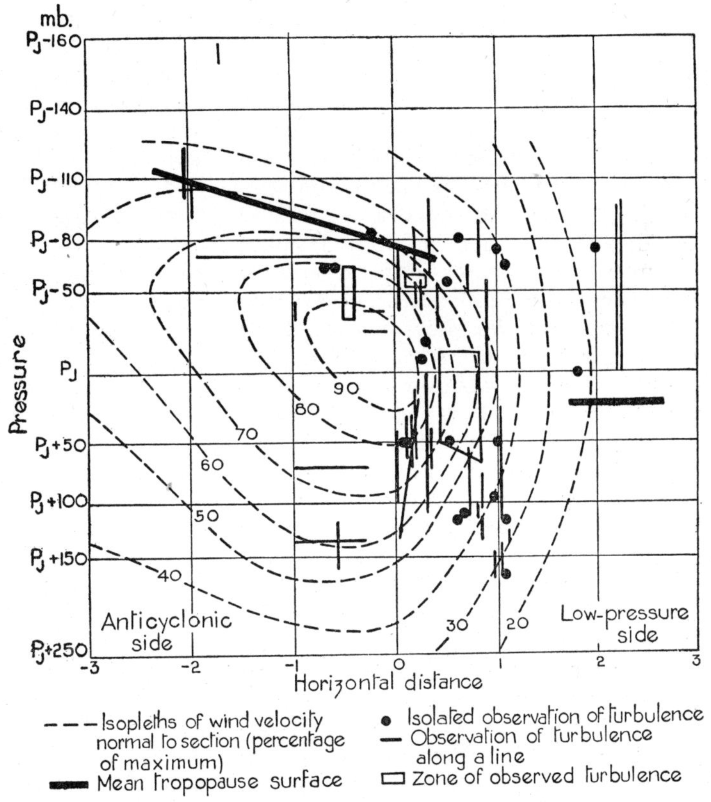

Fig. 8. Positions of occurrences of severe turbulence relative to a jet-stream axis. The cross section of the jet-stream is drawn from the mean of three typical jet-streams. P_j is the pressure at the axis of the jet (for the three jet streams $P_j = 285$ mb). The unit of horizontal distance on the low-pressure side of the jet axis in which the wind falls to half its maximum value (for the three jet-streams, 106 nautical miles). (According to J. K. BANNON (1952.)

special locations near to the jet region and vertically above each other a rather deep layer of the atmosphere becomes hydrodynamically, but nearly at the same time also hydrostatically unstable. A new mass adjustment has to be made. There appears strong cyclogenesis, which in turn gives rise to strong outbreaks of polar air towards more southern latitudes and the zonal circulation type (zonal with reference to the zonal form of polar jet) breaks down and changes rather rapidly into a meridionally meandering type, DEFANT, FR. and TABA, H. (1958 b). However, a similar structure of the atmosphere appears, if polar front jet and polar atmosphere move southward and come close to the subtropical jet, or come in contact with the subtropical atmosphere in lower latitudes (near 30° N). Here the same operative mechanism should exist. The polar system has undergone an air mass transformation during its north-south movement and the meridional contrasts in temperature are much weaker. Only cyclogenesis of normal intensity may then appear, but there are set bounds to a further advance of the already modified polar air towards south and changes in the circulation type are less obvious.

(b) If the subtropical system remains restricted to the space south of 30° N contrasts of the kind described by aid of Fig. 1 are entirely impossible. At the polarfront polar air masses are in a much weaker contrast to moderate warm air. An inclination of the tropopause as in Fig. 1 is then equally impossible and the meridional temperature contrast near the tropopause or above it remains weak. Therefore no upper frontlike tropopause with an opposite inclination (relative to polar front) as in Fig. 1 exists. Due to much less pronounced wind decrease with height above the maximum wind no hydrodynamic instability can occur in the upper region between maximum wind and tropopause, as was the case in Fig. 1. Normal cyclogenesis of moderate intensity may still occur due to instability at the polar front, but never such spectacular developments.

(c) We may now ask for reasons for the generation of meandering behaviour or sudden northward advances of the subtropical jet stream, which later cause the above described critical situations in northern latitudes.

Normally troposphere temperature contrasts in the troposphere are weak near 30° latitude (no polar front), but the wind maximum of subtropical jet is rather pronounced so that the wind decreases rapidly above the wind maximum. For that reason hydrodynamic instability in the subtropical jet can only occur in this upper region just below the tropopause (about 200 mb) (no polar front instability). Transversal disturbances of the subtropical jet cause therefore oscillations of inertial character in isentropic surfaces around its quasi-zonal position at the 30° parallel. Only if the negative wind shear gets supercritical hydrodynamic instability occurs and as a consequence sudden and strong northward displacements (hyperbolic character) of the subtropical jet develop, which transport rather cold subtropical air near to the 200 mb level and above it northward, but advect at the same time warm subtropical air in the middle and lower troposphere towards more northern latitudes. As a further consequence of these "subtropical impulses" strong anticyclonic vortices (blocks) are generated in middle and higher latitudes, which have strong effect on the form and location of the polar front jet. The approach of the jet cores creates these special atmospheric systems which we discussed in point (a) and investigated in this paper.

One may further speculate for the cause of unusual increase in intensity of the subtropical jet, which appears to be necessary for creating hydrodynamic unstable developments in the flow. As a main cause for the increase in velocity one could think on an increase in the intensity of the net tropical—subtropical circulation cell, which according to recent investigations by E. PALMÉN (1952, 1954, 1955) would result in an increase of northward transport of angular momentum in the higher part of the atmosphere across the northern boundary above 30° latitude. This would preferably happen in the western parts of the oceans, because of the asymmetry in the Hadley circulation over both oceans (Atlantic and Pacific). These are definitely the regions where most of these impulses take its origin. But one could also think on extra-terrestrial influences, which would lead to an increase in intensity of the tropical circulation. But there is so far no means to test such ideas. During periods of strongly meandering flow of the polar jet this flow in itself becomes unstable and cold vortices are excluded southward and sometimes even penetrate into the tropical circulation. At the same time polar cold air flows out into the tropical subtropical regions in a shallow ground layer (breaks in the continuous polar front). Both processes may increase the intensity of the tropical circulation by means of increasing the passat winds and their turbulence. It is very likely that operative mechanisms of this kind are the decisive ones for the generation of strong changes in the type of the general circulation. The increase of knowledge in these questions may result in quite a better understanding of the large-scale developments in the general circulation and may serve as an immensely help in practical forecasting, because they would allow the practical forecaster to be in some way prepared for sudden and large changes and could guide him in middle-range forecasting.

Acknowledgements:

The author wants to express his gratitude to the International Meteorological Institute for having the opportunity to stay and work in this institution and the various help and stimulation he got constantly throughout his work from various staff members.

In addition he expresses his thanks to the European Office of the Air Research and Development Command, USAF for sponsoring this and various other works.

The author had also an outstanding help from Mrs. Birgitta Lorensson who drafted the figures and assisted in the computational work.

REFERENCES

BANNON, J. K., 1952: Weather systems associated with some occasions of severe turbulence at high altitude, *Meteor. Mag.*, **81**, No. 958, 97—101.

BJERKNES, J., 1951: Extratropical cyclones, *Compendium, Amer. meteor. Soc.*, Boston, Mass., 599—620.

DEFANT, F. R., 1953: On the Mechanism of Index Changes, *Univ. of Chicago, Dept. of Met., Techn. Report General Circulation Project.*

— 1954 a: Ueber den Mechanismus der unperiodischen Schwankungen der allgemeinen Zirkulation der Nordhalbkugel, *Arch. Meteor. Geophys. Bioklim.*, Ser. A., **6**, 253—279.

— 1954 b: Ueber characteristische Merodionalschitte der Temperatur für High and Low Indextypen der allgemeinen Zirkulation und über die Temperaturänderungen während ihrer Umwandlungsperioden, *Arch. Meteor. Geophys. Bioklim.*, Ser. A., **6**, 280—296.

— 1956: Ueber die Struktur hochtroposphärischer Düsenströme, insbesondere des subtropischen Strahlstromes über Nordamerika, *Ber. d. deutsch. Wetterdienstes*, Nr. 22, Tagung Frankfurt a.M. 1955, 126—133.

DEFANT, FF., and TABA, H., 1957 a: The Threefold Structure of the Atmosphere and the Characteristics of the Tropopause, *Tellus*, **9**, 259—274.

— 1958 a: The strong Index Change Period from January 1 to January 7, 1956, *Tellus*, **10**, pp. 225—242.

— 1958 b: The Details of Wind and Temperature Field and the Generation of the Blocking Situation over Europe, (Jan. 1 to Jan. 4, 1956), *Beitr. z. Physik d. Atm.*, **31**. pp. 69—88.

— 1958 c: The Break down of the Zonal Circulation during the period January 8 to 13, 1956, the Characteristics of temperature Field and Tropopause and its Relation to the Atmospheric Field of Motion, *Tellus*, **10**. pp. 430—450.

MIEGHEM, VAN, J., 1945: Perturbations d'un courant atmosphérique permanent zonal, *Inst. Roy. Meteor. Belg. Mem.*, **18**, 1—33.

— 1948: La stabilité du mouvement permanent, horizontal et isobare de l'air atmosphérique, *Inst. Roy. Meteor. Belg. Mem.*, **28**, 1—60.

— 1950: L'equation aux dérivées partielles de la pression de perturbation associée aux ondulations de grande longeur d'onde du courant géostrophique zonal, *Inst. Roy. Meteor. Belg. Mem*, **39**, 1—45.

— 1951: On hydrodynamic Instability, *Compendium, Amer. Meteor. Soc.*, Boston, Mass., 434—453.

PALMÉN, E., 1951: Aerology of Extratropical Disturbances, *Compendium, Amer. Meteor. Soc.*, Boston Mass., 599—620.

PALMÉN, E. and ALAKA, M. A., 1952: On the Budget of Angular Momentum in the Zone between Equator and 30° N, *Tellus*, **4**, 324—331.

PALMÉN. E., 1954: On the Relationship between Meridinal Eddy Transfer of Angular Momentum and Meridional Circulations in the Earth Atmosphere, *Arch. Meteor. Geophys. Bioklim.*, Ser. A, **7**, 80—84.

— 1955: On the Mean Meridional Circulation in Low Latitudes of the Northern Hemisphere in Winter and the Associated Meridional and Vertical Flux of Angular Momentum, *Soc. Scien. Fennica, Com. Phys.-Math*, **17**, Nr. 8, 1—33.

ALAKA, M. A., JORDAN, C. L., RENARD, J. R., edited by RIEHL, 1953: *The Jet Stream*, Techn. Report, Project Arowa, Chief Bureau of Aeronautics. Univ. of Chicago, 1—84.

RICHARDSON, F. L., 1925: Turbulence and the Vertical Temperature Difference near Trees, *Phil. Mag.* **49**, 81—90.

ROSSBY, C. G., 1947: On the distribution of Angular Velocity in Gaseous Envelopes under the Influence of Large-Scale Horizontal Mixing Processes, *Bull. Amer. Meteor. Soc.*, **28**, No. 2, 55—68.

(Manuscript received February 19, 1958)

A Solution of the Nonlinear Vorticity Equation

By George W. Platzman
The University of Chicago

Abstract

A solution of the barotropic nondivergent vorticity equation is proposed in which the coefficients of a Fourier representation of the solution are developed as series of powers of a parameter. The motion is an invariant wave propagation, and the analysis is restricted by the "beta-plane" approximations.

1. Introduction

In his epochal study of planetary waves, Rossby (1939) developed his results in the context of a perturbation analysis. Subsequently, it was recognized that the solution which he gave for the nondivergent barotropic vorticity equation is a finite-amplitude solution of a linear equation. Generalizations of the Rossby waves, for example by Haurwitz (1940) and by Neamtan (1946), also are finite-amplitude solutions of the linear vorticity equation.

In the discussion to follow, the distinction between a finite-amplitude and a nonlinear solution (that is, a solution of a nonlinear equation) is important. On the "β-plane" the vorticity equation which will be considered here is

$$\frac{\partial \zeta}{\partial t} + \beta \frac{\partial \psi}{\partial x} = \frac{\partial(\zeta, \psi)}{\partial(x, y)} \tag{1.1}$$

where β is the Rossby parameter and $\zeta = \nabla^2 \psi$. There is a class of solutions of this equation in which the right side (the advection of relative vorticity) is zero or is equal to $-U\partial\zeta/\partial x$, where U is an absolute constant. Such solutions satisfy the linear equation

$$\frac{\partial \zeta}{\partial t} + U\frac{\partial \zeta}{\partial x} + \beta \frac{\partial \psi}{\partial x} = 0, \tag{1.2}$$

and may have finite amplitude. For example,

$$\psi = -Uy + A \sin ky + B \sin \mu y \cos \lambda(x - ct)$$

is a solution which satisfies (1.2) provided $U = c + \beta/k^2$ and $k^2 = \lambda^2 + \mu^2$. Furthermore, A and B are completely unrestricted so we may correctly designate this as a finite-amplitude solution.

What is sought here, is to construct a solution of (1.1) in which the vorticity advection does not vanish (or reduce to the advection by a uniform flow). The solution we seek is, in this sense, the solution of a nonlinear equation (and, *ipso facto*, also one of finite amplitude). The method employed for this purpose is to develop the solution as a trigonometric series, the coefficients of which are series of powers of a parameter. This procedure does not yield a closed solution, but at each step in the sequence of approximations the boundary conditions are satisfied exactly. For boundaries we take rigid walls coincident with two latitude circles. A further restriction that is made is to assume at the outset that the motion is organized permanently as a wave propagating zonally at constant speed without change of shape.

A disadvantage of the expansion method is that it imposes the obligation of establishing convergence of the series, which usually is a very difficult matter and is not attempted here.

2. The trigonometric series

We place the origin for y so that the southern boundary coincides with $y = 0$ and the northern boundary with $y = D$ (the width of the "channel"). Take $\psi = 0$ at $y = 0$ and let $\psi(D)$ denote the uniform value of ψ along $y = D$. The quantity $\psi(D)$ is proportional to the total linear momentum; since on the β-plane the latter is conserved, this quantity is an absolute constant. Now let

$$\psi = -Uy + \psi'$$
$$U \equiv -\psi(D)/D,$$

so that ψ' (a function of x, y, t) vanishes at $y = 0$ and $y = D$, and represents the "residual" flow with zero total momentum. Substitution in (1.1) yields

$$\frac{\partial \zeta'}{\partial t} + U\frac{\partial \zeta'}{\partial x} + \beta \frac{\partial \psi'}{\partial x} = \frac{\partial(\zeta', \psi')}{\partial(x, y)}.$$

The term involving U may be suppressed by replacing x by $x - Ut$; hence, since there is no loss of generality, we take $U = 0$. The primes may now be omitted, and we again have (1.1), but with $\psi = 0$ on both boundaries.

Consider the expansion

$$\psi = \sum_{l=0}^{\infty} \sum_{m=1}^{\infty} \hat{\psi}_{l,m} \sin m\mu y \cos l\lambda(x - ct), \qquad (2.1)$$

where $\mu \equiv \pi/D$ and $\lambda \equiv 2\pi/L$. This expansion represents a periodic motion of wave length L propagating without change of shape at the speed c along x. The troughs and ridges of this wave motion are equally spaced, parallel lines $x - ct =$ constant, without tilt. As a function of x, this representation is assumed to be completely continuous and differentiable, so that the x-derivatives required in the differential equation may be obtained through term-by-term differentiation of the series. As a function of y, in accordance with the preceding discussion, ψ vanishes at the end points ($y = 0$ and D) and is assumed to be continuous in the open interval; hence, one termwise differentiation with respect to y is permitted. In order to simplify the problem at this stage, we make the special assumption that the *vorticity* vanishes at both boundaries. Since $\partial^2\psi/\partial x^2 = 0$ at the boundaries in any case, this means that $\partial^2\psi/\partial y^2 = 0$ there also. Consequently, the second and third y-derivatives of ψ (required in the differential equation) may be obtained by termwise differentiation of the series.

Before substitution into the differential equation (1.1) it will be convenient to write (2.1) in the following complex form:

$$\psi = i \sum_{l=-\infty}^{\infty} \sum_{m=-\infty}^{\infty} \psi_{l,m} \exp i\Theta_{l,m} \qquad (2.2)$$

$$\Theta_{l,m} \equiv l\lambda(x - ct) + m\mu y,$$

where $\psi_{0,m} = -\hat{\psi}_{0,m}/2$ and $\psi_{l,m} = -\hat{\psi}_{l,m}/4\,(l \neq 0)$. To make (2.2) reduce to (2.1) we must have

$$\psi_{-l,m} = \psi_{l,m}; \quad \psi_{l,-m} = -\psi_{l,m}. \qquad (2.3)$$

By differentiation of (2.2) we obtain the following expansion for the vorticity $\zeta = \nabla^2\psi$:

$$\left.\begin{aligned} \zeta &= i\mu^{-1}\beta \sum_{l=-\infty}^{\infty} \sum_{m=-\infty}^{\infty} \zeta_{l,m} \exp i\Theta_{l,m} \\ \zeta_{l,m} &\equiv (\mu/c_{l,m})\psi_{l,m} \\ c_{l,m} &\equiv -\beta/(l^2\lambda^2 + m^2\mu^2), \end{aligned}\right\} \qquad (2.4)$$

where $c_{l,m}$ is the Rossby-Haurwitz solution corresponding to the l, m-mode. It should be noted that, because of the special form (2.1), the coefficients $\psi_{l,m}$ and $\zeta_{l,m}$ are real. The factor $\mu^{-1}\beta$ has been introduced in (2.4) in order to render $\zeta_{l,m}$ dimensionless.

To write the inversion of (2.2), or (2.4), it is convenient to define

$$\psi(x, -y, t) = -\psi(x, y, t).$$

Then it follows that

$$\psi_{l,m} = \frac{-i}{2LD} \int_0^L \int_{-D}^D \psi \exp(-i\Theta_{l,m})\, dy\, dx. \qquad (2.5)$$

Further, if two expansions of the type (2.2) are equal, then the respective coefficients are equal.

3. The interaction function

Since the postulated solution is an invariant wave propagation, the left side of (1.1) may be written

$$\partial(-c\zeta + \beta\psi)/\partial x.$$

With the aid of (2.2) and (2.4), one finds that

$$\partial(\beta\psi - c\zeta)/\partial x =$$
$$= \mu^{-1}\beta\lambda \sum_{l=-\infty}^{\infty} \sum_{m=-\infty}^{\infty} l(c - c_{l,m})\zeta_{l,m} \exp(i\Theta_{l,m}).$$

For the sake of a more compact notation, we will write

$$\partial(\beta\psi - c\zeta)/\partial x =$$
$$= \mu^{-1}\beta\lambda \sum_1 l_1(c - c_1)\zeta_1 \exp(i\Theta_1),$$

the subscript 1 designating symbolically the joint operation of the indices l_1, m_1. Similarly, the right side of (1.1) is

$$\partial(\zeta, \psi)/\partial x, y) =$$
$$= \mu^{-1}\beta\lambda \sum_2 \sum_3 (l_2 m_3 - l_3 m_2)(c_3 - c_2)\zeta_2\zeta_3 \times$$
$$\times \exp i(\Theta_2 + \Theta_3),$$

on the understanding that in the summation, each pair of l, m-points is counted only once.

Equating coefficients in the two series, we have

$$\left.\begin{aligned} &l_1(c - c_1)\zeta_1 = Q_1(\zeta) \\ &Q_1(\zeta) \equiv \sum_2 \sum_3 (l_2 m_3 - l_3 m_2)(c_3 - c_2)\zeta_2\zeta_3 \\ &(l_1 = l_2 + l_3, \quad m_1 = m_2 + m_3). \end{aligned}\right\} \qquad (3.1)$$

Equation (3.1) is the vorticity equation in the domain of the coefficients $\zeta_{l,m}$: an infinite set of quadratic equations. We will refer to the quadratic form $Q_1(\zeta)$ as the *interaction function*.[1]

Our task is to construct a nontrivial solution of (3.1); specifically, a solution in which $\zeta_{l,m}$ is nonzero on some *two-dimensional* lattice in the wave-number plane. As an example of a "trivial" solution, we have the case in which only a single ζ-coefficient, $\zeta_{l,m}$ say, is nonzero; then the interaction function vanishes and (3.1) is satisfied by taking $c = c_{l,m}$. This is the Rossby-Haurwitz solution.

4. Exclusion rules; the even lattice

Each of the terms in the interaction function $Q_1(\zeta)$ of (3.1) corresponds to a pair of vectors $\mathbf{k}_2 = l_2, m_2$ and $\mathbf{k}_3 = l_3, m_3$ in the wave-number plane, such that $\mathbf{k}_1 = \mathbf{k}_2 + \mathbf{k}_3$. However, not every pair of vectors $\mathbf{k}_2$, $\mathbf{k}_3$ yields a nonzero contribution in $Q_1(\zeta)$. Indeed, since

$$|l_2 m_3 - l_3 m_2| = |\mathbf{k}_2 \times \mathbf{k}_3|,$$

it follows that every interaction is excluded for which $\mathbf{k}_2$ and $\mathbf{k}_3$ are parallel.

Another general exclusion rule is obtained from a consideration of interactions which make $c_2 = c_3$; since $c_{l,m}$ is an even function of l and m, this occurs whenever

$$\mathbf{k}_2 = l, m \text{ and } \mathbf{k}_3 = l, -m$$

or

$$\mathbf{k}_2 = l, m \text{ and } \mathbf{k}_3 = -l, m,$$

that is, whenever $\mathbf{k}_2$ and $\mathbf{k}_3$ are images in the l or in the m axis.

We will refer to these exclusion rules, respectively, as the "parallel" rule and the "image" rule. One rather evident property of the interactions emerges at once by application of these rules: *auto*-interaction is nugatory. This includes the interaction of a given $\mathbf{k}$ with itself as well as with any of its three images in the other three quadrants. For, if $\mathbf{k}$ is (for example) in the first quadrant, the interactions $\mathbf{k}, \mathbf{k}$ and $\mathbf{k}, -\mathbf{k}$ are excluded by the parallel rule, and the interactions between $\mathbf{k}$ and its second- and fourth-quadrant images are excluded by the image rule.

It is convenient at this stage to define the *parity* of each point (or vector) l, m as the parity of the sum $l + m$ (note that throughout the discussion, l and m are integers). In this way the infinite lattice of points l, m (where $l = 0, \pm 1, \pm 2, \ldots$ and $m = 0, \pm 1, \pm 2, \ldots$) can be divided into two sub-lattices, one of which contains all points of even parity ($l + m$ even) and the other all points of odd parity ($l + m$ odd). These sub-lattices, which are pictured in figure 1, we will term the "even" and the "odd" lattices, respectively.

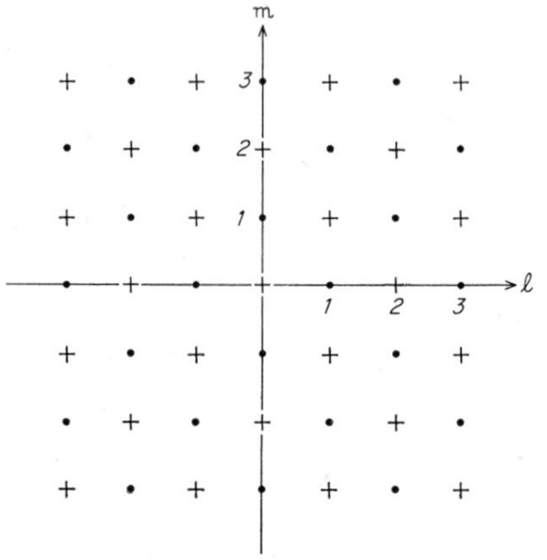

Fig. 1. The even (+) and odd (·) lattices in the wave-number plane.

We now observe that the interaction between two points of the same parity (even or odd) contributes only to a point of even parity, because the parity of $\mathbf{k}_1 = \mathbf{k}_2 + \mathbf{k}_3$ is given by that of

$$l_1 + m_1 = (l_2 + l_3) + (m_2 + m_3) = \\ = (l_2 + m_2) + (l_3 + m_3),$$

from which we see that $\mathbf{k}_1$ has even parity if $\mathbf{k}_2$ and $\mathbf{k}_3$ have the same parity, and further, $\mathbf{k}_1$ has odd parity if $\mathbf{k}_2$ and $\mathbf{k}_3$ have opposite parity. It follows that if *any* points on the odd lattice are included in the solution scheme, then *some* points on the even lattice must also be included (in a nontrivial solution). On the other hand, *a scheme in which only the even lattice is used could be internally consistent.* Since we seek here only a particular solution, we will now assume that $\zeta_{l,m} = 0$ for all points on the odd

[1] SILBERMAN (1954) investigated the function, analogous to $Q_1(\zeta)$ which is obtained when the expansion is carried out in spherical harmonics, On the β-plane, we see that in the quadratic form $Q_1(\zeta)$ the coefficients are $(l_2 m_3 - l_3 m_2)(c_3 - c_2)$. On the sphere, these "interaction coefficients" are much more involved: in place of m_2 and m_3 in the preceding expression, certain integrals appear which are functions of *all six indices* l_i, m_i $(i = 1, 2, 3)$.

lattice, in order to simplify the procedure as much as possible.

An important property of (3.1), to which reference will be made later, is the fact that when $l_1 = 0$, the equation is satisfied identically no matter what values of $\zeta_{l,m}$ enter in the function $Q_1(\zeta)$. This means that $Q_1(\zeta) = 0$ when $l_1 = 0$. To prove this, note that if $l_1 = 0$, then $l_3 = -l_2$, so that the typical term in $Q_1(\zeta)$ corresponds to the vector pair

$$\mathbf{k}_2 = l, m_2; \qquad \mathbf{k}_3 = -l, m_3.$$

For each such term there is a companion corresponding to the pair

$$\mathbf{k}_2 = -l, m_2; \qquad \mathbf{k}_3 = l, m_3.$$

If $m_2 = m_3$, these two pairs of vectors are identical, and in this case the contribution to $Q_1(\zeta)$ is excluded by the image rule, since $\mathbf{k}_2$ and $\mathbf{k}_3$ then are images. If $m_2 \neq m_3$, the two pairs are distinct, but the *sum* of their contributions to $Q_1(\zeta)$ is found to vanish because both $c_{l,m}$ and $\zeta_{l,m}$ are even functions of l. It follows that $Q_1(\zeta) = 0$, so that (3.1) is satisfied identically.

The significance of this property of the equations is that a unique solution is not possible. For, quite apart from any multiplicity that might arise from the nonlinearity of the equations, one should expect that for uniqueness, one non-vacuous member of the set of equations (3.1) should correspond to each coefficient $\zeta_{l,m}$. We have seen, however, that each of the equations which corresponds to $\zeta_{0,m}$ (that is, for which $l_1 = 0$) is vacuous; hence, these coefficients are not determined by (3.1). Their values therefore are restricted only by the requirement that the complete solution must converge.

5. Construction of a particular nontrivial solution

The method that will be adopted is to construct a solution in the neighbourhood of the trivial solution

$$\zeta_{1,1} \neq 0; \quad \zeta_{l,m} = 0 \quad (l, m \neq 1, 1) \quad c = c_{1,1}.$$

This will be done by expansion of $\zeta_{l,m}$ in powers of $\zeta_{1,1}$; since the latter coefficient will appear repeatedly in the discussion, it is convenient to abbreviate

$$Z \equiv \zeta_{1,1}.$$

Further, the following quantities also are convenient:

$$a \equiv \frac{c - c_{1,1}}{c_{1,1}}; \quad a_{l,m} \equiv \frac{c_{l,m} - c_{1,1}}{c_{1,1}}.$$

The first few values of $a_{l,m}$ are, with $\varepsilon \equiv \lambda/\mu = 2\,D/L$:

$$a_{0,2} = (\varepsilon^2 - 3)/4$$
$$a_{1,1} = 0$$
$$a_{1,3} = -8/(\varepsilon^2 + 9)$$
$$a_{2,2} = -3/4$$
$$a_{2,4} = -(3\varepsilon^2 + 15)/(4\varepsilon^2 + 16).$$

In terms of the a's we may evidently write the fundamental equations (3.1) as

$$\left.\begin{array}{c} l_1(a - a_1)\zeta_1 = Q_1(\zeta) \\ Q_1(\zeta) \equiv \sum\limits_2 \sum\limits_3 (l_2 m_3 - l_3 m_2)(a_3 - a_2)\zeta_2\zeta_3 \\ (l_1 = l_2 + l_3, \quad m_1 = m_2 + m_3). \end{array}\right\} \quad (5.1)$$

The advantages of this form are that the a's are dimensionless, and $a_{1,1} = 0$. Note also that $c = c_{1,1}(1 + a)$.

We begin by defining the *order* of any coefficient $\zeta_{l,m}$ as the lowest power of Z in the expansion of $\zeta_{l,m}$ in powers of Z. The crux of the procedure is to establish the order of each $\zeta_{l,m}$; one may then proceed without difficulty by successive approximations.

In the preceding section we demonstrated that without violating the consistency of (5.1), the values of $\zeta_{0,m}$ may be imposed in any way which does not impair the convergence of the solution. Consider the following choice:

$$\left.\begin{array}{ll} \zeta_{0,2} = \sigma Z^2 & \\ \zeta_{0,m} = 0 & (m \neq 2) \end{array}\right\} \quad (5.2)$$

where σ is a parameter independent of Z. This makes $\zeta_{0,2}$ a quantity of the *second order*. (We will assume that (5.2) is an exact expression of $\zeta_{0,2}$ in terms of Z.) Hence, the interaction corresponding to

$$\mathbf{k}_2 = 1, 1; \qquad \mathbf{k}_3 = 0, 2$$

produces a contribution to $\mathbf{k}_1 = 1, 3$ of the *third* order; this evidently is the lowest order of any contribution to $\mathbf{k}_1 = 1, 3$ so that $\zeta_{1,3}$ is a third-order coefficient.

Similarly, the interactions corresponding to

$$\mathbf{k}_2 = 1,\ -1; \qquad \mathbf{k}_3 = 1,\ 3$$
$$\mathbf{k}_2 = 1,\ 1; \qquad \mathbf{k}_3 = 1,\ 3$$

produce fourth-order contributions, respectively, to $\mathbf{k}_1 = 2, 2$ and $\mathbf{k}_1 = 2, 4$; hence $\zeta_{2,\,2}$ and $\zeta_{2,\,4}$ are coefficients of the fourth order, since no interactions of lower order can contribute to these coefficients. Proceeding in this way, the picture shown in figure 2 very quickly emerges. The encircled numbers give the order of each coefficient on the even lattice, in the particular solution generated by (5.2). From (2.1) or (2.3) it is evident that there are no nonzero coefficients on the line $m = 0$. It is not difficult to verify that to be consistent with figure 2, the order of any $\zeta_{l,\,m}$ is

$$p \equiv \frac{1}{2}(l + m + 2) + \frac{1}{2}\left|l - m + 2\right|,$$

except for $l,\ m = 1, 1$ in which case p is the lowest order of any contribution to $\zeta_{1,\,1}$ *from interaction.*

Having established the order of $\zeta_{l,\,m}$ one may solve (5.1) by successive approximations to any desired order. To illustrate, we will obtain the fourth-order solution. For each $\mathbf{k}_1$ of order four or less, we list in table 1 all interactions which produce contributions of order four or less (and, for $\mathbf{k}_1 = 1, 1$ also those of order five).

Table 1. The order (n) of the interaction $\mathbf{k}_2$, $\mathbf{k}_3$ which contributes to $\mathbf{k}_1 = \mathbf{k}_2 + \mathbf{k}_3$ in accordance with figure 2.

$\mathbf{k}_1$	n	$\mathbf{k}_2$	$\mathbf{k}_3$
1, 1	3	1, —1	0, 2
	5	0, —2	1, 3
		—1, —1	2, 2[1]
1, 3	3	1, 1	0, 2
2, 2	4	1, —1	1, 3
2, 4	4	1, 1	1, 3

We now write the equation in (5.1) which corresponds to $\mathbf{k}_1 = 1, 1$. For reasons that will appear presently, we include here interactions through the fifth order:

$$(a - a_{1,\,1})\,\zeta_{1,\,1} = 2\,(a_{0,\,2} - a_{1,\,1})(-\zeta_{1,\,1})\zeta_{0,\,2} + $$
$$+ 2\,(a_{1,\,3} - a_{0,\,2})(-\zeta_{0,\,2})\,\zeta_{1,\,3} + O_7.$$

[1] Excluded by "parallel" rule.

Replace $\zeta_{1,\,1}$ by Z, and $\zeta_{1,\,2}$ by σZ^2 as in (5.2); solving for a, we get, since $a_{1,\,1} = 0$:

$$a = -2\sigma a_{0,\,2} Z^2 - 2\sigma(a_{1,\,3} - a_{0,\,2})\,\zeta_{1,\,3} Z + O_6 \tag{5.3}$$

(The notation O_n signifies the presence of terms of order n in Z.) Since $\zeta_{1,\,3}$ is a third-order term, the second term on the right in (5.3) is of the fourth order. It is clear, then, that the common factor of Z in the equation for $\mathbf{k}_1 = 1, 1$ requires the inclusion initially of terms of order one in excess of the order to which the solution is wanted.

Equation (5.3) determines the propagation speed $c = c_{1,\,1}\ (1 + a)$ in the nonlinear solution.

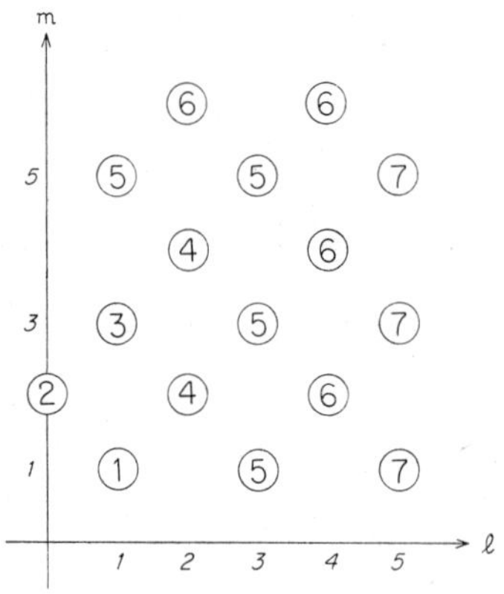

Fig. 2. The order of magnitude (circled numbers) of the expansion coefficients in the particular solution generated by (5.2), at points of the even lattice in the wave-number plane.

To eliminate $\zeta_{1,\,3}$ from (5.3), we write the equation in (5.1) which corresponds to $\mathbf{k}_1 = 1{,}3$:

$$(a - a_{1,\,3})\,\zeta_{1,\,3} = 2\,(a_{0,\,2} - a_{1,\,1})\,\zeta_{1,\,1}\zeta_{0,\,2} + O_5.$$

On the right we introduce $\zeta_{1,\,1} = Z$ and $\zeta_{0,\,2} = \sigma Z^2$, and on the left we may replace a by 0, since a is a quantity of the second order which when multiplied by $\zeta_{1,\,3}$ would yield terms of order higher than four. In this way one finds

$$\zeta_{1,\,3} = -2\sigma(a_{0,\,2}/a_{1,\,3})\,Z^3 + O_5. \tag{5.4}$$

Substitution in (5.3) gives

$$\left.\begin{aligned} a &= 2a_2\sigma Z^2 + 4a_4\sigma^2 Z^4 + O_6 \\ a_2 &\equiv -a_{0,\,2} \\ a_4 &\equiv (a_{1,\,3} - a_{0,\,2})\,a_{0,\,2}/a_{1,\,3} \end{aligned}\right\} \tag{5.5}$$

The "frequency equation" (5.5) shows the propagation speed $c = c_{1,1}(1+a)$ to be a series in even powers of the amplitude parameter Z.

To complete the fourth-order solution, we write the equations in (5.1) which correspond to $\mathbf{k}_1 = 2, 2$ and $\mathbf{k}_1 = 2, 4$. These lead ultimately to

$$\zeta_{2,2} = -8\sigma(a_{0,2}/a_{2,2})Z^4 + O_6$$

$$\zeta_{2,4} = 4\sigma(a_{0,2}/a_{2,4})Z^4 + O_6.$$

With the aid of figure 2, one may proceed without much difficulty to solutions of the fifth and higher orders.

6. Structure and speed of the wave

The quantity β/μ^2 (where $\mu \equiv \pi/D$) is a convenient reference velocity, values of which are listed here for several values of D, and for $\beta = 1.62 \times 10^{-11}$ sec^{-1} m^{-1} (the Rossby parameter at 45° latitude):

D	(deg lat)	30	50	70
β/μ^2	(m sec^{-1})	18.2	50.5	99.0

Unless otherwise noted, all velocities involved in the discussion to follow are assumed to be rendered dimensionless through division by β/μ^2.

The zonal mean flow corresponding to the solution obtained in the preceding section is

$$\bar{u} = -\sigma Z^2 \cos 2\mu y.$$

If $\sigma > 0$, this gives westerlies in the central region and equally strong easterlies at the boundaries. In order to obtain a more realistic velocity profile, we will add a uniform flow (see section 2) equal to σZ^2:

$$\bar{u} = \sigma Z^2 (1 - \cos 2\mu y); \qquad (6.1)$$

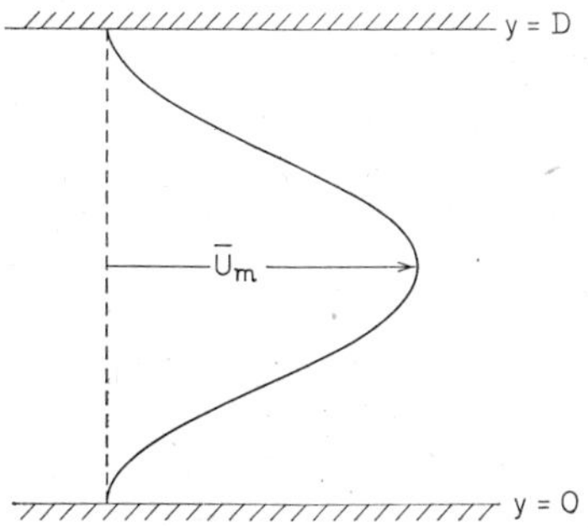

Fig. 3. The zonal mean velocity given by (6.1).

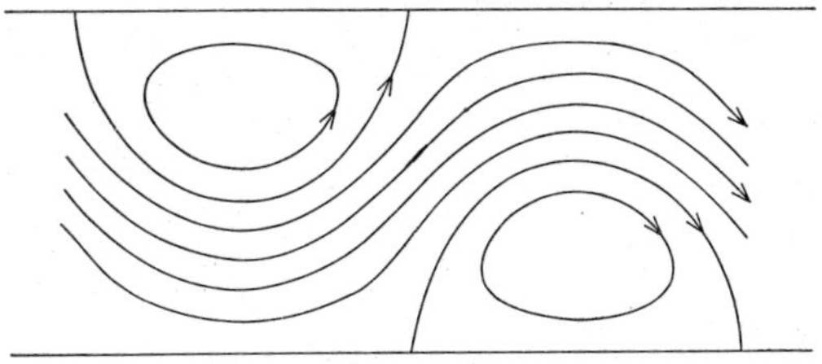

Fig. 4. Second-order streamlines, for $L = 2D$ and $u_{max} = \bar{u}_{max}$.

this causes $\bar{u}$ to vanish at the boundaries, and gives the profile shown in figure 3. Evidently,

$$\bar{u}_m \equiv 2\sigma Z^2 \qquad (6.2)$$

gives the maximum zonal mean velocity.

Through terms of the *third* order, the stream function ψ is given by

$$\beta^{-1}\mu^3\psi = \sigma Z^2\left(-\mu y + \frac{1}{2}\sin 2\mu y\right) + 4(1+\varepsilon^2)^{-1} Z \sin \mu y \cos \lambda x + \frac{1}{4}(\varepsilon^3 - 3)\sigma Z^3 \sin 3\mu y \cos \lambda x + O_4,$$

where $\varepsilon \equiv \lambda/\mu = 2\,D/L$. The corresponding velocity components may be found readily by differentiation. In figure 4 the streamline configuration is shown *to the second order* for $L = 2D$ and $v_{\max} = \bar{u}_m$. The flow pattern is essentially the same as that of the Rossby-Haurwitz waves; in fact, it would probably not be very fruitful to explore the streamline fine-structure associated with higher-order terms in our solution, because the use of the β-plane imposes certain compromises *ab initio* in the geometry of the solution.

With the aid of the expressions given previously (section 5) for $a_{0,2}$ and $a_{1,3}$ in terms of $\varepsilon \equiv \lambda/\mu = 2D/L$, the explicit formula for the wave speed through terms of the fourth order is, from (5.5):

$$c = c_{1,1}(1+a)$$

$$c_{1,1} = -(1+\varepsilon^2)^{-1}$$

$$a = \frac{1}{4}(3-\varepsilon^2)\bar{u}_m - \frac{1}{4}(3-\varepsilon^2) \times \left[1 - \frac{1}{32}(3-\varepsilon^2)(\varepsilon^2+9)\right]\bar{u}_m^2 + O_6.$$

Here we have introduced $\bar{u}_m$ in place of Z through the relation (6.2). The westward wave speed — c

is represented in figure 5 for several values of $\bar{u}_m$. The curves in this figure show only the *dynamic* part of the propagation speed; the kinematic term (equal to $\frac{1}{2}\,\bar{u}_m$) must be added to obtain the total speed.

From figure 5 we see that the effect of allowing for nonlinear terms in the particular manner adopted here is to increase slightly the westward dynamic part of the phase velocity. This statement does not apply to all wave lengths, however, because for hemispheric wave numbers greater than about 5, terms of order higher than four become important, so the approximation obtained above does not suffice. For this reason, the broken curves in figure 5 have not been extended beyond wave number 5.

The solid curve in figure 5 gives the propagation speed of the Rossby-Haurwitz wave. It is important to note that in the latter solution the dynamic part of the phase velocity is not affected by the zonal mean flow, in contrast with the nonlinear solution.

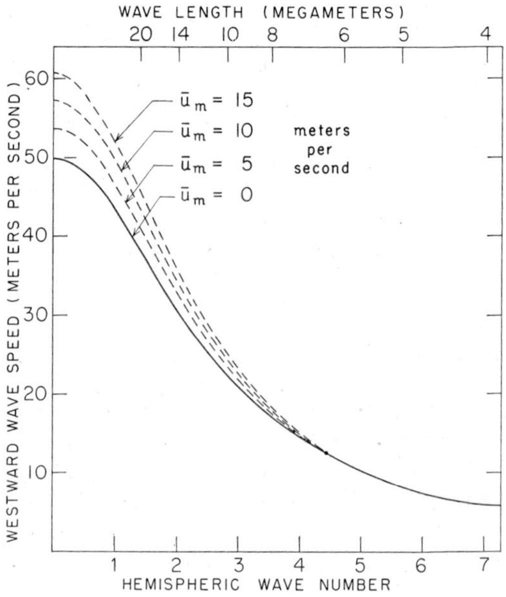

Fig. 5. Westward dynamic propagation speed (ordinate) as a function of hemispheric wave number (abscissa). The solid curve represents the zero-order (linear) solution; the broken curves show the nonlinear solution, through terms of the fourth order.

7. Conclusions

The method presented here for generating a solution of the nonlinear vorticity equation seems to be internally consistent, and to be capable of extension to any order of approximation. The resulting solution, through terms of the fourth order, does not differ drastically from the Rossby-Haurwitz wave, insofar as the streamline geometry and propagation speed are concerned, and reduces to the latter solution as a special case. These aspects of the present results encourage the belief that the infinite series representation which has been used actually converges in the strict mathematical sense.

Another question which is raised by this approach is whether the methods used here can be carried out on the sphere, without making the compromises needed to achieve the geometrical simplicity of the β-plane.

In spite of these uncertainties, it is possible that the solution given here, or any other obtained by similar methods, may be useful in the study of truncation errors arising from nonlinear effects. Thus, the power-series expansion can be extended (by high-speed computer if necessary) to any order of approximation, to yield a nonlinear solution of relatively simple structure, exact to within any specified tolerance. If then a finite-difference scheme is applied to appropriate initial conditions, one would have the means to assess truncation errors in a case where nonlinear effects are included.

Acknowledgement

The spirit of the method of expansion presented here was developed in collaboration with Dr. H. L. Kuo in connection with an investigation of the problem of finite-amplitude convection, to be published in the near future.

REFERENCES

Haurwitz, B., 1940: The motion of atmospheric disturbances. *J. Marine Res.*, **3**, 254—267.

Neamtan, S. M., 1946: The motion of harmonic waves in the atmosphere. *J. Meteor.*, **3**, 53—56.

Rossby, C.-G., and Collaborators, 1939: Relation between variations in the intensity of the zonal circulation of the atmosphere and the displacement of the semi-permanent centers of action. *J. Marine Res.*, **2**, 38—55.

Silberman, J., 1954: Planetary waves in the atmosphere. *J. Meteor.*, **11**, 27—34.

(Manuscript received August 31, 1958)

On the Behavior of Baroclinic Waves[1]

By JÖRGEN HOLMBOE

The University of California, Los Angeles

Professor Rossby's discovery of the dynamic importance of the planetary vorticity gradient is one of the great landmarks in the theory of atmospheric motion. All later developments of the theory have been influenced and stimulated by this discovery. It is an honor to pay tribute to the memory of this great man and friend.

1. Introduction

The new vorticity principle was first applied by ROSSBY (1939) to non-divergent wave perturbations on a uniform barotropic zonal current. He found that these waves, now generally known as Rossby-waves, are stable for all wave lengths, and he showed that the properties of these waves give the key to the understanding of the large scale circulation patterns which are observed in the atmosphere. In a later paper ROSSBY (1942) investigated the properties of long waves in a baroclinic current. Here he used the principles of vorticity conservation and quasi-geostrophic balance synthetically in the derivation of the three-dimensional kinematic structure of long baroclinic waves. He also showed that such waves actually are found in nature. A few years later similar methods were applied to somewhat shorter baroclinic waves by BJERKNES and HOLMBOE (1944) in an attempt to explain the dynamic mechanism wich makes these waves grow in amplitude and develop into cyclones. They showed in a qualitative way that simple wave perturbations on a baroclinic zonal current will develop westward tilt with height, and the wave amplitude will keep on growing if the wave length is shorter than some critical value. The analytical proof of this result was given by CHARNEY (1947), EADY (1949), and FJØRTOFT (1950). They derived the spectrum of normal modes for a baroclinic current. It turns out, however, that the same results may be obtained with less mathematical labor when Rossby's kinematic method is used. Although less powerful than the analytical method of normal modes, Rossby's synthetic kinematic method has the practical advantage that it brings out more clearly the physical mechanism which governs the behavior of baroclinic waves, as is shown in sections 7, 8 and 9 of this note. For convenient reference and comparison the theory of normal modes is reviewed in the earlier sections. Only the simplest baroclinic model of the atmosphere —the so-called "advective model" of Fjørtoft— will be considered.

2. The advective model

This model of the atmosphere is defined as having zero static stability. In the form proposed by FJØRTOFT (1950) the curvature of the earth is ignored. The atmosphere is incompressible, horizontally unbounded and vertically bounded by rigid horizontal planes. The undisturbed motion is a steady zonal current which increases linearly from the bottom to the top of the atmosphere, and has no variation with latitude. This motion is balanced by the proper meridional gradient of the mass field. *The vertical gradient is by definition zero.*

Let U_T denote the total increase of the zonal wind from the bottom to the top in this atmospheric model.[2] Choose a cartesian frame of reference (**i**, **j**, **k**) with the usual orientation, moving with the air at the central level and having the origin at that level. Let the height of the atmosphere be the unit of length. The zonal wind at an arbitrary level is then[3]

$$U = U_T z, \qquad \left(-\tfrac{1}{2} < z < \tfrac{1}{2}\right). \tag{2.1}$$

Let further the mass field be represented by the parameter

$$\varkappa = g \ln \varrho. \tag{2.2}$$

where ϱ is the density and g the acceleration of gravity. Within the approximation consistent with the model the condition for balance of the

[1] The research reported in this paper was sponsored by the Geophysics Research Directorate of the Air Force Cambridge Research Center under Contract No. AF 19(604)-3064.

[2] Later on we shall introduce another thermal wind parameter which is the intrinsically simplest measure for the baroclinity.

[3] Se list of symbols at the end of the paper.

undisturbed zonal flow is the well known "thermal" wind formula

$$fU_T = d\varkappa_0/dy, \qquad (2.3)$$

where f is the Coriolis parameter.

3. The normal modes

Following Fjørtoft we shall consider the normal modes of this system. These are small-amplitude wave disturbances, superimposed on the balanced zonal current, whose elements $(\mathbf{v}, \bar{\varkappa})$ have a sinusoidal variation in the zonal direction with the wave length $L = 2\pi/k$, and no variation in the meridional direction. The amplitude and phase of the wave elements are supposed to be properly adjusted from level to level so that the evolution in time is simple harmonic. In other words the normal modes are wave disturbances whose elements are proportional to $\exp i(kx+nt)$. The mathematical problem is to determine the amplitude factors and the values of $n = n(k)$ for which the corresponding resultant motion

$$\mathbf{V} = \mathbf{U} + \mathbf{v}, \qquad \varkappa = \varkappa_0 + \bar{\varkappa}, \qquad (3.1)$$

is a solution of the atmospheric equations

$$\frac{D\mathbf{q}}{Dt} = \mathbf{q} \cdot \nabla \mathbf{V} + \mathbf{k} \times \nabla \varkappa; \qquad \frac{D\varkappa}{Dt} = 0. \qquad (3.2)$$

Here $\mathbf{q}$ is the vorticity of the resultant motion in the absolute frame, that is

$$\mathbf{q} = \nabla \times \mathbf{V} + 2\boldsymbol{\Omega} = \xi\mathbf{i} + (\eta + 2\Omega_y)\mathbf{j} + (\zeta + f)\mathbf{k}.$$

A slight approximation, similar to that introduced in the balance equation (2.3), has been made in the solenoidal term $\mathbf{k} \times \nabla\varkappa$ in the vorticity equation.

Since the motion is solenoidal and independent of latitude, we may represent its component in the vertical zonal planes by a stream function ψ, and write

$$\mathbf{v} = u\mathbf{i} + v\mathbf{j} + w\mathbf{k} = v\mathbf{j} + \mathbf{j} \times \nabla\psi.$$

The normal modes accordingly are represented by the three scalar fields

$$v, \ \psi, \ \bar{\varkappa} \sim \exp i(kx+nt). \qquad (3.3)$$

The three equations needed to determine these fields are the vertical and meridional components of the vorticity equation and the equation of incompressibility in (3.2). Letting differentiation with reference to height be denoted by a prime, $\partial/\partial z = (')$, these equations with second order terms (as far as they would appear) ignored are

$$\left.\begin{aligned} &\frac{D}{Dt}(\zeta + f) = -f\frac{\partial \psi'}{\partial x}; \quad (\zeta = \partial v/\partial x) \\ &\frac{D}{Dt}(\eta + 2\Omega_y) = fv' + \frac{\partial \bar{\varkappa}}{\partial x}; \quad (\eta = \nabla^2\psi + U_T) \\ &\frac{D}{Dt}(\bar{\varkappa} + \varkappa_0) = 0. \end{aligned}\right\} \qquad (3.4)$$

On the left hand side of the vertical vorticity equation, where the Coriolis parameter f appears under the differentiation sign, its variation with latitude is dynamically significant, as was first noted by Rossby. However, after the differentiations have been performed the resulting Rossby parameter

$$\beta = df/dy = (2\Omega \cos \varphi)/a,$$

and the Coriolis parameter itself are regarded as constants in order to make the equations consistent for the flat Rossby-plane model of the earth. To make the equations look dimensionally homogeneous we shall let the Rossby parameter appear implicitly by defining the corresponding Rossby-velocity

$$U_R = \beta/k^2, \qquad (3.5)$$

and introduce the two frequency parameters

$$\left.\begin{aligned} n_R &= kU_R = \beta/k \\ n_T &= kU_T. \end{aligned}\right\} \qquad (3.6)$$

The product of these, $n_R n_T = \beta U_T$, is a constant for a given system.

The individual time derivatives of the fields in (3.3) with second order terms ignored may be written

$$\frac{D}{Dt} = \frac{\partial}{\partial t} + U\frac{\partial}{\partial x} = i(n + kU) = i\nu,$$

where ν is the local frequency of the air particles. Using (2.1) and (3.6) the local frequency may be written

$$\nu = n + kU = n + n_T z. \qquad (3.7)$$

When the differentiations in (3.4) are performed and the balance equation (2.3) is used, the equations take the form

The reason for the name is explained in the next section. According to this formula the transition from instability to stability ($n_i = 0$) occurs at the wave length of $U_R = U_T/\sqrt{3}$, shown by the dashed parabola in fig. 1. This is a slight overestimate of the instability, but the agreement with the exact values (full drawn curve) is quite good for the atmospheric range of baroclinities.

For other wave lengths the geostrophic approximation is shown by the dashed curve in the upper diagram of fig. 1. We notice that it becomes increasingly better with increasing wave length, and it is quite good down to the wave length where it meets the dotted curve of the short wave approximation. At this point the stabilizing effect of the planetary vorticity gradient may be ignored, and the geostrophic approximation reduces to

$$n_i = n_T/\sqrt{12} = n_{i0}. \tag{4.8}$$

This formula is represented graphically by the dotted-dashed hyperbolas in fig. 1. It is seen that even this great simplification gives a rather good approximation of the rate of growth of the unstable waves over a fairly wide central part of the unstable band of wave lengths. The mathematical simplicity of the growth-rate in (4.8) reflects a corresponding simplicity in the three-dimensional structure and the dynamic behavior of the unstable baroclinic waves, as will be shown later.

5. The geostrophic approximation

It was noticed by Charney (1947) that the approximation which is reflected in the simplified frequency formula (4.7) may be introduced from the start in the basic system of equations (3.4) by ignoring the change of the meridional vorticity component. The meridional vorticity equation then reduces to $fv' \approx -\partial\varkappa/\partial x$, which implies quasi-geostrophic balance of the meridional wind component. The approximation in (4.7) is therefore formally equivalent to the assumption that the meridional component of the wind field is geostrophic. With this "geostrophic" approximation introduced in (3.9) the non-dimensional equations for the normal modes become

$$\left.\begin{aligned}(\nu - n_R)\,v &= i\psi' \\ (v/\nu)' &= 0.\end{aligned}\right\} \tag{5.1}$$

The second of these has the integral $v = \nu$ so, leaving out an arbitrary amplitude factor we have

$$v = i\nu \exp i(kx + nt) \tag{5.2}$$

and hence from (3.8) the perturbation of the mass field is

$$\varkappa = -fU_T \exp i(kx + nt) \tag{5.3}$$

To find the frequency n and the stream function ψ, substitute the value of v from (5.2) into the first equation (5.1), giving

$$\psi' = \nu(\nu - n_R) \exp i(kx + nt)$$

Substitute here from (3.7)

$$\nu(\nu - n_R) = (n_T z)^2 + (n^2 - nn_R) + 2n_T z\left(n - \tfrac{1}{2} n_R\right)$$

and integrate with respect to z. The result may be written

$$\psi = \left[\tfrac{1}{3} z n_T^2 \left(z^2 + 3\,\frac{n^2 - nn_R}{n_T^2}\right) + \right.$$
$$\left. + n_T\left(n - \tfrac{1}{2} n_R\right)(z^2 + B)\right] \exp i(kx + nt).$$

The integration constant B and frequency n are determined by the boundary conditions $\psi = 0$ at the bottom and the top of the atmosphere $\left(z = \pm\tfrac{1}{2}\right)$. We see that both boundary conditions are statisfied when

$$B = 3(n^2 - nn_R)/n_T^2 = -\tfrac{1}{4}.$$

This is just the value of the frequency in (4.7). The corresponding value of the stream function is accordingly

$$\psi = n_T\left(z^2 - \tfrac{1}{4}\right)\left[\tfrac{1}{3} n_T z + \left(n - \tfrac{1}{2} n_R\right)\right] \cdot$$
$$\cdot \exp i(kx + nt). \tag{5.4}$$

From these fundamental complex solutions we get the real solutions by substituting the appropriate value of n from (4.7) and then take the real or the imaginary parts. For every wave length in the unstable band of the spectrum the system has a pair of normal modes whose frequencies are $n = \tfrac{1}{2} n_R \pm in_i$. One of these grows and the other decays at the exponential rate n_i. We shall examine the field elements of the growing or amplifying mode.

6. The amplifying mode

The orbital frequency of this mode is

$$\nu = n_T z + n = n_T z + \tfrac{1}{2} n_R - in_i,$$

so it propagates to the west with the phase velocity $\frac{1}{2} U_R$ relative to the air at the central level. In other words the mode is stationary relative to the air at the level where $U = U_T z = -\frac{1}{2} U_R$. We call this level *the stationary level* of the mode. Let z_0 denote non-dimensional height measured from the stationary level, so we have

$$n_T z_0 = n_T z + \tfrac{1}{2} n_R. \tag{6.1}$$

Substitute these in the fundamental solutions in (5.2), (5.3) and (5.4). The results are the still complex field elements of the amplifying mode with reference to the stationary frame, namely

$$\begin{aligned} v &= (n_i + in_T z_0) \exp(n_i t + ikx) \\ (\tfrac{1}{4} - z^2)^{-1}\psi &= in_T(n_i + i\tfrac{1}{3} n_T z) \exp(n_i t + ikx) \\ \bar{\varkappa} &= -fU_T \exp(n_i t + ikx), \end{aligned}$$

x being now measured with reference to the air at the stationary level.

Take the imaginary parts of these and include the amplitude factor (v_0/n_i) to get the right dimensions. Introducing further the notation[1]

$$v_b = v_0 \exp(n_i t) \tag{6.2}$$

we get the elements of the amplifying mode relative to the air at the stationary level in the form

$$\left.\begin{aligned} v &= v_b \sec\varphi \sin(kx + \varphi); \\ &\qquad (\tan\varphi = n_T z_0/n_i) \\ (\tfrac{1}{4} - z^2)^{-1}\psi &= n_T v_b \sec\Theta \cos(kx + \Theta); \\ &\qquad (\tan\Theta = \tfrac{1}{3} n_T z/n_i) \\ \bar{\varkappa} &= -(fU_T v_b/n_i) \sin kx. \end{aligned}\right\} \tag{6.3}$$

The mass-distribution is very simple in this disturbance. Adding the undisturbed mass field from the balance equation (2.3), we see that the mass-distribution is

$$\varkappa = \varkappa_0 + \bar{\varkappa} = \varkappa_{00} + fU_T(y - v_b/n_i \sin kx),$$

where $\varkappa_{00}$ denotes the value at the reference latitude $y = 0$. The isopycnic surfaces, $\varrho = \text{const}$, are the vertical cylinder surfaces

$$(y - y_0)_\varrho = (v_b/n_i) \sin kx = A_\varrho \sin kx. \tag{6.4}$$

[1] The reason for choosing the subscript b will become clear in section 7.

Since the mass field is conservative, the growth of the amplitude is caused by meridional advection. At the meridians of the crests and troughs of the isopycnic surfaces the meridional velocity has the values $\pm v_b$ at all heights. So the amplitude grows at the rate $\dot{A}_p = v_b$ at the time when its value is v_b/n_i. This explains why it grows at the exponential rate $d(\ln A_\varrho)/dt = n_i$.

The verticals half way between the crests and troughs are stationary nodal lines in the mass field. The flow is here parallel to the isopycnic surfaces. To verify this, consider the resultant of the zonal flow U and the meridional flow v at an arbitrary level. It may be represented by a stream function as follows:

$$\mathbf{U} + v\mathbf{j} = U \nabla [y + (v_b/Uk \cos\varphi) \cos(kx + \varphi)] \times \mathbf{k}.$$

Substituting here from (6.3)

$$Uk \cos\varphi = n_T z_0 \cos\varphi = n_i \sin\varphi,$$

we see that the horizontal streamlines are the sine curves

$$(y - y_0)_s = -(v_b/n_i \sin\varphi) \cos(kx + \varphi). \tag{6.5}$$

At all levels these are parallel to the isopycnic surfaces at the vertical nodal lines of these surfaces.

The mass distribution is the same for all wave lengths but the configuration of the velocity field depends upon the position of the stationary level. This level is lowered with increasing wave length as the stabilizing effect of the planetary vorticity gradient (the Rossby stability) becomes stronger. For sufficiently short waves ($U_R \ll U_T$) this effect is negligible (see fig. 1), and the stationary level coincides very nearly with the central level, as shown in fig. 2. From (4.8) these waves have the approximate growth rate n_{i0}, and the phase of the horizontal flow pattern is $\tan\varphi = 2z_0\sqrt{3}$. The wave tilts westward with increasing height. The horizontal streamlines and the isopycnics are 90° out of phase at the stationary level, and the wave has the total westward phase shift of one third of a wave length from the bottom to the top. The field of the vertical zonal circulation has a smaller westward tilt, $\tan\Theta = 2z/\sqrt{3}$. The phase shift of this field from bottom to top is one sixth of a wave length.

The wave structure in fig. 2 is representative of the central part of the unstable spectral band

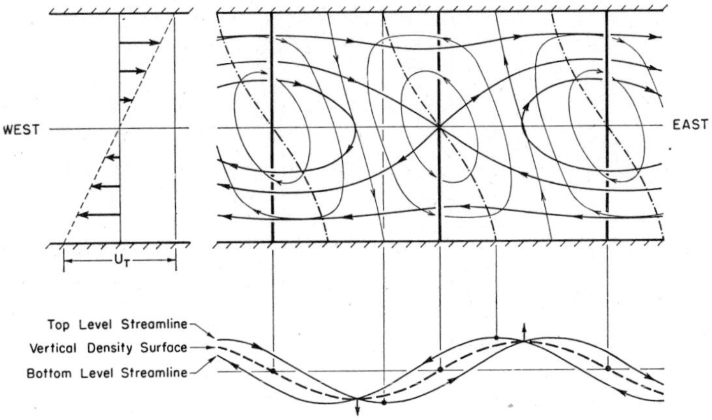

Fig. 2. The amplifying mode in the central part of the unstable band (n_i0-approximation).

where the limiting approximation n_{i0} in fig. 1 is fairly good. However, as we proceed to longer waves the Rossby stability becomes increasingly important. As a consequence the stationary level lies below the central level in the longer waves, and the wave structure is correspondingly modified. Fig. 3 shows a wave near the long wave end of the unstable band ($U_R = \frac{1}{2} U_T$). The stationary level of this wave is located half way down between the central level and the bottom. From (4.7) its growth rate is $\frac{1}{2} n_{i0}$ and the corresponding phase angles in (6.3) are

$$\tan \varphi = 4 z_0 \sqrt{3}, \quad \tan \Theta = 4z/\sqrt{3}.$$

The westward tilt of the meridional field is symmetric with reference to the stationary level. In fact the horizontal flow pattern in the lower half of this particular wave is a replica, level for level, of that in fig. 2 when here the heights and velocities are reduced by a factor of one half. So the westward phase shift with height is doubled in the lower half of this wave, with a phase shift of one third of a wave length from the bottom to the central level. The upper part of the wave has a much smaller tilt due to the strong west winds at high levels. The phase difference between the central level and the top is less than four per cent of the wave length, with practically no tilt near the top. The vertical zonal circulation cells tilt westward too, but these remain symmetric with respect to the central level for all wave lengths. The physical mechanism which is responsible for this wave structure will be explained in the following sections.

7. The evolution of quasi-geostrophic baroclinic waves

We shall now examine the behavior of the baroclinic waves with the aid of Rossby's kinematic method. This method consists in a synthetic application of the principles of quasi-geostrophic balance and potential vorticity conservation. The vorticity principle is used only in situations when the waves are neutral, propagating with the phase

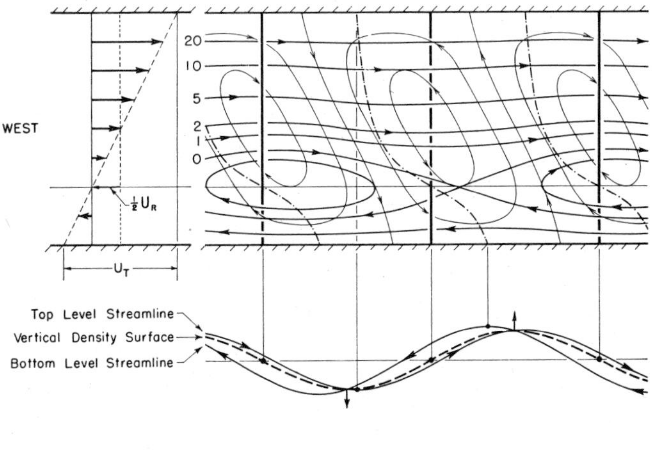

Fig. 3. The amplifying mode near the upper end of the unstable band ($U_R = \frac{1}{2} U_T$).

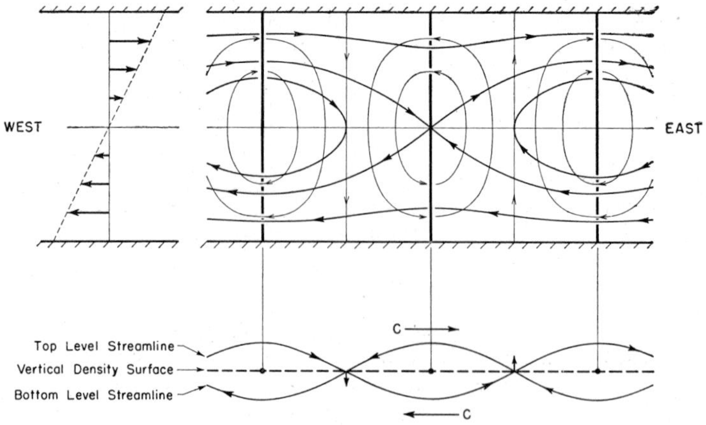

Fig. 4. The non-thermal state of a baroclinic wave. (The b-wave.)

velocity C. For such waves the vertical vorticity equation in (3.4) has the well known form, first introduced by Rossby

$$k^2(U - C - U_R)\,v = f\partial\psi'/\partial x. \qquad (7.1)$$

In words it states that the neutral waves are simple Rossby waves at the level (or levels) of zero horizontal divergence, moving westward with the Rossby velocity U_R relative to the air at these levels.[1] At other levels the neutral waves have horizontal divergence (convergence) to the east of the trough if the zonal wind relative to the wave is greater (less) than the Rossby velocity.

We begin by considering the simple non-tilting wave shown in fig. 4. The small amplitude meridional disturbance,

$$v = v_b \sin kx \qquad (7.2)$$

is here impulsively superimposed on the balanced zonal current (2.1), so the mass field is at that time undisturbed. In order that this initial impulse shall satisfy the geostrophic approximation it can have no shear, so the amplitude v_b is necessarily a constant. In fact the field in (7.2) is the only sinusoidal impulse on the undisturbed mass field compatible with the quasi-geostrophic condition. The lower part of fig. 4 shows the streamlines of the resultant horizontal motion relative to the air at the central level. The vertical circulation cells shown in the cross-section above agree in a qualitative way with the requirements of the vorticity equation (7.1). We shall consider this field in more detail later. The situation in fig. 4 is uniquely defined by the fact that the mass field has no deformations. The wave has no thermal wind so we shall call it the *non-thermal state* of the wave.

Starting from the non-thermal state in fig. 4 the meridional velocity field immediately begins to deform the vertical isopycnic surfaces into

[1] Bjerknes and Holmboe used the name "critical velocity" for this parameter.

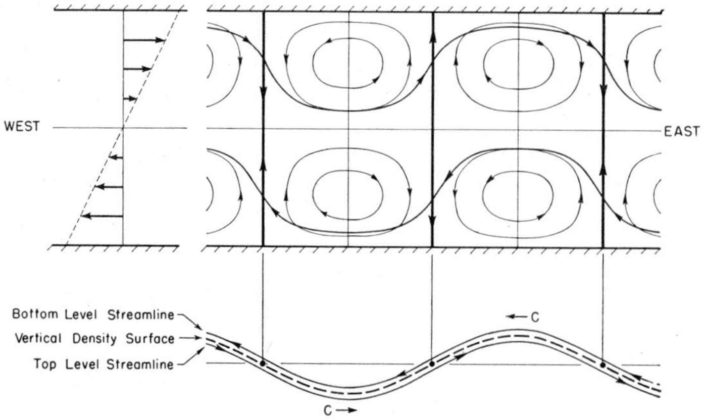

Fig. 5. The thermal state of a baroclinic wave. (The a-wave.)

sinusoidal cylinder surfaces. A short time increment after the undeformed state the mass distribution is therefore

$$\varkappa = \varkappa_{00} + fU_T(y - A_\varrho \sin kx).$$

This mass field in turn gives rise to the meridional thermal wind shear

$$v' = -\frac{1}{f}\frac{\partial \varkappa}{\partial x} = kU_T A_\varrho \cos kx. \qquad (7.3)$$

The amplitude of the corresponding thermal wind field increases linearly with height, so there is one level—not necessarily within the bounds of the atmosphere—where this amplitude is zero. In a frame of reference which moves with the air at that level the entire motion is zero at the points where the nodal verticals of the mass field meet that level; and the wind is purely thermal—that is parallel to the isopycnics—everywhere else on these nodal verticals. The mass field deformation accordingly has no progressive motion relative to the air at this reference level, so we may call it the *stationary level* of the wave.

The corresponding thermal part of the meridional field, from (7.3), is

$$v = kUA_\varrho(t) \cos kx, \qquad \text{(thermal part)} \quad (7.4)$$

where U is the zonal wind in a frame of reference which moves with the air at the stationary level. That is the frame in which the mass field deformation remains stationary at all times, so we shall call it the stationary frame.

The remaining non-thermal part of the meridional field has no variation with height. It has a 90° phase difference from the thermal field, so it is given by

$$v = v_b(t) \sin kx. \qquad \text{(non-thermal part).} \quad (7.5)$$

This part of the field continues to deform the mass field at the rate $\dot{A}_\varrho = v_b$. At an arbitrary time the changes of the thermal and the non-thermal parts of the wave are therefore in some way coupled by the growth rate of the mass field deformation

$$n_i(t) = \frac{d}{dt}(\ln A_\varrho) = \frac{v_b}{A_\varrho}. \qquad (7.6)$$

The total meridional field is the sum of the thermal and the non-thermal part of the wave,

$$v = v_b \sin kx + kUA_\varrho \cos kx. \qquad (7.7)$$

This then is the meridional field at an arbitrary time of a wave which is started impulsively in the non-thermal state (7.2) with no deformation of the mass field. During the evolution of the wave both the thermal and the non-thermal part will change. The change of the thermal part is determined by the growth rate parameter n_i in (7.6). This change is a direct consequence of the quasi-geostrophic condition. The change of the non-thermal part is primarily a consequence of the vorticity condition, as will be explained presently. However it is useful to study the consequences of the geostrophic condition a little further before the vorticity condition is invoked.

We first note that the thermal and the non-thermal components of the wave combine into the single wave

$$v = v_b \sec \varphi \sin (kx + \varphi). \qquad (\tan \varphi = kU/n_i) \quad (7.8)$$

The phase of the wave determines the growth rate of the mass field. We also see that the tangent of the phase is proportional to the height above

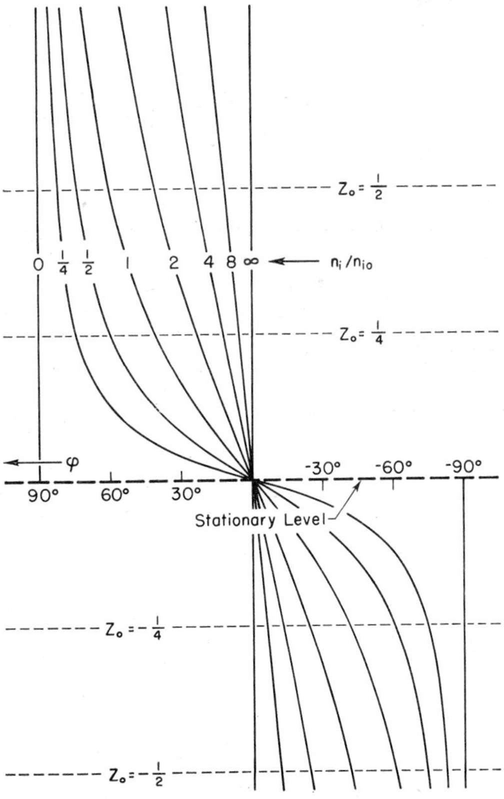

Fig. 6. Successive positions of the trough line in a baroclinic wave during its evolution from the non-thermal to the thermal state.

the stationary level, as shown in fig. 6. The diagram shows successive positions of the trough line in the evolution from the non-thermal state in fig. 4, labeled by the values of the growth rate of the thermal component.

The corresponding growth rate of the non-thermal component is obtained by logarithmic time differentiation of the phase equation in (7.8) and subsequent substitution of n_i from (7.6), thus

$$\frac{d}{dt}(\ln v_b) = (kU - \dot{\varphi}\sec^2\varphi)\cot\varphi. \qquad (7.9)$$

In the non-thermal state ($\varphi = 0$) the right hand side of this equation becomes infinite unless $\dot{\varphi} = kU$. However an infinite growth rate would violate the energy principle. So the wave moves instantaneously westward with the phase velocity $-U$ relative to the stationary level in the non-thermal state. In other words the vertical trough line (fig. 6) is turning westward about the point where it meets the stationary level at the same rate that the vertical air columns are turned eastward by the zonal wind shear.

The growth rate of the wave in the non-thermal state can not be seen immediately from (7.9) since the right hand side is indeterminate. However, if the states of negative phase are added in fig. 6, it will be evident that the evolution is symmetric around the non-tilting state ($\varphi = 0$). The phase velocity in that state must be an extreme value ($\ddot{\varphi} = 0$) so, by l'Hospitals rule applied in (7.9), it follows that the growth rate of the wave is zero in the non-thermal state.

Thus we have shown that the non-thermal wave in fig. 4 is an instantaneously neutral non-tilting wave moving at every level with the phase velocity $-U$ relative to the stationary frame, or with the phase velocity $-2U$ relative to the air at every level. We may therefore apply the vorticity condition in the simple form (7.1) to the wave in the non-thermal state (7.2). It gives

$$f\psi' = -k(2U - U_R)v_b \cos kx. \quad \text{(non-thermal state)}.$$

The stream function amplitude in the non-thermal wave has a parabolic height variation with zeros at the bottom and the top of the atmosphere and a level of non-divergence ($\psi' = 0$) in the middle, as shown in the lower diagram in fig. 7. At that level the vorticity is conserved, and the wave moves with the Rossby velocity westward relative to the air. The stationary level of the wave is therefore the level where the air moves westward relative to the air at the central level with one half of the Rossby velocity.

As soon as the wave has moved out of the non-thermal state it is no longer neutral. The thermal wave component begins to appear and keeps on growing at the rate in (7.6) and the non-thermal component begins to change at the rate in (7.9), as the resultant wave successively moves through the increasingly westward tilting states shown in fig. 6. As this evolution continues one of two things may happen:

(i) The wave has some state of stationary phase ($\dot{\varphi} = 0$). If such a state exists, the wave can not move past it in its evolution from the non-thermal state. Indeed, the stationary state is approached asymptotically ($\dot{\varphi} \to 0$), and in the limit both the thermal and the non-thermal wave component keep on growing at the same stationary rate. The stationary state accordingly is the state of the stationary amplifying mode in (6.3). And we see that the non-thermal wave must move into this state and become stationary if it exists.

(ii) The wave has no state of stationary phase. In that case the phase of the wave must keep on changing. After a certain time interval the wave arrives in the state of $\varphi = 90°$ shown in fig. 5. From fig. 6 [or directly from the phase equation in (7.8)] we see that the growth of the thermal component has stopped here, and the non-thermal component has disappeared. Thus in the evolution from the non-tilting state in fig. 4 to the new non-tilting state in fig. 5 the wave changes from a non-thermal into a thermal wave. We shall call this second neutral non-tilting state the *thermal state* of the wave. We have for the moment excluded the possibility that the thermal state is stationary, so the wave must pass through the thermal state in the same sense as in the non-thermal state. In the subsequent evolution the wave moves on to a new non-thermal state, with eastward tilting wave troughs in the intermediate states. The evolution is therefore quite simple when observed from the stationary frame which we recall is fixed to the mass field deformation. Above the stationary level the wave moves westward and below the stationary level it moves eastward relative to the permanently non-tilting thermal wave component. At the time when the upper and the lower through coincide the wave is non-thermal with an undeformed mass field. Half a period later the wave is thermal with a maximum deformation of the mass field. In both these states the wave is non-tilting. In all intermediate states the wave is a partly thermal and partly non-thermal tilting wave.

It remains to decide which waves have a state of stationary phase and which waves have not. This question is easily answered by the application of the vorticity condition to the neutral thermal state of the wave. We first note that the non-tilting constant-amplitude deformation of the mass field in fig. 5 is the only thermal state which is compatible with the quasi-geostrophic principle. This geostrophic uniqueness of the thermal state in fig. 5 is perhaps not quite so obvious as the uniqueness of the non-thermal state in fig. 4. But it is not difiicult to see that any other mass distribution leads to a contradiction if weassume that the field is thermal, and apply the geostrophic condition: A field will be defined as thermal if it has at least one level where the streamlines are parallel to the isopycnics (isotherms). According to the geostrophic condition the wind shear at that level is everywhere parallel to the isotherms, so the streamlines have the same amplitude and phase at the adjacent levels above and below. However if the same consideration is repeated at these levels, we get different answers for the streamline at the middle level depending on whether we return to it from above or from below, unless the isotherms have the same amplitude and phase at all three levels.

It is interesting to note that the quasi-geostrophic condition automatically excludes any variation with height of the temperature field. It is therefore redundant to introduce the latter as an independent restriction on the atmospheric model. This was clearly recognized by ROSSBY (1942), who also showed that the waves which are observed in the atmosphere have a practically non-tilting temperature field.

8. The non-tilting states of the baroclinic wave

We have seen that the non-tilting state in fig. 4 is the only possible purely non-thermal state of the quasi-geostrophic baroclinic wave, and the non-tilting state in fig. 5 is the only possible purely thermal state of the wave. All other permissible states are partly thermal and partly non-thermal. In a mathematical sense the two non-tilting states are linearly independent. By a linear combination of them with arbitrary amplitude ratio and phase difference, we can construct the most general state which the quasi-geostrophic wave can have. By adding them 90° out of phase (directly as they are shown in fig. 4 and 5) we may by proper adjustment of the amplitude ratio construct any one of the intermediate tilting states in fig. 6, or the corresponding eastward tilting states with a negative amplitude ratio. Each of these is a legitimate quasi-geostrophic initial state of the wave whose evolution in time has been described already. If the non-tilting components are added with a phase difference other than 90° we get more complex initial states whose evolution may be anticipated in a general way by considering the evolutions of the thermal and non-thermal component separately. Finally by adding the non-tilting wave components in phase we may by proper adjustment of the amplitude ratio construct neutral waves which move with the same phase velocity at all heights, provided the wave has no state of stationary phase. These are the stable long normal modes of the system.

The non-tilting wave components share with the normal modes the property that they can be used to construct waves which satisfy arbitrary initial conditions. In a mathematical sense they may be regarded as different pairs of linearly independent solutions of the quasi-geostrophic atmospheric equations. Each pair has its advantages and drawbacks. The normal modes have a simple evolution in time but have a rather complex wave structure. If we wish to find the evolution of a localised disturbance which contains a whole spectrum of waves, the Fourier integral of the spectrum of normal modes is probably the simplest method to use. However the physical wave mechanism may be better understood in terms of the non-tilting wave components, with their simple structure and easy mathematical derivation.

Since these components will be frequently referred to in the following, it is desirable to have suitable short and simple names for them. Adopting a terminology which was introduced earlier by the author in a similar analysis of Rayleigh waves in triple Couette flows (HOLMBOE, 1953), we shall call the thermal wave in fig. 5 the *a-wave*, and the non-thermal wave in fig. 4 the *b-wave*. And we shall use the corresponding subcripts for their phase velocities relative to the massfield deformation (the stationary frame). Thus we have by definition

The a-wave (thermal)	$C_a = -\dot{\varphi}_a/k$	$(\varphi = 90°)$
The b-wave (non-thermal)	$C_b = -U$	$(\varphi = 0°)$

The phase velocity of the a-wave is obtained by time differentiation of the phase equation (7.8),

$$-\dot{n}_i = kU\dot{\varphi}\csc^2\varphi.$$

Applying this relation to the thermal state ($\varphi = 90°$) where $\dot{\varphi}$ is the phase frequency of the a-wave, we see that the product of the phase velocities in the non-tilting states has the same value at all levels. This is quite evident if we inspect the adjacent tilting states in fig. 6. If the wave has no state of stationary phase, its phase velocity has the same sign in all states, so the product of the phase velocities in the non-tilting states is positive. Let us denote it by

$$C^2 = C_a C_b = -C_a U. \tag{8.1}$$

Its value is obtained by using the vorticity condition (7.1) in the thermal state (7.4), which gives

$$f\psi' = k^2(U - C_a - U_R)\,UA_\varrho \sin kx \quad \text{(thermal state)}$$

When the value of C_a is substituted here from (8.1), we see that the divergence is zero at the levels where $U^2 + C^2 = U_R U$, that is the levels where the air moves relative to the stationary frame with the velocity

$$U = \tfrac{1}{2}U_R \pm \sqrt{\tfrac{1}{4}U_R^2 - C^2}. \tag{8.2}$$

Since the air at the central level moves with one half of the Rossby velocity in the stationary frame (see the b-wave in fig. 7), the levels of non-divergence in the a-wave are located symmetrically above and below the central level. The main physical significance of these levels is not so much that the divergence is zero, but rather that the vorticity is conserved and that the wave is a simple Rossby wave at these levels. To emphasize this we shall call them the *Rossby-levels*. Although symmetrically placed in the atmosphere, the Rossby-levels are asymmetric with reference to the stationary level. If the vorticity condition is satisfied at one of the Rossby-levels, it is automatically satisfied at the other, so it is sufficient to consider one of them. It turns out that the upper level is most convenient to use, so the upper level is intended when we speak of the Rossby-level in the a-wave, or the Ra-level for short.

Let us now introduce the symbol U_T to denote the increase of the zonal wind from the lower to the upper Rossby level in the a-wave (see fig. 7). No confusion should arise from the different meaning of this symbol in the review of Fjørtoft's theory for the normal modes. In that theory the Rossby levels were not available, so the increase of the zonal wind from the bottom to the top of the atmosphere appeared to be the simplest measure for the baroclinity. However in the present analysis the relative zonal wind of the two Rossby levels turns out to be by far the best intrinsic measure of the baroclinity.

With this new meaning of U_T, equation (8.2) may now be written

$$C^2 = \tfrac{1}{4}(U_R^2 - U_T^2) = C_a C_b. \tag{8.3}$$

It remains to find the precise positions of the Rossby-levels in the a-wave: Since the divergence has a parabolic height distribution with zeros at the Rossby levels, the stream function is cubic with one zero at the central level and the other zeros at the bottom and the top. So, apart from an irrelevant constant, the stream function amplitude in the a-wave is

$$\psi_a = z\left(z^2 - \tfrac{1}{4}\right)$$

where z denotes non-dimensional height measured from the central level. The vertical distance between the Rossby levels is therefore $\left(1/\sqrt{3}\right)$, that is a little more than one half of the height of the atmosphere.

It may be noted that the velocity parameter C in (8.3) happens to be the phase velocity of the quasi-geostrophic normal mode in (4.7). The new intrinsic choice of the thermal wind parameter U_T makes the dispersion formula symmetric in U_R and U_T. The phase velocity of the normal mode emerges here as the geometric mean of the phase velocities in the non-tilting states of the wave.

The dispersion equation in (8.3) may be derived with little effort from the fact that the wave is a Rossby-wave at the Rossby levels in the non-tilting states. Once the positions of these levels are known, we merely let the wave move through the air with the Rossby velocity at these levels, and the dispersion formula follows. The formula (8.3) applies to all levels, but since C_a and C_b are inverse, it is sufficient to derive it at one particular level. The best choice turns out to be the upper Rossby level in the a-wave—that is the Ra-level in fig. 7. Following the procedure just mentioned it is readily seen that the phase velocities in the non-tilting states at that level are

$$\left.\begin{aligned} C_a &= -\tfrac{1}{2}(U_R - U_T),\\ C_b &= -\tfrac{1}{2}(U_R + U_T).\end{aligned}\right\}\ \text{(at Ra-level)} \tag{8.4}$$

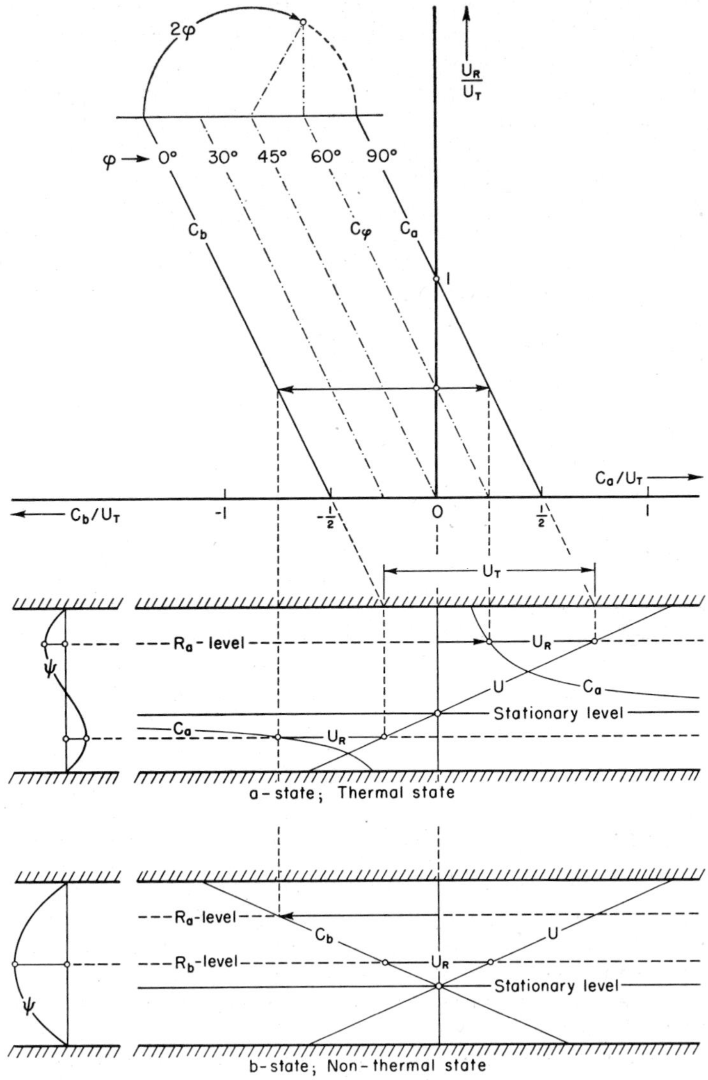

Fig. 7. Lower diagram shows how the stationary level is found from the Rossby velocity at the central Rossby level in the non-thermal state. Middle diagram shows how the phase velocity in the thermal state is found from the Rossby velocity at the upper Rossby level. Upper diagram shows the wave velocity relative to the mass field as a function of the Rossby velocity.

The product of these gives the dispersion formula in (8.3). However the representation in (8.4) is more useful. In the following we shall mainly consider conditions at the Ra-level, and let C_a and C_b have the fixed meaning in (8.4) for that level.

The upper diagram in fig. 7 shows the linear variation of these phase velocities with increasing Rossby velocity, that is with the square of the wave length. Foı all wave lengths their sum is the Rossby velocity and their difference is the relative zonal motion of the Rossby levels. The wave moves westward in both non-tilting states if $U_R > U_T$, so the waves whose Rossby velocity is larger than the relative velocity of the Rossby levels have no state of stationary state. However, if $U_R < U_T$, the wave moves westward in the *b*-state and eastward in the *a*-state at the Ra-level. These shorter waves can not reach the thermal *a*-state in the evolution from the non-thermal *b*-state, so they must have an intermediate stationary westward tilting state with a stationary growth rate.

It is rather plausible that the position of the stationary tilting state is determined by the phase velocity ratio of the non-tilting states. The stationary phase is easily obtained if we make use of the fact that (8.3) is the dispersion equation for the normal modes. For the shorter waves ($U_R < U_T$) it becomes the equation for the growth rate of the modes

$$n_i^2 = -k^2 C_a C_b.$$

Combining this with the phase equation in (7.8) we get

$$\tan \varphi = -\frac{kC_b}{n_i} = \frac{n_i}{kC_a}$$

or, when n_i/k is eliminated,

$$0 = C_a \sin^2 \varphi + C_b \cos^2 \varphi.$$

This happens to be a special case of a more general formula which applies to all waves. For lack of space I give the general formula without proof. It is

$$C_\varphi = C_a \sin^2 \varphi + C_b \cos^2 \varphi, \quad \text{(at Ra-level)} \qquad (8.5)$$

where C_φ is the phase velocity of the wave at the upper Rossby-level at the time when the wave has the phase φ at that level. Introducing here the values of C_a and C_b from (8.4), we see that the phase velocity of the wave at the upper Rossby level relative to the stationary frame (the mass field deformation) is

$$C_\varphi = -\tfrac{1}{2}(U_R + U_T \cos 2\varphi) \qquad (8.6)$$

The C_φ-isopleths as obtained from this formula are shown in the upper diagram of fig. 7. All the isopleths are parallel lines in the stripe bounded by the isopleths of the non-tilting states. The shorter waves ($U_R < U_T$) have the stationary phase of the isopleth $C_\varphi = 0$. The longer waves have no state of stationary phase.

The information we have found so far about the behavior of the baroclinic waves has now been transferred in graphical form to the diagram in fig. 7. It remains to examine the physical interpretation of these results a little further.

9. The unstable baroclinic waves

We begin by considering the relatively short waves whose Rossby velocity is negligible compared to the relative zonal motion of the Ra-levels. Let us for a moment ignore the Rossby velocity all together. The wave then exhibits the baroclinic instability of the system in pure form. It is stationary at the central level and moves in the non-tilting states with equal velocities in opposite directions at the Ra-level. From either one of these states the wave moves with the same speed asymptotically toward the stationary amplifying state half way between them which is shown in fig. 2.

The phase velocities at other levels in the non-tilting states (and hence the motion of the air through the wave) is determined by the respectively linear and inverse change with height of these phase velocities. This relative motion combined with the zonal vorticity gradients of the meridional field determines the strength of the divergence field and hence the strength of the vertical circulation. The relative motion in the wave is the same for all wave lengths if their Rossby velocity is ignored. But the vorticity gradient and hence the strength of the vertical circulation increases with decreasing wave length.

This explains why the geostrophic approximation breaks down for the shorter unstable waves. We recall from (3.4) that the geostrophic approximation ignores the meridional vorticity component, or rather the changes of this component. As the wave length decreases the vertical circulation ultimately becomes so intense that the meridional vorticity changes can no longer be ignored.

I cannot go any further into the dynamic properties of the short non-geostrophic waves here. I will discuss them more fully in a later article.

For waves in the upper part of the unstable band the meridional circulation and its vorticity is so weak that the action of this vorticity is no longer an important dynamic factor. The motion is in this sense quasi-geostrophic, and the approximation is clearly better the longer the waves are, because of the further weakening of the meridional vorticity. However, as the wave length is increased, the Rossby stability of the wave can no longer be ignored. The stationary level is increasingly lowered below the central level and the wave structure *within the atmosphere* is increasingly modified. More properly stated the Rossby stability tends to push the whole wave westward through the atmosphere. This is the physical mechanism which brings the Rossby stability into operation as a check on the shearing instability of the baroclinic motion of the wave. At the Ra-level the eastward motion of the wave in the thermal a-state is now slower than its westward motion in the non-thermal b-state, as indicated for the wave of $U_R = \tfrac{1}{2} U_T$ in fig. 7. As a consequence the stationary state lies nearer the thermal state ($\varphi_s = 60°$), and the growth rate of the wave (fig. 6) is correspondingly reduced.

The wave whose Rossby velocity is equal to the relative zonal motion of the Ra-levels is stationary relative to the air at the lower of these levels. The non-tilting thermal a-state of this wave is a stationary neutral wave. For this wave is a stationary Rossby wave at the upper Rossby level and it has no horizontal motion at the lower Rossby level. So the vorticity is conserved at both Rossby levels. In any other state this wave moves toward the a-state and its growth rate ultimately becomes linear, as this state is asymptotically approached. This wave marks the upper limit of the "unstable" spectral band of waves with a stationary tilting state. It was this stationary a-wave which was anticipated by BJERKNES and HOLMBOE (1944).

10. The long stable baroclinic waves

All waves longer than the stationary a-wave will be called long baroclinic waves. The long wave has no state of stationary phase. At levels above the stationary level it moves at all times westward relative to the mass field oscillation. The stationary level lies below the lower Ra-level, and for waves roughly thirty per cent longer than the stationary a-wave the stationary level is a fictitious level below the surface of the earth. The wave then moves westward at all atmospheric levels relative to the mass field oscillation. This oscillation in turn moves westward with one half of the Rossby velocity relative to the air at the central level of the atmosphere. So from (8.6) the wave moves westward at the upper Ra-level relative to the air at the central level with the phase velocity,

$$C_\varphi = -U_R - \tfrac{1}{2} U_T \cos 2\varphi \qquad (10.1)$$

Thus the long waves move on the average westward through the atmosphere with the Rossby velocity. The wave excites the oscillation in the mass field which in turn propagates westward through the air with one half of the Rossby velocity. The wave in turn overtakes this oscillation with on the average the double speed; that is just the speed needed to keep the oscillation synchronous with the wave.

The rhythmic variation of the wave speed during the westward propagation of the wave is intimately connected with the rythmic growth and decay of the wave energy. When the wave is in the non-tilting b-state with a flat mass field the wave energy is uniformly distributed with the same amount at all heights. On the other hand when the wave is in the thermal a-state the wave energy is concentrated at the upper levels.

When the wave is in an intermediate tilting state it may be regarded as the sum of a thermal and a non-thermal component with a 90° phase difference (7.7), and the total wave energy is the sum of the energies of these components. As the wave moves from the non-thermal to the thermal state the non-thermal wave energy decays (7.9) and the thermal wave energy grows (7.6). When the wave is half way between the non-tilting states at the upper Rossby level, the wave energy is exactly half thermal and half non-thermal. As the non-tilting thermal state is approached, the non-thermal part of the energy decays to zero and the thermal energy grows to a maximum which represents the total wave energy in the non-tilting thermal a-state. The wave energy is larger in the thermal state than in the non-thermal state for all wave lengths. This is quite clear for the "shortest" long waves near the stationary thermal a-wave. We recall that this wave ultimately grows linearly with time when approached from the non-thermal state. Waves which are just a little longer behave quite similarly. They slip easily past the temporarily non-existent deformation of the mass field with fairly good speed, but slow down and linger for a relatively much longer time in the quasi-thermal states, thus giving the wave plenty of time to acquire thermal energy before the thermal state is reached and to get rid of it again after this state is passed. This behavior of the wave also explains in another way why the geostrophic adjustment is so good in these waves. The field moves slowly and has plenty of time to adjust itself to the mass distribution just at the time when much adjustment is needed.

What has been said so far applies to the upper wave near and above the upper Rossby level. To get an idea of the behavior of the entire wave, let us consider the evolution of a wave which has the stationary level below the ground through one complete cycle of the mass field oscillation, starting at the moment when the mass field is flat. At that time the wave is uniformly weak at all levels and moves on the average westward through the atmosphere with the Rossby velocity. It moves faster at high levels where the streamline amplitude is small and slower at low levels where the streamline amplitude is great. As the wave begins to set up the next deformation of the mass field ahead of itself with crests to the west of the wave crests, this deformation moves westward through the atmosphere as a growing "wave" in the vertical isopycnic surfaces with one half of the Rossby velocity. The wave, moving on the average twice as fast, overtakes the mass wave, and in so doing it grows stronger and slows down at high level and it decays and speeds up at low levels. At the half way point the wave has the strongest westward tilt and moves with the Rossby velocity at all levels. The upper wave keeps on growing and slowing down and the lower wave keeps on decaying and speeding up until the entire wave catches up with the mass wave. At that moment the wave moves *through the air* with the Rossby velocity at both Rossby levels, so the relative propagation of the upper and lower wave is now reversed. The upper wave which carries the major part of the wave energy has reached maximum strength and minimum speed, while the lower wave has minimum strength and maximum speed. At the central level both the wave speed and the energy remain roughly the same all the time. During the next half period the same sequence of events follows in reverse order with the mass field returning to the undeformed state again.

Very briefly then the main feature of the long wave propagation in a baroclinic current is the overall westward propagation of the wave with the Rossby velocity. The wave must put the mass field into synchronous oscillations, and the resulting oscillating thermal wind field keeps the through- and crest-lines wagging back and forth and pumps the wave energy from low to high level and back again during each cycle.

While these vacillations are quite conspicuous for the "shorter" long waves, they become rapidly unimportant as the wave length is increased. For example a wave which is about sixty per cent longer than the stationary thermal wave has the "stationary level" at a depth below ground equal to one quarter of the atmospheric column. So its ground level in fig. 6 would be the level marked $z_0 = \frac{1}{4}$. To see the entire atmosphere, the diagram would have to be extrapolated upward twice as far as it goes. We notice that already in this wave the wagging of the trough line is relatively small, particularly at high levels. The Rossby velocity of this wave is about 2.5 U_T, more than twice the total change of the wave speed at the Rossby levels.

It appears therefore that the longer the waves are the more nearly do they move with the Rossby velocity at all levels, and the less noticeable is the wagging of the wave. The vorticity is therefore nearly conserved at all levels in the very long baroclinic waves, which is another way of saying that the divergence field and the vertical circulation is extremely weak in these waves. If the dynamic effect of the divergence is ignored we have the *solenoidal* approximation whose influence on the normal mode frequency is shown in fig. 1. Even for strong baroclinities the solenoidal approximation appears to be fairly good when the wave is more than fifty per cent longer than the stationary thermal wave.

With the solenoidal approximation introduced, the wave becomes a simple non-tilting Rossby wave with practically the same amplitude and the same wave energy at all heights. This wave of course still keeps the mass surface in synchronous oscillations with the wave, but these oscillations are now dynamically neutral, somewhat like weightless flags fluttering in the wind. They offer practically no resistance to the wave-motion since the slight amount of vertical energy transfer between the thermal and non-thermal state of the wave is an insignificant part of the total wave energy.

In conclusion it may be remarked that this long quasi-solenoidal Rossby wave, even though it is a neutral wave, is not to be identified with the corresponding quasi-solenoidal mode in (4.6). Indeed it is the resultant of both modes with equal amplitudes of the mass field deformations. The modes taken separately have a more complicated structure, but their resultant is very simple and probably more like the long waves we find in the atmosphere.

The behavior of the long baroclinic waves as summarized here was clearly understood and explained by Rossby in his 1942-article. However, Rossby's, in my opinion, most important scientific achievement was his discovery that the baroclinic atmosphere behaves essentially as if it is a barotropic, vorticity conserving medium in the large scale semi-permanent features of the planetary circulation. Rossby, with visionary physical intuition, recognized at a very early date that this must be true, and he felt no need for a formal mathematical proof of this principle.

Acknowledgement

I wish to thank my colleagues Drs. Palmer, Charney, Döös, Kao, Wurtele and Gates for useful discussions during the preparation of this note.

LIST OF SPECIAL SYMBOLS[1]

A_ϱ: Amplitude of mass field deformation (6.4).

C_a: Phase velocity in thermal state (8.1).

C_b: Phase velocity in non-thermal state (8.1).

n_i: Growth rate of mass field deformation (7.6).

n_{i0}: Limiting growth rate for short waves when Rossby stability is ignored (4.8).

$n_R = kU_R$: Rossby wave frequency (3.6).

$n_T = kU_T$: Thermal wind frequency parameter (3.6).

$U_R = \beta/k^2$: Rossby velocity (3.5).

U_T: In theory of normal modes (sections 2 through 7), increase of zonal wind from bottom to top of the atmosphere (2.1).

U_T: In theory of non-tilting states (sections 8 through 10): Increase of zonal wind from lower to upper Rossby-level in thermal state.

v_b: Amplitude of meridional velocity in non-thermal part of wave (6.2) and (7.5).

z: Non-dimensional height measured from central level (2.1).

z_0: Non-dimensional height measured from "stationary level" (6.1).

$\varkappa = g \ln \varrho$, mass variable (2.2),

$\varkappa_0$: Mass field in undisturbed state (2.3),

$\bar{\varkappa}$: Mass field perturbation in normale mode (3.1).

ν: Local particle frequency (3.7).

$\sigma = \sqrt{\frac{1}{4}n_R^2 + 1}$ (4.2).

$(')$: Differentiation with reference to height (3.4).

[1] Numbers in parentheses indicate equation where symbol is introduced.

REFERENCES

BJERKNES, J., and HOLMBOE, J., 1944: On the theory of cyclones. *J. Meteor.* **1**, No. 1.

CHARNEY, J. G., 1947: The dynamic of long waves in a baroclinic westerly current. *J. Meteor.* **4**, No. 5.

EADY, E. T., 1949: Long waves and cyclone waves, *Tellus*, **1**, No. 3.

FJØRTOFT, R., 1950: Application of integral theorems in deriving criteria of stability for laminar flows and for the baroclinic circular vortex. *Geof. Publ.* **17**, No. 6.

HOLMBOE, J., 1953: Two-Dimensional Barotropic Flow. Part I. Straight Parallel Flow with Larnear Profiles. Final Report. *The Upper Level Winds Project.* Contract W 28—099 ac-403, Geophysical Research Directorate, Air Force Cambridge Research Center, Cambridge, Mass.

ROSSBY, C. G., and collaborators, 1939: Relation between the intensity of the zonal circulation of the atmosphere and the displacements of the semipermanent centers of action. *J. Marine Res.* 2, No. 1.

ROSSBY, C. G., 1942: Kinematic and hydrostatic properties of certain long waves in the westerlies. *University of Chicago, Dept. of Meteorology, Misc. Reports* No. 5.

(Manuscript received September 4, 1958)

Some Statistical Aspects of the Dynamical Processes of Growth and Occlusion in Simple Baroclinic Models[1]

PHILIP DUNCAN THOMPSON[2], Lt. Colonel, U.S. Air Force

Joint Numerical Weather Prediction Unit, Washington, D.C.

Abstract

By combining the vorticity and continuity equations for the general two-level model, it has been found possible to derive relatively simple expressions for the average rate of growth (or increase of rotational energy) and the average rate of occlusion of large-scale baroclinic disturbances. The growth rate depends primarily on the area correlation between the vertical air speed and the deviation of the temperature from its zonal average; the rate of occlusion depends on the area correlations between the vertical air speed and the deviations of both temperature and pressure from their zonal averages.

At least in cases when the horizontal velocity field is independent of the north-south coordinate, it is found that disturbances in which the temperature field precedes the pressure field tend to die out undetected. Disturbances in which the temperature field lags behind the pressure field, on the other hand, grow in amplitude as long as they maintain that phase relationship. Simultaneously and as a dynamical consequence of the growth process, the temperature field in such disturbances gradually catches up with the pressure field, and the flow approaches a state of quasi-barotropy. At the instant this state is reached, growth ceases and there is no further change in the relative phase of the pressure and temperature fields. In the absence of heating and viscosity, the flow would tend to remain quasi-barotropic, verifying an hypothesis proposed by Rossby almost twenty years ago.

1. Introduction

Over the past three years the Joint Numerical Weather Prediction Unit has computed two barotropic forecasts daily, beginning with current initial data at the two daily observing times, and over most of that period has computed parallel forecasts based on either or both of two simple baroclinic models. Thus, in a large and representative sample of cases, it has been possible to compare the performances of physically different models—the barotropic model, the 3-level model proposed by CHARNEY and PHILLIPS (1953), and a 2-level model generically the same as the "thermotropic" model described by THOMPSON and GATES (1956).

Although this entire mass of data has not been given the systematic and intensive study it deserves, certain conclusions can be drawn from statistical indices of the errors of many numerical forecasts and from a case-by-case inspection of long series of individual forecasts. One inescapable and rather surprising conclusion is that the behaviour of the large-scale flow patterns in midtroposphere is very similar to that of initially equivalent flow patterns in a barotropic fluid. On the whole, the barotropic 500 mb forecasts account for most of the day-to-day change in the large-scale flow patterns—at least in regions where the forecasts are relatively unaffected by conditions around the boundary of the forecast area and/or by large errors in the analyst's reconstruction of the initial flow pattern.

Even more striking, perhaps, is the fact that the root-mean-square wind error of the barotropic forecasts is no greater than that of the 500 mb forecasts based on either of the baroclinic models. Superficially, at least, this result is not difficult to understand, since the atmosphere as a whole does maintain itself in a state of quasi-barotropy, in the sense that the isotherms of an isobaric surface very nearly coincide with its contours. Such conditions, of course, have long been recognized as unfavorable to the growth of

[1] Published with permission of the Commander, Air Weather Service, U.S. Air Force.

[2] Currently assigned to the International Meteorological Institute, Stockholm.

new circulation centers, but it has only recently become apparent that many developments which the weather forecaster might once have regarded as "new" can be ascribed to the reorganization of previously existing circulation centers. Moreover, although prediction methods based on the barotropic model cannot forecast the creation of genuinely new circulation centers, such developments are relatively rare in midtroposphere (especially in regions of good data coverage) and are confined to a few small areas at any given time.

The facts outlined above are, of course, only ostensible reasons for the remarkable success of the barotropic model. The fundamental question is this: Why does the baroclinic atmosphere tend toward a quasi-barotropic state? Is this behaviour a consequence of the dynamical properties of the atmosphere itself and, if so, which properties?

These questions are particularly interesting from the theoretical standpoint, for the very concept of a many-level baroclinic model presupposes that the vertical distribution of horizontal motion possesses indefinitely many degrees of freedom—i.e., that it can presumably exhibit all the irregularities and complexities of, say, the motion of air heated by the end of a cigarette. From this point of view, the simplicity and regularity of the vertical structure of the large-scale horizontal motions is truly amazing. If, in fact, it turns out that the atmosphere's dynamical properties drive it toward a quasi-barotropic state, then the number of degrees of freedom (required to characterize the vertical distribution of horizontal motion) must be somehow limited. This further suggests that a more systematic (but much more ambitious) study of what determines the vertical structure of large-scale flow patterns might reveal an alternative to merely increasing the number of levels in a baroclinic model.

Beyond the very general observations stated above, it is extremely difficult to come to any definite conclusions about the defects of the baroclinic models currently under investigation. In individual cases, numerical forecasts are contaminated by many different types of error—truncation error, errors due to the imposition of arbitrary lateral boundary conditions, errors in the initial analysis, and errors in the verifying analysis—none of which can be completely isolated or removed. Added to these obstacles is the fact that the equations for even the simplest of baroclinic models are mathematically quite complicated, making it extremely difficult to interpret a numerical forecast in simple physical terms and to understand how it evolved from the given initial state.

In the face of such difficulties, it is natural to inquire whether or not one can derive equations that govern the statistical or "general" aspects of the behaviour of various models, from the dynamical equations that describe their behaviour in detail. If so, and if those equations are simple enough, they might serve as an aid in interpreting numerical forecasts, and might provide a clearer understanding of the general behaviour of fairly complicated models.

Having discussed the various reasons for approaching the dynamics of baroclinic flow from a statistical standpoint, we can now state briefly the main purpose of this article. It is simply to derive a pair of equations that describe how, on the average, the phase of the temperature field (relative to the pressure field) changes with time, and how the average rotational or kinetic energy of the large-scale disturbances increases or decreases. These equations are first derived from the vorticity equations for a rather general non-geostrophic model, and are later specialized in the case of "quasi-nondivergent" flow—a procedure that enables us to isolate the effects of certain common types of approximations on the statistical behaviour of the models.

By considering the evolution of a whole family of initial states, one can deduce the existence of certain phenomena that are commonly observed in the true atmosphere. One finds, for example, that the simple 2-level model has a selective preference for disturbances in which the temperature pattern lags behind the pressure pattern; its dynamical properties are such that disturbances in which the temperature field precedes the pressure field die out and remain undetected, while disturbances in which the temperature field lags behind are amplified. Finally, through the very same mechanism by which "out-of-phase" disturbances grow, the temperature field is gradually brought into phase with the pressure field, and the atmosphere approaches a statistical state of quasi-barotropy. As the temperature and pressure fields come into phase, the growth of average rotational energy ceases, and there is no further change in the relative phase of the temperature and pressure fields. Left to itself, the atmosphere would remain in this quasi-barotropic state. This result may be taken as a rather belated theoretical justification for the intensive studies of the barotropic model proposed and initiated by ROSSBY (1939), and, in some measure, accounts for their remarkable and unexpected success.

The irreversibility of the sequence of events outlined above, together with the quasi-barotropy of the state toward which these events tend, make it clear that an entirely different process must be postulated to account for the removal of accumulated rotational or "eddy" kinetic energy. It is evident, moreover, that the mechanism required to do so is necessarily operative in quasi-barotropic flow, a result that is certainly in accord with the experimental and theoretical studies of KUO (1951), LORENZ (1955) and PHILLIPS (1956). Lastly, the fact that the process of development in an adiabatic nonviscous flow destroys the conditions that are initially favorable to growth strongly suggests that the ultimate causes of baroclinic development cannot lie within a closed system, but must arise from nonadiabatic heating —either by eddy conduction from the surface, release of latent heat and/or by absorption or emission of radiant energy.

2. The equations for a nongeostrophic two-level model

We begin with the general vorticity equation for adiabatic nonviscous flow, written in the form

$$\frac{d\eta}{dt} + \eta \nabla_\Theta \cdot \mathbf{v} = 0 \tag{1}$$

in which $\eta = f + \zeta$; $\zeta = \mathbf{k} \cdot \nabla_\Theta \times \mathbf{v}$; $\mathbf{k}$ is a unit vector directed vertically upward; $\mathbf{v}$ is the horizontal projection of the velocity vector; and ∇ is the horizontal vector derivative. The subscript Θ indicates that the differentiation is to be carried out along surfaces of constant potential temperature Θ. Unless otherwise stated, all notation is standard. Now, in general,

$$\nabla_\Theta \cdot \mathbf{v} = \nabla \cdot \mathbf{v} + \frac{\partial \mathbf{v}}{\partial p} \cdot \nabla_\Theta p$$

where the vector derivative without subscript denotes differentiation along isobaric surfaces, and differentiation with respect to the pressure p is carried out along the vertical. Since the flow is almost geostrophic, the vector $\partial \mathbf{v}/\partial p$ is very nearly perpendicular to the vector $\nabla_\Theta p$, so that $\nabla_\Theta \cdot \mathbf{v}$ is approximately equal to $\nabla \cdot \mathbf{v}$. Accordingly, the continuity equation may be written in the following form:

$$\nabla_\Theta \cdot \mathbf{v} = \nabla \cdot \mathbf{v} = -\frac{\partial \omega}{\partial p} \tag{2}$$

where ω is the total derivative of pressure. Finally, combining Eqs. (1) and (2), we may rewrite the vorticity equation as

$$\frac{\partial \zeta}{\partial t} + \mathbf{v} \cdot \nabla \zeta + \mathbf{v} \cdot \nabla f + \omega \frac{\partial \zeta}{\partial p} - (\zeta + f) \frac{\partial \omega}{\partial p} = 0 \tag{3}$$

It is now understood that differentiations with respect to time are carried out with p held fixed. Eq. (3) is the general form of the vorticity equation on which most baroclinic models are based.

We next apply Eq. (3) at the 400 and 800 mb surfaces, and approximate the vertical derivatives $\partial \zeta / \partial p$ and $\partial \omega / \partial p$ by finite differences. For simplicity, we shall assume that ω vanishes at 200 and 1,000 mb, and that its vertical profile is symmetrical around the 600 mb surface[1]. Thus,

$$\frac{\partial \zeta_1}{\partial t} + \mathbf{v}_1 \cdot \nabla \zeta_1 + \mathbf{v}_1 \cdot \nabla f + \frac{A\omega}{P}(\zeta_2 - \zeta_1) - \frac{\omega}{P}(\zeta_1 + f) = 0$$

$$\frac{\partial \zeta_2}{\partial t} + \mathbf{v}_2 \cdot \nabla \zeta_2 + \mathbf{v}_2 \cdot \nabla f + \frac{A\omega}{P}(\zeta_2 - \zeta_1) + \frac{\omega}{P}(\zeta_2 + f) = 0$$

in which the subscripts 1 and 2 denote conditions at the 400 and 800 mb surfaces, respectively, ω without subscript is its value at 600 mb, $\omega_1 = \omega_2 = A\omega$ and $P = 400$ mb. It turns out that it is more convenient for later purposes to consider an equivalent pair of equations, obtainable by forming the sum and difference of the equations above. After some rearrangement, we find that

$$\frac{\partial \zeta^*}{\partial t} + \mathbf{v}^* \cdot \nabla \zeta^* + \mathbf{v}' \cdot \nabla \zeta' + \mathbf{v}^* \cdot \nabla f - \frac{\omega \zeta'}{P}(2A + 1) = 0 \tag{4}$$

$$\frac{\partial \zeta'}{\partial t} + \mathbf{v}^* \cdot \nabla \zeta' + \mathbf{v}' \cdot \nabla \zeta^* + \mathbf{v}' \cdot \nabla f - \frac{\omega}{P}(\zeta^* + f) = 0 \tag{5}$$

where a "starred" quantity is half the sum of its values at the 400 and 800 mb surfaces, and

[1] It should be noted that ω is very nearly proportional to the vertical mass transport ϱw. Thus, ω is much smaller in magnitude near a flat ground surface than it is in midtroposphere, where it attains its extreme values. It has also been shown by THOMPSON (1956) that the vertical air speed must reverse sign somewhere above the tropopause, owing to the reversal of temperature gradient above that level.

a "primed" quantity is half the difference between its values (upper minus lower) at those surfaces.

In exactly the same way, we apply Eq. (2) at the 400 and 800 mb surfaces, with the result that

$$\nabla \cdot \mathbf{v}_1 + \frac{\omega}{P} = 0 \qquad \nabla \cdot \mathbf{v}_2 - \frac{\omega}{P} = 0$$

from which it follows that

$$\nabla \cdot \mathbf{v}^* = 0 \qquad \nabla \cdot \mathbf{v}' = -\frac{\omega}{P} \tag{6}$$

Eqs. (4), (5), and (6) provide the physical basis for most of the remaining discussion.

3. An equation for the growth of total rotational energy

Our next concern is to derive an equation that relates the instantaneous increase of total rotational energy (or average amplitude) to the current fields of horizontal and vertical motion. To do so, we first multiply Eq. (4) by ζ^*, multiply Eq. (5) by ζ', and add those equations together. Factoring and making use of standard vector identities, we find that

$$\frac{1}{2}\frac{\partial}{\partial t}(\zeta^{*2} + \zeta'^2) + \frac{1}{2}\mathbf{v}^* \cdot \nabla(\zeta^{*2} + \zeta'^2) + \mathbf{v}' \cdot \nabla(\zeta^*\zeta')$$
$$+ (\zeta^*\mathbf{v}^* + \zeta'\mathbf{v}') \cdot \nabla f - \frac{f\omega\zeta'}{P} - \frac{\omega\zeta'\zeta^*}{P}(2A + 2) = 0 \tag{7}$$

Now, from Eq. (6), it follows that

$$\mathbf{v}^* \cdot \nabla(\zeta^{*2} + \zeta'^2) = \nabla \cdot (\zeta^{*2} + \zeta'^2)\mathbf{v}^*$$
$$\mathbf{v}' \cdot \nabla(\zeta^*\zeta') = \nabla \cdot \zeta^*\zeta'\mathbf{v}' + \frac{D\omega\zeta^*\zeta'}{P}$$

where D is a constant which is actually unity. In the socalled "quasi-nondivergent" models, however, the vector $\mathbf{v}'$ is regarded as nondivergent wherever it enters *explicitly* in Eqs. (4) and (5). Accordingly, the constant D takes on the value "zero" in the special case of "quasi-nondivergent" flow. Eq. (7), when combined with the expressions above, then becomes

$$\frac{1}{2}\frac{\partial}{\partial t}(\zeta^{*2} + \zeta'^2) + \frac{1}{2}\nabla \cdot (\zeta^{*2} + \zeta'^2)\mathbf{v}^* + \nabla \cdot \zeta^*\zeta'\mathbf{v}'$$
$$+ (\zeta^*\mathbf{v}^* + \zeta'\mathbf{v}') \cdot \nabla f - \frac{f\omega\zeta'}{P} -$$
$$- \frac{\omega\zeta'\zeta^*}{P}(2A + 2 - D) = 0 \tag{8}$$

The next step is to form the average of each term of Eq. (8) taken over the entire area of the earth. Thus,

$$\frac{1}{2}\frac{\partial}{\partial t}\overline{\zeta^{*2} + \zeta'^2} = \frac{\overline{f\omega\zeta'}}{P} - \overline{(\zeta^*\mathbf{v}^* + \zeta'\mathbf{v}') \cdot \nabla f} +$$
$$+ \frac{\overline{\omega\zeta'\zeta^*}}{P}(2A + 2 - D) \tag{9}$$

where a "bar" above a quantity denotes its area-average. The area-averages of the second and third terms on the lefthand side of Eq. (8) vanish, since the area integral of the divergence of any continuous vector vanishes, when taken over a closed surface.

Eq. (9) may be simplified considerably by assuming, as is customary, that $\mathbf{v}'$ is nondivergent where it enters explicitly in Eqs. (4) and (5) and, hence, where it enters Eq. (9) as well. Thus, there must exist a streamfunction ψ', such that $\mathbf{v}' = \mathbf{k} \times \nabla\psi'$. Similarly, in view of Eq. (2), there must exist a streamfunction ψ^*, such that $\mathbf{v}^* = \mathbf{k} \times \nabla\psi^*$. The second term on the righthand side of Eq. (9) then takes the form

$$\overline{(\zeta^*\mathbf{v} + \zeta'\mathbf{v}') \cdot \nabla f} = \beta\,\overline{\left(\frac{\partial\psi^*}{\partial x}\nabla^2\psi^* + \frac{\partial\psi'}{\partial x}\nabla^2\psi'\right)} \tag{10}$$

where x is the coordinate distance directed toward the east, and β is the Rossby parameter. We note, however, that

$$\frac{\partial\psi^*}{\partial x}\nabla^2\psi^* \equiv \nabla \cdot \frac{\partial\psi^*}{\partial x}\nabla\psi^* - \frac{\partial}{\partial x}\left(\frac{1}{2}\nabla\psi^* \cdot \nabla\psi^*\right)$$
$$\frac{\partial\psi'}{\partial x}\nabla^2\psi' \equiv \nabla \cdot \frac{\partial\psi'}{\partial x}\nabla\psi' - \frac{\partial}{\partial x}\left(\frac{1}{2}\nabla\psi' \cdot \nabla\psi'\right)$$

Thus, if we also regard β as a constant, the entire righthand side of Eq. (10) vanishes, simply because area integrals of the expressions immediately above transform exactly into line integrals which vanish when (in the limit) they enclose a single point in a closed surface.

Moreover, the third term on the right hand side of Eq. (9) may also be omitted, since ω, ζ' and ζ^* all oscillate around zero and have the same characteristic scale. Under the latter conditions, it can be shown that three-factor correlations—e.g. $\overline{\omega\zeta'\zeta^*}$—tend to be uniformly small, without regard to the relative phases of the individual factors.[1] Thus, introducing all these results into Eq. (9) and recalling the definitions of ζ^* and ζ', we find that

$$\frac{\partial}{\partial t}\overline{\zeta^{*2} + \zeta_1^2} = \frac{1}{2}\frac{\partial}{\partial t}\overline{\zeta_1^2 + \zeta_2^2} = 2\frac{\overline{f\omega\zeta'}}{P} \qquad (11)$$

Since the quantity $\overline{(\zeta_1^2 + \zeta_2^2)}$ is a measure of the total "rotationality" of the flow, one may think of Eq. (11) as a relationship between the instantaneous increase (or decrease) of average circulation amplitude and the current fields of vertical and horizontal motion.

In order to interpret Eq. (11) in simple physical terms, let us estimate the correlation $\overline{f\omega\zeta'}$ in quasi-geostrophic flow. Replacing ζ'/P by $-\frac{1}{2}\partial\zeta/\partial p$, and making use of the hydrostatic equation, we find that

$$\overline{f\omega\zeta'} = \frac{R}{3}\overline{\omega\nabla^2 T}$$

where R is the universal gas constant, and T is the absolute temperature at 600 mb. Thus, assuming for the sake of argument that most of the power in the entire spectrum of disturbances is concentrated in a narrow band around wave-number α,

$$\overline{f\omega\zeta'} = -\frac{R\alpha^2}{3}\overline{\omega(T - T_0)}$$

in which T_0 is a zonally symmetric temperature field in which $\nabla^2 T_0 = 0$, and whose average meridional gradient is that in the true atmosphere. Referring back to Eq. (11), we see that the average circulation amplitude increases when there is a negative correlation between ω and $(T - T_0)$. This corresponds to the case when, on the average around all latitude circles, cold air ($T < T_0$) is sinking ($\omega > 0$), and warm air is rising. This result, of course, is in accord with the classical view of the growth process.

To carry the interpretation a little further, we note that ω tends to oscillate around zero along a latitude circle, so that the preceding equation becomes approximately

$$\frac{\overline{f\omega\zeta'}}{P} = -\frac{R\alpha^2}{2p^*}\overline{\omega T} = -\frac{\alpha^2}{2}\overline{\left(\frac{\omega}{\varrho^*}\right)} \qquad (12)$$

[1] This can be easily seen in the case of three sinusoidal functions whose wave-numbers are equal, but whose phases are arbitrary. The proof in the general case hinges on the identity $4\overline{\omega\zeta^*\zeta'} \equiv \overline{\omega(\zeta^* + \zeta')^2} - \overline{\omega(\zeta^* - \zeta')^2}$ and on the fact that ω, ζ^*, ζ', $(\zeta^* + \zeta')$ and $(\zeta^* - \zeta')$ all have the same characteristic scale. As will be shown later, both of the terms on the righthand side of this identity tend to be uniformly small.

Thus, from the adiabatic and continuity equations,

$$\frac{\overline{f\omega\zeta'}}{P} = -\frac{\alpha^2 C_p}{2}\overline{\frac{dT}{dt}} = -\frac{\alpha^2 C_p}{2}\overline{\left[\frac{\partial T}{\partial t} + \nabla\cdot T\mathbf{v} + \frac{\partial}{\partial p}(T\omega)\right]}$$

But the second and third terms in the square brackets of the equation above vanish: one, because $T\mathbf{v}$ is a continuous vector, and the other, because ω was assumed to vanish at 200 and 1,000 mb. Finally, substituting the results above into Eq. (11),

$$\frac{1}{\alpha^2}\frac{\partial}{\partial t}\overline{(\zeta_1^2 + \zeta_2^2)} + 2\frac{\partial}{\partial t}\overline{C_p T} = 0 \qquad (13)$$

Now, it is a well-known fact that the potential energy of a fluid in hydrostatic equilibrium is proportional to its internal energy, and that the area-average of the sum of these two forms of energy (per unit mass) is equal to $\overline{C_p T}$. Accordingly, Eq. (13) states that any net transformation of internal and potential energy in the atmosphere must result in a change of total rotational energy.

From more general considerations, it can be shown that the equation for conservation of *total* kinetic, internal and potential energy may be written as

$$\frac{1}{2}\frac{\partial}{\partial t}\overline{(\mathbf{v}_1\cdot\mathbf{v}_1 + \mathbf{v}_2\cdot\mathbf{v}_2)} = -\frac{2AR\overline{\omega T}}{p^*}$$

Now, combining Eq. (11) with Eq. (12), we find that

$$\frac{1}{2}\frac{\partial}{\partial t}\frac{\overline{(\zeta_1^2 + \zeta_2^2)}}{\alpha^2} = -\frac{R\overline{\omega T}}{p^*}$$

Thus setting $A = \frac{1}{2}$, and comparing the two equations above, we see that the rate at which the *total* kinetic energy per unit mass $\overline{(\mathbf{v}_1\cdot\mathbf{v}_1 + \mathbf{v}_2\cdot\mathbf{v}_2)}/2$ changes is just the rate at which $\overline{(\zeta_1^2 + \zeta_2^2)}/2\alpha^2$ changes. We are thus led to conclude that virtually all of the transformed potential energy goes directly into an increase of the kinetic energy of the disturbances and/or into intensification of the maximum of the zonally-averaged westerlies, and that relatively little goes *directly* into a uniform increase of the average westerly flow. This result, of course, is also in accord with the recent studies of LORENZ (1955) and PHILLIPS (1956).

4. An equation for the average rate of occlusion

It was pointed out in the preceding section that Eq. (11) may be regarded as a means of calculating the average increase in the amplitude of disturbances. Our next concern is to derive a similar equation that expresses the instantaneous change in the phase of the temperature field (relative to the pressure field) in terms of the current state of vertical and horizontal motion. To do so, we multiply Eq. (4) by ζ', multiply Eq. (5) by ζ^*, and add those two equations together. Factoring and making use of the rules for vector differentiation, we find that

$$\frac{\partial}{\partial t}(\zeta^*\zeta') + \mathbf{v}^* \cdot \nabla(\zeta^*\zeta') + \tfrac{1}{2}\mathbf{v}' \cdot \nabla(\zeta^{*2} + \zeta'^2) + $$
$$+ (\zeta^*\mathbf{v}' + \zeta'\mathbf{v}^*) \cdot \nabla f - \frac{\omega\zeta'^2}{P}(2A+1) - \frac{\omega\zeta^{*2}}{P} - $$
$$- \frac{f\omega\zeta^*}{P} = 0 \qquad (14)$$

Now, from Eq. (6), it follows that

$$\mathbf{v}^* \cdot \nabla(\zeta^*\zeta') = \nabla \cdot \zeta^*\zeta'\mathbf{v}^*$$

$$\mathbf{v}' \cdot \nabla(\zeta^{*2} + \zeta'^2) = \nabla \cdot (\zeta^{*2} + \zeta'^2)\mathbf{v}' + \frac{D\omega}{P}(\zeta^{*2} + \zeta'^2)$$

Thus, when combined with the expressions above, Eq. (14) becomes

$$\frac{\partial}{\partial t}(\zeta^*\zeta') + \nabla \cdot \zeta^*\zeta'\mathbf{v}^* + \tfrac{1}{2}\nabla \cdot (\zeta^{*2} + \zeta'^2)\mathbf{v}' + $$
$$+ (\zeta^*\mathbf{v}' + \zeta'\mathbf{v}^*) \cdot \nabla f + \frac{\omega\zeta'^2}{P}\left(\frac{D}{2} - 2A - 1\right) + $$
$$+ \frac{\omega\zeta^{*2}}{P}\left(\frac{D}{2} - 1\right) - \frac{f\omega\zeta^*}{P} = 0 \qquad (15)$$

As before, we next average each term of Eq. (15) over the entire area of the earth. Since the area-integral of the divergence of any continuous vector vanishes when taken over a closed surface, the area averages of the second and third terms on the lefthand side of Eq. (15) vanish, with the result that

$$\frac{\partial}{\partial t}\overline{\zeta^*\zeta'} = \frac{\overline{f\omega\zeta^*}}{P} - \overline{(\zeta^*\mathbf{v}' + \zeta'\mathbf{v}^*) \cdot \nabla f} + $$
$$\frac{\overline{\omega\zeta'^2}}{P}\left(2A + 1 - \frac{D}{2}\right) + \frac{\overline{\omega\zeta^{*2}}}{P}\left(1 - \frac{D}{2}\right) \qquad (16)$$

Assuming (as is usual) that $\mathbf{v}'$ may be regarded as nondivergent where it enters *explicitly* in Eqs. (4) and (5), we may put the second term on the righthand side of Eq. (16) in the form

$$\overline{(\zeta^*\mathbf{v}' + \zeta'\mathbf{v}^*) \cdot \nabla f} = \beta\overline{\left(\frac{\partial\psi'}{\partial x}\nabla^2\psi^* + \frac{\partial\psi^*}{\partial x}\nabla^2\psi'\right)}$$

We note, however, that

$$\frac{\partial\psi'}{\partial x}\nabla^2\psi^* + \frac{\partial\psi^*}{\partial x}\nabla^2\psi' \equiv \nabla \cdot \left(\frac{\partial\psi'}{\partial x}\nabla\psi^* + \right.$$
$$\left. + \frac{\partial\psi^*}{\partial x}\nabla\psi'\right) - \frac{\partial}{\partial x}(\nabla\psi' \cdot \nabla\psi^*)$$

Thus, if we treat β as a constant, the second term on the righthand side of Eq. (16) vanishes, simply because the area integral of the expression immediately above transforms exactly into a line integral enclosing a single point.

Let us now investigate correlations of the type

$$\overline{\omega\zeta'^2} \equiv \overline{\omega}\,\overline{\zeta'^2} + \overline{\omega(\zeta'^2 - \overline{\zeta'^2})}$$

In the first place, Eq. (6) implies that $\overline{\omega} = 0$, so that the first term on the righthand side of the equation above vanishes. We next note that ζ' fluctuates fairly regularly around zero, so that ζ'^2 usually has a minimum (zero) between each minimum of ζ' and its adjacent maxima. On the average, therefore, ζ'^2 has twice as many minima as ζ' in any given direction, and the scale of fluctuations of ζ'^2 is half the scale of fluctuations of ζ'. Finally, since the characteristic scale of ω is the same as that of ζ', and because $(\zeta'^2 - \overline{\zeta'^2})$ oscillates around zero with double the frequency of ω, the three-factor correlation $\overline{\omega\zeta'^2}$ tends to be uniformly small without regard to the relative phase of ω and ζ'. A similar argument may be invoked to show that $\overline{\omega\zeta^{*2}}$ is also uniformly small. Introducing all of these results into Eq. (16) we find that

$$\frac{\partial}{\partial t}\overline{\zeta^*\zeta'} = \frac{\overline{f\omega\zeta^*}}{P} \qquad (17)$$

Since $\overline{\zeta^*\zeta'}$ depends on the correlation between the fields of ζ^* and ζ', this equation obviously implies something about the rate at which the relative phase of ζ^* and ζ' changes with time.

The quantity $\overline{\zeta^*\zeta'}$ does not, however, depend solely on the phase of ζ^* relative to that of ζ', for it is conceivable that $\overline{\zeta^*\zeta'}$ might increase without change of relative phase—merely as a result of an increase in the amplitudes of both ζ^* and ζ'. Accordingly, we shall define a kind of correlation index r, which is quasi-normalized with respect to the amplitudes of ζ^* and ζ'.

$$r = \frac{N}{K} \qquad N = \overline{\zeta^* \zeta'} \qquad K = \overline{\zeta^{*2} + \zeta'^2}$$

As can be seen by substituting a constant multiple of ζ' ($k\zeta'$, for example) for ζ', r is not independent of k and is not, therefore, entirely independent of amplitude. On the other hand, $\overline{\zeta^{*2}}$ and $\overline{\zeta'^2}$ tend to increase in about the same ratio, so that r is primarily a measure of the relative phase of the fields ζ^* and ζ'. Another important property of r, derivable by simple algebraic manipulation, is that it never exceeds $^1/_2$.

Differentiating r with respect to time, we obtain

$$\frac{\partial r}{\partial t} = \frac{1}{K}\left(\frac{\partial N}{\partial t} - r\frac{\partial K}{\partial t}\right)$$

or, substituting from Eqs. (11) and (17) for $\partial N/\partial t$ and $\partial K/\partial t$,

$$\frac{\partial r}{\partial t} = \frac{1}{K}\left[\frac{\overline{f\omega\zeta^*}}{P} - 2r\frac{\overline{f\omega\zeta'}}{P}\right] \tag{18}$$

This equation provides us with a means of calculating the average rate of occlusion—i.e., the rate at which the correlation (or relative phase) between the fields ζ^* and ζ' changes—in terms of the current fields of horizontal and vertical motion.

5. Dependence of the average rates of growth and occlusion on the relative phase of the pressure and temperature fields.

Since the average rates of growth and occlusion depend on the correlations $\overline{f\omega\zeta^*}$ and $\overline{f\omega\zeta'}$, they are crucially dependent on the phase of the vertical motion pattern relative to the horizontal velocity field. Our next objective is to find out how the phase of the ω-field is related to the horizontal velocity field and how, in turn, the rates of growth and occlusion depend on the relative phase of the pressure and temperature fields.

In order to retain the concept of "relative phase" in a clear and unambiguous way, we shall consider the growth and occlusion of disturbances in which the velocity field is independent of the north-south coordinate. If, in addition, the amplitudes of those disturbances are small, the general relationship between the ω-field and the horizontal velocity field is given by Eq. (8) of THOMPSON (1956). For sinusoidal perturbations whose orbital frequency is much greater than a pendulum day, that equation reduces to

$$\frac{f\omega}{P} = \sigma\,(\beta v' - 2\alpha^2 U' v^*) \tag{19}$$

where

$$\sigma^{-1} = 1 + \alpha^2 c^2/2f^2; \quad c^2 = (R^2T^2/g\Theta)\partial\Theta/\partial z$$

α is the wave-number; β is the northward derivative of the Coriolis parameter; v is the northward component of velocity; and U is the average zonal component of velocity. The "starred" and "primed" quantities carry their earlier meaning. In flows of the type under consideration,

$$\zeta^* = \frac{\partial v^*}{\partial x} \qquad \zeta' = \frac{\partial v'}{\partial x}$$

where x is the coordinate toward the east. Thus

$$\overline{v^*\zeta^*} = \frac{\partial}{\partial x}\frac{\overline{v^{*2}}}{2} = 0 \qquad \overline{v'\zeta'} = \frac{\partial}{\partial x}\frac{\overline{v'^2}}{2} = 0$$

Substituting from Eq. (19) into Eq. (18), and making use of the expressions above, we then find that

$$\frac{\partial r}{\partial t} = \frac{\sigma}{K}\left[\beta\overline{v'\zeta^*} + 4\,r\alpha^2 U'\,\overline{v^*\zeta'}\right] \tag{20}$$

We note, however, that

$$\overline{v^*\zeta'} = \overline{v^*\frac{\partial v'}{\partial x}} = \overline{\frac{\partial}{\partial x}v^*v'} - \overline{v'\frac{\partial v^*}{\partial x}} = -\overline{v'\zeta^*}$$

whence Eq. (20) can be rewritten as

$$\frac{\partial r}{\partial t} = \frac{\sigma}{K}\left[\beta - 4r\alpha^2 U'\right]\overline{v'\zeta^*} \tag{21}$$

Similarly, substitution from Eq. (19) into Eq. (11) yields

$$\frac{\partial}{\partial t}\overline{\zeta_1^2 + \zeta_2^2} = 8\sigma\alpha^2 U'\,\overline{v'\zeta^*} \tag{22}$$

The two equations immediately above express the average rates of growth and occlusion in terms of the static stability, the scale of the disturbances, the average vertical wind shear, and the correlation between the fields of v' and ζ^*.

Let us now consider a whole family of initial velocity fields in which the phase difference between v^* and v' takes on all possible values, and trace first the evolution of those disturbances in which the v'-field lags behind the v^*-field. A disturbance of this type is shown schematically in Figure 1, on which the solid lines are streamlines and the dashed lines are "streamlines" for the vertical wind shear. Approximately, of course,

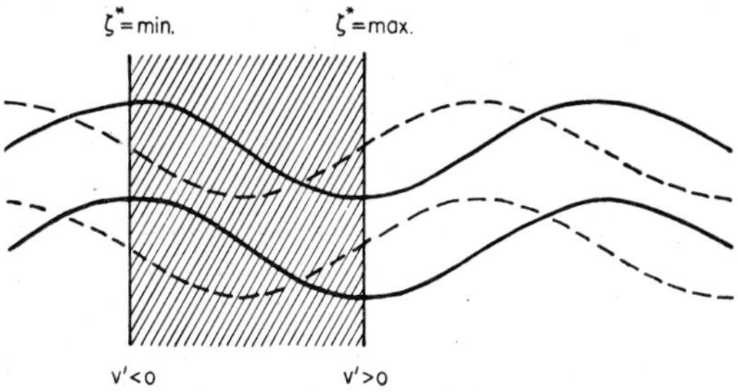

Fig. 1. Streamlines (solid) and "streamlines" for the vertical wind shear (dashed) in a typical disturbance whose temperature field lags behind the pressure field.

the solid lines are isobaric contours and the dashed lines are isotherms. In the case shown, v' is positive where ζ^* reaches its maximum values, and vice versa, so that $\overline{v'\zeta^*}$ is positive. We see, moreover, that $\overline{v'\zeta^*}$ is positive as long as the coldest air (along a latitude circle) lies in the shaded region between the pressure trough and the pressure ridge following it. Now, the average static stability is positive, and the average temperature gradient is directed from north to south, so that U' is also positive. Thus, according to Eq. (22), the average amplitude of the disturbances (or, more precisely, the total rotational energy) increases as long as the temperature field lags behind the pressure field. The rate of growth, of course, depends on the phase difference between the fields of pressure and temperature, being greatest when the temperature field is 90° behind the pressure field and becoming smaller and smaller as the fields are brought into phase.

Let us now suppose that the wave numbers of the disturbances are small—small enough that, even if r approaches its maximum value of $^1/_2$, the expression in square brackets in Eq. (21) remains positive.[1]

In the case discussed above, then, Eq. (21) states that the correlation between the pressure and temperature fields increases as long as the temperature field lags behind the pressure field; that is to say, the temperature field tends to catch up with the pressure field. It is important to note that the rates of growth and "occlusion" both depend on the same correlation $\overline{v'\zeta^*}$, and that the structure of the disturbances enters only into that correlation. This means that the physical mechanism of occlusion is the same as that by which the total rotational energy increases, and that occlusion takes place as an inevitable dynamical consequence of the process of baroclinic development.

Carrying the foregoing arguments to their conclusion, we see that a temperature field which initially lags behind the pressure field will continue to catch up until it is in phase with the pressure field. At that point, $\overline{v'\zeta^*}$ vanishes, the pressure and temperature fields undergo no further change in relative phase, and simultaneously the disturbances stop growing. Left to themselves, disturbances of this type would remain in this final state of quasi-barotropy.

We now turn to the remaining class of disturbances—namely, those in which the temperature field precedes the pressure field. A disturbance of this type is shown in Figure 2. In this case, the correlation $\overline{v'\zeta^*}$ is negative as long as the coldest air (around any latitude circle) lies in the shaded region between the pressure trough and the pressure ridge preceding it. According to Eq. (21), therefore, the correlation between the pressure and temperature fields decreases, and the temperature field tends to become more and more out of phase with the pressure field. This process continues until the pressure and temperature fields are exactly 180° out of phase, when $\overline{v'\zeta^*}$ vanishes and r can decrease no further. The important aspect of the behaviour of this class of disturbances, however, is that their amplitudes decrease with time in accordance with Eq. (22). Thus, if disturbances of this type are very small to begin with, they will become even less perceptible as time goes on.

6. The general behaviour of large-scale disturbances in baroclinic flow

Let us next imagine that a horizontally uniform zonal flow is slightly and intermittently disturbed

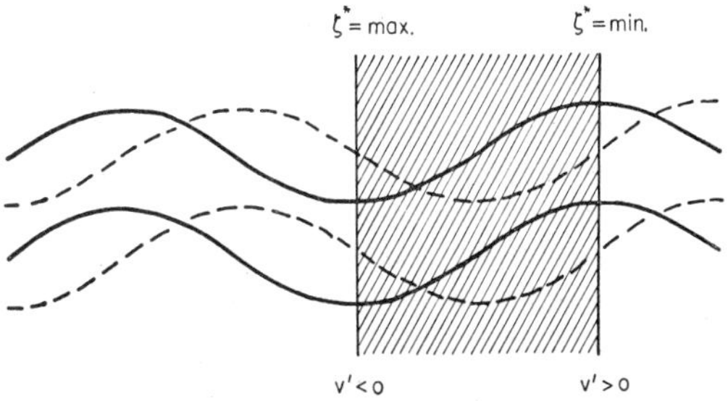

Fig. 2. Streamlines (solid) and "streamlines" for the vertical wind shear (dashed) in a typical disturbance whose temperature field precedes the pressure field.

[1] In actuality, r does not attain its theoretical upper limit, and the factor in question generally remains positive. It does, however, become very small when the temperature and pressure fields are in phase.

in such a way that the velocity field remains independent of the north-south coordinate, but such that the initial temperature field precedes the associated pressure field just as often as it lags behind it. According to the arguments outlined in the preceding section, however, one would not expect that equal amounts of energy would be found in the two ranges of relative phase at some *later* time. As we have seen, the disturbances in which the initial temperature field precedes the pressure field will die out undetected, but will remain in the same range of relative phase. The maximum energy will tend to accumulate in those disturbances in which the temperature and pressure fields are almost exactly in phase, but in which the temperature field *originally* lagged behind the pressure field. At any given time, on the average, one would also expect to find considerable energy associated with disturbances in which the temperature field lags behind the pressure field, the amount of energy varying inversely with the current phase difference between those fields. From one time to the next, disturbances of this latter type increase in amplitude; simultaneously, their temperature fields come more and more into phase with the pressure fields, and gradually approach a final state of quasi-barotropy.

This description of the general behaviour of large-scale disturbances in baroclinic flow is, of course, necessarily lacking in detail—being deduced as it was from very simple dynamical and statistical considerations. Nevertheless, it conforms remarkably well with the gross features of the observed behaviour of disturbances in the true atmosphere. It is, in fact, observed that the atmosphere has a predilection for disturbances in which the temperature field lags behind the pressure field; the reverse phase relationship is rarely observed, and is never associated with large amplitudes. The sequence of events in the evolution of baroclinic disturbances, as deduced from the theory, is also in striking agreement with the history of the typical large-scale storm, even to the simultaneous operation of the processes of growth and occlusion. Finally, it appears that the observed tendency toward an average state of quasi-barotropic motion is a consequence of the dynamical properties of relatively simple baroclinic models.

7. Summary

A brief resumé of the main results is given in the last three paragraphs of the introduction.

Acknowledgement

The author is indebted to Mr. Aksel Wiin-Nielsen for pointing out an error in the original manuscript which, although it fortunately did not affect the main conclusions, would have seriously misled the reader.

Note

As pointed out in Section 5, the foregoing conclusions apply only when the wave number α is sufficiently small or, to be exact, when $\beta - 2\alpha^2 U'$ is greater than zero. If α^2 is greater than a certain critical value, equal to $\beta/2U'$, then the bracketed factor is Eq. (21) changes sign as r passes through the value $r_0 = \beta/4\alpha^2 U'$. Thus, since r decreases when r exceeds r_0 and vice versa, r_0 is a stable stationary value of r. This value of r is generally less than its maximum value, which is attained when the pressure and temperature fields are in phase. Accordingly, Eq. (21) implies that *there exists a stable stationary phase lag between the temperature and pressure fields*, provided α^2 exccds $\beta/2U'$.

REFERENCES

CHARNEY, J. G. and PHILLIPS, N. A., 1953: Numerical integration of the quasi-geostrophic equations for barotropic and simple baroclinic flow. *J. Meteor.*, **10**, pp. 71—99.

KUO, H.-L., 1951: Dynamical aspects of the general circulation and the stability of zonal flow. *Tellus*, **3**, pp. 268—284.

LORENZ, E. N., 1955: Available potential energy and the maintenance of the general circulation. *Tellus*, **7**, pp. 157—167.

PHILLIPS, N. A., 1956: The general circulation of the atmosphere: a numerical experiment. *Quart. J. R. Meteor. Soc.*, **82**, pp. 123—164.

ROSSBY, C.-G., and collaborators, 1939: Relation between circulation of the atmosphere and the displacement of the semi-permanent centers of action. *J. Marine Res.*, **2**, pp. 38—55.

THOMPSON, P. D., 1956: A theory of large-scale disturbances in non-geostrophic flow. *J. Meteor.*, **13**, pp. 251—261.

— 1956: A two-level nongeostrophic model suitable for routine numerical weather forecasting. *JNWP Unit Tech. Memo.*, **11**.

— and GATES, W. L., 1956: A test of numerical prediction methods based on the barotropic and two-parameter baroclinic models. *J. Meteor.*, **13**, pp. 127—141.

(Manuscript received October 14, 1957)

The Propagation of Frequency in Experimental Baroclinic Waves in a Rotating Annular Ring

By D. Fultz and R. Kaylor[1]
University of Chicago

Abstract

Measurements on the properties of certain types of simple group behaviour exhibited by baroclinic waves in a rotating annular ring of fluid are described. They occur when a sloping base is used and exhibit definite evidence of effects of the depth variations equivalent to the influence of the β-parameter in simple Rossby waves.

1. Introduction

A characteristic example of the type of far-seeing contribution made by C. G. Rossby to our quantitative and qualitative understanding of the dynamical behaviour of the atmospheric and oceanic media is that connected with his discussion of the energy transport characteristics of certain types of possible wave motions. In a succession of papers (Rossby 1945, 1949) on the propagation of frequencies and energy in several types of dispersive long waves, he breathed new life into the analysis of wave propagation under fairly realistic hypotheses. He did this by a penetrating application of classical ideas connected with group velocity to wave trains having some of the types of variability in space and time characteristic, for example, of atmospheric large-scale motions. His analysis stimulated both theoretical work (e.g. Yeh 1949) and synoptic work (e.g. Cressman 1949) and pointed out the probable relevance of his ideas to observed phenomena connected with blocking and the index cycle in the atmospheric upper waves (Namias 1947, Riehl and c. 1952).

Several of Rossby's applications of these ideas were to the group and energy transport properties of the famous barotropic Rossby long waves (Rossby and c. 1939) whose frequency equation depends on the variation of the Coriolis parameter with latitude (the Rossby parameter β) and on the principle of conservation of absolute vorticity ($f+\zeta$) where f is the Coriolis parameter and ζ the vertical component of relative vorticity. The work to be described here arose in the following way from a systematic attempt at establishing a number of experimental models exhibiting dynamical features similar to those operating in the atmosphere and ocean (Fultz 1951): a group of these experiments involving thermally driven motions in a layer of liquid in a rotating cylinder (heated at the rim and cooled near the pole) have, in a suitable range of thermal Rossby numbers R_{0T}^* (see below), been shown to exhibit a large number of quantitative features comparable to atmospheric ones (Fultz 1956, Fultz et al. 1958). These include baroclinic progressive wave systems and jet streams having a very realistic vertical structure (Riehl and Fultz 1957). The rotation rates are sufficiently low, however, that the layers are essentially flat and the Coriolis parameter $f \equiv 2\,\Omega$ is constant (where Ω is the absolute rotation rate of the container). In consequence, there is no direct β-effect in the wave motions and the question of how this is to be reconciled in detail with the importance ascribed to β in atmospheric dynamics is still open. In connection with these cylinder convection experiments, Hide was the first to show that if an inner cylinder is used as the cold source, very regular and comparatively simple baroclinic wave trains are obtained in the atmospheric range of Rossby numbers (Hide 1953, 1958) and considerable later work has been done on them at Chicago (Fultz 1952, 1956; Fultz and c. 1958). The properties of these regular annulus waves are much easier to measure with precision than the more irregular Rossby regime meteorological-type motions and yet the fundamental dynamic correspondences remain (Riehl and Fultz 1957).

Concurrently with the above developments, two major types of barotropic (homogeneous fluid) experiments, among others, have estab-

[1] The research reported herewith was made possible through support extended by the Geophysics Research Directorate, Air Force Cambridge Research Center, under contract AF 19 (604) — 1292.

lished quantitatively, within certain approximations, that it is possible to make use of the potential vorticity conservation law $f+\zeta/D =$ individual constant to produce equivalent-β effects by utilizing variations of the depth D in a suitable geometrically transformed experimental model. One of these was the demonstration by LONG (1952; FULTZ and FRENZEN 1955) that Rossby β-waves could be produced experimentally by suitable mechanical generation in a rotating hemisperical shell of liquid and that the vorticity changes could be interpreted interchangeably as due to the β-effect or to the depth variations of fluid columns parallel to the rotation axis. The second was the demonstration by VON ARX (1952) that the wind driven Gulf Stream circulation, due according to the Munk-Stommel theory to β-effects, could be produced on a rotating paraboloid only if depths are suitably adjusted as a function of radius (at equilibrium rotation of the paraboloid the depth effects exactly cancel the β-contributions to vorticity change). Later, he and Faller (VON ARX 1957) established that as good a model of an ocean circulation could be produced on a flat disk with constant Coriolis parameter by replacing the β-effect entirely by an equivalent depth term.

Now, the analysis which is valid for a barotropic fluid is by no means so immediate when a baroclinic density field is present. The basic idea, involved in the present results, however, was to see whether, in spite of the much greater complication of a baroclinic system, any quantitative effects that could be ascribed to the operation of an equivalent-β effect could be detected utilizing the regular annulus waves as test objects. This was done by comparing wave systems obtained with fixed radii of the annulus walls for various bases varying from the flat plane of previous work to several cones of varying steepness sloping either up toward the pole (equivalent to positive β) or up toward the rim (equivalent to negative β). It was, in fact, found (in March, 1955) as is detailed below that, when the base was conical, very considerable changes occur in the wave characteristics and, in particular, very pronounced amplitude and pattern changes propagate relative to the wave trains in a manner forcibly suggesting the behavior of a simple group (in the kinematic sense) of harmonic waves. Measurements on these propagation phenomena turned out to be associatable with the equivalent-β effects for which we were looking, though not in as simple a manner as we had hoped.

2. Theoretical comments

We will give here only the translation which, on the simplest possible hypotheses, transforms Rossby's solution for simple non-divergent waves on the β-plane to a form involving the depth effects. Complications will be touched on later, but we will here consider the motion barotropic and the geometry Cartesian with a plane bottom having a slope toward the north or south (thus refinements appropriate to the curved geometry of the cylindrical ring are ignored). We start then with the potential vorticity conservation principle:

$$\frac{d}{dt}\left(\frac{f+\zeta}{D}\right)=0 \tag{1}$$

With v the positive northward velocity component this expands to:

$$\frac{d\zeta}{dt}+\beta v=(f+\zeta)\frac{d\ln D}{dt} \tag{2}$$

Making use of the restriction that depth of the layer varies only toward the north

$$\frac{d\zeta}{dt}+\beta v=(f+\zeta)\,v\frac{\partial\ln D}{\partial y} \tag{3}$$

$$\frac{d\zeta}{dt}=v\left[-\beta+(f+\zeta)\frac{\partial\ln D}{\partial y}\right] \tag{4}$$

Now, if we neglect ζ relative to f on the right (an approximation made in many comparable theoretical discussions) and replace $\partial\ln D/\partial y$ by a constant mean value, the result

$$d\zeta/dt\approx v\left[-\beta+f\,\overline{\frac{\partial\ln D}{\partial y}}\right] \tag{5}$$

is a differential equation with (assumed) constant coefficients that is precisely the same in form as that from which ROSSBY (1939) started. The depth equivalent of β is represented by

$$\beta_{eq}\equiv-f\,\overline{\frac{\partial\ln D}{\partial y}} \tag{6}$$

and all later results for the depth-effect barotropic waves can be obtained simply by replacing β by $(\beta+\beta_{eq})$. Thus for plane small-amplitude waves in an infinite north-south region, the frequency equation for our situation is Rossby's

$$c=U-\beta_{eq}/k^2 \tag{7}$$

where U is the (constant) basic zonal current, c the phase speed, and k is the wave number $= 2\pi/\lambda$ (λ being wave length) since $\beta \equiv 0$.

Two changes will be convenient for purposes of giving the experimental values: first, to change to dimensionless variables appropriate for atmospheric comparisons (FULTZ 1951) and second, to change from linear velocities to angular velocities for zonal displacements in the ring since these latter are the most accurately measurable in the experiments. With respect to the first, we measure all lengths in units of r_0, the outer radius (6,000 km for the earth), all linear velocities in units of $r_0\Omega$ (465 m/s for the earth), and all angular velocities in units of Ω. Dimensionless variables will be distinguished by primes (′) eg. $U' \equiv U/r_0\Omega$, $\lambda' \equiv \lambda/r_0$, $k' \equiv r_0 k$, $r' \equiv r/r_0$, etc. With respect to the second, we will convert formulae appropriate to linear velocities in a Cartesian geometry by replacing any zonal velocities U' by $\bar{r}'\omega'$ where $\bar{r}' \equiv \bar{r}/r_0$ is the mean radius of the ring in r_0 units ($\bar{r}' = .66$ in all the present experiments) and $\omega' \equiv \omega/\Omega$ is the corresponding angular velocity in Ω units.

The translated Rossby frequency equation (7) is now

$$\bar{r}'\omega'_w = U' - \beta'/k'^2 \tag{8}$$

where $\omega'_w \equiv \omega_w/\Omega$ is the non-dimensional phase speed of the waves relative to the container coordinate system

and $$\beta' \equiv \frac{\beta_{eq} r_0}{\Omega} = -2\frac{\partial \overline{\ln D}}{\partial y'}$$

The numerical values of this quantity given later will be calculated from

$$-\frac{2(D_i - D_o)r_0}{\bar{D}\,\Delta r} \tag{9}$$

where D_i is the inner, D_o the outer, and $\bar{D}$ the mean depth, while Δr is the width of the annulus.

We will need also the purely kinematic relation connecting the group velocity C_g in a train of dispersive waves with the phase velocity c (LAMB 1932).

$$C_g = c + k\frac{dc}{dk} \tag{10}$$

For a train of waves in which the wave lengths vary slowly downstream and phase speed is a function of k only, c_g represents a velocity with which wavelengths, wave numbers or frequency propagate through the wave train. If, in addition, c and c_g vary in space and time as they will in the experimental examples, slow variations in frequency, k, etc. will occur at points moving with the speed c_g and additional convergence or divergence of the energy fluxes will occur (ROSSBY 1945). We will mostly deal with the approximation in which these latter changes are negligible in a limited portion of the wave train.

We will use $\omega'_w \equiv \omega_w/\Omega$ for the angular phase speed of the waves (e.g. of wave troughs) and $\omega'_g \equiv \omega_g/\Omega$ for the angular kinematic group velocity. The non-dimensional translations for the group velocity formula are then

$$\bar{r}'\omega'_g = \bar{r}'\omega'_w + k'\frac{d(\omega'_w\bar{r}')}{dk'} \tag{11}$$

or

$$\omega'_g = \omega'_w + k'\frac{d\omega'_w}{dk'} \tag{12}$$

The difference

$$\omega'_g - \omega'_w \equiv \omega'_{gw} = k'\frac{d\omega'_w}{dk'} \tag{13}$$

represents the group angular rate measured relative to the wave crests. For the simple Rossby waves involving the equivalent-β effect the phase speed equation becomes

$$\bar{r}'\omega'_w = U' - \beta'/k'^2 \tag{14}$$

and

$$\bar{r}'\omega'_g = U' + \beta'/k'^2 \tag{15}$$

so that

$$\omega'_g - \omega'_w \equiv \omega'_{gw} = 2\beta'/\bar{r}'k'^2 \tag{16}$$

It is through this last relation that we have found the most significant results in the experiments.

3. Experimental results

The experiments were carried out on a rotating ring bearing used in previous work (FULTZ and c. 1958) and fully described there. The container was a copper-walled circular cylinder of inner radius *19.5* cm (Fig. 1) that was wrapped with a resistance heater element. The inside copper cylinder of radius *6.4* cm (Fig. 1) was placed on the removable base and was kept filled with thermostatically controlled water to form the cold source. The bases used were several truncated circular cones of varying slopes which formed an inclined bottom for the ring. Some of these cones could either be placed as shown in Fig. 1 (positive equivalent-β') or could be inverted to

Fig. 1. View of the experimental apparatus with a conical base in position in the dishpan. The terminals in the foreground are connections for the rim heating elements and the cylinder in the center is the "cold-source". Thermocouples are carried on the rack-and-pinion assemblies on opposite sides of the mounting ring. The pan is shown partially filled with water to indicate the slope of the base.

give upward slopes toward the rim (negative equivalent-β'). The ring was filled to a depth which in all experiments, regardless of the base used, gave a mean liquid depth $\overline{D}$ of about 5.3 cm.

The types of regular baroclinic waves obtained in the usual experiments depend on a number of parameters (HIDE 1958, FULTZ and c. 1958) but only two of the most important will be used here. The horizontal radial temperature gradient driving the whole convection has an associated thermal wind and a convenient dimensionless parameter is the thermal Rossby number

$$R_{0T}^* \equiv \frac{g\varepsilon(\Delta_r T)\overline{D}}{2r_0\Omega^2\Delta r} \qquad (17)$$

where g is the gravity acceleration, ε the coefficient of expansion, $\Delta_r T$ an average radial temperature difference, and Δr the width of the annulus.

R_{0T}^* is the average thermal wind through depth $\overline{D}$ in $r_0\Omega$ units and for the troposphere in middle latitudes has values in the range 0.01 to 0.05.

The temperature field spontaneously develops positive gradients with height as seen in Fig. 9 that imply a hydrostatic stability comparable to that associated with the potential temperature increase upward in the troposphere. A suitable vertical stability parameter is:

$$S_z^* \equiv \frac{g\varepsilon(\Delta_z T)\overline{D}}{4\Omega^2(\Delta r)^2} \qquad (18)$$

where $\Delta_z T$ is an average vertical temperature difference. S_z^* for the troposphere in middle latitudes has values in the range of about 0.02 to 0.07.

The experiments were carried out with the various bases at as nearly as possible entirely constant conditions in all other respects. The rotation Ω was uniformly .30 sec^{-1}, $r_0\Omega$ was 5.86 cm/sec, and the heating rate was maintained at 75 Watts. The cold source temperature was controlled at 10.7° C, the average mean working liquid temperature was 21° C, but there were air temperature fluctuations in the range 17—24° C. In any given run, the experiment was started and the wave motions maintained for a couple of hours to be certain that a steady state was reached. Visual observations were then taken on the wave propagation speeds, a long series of streak photographs (several per revolution) were made of the top surface flow, and a series of temperature measurements sufficient to determine a reasonably detailed average meridional temperature profile were recorded. It had been expected that at least some tendencies in the direction called for by equation (14) would be detected in the wave phase speeds ω_w'. That is, for positive slope toward the pole and positive β', that ω_w' would be less than for a comparable flat base experiment. This turned out not to be the case (the point will be discussed further below) as will be seen from Table 1. ω_w' instead increases as β' increases. However, this is undoubtedly connected with the fact that, in spite of the constancy of the other imposed conditions, as the base slope increases the motion so adjusts that the average thermal Rossby number R_T^* increases even more strongly than ω_w'.

While the expected effect on the phase speed thus failed, it was noticed immediately in the initial experiments that, with the conical bases, systematic differences were present between the individual waves of the three or four in the ring and that these *differences were travelling in the wave train at a rate different than the phase speeds* in just the manner that a simple group travels at a different rate than the wave crests in a general dispersive wave motion. The nature of these differences is exemplified by Fig. 2 (b). One of the wave troughs (No. 2) is distinctly sharper and characterised by a more nearly meridional flow than the other three which are broader and also in Fig. 2(b) possess small upper closed lows. While certain intermediate phases would not show such distinct differences between the

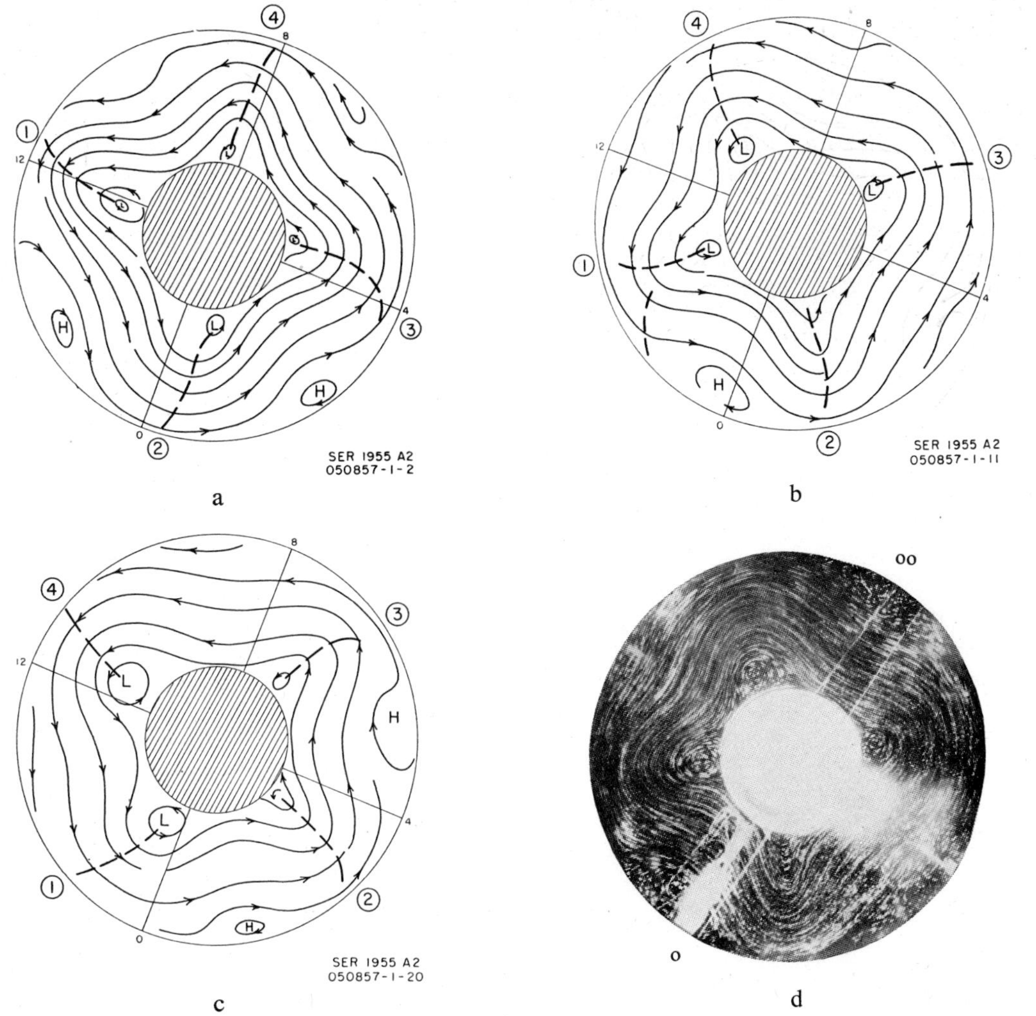

Fig. 2. Free surface streamlines of a steady state, four wave convection (050857-1) with one sharp and three broad waves. The waves are identified in successive figures by the numbers around the edge. The streamlines are drawn for direction only and do not indicate velocity. (a) The sharpest trough pattern is progressing from wave 4 to wave 1, with 2 and 3 showing broad looped troughs. (b) 1.36 revolutions later, the sharp trough has progressed to wave 2. (c) 1.40 revolutions later, the sharp trough is progressing from wave 2 to wave 3. Waves 4 and 1 now have the broad looped troughs. (d) Original streak photograph of fig. (b) Conditions: Base BC-4 D_i=2.70 cm, D_0=7.95 cm, β'=2.84, $\overline{\omega}'_w$= .060, ω'_{gw}=.170, $2\beta'/\bar{r}'k'^2$=.234, R_{0T}^*=.132, S_z^*= .100.

troughs, careful observation in time would show this general trough sharpening reappearing successively at each downstream trough. The rate of motion, which we identify with the group velocity ω'_g, was comparatively rapid and consistent with what would be expected qualitatively from equations (15) or (16). Thus in figure 2, $\overline{\omega}'_w$ is *.06*, meaning that the waves travel one revolution relative to the pan in about *17* pan revolutions (days), while ω'_g is *.24*, meaning that the shape and amplitude change travels one revolution in about *4* pan revolutions. ω'_{gw} is *.17*, meaning that the pattern returns to the original position relative to the troughs in about *6* pan revolutions. All these speeds could be measured both visually, from the photographs, and from the temperature records as checks. Streak photographs of the top surface velocities (Fig. 2(d)) are extremely useful checks on the visual observations, as well as yielding data

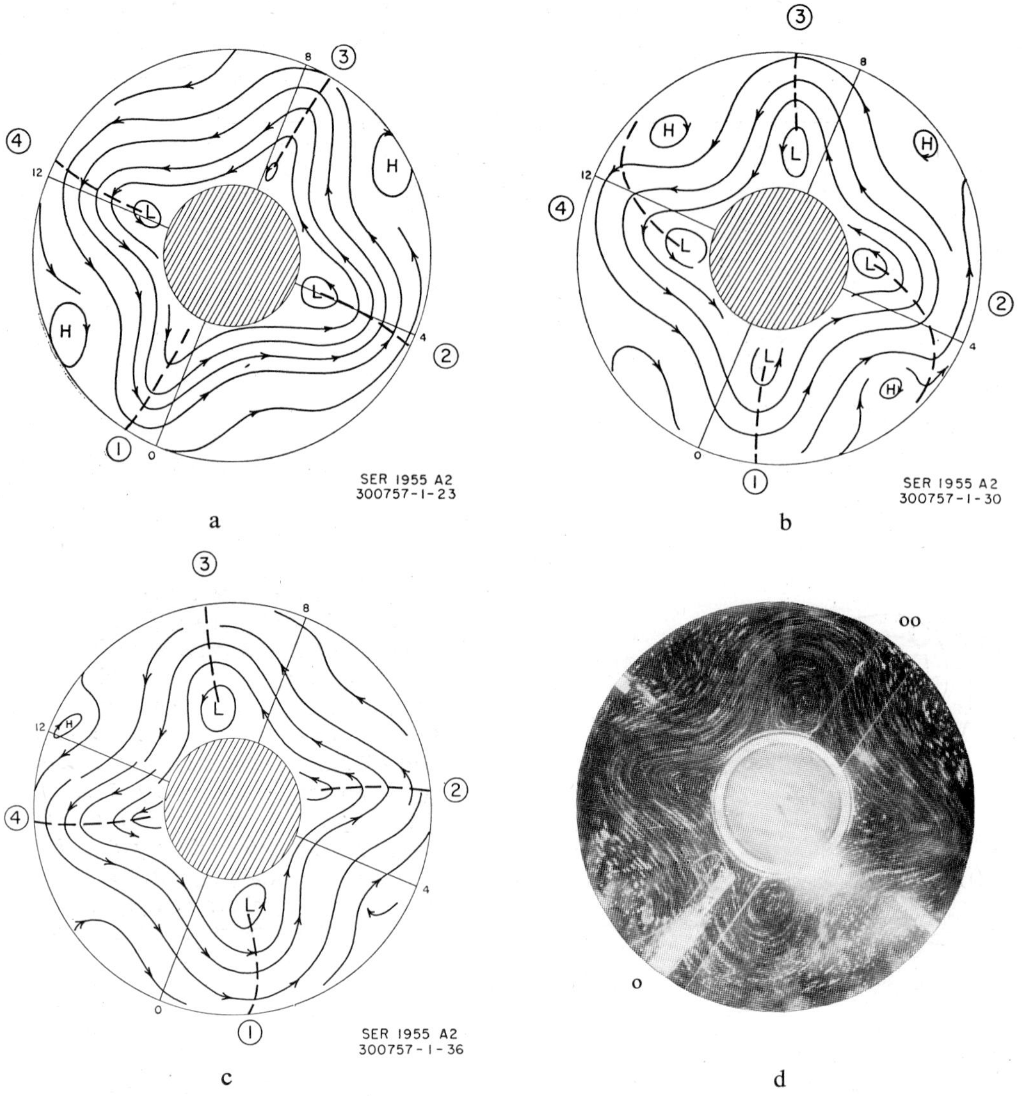

Fig. 3. (a) Free surface streamlines of a steady state, four wave convection (300757-1) with broad and sharp waves in opposite pairs. Waves 2 and 4 show closed vortices in the trough centers and a general looped appearance. (b) 0.97 revolutions later, approximately half way through the group progression from one wave pair to the other. (c) 0.89 revolutions later, the group pattern has completed the transfer to waves 2 and 4. (d) Original streak photograph of fig. (c). Conditions: Base BC-6, $D_i = 3.90$ cm, $D_0 = 6.60$ cm, $\beta' = 1.55$, $\overline{\omega}_w' = .049$, $\omega'_{gw} = .13_0$, $2\beta'/\bar{r}'k'^2 = .128$, $R_{0T}^* = .120$, $S_z^* = 138$.

which cannot be taken during the experiment, such as individual wavelengths and trough speeds. In several instances, variations which were too small or rapid to allow visual observations became evident after a careful examination of the streak photographs. Fig. 3 shows another positive β' example where alternate troughs are sharp and broad, two by two. Here there is an intermediate phase where the troughs systematically tilt in pairs and are more nearly equal in amplitude (Fig. 3 (b)). Because of the pairwise symmetry in this case, it is difficult to decide whether the pattern is propagating relative to the waves toward the east or west. But a careful comparison of intermediate photographs establishes an eastward propagation and the value $+.13$ for ω'_{gw}.

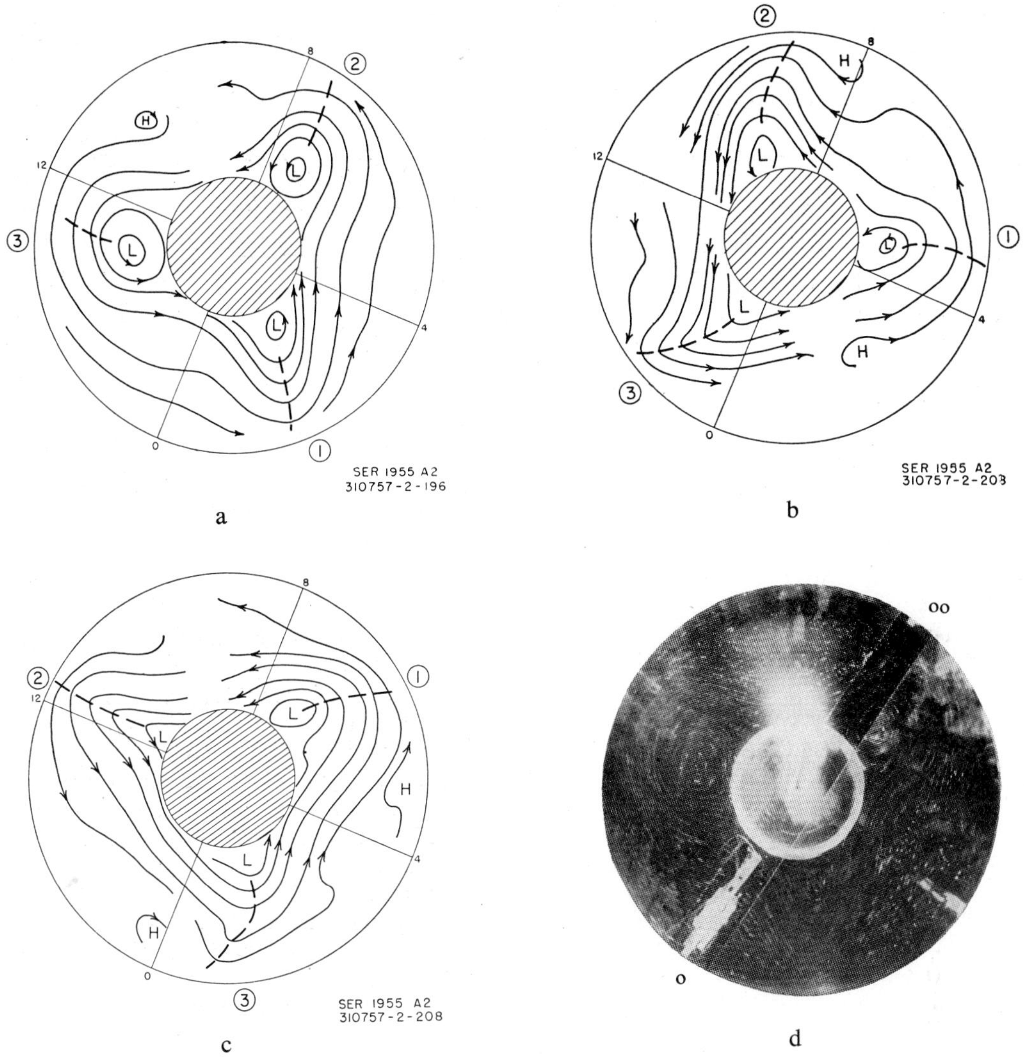

Fig. 4. Free surface streamlines of a steady state, three wave convection (310757-2) with inverted cone base. (a) Several small irregular vortices near the outer rim distort the streamlines, but do not seem to be significant. (b) 3.51 revolutions later, the waves have progressed counter-clockwise in the normal manner, but the group pattern has progressed clockwise from wave 1 to wave 3. (c) 2.50 revolutions later, the group system is progressing clockwise from wave 3 to wave 2. (d) Original streak photograph of fig. 2 (a). Conditions: Base BC-5 Inverted, $D_i = 5.65$ cm, $D_0 = 4.70$ cm, $\beta' = -0.58$, $\overline{\omega}'_w = .047$, $\omega'_{gw} = -.095$, $2\beta'/\overline{r}'k'^2 = -.084$, $R_{0T}{}^* = .088$, $S_z{}^* = .151$.

Finally, the third example of this type in Fig. 4 establishes the very important fact (again consistent with equation (16)) that a negative slope and β' reverses the group propagation relative to the waves to westward. Here one has the very striking situation that the wave phase propagation is in one direction while the group propagation is in the opposite direction. A similar unusual situation occurs for the propagation of certain types of internal waves in the vertical direction in a stratified atmosphere (ELIASSEN and KLEINSCHMIDT 1957, p. 56). Fig. 5 gives a second type of evidence, that is perhaps even more convincing, for the conclusion that the wave train is behaving in a manner like that of a simple group. A thermocouple fixed in the pan that is measuring either a point temperature or a temperature difference exhibits a strong modula-

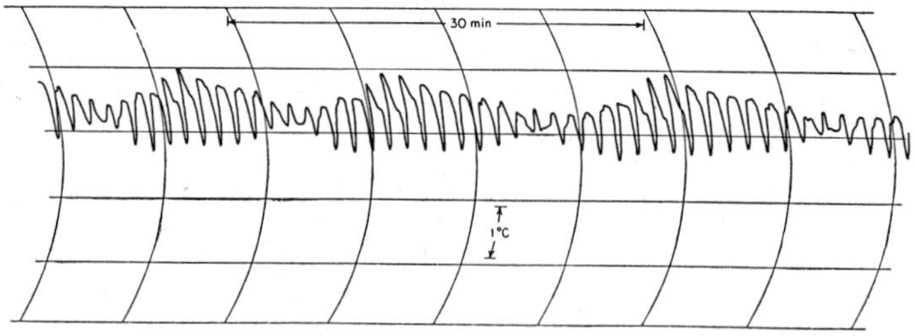

Fig. 5. Representative temperature record (171257) of a thermocouple rotating with the pan. The short term oscillations are the individual wave passages and the long term modulation envelope is produced by the group amplitude and pattern variation in the wave train as it passes the couple position. The maximum range of temperature as the waves pass is 1.5° C. The change in the period of the modulation is due to a gradual increase in the temperature gradient, as the system was not yet in a steady state. The base and other conditions are similar to Fig. 2.

tion produced by the difference between the individual wave periods and the group period. The modulation period on the record is the least common multiple of these periods. Note particularly the repetition of quite small details in the individual wave traces at corresponding positions relative to the modulation. A third type of confirmatory data was found to be possible to obtain from careful detailed measurements of the trough positions on the photographs. In a simple group of dispersive waves, wave length variations occur between troughs, the individual trough phase speeds varying accordingly, and the wave length variations should propagate relative to the wave crests at the group rate ω'_{gw} (ROSSBY 1945). In addition, ω'_{wg} should be related to the slope of the phase speed vs. wave length curve according to

$$\omega'_{gw} = -\lambda'\frac{d\omega'_w}{d\lambda'} \qquad (19)$$

obtained from equation (13) by substituting $k' = 2\pi/\lambda'$.

It was found by measuring longitude angles of the trough lines on the photographs (at mid-radius of the ring or averaged toward the cold source for strongly tilted troughs) that systematic wave length differences occurred and that variations in speed of the individual troughs were detected. For positive β', the longest trough to trough wave lengths were generally downstream of the "sharpest" trough and for negative β', upstream. If a longitude-time diagram of the wave lengths and displacements was plotted in wave coordinates, isolines of wave length, for example, could be drawn that sloped in strips corresponding to the speed ω'_{gw}. On several experiments a number of pairs of values of individual wave lengths and corresponding trough displacement speeds ω'_w were measured. There were some difficulties in this because of the small number of waves, the difficulty of precisely defining wave phase locally, and the difficulty of getting long enough displacements for accurate ω'_w values in view of the rapid group propagation of wave lengths through the wave train. Attempts were made to average wave lengths to improve accuracy and make them correspond better to the mean time and position of the displacements but this suppressed too much of the real variability so that no consistent relations emerged. It was found that if trough-trough wave lengths were measured in such a way that the group propagation would approximately center this wave length on the trough at the mid-time of the trough displacement used, consistent results could be obtained. For positive β', the upstream wave length was paired with a suitable subsequent trough displacement, while for negative β', the downstream wave length was so paired. Figs. 6 and 7 give examples in the form of scatter diagrams of the results for a positive β' and a negative β' experiment respectively. Individual trough ω'_w values show the correct dependence on local wavelength; that is ω'_w decreases with increased λ' for the positive cone and increases with increased λ' for the negative cone. The solid lines show the slope of the phase speed wave length relation calculated from the *visually observed* ω'_{gw} according to equation (19) and

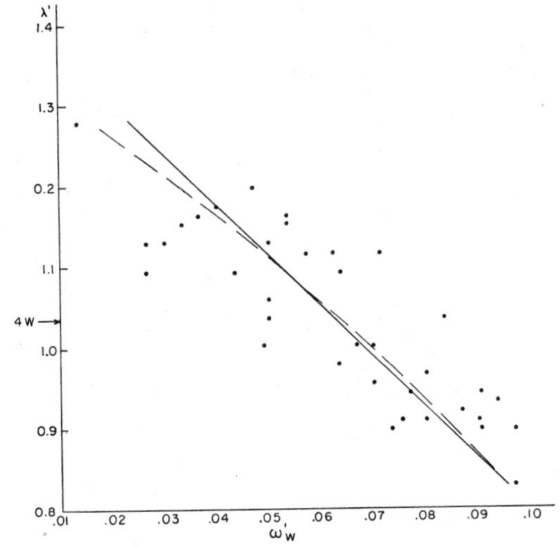

Fig. 6. Individual wave phase speeds vs. upstream wavelength (171257—4) for conditions similar to figure 2. The solid line is the tangent to the phase velocity curve drawn through the mean wavelength and wave speed with a slope $d\omega'_w/d\lambda' = -0.160$ that is calculated from the visually observed group propagation rate ω'_{gw}. (Arrow on λ' axis indicates wavelength for 4 waves). The dashed curve is a least-squares fit to the equation $\omega'_w = a_0 + a_2\lambda'^2$. Mean wavelength$=1.03$, mean wave speed $\overline{\omega}'_w = 0.06$, $a_0 = 0.15$, $a_2 = -0.083$.

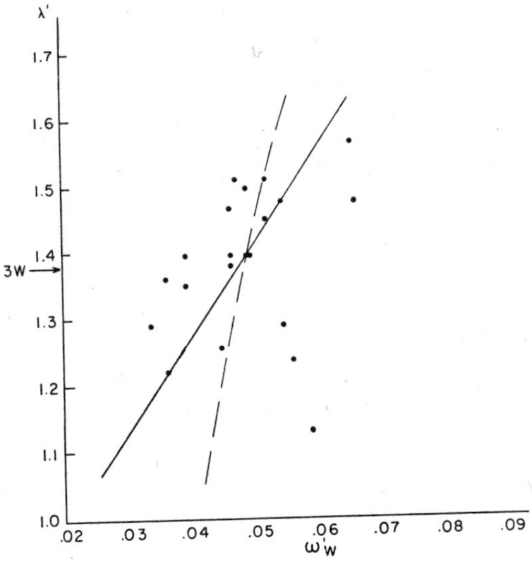

Fig. 7. Individual wave phase speeds vs. downstream wavelength (310757-2) for conditions of fig. 4. The arrow on the λ' axis indicates wavelength for 3 waves. The slope of the phase speed curve (solid line) $d\omega'_w/d\lambda' = 0.069$, calculated from the observed ω'_{gw}. Mean wavelength$=1.382$, mean wave speed $\overline{\omega}'_w = 0.047$. Coefficients of least-squares curve $a_0 = 0.03$, $a_2 = 0.008$.

Table I: Representative values

Base	β'	$2\beta'/\bar{r}k'^2$	ω'_w	ω'_g	ω'_{gw}	$\bar{u}'_s$	R^*_{0T}	S^*_z	n
BC-7	4.19	.346	.080	.26	.181	.065	.172	.134	4
BC-4	2.84	.234	.068	.22	.154	.045	.129	.129	4
BC-6	1.55	.128	.052	.19	.137	.038	.093	.111	4
BC-3	1.43	.118	.047	.17	.128	.040	.092	.095	4
BC-5	0.57	.046	.040	—	—	,025	.055	.118	4
Flat	0	0	.034	—	—	.025	.052	.116	4
– BC-5	– 0.58	– 0.084	.047	– .048	– .095	—	.088	.151	3

Note: n is total number of waves.

passed through the visually observed mean $\overline{\omega}'_w$ point. The dashed lines are a least squares fit of an equation of the form of (14) to the observed points. In view of the difficulties of measurement and scatter of the points, the agreement in both cases is very satisfactory. Particularly, the agreement with the purely kinematic relation (19) is an excellent independent check on the reality of the apparent behaviour as a simple group. Some diagrams for experiments with positive β' show more scatter than Fig. 6, but the general agreement is still very good for all except the flattest cone in Table 1 where no distinct group behaviour was detected.

The most important quantitative evidence for the presence of an equivalent-β' effect in these baroclinic waves is that given for ω'_{gw} in Fig. 8 and Table I. In contrast to the failure of a direct effect for ω'_w, the group speeds relative to the wave crests, ω'_{gw}, not only are correct in sign

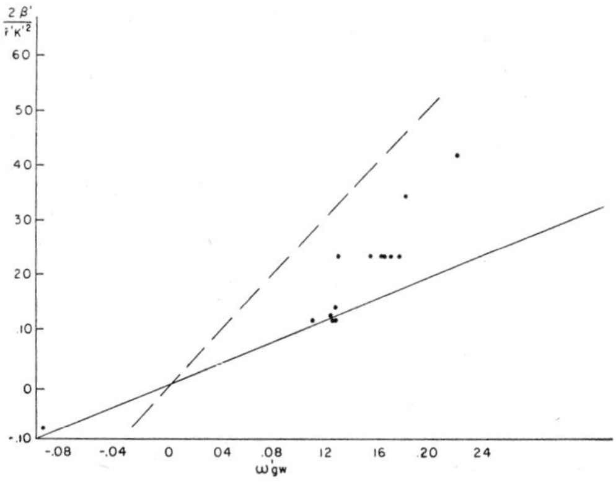

Fig. 8. Observed group speeds relative to the waves ω'_{gw}vs. $2\beta'/\bar{r}'k'^2$. The solid line is the theoretical curve for the barotropic equation on an infinite β'-plane, the dashed line is the same curve corrected for finite width. All data and the lines are for cases where the number of waves is four and $k'^2 = 36.7$ (except the negative β' point where there are three waves).

(reversing for the negative cone) but also agree approximately with the value expected from equation (16) (i.e. $2\beta'/\bar{r}'k'^2$ as calculated from the slope of the base) for the analog to simple Rossby waves on an infinite β-plane. This is the solid straight line in Fig. 8. If one makes the same finite width correction calculated by HAURWITZ (1940) for the Rossby waves to allow for the limitation of the waves to a ring, the effect is merely to multiply the right side of equation (16) by a factor depending on the ratio of the squares of the wave number in the y-direction $k_y'^2$ to the previous longitudinal wave number k'^2 If we approximate k_y' by a value corresponding to the ring width as a half wave-length in that direction, this factor is *0.39* and the dashed line in Fig. 8 is the corresponding curve. We may note that the agreement in Fig. 8 depends only on the ω'_{gw} measurements which could be made in two or three independent ways with good precision and are not subject to anywhere near the uncertainties of the data in Figures 6 and 7.

It will be obviously desirable in future work to apply baroclinic theories and try to understand in detail how the equivalent-β effect is operating, but from the experimental side this will require elaborate three-dimensional internal measurements for comparison. The general nature of the average meridional temperature field is illustrated by Figures 9 and 10 comparing a flat base with a conical base experiment. The major difference is the strong tendency, true for all the positive cones, for the mean isotherms to run parallel to the cone with a stronger packing with increasing slope corresponding to the increasing R_{0T}^* values in Table 1.

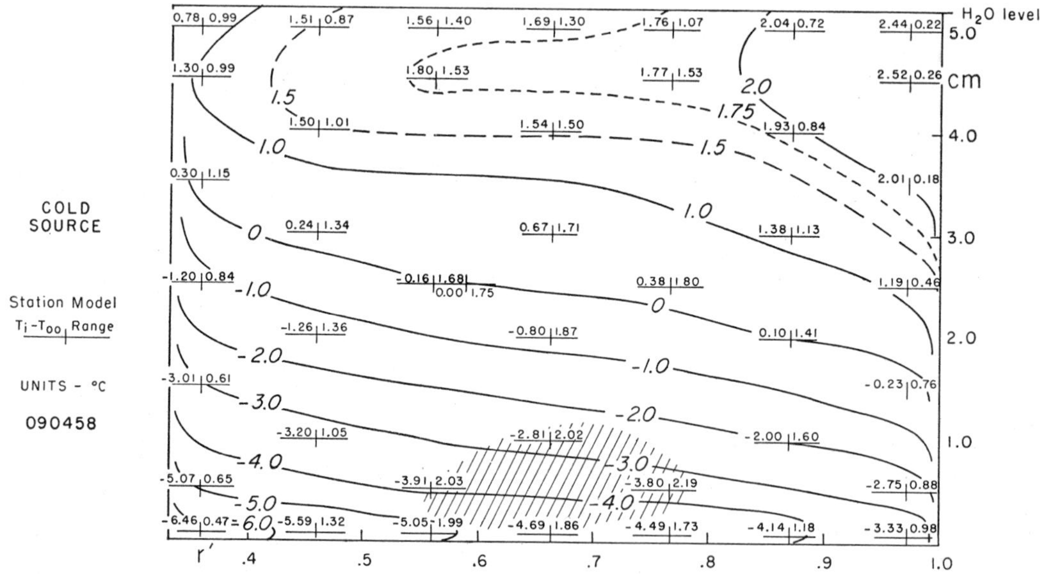

Fig. 9. Longitudinally averaged temperature cross-section of a four wave convection (090458) with conditions similar to all other experiments except that the base is flat ($\beta' = 0$). Isolines are deviations from an overall mean temperature T_{00} in units of Centigrade degrees. Figures on the left are average temperature deviations; on the right, the range in degrees about this average. The hatching indicates the region where the range exceeds 2 degrees. $T_{00} = 21.0°$ C.

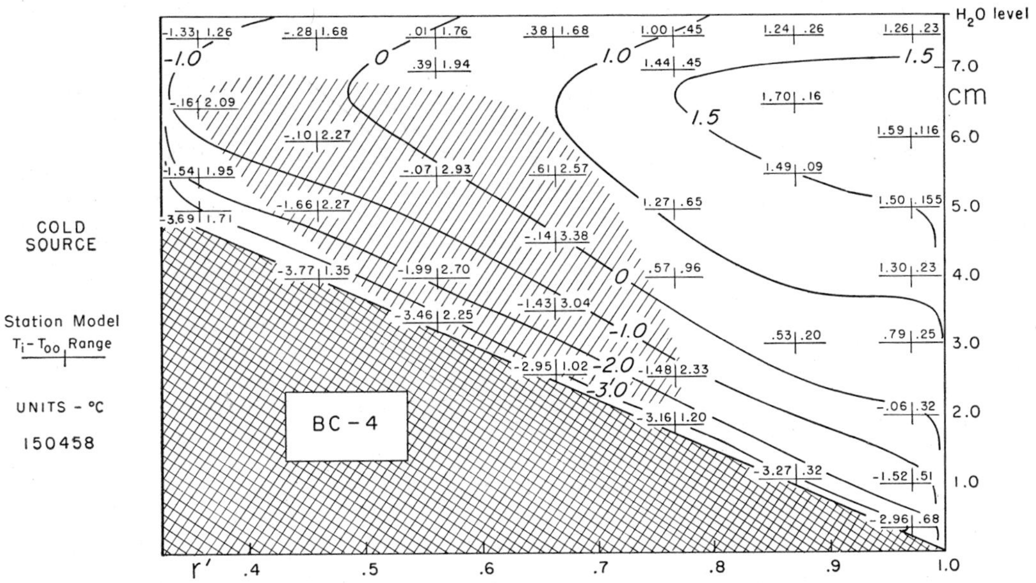

Fig. 10. Longitudinally averaged temperature cross-section of a four wave convection (150458) with conditions similar to Fig. 2. Isolines and units as in Fig. 9. $T_{00}=23.4°$ C. Note the strongly increased slope and horizontal gradient compared with Fig. 9 and the tendency to parallelism of mean isotherms and the base.

Some comparisons with baroclinic theory can be made, for example, with frequency equation results given by Kuo (1953). His expression for the real phase speed translates to:

$$\bar{r}'\omega'_w = (\bar{u}'_s - 1/2R^*_{0T}) - \beta'/k'^2 \left\{\frac{k'^2\Delta r'^2 S^*_z + 4}{k'^2\Delta r'^2 S^*_z + 8}\right\} \quad (20)$$

where $\bar{u}'_s$ is the top surface mean zonal current and $(\bar{u}'_s - 1/2R^*_{0T})$ is an estimate for the overall mean zonal current used by Kuo.

(Unfortunately this is a result valid only for unstable waves and it does not reduce to (14) in the barotropic case but the general nature of the corrections is similar to those for neutral waves.) A corresponding expression for ω'_{gw} is again the same in form as equation (16) but with a factor depending on the terms in the bracket above. Examples of the longitudinally averaged top surface zonal speeds are given in Fig. 11 for increasing base slopes and of the corresponding $\bar{u}'_s$ values in Table I. Unfortunately (20) or similar expressions do not improve the correspondence of calculated ω'_w vs. observed. The error is in the same direction as the error of equation (14), both calling for too low wave speeds (retrogression), but the baroclinic value (20) is better.

For the experiment with BC-4 in table I, (14) calls for $\omega'_w = -.147$ and (20) calls for $\omega'_w = -.075$, the observed value being *.0676*. In respect of this question of the phase speeds, our qualitative impression has been that the increase over flat base values, and over any of the theoretical values, of the observed values is due somehow to a strong tendency for katabatic flows down the positive cone and a consequent abnormally strong meridional cell component of the velocity field changing the equivalent mean zonal flow in, say, equation (14). This is also suggested by the changes in surface velocity profiles with increasing cone slope in Fig. 11 which are very much in the direction of increasing resemblance to the profiles of a symmetrical Hadley regime motion (Fultz 1956).

The effects of baroclinic corrections to equation (16) are relatively slight once the finite width change has been made. Thus the analogue of equation (16) from (20) gives for the BC-4 case $\omega'_{gw} = .080$, (16) with the width correction gives $\omega'_{gw} = .091$, and the observed value is *.154*. The discrepancies are obviously worse for the phase speeds and deserve careful study in the future.

4. Conclusions

We believe it is clear that much remains mysterious in the behaviour of these waves that will

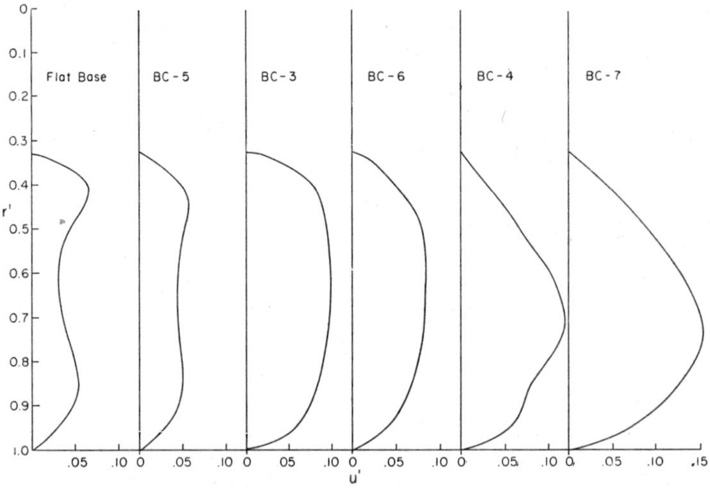

Fig. 11. Top surface longitudinally averaged zonal velocity profiles for various bases. Velocity scale is in units of $r_0\Omega$ and the radius scale in units of the total pan r_0. The cold source extends to $r'=.329$. The slope of the bases increases from left to right. The profiles to the right have characteristics resembling those of axially symmetric Hadley regime convection.

yield only to extensive further work, but it seems hardly possible to doubt that in some manner an equivalent-β effect is being produced by the depth variations in spite of the baroclinicity. Quite aside from this question however, the presence of such obvious wave energy, frequency, and wave length variations propagating thru the train is of the highest interest. The time variations in individual waves sometimes have very close resemblances to those that develop with index cycle (vacillation) fluctuations (FULTZ and c. 1958). It is very probable that, with suitably precise estimates of the wave energy, the time variations of this energy can be associated with convergence and divergence of the local group velocity in the manner expected by ROSSBY (1945) and investigated for the atmosphere by CRESSMAN (1949).

That understanding of these phenomena in the experiments will have a strong relevance to general problems of development in the atmosphere can confidently be expected and the experiments have the advantage for purposes of theoretical understanding and suggestion of making possible the isolation of very vigorous and well-defined effects. We hope that developments of the sort that Rossby was a master at encouraging will occur in this connection.

REFERENCES

CRESSMAN, G. P., 1949: Some effects of wave-length variations of the Long Waves in the upper Westerlies, *J. Meteor.* **6**, 56—60.

ELIASSEN, A., and KLEINSCHMIDT, E., 1957: Dynamic Meteorology, *Handbuch Der Physik*, **48**, 1—154.

FULTZ, D., 1951: Non-dimensional equations and modeling criteria for the atmosphere, *J. Meteor.* **8**, 262—267.

— 1951: Experimental Analogies to Atmospheric Motions, *Compendium of Meteor.*, ed. T. Malone, Amer. Meteor. Soc., 1235—1248.

— 1952: On the possibility of experimental models of the polar-front wave, *J. Meteor.* **9**, 379—384.

— 1956: A survey of certain thermally and mechanically driven fluid systems of meteorological interest, ed. R. R. Long, Johns Hopkins Univ. *Proc. 1st Sympos. Geoph. Models*, Sept. 1953; 27—63.

FULTZ, D., and FRENZEN, P., 1955: A note on certain interesting ageostrophic motions in a rotating hemispherical shell, *J. Meteor.* **12**, 332—338.

FULTZ, D., LONG, R. R., OWENS, G. V., BOHAN, W., KAYLOR, R., and WEIL, J., 1958: Studies of thermal convection in a rotating cylinder and Large-scale atmospheric motions, *Meteor. Monog., Amer. Meteor. Soc.* (in press).

HAURWITZ, B., 1940: The Motion of Atmospheric Disturbances, *J. Mar. Res.* **3**, 35—50.

HIDE, R., 1953: Some experiments on thermal convection in a rotating liquid, *Quart. J. Roy. Meteor. Soc.* **79**, 161.

HIDE, R., 1958: An experimental study of thermal convection in a rotating liquid, *Phil. Trans. Roy. Soc. Lond.* (A) **250**, 441—478.

KUO, H. L., 1953: The stability properties and structure of disturbances in a baroclinic atmosphere, *J. Meteor.* **10**, 235—243.

LAMB, H., 1932: *Hydrodynamics*. Cambridge Univ. Press, sixth edition, 738 p.

LONG, R. R., 1952: The flow of a liquid past a barrier in a rotating spherical shell, *J. Meteor.* **9**, 187—199.

NAMIAS, J., 1947: Physical Nature of some fluctuations in the speed of the zonal circulation, *J. Meteor.* **4**, 125—133.

RIEHL, H. and collab., 1952: Forecasting in Middle Latitudes, *Meteor. Monog.* 1, No. 5, Amer. Meteor. Soc., Boston.

RIEHL, H., and FULTZ, D., 1957: Jet stream and Long waves in a steady rotating-dishpan experiment: structure of the circulation, *Quart. J. Roy. Meteor. Soc.* **83**, 215—231.

ROSSBY, C.-G., 1945: On the propagation of frequencies and energy in certain types of oceanic and atmospheric waves, *J. Meteor.* **2**, 187—204.

ROSSBY, C.-G., 1949: On the dispersion of planetary waves in a barotropic Atmosphere, *Tellus* **1**, 1—5.

— and collab. 1939: Relation between variations in the intensity of the zonal circulation of the atmosphere and displacements of the semi-permanent centers of action, *J. Mar. Res.* **2**, 38—55.

VON ARX, W. S., 1952: A laboratory study of the wind-driven ocean circulation, *Tellus* **4**, 311—318.

— 1957: An experimental approach to problems in physical oceanography, *Phys. and Chem. Earth* **2**; ed. Ahrens and c., Pergamon, London; 1—29.

YEH, T. C., 1949: On energy dispersion in the atmosphere, *J. Meteor.* **6**, 1—16.

(Manuscript received November 6, 1958)

A Laboratory Model of Air Flow over the Sierra Nevada Mountains

By Robert R. Long[1]
The Johns Hopkins University, Baltimore, Maryland

Abstract

A description is given of a liquid model of the flow of air over the Sierra Nevada Mountains in the vicinity of Bishop, California. A theoretical discussion indicates that the modeling can be attempted by requiring geometric similarity of the boundaries in the fluid systems and equality of the internal Froude numbers, suitably defined. The experimental model has flow patterns that resemble the prototype quite closely although in some cases at somewhat different internal Froude numbers.

1. Introduction

The air flow over the Owens Valley east of the Sierra Nevada ridge has been studied recently by members of the Department of Meteorology, University of California at Los Angeles, under a contract with the U.S. Air Force (Holmboe and Klieforth, 1954, Klieforth, 1957). The observational part of this research has produced several vertical cross-sections of the flow patterns for various distributions of "upstream" velocity and stability (figures 1—2).

The effort to model this atmospheric phenomenon had several motivations: First, a desire to apply to a practical problem some of the findings of the author's research on stratified fluids (Long, 1953 a, 1954, 1955, 1956); second, a hope to improve the author's first attempt to model air flow over mountains (Long, 1953 b); and finally, the availability of the observed flow patterns for comparison with experiment.

2. Modeling problem

Numerous problems arise in constructing a model of flow over mountains. An important one concerns friction, since it is impossible to obtain equality of Reynolds number in model and prototype. In the atmosphere a typical value is $R = 10^{10}$; in the model $R = 10^4$. Since the flow in the model is basically laminar and that in the atmosphere turbulent, adopting the terminology of Reynolds[2] (1894), we must compare the mean motions in the model with the mean-mean motions in the atmosphere at corresponding points. The equations of motion in the model are the familiar Navier-Stokes equations, while those for the atmosphere are Reynolds equations of mean-mean motion with both molecular friction and Reynolds' stress terms. The forms of these two sets of equations differ fundamentally unless (1) molecular friction and turbulent friction terms are neglected in both systems, or (2) molecular friction is negligible compared to turbulent friction in the atmosphere *and* the turbulent friction is expressible in terms of mean-mean motion and has the same form as in the equations of Navier-Stokes, viz. proportional to the Laplacean of the respective velocity component.

If we adopt viewpoint (1) the Reynolds number criterion for similarity no longer need be applied. Viewpoint (2) includes the assumption of a mixing length theory of turbulence with constant coefficient of eddy viscosity. It is known that this theory is exceedingly crude.

Experimental evidence in the flow of stratified liquids is enlightening in this regard. The author (Long, 1955) was able to compare exact, perfect fluid solutions, yielding certain types of stratified

[1] This research was sponsored by a contract with the U.S. Weather Bureau.

[2] Reynolds called the velocity components u_i that occur in the Navier-Stokes equations components of "mean motion" because heat motions are already averaged out. Velocity components $\bar{u}_i$ obtained by averaging u_i over macroscopic intervals of space or time are called "mean-mean motions".

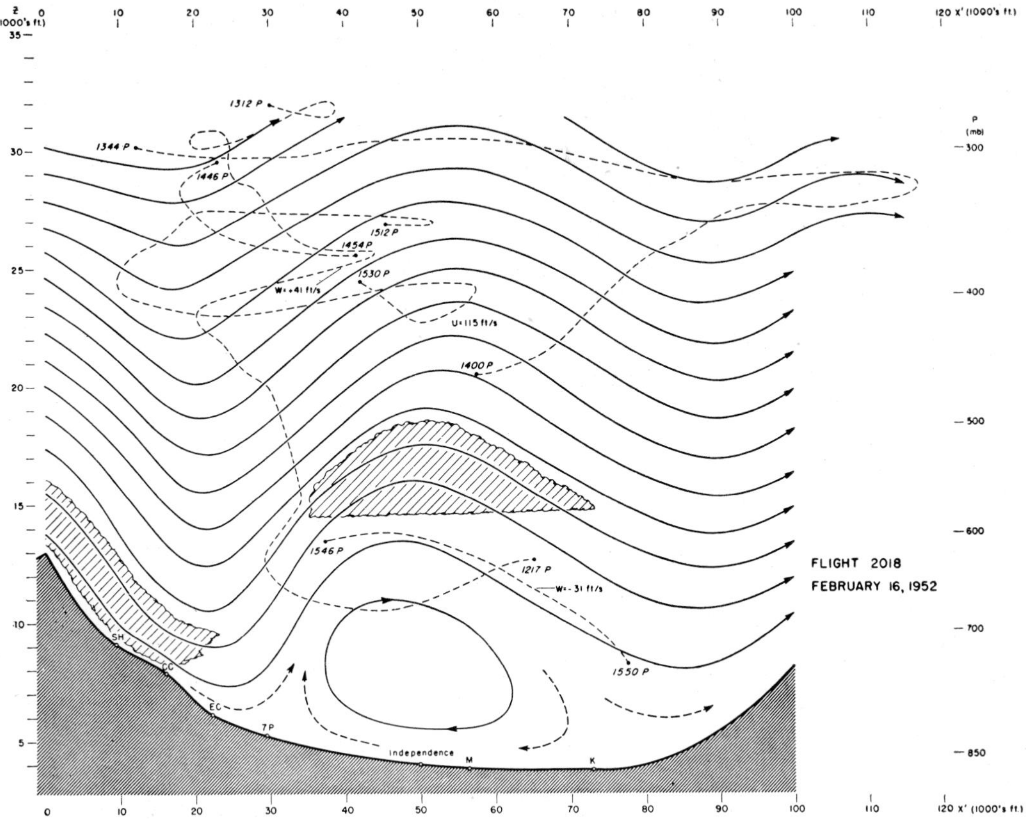

Fig. 1. Vertical cross-section of flow afternoon of February 16, 1952. Conditions upwind at Merced, California: height of tropopause, $h = 11$ km.; relative potential density difference in troposphere, $\Delta\varrho/\bar{\varrho} = 0.14$; mean wind speed, $\bar{u} = 29$ m. sec^{-1}; $Fi = 0.24$. (Estimated from sounding and wind profile.)

flow, with similar experimental models. The agreement was very good in most respect and it was obvious that the only important effects of friction were a damping[1] of wave patterns downstream and the generation of an eddy under the first wave crest in the lee of the obstacle due to boundary layer separation. One may conclude that friction does not have a fundamental importance in the model and can be neglected for most purposes. Although there is no direct evidence, it is likely that the same comments are valid for the atmosphere. This is indicated by the fact that the ratio of inertia terms to Reynolds stress terms is about the same order of magnitude as the Reynolds number in the experiment.

In summary, it seems possible to neglect friction in both model and prototype in connection with the flow in the great bulk of the fluids. If we model perfectly in all other respects, we would still expect certain differences, mainly near boundaries due to boundary layer effects, unless we adopt viewpoint (2) above and attempt to obtain equality of Reynolds numbers composed of a coefficient of virtual or eddy viscosity in the case of the atmosphere. Indeed, if we use any reasonable value of virtual viscosity we find that the Reynolds numbers defined in this way are about the same order of magnitude. This crude approach may have some merit since, as we see later, boundary layer separation effects seem to be similar in model and prototype.

If we agree, however, to model on the basis of the perfect fluid equations, and if we assume a steady state in both systems, the governing equations may be written (LONG, 1956)

$$\frac{\partial(v, y)}{\partial(x_0, y_0)} + \frac{\partial(u, x)}{\partial(x_0, y_0)} - \frac{\partial(u_0, x_0)}{\partial(x_0, y_0)} - \frac{1}{u_0\varrho}\frac{d\varrho}{dy_0}\left[\frac{u^2+v^2}{2} + g(y - y_0)\right] = 0, \qquad (1)$$

[1] The damping was pronounced only when the motion in the waves was turbulent.

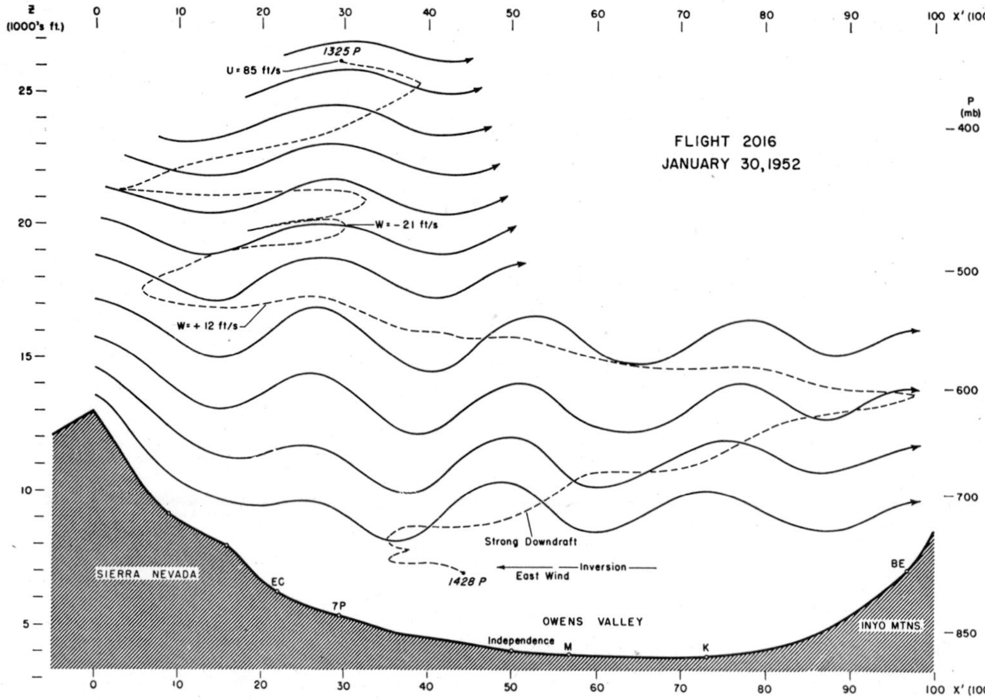

Fig. 2. Vertical cross-section of flow afternoon of January 30, 1952. Conditions upwind at Merced, California: $h = 9$ km.; $\Delta\varrho/\bar{\varrho} = 0.14$; $\bar{u} = 15$ m sec^{-1}; $F = 0.14$. (Estimated from sounding and wind profile.)

$$u = u_0 \frac{\partial x}{\partial x_0}, \quad v = u_0 \frac{\partial y}{\partial x_0}, \tag{2}$$

$$\frac{\partial(x, y)}{\partial(x_0, y_0)} = 1 + \left[\frac{u^2 + v^2 - u_0^2}{2\,c_0^2} + \frac{g(y - y_0)}{c_0^2} + \ldots\right], \tag{3}$$

subject to the following comments and definitions:

(a) x is horizontal, y is vertical and the corresponding velocity components are u and v.

(b) $x_0 = u_0 t_0$, where $u_0(y_0)$ is the upstream basic velocity distribution and t_0 is the time a given particle passed a certain cross-section far upstream. The height of the particle at time t_0 is y_0. Thus x_0 and y_0 are Lagrangian variables.

(c) ϱ is density in the model and potential density in the atmosphere, i.e. the density of a parcel if reduced to some standard pressure.

(d) $\frac{d\varrho}{dt} = 0$ in both cases, i.e. $\varrho = \varrho(y_0)$. These are excellent approximations for phenomena of such small time scales.

(e) c_0 is the speed of sound in the atmosphere at height y_0 upstream.

(f) The flow is two-dimensional and the earth's rotation is negligible.

(g) The flow and density distributions upstream vary only with y_0.

(h) The terms in square brackets in equation (3) are absent in the model.

Some discussion of the assumption of steady state is necessary. Since we are using the equations of mean-mean motion for the atmosphere (neglecting turbulent and molecular friction terms) the essential unsteadiness of ordinary atmospheric turbulence will not vitiate the assumption of a steady state. On the other hand theory indicates (LONG, 1955) that an assumed steady-state flow of a stratified fluid over barriers above a certain size ceases to exist in a mathematical sense. Accompanying experiments indicate that this unsteadiness takes two forms:

(1) Wave effects (blocking waves) propagate upstream altering upstream density and velocity distributions.

(2) Large-scale eddies of the size of the depth

of the fluid appear and introduce turbulent fluctuations.

In a strict sense, then, we cannot use the equations (1)—(3) as a basis for modeling in the interesting range of conditions that lead to (1) and (2) above. As a practical matter, however, we note that the unsteadiness (1) is a local affair which ultimately propagates so far upstream that conditions in the vicinity of the obstacle are no longer unsteady from this effect. The unsteadiness (2) is more serious. The time dependence can be averaged out by considering that the equations of the model refer to mean-mean motions. But this introduces Reynolds stress terms whose magnitudes are considerable. In fact, the loss of energy as the fluid passes through these eddies is very noticeable in the experiments. The position and general shape of the eddies, however, are as given by perfect fluid theory, and we may hope to model these general features of well-developed flow patterns.

If we accept equations (1)—(3) as the basis for modeling we notice first that the forms of the governing equations are identical if:

(1) We compare density in the liquid model to potential density in the atmosphere.

(2) If the square of the Mach number is small compared to 1.

(3) If the vertical scale of the atmospheric motion is sufficiently small.

Conditions (2) and (3), if met, lead to identities of the equation of continuity (3). Condition (2) is not an important restriction since atmospheric velocities are small compared to the speed of sound. Condition (3) is troublesome and is not satisfied when vertical displacements are much larger than 1 km, as they are, for example, in well-developed Sierra waves. Some error may be expected in this connection despite evidence that considerably larger vertical displacements are tolerable (LONG, 1956).

In view of the above discussion we use the Eulerian form of equations (1)—(3) (after neglecting the terms in brackets in (3)) and associated boundary conditions, as our basis for modeling. As shown by the author (LONG, 1955) this is equivalent to a single equation

$$\nabla^2 y_0 + \frac{1}{2}[(\nabla y_0)^2 - 1]\frac{d}{dy_0}\ln(\varrho u_0^2) - \frac{g}{u_0^2\varrho}\frac{d\varrho}{dy_0}(y_0 - y) = 0, \tag{4}$$

with independent variables x, y. Let L be a representative length scale (horizontal dimension of barrier or mountain ridge), $\bar{u}$ a representative velocity (average basic velocity through the depth of the liquid or troposphere) and $\bar{\varrho}$ a representative density (average density or potential density through the depth of the liquid or troposphere). Defining

$$y_0' = \frac{y_0}{L},\quad x' = \frac{x}{L},\quad y' = \frac{y}{L},\quad u_0' = \frac{u_0}{\bar{u}},\quad \varrho' = \frac{\varrho}{\bar{\varrho}}, \tag{5}$$

equation (4) becomes

$$\nabla^2 y_0' + \frac{1}{2}[(\nabla y_0')^2 - 1]\frac{d}{dy_0}\ln(u_0'^2\varrho') - \frac{gL}{\bar{u}^2 u_0'^2\varrho'}\frac{d\varrho'}{dy_0'}(y_0' - y') = 0. \tag{6}$$

Necessary conditions that $y'_0\,(x', y')$ be identical in two experiments (or in the atmosphere and its experimental model) are the equalities of the functions $u_0'\,(y_0')$, $\varrho'(y_0')$ and of $F^2 = \bar{u}^2/gL$. This appears to be possible experimentally, but in the present research it was decided to assume that the entire middle term in equation (6) is negligible and require equality of

$$\frac{1}{F^2 u_0'^2\varrho'}\frac{d\varrho'}{dy_0'}. \tag{7}$$

This approximation implies that F^2 is very small and this is well satisfied in the atmosphere and model. Notice that we demand only equality of $y_0'\,(x', y')$. This insures a similarity of flow patterns but not a similarity of velocities.

The only difficulty in modeling on the basis of (7) is that the atmosphere is hundreds of kilometers deep while we are only interested in the flow in the lowest 10 km. This means that any strict model of reasonable size would consign the "troposphere" to such a small layer that boundary layer effects might dominate. This difficulty requires one of two approximations:

(a) We may ignore all of the atmosphere above the troposphere by creating a model of the troposphere only. In effect, since the model has a free surface which remains sensibly undisturbed, we assume that atmosphere has an enormous stability at the tropopause. The stability at and above the troposphere is very great compared to that in the troposphere so that there is some possibility that this approximation may lead to reasonable results.

(b) We may model the troposphere and the lower 10—20 km or so of the stratosphere. This seems to be a more reasonable approach if we accept the intuitively appealing viewpoint that conditions in the very high atmosphere will not seriously affect the flow near the ground. This model is difficult to construct, however. The primary problem is to maintain against strong mixing in the experiments a density distribution resembling that in the stratosphere. A simpler variation of this procedure, and the only model of this type used in the experiment, is to put layers of lighter fluids on top of the model "troposphere". This may be considered as a rough representation of the stability in the stratosphere.

In either of the above approximations we attempt to equate (7) in the actual and model troposphere. Since we move the barrier in a resting channel of fluid we obtain $\bar{u}$ = const far upstream if no disturbance is propagated upstream. We will assume this is the case for the sake of argument although, as we will notice later, the velocity distribution is curved at moderate distances upstream. In addition experiments with stratified fluids (LONG, 1955) when compared to a theoretical model with linear density gradient, revealed that the effect of curvature of the density profile is very slight provided the density difference from top to bottom of the channel is the same. On this basis, we assume a linear density and potential density profile in both model and prototype, and uniform velocity profiles. If, further, we assume that the density difference from top to bottom satisfies $\Delta\varrho/\bar{\varrho} \ll 1$ and if we use the fact that there is geometric similarity, equality of (7) is equivalent to equality of

$$F_i = \frac{\bar{u}}{\left(g \dfrac{\Delta\varrho}{\bar{\varrho}} h\right)^{1/2}}, \tag{8}$$

where h is the depth of the troposphere. F_i is called the modified Froude number. This is the criterion for similarity used in the modeling. The most serious deficiency probably is due to the strong wind increase with height in the atmosphere. A comparison of model and atmosphere may be made in this case if we use the mean wind in the troposphere. The arguments above indicate that this criterion is the most important one in the model of type (a) above. The few examples of type (b) attempted made no effort to model (7) in the stratosphere, but were used simply to provide a reduction of the stability at the free surface.

Fig. 3. Idealized cross-section of topography of Sierra Nevada ridge near Bishop, California. The section is oriented WSW-ENE. (Left-right in figure.) Length is 1 meter, maximum height 4 cm.

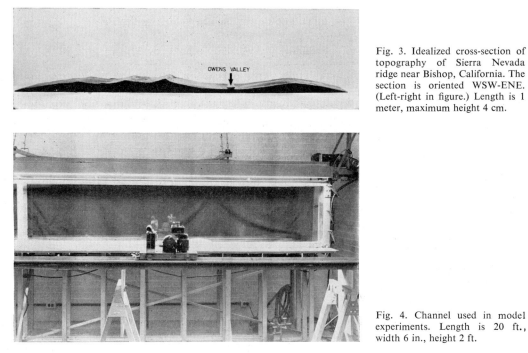

Fig. 4. Channel used in model experiments. Length is 20 ft., width 6 in., height 2 ft.

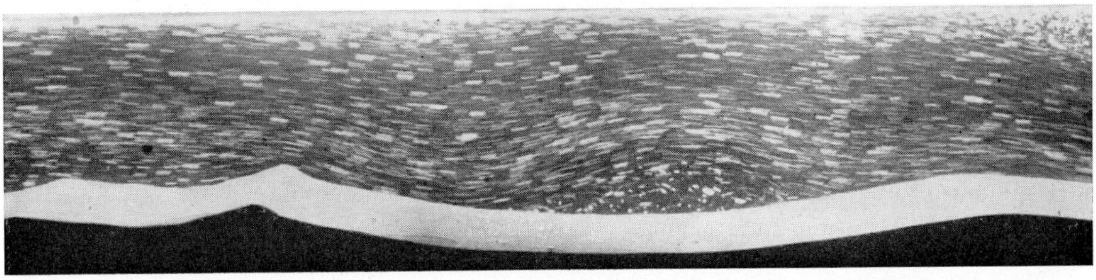

Fig. 5. Single-fluid flow over barrier. Total depth of fluid 13 cm., $F_i = 0.240$.

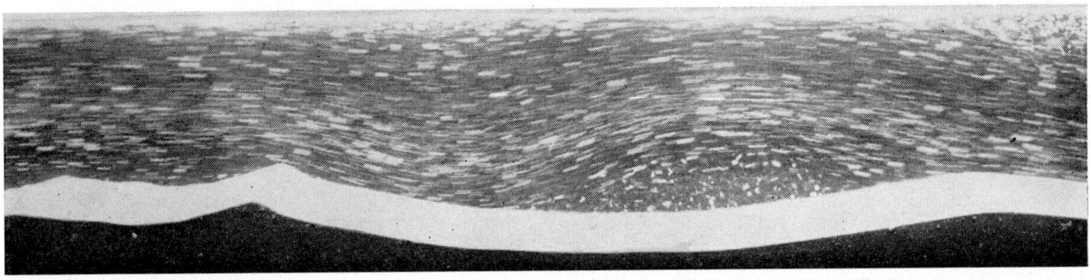

Fig. 6. Single-fluid flow over barrier. Total depth of fluid 13 cm., $F_i = 0.258$.

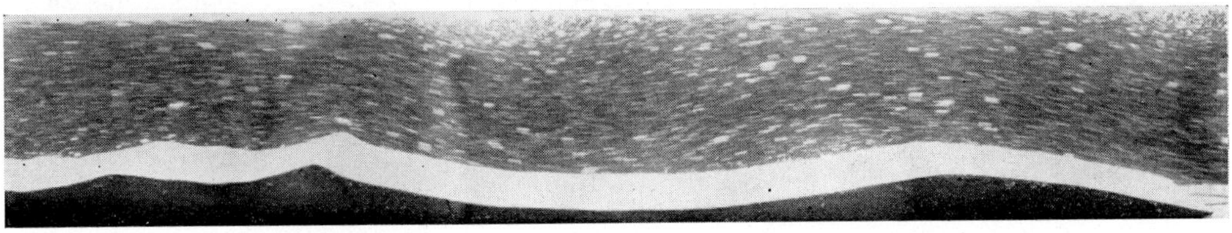

Fig. 7. Single-fluid flow over barrier. Total depth of fluid 13 cm., $F_i = 0.283$.

3. Experiments with a single-fluid system

In this section we describe experimental observations of flow over a model of the Sierra ridge, in the vicinity of Bishop, California. Pictures of the obstacle and channel are in figures 3 and 4. The fluid is a mixture of water and salt which has a basic density distribution that is very roughly linear with height. The obstacle is moved along the bottom at a known speed, and time exposures of the streaks due to aluminium particles are made on the plate of a camera moving with the barrier on a parallel track.

As indicated in the previous section it was assumed that geometric similarity of the boundary forms and equality of F_i insured similarity of the flow patterns. Since the geometry is unchanging each experimental photograph is identified by the Froude number of the experiment.

Figures 5—7 show the flow at high velocities. There is a single wave crest over the valley which moves downstream as the speed is increased. Figure 5 has a Froude number closest to that of the prototype of figure 1 and there is a strong resemblance.

Figure 8 shows the effect of a reduction of Froude number. In this picture and in the range F_i = 0.09—0.17 there are two wave crests in the valley. Between 0.05 and 0.09 there are 3 wave crests as in figure 9. Below this the flow is confused. In the lower layers over the valley there are ill-defined turbulent wave patterns with two or more horizontal jets, one just at the level of the Sierra ridge.

The normal state of affairs upstream in the atmosphere is a very marked increase of wind with height. Sufficiently far upstream in the model we assume a basic flow uniform with height. We notice, however, as in figures 8 and 9, that the massive barrier has a considerable effect in causing long waves to propagate upstream and change the upstream distribution of density and velocity. Close inspection of the photographs of flow at large Froude numbers show that there are great reductions of wind velocity upstream

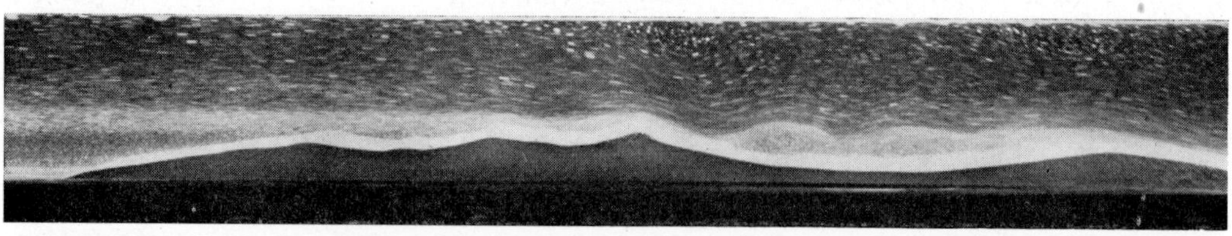

Fig. 8. Single-fluid flow over barrier. Total depth of fluid 13 cm., $F_i = 0.103$.

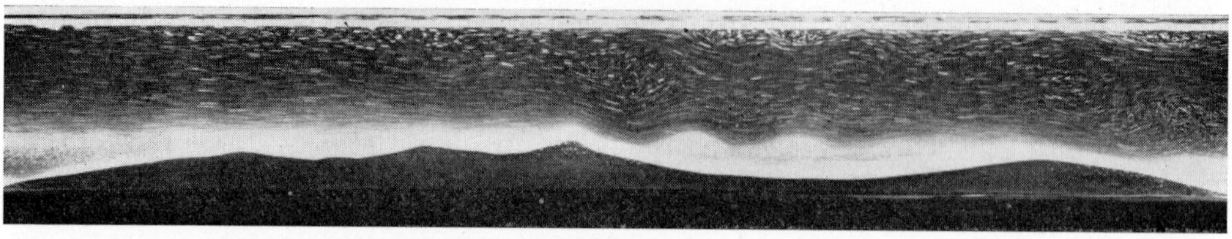

Fig. 9. Single-fluid flow over barrier. Total depth of fluid 13 cm., $F_i = 0.058$.

Fig. 10. Multi-fluid flow over a barrier. Of the total depth of 26 cm., the lower 13 cm. is a salt-water mixture with density 1.18 at the bottom and 1.05 at the top of the mixture. Above this are 5 layers of fluids of densities 1.00, 0.94, 0.89, 0.84, 0.79. The Froude number based on $h = 13$ cm., $\Delta\varrho/\bar{\varrho} = .117$, is $F_i = 0.105$.

in the lower layers and increases aloft. This is in the desired direction for improving the resemblance to the atmosphere. For moderate or small Froude numbers the speed upstream is reduced near the bottom and increased just above, but still higher in the fluid the speed decreases again. If the Froude number is low there are several layers of alternately high and low speed fluid.

We note that there is a resemblance between the flow in figure 2 in the prototype and in figure 9 in the model. The difference in Froude numbers is considerable, however. This may be caused by the dissimilar form of the velocity profiles upstream. At low fluid or wind velocities, the speed near the ground may be more important in determining the phenomena than the mean wind speed in the troposphere. Another possibility is the large stability of the "tropopause" (free surface) in the model. This is discussed in the next section.

4. Experiments with a multi-fluid system

As mentioned in Section 2 qualitative efforts were made to simulate the effect of the stratosphere. This was attempted by putting several layers of immiscible fluids on top of the salt-water mixture used in Section 3. In this way the density was reduced in steps over a considerable depth instead of by a sudden reduction at the free surface. (The air-fluid interface with its enormous stability still exists but its distance from the bottom is doubled and one may hope that it will have a minor effect on phenomena near the "ground".)

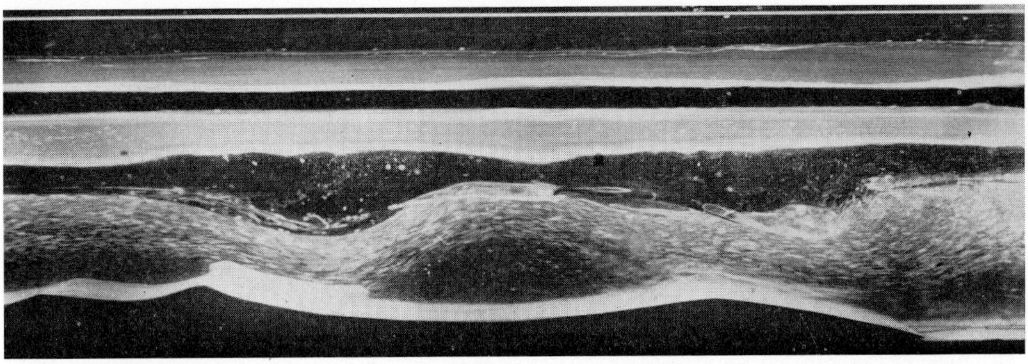

Fig. 11. Multi-fluid flow over barrier. Of the total depth of 26 cm., the lower 13 cm. is a salt-water mixture with density 1.17 at the bottom and 1.05 at the top of the mixture. Above this are 5 layers of fluids of densities 1.04, 0.97, 0.91, 0.85, 0.78. The Froude number based on $h = 13$ cm., $\Delta\varrho/\bar{\varrho} = 0.108$, is $F_i = 0.219$.

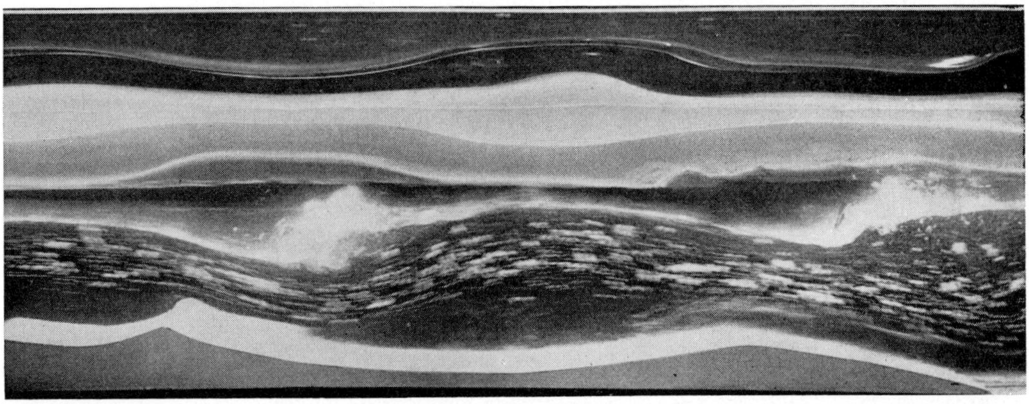

Fig. 12. Multi-fluid flow over barrier. Of the total depth of 26 cm., the lower 13 cm. is a salt-water mixture with density 1.16 at the bottom, and 1.05 at the top of the mixture. Above this are 5 layers of fluids of densities 1.00,0.91, 0.89, 0.84, 0.79. The Froude number based on $h = 13$ cm., $\Delta\varrho/\bar{\varrho} = 0.105$, is $F_i = 0.264$.

Experiments indicate that for a given Froude number based on the height and density difference of the "troposphere", the effect of the added layers is negligible for Froude numbers less than about 0.060. In this range all interfaces are sensibly undisturbed and the flow patterns are not noticeably changed. For moderate values of F_i, as in figure 10, the interfaces remained nearly undisturbed but there is a slight tendency for the flow patterns to resemble those associated with lower Froude numbers in a single-fluid system. (Compare figures 8, 9 and 10.) This tendency is reasonable from a physical viewpoint; for example if the Froude number in figure 10 is based on the total density difference and total depth of all fluids we obtain $F_i = 0.040$ instead of 0.105.

An increase of Froude number leads to a marked deformation of the first interface as in figure 11. The other interfaces remain undisturbed and the flow pattern in the "troposphere" is qualitatively similar to the free-surface flow at this Froude number. Still larger values of F_i cause strong deformations of all internal interfaces. As indicated by figure 12, internal hydraulic jumps begin to appear at some of the interfaces.

We remark in conclusion that there is some indication that a boundary layer separation occurs in the valley both in the prototype and in the model. Certainly the occurrence of east winds near the valley floor implies a separation and the streamline configuration near the ground in figure 1 is very suggestive. The photographs of the model, for example figure 5, show the separation very clearly, just as the fluid in the boundary layer must be entering the region of adverse pressure gradient as it moves toward the first wave crest. In the atmosphere the vorticity of the boundary layer, when carried into the main body of the fluid, may account for the circulation of the type associated with the "rotor cloud" phenomenon.

Acknowledgements

The author wishes to thank Mr. Rudolf Kuster for supervising the experimental observations and designing the equipment. He wishes also to thank Mr. Harold Klieforth for permitting reproduction of two figures in his paper and for supplying the sounding and wind profiles at Merced for January 30, 1952.

REFERENCES

HOLMBOE, J., and KLIEFORTH, H., 1954: *Sierra Wave Project*. Final Report of Contract AF 19(122)—263, University of California at Los Angeles.

KLIEFORTH, H., 1957: Meteorological aspects of the Sierra Wave, *Swiss Aero. Review*, **3**.

LONG, R. R., 1953 a: Some aspects of the flow of stratified fluids. I. A theoretical investigation. *Tellus*, **5**, 42—58.

— 1953 b: A laboratory model resembling the "Bishop-Wave" phenomenon. *BAMS*, **34**, 205—211.

— 1954: Some aspects of the flow of stratified fluids. II. Experiments with a two-fluid system. *Tellus*, **6**, 97—115.

— 1955: Some aspects of the flow of stratified fluids. III. Continuous density gradients. *Tellus*, **7**, 341—357.

— 1956: Models of small-scale atmospheric phenomena involving density stratification. *Fluid Models in Geophysics*, U.S. Government Printing Office, Washington, D.C.

REYNOLDS, O., 1894: On the dynamical theory of incompressible viscous fluids and the determination of the criterion. *Phil. Trans.* A, **186**.

(Manuscript received August 20, 1957)

On Production of Kinetic Energy from Condensation Heating

By HERBERT RIEHL
The University of Chicago

Abstract

Warm anticyclones extending to the high troposphere are usually regarded as "dynamic" anticyclones. In this paper a situation is presented where a warm high was of thermal origin, produced and maintained by release of latent heat of condensation. The interior of the high was filled with cloud and rain; maximum precipitable water content of the air was found in the central parts of the high.

This situation occurred over the Gulf of Mexico and the southeastern United States during September 1957. It is now known that this type of circulation occurs fairly frequently in subtropical and tropical latitudes. Therefore, the warm thermal high should be added to the types of disturbances known to exist in the atmosphere. Such a high affords simple direct means for converting latent heat energy to potential and then to kinetic energy. Calculations of the energy budget of the high showed that, over the four days analyzed, there was little export or import of heat through the boundary. A gradual increase in the intensity of the system was produced by an excess of local heat source at the ocean surface over net outgoing radiation.

The warm thermal high is associated with a "direct" mass circulation: inflow and convergence near the surface, outflow with divergence near the top. From vorticity and balanced wind considerations low pressure should develop at the surface underneath the warm high, and this took place. Thus the mass circulation was directed everywhere toward lower pressure; it released potential and produced kinetic energy. A large export of kinetic energy took place through the boundaries of the system, manifested by formation of two jet streams on its northern and eastern peripheries.

Introduction

A simple model of a thermal atmospheric heat engine may be summarized as follows. Given an area with heat source (radiation or condensation), air converges toward this area at low altitudes and high pressures, and it diverges from it at high altitudes and low pressures. Ascent takes place at higher temperatures than descent, hence potential energy is released. For steady state, continued heating restores the potential energy, because the heating occurs at high pressures relative to the compensatory cooling, which will be the net radiation cooling of the atmosphere at large.

Applying the theorem of conservation of potential vorticity, the inflowing current will develop cyclonic rotation and the outflowing current anticyclonic rotation. If the system is large enough so that quasi-gradient balance of forces is maintained, the pressure at the center of the heated area will be low relative to its surroundings on the horizontal plane in the layer of inflow; it will be high relative to the surroundings in the layer of outflow. The horizontal motion will be directed everywhere from high to low pressure, and this results in generation of kinetic energy. The efficiency of the heat engine in converting heat to kinetic energy may be defined as the ratio of kinetic energy produced by pressure forces to the strength of the heat source, condensation heating in the case to be considered here.

While features of the general circulation such as whole trade wind cell and the monsoons bear resemblance to the scheme outlined, cases of simple heat engines have not been observed in the daily or secondary disturbances of the tropics apart from hurricanes. Such circulations should exist in the tropics where most condensation heating occurs, as counterpart to the kinetic energy releasing cyclones of middle and high latitudes. Most evidence, however, has been discouraging as brought out earlier by the writer (RIEHL, 1948). Even the equatorial trough zone does not have a warm core structure everywhere (SIMPSON, 1947). Precipitation in the tropics tends to occur in and around cold-core troughs or cyclones in the upper troposphere, while the upper anticyclones are the well known "dynamic" highs where the high temperatures are produced by subsidence. This situation introduces considerable difficulties (cf. RIEHL, 1954, p. 247 ff.) because all these systems are "indirect" circulations which, for genesis and maintenance, must depend on energy releases elsewhere. As yet the energy cycle maintaining such systems has remained intractable.

The increasing amount of upper-air data collected in the tropics since the 1940's, especially the advent of rawin observations, has confirmed the frequent association of precipitation with cold-core disturbances. Occasionally, however, other types of patterns have also appeared. Some years ago the writer first published a description of a case where condensation heating may have contributed materially to the building of an upper anticyclone (RIEHL and BURGNER, 1950). This type of association has also been suspected in other cases observed since that time, but documentation was too fragmentary to warrant detailed inquiry. It is only with expansion of the raob-rawin network over the United States in recent years, and establishment of a large number of upper-air stations around the Caribbean Sea and Gulf of Mexico by the National Hurricane Research Project of the United States Weather Bureau, that a minimal amount of information has become available for quantitative evaluation of energy cycles.

It is the purpose of this paper to demonstrate the existence of a simple heat engine, as described initially, for a specific situation and then to calculate the energy transformations executed by this heat engine as best possible. It must be emphasized that the latter objective cannot be carried out perfectly with existing data, and that therefore the present work must be regarded as no more than a first attempt to effect a transition from the qualitative to the quantitative stage in tropical weather forecasting. Nevertheless, the mere existence of the circulation to be described—as nearly a "prime mover" as one may hope to find—is believed to warrant presentation of the following case history.

The Weather Situation, September 15—18, 1957

Analysis of tropical circulations over the oceans has always been handicapped due to lack of station networks; it has seldom been possible to obtain more than a passing and fragmentary view of any development one wished to follow. In this respect the Gulf of Mexico offers superior opportunities. While there are no weather ship stations inside this body of water, it is at least ringed by a sizable number of upper-air stations (fig. 1). The Gulf is sufficiently small that gross aspects of the weather situation over the water are fairly well described by this ring, which has a nearly elliptical shape as will be called the "Gulf ellipse".

Surface: Figures 2—22 describe the situation observed during the period September 15—18, 1957. Only 24-hour continuity is shown. At the surface we observe at first a wave disturbance in the easterlies in the eastern part of the Gulf (fig. 2); this disturbance had moved westward into this area from the Atlantic and Caribbean during the preceding day. Shortly after our map time a cyclonic center began to develop in the trough and drift north-northwest with the prevailing tropospheric current. This center was well defined on the next day (fig. 3); it is the principal thermal cyclone of the case.

Proximity to the coast prevented further deepening of this center, but on September 17 (fig. 4) another low appeared in the southwestern Gulf. Data over Central America confirm that

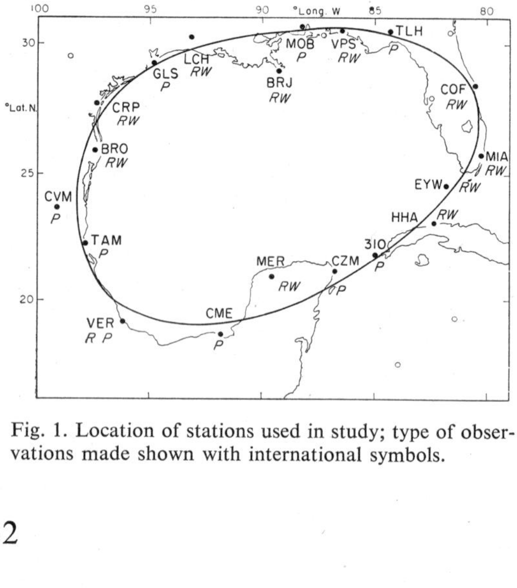

Fig. 1. Location of stations used in study; type of observations made shown with international symbols.

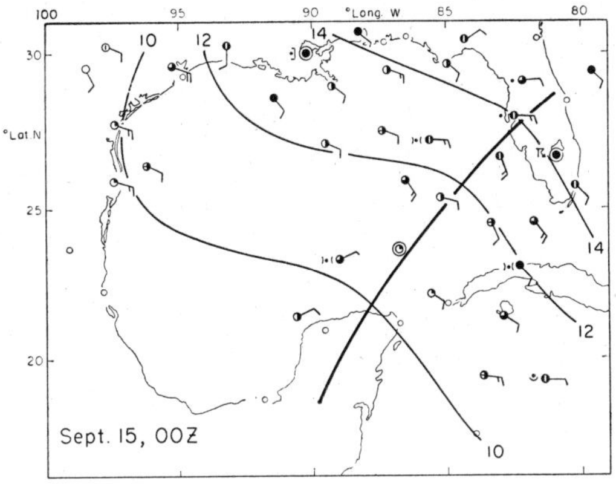

Fig. 2. 1000-mb chart, Sept. 15, 1957, OOZ. Contours in tens feet. Heavy line denotes axis of wave trough. International weather and sky symbols used.

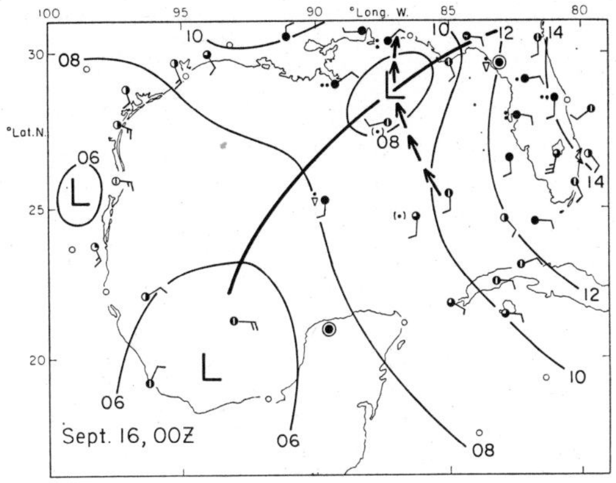

Fig. 3. 1000-mb chart, Sept. 16, 1957, OOZ.

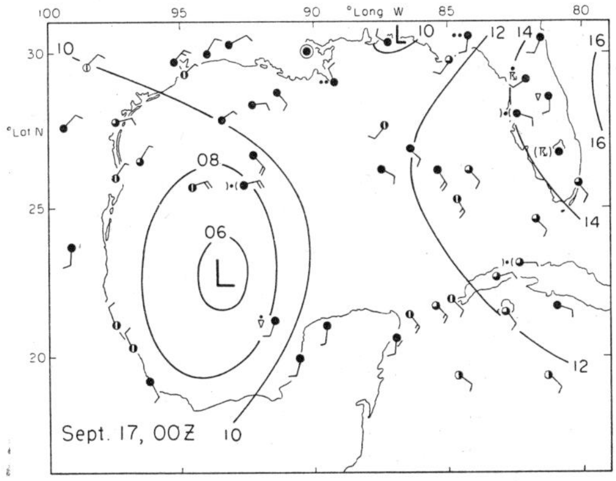

Fig. 4. 1000-mb chart, Sept. 17, 1957, OOZ.

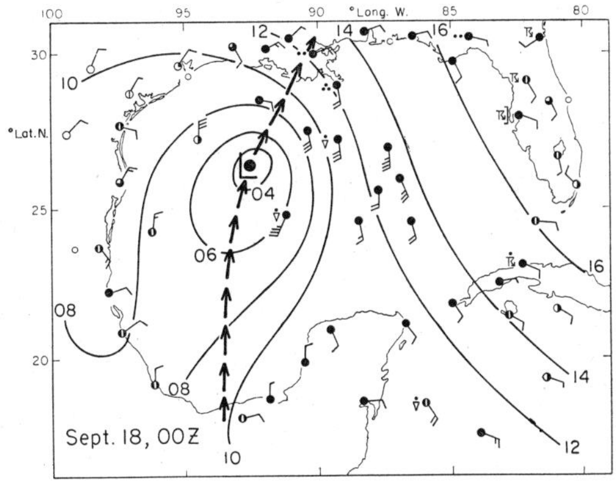

Fig. 5. 1000-mb chart, Sept. 18, 1957, OOZ.

this second center had been drawn northward across Central America from the equatorial trough zone of the Pacific. It must be regarded as a feature extraneous to the initial development of the simple heat engine over the Gulf, which was then brought in contact with it. This combination at once suggests the possibility of hurricane formation. Indeed, on September 18 (fig. 5) the center had developed into a tropical storm with strongest winds above 50 knots. The hurricane, however, failed to materialize, and the disturbance entered the coast near New Orleans as a rather weak storm.

850-mb: All upper-air observations around the Gulf have been reproduced at 850 mb and higher levels. It must be noted that the radiosonde observations at several stations were subject to systematic errors; based on experience, these errors have been adjusted in the analysis. Initially, we observe a marked trough over the eastern Gulf (fig. 6) above the position of the surface trough line. The current passing through this trough had even larger amplitude on the preceding day, when the disturbance extended from the Bahamas across Cuba to the Caribbean. At that time the 850-mb trough also was much better developed than the surface trough, suggesting a cold-core structure of the wave as normally encountered at low levels in the easterlies. The change from September 14 to 15 indicates that the wave structure was not steady, but that transition to a warm-core system was taking place, as evidenced also by the formation of a surface center during September 15.

Present on September 15 also was cyclonic turning of the winds over the southwestern Gulf.

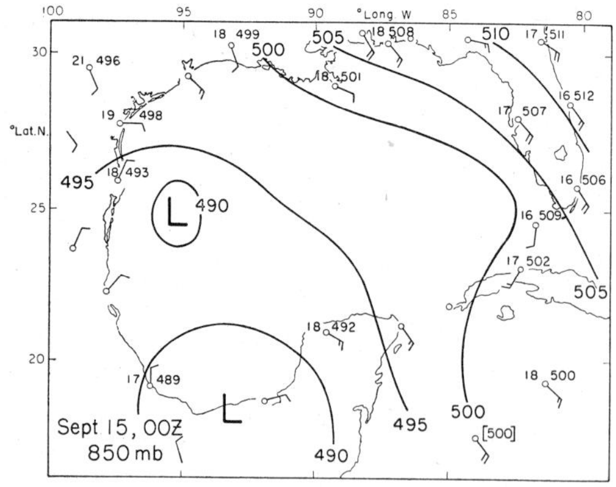

Fig. 6. 850-mb chart, Sept. 15, 1957, OOZ. Heights in tens feet, temperatures in deg. C.

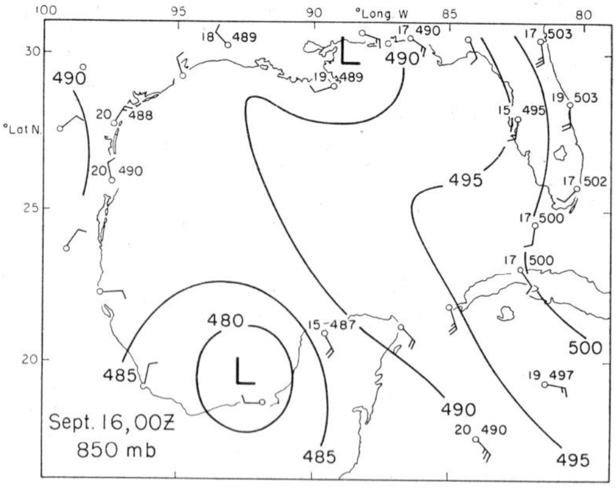

Fig. 7. 850-mb chart, Sept. 16, 1957, OOZ.

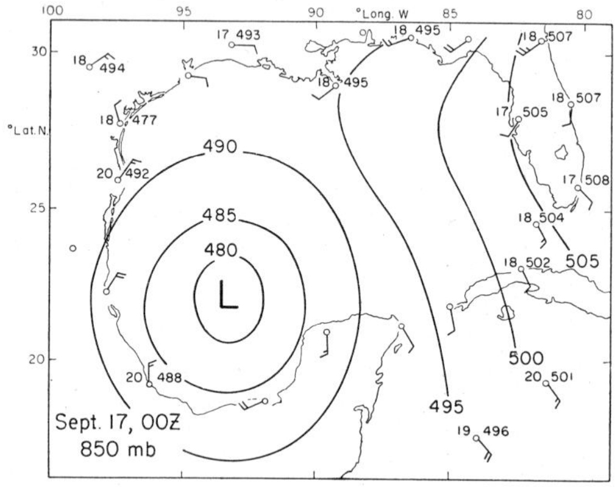

Fig. 8. 850-mb chart, Sept. 17, 1957, OOZ.

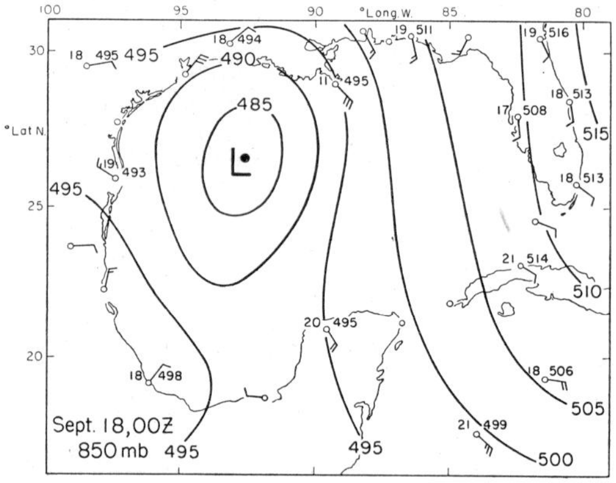

Fig. 9. 850-mb chart, Sept. 18, 1957, OOZ.

On the next day (fig. 7) a low pressure center clearly had entered this area, as already noted on the surface analysis. The trough in the northeastern Gulf weakened from the preceding day. As shown by the Burrwood observation (BRJ in fig. 1), the 850-mb trough was situated well to the north of the position of the surface low, indicating further warm-core development. The amplitude of the trough over Florida also had greatly diminished.

The map for September 17 (fig. 8) is spectacular. Strong cyclonic growth has occurred in the western Gulf as the disturbance located there came into contact with the thermal heat engine over the Gulf. In its gross features the map resembles that of June 25, 1957 when formation of a hurricane of great intensity ensued. On the last day of the series (fig. 9) the cyclone approached the northern Gulf coast under the steering influence of a strengthening Bermuda high to the east.

250-mb: The preceding charts outline the low-level circulation. As frequently emphasized by the writer (cf. RIEHL, 1954, p. 253) the tropical troposphere tends to be divided into two portions, each with a distinct circulation regime. The transition occurs near 500 mb, where winds are often weak and confused. This was true in the present case; hence we shall omit the middle troposphere and pass on directly to the high troposphere. The level for presentation will be 250 mb, chosen because B-47 aircraft operated by the National Hurricane Research Project was flying near this pressure surface and supplying critical information over otherwise uncharted areas.

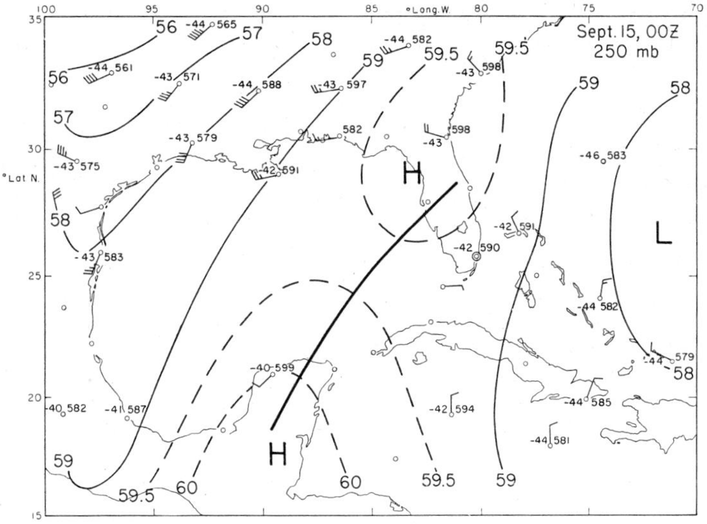

Fig. 10. 250-mb chart, Sept. 15, 1957, OOZ. Contours in hundreds feet, base 30,000 feet.

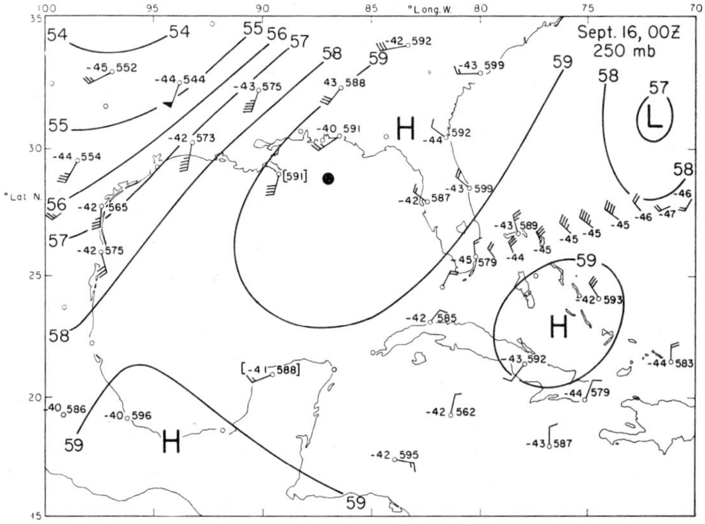

Fig. 11. 250-mb chart, Sept. 16, 1957, OOZ. Heavy dot denotes surface center.

On September 15 a ridge extending from the Yucatan peninsula to the southeastern United States was already in evidence (fig. 10). The surface trough line has also been entered. It was situated almost directly under the upper ridge after westward displacement from the area of cyclonic circulation at 250 mb in the west-central Atlantic. The map, therefore, shows the period of organization of the heat engine, brought about by relative motion of the low-level disturbance traveling under the influence of the easterlies to a position underneath the high-tropospheric ridge. Deepening in the low-level trough began shortly after the superposition took effect.

On the next day (fig. 11) the wind circulation about the upper high increased considerably. While the data do not permit precise drawing of the contours, there can be little doubt that air was crossing the 250-mb contours toward lower pressure on both sides of the high, and that this movement represented the outflow of mass funneled upward in the convergence zone attending the surface center. Since this center with its heavy precipitation area was situated almost

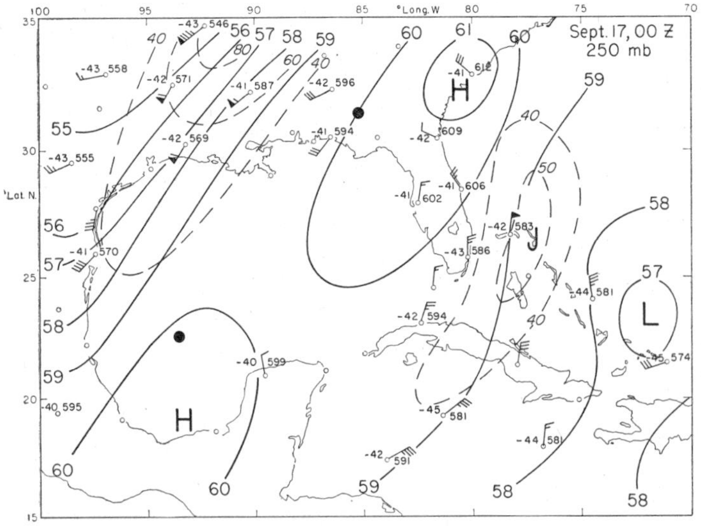

Fig. 12. 250-mb chart, Sept. 17, 1957, OOZ. Includes isotachs (dashed, in knots).

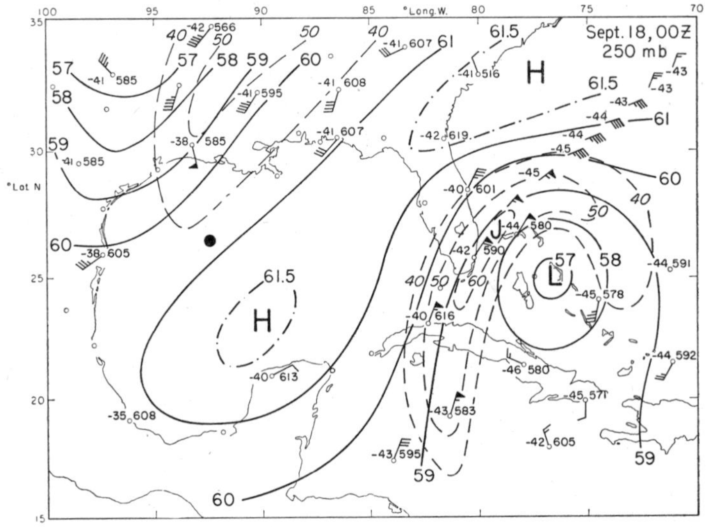

Fig. 13. 250-mb chart, Sept. 18, 1957, OOZ. Includes isotachs and B-47 aircraft flight data east of Florida.

centrally underneath the upper high, the thermal heat engine was fully developed at this time.

By September 17 (fig. 12), continued building of the upper anticyclone resulted in the appearance of two jet streams which developed on eastern and western margins of the heat engine. Even more spectacular are figs. 13 and 14. The cyclone in the western Gulf acted to strengthen the southwesterly jet stream, with strong movement of air toward lower pressure evident in fig. 13, especially at Lake Charles (LCH). In addition, the eastern jet stream was reinforced by westward advance of a large cold low from the Atlantic.

The thickness field for the layer 850—250 mb (figs. 15—18) reveals a gradual increase in internal energy associated with the growth of the thermal heat engine. Both surface centers have been entered with heavy dots in the thickness charts. They were situated along the axis of warmest air, definitely establishing their warm-core nature.

Total moisture charts: Formerly, the moisture element of the radiosonde instrument was considered too unreliable to warrant computations

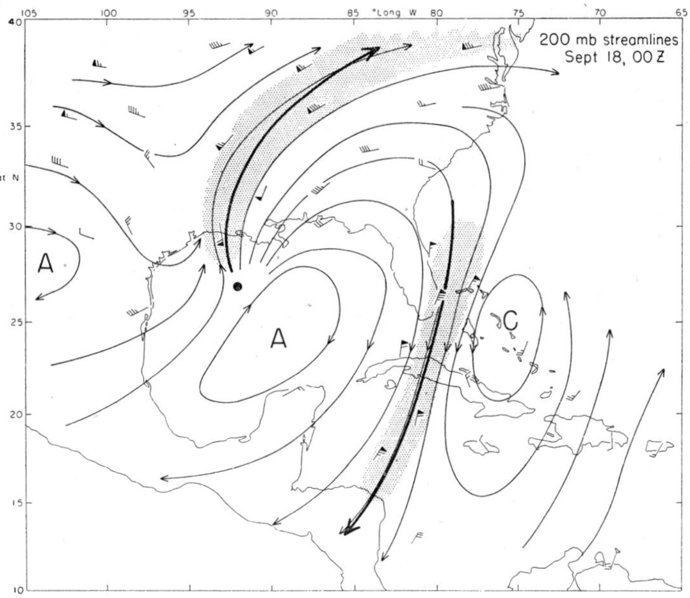

Fig. 14. Streamlines at 200 mb, Sept. 18, 1957, OOZ. Area with winds above 60 knots shaded.

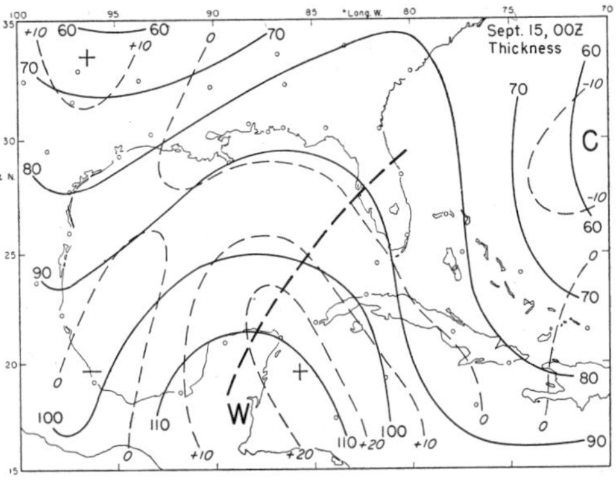

Fig. 15. Thickness 850—250 mb (tens feet, base 30,000 feet), Sept. 15, 1957, OOZ. 24-hour thickness changes (tens feet) dashed.

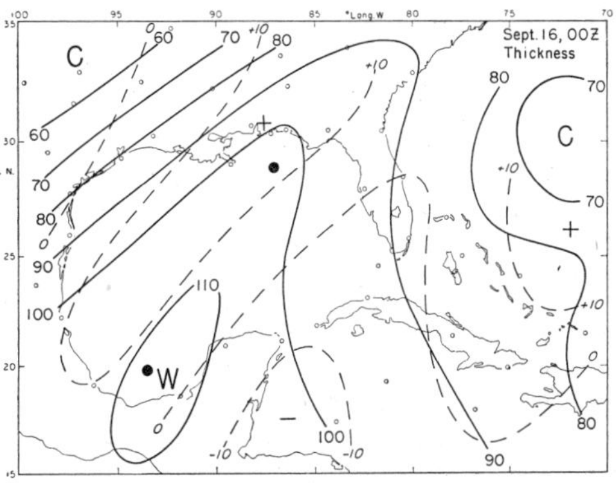

Fig. 16. Thickness 850—250 mb, Sept. 16, 1957, OOZ.

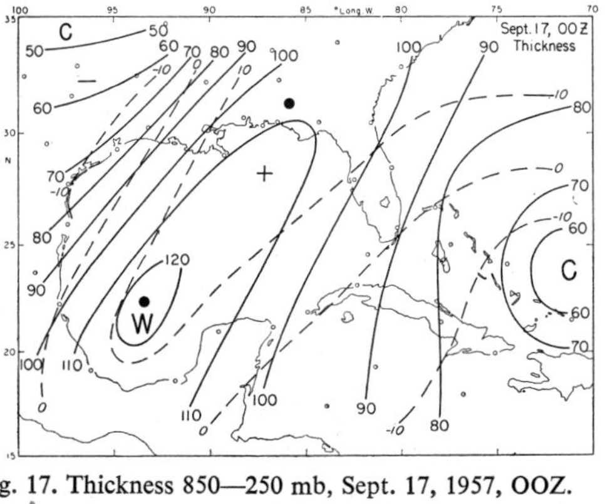

Fig. 17. Thickness 850—250 mb, Sept. 17, 1957, OOZ.

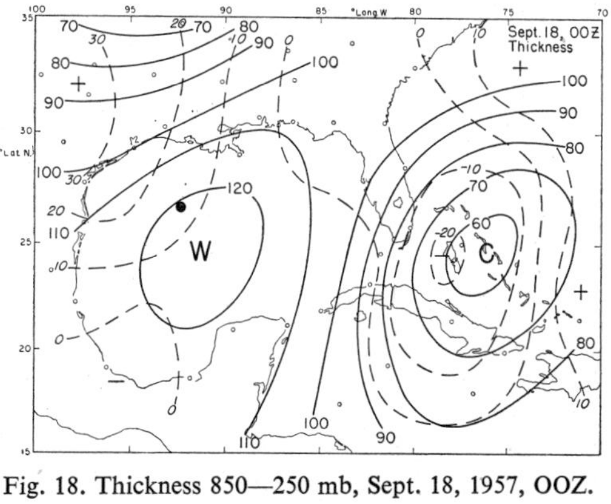

Fig. 18. Thickness 850—250 mb, Sept. 18, 1957, OOZ.

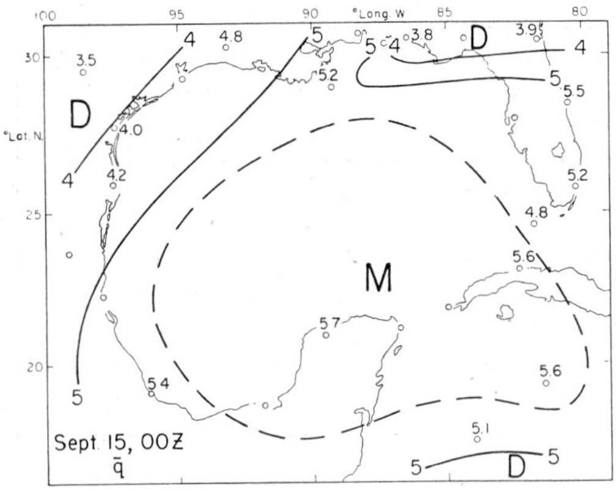

Fig. 19. Total moisture content (g/cm²), Sept. 15, 1957, OOZ.

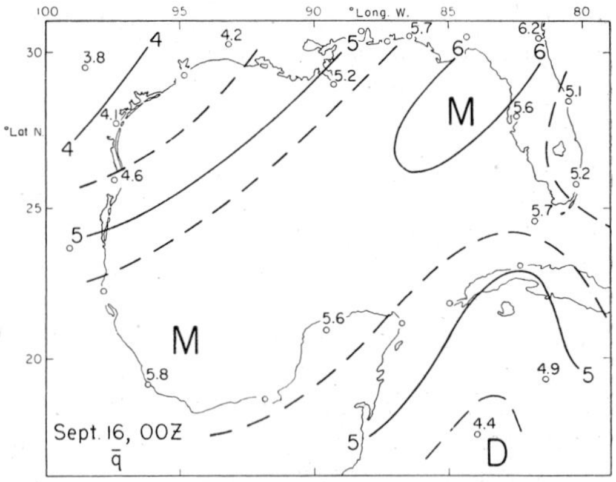

Fig. 20. Total moisture content, Sept. 16, 1957, OOZ.

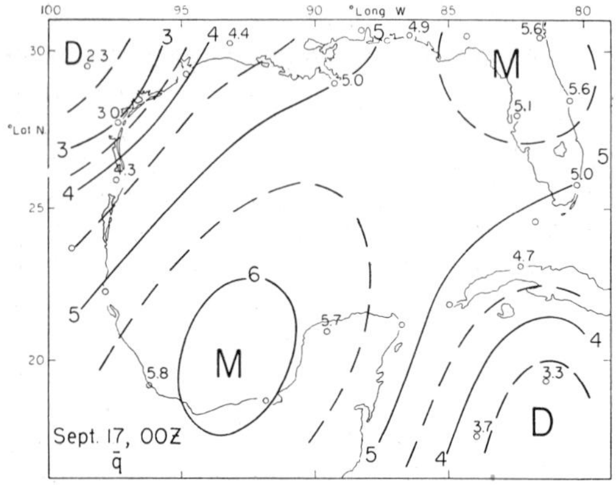

Fig. 21. Total moisture content, Sept. 17, 1957, OOZ.

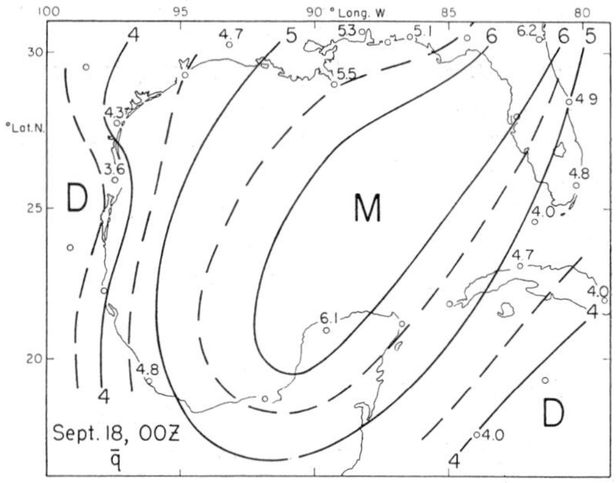

Fig. 22. Total moisture content, Sept. 18, 1957, OOZ.

of total precipitable water content of the air. Further, one might expect that, on account of small-scale moisture gradients in the tropics, the total moisture determined by any particular ascent would be unrepresentative for analysis of a station network with spacing of stations as shown in fig. 1. Nevertheless, recent experimentation with total moisture charts in tropical Atlantic and Pacific has brought out that in general the patterns are broad-scale, that they can be traced readily from map to map, and that the time sequence of total moisture at one station generally follows a regular course. For these reasons the analyses of figs. 19—22 are considered quite reliable. Since a high correlation between total moisture and cloudiness and weather may be expected, the total moisture charts provide a good measure of the weather distribution over tropical areas. Previously, owing to the showery nature of rainfall and local influences over land and at coastlines, it had been difficult in many cases to obtain reliable knowledge of the location of disturbed and undisturbed areas.

After the first day, moisture gradients were strong and well organized over the Gulf area. Isolines almost paralleled the 250-mb contours and the 850—250-mb thickness lines. The axes of high temperature and high moisture coincided, *revealing clearly that the high temperatures were derived from condensation heating*. This is the final piece of evidence needed to establish the existence of a thermal heat engine. It is of more than casual interest that the moisture gradient on both sides of the wet area increased with time, indicating subsidence in the periphery. Further, since the moisture decreased from the stationary maximum over the Gulf not only toward northwest but also *toward* southeast—with low-level air motion into the Gulf *from* southeast— it is evident that the deep moist layer over the Gulf was not produced by horizontal advection from the equatorial zone but by low-level convergence in the inflowing southeasterly stream. As stressed earlier by the writer (RIEHL, 1954, pp. 51—53), dynamic features of the wind field govern the observed gradients of temperature and moisture above the mixed subcloud layer.

Mass Balance

While it was a rather simple task to demonstrate the existence of the heat engine qualitatively, quantitative determination of the energy transformations is difficult. The only possible approach is by means of line integrals, and for these only one line of stations is available, the Gulf ellipse of fig. 1. It would be preferable to develop coordinate systems fitted with respect to the upper anticyclone, and also to place the origin of polar coordinate systems in the two cyclones. None of these things can be done unless the analyses of figs. 2—22 and of other constant pressure surfaces are considered sufficiently reliable for mass flow, divergence, cross-isobar flow, etc. This is not the case, and the only quantitative use of the analyses will be determination of total energy and moisture inside the volume bounded by the ellipse.

We place a coordinate system s, n with velocity components c_s, c_n along the ellipse. The s-axis is parallel to the ellipse; cyclonic c_s is considered positive; c_n is normal to c_s and taken positive inward. Quantities averaged around the ellipse will be denoted with a bar, deviations from such means with primes. At first we shall compute the mean circulations $\bar{c}_n$, $\bar{c}_s$ for each day. Since $\bar{c}_n$ is the mean ageostrophic indraft or outdraft, the computation is quite critical. This important component is quite small, and its integrated value around the ellipse and from the surface to the top of the circulation cell must vanish when calculated to the nearest 1/10 mps. The reason for this lies in the fact that the net change of mass within the ellipse is very small percentually (one tenth of one per cent of total mass), hence will be treated as zero.

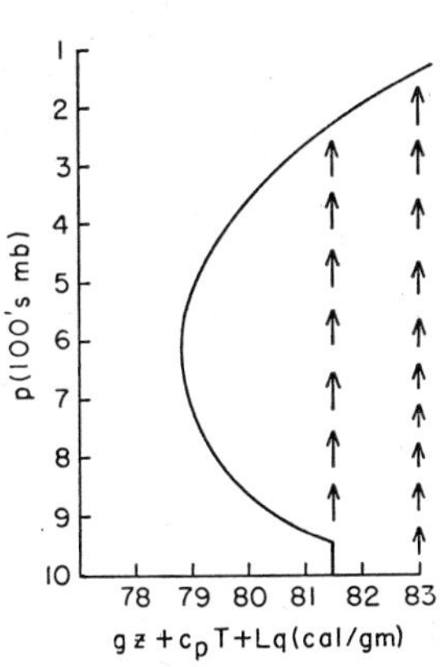

Fig. 23. Average distribution of total heat content in Gulf area during period as function of pressure. Arrows denote adiabatic ascent at mean and extreme heat content observed at surface.

Of course, $\bar{c}_n$ and $\bar{c}_s$ as such are not of great significance for the present problem because the boundary is not a special one chosen from physical considerations but from geography. The interest resides mainly in total energy fluxes; to obtain these, the transport by the mean ageostrophic circulation, possibly a large term, must nevertheless be calculable.

The top of the circulation cell is defined as the lowest pressure to which air can penetrate from the surface through buoyancy following the parcel ascent. Studies made by the Thunderstorm Project (BRAHAM, 1952) and recent work on the heat balance in the equatorial trough zone (RIEHL and MALKUS, 1958) have shown that much of the net ascent in convective clouds takes place in cumulonimbus cores protected by surrounding cloud matter from entrainment of unsaturated air during ascent. Hence the parcel ascent really occurs; it plays a considerable role in establishing temperatures and heights of isobaric surfaces in the upper troposphere where the rising mass spreads laterally. Given the surface properties of the air and the mean vertical sounding, the top of the circulation cell can be found from a thermodynamic chart. Alternately, one can compute the vertical distribution of heat and potential energy of the atmosphere and find the pressure to which air with the observed surface properties can rise. This ascent can be represented on a diagram of $Q = gz + c_pT + Lq$ against pressure (fig. 23). Here, g is the acceleration of gravity, z height, c_p specific heat of air at constant pressure, T temperature, L latent heat of condensation, and q specific humidity. The parcel ascent is represented by a straight line on this diagram. At the surface (subscript zero) the potential energy is nil, so that $Q_0 = (c_pT+Lq)_0$. Two parcel ascents, at the mean and extreme values of Q_0, have been entered in fig. 23, together with the average distribution of Q against pressure for the period. These ascents terminate near 225 mb and 150 mb, and this outlines the height range for the cumulonimbus anvils. There was no

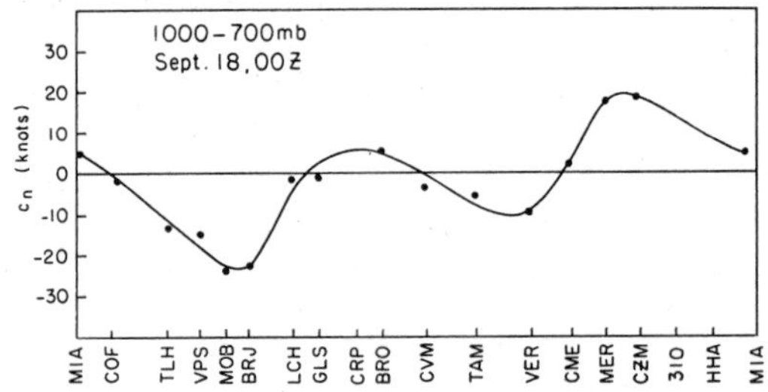

Fig. 24. Wind component normal to Gulf ellipse (knots) for layer 1000—700 mb, plotted as function of distance around Gulf on Sept. 18, 1957, OOZ.

indication of strong variations in the mean sounding over the period which would have permitted the top of the convective layer to undergo large height changes. Therefore, the 150-mb surface will be taken as the top of the tropospheric circulation cell. All integration with respect to pressure will be made from 1,000 to 150 mb, neglecting the mass at pressures higher than 1,000 mb. It should be noted that there is no requirement for $\bar{c}_n$ to vanish at 150 mb as there may be stratospheric cells higher up; these cannot be analyzed, as the frequency of soundings diminished rapidly above 200—150 mb.

The method one would like to use in computing $\bar{c}_n$ is to average c_n at all rawin stations for each reporting level and then to draw a curve of $\bar{c}_n$ so obtained against pressure. Unfortunately, this approach does not work. Since this study deals with daily and not time-averaged maps, details of the flow patterns must be taken into account, such as the jet streams in figs. 12—14 which may be centered between observing stations. Further, there is a large gap in the rawins between Brownsville (BRO) and Merida (MER). Two more rawin stations are needed: at Tampico (TAM) and Vera Cruz (VER). If these were available, one could readily construct vertical cross sections of c_n around the ellipse, read c_n at evenly spaced grid points, and obtain mass balance with little need for adjustment. On account of the data gap, various techniques were tried out. The results shown in figs. 25—26 were obtained as follows.

At first c_n was averaged with respect to pressure in layers of 100-mb thickness (and over 50 mb from 200 to 150 mb) at all stations, including pilot balloon stations. In order to minimize the danger of including sea breeze effects, computations were made for the 0000 Z (1800—1900 local time) observations. Where data was missing, however, soundings six and even twelve hours earlier or later were used. With these auxiliary winds and a few extrapolations to 10,000 feet, c_n was available for all stations on each day for the layer 1,000—700 mb. This quantity was plotted on a diagram, with c_n as ordinate, and distance around the ellipse as abscissa. It is seen in fig. 24 that a smooth curve can be fitted closely to all data points; from this curve the mass circulation in the layer 1,000—700 mb may be considered as well established.

Next, all values of c_n averaged over layers of 100-mb thickness were plotted and analyzed on cross sections with pressure on a linear scale as ordinate and distance around the ellipse as abscissa. Values were read at 20 evenly spaced grid points in each layer from the analyses, and averaged. As expected, mass balance was not fully obtained. Adjustment of the analyses was then made in the data gap along the Mexican coast with qualitative aid from the upper-air charts. Undoubtedly, there remains an arbitrary element in the upper portions of the profiles of fig. 25; the original aim to proceed on a purely numerical basis could not be carried through except for the layer 1,000—700 mb. Quantitative procedures will become possible in the future if the number of upper-air stations will continue

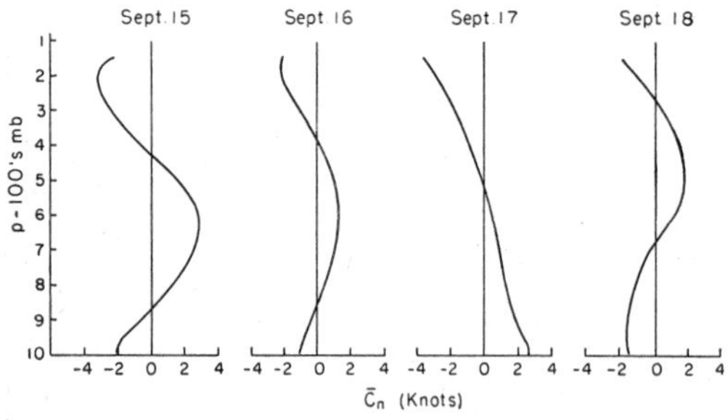

Fig. 25. Profiles of mean ageostrophic mass circulation $\bar{c}_n$ (knots).

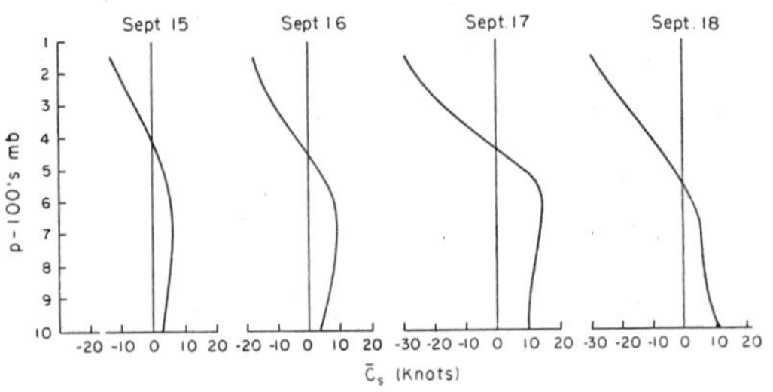

Fig. 26. Profiles of mean tangential component $\bar{c}_s$ (knots).

to increase as in recent years; as stated initially, the present effort is only a first attempt. In spite of their shortcomings, the mass flow curves of fig. 25 are considered to be sufficiently reliable to permit calculation of heat and energy fluxes through the ellipse.

According to fig. 25, outflow of variable intensity took place in the high troposphere on all days, also inflow in the lower troposphere on the first three days, as is consistent with the picture of the thermal heat engine. A remarkable reversal followed on September 18 (see also fig. 24). The distribution of c_s (fig. 26) shows cyclonic circulation in low and middle troposphere and anticyclonic circulation, increasing with time, in the high troposphere.

Balance of Internal, Potential, and Latent Heat Energy

Energy equations are treated in numerous textbooks. Therefore, no derivations will be offered here, only the final expressions used for calculation. The general equations contain all energy forms. As is well known, however, the terms containing kinetic energy are one or two orders of magnitude smaller than the other terms. Therefore, the energy balance will at first be computed neglecting kinetic energy. Later a separate kinetic energy budget will be determined.

Assuming no vertical motion at 150 mb and integrating over the boundary of the Gulf ellipse, the energy equation then takes the form

$$\frac{\partial}{\partial t}(I+P+M) = \iint (gz+c_pT+Lq)c_n ds\frac{dp}{g} + Q_e + Q_s + R - R^*\frac{\partial}{\partial t}\iint T\cdot dA\frac{dp}{g}. \qquad (1)$$

Here, I, P, and M are internal, potential, and latent heat energy integrated over the ellipse; p is pressure, R^* the gas constant for air, and t time. The heat source (S) within the ellipse

$$S = Q_e + Q_s + R \qquad (2)$$

consists of latent (Q_e) and sensible (Q_s) heat exchange between air and ocean, and the net tropospheric radiation R. Equation (1) may be subdivided as follows:

$$\frac{\partial}{\partial t}(I+P) = \iint (c_pT+gz)c_n ds\frac{dp}{g} + Q_s + L\pi + R - R^*\frac{\partial}{\partial t}\iint T\cdot dA\frac{dp}{g}, \qquad (3)$$

$$\frac{\partial M}{\partial t} = \iint Lqc_n ds\frac{dp}{g} + Q_e - L\pi, \qquad (4)$$

where π is precipitation. Equation (4) permits separate determination of the moisture budget.

As shown in textbooks $I+P = -p_T\tilde{Z}_TA + c_p\int TdA\frac{dp}{g}$, where A denotes area, $\sim$ averaging with respect to area, and the integration is extended from the surface to the pressure surface p_T (top). The first term in this expression is negligible, so that $I+P$ could be determined readily from thickness charts for the layer 1,000—150 mb. Strictly, the dry temperature should be used, whereas the thickness is obtained from the virtual temperature. Since the total moisture was fairly constant through the period and only time derivatives are wanted for evaluating Eqs. (1)—(4), use of thickness charts does not introduce appreciable error. The thickness and also the total moisture content were tabulated on a 22-point grid spread evenly over the interior of the ellipse and averaged. Then the integrated values were plotted against time, curves drawn, and the time derivative determined from the slope of the curves.

Transport terms: For the transport of c_pT+gz and of Lq through the boundary, it was necessary to analyze these quantities on a vertical cross section around the Gulf just as in the case of the c_n component, and then read values from the analyses for the same grid points that were used to determine c_n. This proved a relatively easy task because Vera Cruz (VER) has a daily radiosonde observation, hence there was no large data gap on the western boundary of the ellipse. At first c_pT+gz and Lq were averaged vertically over layers of 100-mb thickness for each sounding, and then the mean of all ten radiosonde stations (Key West omitted) was computed for each layer to obtain $c_p\overline{T}+g\overline{z}$ and $L\overline{q}$. Stations were sufficiently evenly spaced that no further adjustment proved necessary. Then the deviations $(c_pT+gz)'$ and Lq' were computed at each station for each layer and plotted on cross sections. After analysis, the products $\overline{c_n(c_pT+gz)'}$ and $\overline{c_nLq'}$ yielded the heat and moisture transport by the asymmetrical part of the circulation, the products $\overline{c}_n(c_p\overline{T}+g\overline{z})$ and $\overline{c}_nL\overline{q}$ the transports by the mean ageostrophic circulation.

Heat sources and sinks: A mean daily cooling rate of 1° C/day was assumed for the net outgoing radiation, following previous calculations of the radiational heat loss in the tropics. Day-to-day variations could not be assessed. Q_e was computed from the formula

$$Q_e = 1.71 \times 10^{-6} L \int (q_w - q_a) V_0 dA, \quad (5)$$

where q_w and q_a are specific humidity at ocean surface and ship's deck level, and V_0 is wind speed at ship's deck level. This formula, derived from the turbulence theory, has been applied, for instance, by the writer (RIEHL *et al*, 1951) for calculation of the evaporation in the northeast trade of the Pacific Ocean. The formula has shortcomings which were discussed in the earlier paper and will not be reviewed here. The quantities q_w and q_a were obtained by plotting for the four-day period, on 6-hourly charts, all dewpoints and sea surface temperatures reported by ships. Variations were irregular, so that finally all dewpoints and all sea surface temperatures were combined on one map each. Figure 27 contains the plot of the ocean temperatures. Variation appeared to be random, hence a single value for the mean surface temperature of the Gulf was computed; this amounted to 85° F, a very high value, which exceeded the seasonal mean by 2° F. Distribution of dewpoints was also irregular; the mean dewpoint temperature was 77° F. Because of the lack of determinable gradients in sea surface temperature and dewpoint, $(q_w—q_a)V_0$ in Eq. (5) may be replaced by $(\tilde{q}_w — \tilde{q}_a)\tilde{V}_0$. From the temperature data $\tilde{q}_w — \tilde{q}_a = 6.5$ g/kg, a large difference. $\tilde{V}_0$ ranged from 5.1 mps on September 16 to 9.8 mps on September 18 when the tropical cyclone reached peak intensity. With these high winds and the large $\tilde{q}_w — \tilde{q}_a$ the evaporation was also large, ranging from 0.51 to 0.98 cm/day. Since the mean seasonal evaporation has been estimated near 0.5 cm/day, the first of these values is average, but the second value is exceptional and clearly related to the map situation. It is seen that large interdiurnal variations in heat source may be expected in the tropics with varying wind conditions.

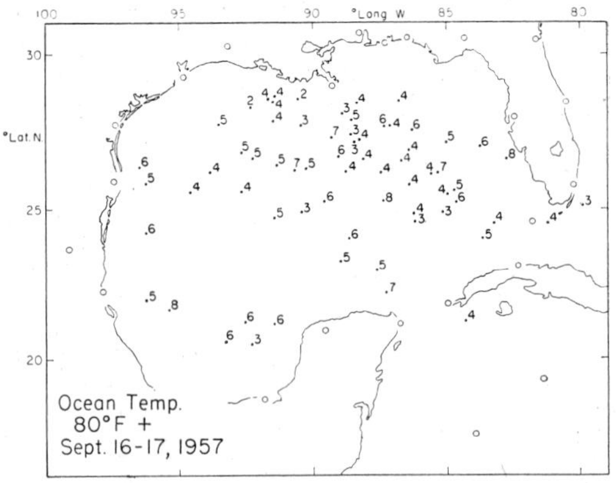

Fig. 27. Sea surface temperatures Sept. 16—17, 1957; departures from 80° F.

The sensible heat transfer Q_s, formerly considered to be a very small fraction of Q_e, has been assessed by HOUGHTON (1954) as 40 per cent of Q_e for the annual heat balance of the globe. RIEHL and MALKUS (1958) found that the same ratio holds for the equatorial trough zone alone. These estimates apply only to averages over long periods and large areas. For want of better information, however, the ratio of 40 per cent will be applied to the present Gulf case. Since Q_s depends on wind stirring, and following RIEHL and MALKUS (1958), on the amount of cumulonimbus downdrafts, it is plausible that the sensible heat exchange between sea and air increased materially over the period analyzed.

With the assumptions and procedures as just discussed, the heat source was computed for each day, with results as given in Table 1. To the extent that this table may be accepted as valid, large fluctuations in the heat source occurred, corresponding to progressive organization of the whole heat engine and development of the tropical storm.

Heat budget: Table 2 shows the heat energy budget determined from evaluation of all terms in Eq. (1); the residual imbalance is brought out through comparison of the local change of $I + P + M$ determined from the curve and computed from advection and heat source. While there may be a systematic overvaluation of the source, the result as a whole appears fairly satisfactory. It must be remembered that rather crude methods had to be employed for evaluation of all terms; they may all contribute to the

Table 1. Heat Sources and Sinks (10^{14} cal/sec)

Date (Sept.)	$\tilde{V}_0$ m/sec	$\tilde{q}_w - \tilde{q}_a$ (g/kg)	Evap. (cm/day)	Q_e	Q_s	$Q_s + Q_e$	R	Net Heat Source
15	6.2	6.5	.62	.68	.27	.95	—.38	.57
16	5.1	6.5	.51	.56	.22	.78	—.38	.40
17	7.0	6.5	.70	.77	.31	1.08	—.38	.70
18	9.8	6.5	.98	1.08	.43	1.51	—.38	1.13

Table 2. Heat Energy Budget (10^{14} cal/sec)
(evaluation of Equation 1)

Date (Sept.)	$\frac{\partial}{\partial t}\cdot(I+P+M)$ from curve	$\frac{\partial}{\partial t}\cdot(I+P+M)$ from right side	=	Advection	+ Source	$-R^*\frac{\partial}{\partial t}\iint T\,dA\,\frac{dp}{g}$
15	.74	.91		.34	.57	—.12
16	—.19	—.34		—.74	.40	.00
17	.45	.87		.17	.70	—.09
18	.66	1.33		.20	1.13	—.23
Total 15-18	1.66	2.77		—.03	2.80	—.44

Table 3. Latent heat Energy Budget (10^{14} cal/sec)

Date (Sept.)	Local change (from curve)	=	Advection by mass circ.	+ Advection by asymmetries	$+ Q_e$	$- L\pi$ (residual)	Precip. cm/day
15	.34		.29	.60	.68	—1.23	1.10
16	—.19		.12	—.34	.56	— .54	.49
17	.14		.97	.08	.77	—1.68	1.50
18	—.14		—.26	.13	1.08	—1.09	.99
Total 15—18	.15		1.12	.47	3.09	—4.54	1.02

Table 4. Budget of $c_pT + gz$ (10^{14} cal/sec)*

Date (Sept.)	$\frac{\partial}{\partial t}(I+P)$ from curve	$\frac{\partial}{\partial t}(I+P)$ from right side	=	Advection by mass circ.	+ Advection by asymmetries	$+ R$	$+ Q_s$	$+ L\pi$	$-R^*\frac{\partial}{\partial t}\iint T\,dA\,\frac{dp}{g}$
15	.40	.45		— .70	.15	— .38	.27	1.23	—.12
16	0	— .15		— .32	—.20	— .38	.22	.53	.00
17	.31	.64		—1.14	.26	— .38	.31	1.68	—.09
18	.80	1.24		.33	0	— .38	.43	1.09	—.23
Total 15—18	1.51	2.18		—1.83	.21	—1.52	1.23	4.54	—.44

* If Q_s had been computed with the classical method, the difference between $\frac{\partial}{\partial t}(I+P)$ from the curve and from the right side of the table would be materially reduced.

residual imbalance. The main result is that the net heat exchange through the boundary was nearly zero, so that the entire build-up of $I + P +$ $+ M$ over the Gulf took place by means of the local heat source.

Tables 3 and 4 show the budgets of M and of $I + P$ separately. Of these, Table 3 is considered most reliable because the moisture exchange takes place in the low levels. The moisture balance is hardly affected by errors in drawing the c_n-profiles in the upper troposphere. Therefore, all unbalance of Table 2 has been placed into Table 4.

The moisture budget contains the precipitation as residual that could not be measured. Because of the large size of the Gulf, one should expect only moderate precipitation depths in the mean over the whole area. This requirement is satisfied, as seen from the last column in Table 3. It is of interest that the computed rainfall was highest on the two days when the cyclones were developing. Precipitation decreased sharply on September 16 when the first cyclone was entering land, and again on September 18 in spite of the tropical storm. This result may be attributed to the reversal of the whole circulation cell on that day (fig. 25), which led to subsidence and drying everywhere except in the immediate vicinity of the cyclone.

Table 3 shows that a strong moisture import took place through the boundary, accomplished mainly by the mean ageostrophic mass circulation. It is clear that without careful determination of this mass circulation it would be impossible to obtain a correct view of the energy transformations carried out by the heat engine over the Gulf. As already seen, the total heat flux through the boundary was nearly zero in the mean over the four days. Thus, the cell acts in part to convert imported latent heat to $gz + c_pT$, which must then be exported. This is confirmed by Table 4, which also shows that transports due to ageostrophic mass circulation and due to asymmetries must be computed. One cannot assume the net mass circulation to be zero; nor can one make the assumption of horizontally uniform temperature and moisture, in spite of the relative homogeneity of the tropical air mass.

Table 4 indicates further that a small part of the precipitation is used to balance the excess of R over Q_s; that a large part is used for the sensible heat export as just mentioned; and that all increase in $I + P$ results from precipitation heating when the change over the four days is considered. With this, a quantitative demonstration of part of the simple heat engine has been given. For an estimate of conversion of latent heat released to kinetic energy through building up the potential energy over the Gulf, we now turn to the kinetic energy budget.

Budget of Kinetic Energy

If the kinetic energy equation per unit mass is integrated over the mass inside the ellipse, one obtains, neglecting vertical kinetic energy,

$$\frac{\partial K}{\partial t} = -\tfrac{1}{2}\int\limits_p\int\limits_s V^2 c_n ds \frac{dp}{g} - \int\limits_p\int\limits_A \mathbf{V}\cdot\nabla h\, dA\, dp + \int\limits_p\int\limits_A \mathbf{V}\cdot\mathbf{F}\, dA \frac{dp}{g}. \quad (6)$$

Here, K is the integrated kinetic energy of the mass inside the ellipse, V scalar wind speed, $\mathbf{V}$ vector wind, and ∇ the two-dimensional gradient operator. For calculation of local change and transport terms, the techniques already outlined for the heat energy budget were applied, except that determination of K was made from isotach analyses at six levels. There was much leeway in drawing the lines in the middle troposphere, where the change from lower to upper circulation occurred. This proved to be without importance, because most kinetic energy was concentrated in the two jet streams and the tropical storm, all of which could be described with fair certainty.

Evaluation of the production of kinetic energy by pressure forces could not be fully carried out because knowledge of the three-dimensional distribution of $\mathbf{V}\cdot\nabla h$ is required. Only a partial computation can be made after the following transformations (cf. STARR, 1951). We can write

$$-\iint \mathbf{V}\cdot\nabla h\, dA\, dp =$$
$$= -\iint \nabla\cdot(\mathbf{V}h) dA\, dp + \iint h\,\nabla\cdot\mathbf{V} dA\, dp.$$

Now

$$-\iint\nabla\cdot(\mathbf{V}h)\, dA\, dp = \int h c_n ds\, dp =$$
$$= s\int \bar{h}\bar{c}_n dp + s\int \overline{h' c_n'}\, dp.$$

This term represents the work done by pressure forces through the ellipse. Nearly all of this was accomplished by the mass circulation, so that the $h'c_n'$ term can be neglected as a secondary effect.

The term

$$\iint h\,\nabla\cdot\mathbf{V} dA\, dp = A\int \overline{h\,\nabla\cdot\mathbf{V}}\, dp + \iint \overline{h'\,\nabla\cdot\mathbf{V}'}\, dA\, dp.$$

Since

$$\overline{\nabla \cdot \mathbf{V}} = -\frac{1}{A}\int c_n ds,$$

$$A\int \tilde{h}\, \overline{\nabla \cdot \mathbf{V}}\, dp = -s\int \tilde{h}\bar{c}_n dp.$$

The production term can now be written

$$-\iint \mathbf{V} \cdot \nabla\, hdAdp =$$

$$= s\int \left(\bar{h} - \tilde{h}\right)\bar{c}_n dp + \iint \overline{h' \nabla \cdot \mathbf{V}'}\, dAdp. \quad (7)$$

In this formula the first term on the right-hand side can be determined from the ellipse boundary data and the constant pressure charts. It measures the production of kinetic energy by the mass circulation acting on the mean pressure difference between boundary and interior. With inflow toward lower pressure near the ground and outflow from the upper anticyclone also toward lower pressure at high levels, this term will make a positive contribution to kinetic energy generation. The second term essentially measures the production that arises, for instance, from the penetration of the flow toward small areas of particularly low pressure within the general envelope during convergence. From the well known association between convergence and vorticity, and hence indirectly with the pressure field through the gradient wind equation, we must assume that this term will be large and may be dominant. Variations in the efficiency of the thermal heat engine in converting latent heat to kinetic energy will largely depend on the role played by this term. Highest efficiency will evidently be attained in hurricanes, where most inflowing mass penetrates to a local area of very low pressures before converging and ascending. It is this important term that cannot be computed from the ellipse data and must be treated as residual.

The frictional force per unit mass $\mathbf{F} = \frac{1}{\varrho}\frac{\partial \tau}{\partial z}$, where τ is the shearing stress vector. Therefore the frictional dissipation of kinetic energy

$$\int \mathbf{V} \cdot \mathbf{F} dA \frac{dp}{g} = \int_\alpha \mathbf{V} \cdot \frac{\partial \tau}{\partial z}\, d\alpha =$$

$$= \int_\alpha \frac{\partial}{\partial z}\, \mathbf{V} \cdot \tau d\alpha - \int_\alpha \tau \cdot \frac{\partial \mathbf{V}}{\partial z}\, d\alpha,$$

where α denotes volume. The first of the terms on the right-hand side gives the dissipation at upper and lower boundaries, the second the internal dissipation within the atmosphere (cf. PALMÉN and RIEHL, 1957). Dissipation at the top is presumably negligible. Therefore we obtain

$$\int_\alpha \frac{\partial}{\partial z}\mathbf{V} \cdot \tau d\alpha = -\int_A (\mathbf{V} \cdot \tau)_0 dA \quad (8)$$

after integration. Further, τ_0 may be expressed through the well known formula $\tau_0 = k\varrho_0 \mathbf{V}_0 \mathrm{V}_0$, where $\mathbf{V}_0$ is the vector wind at ship's deck level, ϱ_0 the density of the air at the surface, and k an areodynamic constant. Then $-\int (\mathbf{V} \cdot \tau)_0 dA = -k\varrho_0 \tilde{\mathrm{V}}_0^3 A$. This term can be computed because fairly reliable isotachs could be drawn over the water from ship observations. We shall assume that the surface stress is 1 dyn/cm^2 at normal trade wind speeds of 7 mps. Given $\varrho_0 = 1.2 \times 10^{-3}$ g/cm^3, $k = 0.0017$. Excepting a small area around the center of the tropical storm, wind speeds did not vary enough over the period analyzed to require consideration of variations of k with V_0 on account of changes in surface roughness.

Very little is known about the internal dissipation of kinetic energy. We shall assume, following BRUNT (1939) and PALMÉN (1958), that it does not exceed the dissipation due to ground friction. Certainly we should expect that, as the surface winds and vertical shears increased over the period studied, the internal dissipation also increased. While the results of computations made with the foregoing assumptions will necessarily be rough, it is nevertheless believed that the relative importance of all terms in the kinetic energy budget and their variations with time are fairly well represented in Table 5.

According to the table, the total kinetic energy continually rose over the four days. At first the increase was concentrated at high levels, leading to development of the jet streams; later in the low troposphere during the tropical storm development. Altogether, the kinetic energy nearly tripled during the period. This increase was overshadowed by a large export of kinetic energy, concentrated in the two jet streams on September 17 and 18. Export by the asymmetric part of the circulation—the jet streams—predominates strongly over export by the mass circulation (right-hand side of Table 5). It is clear that for computation of a kinetic energy budget symmetrical models cannot be used.

The rate of frictional dissipation rose by almost an order of magnitude during development of

Table 5. Kinetic Energy Budget (10^{12} cal/sec)*

Date (Sept.)	$\frac{\partial k}{\partial t}$	=	Import	+ Production by mass circ.	+ Production by $\overline{h'\nabla\cdot v}$ (residual)	— Dissipation by friction (ground plus internal)	Efficiency of heat engine (%)	Total kinetic energy (10^{16} cal)	Dissipation by friction (10^{16} cal/day)	Export by mass circ.	Export by asymmetries
15	.37		— .13	.50	.44	— .44	0.8	7.1	3.8	—.07	— .06
16	.48		— .35	.42	.71	— .30	2.1	11.1	2.6	—.09	— .26
17	.48		—1.52	1.70	1.18	— .88	1.7	15.4	7.6	—.24	—1.28
18	.37		—2.02	— .35	4.88	—2.14	4.1	19.1	18.5	—.07	—1.95
Total 15—18	1.70		—4.02	2.27	7.21	—3.76					

* For purpose of comparison with the heat energy budget units of cal/sec have been chosen rather than mechanical units.

the tropical storm and the jet streams to attain values comparable with those computed by PALMÉN and RIEHL (1957) for a fully mature hurricane (3.6×10^{12} cal/sec for the ground friction term for a comparable area). In this situation, as in other tropical storm cases, large frictional dissipation at the ground arose from the fact that winds of moderate intensity were spread over a large area, whereas in hurricanes, very strong winds cover a small core. On the first three days (cf. Table 5) the dissipation rate per day was one half to one third of the total kinetic energy in the air over the Gulf; on the last day the dissipation per 24 hours approximately equalled the total kinetic energy; this also corresponds to PALMÉN and JORDAN's (1955) findings in hurricanes. Thus, though no hurricane developed, the picture is quite comparable as far as dissipation is concerned.

This must be true also for production of kinetic energy. In Palmén's computation there was no kinetic energy export through the hurricane boundary; in the present situation there was a large export, roughly equalling the frictional dissipation. Therefore the production term is large on all four days, and on September 18 Palmén's value of 3.6×10^{12} cal/sec is exceeded. Nevertheless, no hurricane formed; the excess kinetic energy produced was largely exported. On the first three days production by the mass circulation was important and equal to the $\overline{h'\nabla\cdot\mathbf{V}'}$ term, especially on September 17. A marked difference occurred on the 18th. With the reversal of mass circulation the mean cell tended to become "indirect", consuming rather than releasing kinetic energy. All production became localized in the tropical storm. Table 5 contains a column showing the efficiency of the thermal heat engine, defined here as the ratio of kinetic energy produced to latent heat released through condensation. On the first three days the efficiency was 1—2 per cent, in accordance with usual estimates; it rose to 4 per cent on the 18th, according to the table. If this figure is reliable, it denotes that the ascending portion of the mass circulation became entirely concentrated in the tropical storm, whereas there was widespread ascent on the 17th.

Comparison of the Cyclone of September 17—18 and Hurricane Audrey

As evident from Table 5, the event analyzed was of large magnitude as far as kinetic energy production in secondary circulations of the tropics is concerned. The question may be raised why the tropical storm, after a good start, failed to become a hurricane. This question cannot be answered fully, because the sufficient conditions for hurricane formation are not known. Some suggestions, however, are contained in the foregoing material. Moreover, analysis was made for the development period of hurricane Audrey (June 24—27, 1957) in the Gulf, similar to that just described. On June 24 the situation over the Gulf resembled that of September 16, except that a stronger belt of easterlies covered the northern Gulf coast; motion of the cyclone in the southwestern Gulf also was appreciably

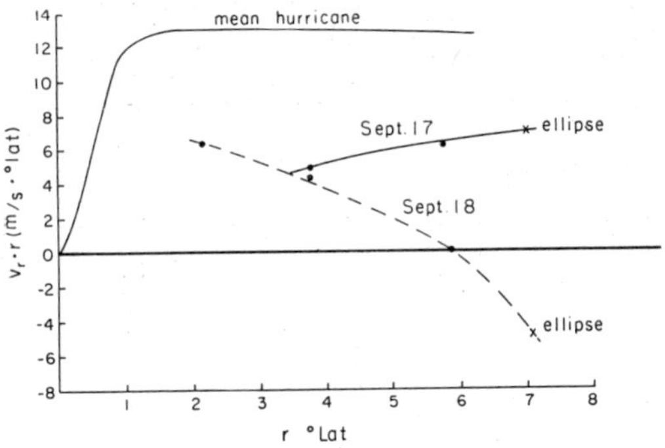

Fig. 28. Distribution of mass circulation ($v_r \cdot r$) at surface against radius (° lat.) in coordinate system centered on tropical storm for Sept. 17 and 18. Ellipse values and profile of mass circulation for mean hurricane are also shown.

slower. The low-level maps of June 25, OOZ were almost identical with those of September 17, OOZ, but development during the next 24 hours differed greatly. While two cases obviously do not suffice for definite conclusions about the trigger mechanism for cyclogenesis, it will nevertheless be of interest to determine the differences between the two situations.

One may ask whether calculations performed for the whole ellipse can be applied readily to a tropical storm centered in the western Gulf and moving northward. For determination of the mass circulation relative to the tropical storm in September, only ship winds and a few low-level reconnaissance winds are available. An attempt was made to determine the mass circulation by plotting all reports within six hours of the OOZ map times on September 17 and 18 on one chart, positioned with respect to the center. The preceding 12*Z* maps were also used to help fill in areas without reports. Results were necessarily rough. Nevertheless, profiles of the mass circulation could be determined for the outskirts of the center (fig. 28); near the core reports were too few to permit calculation. The ellipse computation does not satisfy the geometrical requirements for radial velocity, but surface values from fig. 25 have been entered in fig. 28 at the mean radius of the Gulf, which is 7 degrees latitude.

It is seen that the ellipse data are not contradicted by the ship observations and by the shift of coordinates to a polar coordinate system fixed in the tropical storm. On September 17 inflow and convergence took place around the whole periphery of the center, while on September 18 divergence prevailed over the whole calculable portion of the v_r-profile, with actual outflow beyond the 6° radius. Comparison with the mass circulation of the mean hurricane (PALMÉN and RIEHL, 1957), also shown in fig. 28, indicates that the change in mass circulation from September 17 to 18 may have had a decisive effect on the storm.

This suggestion is also supported by the hurricane Audrey data. Quantitative comparison of the two cases is possible by considering the transport of absolute vorticity through the ellipse boundary. The vorticity equation, neglecting friction, tilting terms and vertical vorticity transport, may be written

$$\frac{\partial \zeta}{\partial t} + \nabla \cdot \mathbf{V}\zeta = 0, \tag{9}$$

where ζ is the absolute vorticity. Integrating over the Gulf between isobaric surfaces,

$$\int \frac{\partial \zeta}{\partial t}\, dA\, \frac{dp}{g} = \frac{\partial}{\partial t} \int c_s ds\, \frac{dp}{g} = - \int \zeta c_n ds\, \frac{dp}{g},$$

or

$$\frac{\partial}{\partial t} \int \overline{c_s} dp = - \int \overline{\zeta c_n} dp = - \int \overline{(f+\zeta_r) c_n} dp, \tag{10}$$

where f is the Coriolis parameter and ζ_r the relative vorticity. In this form of the vorticity equation the quantity ultimately of interest in hurricane prediction—$\frac{\partial \overline{c_s}}{\partial t}$—appears explicitly. In view of the restricted form of Eq. (9), application of Eq. (10) should only be made to changes of $\frac{\partial \overline{c_s}}{\partial t}$ integrated over deep layers of the troposphere. When used in this way, good results were obtained. One would prefer to evaluate the equation for layers of 100-mb thickness. This did not prove feasible, presumably on account of strong vertical vorticity advection. Nevertheless, it is of interest to discuss the vertical distribution on $\overline{\zeta c_n}$. On September 17, the calculation predicted an increase of $\overline{c_s}$ of 3.5 knots/24 hours for the layer 1,000—600 mb and a decrease of 4 knots/24 hours for the layer 600—200 mb, with level of nondivergence at 600 mb. The same level of nondivergence was found on June 25, but on this occasion the calculated changes of $\overline{c_s}$ were + 18 knots/24 hours for the lower troposphere and —10 knots/24 hours for the upper troposphere. There was, then, a large difference in the intensity of the acceleration of circulation as produced by convergence around the Gulf, in spite of the superficial resemblance of the charts. In addition, a distribution of low-level inflow and high-level outflow through the ellipse continued on June 26 and 27, though much weaker than on June 25. There was no reversal as on September 18.

In other respects both situations were quite comparable. The total heat flux through the boundary was small. Internal energy and total moisture actually were a little lower in the June than in the September case. The evaporation also was stronger in September, at least prior to establishment of hurricane Audrey. Dewpoints averaged near 77° F in both cases, but the sea surface temperature was 85° F in September compared to 83° F in June; thus, the difference $\tilde{q}_w - \tilde{q}_a$ was 6.5 g/kg in September and 5 g/kg in June, rendering the September situation more favorable from the ocean temperature viewpoint.

It follows that the only evident difference of importance between the two cases lay in the mechanical concentration of vorticity $\overline{c_n\zeta}$, and this difference was brought about by an entirely different evolution of the flow over the United States. Riehl (1948) has pointed out that hurricane formation is likely to occur when an upper-air trough of large amplitude in the north, propagating eastward, passes a well-developed wave in the easterlies or equatorial shear line with incipient vortex. Principal deepening occurs after the middle latitude trough has moved well to the east of the tropical disturbance and fracture of the two systems is taking place. Exactly this sequence of events happened on June 24—26, with fracture occurring early on June 25. In contrast, no trough passage was observed during September 16—18 (figs. 11—13); southwesterly winds persisted north of the Gulf coast.

On account of lack of sufficient data it has never been possible to compute the mechanism by which eastward passage of a trough in the north influences an incipient tropical storm far to the south. From the details of the c_n distribution around the Gulf in the Audrey situation it can be seen that a strong injection of air into the Gulf in low and middle troposphere took place to the rear of the upper trough across a large portion of the northern Gulf coast. This fresh inflow, coupled with preexisting inflow from the south into the tropical disturbance, led to the strong net inflow in the low troposphere (4 knots) and to the resulting high values of $\overline{\zeta c_n}$.

Conclusion

The preceding comparison of the tropical cyclone situations of June and September 1957 leads to the hypothesis that mechanical forcing from neighbouring disturbances is an important factor in the deepening of tropical disturbances to hurricane strength. It will be necessary to test this hypothesis in a large number of cases to ascertain its validity. Even if successful, an ultimate understanding of the hurricane would not be obtained. For, since gradient wind balance is closely fulfilled in tropical storms, it is necessary to arrive at an understanding of the pressure gradient requisite to maintain the c_s field calculated from the vorticity equation under gradient wind conditions. This problem cannot be solved with observations as utilized in this report, but may be attacked with research aircraft missions into storm centers as flown by the National Hurricane Research Project of the United States Weather Bureau.

This study has shown that thermally direct circulations which produce and export large amounts of kinetic energy can occur in the tropics even without a hurricane or typhoon. In fact, it has been seen that existence of a direct cell is not a sufficient condition for deepening of a tropical disturbance. It will be of interest in subsequent work to determine the frequency of such systems and their contribution toward maintaining the general circulation. Further, it will be necessary to investigate the circumstances that permit their development and control the duration of their existence.

Acknowledgements

This report was prepared under a contract between the Office of Naval Research, United States Navy, and The University of Chicago. All observations and charts used during the research were furnished by the National Hurricane Research Project through the courtesy of its director, Mr. R. H. Simpson.

REFERENCES

BRAHAM, R. R., 1952: The water and energy budgets of the thunderstorm and their relation to thunderstorm development. *J. Meteor.*, **9**, 227—242.

BRUNT, D., 1939: *Physical and Dynamical Meteorology.* Cambridge: The University Press, 428 pp.

HOUGHTON, H. G., 1954: On the annual heat balance of the northern hemisphere. *J. Meteor.*, **11**, 1—9.

PALMÉN, E., and JORDAN, C. L., 1955: Note on the release of kinetic energy in tropical cyclones. *Tellus*, **7**, 186—188.

PALMÉN, E., and RIEHL, H., 1957: Budget of angular momentum and energy in tropical cyclones. *J. Meteor.* **14**, 150—159.

PALMÉN, E., 1958: Vertical circulation and release of kinetic energy during the development of hurricane Hazel as an extratropical storm. *Tellus*, **10**, 1—24.

RIEHL, H., 1948: On the formation of West-Atlantic hurricanes. *Dept. of Meteor., The Univ. of Chicago, Misc. Report* 24, Part I, 102 pp.

RIEHL, H., and BURGNER, N. M., 1950: Further studies of the movement and formation of hurricanes and their forecasting. *Bull. Amer. Meteor. Soc.*, **31**, 244—253.

RIEHL, H. *et al.*, 1951: The northeast trade of the Pacific Ocean. *Quart. J. R. Meteor. Soc.*, **77**, 598—626.

RIEHL, H., 1954: *Tropical Meteorology.* New York: McGraw-Hill Book Co., Inc., 392 pp.

RIEHL, H., and MALKUS, J. S., 1958: On the heat balance in the equatorial trough zone. *Palmén 60th anniversary volume.*

SIMPSON, R. H., 1947: Synoptic aspects of the intertropical convergence near Central and South America. *Bull. Amer. Meteor. Soc.*, **28**, 335—346.

STARR, V. P., 1951: Applications of energy principles to the general circulation. In *Compendium of Meteorology*, T. F. Malone, ed. Boston: American Meteorological Society, 568—574.

(Manuscript received July 8, 1958)

Physics of Winter Precipitation in the Desert

By Horace R. Byers[1]
The University of Chicago

Abstract

Airplane and radar measurements in winter rain situations in the vicinity of Tucson, Arizona, are plotted and discussed. A combination of stratified cloud layers and convective cells predominates, the cellular types being more in evidence than in winter situations of the more humid regions of this and higher latitudes. The cloud droplet sizes and liquid water contents are similar to those measured elsewhere in the given ranges of temperature.

A tabulation of the freezing level on rain days shows that it varies widely but has a median around 8,500 feet in January—March, which is 2,500 feet lower than the mean for all winter days. In some cases precipitation occurs by an all-water process. Counts of giant salt nuclei are high enough to play a role in such a process.

1. Introduction

Winter rains of desert lands are important for providing storage in the mountains and for fortifying the sparse vegetation against subsequent dry, hot periods. Grasses particularly are dependent on rains at this season and in turn, the livestock in their lowland winter grazing areas need the grass. Cloud modification aimed at increased rain production is an attractive prospect for stockmen and others in critical situations during winter.

The two-season pattern of Arizona rainfall (midsummer and midwinter) has been emphasized by Jurwitz (1953). Of the two seasons, the summer is the most striking, with July and August having almost daily convective showers at various places over the mountains, and often spreading over the valleys. In winter, the rain or snow usually occurs with moving cyclonic disturbances which under normal circumstances are infrequent in this region, much as is the case in Southern California. During the four months December through March there has been, in the past 10 years, an average of five days per month on which more than a trace of rain occurred at one or more of six stations located in and around Tucson.

[1] Research performed at and under the support of the University of Arizona, Institute of Atmospheric Physics.

As might be expected, the winter rains fall from more uniform and widespread cloud systems than do those of summer. Des Jardins (1958) shows that one of the principal distinguishing characteristics between summer and winter rains is the greater preponderance of low stratified clouds in the latter. However, this winter characteristic is not as striking in contrast with summer as it is in the eastern part of the country, nor are the winter cloud systems as uniform as they are on the California coast. Examination by aircraft and radar of rainstorms having a continuous cloud cover, reveals, even in such areas of homogeneous rain as New England (Austin, 1951, Cunningham, 1951, Cunningham and Atlas, 1954), a cellular structure of precipitating clouds. In Arizona it is unnecessary to use radar and aircraft in order to detect the cellular nature of most storm situations in winter. The convective cells occur separately during part of each storm or part of each rainy day.

2. Flight and Radar Data in Arizona

Having studied the physical properties of summer clouds in Arizona, the University of Chicago flight group, with the Air Force B-17 airplane assigned to it, made physical measurements in the clouds of winter rain situations during January and the first half of February 1956. Ground radars of the Institute of Atmospheric

Physics of the University of Arizona were used in conjunction with the flights which were carried out as part of a University of Arizona cloud study. There were eight "rain days" (more than a trace at one or more of six stations in and around Tucson) during the six weeks' period and there were flights on six of them, though on one only a few stratocumulus clouds remained by the time the flight got under way. Only two flights represented operations according to plan, that is, penetration of clouds in depth. In the planning, the assumption had been made that on rain days there would be deep, continuous clouds in those regions where Air Traffic Control would permit instrument flights. On four of the six days it was necessary to seek out the clouds, which were located in mountains or in regions where penetration in depth on instruments was impossible.

During the period of study, a 3-cm wavelength range-height-indicating radar (AN/TPS-10) scanning through the full 360 deg. of azimuth was operated on the campus of the University of Arizona near the center of Tucson and a K-band (1.25 cm) radar with vertically directed antenna was operated at the Ryan air-navigation radio-station approximately 12 miles southwest of the University. The "normal" flights were operated on one of the Ryan Radio beams and over the station on standard instrument let-down and clumb-out patterns of the Tucson traffic control.

The B-17 also carried a nose radar (AN/APQ-13) of 3-cm-wavelength with antenna rotating around the longitudinal axis of the airplane, operated as previously described (BRAHAM, BATTAN and BYERS, 1957).

3. General Characteristics of Clouds and their Echoes

The flights and the radarscope photographs reveal that characteristically in the winter-rain situations there is an intermittent or broken low-cloud layer identified as stratus, nimbostratus or stratocumulus covering large areas. Over a considerable portion of this cloud layer precipitation echoes are returned to the 3-cm radar. Above this, other stratified layers are found, usually without echoes. Embedded in these clouds, often surrounded by small relatively cloud-free areas, are tall convective-type cells producing intense echoes and moderate to heavy rains.

Where only the stratified layers appear, the rain is light and the echoes mostly faint. Broad areas of low echoes, fairly weak but extending essentially to the ground, are observed in the low clouds. Many of these echoes are at temperatures entirely above freezing, but there are strong indications that snow may be filtering down to them from above. Winds from the snow layers may scatter ice crystals over a large area after the manner described by K. L. S. GUNN, DENNIS, *et al.* (1954, 1955). These low echoes sometimes are interpreted as extensive "bright-band" returns and, in some instances are arranged with respect to the melting level so as to meet the definition of such a band. Except in the tall rain cells, echoes are found only in the lower parts of the stratified clouds. The larger cells extend above 15,000 feet m.s.l., but many go only to 10,000 or 12,000. The median height of the freezing level is around 8,500 feet in the winter storms, but there is considerable variation.

By far the greater portion of the space covered by radar echoes as perceived by the 3-cm radars is below 10,000 feet. There is a diurnal variation in the amount of cloud and echo in these lower rain layers, especially in the broad valleys such as that in which Tucson is located. The clouds and their echoes are less extensive in the afternoon than in the morning, although there is a tendency for them to cling to the mountains all day on rainy days. The effect of solar heating in regions of downslope wind probably starts the dissipation of the stratified layers. The clouds and echoes become more cellular as the day goes on.

4. Clouds on the Flight of January 21, 1956

Flight 266 of January 21, 1956 was the best of the two flights operated according to plan; the

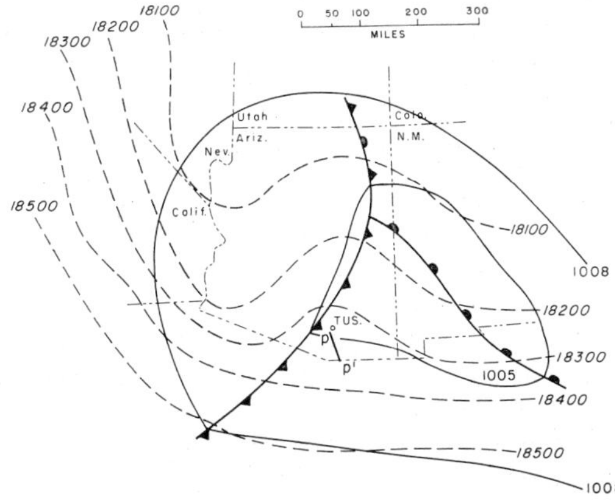

Fig. 1. Synoptic pattern at sea level and 500 mb for Jan. 21, 1956. The flight path south of Tucson (TUS) is shown by the line segment *pp′*.

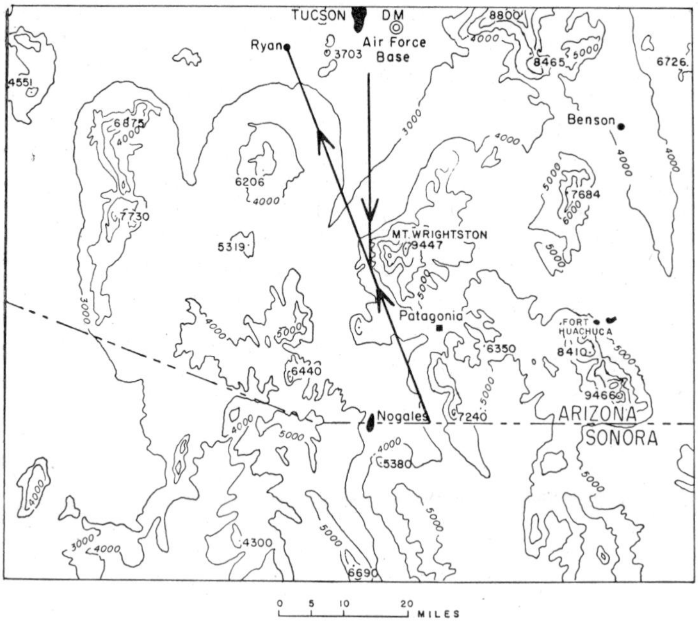

Fig. 2. Map showing path of flight 266. Elevations in feet above sea level.

cloud and rain situation was about ideal and essentially all of the equipment, airborne and ground-mounted, was working. Mr. Edward L. Harrington of the University of Chicago Cloud Physics Laboratory who was in the controller's position on the airplane has prepared the following account and sketches of the flight.

When flight 266 was planned, intermittent, light precipitation had been occurring at Tucson for a period of about nine hours from a nimbostratus overcast. Fig. 1 shows the general synoptic pattern prevailing. The situation appeared to be precisely what the project had been set up to study.

Fig. 2 shows the track of the aircraft during the operation. In Fig. 3 may be seen a scheme of representation of the clouds encountered. This scheme is presented as a cross-section along the southeast leg of the Tucson low-frequency radio range. The axis of the cross-section is graduated in miles from the Ryan range station. Where the flight was not made on the range, data and observations have been projected onto the plane of the cross-section. Likewise radar echoes are shown as appearing in the plane of the cross-section regardless of their actual position (radar was on four mile range). At no time did the aircraft penetrate radar echo. Where this appears to be the case in the diagram the echoes were abeam the aircraft. The echoes appearing from ten to seventeen miles from the range were observed on the return leg of the flight when the aircraft was at an approximate altitude of twenty thousand feet.

The cross-section represents approximately twenty-nine hundred seconds. During that time the aircraft climbed as indicated from four thousand feet through two stratified cloud layers to twenty-three thousand feet, a thousand feet above the top of the upper layer. The headings were generally as shown in Fig. 2. The inbound heading was taken while the climb was still in progress when the Mexican border was reached.

The cloud system was essentially two layers of stratus. In Fig. 3 cloud bases and tops are drawn as horizontal extensions of the points at which the aircraft penetrated and emerged.

Prior to the beginning of the climb the aircraft cruised in the area between Davis-Monthan Air Force Base and Ryan at an altitude of about four thousand feet. During this period several showers were observed in the area.

After the climb was commenced, as the lower cloud layer was approached, it became apparent that the elevation of the cloud base was irregular. By the time the cloud was finally entered several minutes had eclapsed since the aircraft had passed through the level of some of the cloud bases. Quite possibly the aircraft ascended into a hole in the cloud. Immediately upon penetration rime icing was encountered, making visibility

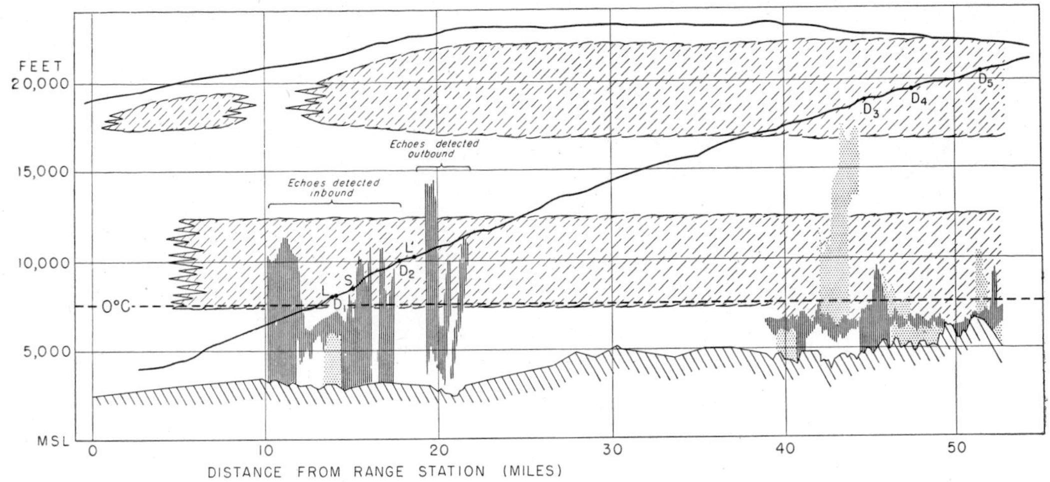

Fig. 3. Flight 266 cross section, Jan. 21, 1956. Heavy ascending line represents outbound flight path through the two cloud layers; inbound flight above. The light stippling represents weak radar echoes and the vertical-line shading designates strong ones. Isotherm of 0°C is just above the base of the lower cloud layer.

out of the aircraft difficult. When the aircraft passed through 10,400 feet a break in the cloud was encountered at which time the sun became visible for a short time. However, when the aircraft emerged from the lower deck, the multi-layer characteristics of the system became evident and there was no indication of breaks in the upper layer. As the aircraft ascended between the two layers there was no visible indication of build-up from the lower layer, at least within the limits of visibility as restricted by subdued light. This condition of semi-darkness, along with the diffuseness of the periphery of the upper layer, made it impossible to determine precisely when the upper layer was entered. This difficulty was encountered again upon exit at the top into the sunlight.

As the aircraft approached Ryan on the return leg the top of the upper layer was seen to become lower and the aircraft consequently was able to descend, maintaining a required one-thousand-foot clearance.

Approximately fifteen miles from Ryan the upper layer became broken. Ten miles from Ryan there was only the lower layer. Six miles out this layer, too, became broken with the ground becoming visible.

As the aircraft passed over the range station the only clouds evident were an estimated fifty per cent coverage of stratocumulus.

The aircraft descended in clear air in the region between Ryan and the city of Tucson. As the aircraft descended the high overcast reappeared. At this time a cumulus congestus, with its top at an estimated altitude of eleven thousand feet, appeared over the Tucson Mountains between Ryan and Tucson.

At the end of the descent aircraft returned to Davis-Monthan Air Force Base. Within an hour after the termination of the flight a thunderstorm occurred in the vicinity of Tucson Municipal Airport.

Harrington's flight cross section shows the characteristic low-level echo pattern in the southern third of the section. There is also a low radar band about three miles long connecting the northernmost cells. The question arises as to whether or not these represent bright-band echoes. In a discussion of his flight report, Harrington made a comparison with computations by R. Wexler (1955) of melting depth as a function of drop size, snowflake type and lapse rate. Wexler considers a diameter of 3 mm to be the upper limit of drop size for continuous rain from stratiform clouds. Allowing these limits and taking the mean melting depth for this flight as 1,500 ft and a lapse rate of between 6 and 7° C per km, Harrington does not obtain values within the realm of Wexler's consideration. The cross section has much the same appearance as some of the flight sections of Cunningham (1951) which show extensive low-level echoes only part of which the author definitely ascribed to the bright band.

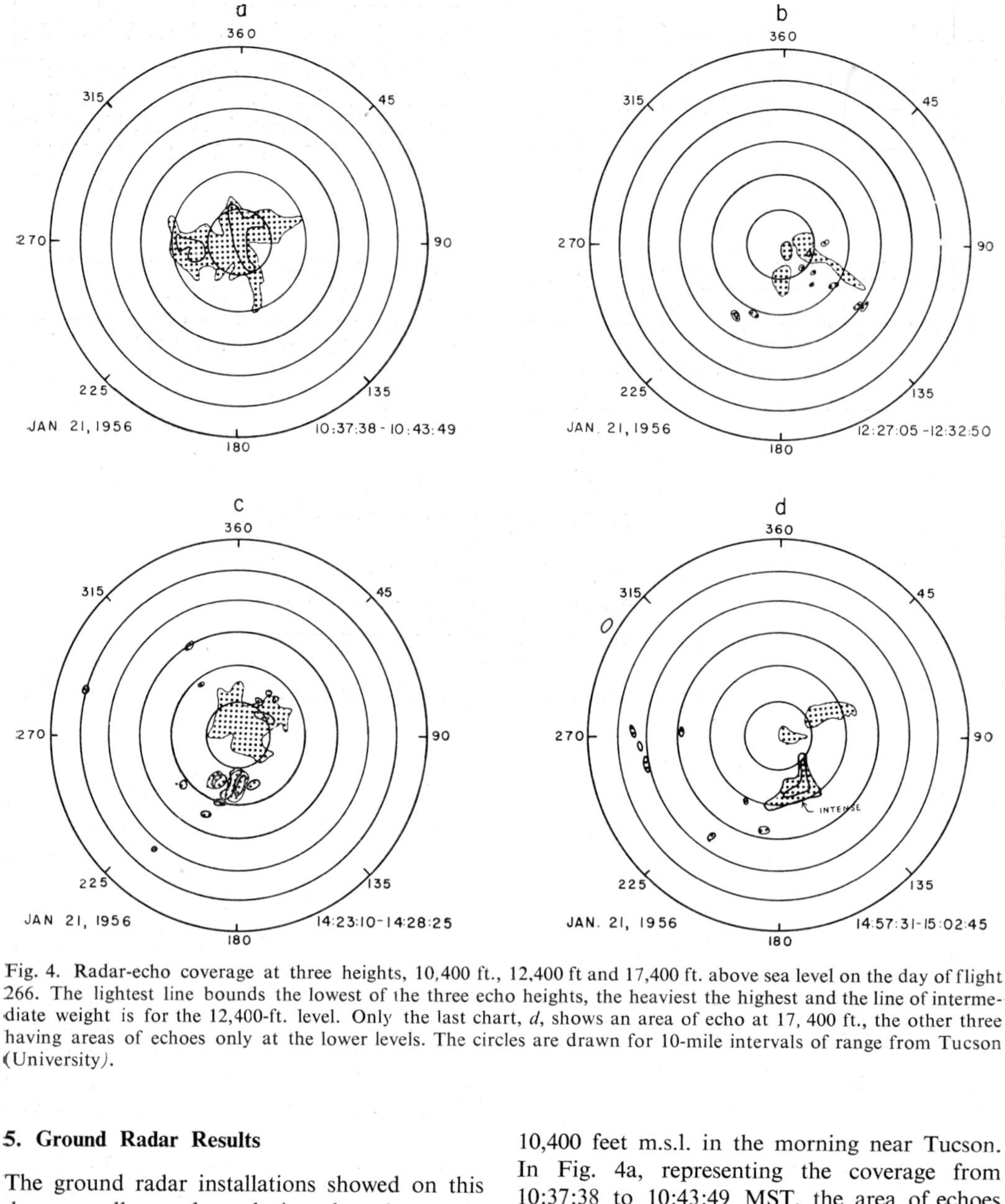

Fig. 4. Radar-echo coverage at three heights, 10,400 ft., 12,400 ft and 17,400 ft. above sea level on the day of flight 266. The lightest line bounds the lowest of the three echo heights, the heaviest the highest and the line of intermediate weight is for the 12,400-ft. level. Only the last chart, *d*, shows an area of echo at 17, 400 ft., the other three having areas of echoes only at the lower levels. The circles are drawn for 10-mile intervals of range from Tucson (University).

5. Ground Radar Results

The ground radar installations showed on this day as well as others during the winter rain period, a great preponderance of echo area below 8,000 feet above the radar, or 10,400 ft m.s.l. (a level more or less arbitrarily chosen to separate low and medium-height echoes). Although these are extensive in areal coverage, it is doubtful that they represent the melting or bright band in very many cases.

On January 21, 1956, the day of the flight, there was a very extensive echo-producing layer below 10,400 feet m.s.l. in the morning near Tucson. In Fig. 4a, representing the coverage from 10:37:38 to 10:43:49 MST, the area of echoes below 10,400 feet is at least four times that at 12,400 ft m.s.l. No echoes within range reached as high as 17,400 feet at that time. By 12:30 MST, as seen in Fig. 4b, the extent of low echo is considerably less than it was two hours previously, and there are still some areas of echo extending above 12,400 feet. At 14:23:10 to 14:28:25 (Fig. 4c), just after flight 266 started on its climb toward the south, extensive echoes are shown again below 10,400 ft and a dozen

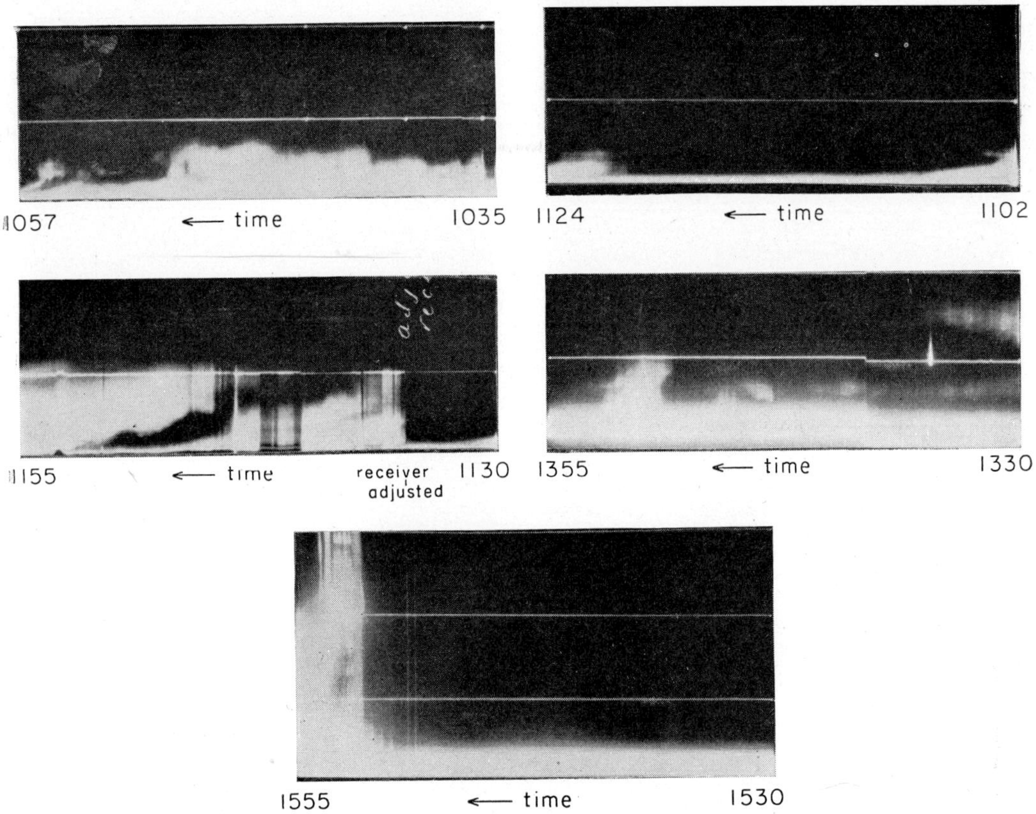

Fig. 5. Film strips of Jan. 21, 1956 from the K-band radar, located at Ryan radio station (see map, Fig. 2). The altitude lines are for intervals of 10,000 feet above the radar which itself is at an elevation of 2413 feet above sea level.

cells have penetrated through 12,400 feet. Thirty-five minutes later, from 14:57:31 to 15:02:45 (Fig. 4d) just after the airplane had started back from 52 miles out, a large echo extending above 17,400 feet is returned from a range of approximately 10 to 20 miles and azimuth approximately 145 to 190 deg. It was by far the most intense echo of the day. It apparently is the echo system, part of which was picked up by the aircraft radar within the four-mile range of the flight path at approximately 1509 to 1512 MST at a distance of 10 to 17 miles from the radio-range station. Around this cellular system there apparently gathered the clouds that produced the thunderstorm after landing. An extensive area of low echo is still to be noted to the east and east-northeast of Tucson.

An approximately continuous series of three film strips of the K-band radarscope taken in the morning and two separate sequences in the afternoon are reproduced in Fig. 5. The sheet of continuous white along the ground represents a peculiarity of the equipment rather than a natural echo condition. The band of low clouds is quite apparent on the first picture, but it is almost entirely absent on the second. This layer probably is not a melting band; most of the time it seems to be too low, and, also, one might expect this high-frequency radar to detect the snowflakes before melting. The third film shows two or three sloping layers, exceeding 10,000 feet in height above radar during the latter part of the period. The third photo shows a faint layer at 6,000 to 8,000 feet above radar with a gradually thinning layer near 15,000 feet above radar. A more cellular type of cloud appears toward the end of the sequence. The pip at 1335 is an airplane. On the last film strip, a convective cell extending above 30,000 feet makes an appearance overhead at about 1550 MST. Apparently this is an edge of the thunderstorm mentioned previously.

6. Temperatures, Droplet Samples and Liquid Water of the Flight

Temperature data for the flight plotted on an adiabatic chart are shown in Fig. 6, as computed by Harrington. Curve A is from data taken during the ascent and thus may be regarded as the "in-cloud" sounding. Curve B is the sounding during the descent, which was in clear air. Curve C is from the radiosonde balloon launched at the Tucson airport U.S. Weather Bureau station at 1400 MST. The temperature measurements in A were made over a horizontal distance of approximately 60 mi while those in B occurred in a distance of about 10 mi. At 410 mb the ascent and descent points were 25 miles apart; at 845 mb there was a time separation of about 1 hr 13 min between the two. Both aircraft soundings exhibit small-scale fluctuations which may be attributed partly to horizontal variations. If the radiosonde observation represents the average condition, then the deviations found by the aircraft might be taken as evidence of convective activity.

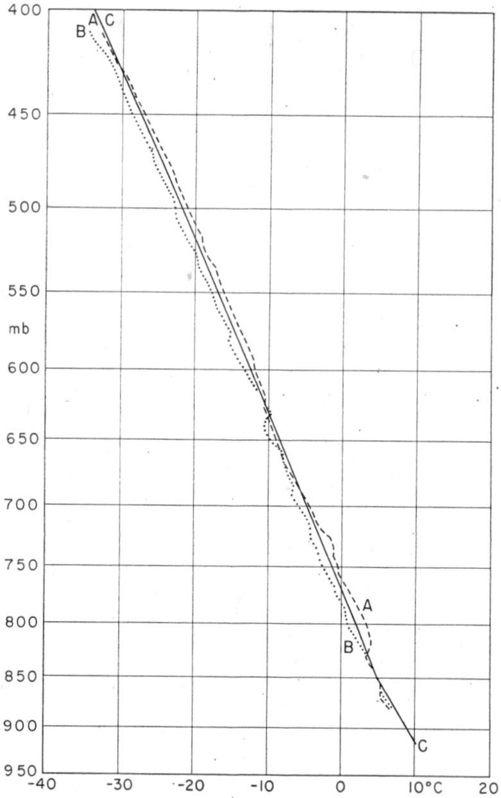

Fig. 6. Temperatures measured on flight 266 ascent (*A*), descent (*B*) and on the radiosonde ascent (*C*) made at approximately the same time at Tucson.

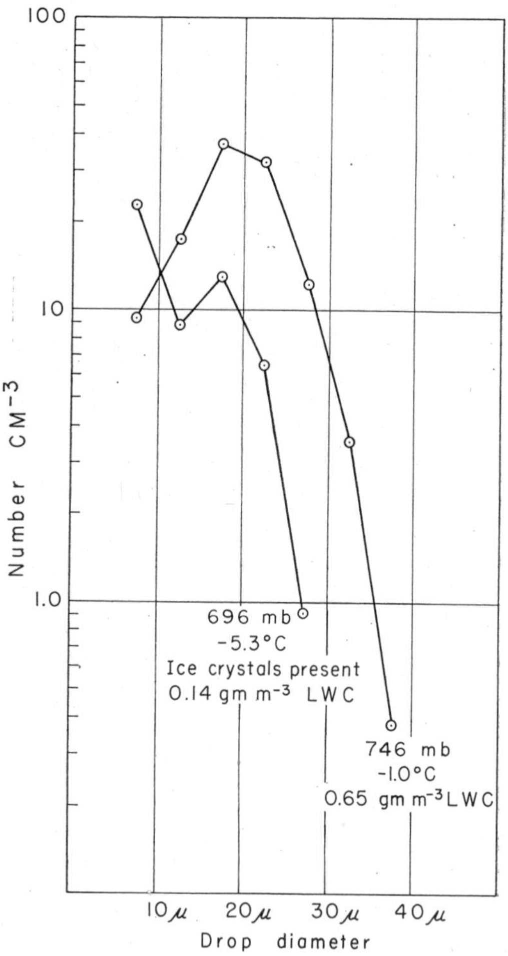

Fig. 7. Concentration of droplets of different sizes taken in samples at 746 mb (point D_1 of Fig. 3) and at 696 mb (point D_2 of Fig. 3). The liquid water contents were 0.65 g m^{-3} and 0.14 g m^{-3}, respectively, computed from the droplet samples. These values should be compared with those measured by the liquid-water meter and represented in Fig. 8.

Points D_1, D_2, D_3, D_4, and D_5 in Fig. 3 denote locations at which droplet samples were taken. Samples at D_1 were entirely liquid droplets. At D_2 some ice crystals appeared among liquid droplets. Samples D_3, D_4 and D_5 showed ice crystals only. At point D_1 the temperature was around $-1°$ C and at D_2 it was about $-5°$ C. Thus it is seen that a mixed cloud of crystals and undercooled droplets existed already at $-5°$ C. The three samplings in the higher cloud layer which produced nothing but ice crystals were

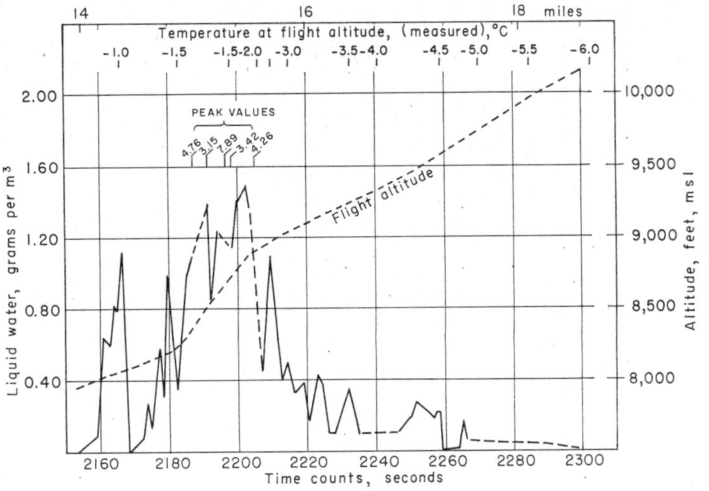

Fig. 8. Values of liquid-water content measured by the Australian meter on flight 266. The points D_1 and D_2 of Figs 3. and 7 are at counter Nos. 2160 and 2280, respectively. It is believed that after about 2280 the instrument could no longer record effectively because of ice. The peak values indicated above the 1.60-gram line have been discarded as due to the paper's being flooded or otherwise disturbed by large drops. Point *S* of Fig. 3 was at about 2190 secs.

made at temperatures of between −24 and −28° C, approximately.

In Fig. 7 the distributions of droplet sizes in the samples at the two levels D_1 and D_2 are plotted. The values are within the range of those found in summer cumulus congestus at about this temperature as reported by Battan and Reitan (1957). From the droplet samples, Harrington computed liquid water contents of 0.65 grams m^{-3} at D_1 and 0.14 g m^{-3} at D_2.

It was not possible to obtain much information about the nature of the ice crystals from examining those slides which contained them. They were too often in clusters. Occasionally a single plate or column could be identified, and in a few such cases on this flight it was possible to identify plates with diameters of between 150 and 200 microns.

Between the points marked L and L′ in Fig. 3, recordings of liquid water content made from the Australian paper-tape sensing device were made. The values are shown in Fig. 8, plotted as a function of time with an altitude curve included. The highest consistent values, around 1.5 g m^{-3}, occurred shortly after the airplane passed through an area of precipitation which was audible as it hit the airplane, including snow or ice pellets (point S in Fig. 3). The momentary peaks exceeding 4 or even 7 g m^{-3} are rejected and may represent flooding of the paper tape. There is no doubt that the instrument ultimately ceased to function because of icing, but there is no way of telling when the readings might have become unreliable. It should be noted that at D_1 and D_2 of Fig. 3, about 8,000 and 10,000 ft, respectively, the liquid-water contents as computed by the droplet samples are in reasonable agreement with those measured by the liquid-water-content meter.

In summarizing the flight and the measurements, Harrington writes:

"Despite the stratified structure of the clouds prior to and during the flight, several findings suggest that precipitation from these clouds was convective in form. Showery precipitation was observed before the aircraft began its climb. Radar photographs of precipitation show vertically developing echoes and the aircraft possibly passed through one of these at the point where graupel was heard to hit the aircraft. The steep lapse rate was favorable to convection. The horizontal temperature behavior as presented in Fig. 6 suggests the presence of convective activity. In view of these points, then, the appearance of a cumulus near to the end of the flight, and the ensuing thunderstorm, are not surprising."

7. Radar Patterns for Other Days

It rained on a few other days in January and early February 1956 in the Tucson area. The radar-echo patterns again showed widespread areas of low-level precipitation developing into scattered cellular structures. In the few cases studied there appeared to be no marked tendency for the cells to form over the higher mountains. The amount of data is insufficient for drawing conclusions about the relative effects of terrain height, but the results suggest that the generation of the echoes depended mainly on other than orographic factors.

As examples of echo distributions, eight plots are reproduced in Fig. 9. The two plots about one hour apart on January 27 show the development of a low-level echo area into a large cell extending above 17,400 feet. The unusual feature about this cell is that it covers essentially the same area from the low levels to above 17,400 feet with no extensive lower bands. The two plots for January 28 show the development of scattered echoes at low levels followed by two broadly based cells penetrating the 17,400-foot level and one small one east of Tucson reaching above 12,400 feet. The latter is in the Rincon Mountains where the peaks are themselves near 10,000 ft. The large cell to the northwest seriously interfered with flights on the Tucson-Phoenix airway. An unpleasant icing situation was experienced by the B-17 at 14,500 ft (– 10° C) in clouds over mountains far to the northeast of Tucson. In the February 1 case there were echoes below 17,400 ft covering a large area in the morning but by 1300 MST there were only three small cells, the tallest one 16 mi NNE of Tucson on the western slope of the Catalinas. The two plots for February 8 show that at noon there were large areas of echo both above and below 12,400 ft while later there were some cells 20 to 40 miles out in addition to the large area of echo around Tucson. The freezing level was between 5,500 and 6,000 ft on that day.

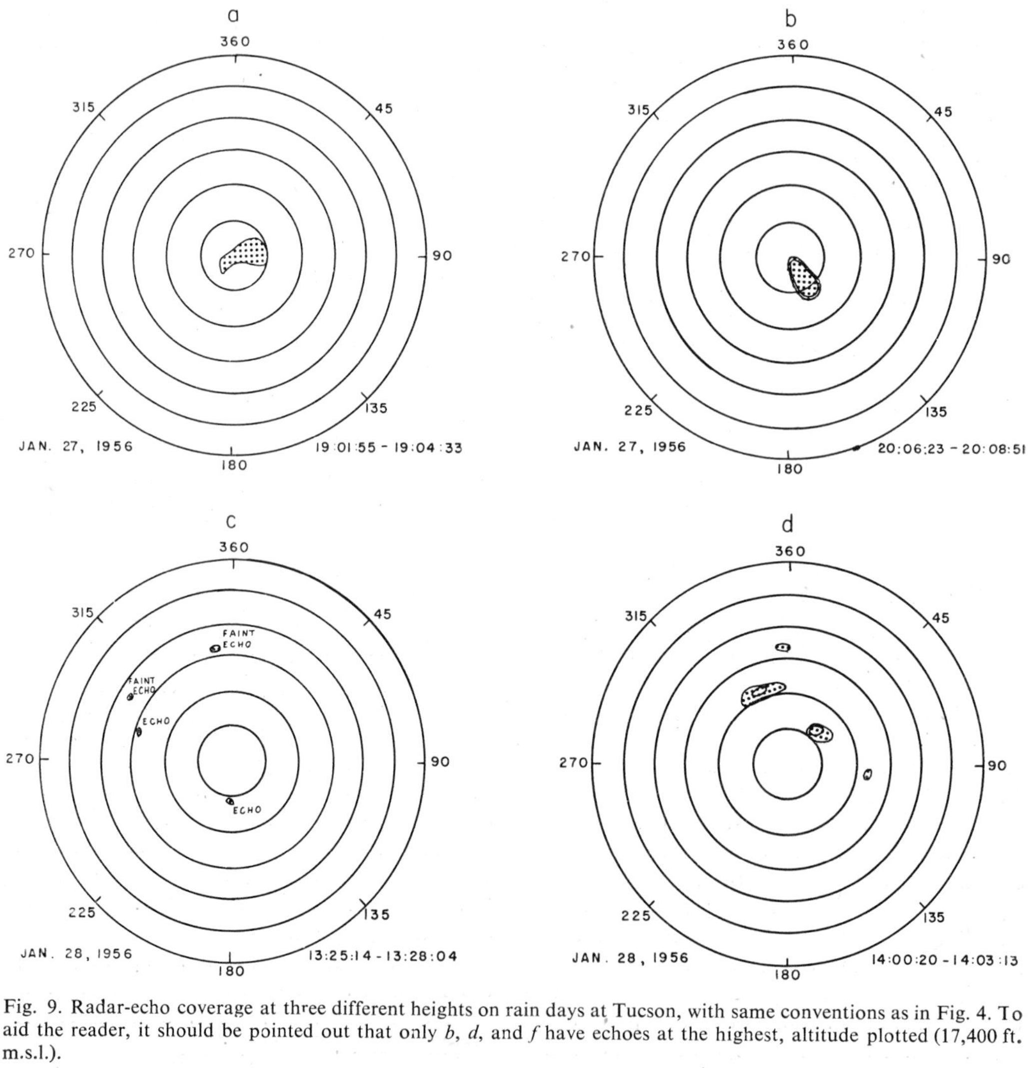

Fig. 9. Radar-echo coverage at three different heights on rain days at Tucson, with same conventions as in Fig. 4. To aid the reader, it should be pointed out that only *b*, *d*, and *f* have echoes at the highest, altitude plotted (17,400 ft. m.s.l.).

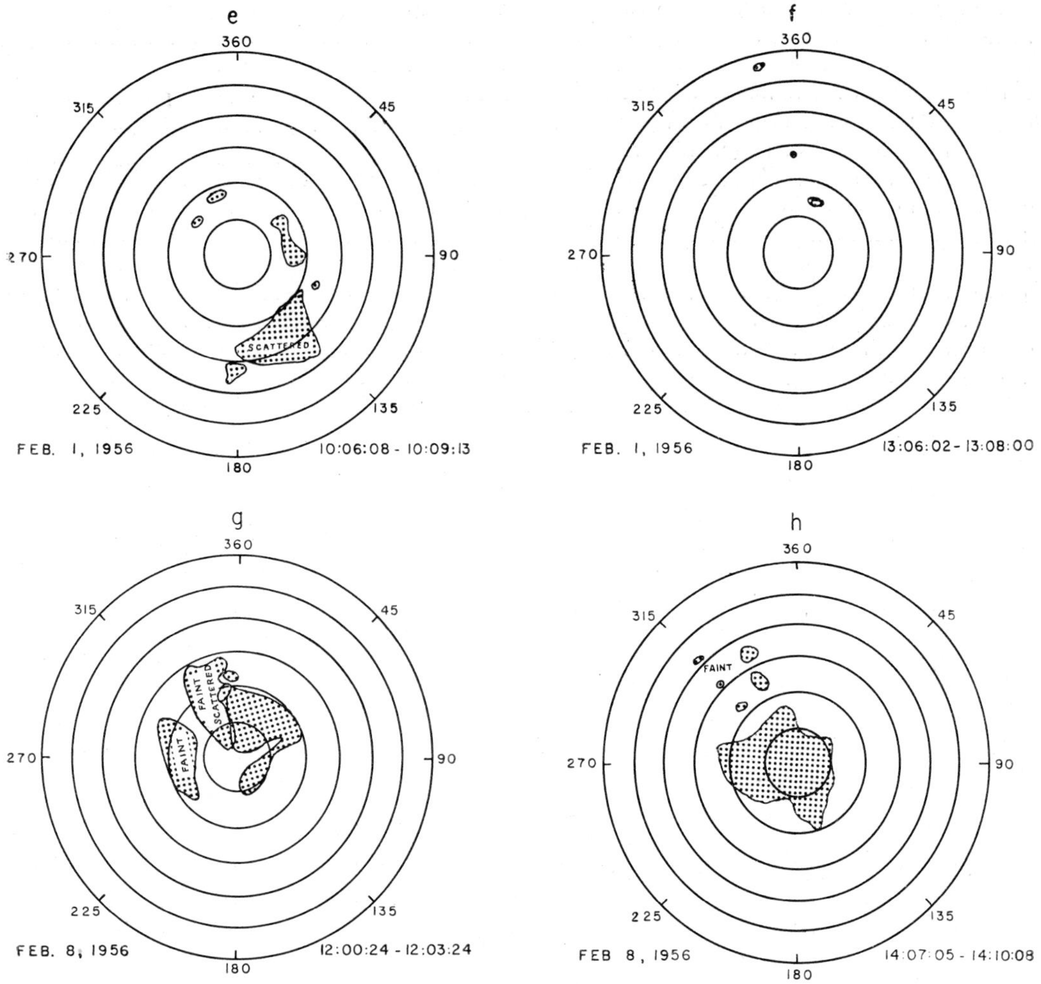

Fig. 9. Explanation see previous page.

From a consideration of all of the available radar data plus visual observations from the air and from the ground it appears that over the *broad* areas of *light* rain in winter storms, the principal drop growth is in the layer clouds below 10,000 ft, but the generating levels of the precipitation are to be found from higher clouds, perhaps even cirrus. It is suggested that ice crystals in sizes and quantities too small to be detected by the 3-cm TPS-10 radar are floating down to these lower clouds. These clouds are then either naturally seeded by the ice crystals or provide accretion growth of the ice particles. Whether or not the low layers represent a "bright band" or melting layer is irrelevant to the present argument. *Moderate* to *heavy* rains are from convective-type cells either embedded in the stratified layers or standing separately.

One might expect that the K-band radar would be able to detect the upper-level particles which the TPS-10 would not find. However, in the type of situation described, attenuation of the radar pulse within the lower cloud probably defeats this purpose. Insufficient experience and observation with the K-band radar were obtained to verify this point. The film strips on January 21 suggest that the upper layer is detected only when the lower one is thin.

When the state of the sky has permitted, the author has seen ice crystals falling from high and middle clouds on frequent occasions in winter in the Tucson area as well as other parts of the mountain states. Observers in the western mountain areas are well familiar with this type of occurrence which is much more evident than in more humid areas. The falling crystals can be observed on occasions to go into lower clouds and initiate rain out of them. This sometimes causes the entire system to become cellular in character. In some instances, with otherwise clear air, it looks as though snow falls from these upper clouds for a long enough time to bring the air to saturation to form a thin veil of cloud below the generating layer which, sooner or later, can be observed to create a light rain shower at the ground.

The extent to which these conditions also exist in more humid regions is indicated in the report by HALL (1957) of precipitating cloud situations in western Washington and Oregon. He states: "Usually one could define an upper and lower cloud deck, the lower containing the primary water supply and the upper furnishing ice crystals which fell into the lower deck and rapidly increased in size. These two decks correspond to what Bergeron has termed the 'releaser' and the 'spender' clouds. On some occasions, however, the upper deck would be absent, with the ice crystals being generated in the upper portions of the lower deck. At other times, the lower deck would be missing and precipitation was limited to snow showers aloft which usually evaporated before reaching the ground."

8. Factors Related to Seedability

It is probably improper to examine data concerning clouds in a region and state emphatically whether or not artificial cloud modification would produce desirable results. Certain modifications have been indicated in preliminary, as yet unpublished, summer tests in the Tucson area by Battan and Kassander. In judging the feasibility of such methods in winter situations, certain features stand out as being important. The following factors and their characteristics in the winter situations are listed:

1) Frequency of rain-producing clouds. While in summer such clouds occur over the mountains nearly every day, in winter they occur irregularly, averaging five days per month, but highly variable. (In 1958 there were no rain days in Tucson in January but a record-breaking 18 in March. If the 10-year period used in this study had not included 1958, March would have had fewer rain days in 10 years than January.)

2) Area of Occurrence. The tendency for the clouds to form in favored, usually predictable,

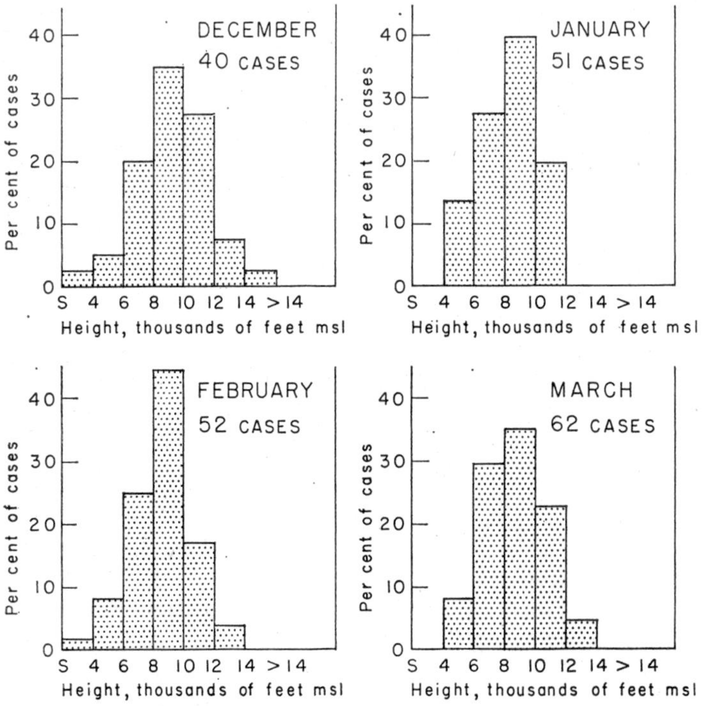

Fig. 10. Height of the freezing level on rain days in winter months at Tucson for the 10 years December 1948 to March 1958, inclusive.

locations over the mountains in summer is not repeated in winter.

3) Temperature lapse rates. The temperature decrease with height in winter rain situations is not entirely unfavorable for upward diffusion of such materials as silver iodide smokes. Except for morning conditions or in occasional situations of marked stratification, the temperature lapse rate is nearly as great in winter as in summer in many rain-producing cases.

4) Nature of precipitation process. A great deal of natural seeding by ice crystals, as described previously, exists in the winter clouds. In the flight of January 21, ice crystals already were present at a temperature of $-5°$ C.

5) Height of the freezing level. On rain days in Tucson, selected on the basis of more than a trace of rain at six stations in and around Tucson, the height of the freezing level, averaged by months for a 10-year period of record, is shown in Fig. 10. Cumulative percentages for different heights are shown in Fig. 11. (Only December is sufficiently distinct from the other three months to warrant a separate curve.) The height of the freezing level is quite variable, having extremes ranging from the surface to above 14,000 feet. The median is at about 9,500 feet in December and at about 8,500 feet in the other three months. For January, February and March, the freezing level on rain days is below 7,200 in one-fourth of the cases, above 9,800 in one-fourth and between these two levels in the remaining half of the cases. It is interesting to note that, averaged for all days (mostly rainless), the 0° C level is near 10,000 feet. This merely indicates that extratropical cyclones tend to be cold aloft, which is a well-known statistic of meteorology.

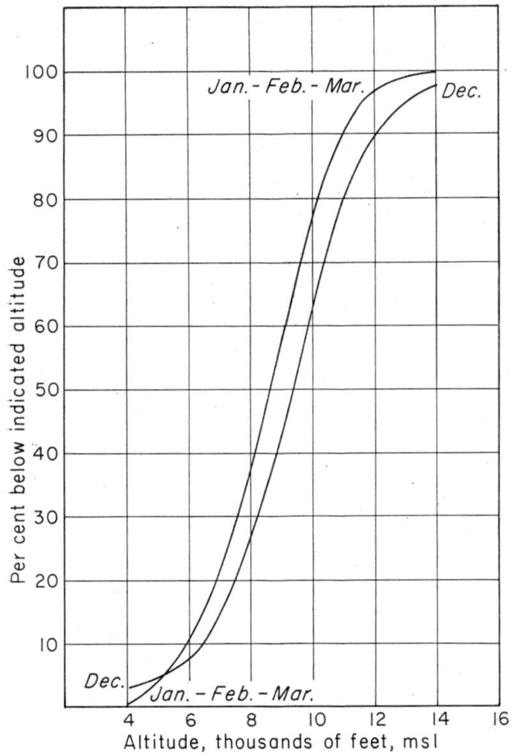

Fig. 11. Height of freezing level for rain days at Tucson corresponding to Fig. 10 but represented in cumulative percentages. January, February and March are sufficiently alike to be combined in one curve, but December is represented separately.

In connection with some of the cases with high freezing levels, the possibility of rain from an all-liquid process should not be ruled out. A number of warm rains have been observed personally by the author in which indirect evidence indicated no ice crystals were present.

9. Chloride Particles in Winter

On several of the flights in the first half of February 1956 chloride particles were collected by the Chicago group using the technique developed at Chicago for collecting and counting on membrance filters. The sizing and counting was done by personnel of the University of Arizona. The results are presented in Table 1, averaged for the eight flights and separated according to whether the diameter of the particle was greater or less than 3 microns.

Some of the extreme values can be explained in terms of the prevailing weather situations. On February 8 cyclonic conditions with a steep lapse rate prevailed over Arizona, with a cut-off low on the 500-mb chart to the NNW. On February 10 Arizona was in the eastern end of a large Pacific anticyclone with strong indications of subsidence appearing in the sounding.

The separation of the data into classes of particles of dry diameters greater or less than 3 microns follows a practice started in earlier Chicago data. At sizes from 3 to 10 microns we are getting into the range of the so-called giant nuclei which, upon reaching saturation, produce drops so large as to start the precipitation process by accretion.

On any given day the counts tended to decrease with height, but not always. The interdiurnal changes were of the same order of magnitude as the altitude changes, within the height range investigated.

Table 1. Results of Chloride Particle Collections in Arizona. February 1956.
Numbers of Particles per Cubic Meter

Date	Altitudes, ft.	$< 3\mu$	$> 3\mu$	Total
Feb. 2	6,000—12,000	3.74×10^4	7.4×10^3	4.48×10^4
Feb. 3	4,000—10,000	2.3×10^4	3.7×10^3	2.7×10^4
Feb. 8	11,000—15,000	6.1×10^4	6.0×10^4	1.21×10^5
Feb. 9	4,000—15,000	3.7×10^3	3.0×10^3	6.7×10^3
Feb. 10	4,000—15,000	1.04×10^3	7.6×10^2	1.8×10^3
Feb. 11	400—10,000	3.1×10^3	2.2×10^3	5.3×10^3
Feb. 13[1])	10,000	1.46×10^4	2.2×10^4	3.66×10^4
Average		2.0×10^4	1.42×10^4	3.47×10^4

[1]) Only one filter counted on Feb. 13.

It is of interest to compare the collections on these flights with those made in Arizona in January of 1955. In the 1955 data counts were made only on those filters exposed while flying at the 15,000-foot level. The average number of chloride particles of diameter greater than 3 microns at this height in 1955 (16 flights) was 1.64×10^3. This is an order of magnitude lower than the average for all the 1956 flights, but of three samples taken at 15,000 feet in 1956 (Feb. 8, 9, and 10) the average number greater than 3 microns was 1.74×10^3, although one at 13,000 feet on February 8 (the day of unusually high counts) gave 5.7×10^4. The agreement is considered to be reasonable.

It is interesting also to make a comparison with counts made elsewhere. The numbers are in the same general range as those of some of the flights made in the Middle West and reported by Byers *et al.* (1957). The Arizona values are for the most part lower than in the summer flights of the Middle West but are in close agreement with the counts obtained on some November 1954 flights at Champaign, Ill.

From the data one must conclude that there is no dearth of salt nuclei, even giant ones, in winter in Arizona. The possibility of starting warm rains through condensation and accretion is apparent.

Acknowledgement

This paper represents the results of team research in which the individual contributions have been submerged. Edward L. Harrington was in charge of the flight work and performed the difficult analysis of flight 266. University of Arizona personnel under Dr. A. R. Kassander handled the ground radar data collection and analysis and evaluation of the particle collections.

REFERENCES

Austin, P. M., 1951: Radar observation of a frontal storm, *Bull. Am. Met. Soc.*, **32**, 136—145.

Battan, L. J., and Reitan, C. H., 1957: Droplet size measurements in convective clouds, *in* Artificial Stimulation of Rain, pp. 184—191. New York (Pergamon Press).

Braham, R. R., Jr., Battan, L. J., and Byers, H. R., 1957: Artificial nucleation of cumulus clouds, *in* Cloud and weather modification, *Am. Met. Soc. Monographs*, **2**, No. 11.

Byers, H. R., Sievers, J. R., and Tufts, B. J., 1957: Distribution in the atmosphere of certain particles capable of serving as condensation nuclei, *In Artificial Stimulation of Rain*, pp. 47—72. New York (Pergamon Press).

Cunningham, R. M., 1951: Some observations of natural precipitation processes, *Bull. Am. Met. Soc.*, **32**, 334—343.

Cunningham, R. M., and Atlas, D., 1954: Growth of hydrometeors as calculated from aircraft and radar observations, *Am. Met. Soc.-Roy. Met. Soc. Proc Toronto Met. Conference*, pp. 276—289.

Dennis, A. S., 1954: Initiation of showers by snow, *J. Met.*, **11**, 157—162.

Des Jardins, R. B., 1957: The distribution of clouds at Tucson, Arizona, with respect to type, amount, and time of observation, *Univ. of Ariz. Inst. Atmos. Phys. Sci. Rep.* No. 6.

Gunn, K. L. S., Langleben, M. P., and Dennis, A. S., 1954: Radar evidence of a generating level for snow, *J. Met.*, **11**, 20—26.

Gunn, K. L. S., Langleben, M. P., Dennis, A. S., and Marshall, J. S., 1955: The effect of wind shear on falling precipitation, *J. Met.*, **12**, 339—349.

Hall, F., 1957: The Weather Bureau ACN Project, *in* Cloud and weather modification, *Am. Met. Soc. Monographs*, **2**, No. 11.

Wexler, R., 1955: The melting layer. *Met. Radar Studies Blue Hill Observ.*, No. 3.

(Manuscript received July 21, 1958)

Dynamics of Convective Vortices and Eye Formation

By H. L. Kuo

Massachusetts Institute of Technology, Chambridge, Massachusetts

Abstract

The mechanics that lead to the formation of the eye in convective vortices is analyzed and the dynamical significance in the maintenance and further development of the systems is investigated by applying general integral relations expressing the conservations of absolute momentum, potential temperature and total energy.

The energy integral is first rearranged, with the help of the law of conservation of potential temperature, in such a way as to express the change of the sum of the internal and potential energies along a streamline in terms of the horizontal pressure difference, even though the streamline itself is not horizontal. When this energy integral is combined with the integral expressing the conservation of absolute momentum, it is then found that there exists a limiting radius beyond which the converging current cannot penetrate; it must therefore turn upward and then outward at upper levels. The surface defined by this streamline is identified with the wall of the eye; it separates the vortex into an outer and an inner region.

When friction is included, the absolute momentum is no longer conserved. However, by assuming the net influx of momentum into the region bounded by two concentric circles to be proportional to the flow across the outer circle, a new law of distribution of the tangential velocity along the streamline is found, in which the tangential velocity becomes proportional to the (β-1) power of the radial distance r, where β is called a dissipation factor. The value of β is found to be about 0.4. The radius of the eye obtained from this law of distribution agree quite well with the observed values.

The motion inside the eye and its dynamic significance are discussed. Since the maximum tangential velocity occurs just outside the eye, and there exists a very large horizontal shear, strong lateral mixing will take place and the air inside the eye must be dragged into the upward and outward motion, which reduces the pressure inside the core and in turn strengthens the converging flow. A descending motion will also be induced near the center as a result of the ascending motion near the rim of the eye.

1. Introduction

One of the oddest phenomena in tropical storms is the existence of a central core, across whose boundary precipitation ceases abruptly and the wind subsides suddenly from the highest velocity to a very light or even calm condition. Phenomena of such peculiar nature never fails to raise scientific curiosity and various speculations have been advanced to explain their main features. Haurwitz has argued that in order to have the wind to subside at higher levels, the temperature inside the eye must be higher than outside, which he ascribed to a descending motion near the center. Byers (1944) and Syono (1951) strived to explain the eye as a consequence of the large centrifugal force associated with the strong rotational motion. More recently Abdulla (1953) constructed a two-layer model of the atmosphere, in which motion takes place only in the lower layer and is one-dimensional. He then invoked the combined actions of a circular vortex and a sink to demonstrate the existence of a central core. Such an explanation has also been suggested by many others, for example, by Wexler (1947). The dynamics of such a system is the same as in gas dynamics (see Howarth, 1953). The difficulty of this explanation is that it is impossible to realize it in the atmosphere, and hard to fit into the overall dynamics of the system. Furthermore, the representation of the system by a single uniform layer implies similar motion all over the system, for example, the lowering of the interface toward the center implies a descending motion both inside and outside the eye, which is quite contrary to what is actually happening in a hurricane and is not easily disposed of by some proper interpretation.

The present paper is an attempt to explain the formation of the eye and its role in the further development of the system by the general dynamic principles without much recourse to arbitrary devices. The discussions will be limited to the structure of the system under steady state conditions. The system is assumed to be essentially symmetric with respect to the center within certain distance r_0 from the center. Minor asymmetries are eliminated by integrating the relevant equations with respect to the polar angle λ (see KUO, 1956).

Unlike most other theoretical studies, which usually propose to seek solutions for the dynamic equations for the whole field, we shall concentrate on the lowest branch of the system of currents which is supposed to be converging toward the center, where the pressure is relatively low and the temperature relatively high. The question as to how such a low pressure area is set up will not be discussed in this paper. Also, the system is visualized as a semi-open one. The region outside the radius r_0 is considered as a large reservoir and acts as a regulator, to provide proper cooling or heating and a proper momentum source for the system, so that a quasi-steady state can be maintained.

The essence of the theory is based on the integral relations concerning the distribution of the angular momentum and the total energy along a streamline. In case the motion is frictionless and adiabatic, both these quantities will remain constant along a given streamline. Since the total energy is limited according to the energy integral while the momentum equation depicts inverse proportionality between the tangential velocity and the distance from the center, there exists a minimum radius beyond which the converging current cannot penetrate. Thus this current must turn upward and outward, thereby forming a wall between the outside and inside. This is considered to be the wall of the eye.

Although the value of the minimum radius thus obtained is comparable to the radius of the eye of an ordinary hurricane, it appears to be somewhat too large. This discrepancy is removed when the influence of friction is taken into consideration. It is shown that when frictional dissipation is included, the tangential velocity increases at a much slower rate as the distance r from the center decreases, therefore the converging current can reach a much smaller radius. The values of the minimum radius obtained from this new law are all within the range of the observed radii of the eye of hurricanes.

Concerning the motion inside the central core, it is the writer's opinion that turbulent friction plays a decisive role. Since the tangential velocity reaches its maximum strength just outside the core and since the horizontal shear is very large, strong lateral mixing must be present and the current just outside the eye must drag part of the air inside into its upward and outward journey. A descending motion will then also be set up near the center. As a result of this frictionally driven circulation the pressure inside the core will be reduced and temperature near the center raised, therefore it represents a very important mechanism for the maintenance and further development of the system.

2. The governing equations

Assuming that the hydrostatic approximation is valid for the pressure distribution, it is convenient to take the hydrostatic pressure as the vertical coordinate and replace $w\partial/\partial z$ by $\omega\partial/\partial z_1$, where $z_1 = Hp/p_0$, H being the height of the homogeneous atmosphere and $\omega = dz_1/dt \approx \approx -\varrho w/\bar{\varrho}$. We note that z_1 is in height units but is proportional to p, and therefore increases downward. The advantage of this coordinate is that the continuity equation takes the same simple form of an incompressible fluid,although the effect of compressibility is implicitly included. For the axisymmetric motion[1] we are considering, this equation may be written as

$$\frac{\partial ur}{r\partial r} + \frac{\partial \omega}{\partial z_1} = 0 \qquad (1)$$

where u is the radial velocity in the direction of increasing r, r being the distance from the axis of symmetry. Thus a stream function for the meridional circulation may be introduced, such that

$$u = -\frac{1}{r}\frac{\partial \psi}{\partial z_1}, \qquad \omega = \frac{1}{r}\frac{\partial \psi}{\partial r} \qquad (2)$$

Even though the hydrostatic pressure is being used as the vertical coordinate, we can still preserve the vertical acceleration in the vertical equation of motion, at least approximately. Thus we may multiply the vertical equation of motion by $\frac{H}{p_0}\frac{\partial z}{\partial p}$ and replace $\frac{H}{p_0}\frac{\partial z}{\partial p}\frac{dw}{dt}$ by $\frac{d\omega}{dt}$. The equa-

[1] We consider that the relevant equations have been integrated with respect to the polar angles and minor asymmetries so removed (see KUO, 1956).

tions of motion in the radial, vertical and tangential directions may then be written in the following forms.[2]

$$\frac{\partial u}{\partial t} - \omega\xi - \frac{v}{r}\frac{\partial M}{\partial r} = $$

$$= -\frac{\partial}{\partial r}\left(\Phi + \frac{q^2}{2}\right) + \nu\left(\nabla^2 u - \frac{1}{r^2}u\right) \quad (3)$$

$$\frac{\partial \omega}{\partial t} + u\xi - \frac{v}{r}\frac{\partial M}{\partial z_1} = $$

$$= -\frac{\partial}{\partial z_1}\left(\Phi + \frac{q^2}{2}\right) - \frac{RT}{z_1} + \nu\nabla^2\omega \quad (4)$$

$$\frac{\partial M}{\partial t} + u\frac{\partial M}{\partial r} + \omega\frac{\partial M}{\partial z_1} = \nu D^2 M \quad (5)$$

where v is the tangential velocity, $q^2 = u^2 + v^2 + \omega^2$, $\xi = \frac{\partial \omega}{\partial r} - \frac{\partial u}{\partial z_1}$ is the vorticity of the meridional motion, $\Phi = gz$ is the geopotential of the isobaric surfaces, $M = vr + \frac{1}{2}fr^2$ is the absolute tangential momentum, f the Coriolis parameter, T the absolute temperature, R the gas constant, ν is the viscosity coefficient, $\nabla^2 = \partial^2/\partial r^2 + \frac{1}{r}\partial/\partial r + \partial^2 \partial z_1^2$ and $D^2 = \partial^2/\partial r^2 - \frac{1}{r}\partial/\partial r + \partial^2/\partial z_1^2$.

In addition, we have the first law of thermodynamics, which may be more conveniently expressed in terms of the potential temperature $\vartheta = T(p_0/p)^K$ and is given by

$$\frac{\partial \vartheta}{\partial t} + u\frac{\partial \vartheta}{\partial r} + \omega\frac{\partial \vartheta}{\partial z_1} = Q/c_p \quad (6)$$

where Q denotes the nonadiabatic addition of heat.

Eliminating $\Phi + q^2/2$ from (3) and (4) we obtain the equation for the rate of change of the vorticity ξ. In terms of the stream function ψ we have $\xi = \frac{1}{r}D^2\psi$ and the vorticity equation is given by

$$\frac{\partial}{\partial t}D^2\psi + \frac{1}{r}\frac{\partial \psi}{\partial r}\frac{\partial}{\partial z^1}D^2\psi - r\frac{\partial \psi}{\partial z_1}\frac{\partial}{\partial r}\left(\frac{D^2\psi}{r_2}\right) = $$

$$= -\frac{R}{z_1}r\frac{\partial T}{\partial r} - \frac{2M}{r^2}\frac{\partial M}{\partial z_1} + \nu D^4\psi \quad (7)$$

[2] For ordinary rotating systems, a centrifugal force will be present in the radial equation of motion. This term is absent for earth's atmosphere because of the ellipsoidal shape of the earth.

It is seen that an increase of temperature toward the center along the isobaric surface, which measures the solenoids field in the meridional plane, tends to increase the vorticity ξ.

It may be remarked that if the center of the system is moving with a constant horizontal velocity V, these equations also hold for the motion relative to the moving center 0.

3. Conservative properties for frictionless and adiabatic flow

Since the viscosity of the air is quite small, the general flow pattern will be determined largely by the inertial terms of the equations of motion, except near the ground where internal and ground friction may play some role. We shall therefore at first disregard the viscous effect. Similarly, nonadiabatic effects will also be neglected. The equations (5) and (6) then show that the absolute momentum M and the potential temperature ϑ are then both conserved for the individual particles.

We shall limit ourselves further by assuming a steady state condition. The quantities M and ϑ will then both be conserved along a streamline, i.e.,

$$M = c_1(\psi) \quad (8)$$

$$\vartheta = c_2(\psi) \quad (9)$$

It may be remarked that these results can only be considered as first approximations. The unrealistic part of these distributions are removed by the inclusion of the frictional and nonadiabatic effects.

The equations (3) and (4) may then be written as

$$\frac{1}{r}\frac{\partial \psi}{\partial r}\xi = \frac{\partial}{\partial r}\left(\Phi + \frac{1}{2}q^2 + c_pT\right) - $$

$$-\frac{v}{r}\frac{\partial M}{\partial r} - c_p\left(\frac{p}{P_0}\right)^K\frac{\partial \vartheta}{\partial r} \quad (10)$$

$$\frac{1}{r}\frac{\partial \psi}{\partial z}\xi - \frac{\partial}{\partial z_1}\left(\Phi + \frac{1}{2}q^2 + c_pT\right) - $$

$$-\frac{v}{r}\frac{\partial M}{\partial z_1} - c_p\left(\frac{p}{P_0}\right)^K\frac{\partial \vartheta}{\partial z_1} \quad (11)$$

Multiplying (10) by δr and (11) by δz_1, where δr and δz_1 are the components of a line segment ds, and adding, we then obtain

$$\frac{1}{r}\xi\delta\psi = \delta H + \frac{1}{2}f\delta M - \frac{M}{r^2}\delta M - c_p\left(\frac{p}{P_0}\right)^K\delta\vartheta \quad (12)$$

where $H = c_pT + gz + q^2/2$ is the total energy and δ denotes the change of the quantity along the segment ds.

If ds is taken to be a segment of a streamline, we then have $\delta\psi = 0$. Since M and ϑ remain constant along the streamline, (12) reduces to $\delta H = 0$. Therefore H also remains constant along the streamline. We have

$$H \equiv c_pT + gz + q^2/2 = c_3(\psi) \qquad (13)$$

This is the Bernouilli equation of the system. Thus for this case, all the three quantities M, ϑ and H are conserved along a given streamline.

If, on the other hand, s is not a streamline, we may then divide eq. (12) by $\delta\psi/r$ and obtain

$$D^2\psi = r^2F_1(\psi) - F_2(\psi) - r^2\left(\frac{p}{P_0}\right)^K F_3(\psi) \quad (12\,\mathrm{a})$$

where $F_1(\psi) = \partial\left(H + \frac{1}{2}fM\right)\Big/\partial\psi$, $F_2(\psi) = M\partial M/\partial\psi$ and $F_3(\psi) = c_p\partial\vartheta/\partial\psi$. Since the quantities M, ϑ and H all remain constant along a streamline, F_1, F_2 and F_3 are functions of ψ alone. Hence if M, ϑ and H are given in terms of ψ for any r, for example, at $r = r_0$, then the streamline pattern will be determined by this equation.

Since $T = \vartheta(p/P_0)^K$ and ϑ is conserved along the streamline, it is convenient to write the Bernoulli equation in the following form:

$$H \equiv c_p\left(\frac{p}{P_0}\right)^K \vartheta + gz + \frac{q^2}{2} = c_3(\psi) \quad (13\,\mathrm{a})$$

From this equation it is seen that an increase of the kinetic energy of the particle must be accompanied either by a decrease of the pressure or a decrease of the potential energy. When the motion is purely horizontal, the maximum increase of kinetic energy is measured by the maximum drop of pressure along the streamline. However, in the vertical direction, a decrease of pressure is always accomp nied by an increase of the potential energy. It follows that this equation is not very convenient to apply. We shall therefore transform it into anot er form, so as to express the two quantities $c_pT + gz$ in terms of the horizontal pressure distribution, irrespective of the change of height of the streamline.

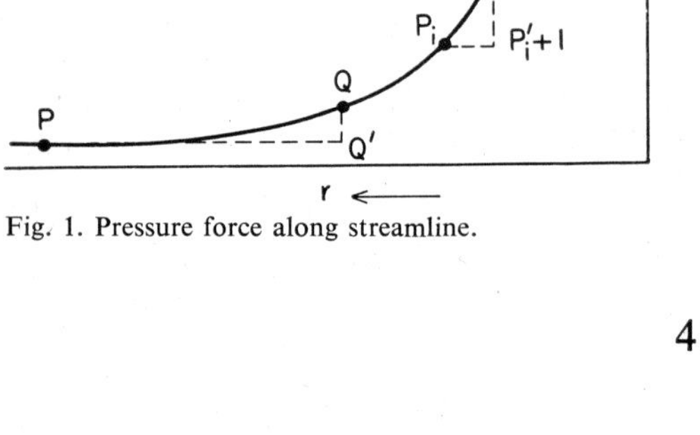

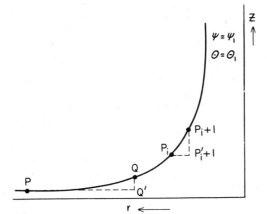

Fig. 1. Pressure force along streamline.

4. Change of kinetic energy in terms of horizontal pressure field

To do this, let us consider the streamline $\psi = \psi_1$ in fig. 1, along which the potential temperature is ϑ_1, and p and Q are two points on this streamline, whose temperature and height are T_0, z_0 and T_Q and z_Q, respectively. We shall take P, where the pressure is p_0, as the reference point, and let Q' be the point at the same height as P but directly below Q. For small values $z_Q - z_0$ we may then write

$$\begin{aligned} c_pT_Q + gz_Q &= c_pT_{Q'} + gz_0 + \\ &\quad + c_p(z_Q - z_0)\left\{\left(\frac{\partial T}{\partial z}\right)_{Q'} + \frac{g}{c_p}\right\} \\ &= c_pT_{Q'} + gz_0 + c_p\left(\frac{p'}{P_0}\right)^K(\vartheta_Q - \vartheta_{Q'}) \\ &= gz_0 + c_pT_0\left(\frac{p'}{P_0}\right)^K \end{aligned}$$

where the relation $\vartheta_Q = \vartheta_P = T_0\,(p/P_0)^{-K}$ has been used, and p' is the pressure at Q'. Therefore the change of q^2 from P to Q along the streamline is given by

$$\delta q^2 = 2c_pT_0\left\{1 - \left(\frac{p'}{P_0}\right)^K\right\} \qquad (14)$$

This formula is strictly valid only for small distance between p and Q, or when the atmosphere is isentropic. For application to large vertical distance and when ϑ varies from streamline to streamline, we may divide the streamline PQ into small segments, one of which is represented by $P_i\,P_{i+1}$ in fig. 1, whose horizontal and vertical projections are $P_iP'_{i+1}$ and $P'_{i+1}P_{i+1}$, respectively. Taking the sum of the changes of q^2 along each small segment we then obtain

$$\left.\begin{aligned}\delta q^2 &= 2c_p \sum_{i=0}^{N} T_i \left\{1 - \left(\frac{p'_{i+1}}{p_i}\right)^K\right\} \\ &= 2\sum_{i=0}^{N} \frac{\Delta p_i}{\varrho_i}\left\{1 + \frac{1-k}{2}\frac{\Delta p_i}{p_i} + \ldots\right\}\end{aligned}\right\} \quad (15\,\text{a})$$

When $\Delta p_i/\varrho_i$ is fairly independent of height, we may take all the horizontal segments at the same level, for example, at the level z_0; then the sum on the right of (15 a) will be the same as that of (14), and the change of the kinetic energy is obtained from the horizontal pressure field at a constant level.

The exact formula for the change of q^2 along the streamline is obtained by integrating δH from P to Q. We then obtain

$$\delta q^2 = -2g\delta z - 2c_p \int_P^{Q'} \left(\vartheta \frac{\partial \pi}{\partial r} + \pi \frac{\partial \vartheta}{\partial r}\right) dr - $$

$$- 2c_p \int_{Q'}^{Q} \left(\vartheta \frac{\partial \pi}{\partial z} + \pi \frac{\partial \vartheta}{\partial z}\right) dz$$

$$= -2c_p \int_P^{Q'} \vartheta \frac{\partial \pi}{\partial r} dr -$$

$$- 2c_p \int_{PQ'Q} \pi \left(\frac{\partial \vartheta}{\partial r} dr + \frac{\partial \vartheta}{\partial z} dz\right)$$

where $\pi = (p/P_0)^K$. Since $d\vartheta = 0$ along the streamline PQ, we may replace the last integral by the integral along the closed curve $PQ'QP$. Applying Stokes circulation theorem we then obtain

$$\delta q^2 = 2c_p \overline{T}_0 \left\{1 - \left(\frac{p'}{p_0}\right)^K\right\} + 2c_p$$

$$\iint_S \frac{1}{\vartheta}\left(\frac{\partial T}{\partial r}\frac{\partial \vartheta}{\partial z} - \frac{\partial T}{\partial z}\frac{\partial \vartheta}{\partial r}\right) drdz \quad (15\,\text{b})$$

where $\overline{T}_0$ is the average temperature along PQ and S is the area enclosed by the curve $PQ'QP$.

We note that the second integral is proportional to the solenoids in the plane area $PQ'QP$, and that when the temperature increases toward the center and when ϑ increases upwards both of the two terms in this integral are negative. Therefore δq^2 is less than that given by the first term.

To estimate the magnitude of the second integral in (15 b), let us take $\Delta_r T = 5°$ C and $\Delta_r \vartheta = 12°$ C. We then find $\delta q^2 \approx -100$ m^2 sec^{-2}, which is only a small fraction of the first integral and may therefore be neglected. Therefore eq. (14) can be used as a first approximation even for large δz.

5. Formation of the eye and determination of its radius

As has been mentioned in the introduction, we shall discuss only the mechanisms that will maintain a steady state, and not the detailed developments that lead to the different stages of the vortex motion. For this purpose we shall begin by assuming that a region of relatively higher temperature and lower pressure is present and the air near the ground is converging towards the low center. Since we are dealing with a steady state condition, the lower margin of this converging current can be represented by a streamline. The origin of this converging current is considered to be the region outside the radius r_0, which we shall consider as a large reservoir, and which is to provide the converging current with specified properties and is to receive the returning current from above. In this way we avoid the necessity of drawing closed streamlines, which invariably will introduce some difficulty, or considering an infinite domain, which is equally undesirable.

According to equation (8) and the definition of M, the tangential velocity v increases with decreasing r and becomes inversely proportional to r for small r. If this streamline is to reach the center, the tangential velocity will become infinite. However, according to equation (14) or (15 a, b), the total kinetic energy that can be gained by the current is limited, therefore this cannot happen. In other words, the converging current cannot penetrate a certain minimum radius r_m and must turn upward and eventually outward at higher levels, since the radial pressure gradient usually decreases with elevation. The surface of revolution defined by this streamline is identified with the wall of the eye.

Since the pressure force $\frac{1}{\varrho}\,\partial p/\partial r$ usually decreases only slightly upward in the lower atmosphere, the actual gain of kinetic energy is a little less than that given by equation (14). Denoting the minimum radius that the lowest streamline can reach by r_m and the surface pressure at this radius by P'_m, we then have

$$\left.\begin{aligned} q_m^2 &= q_0^2 + 2c_pT_0\left\{1-\left(\frac{p'_m}{p_0}\right)^K\right\} \\ &\leqslant q_0^2 + 2c_pT_0\left\{1-\left(\frac{p_c}{p_0}\right)^K\right\}\end{aligned}\right\} \quad (16)$$

where q_0 is the wind speed at P and p_c is the surface pressure at the center. In applying this equation, we may take P far away from the center where q_0^2 may be considered as very small.

For the kind of motion we are studying, the vertical velocity is very small and can be disregarded in q^2. As a matter of fact, if the hydrostatic equation has been used instead of (4), we shall have $q^2 = u^2+v^2$. At the limiting radius $r = r_m$, where the total kinetic energy reaches its maximum, the radial velocity diminishes to zero, therefore we have $q_{\max}^2 = v_{\max}^2$. Accordingly (16) gives

$$v_{\max}^2 \leqslant q_0^2 + 2c_pT_0\left\{1-\left(\frac{p_c}{p_0}\right)^K\right\} \quad (17)$$

If P is chosen as the point where the particle is drawn in with a zero velocity, we then have

$$v_{\max}^2 \leq \frac{2}{\gamma-1}\, a_0^2\left\{1-\left(\frac{p_c}{p_0}\right)^K\right\} \quad (17\,a)$$

where $a_0 = \sqrt{\gamma R T_0}$ is the velocity of sound at temperature T_0.

In addition, the conservation of the absolute momentum M along the streamline demands $M)_{r=r_m} = M_0$, where M_0 is its value at $r = r_0$ and $M)_{r_m}$ the value at the innermost point $r = r_m$. Since $M = vr+\frac{1}{2}fr^2$ and $v = v_{\max}$ at $r=r_m$, we have

$$v_{\max} r_m\left(1+\frac{1}{2}\frac{fr_m}{v_{\max}}\right) = M_0$$

and therefore

$$\left.\begin{aligned} r_m &= \frac{M_0}{v_{\max}\left(1+\dfrac{fr_m}{2v_{\max}}\right)} \\ &\approx \frac{M_0}{v_{\max}}\end{aligned}\right\} \quad (18)$$

since fr_m is much smaller than $v_{\max}$ at the minimum radius r_m.

Combining this equation with (17) we then obtain

$$\left.\begin{aligned} r_m &= \frac{M_0}{a_0\sqrt{\dfrac{2}{\gamma-1}\left\{1-\left(\dfrac{p'_m}{p_0}\right)^K\right\}}} \\ &\geqslant \frac{M_0}{a_0\sqrt{\dfrac{2}{\gamma-1}\left\{1-\left(\dfrac{p_c}{p_0}\right)^K\right\}}}\end{aligned}\right\} \quad (19)$$

This equation shows that if M_0 differs from zero, then r_m is greater than a finite value, which means that the converging current is not able to get any nearer to the center than r_m, and therefore it must turn upward and then outward in the upper levels, leaving a central core to be occupied by another regime of motion.

Equation (19) also shows that this minimum radius r_m increases with the value of M_0, and decreases with the pressure depth $p_0 - p_c$. We note that even when the pressure p_c at the center is zero, r_m is still larger than a certain definite value. Therefore a central core which is impenetrable by the converging current will always be present, unless the law of the conservation of tangential momentum is invalid. Thus the existence of such an inner core must be a common feature of such convective vortex systems.

As numerical examples, we take three different cases, with the pressure ratio p_c/p_0 equal to 0.95, 0.97 and 0.98, respectively, and $T_0 = 290°$A. The velocity q_0 at the far away point is assumed to be zero. We then obtain from (17) $v_{\max} =$ $= 93.7$ m sec^{-1}, 71 m sec^{-1} and 58 m sec^{-1} respectively. It is seen that these maximum velocities are rather comparable with those observed in the hurricanes.

To compute the radius of the eye of the hurricane as given by r_m in (19) we need the value of M_0. Assuming the converging current is drawn in from relative rest, M_0 is then given by $M_0 = fr_0^2/2$, and therefore depends upon the latitude and the outer radius r_0. Since as yet the horizontal dimension r_0 has not been fixed, we shall arbitrarily take $r_0 = 500$ km. On the other hand we shall take three different values of the Coriolis parameter, f equals to 2.5×10^{-5} sec^{-1}, 3.75×10^{-5} sec^{-1} and 5.0×10^{-5} sec^{-1}, respectively, corresponding to storms located at latitude 10°, 15° and 20°. The values of M_0 corresponding to these three latitudes and $r_0 = 500$ km are

3.125×10^6 m² sec⁻¹, 4.7×10^6 m² sec⁻¹ and 6.25×10^6 m² sec⁻¹, respectively. Since $M_0 = fr_0^2/2$, the same value of M_0 may represent different combinations of f and r_0.

Using these values of M_0 and the three values of v_{max} corresponding to $p_c/p_0 = 0.95$, 0.97 and 0.98, we find the minimum radius from eq. (19), which are given in table 1. These values are somewhat too large as compared with the radius of the eye of mature hurricanes. Smaller values of r_m will be obtained if we choose smaller values of M_0. However, this is not really necessary, because the inclusion of ground friction will greatly reduce the theoretical value of r_m, as will be shown in the next section.

Table 1. Values of r_m (km) for various M_0 (10^6 m² sec⁻¹) and p_c/p_0

p_c/p_0	M_0		
	3.125	4.70	6.25
0.95	33.4	50.2	66.8
0.97	44.0	66.2	88.0
0.98	53.8	81.0	107.6

It may be remarked that if the system is of very small horizontal dimension so that the Coriolis force can be neglected even in the outer portions of the system, then the tangential flow around the low center can be either cyclonic or anticyclonic, depending on the momentum $M_0 = r_0 v_0$ of the inflow current. Thus smaller vortices such as tornadoes may have either cyclonic or anticyclonic rotation. However, cyclonic roation may be more common than anticyclonic rotation in tornadoes simply because they are usually formed in regions of cyclonic vorticity.

6. Influence of ground friction

When the effect of frictional dissipation is included, the steady state equation of motion in the tangential direction may be written as

$$\frac{\partial(ruv)}{r\partial r} + fu + \frac{\partial(wv)}{\partial z} = \frac{1}{\varrho}\frac{\partial \tau_\vartheta}{\partial z} \qquad (20)$$

where τ_Θ is the tangential shearing stress.

Under normal conditions, τ_Θ decreases very rapidly with elevation and may be considered as approaching practically zero at a height h, which

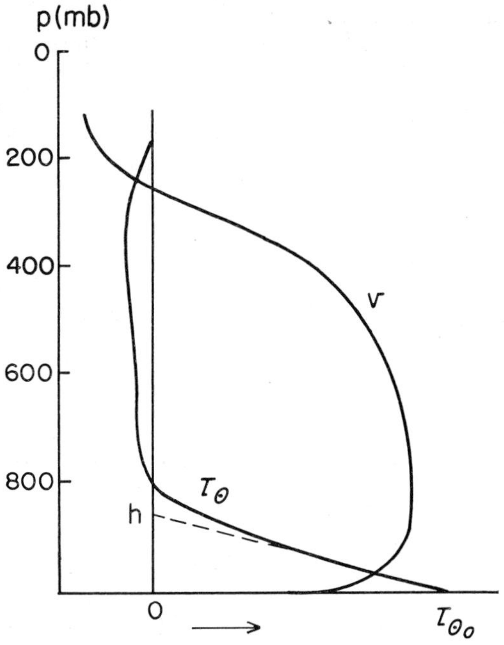

Fig. 2. Schematic vertical distributions of τ_Θ and v.

is of the order of 1 or 2 kilometers. Integrating equation (20) over this surface layer h of the converging current and over the area between the two circles of radii r and $r_1 = r - \delta r$ we obtain

$$(\overline{ruv})_r - (\overline{ruv})_{r_1} + f\tilde{\bar{u}}\frac{r+r_1}{2}\delta r =$$

$$= -\left\{\left(\frac{\tilde{\tau}_\vartheta}{\varrho}\right)_0 + (wv)_h\right\}\frac{r+r_1}{2}\frac{\delta r}{h} \qquad (21)$$

where the bar denotes an average over the depth h, the wavy bar denotes an average over the radial distance δr, and the subscripts o and h denote values at the ground and at the level $z = h$, respectively.

This equation shows that part of the influx of the absolute tangential velocity through the two sides of this annular ring of depth h is being dissipated through friction, and the remaining part is being carried upward into upper levels by the current. We shall now make the two following assumptions: (i) the influx of the relative momentum through the two side-boundaries is equal to a fraction of the flux through the outer circle of radius r, i.e., $(ruv)_r - (ruv)_{r_1} = \alpha uv\delta r$; (ii) the two terms on the right side of equation (21) always bear a constant ratio so that their sum

Table 2a. Velocities at 900 mb and shearing stress τ_{ϑ_0}

r (deg. lat)	1	1.5	2	2.5	3	4	5	6
v m sec^{-1}	28.0	24.7	20.0	17.5	15.0	11.3	7.7	6.7
u m sec^{-1}	9.5	7.6	6.5	5.2	4.5	3.2	2.7	2.2
v/r 10^{-5} sec^{-1}	25.4	14.8	9.0	6.3	4.5	2.5	1.4	1.0
τ_{ϑ_0} dyne cm^{-2}	18.8	9.8	6.1	4.2	3.0	1.8	0.9	0.6

Table 2b. Transport $T_h = \int_0^{1.5\,\mathrm{km}} \left(f + \frac{v}{r}\right) u\varrho dz$ and the ratio τ_{ϑ_0}/T_h

r (deg. lat.)	1	1.5	2	2.5	3	4	5	6
$\left(f+\frac{v}{r}\right) u$ 10^{-2} cm sec^{-2}	29.0	15.4	9.2	6.0	4.3	2.5	1.8	1.3
T dyne cm^{-2}	50.0	26.5	15.8	10.3	7.4	4.3	3.1	2.4
$\tau o/T$	0.38	0.38	0.39	0.41	0.40	0.42	0.29	0.27

can be expressed in terms of $\tau_{\Theta_0}/\varrho_0$ alone. Since $\delta r = r - r_1$ may be taken very small, we may replace $(r+r_1)/2$ by r and omit the wavy bar from the above equation. It can then be written as

$$\alpha \frac{\overline{uv}}{r} + f\bar{u} = -\frac{1+b}{\varrho} \frac{\tau_{\vartheta_0}}{h} \tag{22}$$

where α is a fraction and b is another constant, which is positive if w is positive at $z = h$ and radius r.

It may be remarked that if we treated the radial transport of earth's momentum in the same way as we treated the transport of the relative momentum, the factor α will also occur in the term fu. However, since this latter term will disappear upon integration over the entire depth of the disturbance, it is reasonable to treat these two transports separately.

Since h is relatively small compared with the total depth of the disturbance and since we are not discussing the detailed vertical variations of the various quantities, we may replace each quantity by its mean value within this layer. In this manner the bars can be removed from the equation and τ_{ϑ_0}/h replaced by $\partial\tau_0/\partial z$ (see fig. 2). Thus equation (22) becomes

$$\frac{1}{\varrho}\frac{\partial\tau_\vartheta}{\partial z} = \beta\frac{uv}{r} + \beta' fu \tag{23}$$

where β and β' are two factors representing the fractional contributions to the frictional dissipation of the tangential momentum from the radial transport of the momentum of the relative motion and of earth's rotation, respectively. This relation is considered to be valid in the lowest layer $0 \leq z \leq h$. We may also regard this as an assumption.

The assumption that lead to the establishment of the relation (23) can be justified by the observational fact that the ratio between the surface tangential stress τ_{ϑ_0} and the momentum transfer $\int_0^h \left(f+\frac{v}{r}\right) u\varrho dz = T_h$ remains fairly constant for a large range of r for the average hurricane, as can be seen from the values given in table 2b. The values of the transfer T_h in this table are computed from the velocity components u and v at the 900 mb level given in table 2a, which are obtained from the data given by PALMÉN and RIEHL (1957). The values of the surface tangential stress τ_{ϑ_0} given by these authors are also included in table 2a. In computing the transport T_h it is assumed that the transport at 900 mb is representative of this layer. The depth h is taken to be 1.5 km, $\varrho = 1.15 \times 10^{-3}$ gr. cm^{-3} and the value of f is taken to be 5×10^{-5} sec^{-1}, corresponding to the mean latitude 20 deg.

From table 2b it is seen that for $r < 4$ deg. lat. the ratio τ_{ϑ_0}/T_h has an average value of 0.40 and shows very little variation with r. For the larger radial distances $r = 5°$ and $r = 6°$, this ratio takes a much smaller value 0.28. This characteristic feature is also reflected in the ratio between τ_{ϑ_0} and the total transport $T_H = \int_{100\,\text{mb}}^{p_0} \frac{uv}{r}\frac{dp}{g}$, which is given by PALMÉN and RIEHL (1957) in their table 1. Here again the ratio shows a sudden decrease for $r > 5°$, suggesting that a different mechanism is at work in the outer region. Such a change of the mechanism has also been found by PFEFFER (1956).

Substituting the relation (23) in the tangential equation of motion (20) it reduces to

$$\left\{\frac{\partial v}{\partial r} + (1-\beta)\frac{v}{r} + (1-\beta')f\right\}u + \omega\frac{\partial v}{\partial z_1} = 0 \quad (24)$$

Expressing u and ω in terms of the stream function ψ we find that this equation has the solution

$$\left.\begin{aligned} I &\equiv r_0^{\beta} r^{1-\beta}\left(v + \frac{1-\beta'}{2-\beta}fr\right) \\ &= I_0(\psi) \end{aligned}\right\} \quad (25)$$

showing that this quantity I instead of the absolute momentum M is conserved along the streamline. When $\beta = \beta' = 0$, i..e, when the motion is frictionless, I becomes identical with M and we have the conservation of absolute momentum.

According to this law, the variation of the relative tangential velocity with r is given by

$$r_0^{\beta} r^{1-\beta} v = I_0(\psi) - \frac{1-\beta'}{2-\beta} f r_0^{\beta} r^{2-\beta} \quad (26)$$

For $0 < \beta < 1$, v is still increasing with decreasing r, only at a slower rate than that depicted by the conservation of M. The factor β may very conveniently be called the dissipation factor for the tangential velocity.

As has been mentioned before in connection with table 2, the value of β estimated from the wind data given by PALMÉN and RIEHL (1957) for the average hurricane is about 0.39. For this value of β and not too large r, the second term on the right side of (26) is small and may be neglected. Eq. (26) then gives

$$vr^{0.61} = \text{Const.} \quad (27)$$

Thus as a result of the frictional retardation, the tangential velocity v increases with decreasing r at a much slower rate than that is predicted by the $vr = \text{const.}$ law.

According to HUGHES (1952), the surface tangential wind distribution in hurricanes can be represented by the formulae

$$vr^{\alpha} = \text{Const.}$$

with $\alpha = 0.62$. This agrees quite well with our eq. (27). Thus such wind distributions can be explained by the frictional effect in the surface layer.

7. Radius of penetration in flow with friction

We shall now demonstrate that this frictional effect in the surface boundary layer (large scale) has a very large influence on the minimum radius of penetration r_m; it reduces the values of r_m enormously. Since the effect of friction is not very important in the total energy integral, we shall assume equation (17) to be still valid, so that the maximum value of v is again determined by the values of T_0 and p_c/p_0 as before. Since $r_m \ll r_0$, eq. (26) gives

$$\left.\begin{aligned} I)_{r=r_m} &= r_m^{1-\beta} r_0^{\beta} v_{\max} \\ &= I_0 \end{aligned}\right\} \quad (28)$$

Therefore r_m is given by

$$r_m^{1-\beta} = \frac{I_0 r_0^{-\beta}}{v_{\max}} \quad (29)$$

We note first that in the equations (28) and (29) the exponent of r_m is $1-\beta$ while $I_0 r^{-\beta}$ is proportional to $r_0^{2-\beta}$, thereby reducing the influence of r_0. Secondly, the effect of f has been reduced by the factor $(1-\beta')/2-\beta$. Thus both β and β' tend to reduce the value of r_m. To illustrate these effects, let us take six different sets of values of β and β', two values for β, $\beta = 0.4$ and $\beta = 0.5$, and three values for β', $\beta' = 0$, $\beta' = 0.2$, and $\beta' = 0.4$. As in section 5, we take three different latitudes, 10°, 15° and 20°, with the corresponding values of f equal to 2.5×10^{-5} sec^{-1}, 3.75×10^{-5} sec^{-1} and 5.0×10^{-5} sec^{-1} respectively. The radius of inflow is $r_0 = 500$ km. Thus for each set of β and β' we have three different values of I_0, ($I_0 = \frac{1-\beta'}{2-\beta} f r_0^2$, corresponding to $q_0 = v_0 = 0$).

Since the effect of friction in the energy integral is being disregarded, the value of $v_{\max}$ is given by equation (17) in terms of T_0 and p_c/p_0. We also consider three different values of the pressure depth, that of $p_c/p_0 = 0.95$, 0.97 and 0.98

Table 3. Values of r_m (in km) computed from (29)

a) $\beta = 0.4$, I_0 in 10^6 m^2 sec^{-1}

p_c/p_0	$\beta'=0$			$\beta'=0.2$			$\beta'=0.4$		
	I_0			I_0			I_0		
	3.91	5.88	7.84	3.13	4.70	6.25	2.34	3.61	4.69
0.95	8.0	15.7	25.8	5.5	10.8	17.4	3.4	6.7	10.7
0.97	12.6	24.9	40.1	8.7	16.8	27.6	5.4	10.7	17.1
0.98	17.7	36.3	56.1	12.2	24.6	38.7	7.6	14.8	23.9

b) $\beta = 0.5$, I_0 in 10^6 m^2 sec^{-1}

p_c/p_0	$\beta'=0$			$\beta'=0.2$			$\beta'=0.4$		
	I_0			I_0			I_0		
	4.13	6.27	8.33	3.36	5.02	6.66	2.48	3.76	5.00
0.95	3.7	8.4	14.9	2.4	5.4	9.5	1.3	3.0	5.4
0.97	6.5	14.5	25.9	4.2	9.3	16.5	2.3	5.2	9.3
0.98	9.6	21.8	38.6	6.2	14.0	24.7	3.5	7.8	13.9

respectively; the corresponding values of v_{max} are 93.5 m sec^{-1}, 71 m sec^{-1} and 58 m sec^{-1} as before.

For each set of values of β and β' we computed nine values of r_m, corresponding to the different combinations of I_0 and p_c/p_0. These values of r_m, as computed from eq. (29), are given in the tables 3a, 3b and 3c; the units are km. The three values of the quantity I_0 in each combination, corresponding to the three different values of f, are also given in these tables, the units being 10^6 m^2 sec^{-1}.

Comparing the values of r_m in these tables with those in table 1 it is seen that they are much smaller than the corresponding values for frictionless flow. We note that these computed values agree quite well with the observed radii in hurricanes, which are usually within the range from 7 to 25 kilometers.

This analysis shows that ground friction is very influential in reducing the radius of the eye of the hurricane. It is evident that when the loss of tangential momentum is rapid, the converging air may actually reach the center and the eye will disappear. This is the case when the dissipation factor is equal to or greater than 1.

Another interesting feature of the frictional law of the distribution of tangential velocity (26) is the distribution of the vertical components of the vorticity given by it. Assuming that the motion is purely horizontal we find from (26) that ζ is given by

$$\left.\begin{aligned} \zeta &= \frac{1}{r}\frac{\partial rv}{\partial r} \\ &= \frac{\beta I_0 r_0^{-\beta}}{r^{2-\beta}} - \frac{2(1-\beta')}{2-\beta} f \end{aligned}\right\} \qquad (30)$$

It is seen that for small values of r, the relative vorticity is positive and that it increases very rapidly with decreasing r. Such a vorticity distribution is a common feature in hurricanes (see RIEHL, 1954). At large radial distance, the relative vorticity becomes anticyclonic according to (30).

8. Motion inside the eye and its dynamic significance

According to the arguments advanced above, the converging current is unable to penetrate the minimum radius r_m, and therefore turns upward and outward in the upper levels, to form the wall of the eye. Thus the air inside the central core will not be participating in the dynamically and thermodynamically driven circulation and calm conditions will prevail, except for the translatory motion of the system. If this is so, then the eye is not of any significance for the maintenance of the system. However, this is actually not the case; HAURWITZ's (1935) analysis of the pressure distribution in the hurricane definitely demonstrated the necessity of the existence of a very warm eye, and RIEHL's (1954) investigation shows the high temperature can only be maintained by a continuous descending motion near the center, in addition to the heating by the release of latent heat in the rain area. It is the writer's opinion that such descending motion should be a very natural consequence of frictional drag exerted by the flow just outside the eye; the reason for this is presented below.

Since the inflow takes place near the ground, there must exist a very large vertical shear of the tangential velocity, especially near the eye. As this current turns upward, this shear manifests itself as a large horizontal shear, which is unstable for small disturbances, and thereby creates strong eddy activity and horizontal turbulent mixing. Because of this eddy activity, the rising converging current will drag part of the air inside the eye along with it in its upward and outward journey, and also imparts its large tangential velocity to the air inside. Because of this sucking action and the continuity requirement, the air near the central axis is set in downward motion and spreads out at low levels, and then is dragged along by the ascending current.

The necessity of including the frictional effect in discussing the motion inside the core may be illuminated by another consideration. Since the pressure gradient $-\frac{1}{\varrho}\frac{\partial p}{\partial r}$ and the radial acceleration tend to zero as r approaches zero, M^2/r^3 must also tend to zero, according to the radial equation of motion, which may be written in the form

$$\frac{du}{dt} = -\frac{1}{\varrho}\frac{\partial p}{\partial r} + \frac{M^2}{r^3} - \frac{1}{4}f^2 r + \nu\left(\nabla^2 - \frac{1}{r^2}\right)u \qquad (31)$$

Therefore the tangential velocity v must be proportional to r for small r. Such a velocity distribution is incompatible with any type of meridional circulation when the motion is frictionless, because the conservation of momentum will always give an inward increase of the tangential velocity. Thus if friction is to be neglected completely, the only symmetric motion that can exist is a purely horizontal tangential motion. But even this motion must be dissipated by ground friction.

However, when friction is included, such a tangential motion can be sustained by a laminar meridional circulation, with descending motion near the center and an associated outward flow, the radial velocity being also proportional to r. The possibility of having such motions can be seen directly from the equations of motion (3) to (5); here the momentum is not conserved because of the effect of friction. Such a motion is against the solenoidal field, and therefore must be a forced motion.

Accepting the hypothesis that turbulent friction is present, the high tangential velocity of the inflowing air in the vicinity of the eye will act as a rotating fan, which sucks air from inside into its outward journey, and the pressure inside the core will be reduced. This will in turn increase the strength of the inflow and thereby also increase the tangential velocity, which will in turn increase the sucking action and reduce the pressure near the center further still until a state of balance between the centrifugal force, the pressure force and the frictional force is also reached inside the core.

Since downward motion is produced near the center, a much higher temperature will be produced in this region, which can then account for the very low pressure. As the air descends, it becomes extremely dry and therefore very susceptible to the supply of water from the agitated ocean surface. The latent heat thus obtained will be released as the air joins the ascending current outside the eye, thereby also giving a

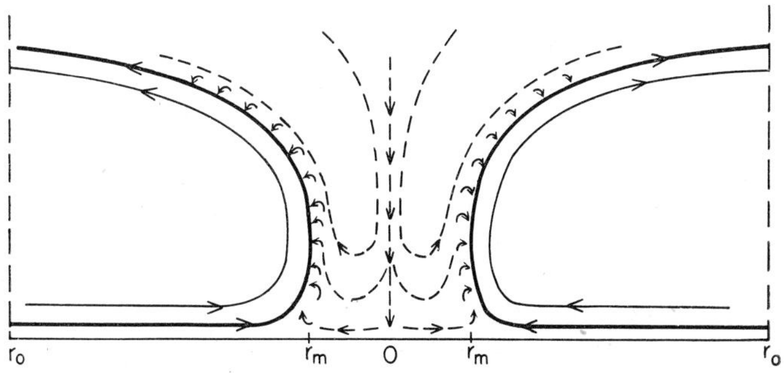

Fig. 3. Schematic flow pattern in meridional plane.

relatively higher temperature to the area of precipitation. Thus even though the motion inside the core is considered to be a frictionally driven circulation, it furnishes a mechanism in reducing the pressure at the center and therefore is of primary importance in the development of the system.

If this frictionally driven motion inside the core is instrumental for the development of the system into hurricane strength, its efficiency depends very much on its dimensions. A very large core is not efficient because the pressure inside cannot be effectively reduced by the frictional sucking and the system can easily be destroyed by asymmetrical motion, while too small a core will also be unable to produce the required work and may easily be destroyed. From this point of view, the selection of the proper size of the system may be determined by the adjustment in producing a proper sized eye.

Fig. 3 illustrates the probable flow pattern in and outside the eye. The heavy curve represents the surface inflow which forms the wall of the eye, and the small curved arrows indicate the effect of turbulent eddy motion, which drags the air inside the eye into the outward flow and set up downward motion in the center. In a steady state, air must flow into the central region at upper levels; however, since the system becomes open at upper levels, this supply is most likely to come from a certain sector and not symmetrically. Such a mechanism has been proposed by RIEHL (1957).

It may be remarked that because of the strong turbulent mixing along the wall of the eye, the eye wall should be diffused and less well defined

REFERENCES

ABDULLA, ABEL JABBAR, 1953: Dynamics of hurricanes, *Meteorological Papers*, New York University, New York.

BYERS, H. R., 1944: *General Meteorology*, McGraw-Hill, New York.

HAURWITZ, B., 1935: The height of tropical cyclones and the eye of the storm, *Monthly Weater Review*, **63**, pp. 45—49.

HOWARTH, L., 1953: *Modern development in fluid dynanics, High speed flow*, Vol. 1, pp. 158—164.

HUGES, L. A., 1952: On the low level wind structure of tropical storms, *J. Meteor.*, **9**, 422—428.

KUO, H. L., 1956: Forced and free meridional circulations in the atmosphere, *J. Meteor.*, **13**, 561—568.

JORDAN, C. L., 1952: On the low level structure of the typhoon eye, *J. Meteor.*, **9**, 285—290.

PALMÉN, E., and HERBERT RIEHL, 1957: Budget of angular momentum and energy in tropical cyclones, *J. Meteor.*, **14**, 150—59.

PFEFFER, R., **1956**: Concerning the mechanics of hurricanes, [Sci. Rep. 4, Contract AF 19(604)-1 000], Cambridge, Mass. Inst. Tech.

RIEHL, H., 1954: *Tropical Meteorology*, McGraw-Hill Book Co., New York, pp. 291—357.

— 1957: On the maintenance of the eye of tropical storms, unpublished manuscript.

SYONO, S., 1951: On the structure of atmospheric vortices, *J. Meteor.*, **8**, 103—119.

WEXLER, H., 1947: Structure of hurricanes as determined by radar. *Ann. N. Y. Acad. Sci.*, **48**, 821—844.

(Manuscript received March 31, 1958)

The Evolution of a Convective Element: A Numerical Calculation[1]

By Joanne S. Malkus
Woods Hole Oceanographic Institution

and

Georg Witt
International Meteorological Institute in Stockholm

Abstract

The evolution of a convective element is studied, starting with the introduction of a specified distribution of buoyancy into a resting stratified fluid. Because of the interaction between temperature and motion fields, the differential equations describing the onset of convection are non-linear and usually intractable to analytic solution, but they are well suited to integration in finite time steps on a high speed computer. The results of several cases programmed for one such machine (BESK) are reported here.

We consider two-dimensional motions in vertical planes with central symmetry in a 640 m by 640 m space. A lower unstable or neutral layer is topped by a more stable one. A potential temperature perturbation is introduced at the initial moment, with amplitude 0.5° C, half-width 160 m, slowly decaying with height. We set up in finite difference form equations governing the vorticity, temperature, and motion fields and solve them in a series of time steps. The calculation is ended after a time corresponding to five to seven minutes due to the growth of numerical errors.

Five cases have been computed and compared to date, varying one of four initial or environmental parameters in each, namely instability, horizontal shape, frictional exchange, and the presence of the ground at the lower boundary of the perturbation. It was found that in each of the cases studied the initial perturbation developed into a mushroom-shaped bubble-like element exhibiting a rounded cap with a concentration of isentropes, and a vortex ring circulation at its edges. The early stage of development of the element has been found to consist of two phases. The first of these is an "organization phase", during which the cap and the vortex ring are formed accompanied by only slight upward motion. The second one is the actual ascent of the bubble.

I. Introduction

This is a study of the initiation of convective motions from rest in a stratified fluid. Convective motions are created and maintained by buoyancy or horizontal gradients in density, so that the different parts of the fluid are acted upon differently by gravity, producing vertical accelerations in restricted regions. In this work, we are interested in the formation and structure of the buoyant elements themselves as a function of time, and only less directly in the grosser properties of the convecting fluid and its transports. We introduce an initial, arbitrarily determined distribution of buoyancy into a fluid of given stratification and study the growth of the elements in a series of time steps for about five to seven minutes.

The direct impetus for this undertaking comes from our interest as meteorologists in the devel-

[1] Contribution No. 967 from the Woods Hole Oceanographic Institution.

opment and structure of thermals and cumuliform clouds. The type of questions we raise and hope to answer have thus mainly been formulated from attempts to learn something concerning this kind of atmospheric convection: We seek to discover what factors control the size, shape, velocity and temperature distribution, onset and decay of cumulus-size buoyant elements; and how they interact with their environment and with each other.

Previous quantitative work on cumulus convection has, of necessity, largely been concerned with the mature and decaying phase in the element's life cycle. The main developments in the field leading up to the present inquiry are three:

1) The "entrainment" model of the cumulus, begun by STOMMEL (1947) and carried further by others at Woods Hole (MALKUS 1952, 1954). This model treats the convection element as a steady-state column discontinuously distinct from the surroundings. It has been of value primarily in relating observations of buoyancy, updrafts, and mixing. It has illustrated the effects of environment properties, such as dryness, stability, and wind shear in inhibiting the growth of cumuli and provided considerable advance over the concept of the non-interacting adiabatic parcel. It was able to say little about the mechanism of entrainment and nothing about the very early or late phases of the life cycle.

2) The "bubble" model, first evolved by SCORER and LUDLAM (1953). These authors proposed an analogy between convection element and a buoyant bubble, which was suggested to them by time-lapse cloud films and their comparison with experiments on air bubbles in water. This formulation had the advantage of dealing with individual elements or "building blocks" of convection. Large cumuli were envisaged as composed of an aggregate or succession of a number of these bubbles and their turbulent wakes. A mechanism for entrainment was suggested, namely "erosion" from the bubble cap, its protuberances being shed into the wake behind. A quantitative formulation was only possible, however, for the very final or decay phase of cumulus towers (MALKUS and SCORER, 1955). The organization, early growth, and interaction of bubbles could only be treated descriptively, nor were the conditions prescribing the rate of erosion clarified.

3) Laboratory experiments on bubbles of controllable buoyancy at Imperial College, London, by SCORER and RONNE (1956). By releasing mud slurry bubbles with realistic (2—15%) density anomalies into a neutrally or stably stratified water tank, these workers attempted to learn more about the processes of erosion and wake formation. It was found that shedding into a wake only occurred with a stably stratified environment. Under conditions of neutral stability, a mushroom-shaped, long stemmed element evolved, with an appearance similar to a typical atomic bomb cloud. These bubbles spread out along a cone and dilution occurred primarily because of the expansion, so that the fluid ahead was engulfed into the circulation. An interesting feature was the vortex ring which appeared at the edge of the element, with up-motions in its center, so that it progressed forward by continually turning inside out, growing wider in the process.

All these studies to date treated bubbles or elements which were already formed and which possessed *ab initio* sharp density gradients at their edges. Although advances from the parcel method were significant, because dilution or mixing with the surroundings was considered, in all cases it was possible to point to a physical entity which existed from the start of the study. Nothing was said about how the bubbles or columns got there in the first place or how the field of motion believed or observed to exist is initially created by buoyancy. The reason for this is obvious, in that the initial organization of convective motions is a basically non-linear process and thus enormously difficult to treat theoretically: Once motions set in, the original temperature field is altered by advection (and also by turbulent transfer). The change in the temperature field creates alterations in the accelerations; the consequent alterations in the motions in turn further alter the temperature field, and so forth. Thus, except in rare and special cases where the thermal field may, to first order, be considered "decoupled" from feedback from the motion field (for example, when a wind blows across a heated island, as studied by MALKUS and STERN, 1953) linearization of the equations to analytically tractable form loses the basic physics of the process. With the advent of high-speed electronic computers to geophysics, however, many problems previously prohibitive due to non-linearity may now be tackled numerically without a stupefying amount of labor. This paper reports a beginning attempt to apply this new technique to convection.

II. The Model

The basis of the enquiry

We consider a resting stratified fluid and impose an initial distribution of buoyancy. Equations describing the subsequent evolution of motion, temperature and vorticity fields are derived and solved numerically under five different sets of conditions each of which differs from the others in only one respect, thus simulating a controlled experiment. We leave aside the important question of how initial buoyancy is brought about, although in one of the five cases we suppose it to be due to the sudden release of condensation heating at a short distance above the ground. In the remaining four cases, the initial density gradient is greatest at ground level; here we attempt to simplify a complex situation in nature by envisaging that the buoyancy is built up by smaller-scale processes prior to the onset of significant convective-sized motions.

The buoyancy is introduced by means of a specified "perturbation" in the undisturbed potential temperature field, which in all cases has a half-width of 160 m, a peak amplitude of 0.5° C, and decays as the cosine squared of elevation to zero in 200 m. There are thus no strong vertical gradients at the outset. The development is studied in a series of finite time steps without, in this preliminary phase of the work, the introduction of any further heat sources.

One of the main questions we sought to answer was whether a concentration of isotherms would develop with time and if so how and under what conditions most favorably. In other words, we wish to know whether a "bubble-like" element with rounded cap and intense packing of isotherms into a "front" at its top will arise spontaneously. We also wish to know whether a vortex ring circulation will develop and at what point, if any, in time it will become closely associated with the buoyant element. We wish to find out whether the element will look like a bubble with a wake, a mushroom, chimney, plume or column, or if all these shapes are possible, what conditions select between them? We wish to enquire about the development of the motion field, the magnitude of the updrafts at various stages, and where they will locate relative to the maximum temperatures. We wish to find out where the air comes from that composes the circulation and how this grows under different initial and environmental conditions.

Equations and assumptions

The basic equations used are those of motion, state, continuity, and heat transfer which have (in order) the following form

$$\frac{d\bar{v}}{dt} = -\frac{1}{\varrho} \nabla p + \bar{g} + \nabla \cdot (k \nabla \bar{v}) \tag{1}$$

$$p = \varrho R T \tag{1}$$

$$\text{div } \bar{v} = -\frac{1}{\varrho}\frac{d\varrho}{dt} \tag{3}$$

$$\frac{d\Theta}{dt} = \nabla \cdot (k' \nabla \Theta) \tag{4}$$

where Θ is potential temperature and the remaining symbols have their usual meaning. The coefficients k and k' refer to eddy transfers of momentum and heat, respectively, the molecular transfer being ignored in comparison.

The simplifying assumptions made are essential in the physical modelling and in the numerical solutions of the equations and are thus stated explicitly as follows:

1) Only two-dimensional fields are treated, due to excessive machine time required by more general cases. The initial stratification and resulting flow are defined in the Cartesian $x-z$ plane and assumed of infinite extent in the normal or y-direction. A trial case of more realistic cylindrical symmetry was begun by hand computation; its development in the first several steps looked sufficiently similar to the two-dimensional results that we feel none of the essentials are lost by this simplification.

2) div $\bar{v} = 0$

Omission of the $\frac{1}{\varrho}\frac{d\varrho}{dt}$ term in similar convection problems in a shallow layer with small velocities has been justified by MALKUS and STERN (1953) and SMITH (1955). Physically it means that the fluid density is altered only by heating and lifting. It also means that the velocity of sound squared is infinitely larger than the squares of any velocities arising in the problem. The latter is helpful in a numerical approach like the present one since it eliminates difficulties of signal propagation due to sound waves, which is not only irrelevant but if permitted could lead to trouble in achieving computational stability.

3) $k = k'$ or the turbulent exchange coefficients of momentum and heat are equal.

4) $g \gg \left|\frac{d\bar{v}}{dt}\right|, \left|k\nabla^2\bar{v}\right|$ so that the latter two terms may be neglected when they appear compared to $\bar{g}$. Physically the neglection here of $\frac{d\bar{v}}{dt}$ means that pressure is to be determined hydrostatically while the important acceleration terms are not neglected. Implicitly we assume that the pressure is constant at the undisturbed upper boundary of the fluid and below this its horizontal gradients are hydrostatically produced. There is no way of evaluating the realism of this view at present. However, neglection of both $\frac{d\bar{v}}{dt}$ and $k\nabla^2\bar{v}$ compared to g was justified retrospectively by calculation of the omitted terms which did not, in fact, contribute in the last decimal place of the computations undertaken.

5) $\frac{k}{\Theta}\nabla^2\Theta = k\nabla^2\varphi$ where $\varphi = \ln\Theta$. It may be demonstrated that the omitted term $\frac{K}{\Theta^2}(\nabla\Theta)^2$ is always more than an order of magnitude smaller than $k\nabla^2\varphi$ when $\Theta \sim 300°$ A.

Introducing these simplifications, taking the curl of equation (1) to obtain a vorticity equation, and defining a stream function ψ such that

$$u = \frac{\partial\psi}{\partial z}; \quad w = -\frac{\partial\psi}{\partial x}$$

we obtain the final set of equations for numerical integration, namely

$$\underset{A}{} \qquad \underset{P}{} \qquad \underset{T}{}$$

$$\boxed{\frac{\partial\eta}{\partial t} = J(\psi, \eta) - g\frac{\partial\varphi}{\partial x} + k\nabla^2\eta} \qquad \text{I}$$

$$\underset{A}{} \qquad \underset{T}{}$$

$$\boxed{\frac{\partial\varphi}{\partial t} = J(\psi, \varphi) + k\nabla^2\varphi} \qquad \text{II}$$

$$\boxed{\nabla^2\psi = \eta} \qquad \text{III}$$

where η is the component of vorticity about the y-axis, $\varphi = \ln\Theta$ and the Jacobian $J(a, b) =$

$$= \frac{\partial a}{\partial x}\frac{\partial b}{\partial z} - \frac{\partial b}{\partial x}\frac{\partial a}{\partial z}$$

Physically, equation I discusses the time rate of change of vorticity (rotation in the $x-z$ plane). The local change is determined by the interaction of production by buoyancy (term P), advection (term A) and turbulent transfer (term T).

Equation II describes the time rate of change of potential temperature (logarithm thereof), the local change being determined by advection (term A) and turbulent transfer (term T).

Equation III relates the vorticity and stream function.

III. Solution of the equations

Basic Method

The non-linear character of our system of equations necessitates the use of numerical methods for the solution, either by hand or on a high-speed electronic computer. The equations are set up in finite difference form in time and space. The region is divided into 32 by 32 grid points located at a distance d = 20 m apart so that "walls" are placed at x = 640 m, z = 640 m. Their effect on a 160 m by 200 m disturbance may thus be expected to be rather small during the first 5—7 minutes, as the results will substantiate. Then we proceed to carry out the solution in a series of time steps of length Δt, with $\eta = \psi = 0$ at $t = 0$ where $\varphi(x, z)$ $\left(\text{and } \frac{\partial\varphi}{\partial x}\right)$ has been specified.

At the end of the first time interval $\eta = -\Delta t \cdot g\frac{\partial\varphi}{\partial x}$ and thus the initial ψ is determined by a first relaxation step. An advection step is then undertaken using this stream function in equations I and II to obtain the new potential temperature and vorticity distribution whereafter a second relaxation step is performed, and so forth. The distribution of temperature, motion and vorticity may be printed by the machine and plotted after each time-step, if desired, but in most cases the development of the convection proceeds slowly enough so that printing at one minute intervals was sufficient.

Computational stability

In order that small computational errors (arising from the finite difference approximation to derivatives and from round-off) do not grow without bounds and rapidly destroy the validity of the calculation, the length of the time step must be restricted, relative to the grid size and the other physical parameters; neither fluid nor energy can be allowed to propagate across the distance between grid points in a single time step. Now, using the methods[1] of previous workers (for example, CHARNEY, FJØRTOFT, and VON NEUMANN, 1950, and COLLATZ, 1951), we can show that, if we solve an advection equation containing an exchange term by using centered time differences, the solution may become numerically unstable, i.e. the errors may increase exponentially with time, even if the above conditions are fulfilled. This difficulty can be avoided if we replace the exchange term evaluated at $t = \tau$ with the time average of the exchange at $t = \tau - 1$ and $\tau + 1$, respectively. In this case the stability criterion for Δt is

$$|u| + |w| \leq \frac{d}{\Delta t}\sqrt{1 - \mu^2}; \quad \mu = \frac{8k\Delta t}{d^2} \qquad (5)$$

where u and v are the horizontal and vertical velocities, k is the exchange coefficient, and d is the grid interval. In the present computations we have used centered time steps and the exchange term was evaluated at $t = \tau$; still our solutions remained stable as long as the above criterion was fulfilled, due to the small exchange coefficient and the relatively low number of time steps. Actually our equations also permit gravity waves, but their restriction on Δt can be shown negligible compared to that prescribed by advection and exchange (for the physical ranges of parameters chosen). When $k = 0$, the criterion depends on the advection velocities only. Considering these cases, we found the right side of (5) frequently approached 4 m/sec by 5—7 minutes and thus our initial Δt of 20 secs had to be cut down to 5 secs by the end of the time period of interest. Further reduction of Δt would lead to prohibitive use of machine time in studying bubble growth at 1 min intervals over 5—7 minutes. With time steps in the range 20—5 sec we found criterion (5) could not be satisfied with values of k in excess of 0.5 m^2/sec and thus we restricted k to two values, namely that or zero in this preliminary study. The meaning and effect of this choice of k is discussed later.

In a few of the cases studied, the test for computational stability was made at each grid point after each time step; in the majority it was found sufficient to test at boundaries and points where velocities were known to be maxima.

[1] The writers are deeply indebted to Dr. Norman Phillips for his generous and persistent aid in their struggles with computational stability.

Procedures and boundary assumptions

After the first time step, central differences in time were used to obtain the ψ, η, and φ fields and central space differences were always used except at certain boundary points where inward differences were the only ones possible. The lower boundary presented difficulties in evaluating vertical gradients. Since in real situations, the lower boundary which may be rough and to some degree conducting exerts a complex and unknown effect, any choice here of evaluation scheme is bound to be arbitrary and unrealistic. Two different procedures were followed in this work, depending on whether k was chosen as zero or as 0.5 m^2/sec. For the cases where $k = 0$, we are concerned only with evaluating u at the lower boundary from $\partial\psi/\partial z$. We chose a constant u from 10 m (one-half grid width) to the surface at one-half the value obtained by central differences for $z = 20$ m. This means that we could use inward differences at these points for the evaluation of the Jacobian (J) terms. Physically we are crudely attempting to simulate a fairly smooth boundary with neither total slip nor complete adhesion. In those cases where $k = 0.5$ m^2/sec, the exchange terms are also evaluated as if the vorticity and the temperature were constant up to 10 m. In these we also arbitrarily reduced the horizontal advection along the lower boundary by one-half in an attempt to model a very rough boundary and to test effect of radically different boundary choices upon bubble development. As will be seen, the different boundary assumptions led to no significant differences in the major features of the convection.

Accuracy of the calculation and numerical errors

The accuracy of the solution of the Poisson equation is determined by the number of iterations carried out in the Liebmann relaxation process. In the actual computations we have continued the iterations until the maximum residual over the entire field remained below a certain tolerance. Assuming that this residual is homogeneously distributed over the entire field (i.e. the most unfavourable case) the corresponding errors in the velocity field can be estimated by conventional methods. The velocity errors can be shown to reach their maximum at the axis of symmetry. According to the tolerance used in the present computations these maximal errors were kept below 10 cm/s and 20 cm/s, respectively.

The major source of error lies in the so-called "truncation" errors of the finite difference approximations. In approximating the second space derivatives, only terms in d^4 and higher were omitted, but in the finite difference approximation to first derivatives terms in $(\Delta t)^2$ and d^2 are left out by the method (see for example ALLEN, 1954). This means physically that the average values of the first derivatives are taken across distance $2d$ and time $2\Delta t$ which become increasingly poor as gradients concentrate and first derivatives begin to vary (i.e. second derivatives become large) across a grid distance. Since advection velocities are also increasing concurrently, this means that errors will propagate as well as grow. In general, errors showed up as wiggles and bumps at the lower edges of the elements and particularly near the ground, first in the field of vorticity, second in potential temperature, and lastly in stream function and velocity. In the potential temperature field these errors become obvious as impossible non-adiabatic changes which in certain regions reach 0.1 C or 20 % of the initial perturbation after 5 minutes (or somewhat sooner in the case of $k = 0$, smooth boundary). The computation was generally ended shortly after this time, although the major outlines of the elements were still clearly defined and readily analyzable at seven minutes.

IV. Choice of parameters: the cases studied

The initial conditions of the cases studied are summarized in Table 1.

In all examples calculated to date the initial perturbation amplitude was 0.5° C. In each a slightly stable layer was placed at a level 200 m above the initial level of maximum Θ. This was necessary to prevent the velocities from growing too large, requiring a prohibitive shortening of the later time steps. This layer usually had a potential temperature increase of 1° C in 400 m and thus was only slightly stable (lapse rate 75 % adiabatic). We have thus not yet studied the effects of strong stability on a convective element.

It was noted that only two values of eddy transfer coefficients have been considered to date; namely $k = 0$ and $k = 0.5$ m²/sec. The latter corresponds to an "Austausch" of 5 c.g.s. units and may seem very low to meteorologists accustomed to Austausch values of 50—500 c.g.s. units or even larger. The value chosen was specified by Richardson's empirical formula

Table 1. Initial conditions for cases studied

Shape of perturbation	Environment	Remarks
1. $\cos\left(\frac{x}{160}\frac{\pi}{2}\right)\cos^2\left[\frac{(z-100)}{200}\frac{\pi}{2}\right]$	Unstable: $\frac{\partial\Theta}{\partial z} = \frac{-0.25\ ^\circ\mathrm{C}}{100\ \mathrm{m}}$ $k = 0.5$ m²/sec	"Up in the air" bubble (100 m) neutral ground layer; slight stability below element's base.
2. $\cos\left(\frac{x}{160}\frac{\pi}{2}\right)\cos^2\left[\frac{z}{200}\frac{\pi}{2}\right]$	Neutral $k = 0.5$ m²/sec	Maximum initial perturbation amplitude at ground. "Rough" lower boundary.
3. $\cos^2\left(\frac{x}{160}\frac{\pi}{2}\right)\cos^2\left[\frac{z}{200}\frac{\pi}{2}\right]$	Neutral $k = 0.5$ m²/sec	Same as 2, except for initial shape in x.
4. $\cos\left(\frac{x}{160}\frac{\pi}{2}\right)\cos^2\left[\frac{z}{200}\frac{\pi}{2}\right]$	Neutral $k = 0$ smooth lower boundary	Same as 2, except no exchange and doubled lower boundary advection.
5. $\cos\left(\frac{x}{160}\frac{\pi}{2}\right)\cos^2\left[\frac{z}{200}\frac{\pi}{2}\right]$	Unstable: $\frac{\partial\Theta}{\partial z} = \frac{-0.5\ ^\circ\mathrm{C}}{100\ \mathrm{m}}$ $k = 0.5$ m²/sec	Same as 2, except for environment stability.

$k = 0.2\ L^{4/3}$ using $L = d = 20$ m. The attempt was to parameterize only the turbulent transfers by the scale of motion smaller than that of the convective element studied, or eddies of size comparable to the 20 m grid spacing (whose effects are lost by averaging across it) and not to include transports by the convective scale itself. It will be seen from the results that this small exchange coefficient affected the development of the elements very little; in fact the turbulent transfer term in equations I and II approaches the advective term only in the late time steps and only then in the regions of strong gradients and weak advection, and most pronouncedly in the regions of fictitiously high gradients due to truncation errors. Introduction of $k = 0.5$ m²/sec, which indeed retarded the growth of fictitious gradients, may thus be regarded primarily as a smoothing device preventing rapid development of numerical errors. We have not yet tested the effects of strong turbulence in inhibiting the growth of convection. Due to the limitation imposed by the computational stability criterion and the questionable physical meaning of larger values of k, we shall probably continue the study of exchange effects by reducing our initial perturbation amplitude rather than by increasing k.

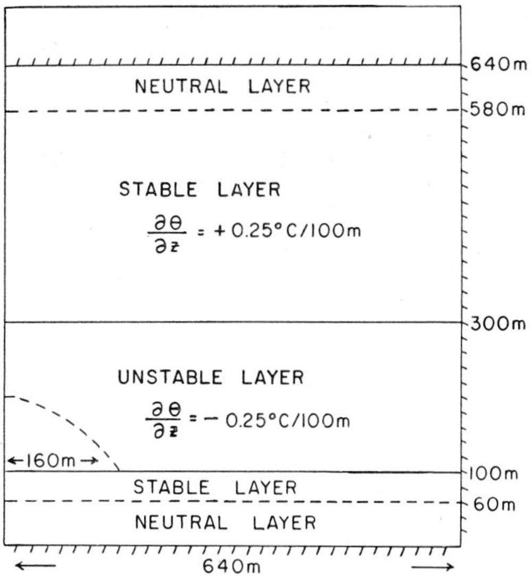

Fig. 1. Schematic outline of the initial conditions for "up in the air" (Case 1, Table 1) bubble. The z-axis is vertical, x-axis horizontal with symmetry about $x = 0$ (left vertical line). The upper neutral layer is inserted only for convenience in programming; the slight stable layer at 60—100 m merely smoothly joins the lower neutral layer and the perturbation and thus is most pronounced at $x = 0$, grading off to neutral at $x = 160$ m. The conditions crudely simulate those over the tropical oceans, a breeding ground for convective clouds.

V. Discussion of results

The selection of initial conditions was devised to investigate in a controlled manner the effects of the following four factors on convection growth, namely environment instability, initial shape, small values of exchange and friction (via differing boundary advection) and the presence or absence of the ground at the level of maximum initial temperature perturbation. The cases in Table 1 represent successive alteration of each of these factors in turn. The resulting convection development will now be described, beginning with Case 1, the "up in the air" bubble. This was believed to be the most satisfactory case undertaken, due to the unimportance of choices concerning the lower boundary, the slower growth of numerical errors (in the remaining cases the ground gave rise to stronger concentrations of high horizontal velocities and gradients in the region of closest packed isotherms), and the greater meaningfulness of starting from rest with an initial finite buoyancy distribution, which can be envisaged here as resulting from the sudden release of condensation heating.

Figure 1 illustrates schematically the conditions for this calculation and Fig. 2 shows the resulting growth of the convection element at one minute intervals for the first five minutes. The computation was actually carried to nearly seven minutes but is shown only through five because by this time numerical errors have become visible. Errors in potential temperature as large as 0.1° C both higher and lower than any original values are seen in the last (lower right) drawing.

We note especially the following features of the convection:

1) Intensification of the vertical temperature gradient into a "front" with formation of a bubble "cap". The potential temperature gradient at the element top increases from — 0.2° C in 40 m initially to nearly 1° C in that distance at 5 minutes, or a five-fold packing of isotherms.

2) Vortex ring circulation, initially centered at about 160 m elevation, which first remains stationary in height as it intensifies. After the first three minutes, it becomes closely associated with the bubble edge and thereafter moves up with it.

3) Growth of the mushroom shape, with colder air pinching in to form the stem.

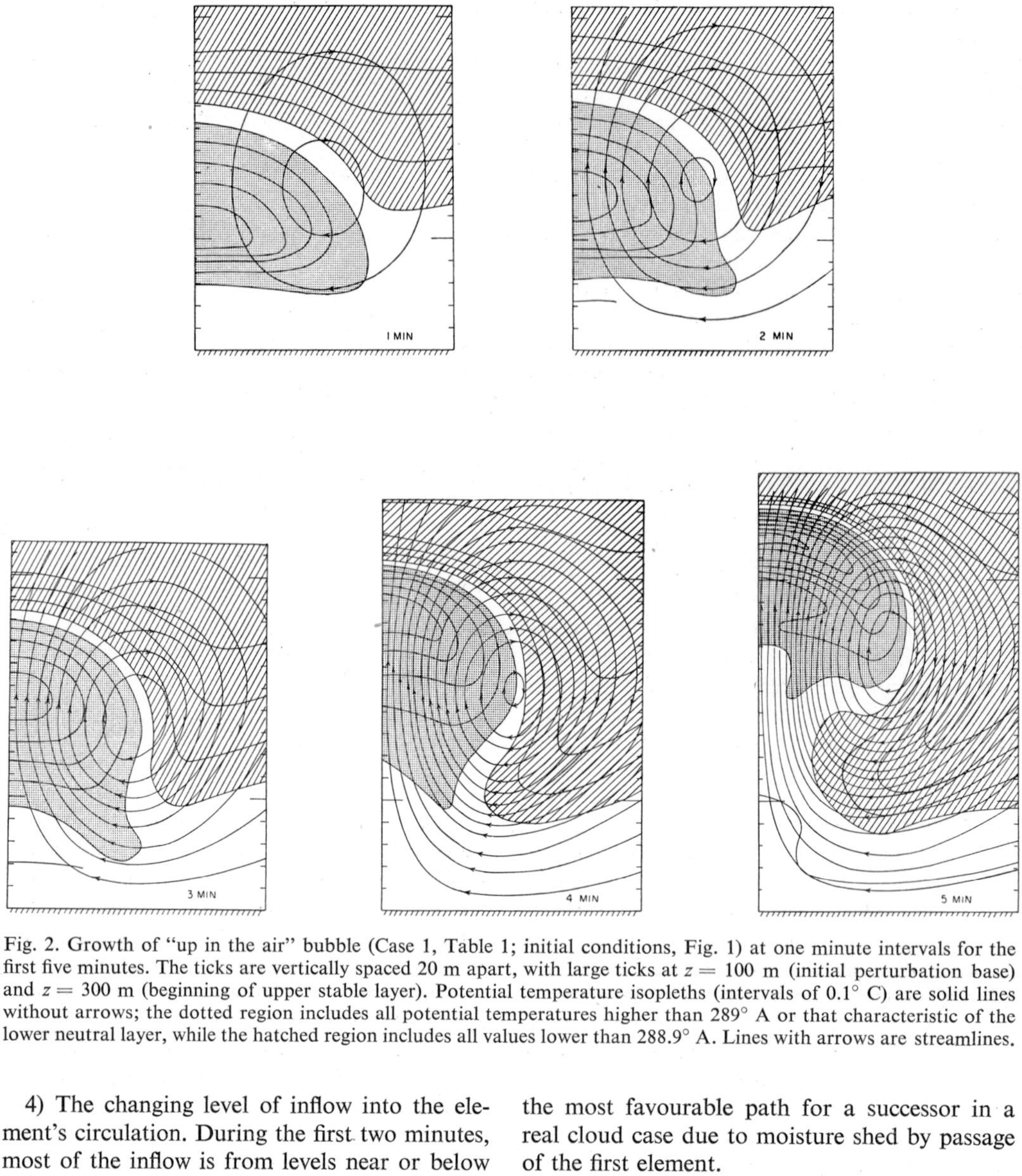

Fig. 2. Growth of "up in the air" bubble (Case 1, Table 1; initial conditions, Fig. 1) at one minute intervals for the first five minutes. The ticks are vertically spaced 20 m apart, with large ticks at $z = 100$ m (initial perturbation base) and $z = 300$ m (beginning of upper stable layer). Potential temperature isopleths (intervals of 0.1° C) are solid lines without arrows; the dotted region includes all potential temperatures higher than 289° A or that characteristic of the lower neutral layer, while the hatched region includes all values lower than 288.9° A. Lines with arrows are streamlines.

4) The changing level of inflow into the element's circulation. During the first two minutes, most of the inflow is from levels near or below 100 m (base of unstable or "cloud" layer). In the later stages, the inflow region rises, so that at five minutes the air entering the circulation comes mainly from levels above 100 m.

5) Favourable conditions at later stages for a new bubble, if available, to follow the first. The stable layer originally below perturbation base has been destroyed and even supplanted by instability. Although the instability is actually greatest in the downdraft zone (where unrealistically the initial stability was weakest) presumably just under the stem region of the element would probably be the most favourable path for a successor in a real cloud case due to moisture shed by passage of the first element.

Figure 3 shows the development of buoyancy (in terms of excess potential temperature over undisturbed environment at same level) and vertical motion at one, three and five minutes. The maximum vertical velocities reach 1 m/sec after three minutes, and 2 m/sec after five (maximum horizontal indrafts attain about 60 % of these values). Maximum downdrafts are about 50 % of the maximum updrafts. Vertical velocities at 100 m (base of unstable layer) are 1 m/sec, diminishing rapidly downward.

It is interesting to note that at five minutes the

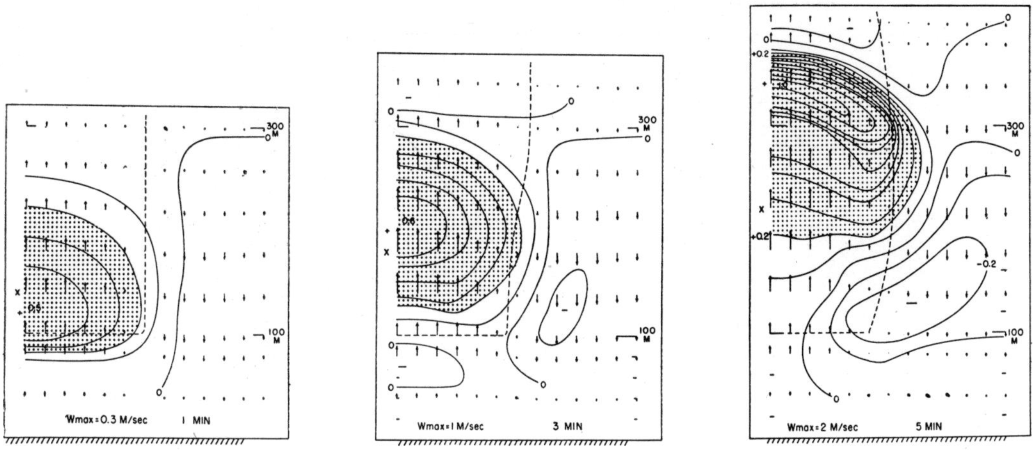

Fig. 3. Development of buoyancy and vertical motion for "up in the air" bubble. Solid lines are isopleths of buoyancy in terms of potential temperature excess $\Delta\ \Theta$ over the undisturbed environment at the same level. They are drawn at intervals of 0.1° C and the dotted region includes buoyancies of $\Delta\ \Theta \geq 0.2°$ C. The level of maximum buoyancy is denoted by the "plus" at the right. The arrows are vertical motions: in the left-hand diagram the longest one is 30 cm/sec; in the middle diagram the longest represents 1 m/sec and in the right diagram, 2 m/sec. The level of vertical velocity maximum is denoted by the cross at the right. The dashed line (except horizontal portion along initial element base at 100 m) separates up from down motions.

buoyancy has doubled its original value of $\Delta\Theta = 0.5°$ C by drawing on instability. At five minutes, 20 % of the buoyancy is due to numerical errors and 80 % is real. The center of maximum buoyancy is now concentrated in the lower part of the stable layer, which begins at 300 m, and now has passed and risen much above the center of maximum updraft. The relationship between these various centers and their motions is illustrated further in Figure 4. In Figure 4A the heights of the centers of maximum Θ (closely coincident with maximum buoyancy), maximum w, and of the vortex ring are plotted as a function of time. These reach the same level at just short of three minutes when the bubble appears to begin rising as an entity and we say that its

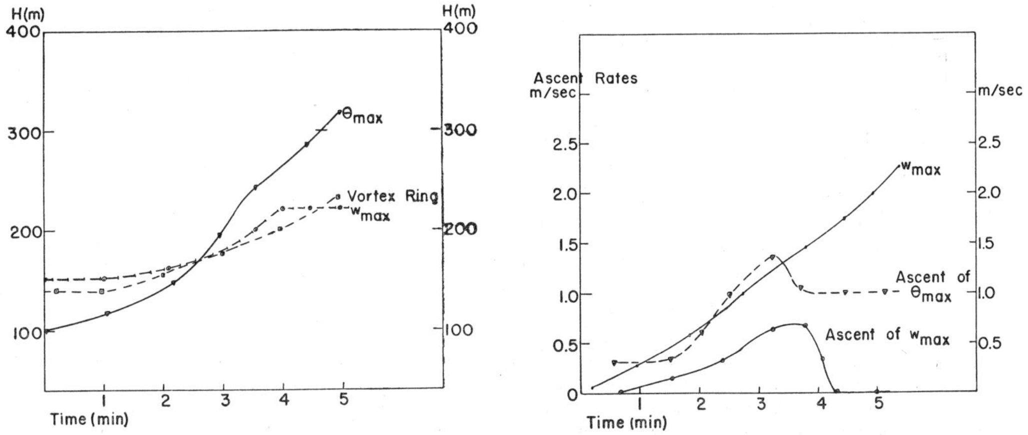

A B

Fig. 4. Behavior of centers for "up in air" bubble. A: Vertical position as a function of time of 1) maximum potential temperature (triangles) 2) maximum vertical velocity (circles) and 3) center of vortex ring (squares). B: Ascent rates as a function of time. The solid curve labelled w_{max} is simply the value of the highest vertical velocity. The dashed curve (triangles) gives the ascent rate of the center of maximum potential temperature, while the lowest solid curve shows the rate of ascent of the center of maximum vertical velocity.

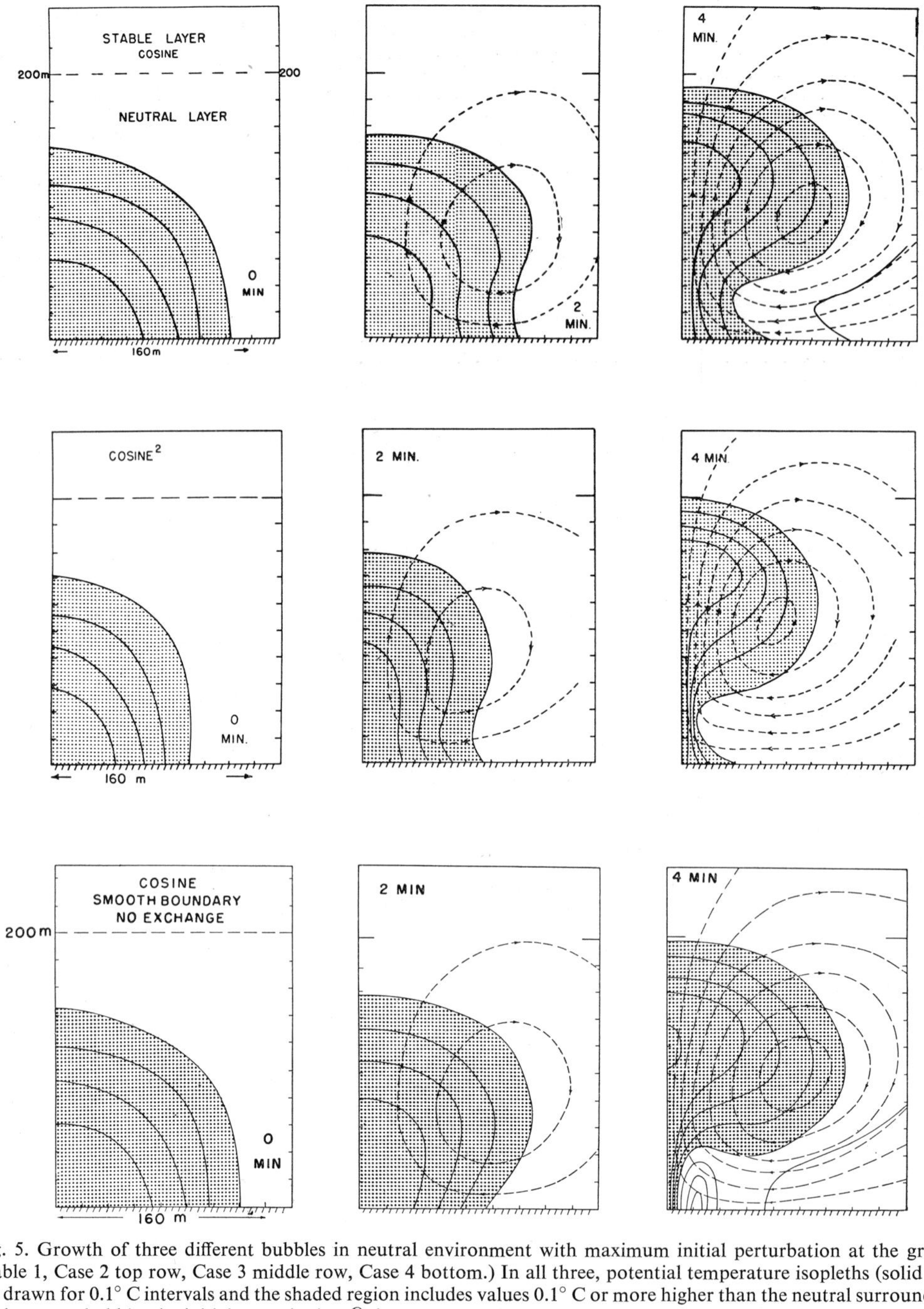

Fig. 5. Growth of three different bubbles in neutral environment with maximum initial perturbation at the ground. (Table 1, Case 2 top row, Case 3 middle row, Case 4 bottom.) In all three, potential temperature isopleths (solid lines) are drawn for 0.1° C intervals and the shaded region includes values 0.1° C or more higher than the neutral surroundings. In the upper bubble, the initial perturbation Θ decays to zero in 160 m as cosine of x. In the middle bubble, it decays to zero at 160 m as cosine squared of x, with everything else unaltered from the first. The lowest bubble differs from the topmost only by the removal of turbulent exchange and by the doubling of lower ($z = 0$) boundary advection. Note in the latter, the more rapid growth of numerical errors in temperature, evidenced by the small hump of impossibly (lower than any initial) cold values near the stem and the 0.1° C impossibly high region in bubble center.

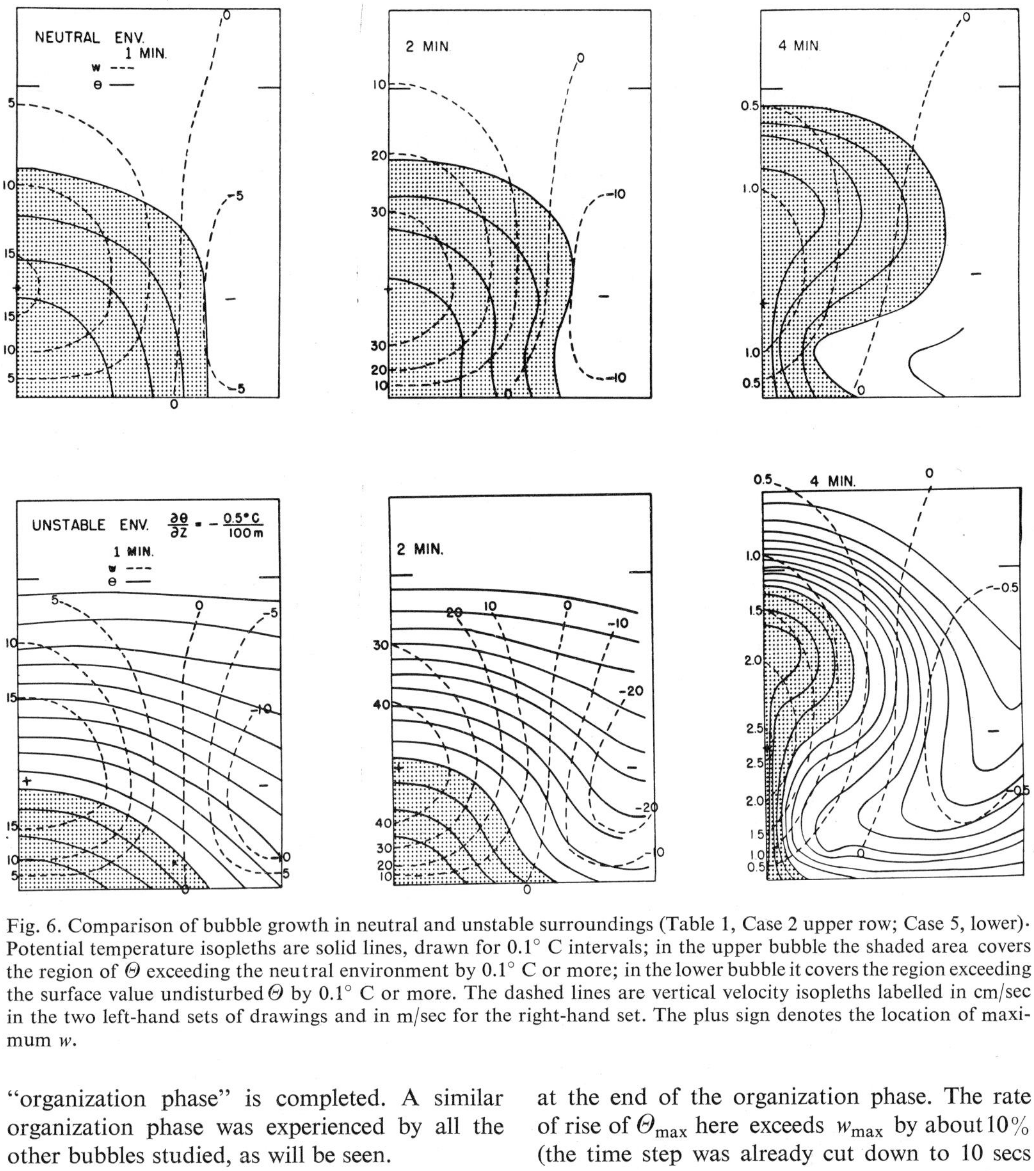

Fig. 6. Comparison of bubble growth in neutral and unstable surroundings (Table 1, Case 2 upper row; Case 5, lower). Potential temperature isopleths are solid lines, drawn for 0.1° C intervals; in the upper bubble the shaded area covers the region of Θ exceeding the neutral environment by 0.1° C or more; in the lower bubble it covers the region exceeding the surface value undisturbed Θ by 0.1° C or more. The dashed lines are vertical velocity isopleths labelled in cm/sec in the two left-hand sets of drawings and in m/sec for the right-hand set. The plus sign denotes the location of maximum *w*.

"organization phase" is completed. A similar organization phase was experienced by all the other bubbles studied, as will be seen.

After this time the Θ_{max} is found increasingly above the level of w_{max}, which appears to have stopped rising in elevation (despite continuously increasing updraft intensity).

Figure 4B shows rates of ascent as a function of time. The strength of the maximum updraft increases continuously and slightly exceeds 2 m/sec after five minutes, while the center of maximum *w* never rises faster than 70 cm/sec and ceases rising altogether after four minutes. The rate of rise of the center of maximum potential temperature has this same characteristic shape in all cases studied, accelerating to a maximum at the end of the organization phase. The rate of rise of Θ_{max} here exceeds w_{max} by about 10% (the time step was already cut down to 10 secs before two minutes so no computational instability results). Naturally this excess of rise rate of Θ_{max} over the maximum advective updrafts can occur only for bubbles with turbulent mixing and comes about because at the "front" or cap region the potential temperature gradients and instability are so great that Θ diffuses upward faster than it is advected, "swallowing" some of the air ahead into the bubble circulation. This effect is slightly more pronounced for the foremost Θ isopleths of the bubble cap and would presumably be even more pronounced (as it was in the Imperial College experiments of SCORER

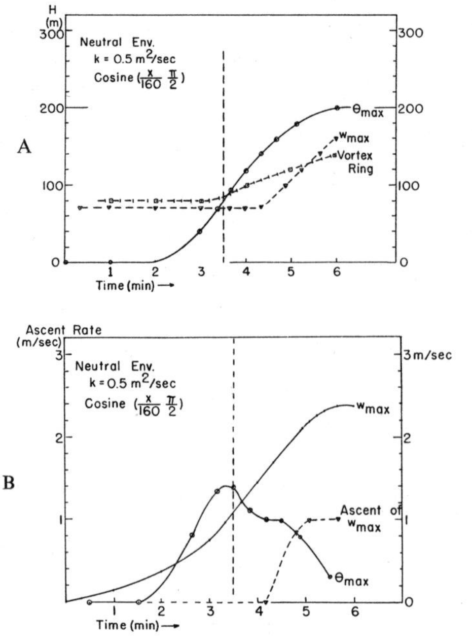

Fig. 7.

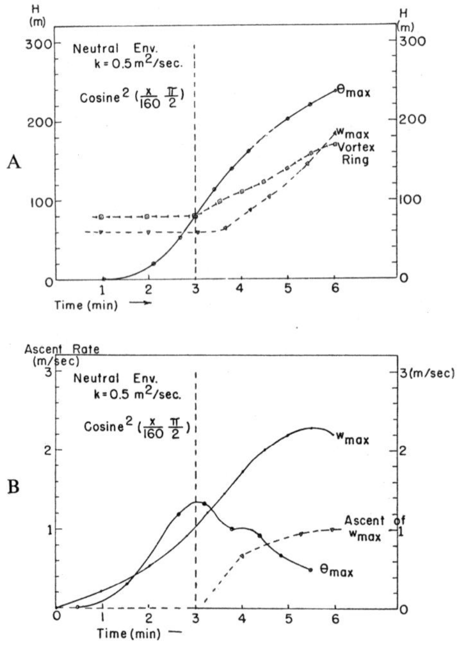

Fig. 8.

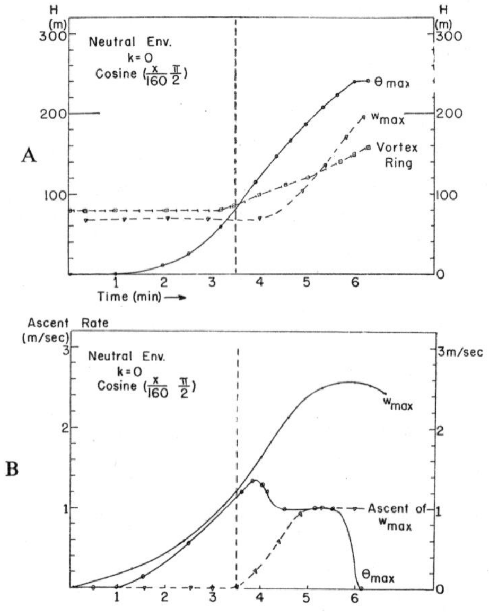

Fig. 9.

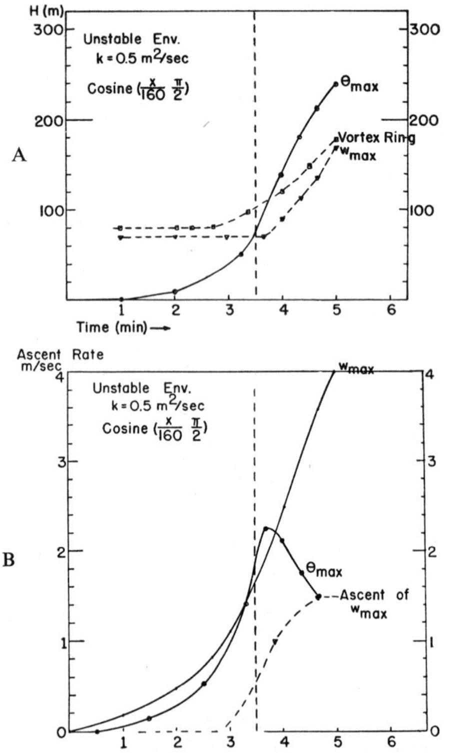

F.g. 10.

Figs. 7—10. Behavior of centers for bubbles starting at ground (Table 1, Cases 2—5 in order). Upper graphs (Figs. 7A—10A) show the heights of the centers as a function of time; the solid curve shows Θ_{max}; the dashed curve with triangles, w_{max}, and the broken curve with squares, the vertical position of the vortex ring.
Lower graphs (Figs. 7B—10B) give the ascent rates as a function of time; the solid curve marked w_{max} gives the actual value of maximum vertical velocity; the dashed curve gives the rate of ascent of its center, and the solid curve marked Θ_{max} gives the rate of rise of the center of highest potential temperature.

and RONNE, 1956) had higher values of exchange relative to buoyancy been used.

Figures 5 and 6 show the development of the remaining bubbles studied, all with the maximum initial potential temperature perturbation at the ground, while Figures 7—10 show the behavior of their various centers and the duration of the organization phase (vertical line). In all these bubbles, the end of the organization phase coincided with the penetration of the maximum vorticity into the central stem region, which could in fact have been used to define it.

In Figure 5 we compare three different bubble developments in a neutrally stratified environment (the only initial instability is contained in the perturbation itself). In the upper two everything is identical except the initial shape of the perturbation which decays to zero in 160 m as the cosine of x in the first and as the cosine squared in the second, thus concentrating the strong potential temperature gradient nearer the center. In the cosine squared case, the vortex ring begins closer to the center and by four minutes the bubble has a more concentrated cap, is higher, and has a narrower stem. The suggestion that its organization phase is completed more rapidly is confirmed by comparison of Figures 7 and 8 in which we see the centers reach the same level with each other 30 seconds sooner. The reason is clarified in Figure 11 comparing the early velocity fields in the two cases. In the cosine squared bubble the maximum horizontal velocity develops closer to the center. The vorticity maximum also originates closer to the center and is advected in sooner, marking an earlier close of the organization phase. The bubble stem is formed sooner. The updraft develops faster and so does a more pronounced downdraft. Initial shape (other things being equal) thus appears to play a very important role in the organization phase of a convective element and throughout at least the first four minutes of its lifetime. Since the cosine squared bubble could perhaps be regarded as effectively one of narrower width than the cosine bubble, this suggests that the duration of the organization phase depends on the ratio of bubble diameter to depth of unstable layer and that these perhaps vary directly. We plan to investigate that question further as the study continues. Figures 7—10 show that for all the remaining bubbles studied, the organization phase was the same, that is, it is not affected by variations in turbulent exchange, boundary friction, or stability. Comparing the first and third rows of Figure 5 and Figures 7 and 9, we see the effect of eliminating turbulent exchange and doubling lower boundary advection. The isotherms pinch more rapidly at the stem and numerical errors grow more rapidly but the basic features of the development are unchanged. On Figure 9 compared to Figure 7, the only difference on the "frictionless" case is a slightly augmented (less than 10%) w_{max} and a rate of rise of Θ_{max} which no longer exceeds advection. The choice of assumptions concerning the lower boundary thus seem to affect the convection negligibly which mitigates the arbitrariness and unreality of those used. A value of k equal to 0.5 m²/sec serves, under these conditions, only to smooth numerical errors and to permit the bubble to grow upward slightly faster than by advection alone.

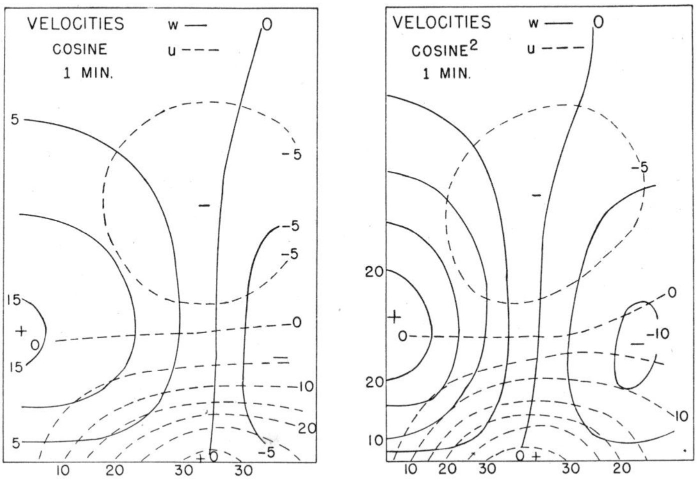

Fig. 11. Comparison of velocities in cm/sec at one minute between cosine bubble (Table 1, Case 2, left diagram) and cosine squared bubble (Table 1, Case 3, right diagram). Vertical velocity isopleths are solid, horizontal dashed. The locations of maxima and minima of each are indicated by the pluses and minuses.

Finally in Figures 6, 7, and 10 we compare the cosine bubble in an unstable and neutral environment to isolate the effect of instability. This produced markedly stronger velocities, with a w_{max} reaching 4 m/sec at 5 minutes and more rapid ascent rates of all centers, but the duration of organization time is the unaltered and the general character of curves and bubble development resemble the other cases.

VI. Conclusion

In general summary, it may be said that we have investigated the early growth of a convective element under very favorable conditions; with no wind shear or initial vorticity present, with an unstable or at worst neutral early environment, with weak or no turbulent mixing, with probably a favorable initial buoyancy distribution and a somewhat exaggerated initial buoyancy amplitude. Under these conditions it may be considered that a bubble or mushroom-like element spontaneously organizes in about three minutes, developing a rounded cap with a "front-like" concentration of isentropes and a vortex ring circulation at its edges.

More specifically we may conclude:

1) That the early life of the element has two phases: the first is an organization phase lasting a time dependent on the initial buoyancy distribution, or probably on the ratio of the depth of the convective layer to the half-width of the element; in our cases the latter was approximately one to one and the organization phase required about three minutes. During this period the element forms its cap and vortex ring and rises little. The second phase is a rising phase which begins when the vortex ring, maximum updraft and maximum buoyancy have come together at the same level.

2) Turbulent transfer coefficients corresponding to an Austausch of 5 c.g.s. units have little important affect on bubbles of these dimensions and initial buoyancy. Large differences in lower boundary advection affect the development only in minor ways.

3) While environment instability favors high velocities and permits the buoyancy to increase with time, it does not alter the organization phase.

4) Downdrafts outside the element are favored by instability and centrally concentrated isentropes initially.

5) Without condensation, or other continued heat source, these elements acquire a mushroom shape and not that of a plume, jet or column.

6) Without condensation, or other heat source, the vertical velocity maximum remains (subsequent to the organization phase) well below the cap and buoyancy maximum.

The results of these preliminary calculations suggest further directions in which we hope to carry the inquiry with this model. In the next stage envisaged, these are primarily three: First, a further investigation of the organization phase, and especially its suggested dependence upon the ratio of dimensions of convective layer to perturbation width. Second, the introduction of heat sources, either dependent upon the coordinates or upon the vertical motions themselves to simulate condensation; this would be an attempt to discover whether a more column-like "cloud" may organize if new sources of buoyancy are available, and to see whether the centers of maximum vertical motion and potential temperatures will coincide more closely if non-adiabatic heating dependent on the former is introduced.

Finally, we hope to investigate, one at a time, factors believed to be inhibitory to convection, such as wind shear, an upper layer of strong stability, and a larger exchange coefficient relative to initial buoyancy.

Acknowledgments

This work has been supported largely by the United States Office of Naval Research, with an important contribution in the early phases from the Munitalp Foundation.

The writers are deeply grateful to Dr. Bert Bolin for his help, advice, and suggestions throughout all stages of the work and to Dr. Norman Phillips who provided indispensable aid on the problem of computational stability and other phases of the numerical calculation. The original formulation of the problem was instigated and assisted by Dr. R. S. Scorer.

REFERENCES

Allen, D. N. DeG., 1954: *Relaxation methods.* McGraw-Hill. New York. Chaps. 4 and 5.

Charney, J. G., Fjørtoft, R., and von Neumann, J., 1950: Numerical integration of the barotropic vorticity equation. *Tellus,* **2**, 237—254.

Collatz, L., 1951: *Numerische Behandlung von Differentialgleichungen.* Springer-Verlag, Berlin-Göttingen-Heidelberg. Chap. III.

Malkus, J. S., 1952: Recent advances in the study of convective clouds and their interaction with the environment. *Tellus,* **4**, 71—87.

— 1954: Some results of a cumulus cloud investigation. *J. Meteor.,* **11**, 220—237.

Malkus, J. S., and Scorer, R. S., 1955: The erosion of cumulus towers. *J. Meteor.,* **12**, 43—57.

Malkus, J. S., and Stern, M. E., 1953: The flow of a stable atmosphere over a heated island. Part I. *J. Meteor.,* **10**, 30—41.

Scorer, R. S., and Ludlam, F. H., 1953: Bubble theory of penetrative convection. *Quart. J. R. Met. Soc.,* **79**, 94—103.

Scorer, R. S., and Ronne. C., 1956: Experiments with convection bubbles. *Weather,* **11**, 151—154.

Smith, R. C., 1955: Theory of air flow over a heated land mass. *Quart. J. R. Met. Soc.,* **81**, 382—395.

Stommel, H., 1947: Entrainment of air into a cumulus cloud. *J. Meteor.,* **4**, 91—94.

(Manuscript received April 8, 1958)

WEATHER FORECASTING

Methods in Scientific Weather Analysis and Forecasting
An outline in the history of ideas and hints at a program

By Tor Bergeron

University of Uppsala

Abstract[1]

Since the first attempts at scientific weather forecasting, weather prognosis has progressed mainly due to improvements of

O. the meteorological *observations*,

T. the *tool* used for making the ever-increasing mass of data accessible to a purposeful mental, graphical or mathematical-mechanical treatment,

M. our *models* of atmospheric structure and their degree of rational physical approach to the problem.

The development of the above factors is treated, from Dove's local method till to-day's mechanical-numerical precalculations of upper flow-patterns.—It is shown that progress has been severely impeded by lack of contact theory-empirie.

Long-awaited radical improvement of weather forecasts will presumably now largely depend on still inconceived fundamental ideas especially as to the factors **O, T** and **M,** also making them more directly related to weather, and on a better utilization of these factors.

1. Introduction

Among events within inanimate Nature predictable in principle by the laws of Mechanics, as outlined once by Laplace,[2] none are more complicated and none rank higher in general interest and importance than *weather* events.

---

[1] Abstract presented to the Scandinavian-American Symposium at Bergen, 1958, but paper not read.

[2] In Laplace's *Mécanique céleste*, Tome I, 1799, "the object of the author..., as stated in his preface, was to reduce all known phenomena of the world to the law of gravity by strict mathematical principles..." (From N. Bowditch's English translation of the Preface, 1829, p. V).

In Laplace's *Essai philosophique sur les probabilités* (p. 3—4) we find this principle in an explicit form:

"Nous devons donc envisager l'état présent de l'univers, comme l'effet de son état antérieur, et comme la cause de celui qui va suivre. Une intelligence qui pour un instant donné, connaîtrait toutes les forces dont la nature est animée, et la situation respective des êtres qui la composent, si d'ailleurs elle était assez vaste pour soumettre ces données à l'analyse, embrasserait dans la même formule, les mouvements des plus grands corps de l'univers et ceux du plus léger atome: rien ne serait incertain pour elle, et l'avenir comme le passé, serait présent à ses yeux."

V. Bjerknes used to render this Laplacian dictum concretely as follows:

Every purely material-mechanical problem could be reduced to stating the present position and motion of all mass-particles involved, and predicting their future positions and motion at a given time by the laws of Mechanics—a problem which should in principle be solvable. Cf. also V. Bjerknes 1904, p. 1.

O. G. Sutton 1951, in an interesting article, has touched the same problem, expounding view-points on the practical indeterminacy and impredictability of weather. Accepting his general view, the weather problem might be inherently unsolvable because of very small random influences having great effects within unstable systems in the atmosphere.—See also R. C. Sutcliffe 1954, p. 14, c); R. B. Carson 1958, p. 670—674.

P. D. Thompson 1957 and R. Berggren 1958 have gone quantitatively into some of these problems, investigating i.a. the effect of observational errors on the prognosis, which may even surpass the effect of the deficiencies of our physical models.—As to thermodynamic processes operating in baroclinic flow, P. D. Thompson (1957a, p. 9) concludes that "the atmosphere tends to be impredictable in situations of strong horizontal temperature gradient and near-adiabatic gradient". — P. Raethjen 1953a considers the atmosphere nearly always to be in the situation of a "Hercules at the cross-roads". Raethjen points out that even minute influences may suffice to change a stable atmosphere into a labile one when the state passes a certain threshold value; and then a "decision" with fundamental consequences may in its turn be triggered. "The manifold lability of the atmosphere will always remain an invincible hindrance to a *physically* founded and exact weather forecasting" (l.c., p. 326).

No other dynamic-thermodynamic problems are subject to such a daily and world-wide idle talk and professional attack, and yet within no comparable field are progress and success so modest.

Since the days when the two Chinese astronomers HI and HO—if we may refer to this old tale—were hanged as a penalty for failing to forecast an eclipse, the progress of Astronomy has been overwhelming. Laymen are nowadays entirely kept outside the field of astronomical forecasts, which are wholly left to the experts and obviously accepted *a priori* as correct.—We all know that by far this is not so in Meteorology.

Turning to Biology—except Man himself—forecasts concerning the developments of the flora and fauna on our planet, and especially regarding cultivated plants, certainly claim very great interest, but not so constantly and to such a world-wide extent as do weather forecasts. Moreover, whenever agricultural forecasts become a dire necessity, this is caused, directly or indirectly, by weather vagaries.—The scientific and technical efforts in Biology, such as the creation of new, useful plant and animal races, or the invention of better cultivation methods, again only enjoy the interest of a limited group of citizens, at least in highly industrialized countries. On the other hand, the corresponding efforts in Meteorology—cloud seeding and other kinds of weather control—already enjoy too great publicity but small success.

Naturally, the evolution and revolutions within our human world—in politics, political economy, social welfare, education, art and science, hygienics and medicine, industry and trade—deserve a supreme and world-wide interest. But in this case, obviously, the events lie far outside the Laplacian, purely mechanical predictability, because of the irrational functioning of human mind and its repercussions in all these fields. Yet, they too are all influenced by the weather.

Thus, the meteorological forecast stands alone as the most important and promising but still unsolved Laplacian problem on our planet.—In fact, the complexity of the atmospheric processes and the difficulty of surveying them simultaneously over a sufficiently vast area made it practically impossible, even for the Giants of Science, to reach any fruitful results at an epoch, say, a hundred years ago, when many important but much "simpler" and/or more surveyable problems of Astronomy, Physics and Medicine had already attained scientific solutions of great practical use.

The great H. VON HELMHOLTZ evidently felt this awkward position of our science quite seriously when, in 1875, he uttered[1] the following memorable words:

"Es regnet wenn es regnen will,
es regnet seinen Lauf,
und wenn's genug geregnet hat,
so hört es wieder auf.

Dies Verslein — ich kann nicht einmal mehr herausbringen, wo ich es aufgelesen habe — (it was by GOETHE) — hat sich seit alter Zeit in meinem Gedächtnis festgehäkelt, offenbar deshalb, weil es eine wunde Stelle im Gewissen des Physikers berührt und ihm wie ein Spott klingt, den er nicht ganz abzuschütteln vermag, und immer, trotz aller neugewonnenen Einsicht in den Zusammenhang der Naturerscheinungen, trotz aller neu errichteten meteorologischen Stationen und unübersehbar langen Beobachtungsreihen, nicht gerade weit vom Ziele trifft. Unter demselben Himmelsgewölbe, an welchem die ewigen Sterne als das Sinnbild unabänderlicher Gesetzmässigkeit der Natur einherziehen, ballen sich die Wolken, stürtzt der Regen, wechseln die Winde, als Vertreter gleichsam des entgegengesetzten Extrems; unter allen Vorgängen der Natur diejenigen, die am launenhaftesten wechseln, flüchtig und unfassbar jedem Versuche entschlüpfend, sie unter dem Zaune des Gesetzes zu fangen."

What HELMHOLTZ said in 1875 holds good in principle even to-day. But the weather problem, which once was the "sore point" in the physicist's conscience, has now been very successfully repressed from his mind.

In 1888, HELMHOLTZ returned to Meteorology a last time in a powerful attack on the fundamental problems of atmospheric motion. It is well known that he succeeded in interpreting the dynamics of the Altocumuli, or billow-clouds, explaining them by the gravitational meso-scale waves that still carry his name. He also had an idea of a world-encircling atmospheric surface of discontinuity in mind, a "Polar front", resulting from the air-motions of the general circulation.[2]—On the whole, though, his attack on the bigger systems of motion broke down, and *had to* do so, because of deficient knowledge of their nature.—This is just one example of what seems to be a rule in our science: *progress is impeded by want of meteorological knowledge on the part of the theoreticians and by a too poor mathematical training of weather-men.*

[1] in a lecture printed in 1884.

[2] l.c., 1888 a, p. 340 (Conclusion): "Der vorliegende Aufsatz sollte zunächst nur zeigen, wie in der Luftmasse es durch continuierlich wirkende Kräfte zur Bildung von Discontinuitetsflächen kommen könne".

Anyhow, the practical result is that the public in hardly any country, as yet, takes the ordinary daily weather forecasts too seriously—even if many a professional forecaster (as a subconscious selfdefence?) unswervingly believes the opposite. The evil repercussions on prestige, available funds and influx of alumni to our science are obvious.

The sad fact, as matters stand now, that public weather forecasting can be said to have started 100 years too early—in 1860[1] instead of in 1960—need not be due, however, to less intelligence or zeal in the meteorologists as compared with contemporary adepts of other sciences. The partly almost insurmountable obstacles will suffice as an excuse in many respects, but not in all: the problems of securing adequate observations, of finding tools for expediently representing and digesting them, and of understanding how the laws of Physics and Chemistry govern the extremely complex processes within a humid and diversely polluted atmosphere on a rotating planet, possibly subject to random influences at the micro-scale level, still having macro-scale effects.—Yet, without these 100 years of official weather forecasting, to-day's Weather Science would have been even more under-developed.

The precarious situation and uncertain future of Weather Forecasting are now becoming widely recognized among meteorologists in leading positions. The discussion has, however, mostly been led only in general terms. Three interesting articles on this subject may be mentioned: O. G. SUTTON 1951, ending with a rather defaitistic conclusion (cf. the footnote above, p. 440); T. E. W. SCHUMANN 1954, asserting that "Synoptic forecasting" is obsolete; V. SCHAEFER 1958, hoping for more students to become interested in our "fascinating and challenging science".—See also the Report of the U.S. Advisory Committee on Weather Services, of 1953.

Thus, an attempt at a more systematic treatment of the problem might be of some value. It seems justifiable then to consider at first the history and present trend of development of Weather Study. By taking a retrospect of it, *epignosis*, and checking its present state, *diagnosis*, one might learn from the errors of the past, and get some hints as to measures that might favour a fruitful future development, *prognosis*.—Thereby it will appear that every great step forward in the science and practice of weather forecasting was brought about by better meteorological *observations* **O**, better *tools* for representing $\mathbf{T}_0$ and digesting $\mathbf{T}_1\mathbf{T}_2$ these observations, and finally better *structure models* **M** of the atmosphere, based on a more realistic and true picture of the general way $\mathbf{M}_0$, and of the specialized structures $\mathbf{M}_1$, in which the processes inherent in our atmosphere follow the general Laws of Nature.[1]

*

The following historical review will mainly deal with certain events in the development of synoptic meteorology in Northwestern Europe. Events after 1950 are mostly considered as lying too near in time to be viewed "historically". Achievements or methods without a clear connection with forecasting weather will generally not be treated. Not even will space permit any account of the advances in the fields of cloud physics, orographic effects or dynamic climatology, in spite of their evident importance to weather forecasting.

It proved impossible to embrace also the parallel and partly analogous development in America prior to 1930, where great men such as ESPY, LOOMIS, FERREL, BLASIUS,[2] BIGELOW, A. L.

[1] LE VERRIER in France at that time explicitly warned FITZROY, though in vain, against starting, already then, a real weather forecasting, even on the basis of the new tool; and the Royal Society in London was severely disturbed by his actions. Cf. Sir GEORGE SIMPSON 1955, p. 168/169.—As to the development of synoptic meteorology in France, see i.a. LE VERRIER 1867, p. 6—7.

[1] These $\mathbf{M}_0$ and $\mathbf{M}_1$ very nearly correspond to P. RAETHJEN'S "masses" and "individuals" (l.c., 1953 a, p. 320 ff.). Very adequately he shows that these individuals —just as in life—are discernible from the mass (1) by their being bounded from this ambient mass, (2) by an inherent pattern of development, (3) by a typical metabolism. However, the present writer had to stick to the word "model" and the symbols $\mathbf{M}_0$ and $\mathbf{M}_1$ (a) since calling $\mathbf{M}_0$ a "mass" would collide with $\mathbf{M}_1$ in the sense "synoptic air-mass", (b) since the word "model" of late has got a second meaning in Meteorology, *viz.* an (ambient) mass of certain general properties (barotropic etc.).

Likewise, R. C. SUTCLIFFE, 1954, states that the atmospheric systems are (1) complex or organized, (2) have an inherent life-history, (3) are "open systems". He distinguishes five magnitude classes of such systems, setting a "hierarchy in predictability". This implies that every extension of the forecasting period requires (a) passing to larger systems, and (b) knowledge of their properties.

[2] However, one cannot mention the name of the German-American WILLIAM BLASIUS — protected by the great scientist LOUIS AGASSIZ, but left outside the meteorological guild—without a quotation from the Preface of his

ROTCH and C. F. BROOKS had ideas in these fields far ahead of their time.

At this review one should bear in mind some psychological factors which, among others, seem to govern the minds of scientists, and which may be worth consideration when using this epignosis (and diagnosis) for an attempt at a prognosis of the future of our science, cf. Sect. 14 below.

(A) At every stage of development of a scientist or a science, *the stock of knowledge already acquired, or the views of a dominating School or personality, will to some extent block the recognition, or even the observation, of certain otherwise obvious facts that do not fit in with this knowledge or view.*

Admittedly, the mediaeval ultra-conservatism of human mind is to-day dispelled, the blind faith in authority is gone, but the tendency may still be there. Moreover, at a given time, the most active scientists and technicians—in the rush of new discoveries and inventions, or in their sturdy adherance to old methods or their own convictions—will never be sufficiently aware of their one-sidedness. The only possible, but by no means reliable, remedy would be to try to learn from History.

(B) Probably thanks to scientific intuition, *a true and valuable discovery may be made from data that at a later inspection turn out (1) not really to represent that phenomenon, or (2) to have been quite unsufficient as a proof.*—Unfortunately, such a discovery is then easily turned down by opponents.

(C) *The value, importance and wide applicability of new observations, methods or deductions will often not be recognized even by the discoverer himself, and may thus be doomed to oblivion.*

(D) Again, in such a complex and unsurveyable field as Meteorology—partly due to inefficiency of international bibliography and terminology, or to lack of reading on the part of the meteorologists themselves—*old knowledge will often be rediscovered and presented under new labels, causing much confusion and impeding progress.*

(E) It is important to notice that in Synoptic and Dynamic Meteorology *the attack has followed two main lines* with regard to the particular processes studied:

(1) *stressing the air-trajectory or air-mass concept*, corresponding to the *Lagrangian* method of mathematical analysis,

(2) *stressing the field concept*, corresponding to the *Eulerian* method.

Of these two aspects the Lagrangian is the more concrete and apparently the more fruitful one in the long run; but it is also the more complicated one to handle mathematically and graphically. Therefore, even when thinking physically in terms of method (1), it is natural to use method (2) when actually dealing with the given data.

2. Early history

When H. W. DOVE in and after 1827—disregarding H. W. BRANDES' synoptic method, presented some years earlier (1820)—developed his system of weather study and weather forecasting based on the *local method*, this meant an enormous step forward as compared with previous attempts in this direction. DOVE'S faculty of *observing* **O** was presumably superior to that of his predecessors. Using only the local method, which has many merits in itself, DOVE naturally did not need any special *tool* **T** for representing and digesting his observations other than his own brain, and evidently it served admirably for this purpose. Thus, he was the first in Europe to introduce real, concrete *structure models* $\mathbf{M}_1$ (of greater extent than for instance a thunder cloud) as a basis of Weather Study, *viz.* the concepts "Polar Current" and "Equatorial Current".[1]

book "Storms", 1875, based on ideas conceived already in 1852:

"Twenty years ago I in vain exhausted every effort to obtain a hearing for what I believe to be the truth, and I have patiently awaited the development of the science" . . "The consequence of the method of observation generally pursued is that an area of barometric depression is considered the storm itself, and the *cause* of the movement of air-currents, while I am certain that the storm is the conflict of air-currents of different temperatures, and the barometric depression the *effect* of their movement. And, in addition, the most important elements in the life of storms—heat, their originator, and the clouds, their embodiments—are those to which least attention has been paid."—A pathetic and farsighted, but at that time vain, appeal for a concrete and Lagrangian philosophy as to **O** and **M**.

BLASIUS' Plate V even shows a schematic vertical cross-section of the troposphere from pole to pole with Polar fronts, main air-masses and circulation wheels practically as we draw them to-day.—Cf. also H. v. FICKER 1927.

[1] Cf. also S. P. CHROMOV 1931,

Already LUKE HOWARD, though, in his "Climate of London" 1820 (1st ed., Vol. II, p. 205—211) and 1833 (3rd ed., Vol. I, p. 124—127), gave striking descriptions of weather situations and developments in terms of cold and warm air-masses alternatingly invading the place of observation at the ground and aloft respectively. At a time when there were as yet no synoptic maps, he drew a vivid and correct three-dimensional "synoptic" picture

Due to the undeniable shortcomings of the local method, to the lack, at that time, of even an elementary hydrodynamics applicable to the atmosphere of a rotating planet, and to faulty application of elementary thermodynamics, DOVE's system was necessarily impaired by certain grave misapprehensions. Nevertheless, he acquired, as we know, a Lagrangian insight in the structure of our atmosphere as to *weather systems* that contained the gist of the fundamental air-mass concepts arrived at 80 years later by the Bergen School.

The edifice erected by DOVE at the very centre of the grounds of our Science—admirable in spite of its deficiencies—shortly afterwards, just a hundred years ago, got completely destroyed at the rediscovery of the synoptic tool and its introduction into practical weather forecasting along strictly Eulerian lines of thought,—with just one salient exception.

Admiral FITZROY—commander of the *Beagle* when CHARLES DARWIN 1831/36 made his voyage around the world—the first chief of Meteorological Office, London, could trace DOVE's weather systems on British synoptic maps.[1] Fig. 1 shows the essence of his findings. They form the very peak of an evolution that was then unfortunately interrupted by FITZROY's untimely death in 1865, and by the overwhelming pressure from the followers of the new isobaric-synoptic method.—That evolution was then not continued until about 1905 by LEMPFERT and SHAW, with their Lagrangian air trajectories and ingenious cyclone model, and by the works of the Bergen School from 1918 and onwards.

Moreover, already at the very outset of the synoptic era, Sir FRANCIS GALTON—a cousin of CHARLES DARWIN and later a pioneer in statistical genetics—had tried to pave the way for a comprehensive, concrete and Lagrangian school of thought and method. His work, "Meteorographica", 1863, contains three European maps a day for the month of December 1861, with pictorial symbols for the winds and main hydrometeors, temperature, wet-bulb depression and pressure. There are also the corresponding 3×93 small maps with (1) stream-lines and rain-areas, (2) the temperature distribution, (3) the pressure distributions, respectively. The introductory text proves that he wanted to demonstrate (a) a practicable technical way of depicting, on the synoptic map $\mathbf{T}_0$, the full observations **O** from all the more than 300 meteorological stations in Europe, (b) how to map and study the air-currents, the weather etc., rationally $\mathbf{T}_1$.—Unfortunately, after 1870, GALTON left active work in Meteorology, and his ideas were not followed up. In fact, nobody in Europe took the pains of performing synoptic work of a similar intensity and with such rational principles until 40—50 years later.

Had the line of thought represented by HOWARD→DOVE→FITZROY→GALTON been guided and supplemented by the synoptic method after 1860, instead of being interrupted by it, then the science of weather forecasting could presumably have kept on an equal footing, for instance, with that of medical anatomy and sur-

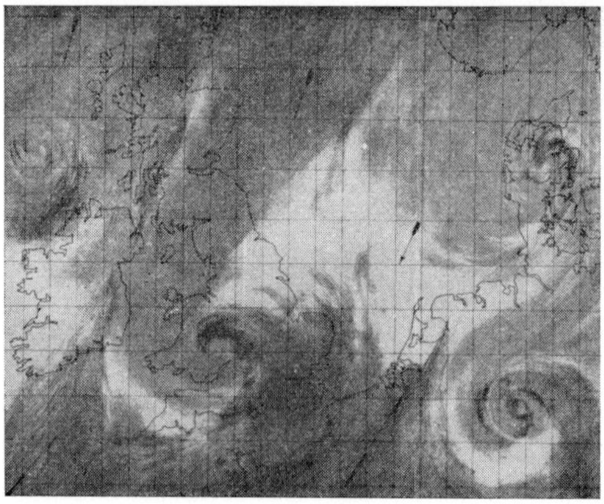

Fig. 1.—FITZROY's weather systems, 1863.—In the original plate the Polar current is blue and the Equatorial current reddish. It shows quite clearly four cyclones, one over S. England with an open warm sector, the others more or less occluded.

of a common kind of (pre-)frontal rain-area and its main air-currents (l.c., 1820, p. 206/7):

"A Southerly current charged with vapour from a warmer region, may be passing Northward, at the same time that a Northerly current may be returning towards the South in its immediate neighbourhood: and these two may rase each other, the colder running laterally under the warmer current, and causing it to flow over laterally in its turn, while each pursues in the main its original course. In this case the country, for a considerable space, extending from about the line of their junction far into the Southerly current, may be the seat of extensive and continuous rain."

He also stood up against HUTTON's rain-theory (prevailing 1784—1874), based on mixing of moist cold and warm air, stating (1) that cloud motion showed mixing of air-masses to be insignificant as compared with the huge output of vast rain-clouds, (2) that the latent heat would oppose the mixing effect.—His findings, based on the local method, were true fore-runners to DOVE's later system, but they were more vaguely expressed and not systematized. Thus, evidently they met with the fate of case (B) and (C) above.

[1] Cf. DIECKMANN 1931; CHROMOV 1933.

gery—provided that a comparable amount of men, brain-power and technical facilities had been put at its disposal. The important scientific and practical results from such a weather science might in their turn have had just that beneficial effect. Firstly, they would have continued to attract to its problems brains of a HELMHOLTZ' and GALTON'S standard even from outside Meteorology; secondly, they would have produced increasing goodwill for Synoptic Meteorology with the public and the governments.—As events developed, however, this did not really happen again until VILHELM BJERKNES was led from Physics to Geophysics, about 1900, with the well-known favourable consequences.

A hundred years ago the technical facilities of Medicine and Meteorology were, in fact, intercomparable, and partly intercomparably poor. None of them possessed any real sounding instrument, and both got it only just before 1900: Medicine the X-rays and Meteorology the kites and sounding balloons (and soon afterwards also the air-planes, see footnote on p. 451).—On the other hand, especially in Great Britain, the network of reporting 2nd order stations was as dense in 1873 as in 1913. Moreover, the "meteorograms" described below appeared only for the twelve years 1869 to 1880.—All these facilities, together with FITZROY'S concrete grip on the subject, meant observations **O**, a technical tool **T**, and a scientific school of thought as to atmospheric models $\mathbf{M}_1$, that would have been quite favourable for reestablishing the essence of DOVE'S system, this time on a sound physical basis. This again would have implied discovering the fronts and the air-masses already before 1870.[1]—The conditions were in these respects partly even less favourable 50 years later, since the daily weather maps of the initiating Bergen School in 1918—20 were very poor outside Scandinavia, meteorograms were no longer available, and the scientific "climate" was then rather inclement towards innovations of Lagrangian character in our science.

The regrettable course taken in this field after 1865 was, however, to a great extent due to DOVE'S own negative and polemic attitude to the synoptic tool and to the results won by it. He did not even allow any improvements of his system in the light of these findings, or resulting from a correct application to the atmosphere of certain dynamic and thermodynamic principles (i.e. the adiabatic change of state) known also to him; case (A).—Hereby the very names of DOVE'S ingenious structure models, "Polar current" and "Equatorial current", became the symbols of a repugnant school of thought, and the underlying concepts were thus strongly rejected by the new weathermen; cf. W. KÖPPEN'S discreet and elucidating answer 1921 to MYRBACH'S article the same year.—Since DOVE was the Director of the Prussian Meteorological Institute till his death in 1879, the evolution of Weather Service in Germany was so severely hampered that G. VON NEUMAYER, when founding the Deutsche Seewarte in 1875, had to invite young KÖPPEN from St. Petersburg to introduce the new methods at the Hamburg Service, "matters otherwise being untenable". Cf. KÖPPEN 1921 (bottom of p. 289) and 1932.

*

As matters developed after 1865, instead, the new tool **T**, the synoptic map, was employed to treat only a minor part of the observations **O** available. Just one rather poor and one-sided structure model $\mathbf{M}_1$ was used: the pressure field at 0-level and its alleged correlation with the weather. Together these **O**, **T** and $\mathbf{M}_1$ provided a most convenient way of handling weather forecasting. So comfortable was this Eulerian method, and so well founded physically it seemed, that its use became world-wide within a short time. Anyone could learn to draw circular or oval shaped isobars around the centers of low pressure, thus showing the Lows, which were supposed to be the real "carriers" of the bad weather, and therefore also hailed as the main object of study for the weather scientist and the practical forecaster. Equally promising and easy seemed the statistical study of the weather within different quadrants of Lows and Highs (not quite dead even in the 1950's), and the tracking of their paths.

[1] This part of the present paper was written before consulting Sir DAVID BRUNT'S important chronicle "A Hundred Years of Meteorology" (1951), which corroborates the above interpretations and views regarding decisive stages in the development of British weather study. BRUNT tells us that the very first report (1867) on the British meteorograms "... gave, as an illustration of what could be achieved by means of self-recording instruments, photographs of charts of pressure and temperature records, exhibiting what we should now call a 'line-squall' (on March 8, 1867)".—Sir NAPIER SHAW, in 1934, commented the same report by stating: "If they had kept 'right on to the end of the road' at that time, the combination of maps and records might have set out the doctrine of fronts in 1869 instead of 1919".—To this BRUNT (l.c., p. 8) remarks: "We might here quote Shaw against himself—'had he kept right on to the end of the road' he might have set up the doctrine of fronts in 1907."—*viz.* on the basis of his cyclone model of 1906, cf. p. below, p. 453, right col.

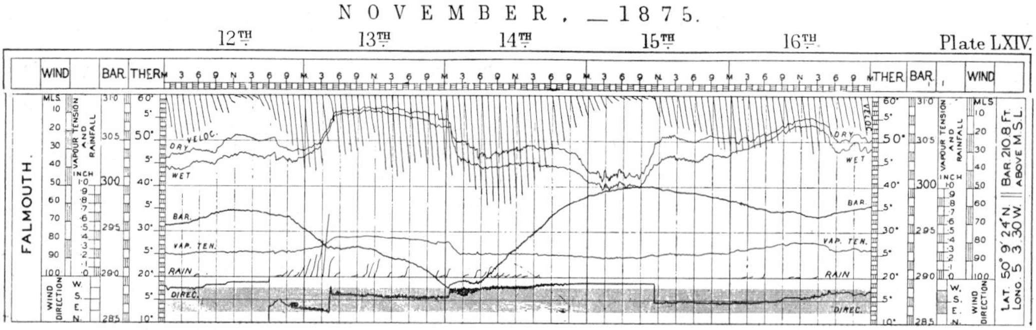

Fig. 2*.—Meteorogram from 1875, showing passage of an ideal warm-sector at Falmouth, 13. XI.

The scientific progress and practical success of Weather Forecasting on such a basis were rapidly declining, or even lacking, and so were the brain-power and the facilities at its command. The meteorological institutes of the world—generally organized in the years 1855 to 1880, some of them with the main task of forecasting weather—were rapidly transformed into administrative-statistical bureaus, mainly loaded with the burden of ruling administratively and digesting statistically the ever-increasing observational data. Even so, the working up and printing of hourly and daily values *in extenso*—i.e. just those data whose prompt publishing forms the material basis of scientific weather study—has been continually reduced from 1880 till to-day in many countries; not least in the United Kingdom, where the start was so brilliant. There is, however, at least one highly creditable exception, the United States, whose publishing of such data has rather been continually increasing in quality and quantity, at any rate until 1950.

Scientific brains were not specially attracted by such a monotonous and "easy" routine work, involving so little success both scientifically and as a career. Thus, they mostly returned to or stayed within related but "superior" sciences, such as Physics or Astronomy, to the great detriment of Meteorology.[1]—The same tendency is still discernible to-day.

3. Efforts and failures

Even during the period 1865—1915, though, with a relative stagnation of Weather Science and Weather Service, several outstanding and very encouraging efforts (some of them already named) were made at improving the observations and tools, and even the structure models.

O.—Already in the 1860's M.O., London, furnished seven observatories in the British Isles with selfrecording instruments for the main meteorological elements: pressure, temperature, humidity (indirectly), precipitation and wind. The publishing in every detail of the data thus secured was started in 1869 in an unparallelled and most ingenious way—again with the advice and support of Sir FRANCIS GALTON— by the so-called *meteorograms* **T**, appearing in the Quarterly Weather Report of M.O., London, for the twelwe years 1869—1880. In this publication the registration curves of all the main elements at these seven observatories were presented in exquisite engraving, day by day, on a common time axis and in Cartesian coordinates. Fig. 2 shows a specimen meteorogram for just five days from one of the observatories, Falmouth, when passed by a typical warm-sector; cf. T. BERGERON 1935, figs. 1 and 2.

The instruments used for these meteorograms were in some important respects even technically superior to modern ones. Thus, the dry and wet bulb mercury thermometers recorded photogra-

[1] Sir DAVID BRUNT 1951, in his interesting account of 100 years of British Meteorology, tells the same story about stagnation, lack of scientific interest, inefficiency and lost opportunities in Weather Study during this epoch. He writes, l.c., p. 5: "... by May 1897, when Shaw became a member of the Meteorological Council, the enthusiasm had entirely gone from the Office. Meteorology was then, indeed, in the Slough of Despond. Such scientific knowledge as could be found in the Office was restricted to the members of the Council," ... "The Council took no interest in forecasting, nor indeed did any of the permanent staff of the Office." ... "By this time, too, physicists in general had ceased to take an active interest in the problems of the atmosphere."

* Indicates that also the original caption of the figure is reproduced here. The same applies to figs. 3, 4 a, 5 c, 7, 9 and 12 below.

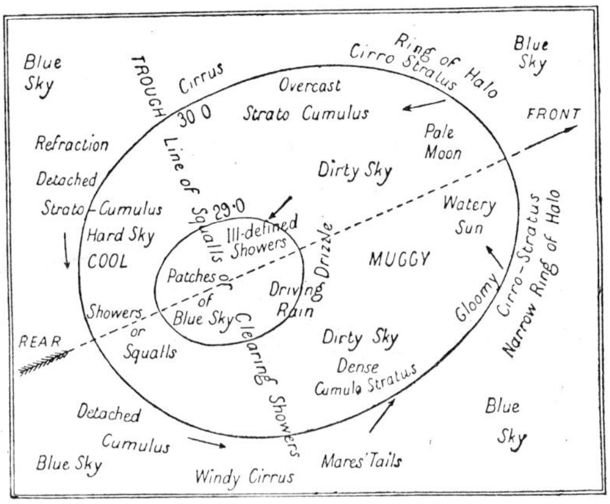

Cyclone Prognostics.

Fig. 3*.—ABERCROMBY's and MARRIOTT's version of the cyclone model, 1883.

phically in orthogonal coordinates. Moreover, GALTON had also invented an instrument, of general application, which i.a. made it possible to protract the vapour-tension trace from the thermograms. Unfortunately, such excellent observations **O** remained confined to the British Isles and, apparently, to the seven stations mentioned. The likewise excellent system of meteorograms **T**, by which these observations became fully accessible and surveyable, was not introduced in other countries; and this British publication ended (in 1891) with the volume of 1880, due to lack of comprehension of its great value (see SHAW 1934, p. 108), and presumably also to lack of funds and personnel—just as is often the case nowadays.

The aim of this wonderful publication is clearly expressed in the Introduction to the first annual volume (1869) by the following words, behind which one feels the genius of GALTON:

"... the advantage as regards weather study which has been gained by such a consecutive graphical record shall be presented to the scientific public in its entirety, instead of being in a great measure lost, as it would be, were occasional, even hourly, tabulations the only information published. The cumbrousness of, and the consequent difficulty in consulting, tables which would give anything like a complete representation of the salient phenomena of our weather, is, in itself, a sufficient reason for adopting a new form of publication."

T.—In his book "Weather" (London 1887) R. ABERCROMBY recommends the use of these meteorograms by stating on pp. 178—179:

"... Of course, if charts could be constructed for every hour of the day, and at stations only five or ten miles apart, there is nothing we learn from meteorograms which we could not also derive from charts; but, as such observations are impracticable, it is of the utmost importance to know precisely how the continuous trace of instruments at any one station can be collated with the intermittent observations at widely scattered localities.—The most striking example of the value of meteorograms in building up the nature of a cyclone is found in the phenomena of the trough. These are confined to a line only a mile or two wide, and it would be utterly impossible from charts alone ever to learn the significance of the turn of the barometer. We might look at fifty charts of different cyclones, and it might happen that the trough was not actually passing over any observing station in any one of them ..." "... The method of the meteorologists is, in fact, analogous to that of the microscopist, who builds up his picture of the organs of an animal by taking a series of their sections, across any portion of it ...".

The general principles of thorough and detailed investigations of atmospheric structure models $\mathbf{M}_1$ by using time-sections could not have been better expressed to-day, when—at last—T. FUJITA 1955 has shown how to perform that kind of small-scale studies rationally on a large scale.—Strangely enough, however, ABERCROMBY himself does not in his printed works give any proof of having applied the fine principles just quoted from him: in a way a first example of instance (C).

M.—In fact, judging from ABERCROMBY's own publications and from contemporary British weather maps (printed in the Quarterly Weather Report, the Daily Weather Report, etc.), the utilization of the good **O** and **T** stayed very poor. In practice he and his followers inaugurated and mainly used sterile isobaric geometry for their synoptic weather study, cf. below, p. 448/49.

Moreover, the interesting cyclone model, fig. 3, often attributed to ABERCROMBY[1], was evidently not regarded by him as representing a physical structure, but rather as a diagram for showing old "weather lore" and recent weather prognostics in their relation to a Low; cf. ABERCROMBY and MARRIOTT 1883 (l.c., p. 28 and p. 44 ff. = the discussion). In fact, fig. 4 a, reproduced from a lecture by CL. LEY (1879 a), held already in 1878, is obviously the prototype of fig. 3., since the latter (not appearing until 1883) was the very first cyclone model of that type published by ABERCROMBY.

It should particularly be noticed that CL. LEY's *model also gives the essence of the three-dimensional structure of a frontal Low as we know it to-day*, by indicating the average air motion in the upper troposphere according to more than

[1] See i.a. "The Weather Map", M.O. 225 i, 1916, 1930, 1939, and even as late as in 1956.

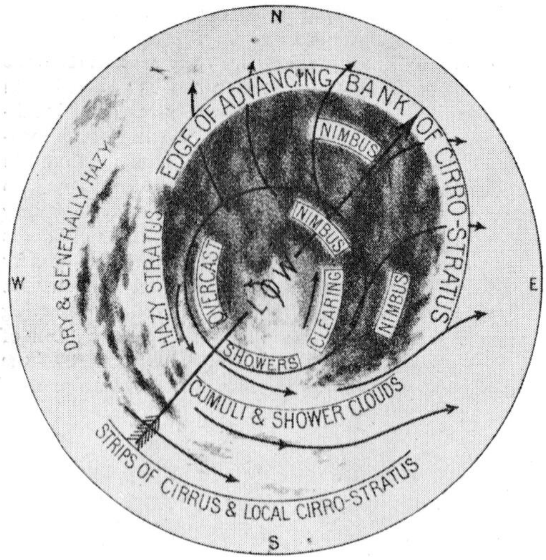

Fig. 4 a.—CL. LEY's cyclone model, 1878.—The streamlines show the motion of upper clouds.

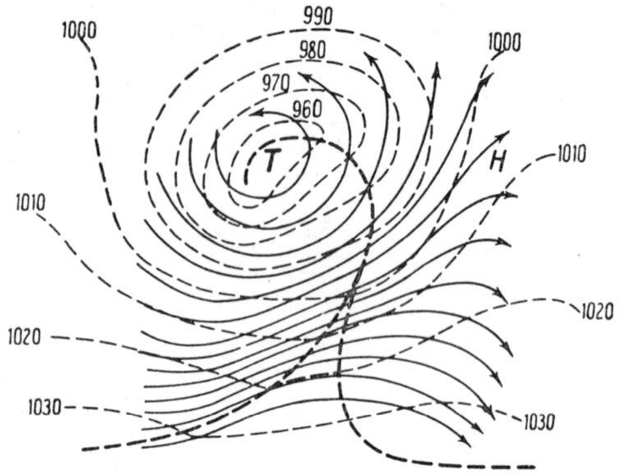

Fig. 4 b.—E. PALMÉN's three-dimensional version, 1931, of the Bergen occlusion model. — — — Front. 990 — — — Isobar at 0-level → Flow aloft.

8,000 observations of cloud drift at those levels.[1] In this respect his model is a true forerunner to E. PALMÉN's three-dimensional model of the flow in a mature cyclone fig. 4 b, published in 1931. (The statistical model presented in 1875, and even as late as in 1900, by H. H. HILDEBRANDSSON, who quotes CL. LEY on this subject, gives rather a less clear picture of that flow.) —Also in another important respect the Rev. CL. LEY was ahead of his time: Opposed by many of his contemporaries (even HILDEBRANDSSON) he claimed (1872; 1877, p. 445; 1879 b) that the cyclone axis would lean backwards, cf. fig. 4 a. This statement, based on his own skilful analysis of the observations and his sound judgement, proved right; his explanation of it, as well as his opponents', though, is debatable.—As a follower of CL. LEY one may mention MAX MÖLLER 1882, a convinced cloud-synoptician who expounded similar ideas in Germany.

The interpretation of fig. 3 advanced above is confirmed by a comparison of figs. 5 a, b & c.—Fig. a shows the fronts, air-masses and rain-areas over NW. Europe on the 14. XI. 1875, at 07—09^{h} LT, analysed by the present author in 1933 on the basis of data that were all published already before 1878 (including the meteorograms)[1]. Consequently, they must have been available also to ABERCROMBY.—Figs. b & c render the "analyses" made by him of exactly the same situation. Fig. b shows only oval isobars and a few plotted stations; the "model" shown in fig. c violates the evidence given by the meteorograms, and also by the majority of cloud and precipitation data given by the dense British network.

It is dejecting to find, in 1958, that the case chosen by ABERCROMBY in 1878 to demonstrate the corrupt cyclone model, fig. 5 c, is the very one with the ideal warm-sector, showing up so beautifully in the meteorogram of fig. 2 above—and this in spite of his fervent recommendation of their use. Evidently, in this case, ABERCROMBY had neither consulted these meteorograms, nor utilized the whole stock of synoptic data, nor even CL. LEY's cyclone model, which all would have led him in an entirely different direction. The same was obviously the case with most synoptic studies and practice during this epoch. —In fact, ABERCROMBY's "Principles" (1885) were in principle based on sheer isobaric geometry, distinguishing seven main isobaric configurations (primary and secondary cyclone, anti-

[1] The NW flow aloft with Ci tractus ("Noah's Ark"), followed rapidly by SE wind below and general rains or snow-fall, is described in some very striking old Swedish sayings, especially from the Bothnian coast, cf. K. EKMAN-DANVER 1941.

[1] Cf. also the corresponding analysis of the previous morning by T. BERGERON (1933) 1935.

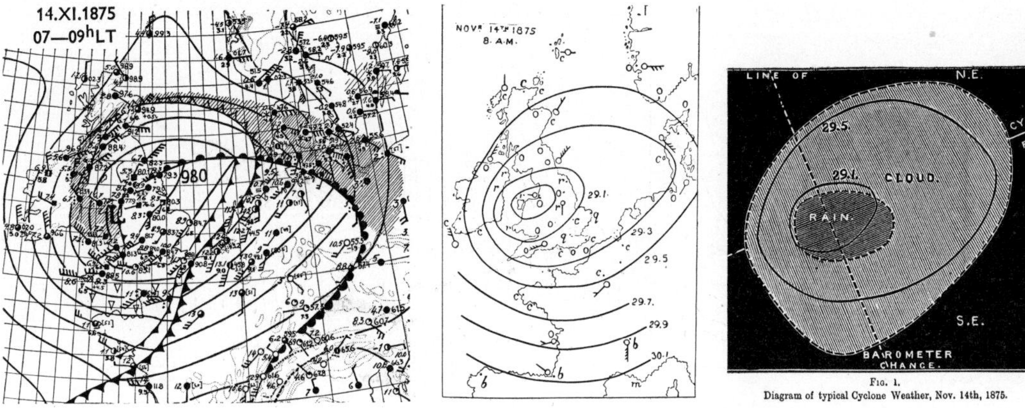

a. T. Bergeron 1935. b.—c*. R. Abercromby 1878

Fig. 5.—Three analyses of the Weather situation 14. XI. 1875, at 07—09^{h} LT.

cyclone, trough, wedge, col and straight isobars) and attributing a rather definite weather type to each of them—and if observations did not conform to these models, so much the worse for the observations.

The above statement on the stagnation of weather study in this period, and an impression of Abercromby as its British Aristotle, is strengthened by the following fact. Sir Napier Shaw (who otherwise did so much for the advancement of Meteorology) in all editions of his "Forecasting Weather" (1911, 1923 and 1940) has taken over 16 pages, literally and within quotation marks, from Abercromby's "Principles" to form the substance of his (Shaw's) Chapter V on "The relation of temperature and weather to barometric pressure".—It can be doubted whether in any other natural science an exposition from 1885 could still serve as a canon fifty-five years later. Cf. also footnote 1 on p. 447.

*

Remembering that a migrating temperate-zone Low, statistically speaking, will show all structures run through by a frontal disturbance (from the initial-wave stage till the fully occluded one, often including a backbent occlusion), it is after all no wonder that the first British cyclone model, figs. 3 and 4 a, contains features from all these stages. The fore part shows the well-known sequence of upslide clouds, ending by "Nimbus" (now Nimbostratus) and continuous rain, and (in fig. 3) a small region containing the warm-sector drizzle or "driving rain". From the reason just mentioned, the latter area is encroached upon by the shower-region and/or the subsidence region, the warm-sector in reality mostly being a "false" one, containing returning mP. Therefore, it may show clear sky (as in fig. 4 a), but over land there will easily develop showers in day-time and fog (with drizzle) at night.—The "squall-line" dividing the fore part from the rear part, may correspond to the cold-front or to the backbent occlusion (especially when of CF-character). The showers and "hard sky" (=excellent visibility) are the equally well-known characteristics of the deep unstable mP in the rear of most big disturbances.—*The main things missing in* Cl. Ley's *otherwise excellent model were the front concept and the developability.*

In fact, already in 1878 Clement Ley, and in 1879 W. Köppen, saw indications of that important phenomenon, or model, which we now call the *cold-front*. Later, Köppen clearly realized that it consisted of a cold-air wedge invading warmer air (e.g. Köppen 1882 a, p. 716; 1914, p. 7), but he gave it a very modest depth (600 m).—These findings or new concepts were, however, never introduced rationally and on a routine basis on the daily synoptic maps, being regarded rather as shallow, local phenomena without too much repercussions on the great-scale synoptics[1] (cf. Durand-Gréville below). Therefore, they never came to be part of a consistent scientific system until rediscovered by the Bergen School

[1] This notion was perhaps after all not so far from truth, since some of the most conspicuous phenomena of cold-front character occurring in Central Europe are pseudo-coldfronts, i.a. those investigated by Köppen.

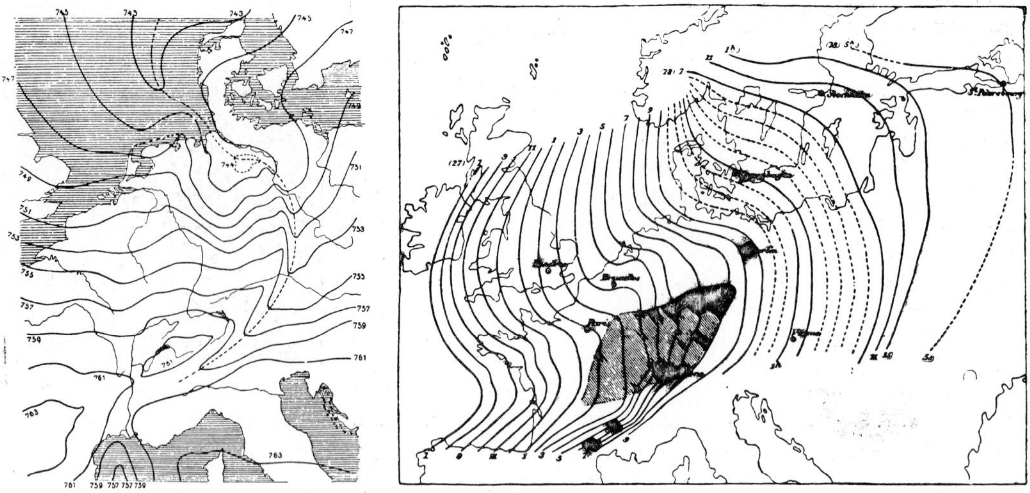

a. Isobars and front of 27. VIII., 21h GMT. b. Isochrones of front. Area of thunder at front-passage.

Fig. 6.—E. DURAND-GRÉVILLE's analysis of the cold-front of 27.—28. VIII. 1890.

in 1918.—The *warm-front*, on the other hand, escaped detection altogether since it is comparatively inconspicuous in the barogram (cf. fig. 2) and in the pressure field.

The French meteorologist E. DURAND-GRÉVILLE, investigating the cold-front of 27 August 1890, called this weather system a "ligne de grain" (squall-line), cf. fig. 6. At an epoch when the isobaric field—in spite of its domination in Meteorology—was generally treated too summarily, and when the connection between flow and pressure field was the only model **M**, DURAND-GRÉVILLE tried to reconstruct the true shape of the pressure field as closely as possible. Besides the synoptic map $\mathbf{T}_0$ he had also consulted the time-sections of the atmosphere rendered by barograms $\mathbf{T}_1$, thereby finding details in the pressure field otherwise unattainable. DURAND-GRÉVILLE, thus, already in 1892 used the method brought to a perfection by FUJITA in 1955.

The marked wedge behind the trough in fig. 6 a, has the shape typical of a *convective system*[1] (thundery rains were reported from part of this region, l.c., p. B. 268—269). Thus, it presumably contained an ordinary cold-front together with a *pseudo-coldfront*.[1] The former is indicated by the front-wave and its secondary Low near Hamburg; had DURAND-GRÉVILLE seen and commented on this connexion, he might now stand as the discoverer of the frontal cyclogenesis.—He calls his "squall-line" an "independent organisme", and states that he is the first to show such a line extending across all Europe, and to connect it with the general pressure distribution, i.e. with the Low over the North Sea, to which it belongs according to him.

In fact, DURAND-GRÉVILLE's analysis, bearing the impress of truth and of an empiric genius, renders exactly the features that we are accustomed to see on modern maps in such situations. Contrary to other known analyses made prior to 1919, it could serve as a model combination of small-scale and large-scale synoptic analysis even to-day.—However, apparently, DURAND-GRÉVILLE published no more such case,[1] and had only a vague notion of its dynamics. If his e m p i r i c craftsmanship had gone hand in hand with theory, and "had he kept right on to the end of the road" (cf. footnote on p. 445), also treating several analogous cases, he might have discovered the Polar front and Life cycle of cyclones.

We may even make another bold statement containing an "if". Had GALTON's meteorographic system of **O** and **T** from the 1860:ies (including the meteorograms, the weather symbolization,

[1] Cf. T. BERGERON 1954, pp. 140—144, especially figs. 5 and 8 h.

[1] His publicationes on squall-lines 1892—1911 seem to be based mainly on his minute analysis of the above single case, although he mentions some other such cases.

and the semi-Lagrangian analytic method) been extended sufficiently in time and space—preferably over all Europe and until present time—and had the ideas as to models $\mathbf{M}_1$ of such men as FitzRoy and Clement Ley been followed up whole-heartedly, no doubt to-day's main knowledge of weather systems and their structure at the earth's surface (including the latest findings at the so-called "meso-scale") could have been gathered long before 1900. Already in about 1890, budding Aerology would then have begun to look rationally into the three-dimensional structure of these systems. Aerology itself would thereby have been strongly stimulated, and promoted by scientists and governments. Aerological stations (with kites and sounding balloons) could have formed a real network in Europe and N. America already in, say, 1905, instead of (with radiosondes) in 1945.

Soon after 1910 meteorological air-plane soundings[1] and radio-transmission of ship's observations were a reality, and the hemispherical upper-air map (over the oceans to begin with based on indirect aerology) could then have been brought into existence.—*Forty or fifty years of further work, till present time, with sufficient observations, a good tool and sound models, might then by now have brought Weather Forecasting past the critical stage.*

4. Stagnation and resignation

The real stagnation or decline of Weather Study came later, after Clement Ley and the young Köppen, and may be represented by fig. 5 c, or by the cyclone model shown in fig. 7, appearing during the 25 years 1901—1926[2] in four editions of the leading German textbook of Meteorology by Julius von Hann. (These models, evidently, had as physical basis the assumption of a general frictional inflow and lifting of the air in the interior of any low pressure area.) Here the Low is no longer organized, except a slightly eccentric cloud-mass with precipitation in its interior, and the indication of "Cirrus" ahead of the Low,

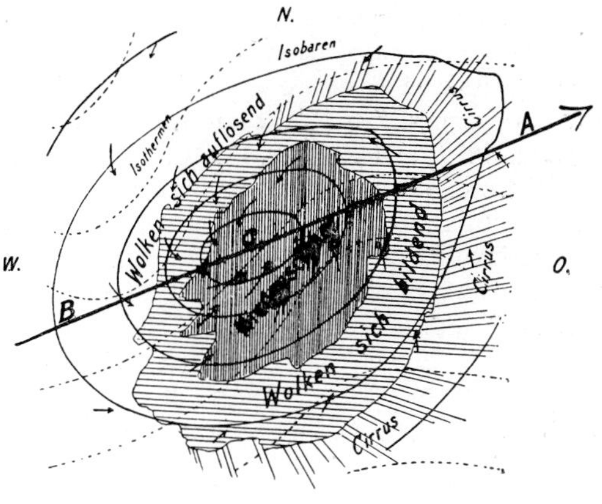

Fig. 49.
Winde und Witterung in der Umgebung eines Barometerminimums.

Fig. 7*.—The cyclone model prevalent in Central Europe 1880—1930.

a feature which is so invariable in Nature that it could not escape von Hann's contemporaries.

Already in 1873 the farsighted Director of the new Danish Meteorological Institute, N. Hoffmeyer, had initiated the construction and publishing of Daily Synoptic Maps of the North Atlantic Ocean and adjacent continents in order to learn from such maps where and how cyclones breed and how they move.[1] From 1881 these maps were edited in collaboration with the Deutsche Seewarte in Hamburg.—**O**. Unfortunately, the quality of the observations and the density of the network turned out mostly to be rather poor, the observations were often not synchronous, and 24 hours showed to be too large a time-interval.—**M**. No fruitful structure models were used; only summarily drawn isobars appeared on the maps. (It is to be hoped that the corresponding publishing of the IGY data from 1957—58 will be much better as to **O**, **T**, and **M**, but there are always ample opportunities of repeating the mistakes of old days and of committing new ones.)

The old Atlantic maps, therefore, proved inappropriate for studying the Lows and Highs over the ocean. The individual cyclones were necessarily often confused, because of unexpected cyclogeneses and the just-mentioned technical map defects. Thus, these maps, and the charts of favoured cyclone tracks at sea, based on them, left weather-men as bewildered as before when this publication stopped with the volume of 1912 because of World War I.

[1] H. C. Cannegieter, of the Royal Dutch Meteorological Institute, already in 1915 inaugurated meteorological routine airplane soundings at Soesterberg, Holland. These were published in full since then and became daily in May 1919. In 1920 the average top-height was 4.4 km, and 5 km were surpassed on 85 days. The chief aviator, J. Bakkenes, was able to pierce even a Nimbostratus without blind-flying instruments. The present writer could witness this on such a flight, in May 1924. —Cf. further Cannegieter 1936.

[2] i.e. even 8 years after the discovery of the Bergen cyclone model.

[1] See N. Hoffmeyer 1876, 1880.

Markedly better were J. VAN BEBBER's "Zugstrassen der Minima" over Europe (1882), and they can now be explained as due partly to local orography, partly to blocking situations. VAN BEBBER, 1882, and KÖPPEN, 1882 b, also realized that the cyclones would move with the average current of the ambient atmosphere, and gave rules for estimating this *steering* current from the pressure and temperature fields at 0-level (VAN BEBBER, l.c., p. 18 and 24—25).—Cf. also the rich literature in this field quoted by HILDEBRANDSSON and TEISSERENC DE BORT (1907, tome I, p. 159—191).

*

No wonder that weather-men in those days, 1865—1915, were prone to an increasing sense of disappointment, or at least indifference[1], since they had to handle all weather situations only with the reports **O** from a scanty network at the earth's surface, given in an incomplete code and without aerology, and since the structure models $\mathbf{M}_1$ were of the just-mentioned misleading kind. —In 1904 N. EKHOLM, at that time a zealous leader of Swedish Weather Forecasting, referring to the deficiencies of the existing European network of weather reports made the following statement (l.c., p. 348):

> "dass diese Mängel nicht schon längst abgeholfen sind, scheint anzudeuten, dass der Wetterdienst als eine Nebensache, ja, vielleicht auch nur als ein unvermeidliches Übel betrachtet wird".

Cf. also the discussion of methods 1 & 2 in Sect. 13 below.

Often enough situations would turn up where several well defined and well separated rain-areas co-existed within one and the same vast Low.—In the case of fig. 8 they would have been left unexplained by the prevalent model, except perhaps the one over the S. Baltic, which in the terminology of those days belonged to a "secondary Low", and the one over Central Scandinavia, which could have been explained as "orographic". (However, the next map, not reproduced here, shows that it had moved west in the general easterly current, and was still maintained, but now on the leeward side of the mountain range.) The air-mass and front methods, already established when this case occurred, easily disclosed the real nature of these rain-areas[2], all of them belonging to different fronts, the one extending from the Orkneys towards NE being connected with a marked Arctic front.

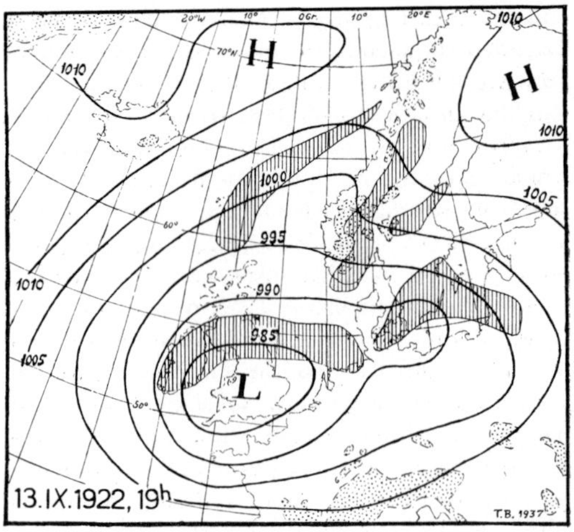

Fig. 8.—A vast Low and its rain-areas.—Rain-areas drawn by G. SCHINZE in 1922.

rain-area   1 000 m plateau

5. Dawn of a new era

At the end of last century a most important step forward was taken as to the system of observations **O** by the start of direct aerological soundings, sporadically in 1880—1900 (especially through L. TEISSERENC DE BORT and R. ASSMANN in Europe, A. LAWRENCE ROTCH in USA), and systematically after 1900 under the auspices of the International Aerological Commission.

As to g e n e r a l atmospheric models $\mathbf{M}_0$, the physical-hydrodynamical fundament of the new era was given by V. BJERKNES' famous circulation theorems, originally expounded in his ordinary lectures of theoretical physics at the University of Stockholm in April 1897, and then published in 1898 (and in their complete form in 1902). In fact, one of these two theorems was published already in 1896 by L. SILBERSTEIN at Krakow, but he regarded the baroclinic state only as a transient one without any real geophysical application: a good example of case (C) on p. 443. V. BJERKNES, on the other hand, saw its great applicability and importance, fought for its recognition and use, and is thus its real discoverer.

During his Stockholm time in 1893—1907 V. BJERKNES often discussed his pioneering meteorological plans and work with his friend NILS EKHOLM. The latter had already in 1891 constructed some synoptic maps with *isopycnics*,

[1] Cf. the quotation from D. BRUNT in footnote on p. 446 above.

[2] See Sect. 7 M (7), p. 458.

which inspired BJERKNES (1898, p. 5) to applying his circulation theorem to the atmosphere.—In 1904, V. BJERKNES could display a rational program for investigations in meteorology and oceanography on the basis of this new "physical hydrodynamics", thereby laying the theoretical foundations of the ensuing Leipzig and Bergen Schools of Meteorology; cf. the two following Sections, and V. BJERKNES 1938.

In 1901 MAX MARGULES showed that the potential energy of a pressure distribution generally equals less than 10 % of the kinetic energy of the wind balancing it. Thereby MARGULES had done nothing less than detronizing the previous *deus ex machina*, the pressure-field, reducing it to a mere cog-wheel in the atmospheric machinery.—He then attacked, on a rational quantitative basis and in a directly applicable way, the problem of the production of cyclone energy, in his famous paper of 1905, whereupon F. EXNER later built part of his dynamic works. See further p. 462, 465.

Shortly afterwards a new and more realistic epoch in concrete weather study was, at last, heralded by W. N. SHAW and R. G. K. LEMPFERT through their Lagrangian work "Life History of Surface Air Currents", published in 1906. This classical paper gave a conclusive proof of the existence of DOVE's and FITZROY's two Main air-currents, and a new Cyclone model,[1] see fig. 9: a great advance as to specialized models $\mathbf{M}_1$. —Here again we meet a striking example of the above case (C). In spite of the evident great merits of these two British discoveries, Sir NAPIER SHAW made no single attempt, as far as

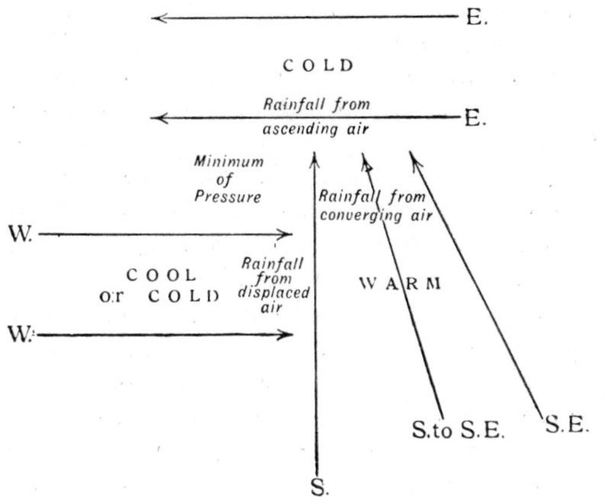

Diagram Representing the Constituent Parts of a Cyclonic Depression.

Fig. 9*.—W. N. SHAW's cyclone model, 1911.

one can see, to apply the air-mass concept or the new cyclone model to any of the numerous synoptic cases treated in his ensuing rich production. Nor were these ideas (so far as is known) ever utilized systematically in British practical weather service, although SHAW for many years was its Director. This failure may be partly ascribed to the afore-mentioned difficulty in finding the foremost convergence line in LEMPFERT's and SHAW's cyclone model (the warm-front), especially when studying it only in the pressure field.[1]—Consequently, the rediscoverers of these concepts and structure models, and the whole Bergen School, who fought for them and used them consistently in practice, deserve the main credit for them.

Moreover, this second British cyclone model —just as the first one—lacked the front concept, and consequently LEMPFERT and SHAW could not find the clue to its life history. The model was undevelopable, a deficiency that might also sufficiently account for its not being used in practice.[1]—It had, however, two advantages over

[1] Already in 1903, SHAW, in a much appreciated lecture before the Royal Meteorological Society, had given an inkling of two kinds of air-trajectories in moving depressions, but as yet no real Cyclone model or Main air-currents.—The new cyclone structure was hinted in 1906, but the generalized, clear-cut model only appeared in SHAW's "Forecasting Weather" 1911.

As early as in 1861—1865 G. JINMAN, master mariner, —opposing strongly to the prevalent Circular Theory of storms—presented an a s y m m e t r i c cyclone model composed of two d i s t i n c t air-currents, crossing each other at two "confluences", the western one (evidently a cold-front or a backbent occlusion) always being more marked (l.c., 1865, p. 4 & p. 60). His model was based on many years' experience of winds and clouds in tropical and extra-tropical cyclones at sea, i.e. on unusually representative data.—JINMAN's excellent observations hardly got due consideration, evidently because they were mingled with absurd notions of the physical cause of atmospheric motion—another regrettable case of lacking contact empirie-theory in our science.

[1] Another and perhaps better reason (not observed when the above lines were written) is given by D. BRUNT, l.c., p. 7—8: "I would regard this memoir as Shaw's greatest written contribution to meteorology. It could have made meteorological history had it only been followed up." . . . "Shaw was so impressed by the ideas put forward by Dines"—the pressure-temperature correlation at 9 km—"that he took no further interest in the consequences of the Life History, and so missed the opportunity of finding the life history of the depressions". —Cf. also below, p. 465, where DINES' statistical results are discussed.

the original version of the Bergen School model (J. BJERKNES' 1919):

(1) it allowed for continuous precipitation in the warm sector, and had an explanation for it ("converging air"),

(2) it contained also a feature that may be interpreted as the trough of the (backbent) occlusion: the "Minimum of Pressure" between the "cold" easterly and "cool" westerly current.

The latter circumstance has probably never been emphasized, and it has only of late occurred to the present author. The explanation for its appearance will be analogous to the reason for the complex structure of CL. LEY's(-ABERCROMBY's) model, see figs. 3—4 a.—This is, again, an example of the above case (C): LEMPFERT and SHAW and their followers evidently never saw the great importance of this feature.

6. The Leipzig School

On the basis of his program of 1904, V. BJERKNES started already in Stockholm, in collaboration with J. W. SANDSTRÖM, to edit a "Dynamic Meteorology and Hydrography". This work was continued after 1907 in Kristiania (Oslo) together with O. DEVIK and TH. HESSELBERG, and resulted in the two classical volumes: I "Statics" 1910, and II "Kinematics" 1911.

When established at Leipzig in 1913—1917, V. BJERKNES tried to complete this great undertaking by editing a Volume III, "Dynamics". Due in the first instance to World War I, which scattered the scientific forces of the *Leipzig School*, this group never accomplished Vol. III. Another and deeper reason was the lack of suitable atmospheric models **M**, either of the general type $\mathbf{M}_0$ (Chicago School) or of the specialized type $\mathbf{M}_1$ (Bergen School), cf. below. —Further, as a first concrete application of his above-mentioned program, V. BJERKNES and his collaborators at Leipzig, now joined by H. U. SVERDRUP, made a large-scale endeavour (till then an unparalleled undertaking in Synoptic Meteorology) at a three-dimensional synoptic representation of atmospheric states[1] selected among the so-called International Aerological Days in 1900—1913.

The ingenious British mathematician and meteorologist L. F. RICHARDSON, inspired by these attempts at a rational diagnosis of the atmospheric structure, endeavoured in 1911/22 to provide, analogously, the prognosis of one such case (20. V. 1910, 07^{h} GMT). Following V. BJERKNES' fundamental lines of thought, RICHARDSON tried to "predict" the atmospheric state over Central Europe only 6 hours after the "known" initial stage by taking account of all atmospheric variables and all conceivable influences within a vast region around the "prognostic district". —This large-scale effort (RICHARDSON's report occupies 236 pp. 4:o) to realize a forecast according to what might be called the complete theoretic-physical method (no. 3 in Table III below) was, however, at that time bound to fail. This was so, partly because of the inevitable errors and lacunae in the network of observations, especially aloft, and the ensuing considerable errors in the analysis of the initial state,[1] but mainly because the equations used were too general. The computational scheme suggested was unstable, which in practice meant the occurrence of undamped micro-scale disturbances (fictitious waves) creeping in and spoiling the result.

Unfortunately, RICHARDSON's unsuccessful trial has till now withheld theoreticians within Meteorology from making a renewed attack on our main problem along the lines of this forecasting method—apparently in part offering another case of the effect of lacking contact theory-empirie.

*

In spite of many rebuffs and other difficulties the general philosophy of V. BJERKNES and his adepts remained unshaken and even ripened during all their work. Some items of this philosophy may be listed here; cf. V. BJERKNES 1913, 1922.

1. An unswerving belief in the possibility of treating the weather-forecast problem with rational physical methods: *the rational physical approach.*

2. The necessity and possibility of applying these physical laws to the atmospheric states at any moment, and not only to average values: *the principle of case studies.*

3. The necessity of getting observations **O** within distances in time and space that could be regarded as differentials: *the principle of dense network.*

4. The recognition of *the necessity of perfecting the synoptic tool* **T**.—For the first time since 1860 a radical improvement of the synoptic map $\mathbf{T}_0$ was established. Realizing that the earth's surface

[1] Synoptische Darstellungen... Leipzig 1916/19.

[1] Cf. P. D. THOMPSON 1957, mentioned in footnote 2 on p. 440.

supplies the main boundary conditions of the atmosphere, orography was shown quantitatively on the maps, by appropriately generalized height steps.[1]—$\mathbf{T}_1$. The wind field got a rational kinematic treatment by isogones (or stream-lines) and isotachs. The upper-air state was shown on constant-pressure maps (instead of on constant-level maps).

5. The attitude that every apparently correct individual observation, however deviating it might seem, should be heeded, explained and incorporated rationally into the pattern of the case studied: *the respect before the empiric facts*—and *the idea of specialized atmospheric structure models* $\mathbf{M}_1$.

This philosophy and all the work of the Leipzig School evidently formed a necessary and sufficient condition for the budding of new and fruitful ideas in the receptive minds of V. BJERKNES' youngest Norwegian assistants at Leipzig: J. BJERKNES and H. SOLBERG.

7. The Bergen School

The findings and works of the Bergen School will be too well-known to need a presentation. The achievements of the period 1918—1930 are by now lying so far off in time that they can be stated to have established the new era in scientific weather forecasting foreshadowed at the turn of the century. They were based on considerable improvements of all the three factors **O**, **T**, **M** mentioned in the Introduction, and represent a final, successful fusion of the technique and concepts of DOVE's local method and those of the synoptic method, based on a general physical understanding of the atmospheric processes, treated as far as practicable from the Lagrangian aspect.

O.—The main improvements as to observations were the following.

1. The initial discoveries of J. BJERKNES and H. SOLBERG, until 1918, were made possible only by applying the above principle of the *dense "surface" network*. In opposition to elder, and apparently more experienced, colleagues, these two very young fellows, already at Leipzig in 1916/17, had adhered to this principle and utilized every available station and information from the earth's surface, although the network of upper-air information was two orders of magnitude sparser.—In 1918, together with V. BJERKNES, they even personally erected and instructed the numerous reporting stations of a new, at least 10 times denser network in Norway. The results proved that they were right.—Here it may be interesting to notice that this successful attitude to the problem, just as the ensuing discoveries made with the dense network, apart from the reasons listed in Sect. 6, must have been due to the fact that the three just-mentioned investigators were not beforehand overburdened with meteorological knowledge and therefore were unbiassed and open to new ideas; cf. the above case (A).

2. For want of direct observations from the upper air, a method of *indirect aerology* was gradually developed. It was mainly based on the indirect evidence of motion, humidity and temperature conditions aloft given by the observations of clouds and other hydrometeors taken from the earth's surface.—A first test of this method was offered when, at last, in 1917/18, after 60 years of synoptic maps, the warm-front was discovered and its structure disclosed.

3. Therefore, the Bergen School after 1919, aided by British, French and other colleagues, fought for and attained a better international reporting system, supplying much richer data also on *clouds*, *visibility* and *precipitation*[1].

T.—Also the synoptic map, the chief tool for digesting the dense network of reporting and/or climatological stations in Central Europe and Scandinavia, was reformed on the basis of the experiences won at Leipzig.

Firstly, *orography* was shown as clearly as possible on the synoptic base maps $\mathbf{T}_0$. Only so was the ensuing rapid discovery of different new orographic effects in wind and precipitation made possible.

Secondly, contrary to the practice of most other investigators and weather services, we took pains to enter not only all stations, but also all meteorological elements from every station as neatly as possible on one and the same map: the *composite map* $\mathbf{T}_0$—a necessary prerequisite for really being able to combine and criticize, rapidly and unerringly, the different elements at all stations and so to perform a rational weather study.—Cf. GALTON's meteorographic system of 1863 and his text, l.c., p. 3.

[1] A few years ago orography was deleted from certain British Weather Service maps, on the argument that it encumbered these maps.

[1] These were also necessary for the study of "cloud systems" inaugurated in France by SCHERESCHEWSKY and WEHRLÉ 1923.

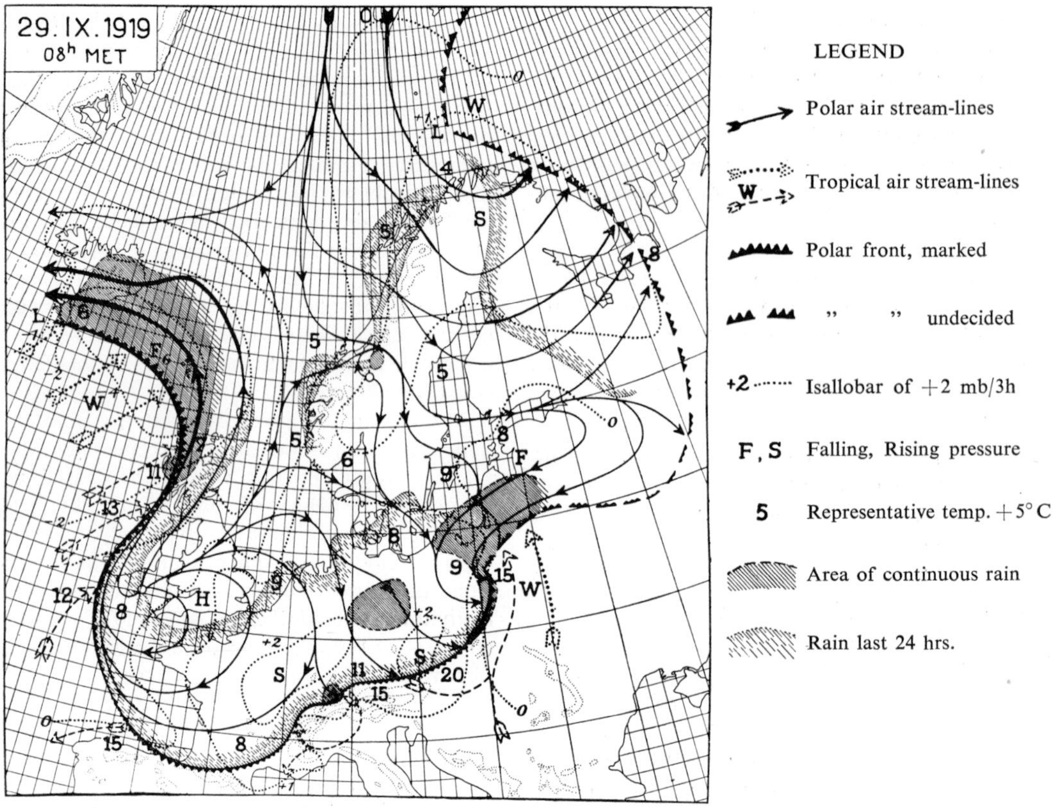

Fig. 10.—Bergen weather map of 29. IX. 1919, showing a Polar front. — Analyzed with streamlines by T. BERGERON in October 1919 (before the occlusion process was discovered).

Thirdly, the wind-field was represented by *stream-lines* T_1, cf. fig. 10. This kind of representation, though Eulerian in itself, as we know, gives an approximation to the air-trajectories whenever the wind-field is quasi-stationary. Therefore, it will often help a Lagrangian attack on the problem. The method was not new in itself. As stated above it became used systematically by the Leipzig School, over larger areas and in a denser network than formerly, and during 1918—1919 it was even used on the daily maps of the Norwegian weather service. After the summer of 1919, though, isobars were reintroduced on those weather maps, and stream-lines were no longer regularly drawn. But they had already served their purpose: two kinds of lines of convergence—later labelled *warmfront* and *coldfront*—and the Bergen model of a *young front cyclone*, had been discovered, achievements that might have come even much later without this highly improved tool, which laid emphasis on the wind-field, and without the general Lagrangian trend of thought.

M_1.—The main accomplishment of the Bergen School evidently lay in introducing realistic Lagrangian *structure models* of the atmosphere, which were fit to account for all the meteorological elements reported (made digestible by the composite map), and which were truly and directly connected with the very weather that the forecaster has to predict—as opposite to the earlier one-sided and sterile isobaric-geometric "weather" study.

Some little known circumstances related to the development during the initial phase of the Bergen School shall be put in the spotlight here.

The case of 24.VII.1918, treated in J. BJERKNES' and H. SOLBERG's classical paper "Meteorological Conditions for the Formation of Rain" (Kristiania 1921), shows their model cold-front invading Europe from WSW and just reaching S.

Scandinavia. Utilizing the lucky circumstance that the meteorological offices both in England, France and Germany had delivered, to V. BJERKNES, extracts from the meteorological ascents made by the air-force stations at and behind the military front, the authors could, on the basis of direct aerology, aim at reconstructing the three-dimensional structure of this model: the cold-front. Thereby the two following points deserve attention:

(1) The network of soundings, only 7 stations in all (cf. l.c., fig. 9), was so loose that it would have been pointless to undertake this three-dimensional study without the reliable information on the position of the cold-front at the ground, and its general properties (rain-area, cloud-system, etc.), given by the composite map at 0-level with its dense network,[1] cf. l.c., figs. 7 a—b.

In fact, *it will pay even to-day always to base the upper-air analysis on the more comprehensive and detailed composite-map analysis* (and *vice versa:* to control the latter by the former).

(2) J. BJERKNES and H. SOLBERG unhesitatingly identified the inversions in the soundings (*vide* l.c., fig. 8) with the upper limit of the cold-air wedge constituting the cold-front.—The ensuing development within aerology, showing frequent so-called "dry" subsidence inversions below front surfaces, or elsewhere within a homogeneous air-mass, cast a shadow of doubt on the interpretation given by the authors, the more so as there were no humidity values in their figure 8.—So compact was, in fact, the opposition on this and other points from leading quarters in Europe, especially the Vienna School (cf. case A on p. 443), that the ideas of the initiating Bergen School made very little headway to begin with outside Norway. Its adepts were severely discouraged and might even have given up using their ideas and findings in practice, as had been the case with some of their fore-runners. —However, recent analyses for fronts in cross-sections[2] have shown that most inversions, isothermies etc., found between the 1 km-level and the tropopause, irrespective of their humidity change, are of frontal character or origin. Therefore, the present author has now been led to the conviction that the original interpretation of the cold-front of 24. VII. 1918 was correct. This, again, offers an example of the above case (B 2).

A few other items may also deserve mention in this connexion.

(3) The cold-front was, after all, as we have seen, not a new concept in 1918.—A greater deed was, in fact, J. BJERKNES' and H. SOLBERG's discovery of the warm-front, which had escaped notice both in the British meteorograms and on the weather maps of 60 years in all Europe, because it was so much less conspicuous in the pressure field (cf. also Sect. 3 above).

(4) The Low of 15. VIII. 1918, by which the cyclone model was definitely discovered, was on that date in reality an occluded cyclone. The same applies to the Low of 27. VIII. 1919 over Norway, published as a good example of the cyclone model (J. BJERKNES and H. SOLBERG 1921). And yet this did not impair the truth and value of the discovery as such.—Here we meet two more instances of case (B) above.

(5) The *occlusion* process, discovered 18. XI. 1919 by T. BERGERON, made the cyclone model developable and gave the clue to the life history of cyclones.—As seen from fig. 11, even in this case the discovery was better than the data by which it was achieved, cf. (B2), p. 443, Firstly, the *seclusion*, indicated near Lofoten in fig. 11, represents a hypothesis that later had to be retracted. Secondly, over S. Germany (not shown in fig. 11) the upper cold-front is so far advanced on this map that it would imply an abnormal speed of displacement since the morning; also, there were no observations to verify such a position. Thirdly, there were only the kite ascents of Lindenberg and Tarp (none reaching above 2,600 m ab. s.-l.) to support the assumed three-dimensional structure of the occluding process.—Yet, the analysis of fig. 11 over Sweden and N. Germany can still stand for criticism, and the occluding process has of late, at last, been fully confirmed aerologically.

(6) Up to 1919 the prevailing isobaric methods were just as repugnant to the Bergen adepts as DOVE's methods had been to the first synopticians after 1865; cf. p. 445 above. Therefore, there was, at first, a tendency at Bergen to a corresponding one-sidedness by clinging to the stream-lines and refraining from the use of the pressure-field; case (A) above.—However, when in Sept. 1919 the new Bergen Weather Service was for the first time

[1] In U.S.A. now misleadingly called "meso-scale" network. In reality, this has been the ordinary network density in NW. and Central Europe for at least 40 years. — This again is a good example of the above case (D).

[2] See T. BERGERON 1957, pp. 133/35, 144/52, 164/69 and figs. 115—117, 120, also rendering frontal upper-air analyses by PALMÉN, BERGGREN, and VUORELA.

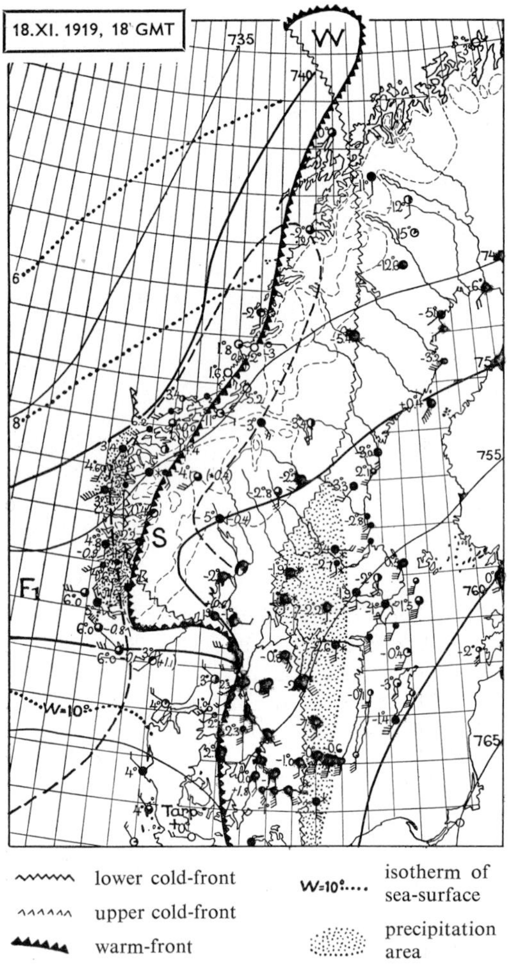

Fig. 11.—The "first" occlusion, 18. XI. 1919, 18h GMT.—Analyzed by T. BERGERON; redrawn in 1920. Only published in Russia, 1934 a.

charged with the great responsibility of issuing autumn and winter storm-warnings for its very exposed coastal section, it became necessary to introduce the isobars on the Bergen maps, cf. Sect. 7 **T** above. The present writer, who in 1908 and later had picked up the Swedish allobaric storm-warning methods (No. 2 in Table III below) directly from NILS EKHOLM and his assistant MARTIN JANSSON, strongly supported this step. Thus, it was also natural then to work for incorporating the allobaric method into the Bergen system as a physically explainable and practically useful analytic and prognostic tool, $\mathbf{T}_1+\mathbf{T}_2$ (see T. BERGERON 1934 b, 1939).—Cf. the paragraph on EKHOLM and V. BJERKNES on p. 465 below.

(7) At the continued synoptic activity at Bergen, and consolidation of the Bergen School, especially 1920—25, E. G. CALWAGEN'S, G. SCHINZE'S and F. SPINNANGR'S devotion to the task, their synoptic experience and enthusiasm, their analytic skill and method, formed more material assets than is generally recognized. They founded a school in keeping up a consistent, reliable, technically clear and thorough analysis of the new models $\mathbf{M}_1$ at the daily weather service and in special studies. Thereby, they helped to produce a fundament for further progress (cf. fig. 8 above), i.a. by showing the existence of the *cyclone series* and by helping to classify the *air-masses*. CALWAGEN'S posthumous paper 1926 contains one of the few exhaustive studies of *air-trajectories* after LEMPFERT'S and SHAW'S. It is partly based on air-plane soundings that formed the first *direct aerology* within the Bergen School, an activity that CALWAGEN had personally initiated and carried through, and which led to his untimely death—thus interrupting a most promising life-work in Synoptic Meteorology.—See also i.a. SCHINZE 1932.

The endeavour underlying all the work of the Bergen School was to minimize the previous unnecessarily great subjectivity of forecasting by trying to arrive at explicit and physically explainable rules for the displacement and development of well-defined weather systems $\mathbf{M}_1$ under different general conditions.—These principles are also illustrated by the improved three-dimensional occlusion model, showing eight *weather regions* (T. BERGERON 1934 a; 1937; 1953, fig. 1).—The more subjective parts of the weather study and forecasting would thus become confined to more and more subtle and detailed weather features, and to processes not yet accessible to a rational explanation and/or a quantitative treatment.

Therefore, *one should not accept the present strict distinction made between "subjective" and "objective" methods in weather analysis and forecasting. In fact, all such methods have a subjective and an objective part, and our endeavour is continually to advance the limit of the objective part as far as possible, thereby letting the continually shrinking subjective part deal with more and more delicate tasks.*

Moreover, *every new weather analysis is to a certain extent a discovery and cannot be achieved purely mechanically: support from intuition will be necessary. This holds good fully with analyses made for scientific purposes, but partly even for practical forecasting.*

A monument on VILHELM BJERKNES' life's work in Meteorology, edited by C. L. GODSKE, was at last accomplished in 1951, trying to render the spirit and main achievements of the Leipzig-Bergen School.[1]

8. The Chicago School

The Bergen methods were certainly to some extent quantitative, but not enough, and mainly with regard to "small synoptic systems" (SUTCLIFFE's classification, l.c., 1954, p. 11). Therefore, they were not able to tackle quantitatively the problem of interaction between several weather systems, and of the weather systems as links in the general circulation, at least not for periods much longer than 24 hours.

Thus, it may well be said that a new era was once more inaugurated in scientific forecasting by the works of C.-G. ROSSBY, as *spiritus rector* and chief promoter of the Chicago School[2]; and naturally much credit is due also to his numerous collaborators from different countries, not least to E. PALMÉN. A special homage must be paid to ROSSBY's many followers and patrons in U.S.A., too numerous to be listed here.—The *isentropic analysis*, and divers studies of the general circulation started by ROSSBY at M.I.T., Cambridge, Mass., in 1937, and pursued by his first followers, H. R. BYERS, J. NAMIAS, H. WEXLER, H. C. WILLETT and others, formed an important forerunner to the later work in Chicago. Cf. ROSSBY and COLL. 1937—1939.

There is a remarkable analogy between C.-G. ROSSBY and V. BJERKNES: although both were mainly hydrodynamists and not weather-men, their interest for long periods focussed on the problem of practical weather forecasting, and they never lost it wholly out of sight.[3] Even ROSSBY's last studies, on atmospheric chemistry,[4] were synoptical with important bearings on air-mass meteorology.

[1] C. L. GODSKE, T. BERGERON, J. BJERKNES & R. C. BUNDGAARD: Dynamic Meteorology and Weather Forecasting. Boston & Washington 1957.

[2] Called so by analogy with the names Leipzig School and Bergen School. Calling a scientific "school" by the name of a country or a person seems unjust to the collaborators, often being even of foreign extraction.

[3] V. BJERKNES, in his installation lecture at Leipzig in 1913, states explicitly (l.c., p. 14) that Weather Forecasting is the most important task of (applied) Meteorology.

[4] See ROSSBY and EGNÉR 1955.

The developments and discoveries connected with the Chicago School are well-known and still in progress. Hence, it is not necessary to review them here; to appreciate them justly is as yet impossible. They will, therefore, be regarded mainly from the view-points of long personal synoptical experience, of the historical development outlined above, and of the three fundamental promoting factors or conditions **O**, **T** and **M** mentioned in the Introduction.—In fact, even the outstanding achievements of the Chicago School were made possible only by great improvements as to the factors **O** and **T**, and by appropriate adaption of **M**.

Three features of this new era in Weather Forecasting seem to have received special attention and publicity:

(a) The introduction of (1) simplified general models $\mathbf{M}_0$ of the atmospheric large-scale dynamics, (2) a new specialized model $\mathbf{M}_1$, the *jet-stream*[1], and (3) new, practicable methods T_2 for handling these models mathematically, aiming at a more inherently quantitative forecast on a physical basis—previous methods being either non-physical, impracticable or mainly qualitative (cf. table III below).

(b) The utilization of electronic computers **T** at the forecasting procedure, and lately also at the analysis.

(c) The claim that, thanks i.a. to (a) and (b), the new tools and methods could produce "weather" forecasts that were "objective", in contrast to the "subjective" forecasts of "conventional methods".

9. Comparison of tools and models

T.—Using electronic computers for meteorological analysis and forecasting is apparently regarded as a technical step forward of unrivalled magnitude, and as *the* means by which not only forecasting but also the analysis can be made "objective".— Certainly, engineering has never before produced anything comparable with the "electronic brains".

Yet, whether mental or mechanical, the weather-service tools **T** are used:

$\mathbf{T}_0$ for ordering the enormous mass of "surface" or upper-air data, $\mathbf{T}_1$ for combining them for further treatment, and $\mathbf{T}_2$ for achieving certain computations along the direction lines of the general atmospheric models $\mathbf{M}_0$ (or $\mathbf{M}_1$).

We must then first distinguish between two

[1] E. PALMÉN 1948, 1951.

cases: the plotting $\mathbf{T}_0$ and analysing $\mathbf{T}_1$ are made (a) mentally-graphically ("conventional method") or (b) mechanically (by electronic computer). Even in numerical forecasting the analytic stage is performed by either method.—In case (a) the plotting $\mathbf{T}_0^G$ and analysis $\mathbf{T}_1^G$ are separate operations, following their specific rules: entirely objective for $\mathbf{T}_0^G$; explicit, heeding and combining all elements, and approaching objectivity as far as possible, for $\mathbf{T}_1^G$.—In case (b) (where till now only upper-air data occur) these operations are combined, $\mathbf{T}_0^N + \mathbf{T}_1^N$, ruled by the "coding" and performed by the machine, in principle objectively and with less errors, but hitherto only treating one element at a time.

As to operation $\mathbf{T}_0$, it seems justifiable then to claim that the introduction of the electronic computer is comparable with, but not surpassing in importance, the introduction of the classical synoptic implements: the weather code, the synoptic base map (or vertical cross-section blank) and station model (including its symbols).

A concrete comparison will help to prove the justness of the above proposition. It is evident that even an expert follower of the numerical forecasting methods would be entirely at a loss if put before the great mass of aerological data of to-day without any implement, graphical or electronic, to digest them and make them accessible to further treatment.—It is, however, just as evident that a forecaster using "conventional methods" could not make anything out of the 100,000 figures of one observational hour, giving "surface" and upper-air data, appearing in an endless succession on the teleprinter strips, by merely scanning them as they stand there—and yet they are already available in a considerably more condensed and understandable form thanks to the international code.

As to operation $\mathbf{T}_1$, using an electronic computer (case b) is comparable to performing the main graphical-analytic operations (case a), with their subordinate rules of analysis, in a strictly professional way.

Again, to the unexperienced or dilettantish analyst the maze of figures and symbols on the map (especially the composite map) will not make (much) sense, even when appropriately plotted. But with knowledge and training, i.e. a professional standard, one may do it fairly rapidly and unerringly.—Even when including the preparatory work done outside the machine, it will perform this task in shorter time and without individual variations, but not necessarily "better" (and hitherto only for upper-air scalar fields). The ideal analysis is, in fact, not the most "objective" one, but the most "probable" one, i.e. the analysis that by all probability lies nearest to the true atmospheric state.

Operation $\mathbf{T}_2$.—(a) The mental method consists here in performing certain graphical computations or estimates $\mathbf{T}_2^G$ according to the inherent properties and life history of the specialized models $\mathbf{M}_1$ and their reaction on the general conditions prevailing (both shown by the analysis).—(b) With the mechanical method the "coding" depends on the kind of general model used $\mathbf{M}_0$, and the calculation is performed by $\mathbf{T}_2^N$.

In both cases, however, in the first instance only a *general forecast* is obtained. The so-called *special forecast* cannot as yet be performed by method (b), and it is mostly left out or performed only summarily with method (a).

The very computations $\mathbf{T}_1^N$ and $\mathbf{T}_2^N$ are made, say, 10^4 to 10^5 times faster than the corresponding man-made ones, and certainly also with less error. But the fact that forecasts of the type $\mathbf{T}_2^N(\mathbf{M}_0)$ also have been accomplished graphically in a few hours (FJØRTOFT 1952), shows that in this case the electronic machines mainly represent a higher speed and accuracy.—Moreover, the computers have not yet disclosed any new specialized models $\mathbf{M}_1$ to us.—The further discussion of the relative merits of methods (a) and (b), as to all the operations $\mathbf{T}_0$, $\mathbf{T}_1$ and $\mathbf{T}_2$, has to be deferred to a later occasion.

$\mathbf{M}_0$.—D. P. MCINTYRE 1951 pertinently characterizes the philosophy of ROSSBY as founder of the Chicago School by these words: "Thus one should focus one's attention on air motion and leave the pressure to adjust itself to the air trajectories" .... "This is the basis of the Chicago School approach to atmospheric dynamics in which we first determine the development of air movement and the pressure distribution is obtained as a by-product."

It will not diminish the greatness of anyone when we state that V. BJERKNES, together with the adepts of the Bergen School, advocated and fought for this very philosophy throughout a life-time, and that C.-G. ROSSBY and his School, having learnt it from the former, are those who have been most successful in carrying through such a Lagrangian program.—The very same philosophy was even vindicated by W. BLASIUS in 1852—1875 (cf. footnote on p. 442—443 above), and by MARGULES 1901.

In order to make the atmospheric large-scale problem solvable quantitatively at that stage of our science and technique, ROSSBY decided at the outset in 1938/40 to avoid the main difficulties by throwing out the thermodynamic solenoids, friction, radiation and the water-vapour cycle of the atmosphere. The production and depletion of kinetic energy in connection with baroclinicity and friction thereby became excluded in a majority of Chicago School works that up till 1950 mostly have followed these leading lines.

It is well recognized, however, that these approaches imply so great a simplification that the models can hardly be called realistic. The hydrodynamics underlying the barotropic, fundamental model $\mathbf{M}_0$ of the Chicago School is no longer the "physical hydrodynamics" introduced by V. BJERKNES, and applied to forecasting in the single case of L. F. RICHARDSON's trial in 1922. Instead, the theorem of vorticity conservation, and its simplest corollary, ROSSBY's famous wave formula, formed a corner-stone of the hydrodynamical system of the Chicago School.—An indispensable part of this model $\mathbf{M}_0$ was the introduction of the quasi-geostrophic approximation in such a manner (J. CHARNEY 1948) that it filtered away the "meteorological noise" without sacrificing too much of the accuracy in the result as to large-scale motions.

10. Jet-stream and circumpolar aerology

O.—One circumstance in connection with the Chicago School is easily overlooked, although it formed a "conditio sine qua non" to the great development in Synoptic Meteorology brought about by this School during World War II. The needs of warfare had then made Meteorology a Key science, which resulted in the organization of the first circumpolar network of regular daily radio-soundings, and in the training of more than 2,000 new meteorologists a year only in America.—Without these vast "proving grounds" and great general interest in this kind of studies, the new ideas, which are essentially applicable to motions on a global scale, would perhaps not have been found worth while to follow up efficiently.

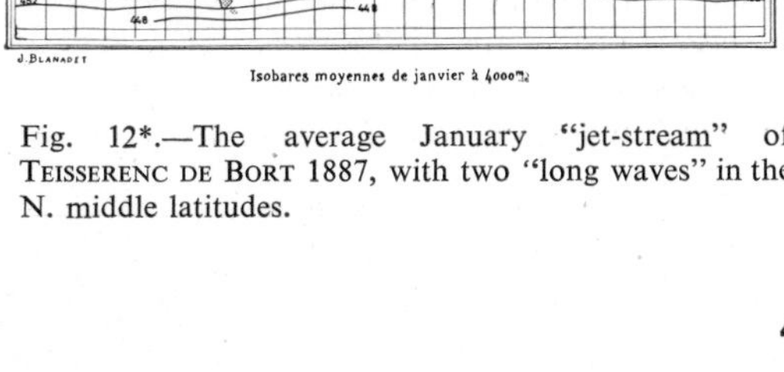

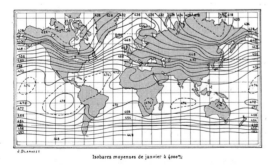

Fig. 12*.—The average January "jet-stream" of TEISSERENC DE BORT 1887, with two "long waves" in the N. middle latitudes.

In the rush of the technical developments of Atomic Age, many a reader might be inclined to think that this meant Man's very first quantitative knowledge of the state aloft circumpolarly, and that the old idea of a "polar vortex" only had the vague sense of world-embracing westerlies at all latitudes outside the equatorial region. That was indeed not the case, though.

From fig. 12, designed by L. TEISSERENC DE BORT already in 1887[1] and based on *indirect* aerology, we may deduce geostrophically what is now called "the jet-stream" as a rather well defined zone of intense westerlies at 30°—50° N lat., forming two stationary major waves just at the places where we usually find them to-day. This knowledge of 70 years ago, it is true, was confined to the *lowest 4 km* of the atmosphere (≦ 600 mb-surface), and it only concerned the *mean* and *geostrophic* wind. Moreover, the explanation of the two waves was thought to be purely *thermal*.—Anyhow, had TEISSERENC DE BORT been able also to construct the corresponding *daily* maps, and had his friend and collaborator H. H. HILDEBRANDSSON had the hydrodynamical training of H. VON HELMHOLTZ (who really had studied the problem of the general atmospheric circulation some ten years earlier, cf. above) or a close collaboration with the latter, then the joint work of TEISSERENC DE BORT and HILDEBRANDSSON: *Les bases de la météorologie dynamique* (1900 & 1907), might have become really dynamical instead of mainly historical and statistical.—The same applies, of course, to any other contemporary scientific group in Meteorology. It could then have treated the dynamics of global wave motion as controlled by the factor $\beta = 2\Omega \cos \varphi / R$, obtaining results similar to those won by the Chicago School, including the wave formula, already before 1900.—In reality, the imperfect contact (to put it mildly) between hydrodynamics and empirical meteorology up

[1] Printed 1889.

to 1900 made the big *œuvre* of those two pioneers in European aerology a descriptive-statistic work. Moreover, contrary to what could be expected from the title, there is not even one dynamic equation in it. This seems all the more strange since C. M. GULDBERG and H. MOHN already in 1876/80 had given the strict mathematical formulation of BUYS-BALLOT's law of 1860.

Naturally, the just-mentioned limitations in 1887, and till the 1930:ies, as to empiric knowledge may serve as an excuse for the lack of rational dynamical studies of the world-wide extra-tropical flow-patterns. Even the Leipzig School 1913—17 was not able to make considerable progress in this field, apparently because of too loose and restricted a network of aerological soundings, and lack of experience as to existing wave mechanisms in the atmosphere (see Table I). Moreover, with the Eulerian method used, the effect of the parameter β on individual air-currents (air-masses) would escape notice.

The air-mass and front method of the Bergen School, on the other hand, is decidedly Lagrangian.—The splitting of the subtropic high-pressure belt in the South Pacific was stated to be inexplicable thermally or by local orography and its fundamental character pointed out by T. BERGERON already in 1930. The dynamical explanation of this phenomenon, by long jet-waves, was at that time missed, though, due to lacking contact empirie-theory. It was given by ROSSBY 1939 (l.c., p. 46 and tables III—IV), and treated more fully by J. CHARNEY & A. ELIASSEN 1949, and by B. BOLIN 1950.

The jet-stream itself is clearly shown in the two mean vertical cross-sections of the atmosphere in figs. 114 and 115 of "Physikalische Hydrodynamik", published by V. BJERKNES and COLL. in 1933. This W-wind maximum is also described in the text (although the name "jet" was not coined yet), but evidently again a certain lack of contact empirie-theory at that time prevented us to see how it could be utilized.—V. BJERKNES, working on the same problems from the theoretical side, always strongly advocated the Lagrangian way of attack. However, his circulation theorem, in its complete, non-linear form, we know, could only tell what will happen to the motion of an air-mass during the next instant. Therefore, at that time, when modern successive integrations were not yet introduced, it could not be used for predicting or explaining any large-scale flow-patterns.

11. Waves and vortices

After 1900 Vienna possessed several meteorologists of highest ability in different fields related to the problem of atmospheric mechanics: MAX MARGULES, thermodynamics; FELIX EXNER, general and dynamical meteorology; H. VON FICKER, empiric-synoptical and alpine meteorology; A. DEFANT and WILHELM SCHMIDT, thermodynamics, turbulence etc.; and others.

The works of this Vienna School certainly gave numerous very important contributions to our science, helpful also to Weather Forecasting. But now afterwards we may state that they did not leave a lasting solution of the general problem put by HELMHOLTZ and later attacked with success by V. BJERKNES, C.-G. ROSSBY and their hydrodynamical collaborators.—Plausible reasons for this failure would once more be *lack of contact theory-empirie* and *lack of a rational dynamic-thermodynamical program* corresponding to V. BJERKNES' of 1904.

Just to take one example: it is amazing that the Vienna School did not soon succeed in continuing HELMHOLTZ' work, solving the general problem of atmospheric wave motions of greater wave-lengths than the billow-cloud waves (cf. Table I), and of the corresponding cellular motions.[1]—Particularly, it now seems almost inaccountable how the short gravity-inertia waves or lee-waves could escape both professional observation and explanation so long in mountainous Central Europe, where several meteorological institutes then had had their site for at least 50 years, and where the lee-wave clouds occur regulary, being known to the people as "Moazagotl"-clouds for hundreds of years. These clouds did not appear in the International Cloud Atlas until 1910, and they had to wait till late in the 1930:ies for a rational dynamical interpretation (QUENEY 1936, 1948; KÜTTNER 1938; LYRA 1943).—In fact, v. FICKER knew a lot about these clouds and waves empirically, and his contemporary, EXNER, at the same institute, knew enough dynamic theory: together they might have solved the problem.

H. VON FICKER's interesting and extensive synoptic studies (1910, 1911) on the spreading of cold and warm air in Russia and Siberia have often been credited the Vienna School as a pioneer work on the Polar front; cf. also v. FICKER's own historical account 1923.—The present author cannot share this opinion, however

[1] Cf. F. EXNER, 1906, 1907, 1910, 1911.

Table I.—Atmospheric waves

Year	Name	Type	Wave-length km
	↑ Ultra-sound	C	$< 2 \cdot 10^{-5}$
	• Ordinary sound (tones)	C	$2 \cdot 10^{-5}$ to 10^{-2}
	Explosion waves	C	10^{-2} » 10^{-1}
1888	Helmholtz waves (Sc und, Ac und)	G	10^{-1} » 1
1933	↓ Short lee-waves (Ac len, Cc len)	G	1 » $2 \cdot 10$
1950	↑ Long lee-waves (nacreous clouds, precip.)	G(I)	$2 \cdot 10$ » 10^2
1918	• Short jet-waves (frontal)	GI(V)	10^2 » $5 \cdot 10^3$
1940	↓ Long jet-waves	V	$5 \cdot 10^3$ » 10^4
	Tidal waves	(G)	$\leqq 2 \cdot 10^4$

Wave type:
C compression, longitudinal.
G gravitational, I inertial, V vorticity-gradient — transversal.

valuable that work may otherwise be. Firstly, v. FICKER's idea met with the fate of case (C), cf. p. 443. Secondly, for convenience, his work was mainly based on 24-hourly mean pressure and temperature differences and thus could not arrive at a well-defined front concept. Therefore —and probably again due to want of contact empirie-theory—it did not lead to any dynamic-thermodynamic description and explanation of the life cycle of cyclones (Bergen School) or of cyclone series (Chicago School). Moreover, during the colder seasons, the most conspicuous "warmings" occurring in Russia-Siberia will generally be caused by removal of a marked "surface" inversion through precyclonic wind-increase, and not by a true warm-front passage connected with the Polar front.

The idea of "steering" of the Vienna and Frankfurt Schools about 1925—40 (just as N. EKHOLM's penetrating synoptic work, 1904 ff.) was mainly centered on the behaviour of allobaric systems, and it did not hit the main problem, namely the dynamic processes underlying the formation and changes of the "steering" upper flow-pattern itself. Further, the Frankfurt School to begin with expelled the origin and steering of the pressure variations from the troposphere to the lower stratosphere,[1] i.e. to an unreasonably high level (above which only 10 to 20 % of the atmospheric mass is left), a hypothesis to which the Bergen School firmly opposed (cf. T. BERGERON 1928, p. 5—11). See also E. PALMÉN 1931 b.

Even much earlier, in 1872, the realistic Rev. CLEMENT LEY had stood up against similar tendencies, writing (l.c., p. 149): . . . . "the upper current has been employed by meteorologists as a sort of *Deus ex mâchina*, to explain the obscurities of the science."—These almost prophetic words hit the idea of the "stratospheric steering", 60 years later, with full force.—At last, after 1940, the Chicago School definitely succeeded to set this "steering" near the mid-troposphere, since that level, as to air-flow, may well represent the average conditions in the "weather-sphere", and since it lies near the level of non-divergence.

R. SCHERHAG, one of the most successful adepts of the Frankfurt School as to practical forecasting methods, inaugurated, in about 1935, a combination of quantitative direct and indirect aerology, at a time when direct aerology was still restricted to a very small area in Europe. His advection of allobaric systems and his "divergence theory" (cf. SCHERHAG 1934, 1948) certainly indicated a sound Lagrangian trend of thought and proved useful in practice; but they did not—at that time—lead further for lack of a strict hydrodynamical foundation.

A rational dynamic treatment of the prognostic value of the divergence was taken up by SUTCLIFFE 1939, and pursued 1947, following the Chicago-School line of thought. Thereby, he arrived at results concerning the thermal steering and development of disturbances that are susceptible both to physical interpretation and practical test, and have done well in practice.

*

[1] e.g. G. STÜVE 1926, R. MÜGGE 1932.

Physics managed to solve the problems of electromagnetic waves by the theoretical genius MAXWELL followed by the more empirical genius HERTZ, who were not even compatriots.—In Meteorology the above-mentioned great Austrian pair of contemporary scientists could not achieve the corresponding deed. Evidently, our science is too complex; we need a "Maxwell-Hertz" or an "Exner-Ficker in one person. The nearest approximation to this complex person as yet in Meteorology were V. BJERKNES and J. BJERKNES, father and son, and there lies maybe the reason for the birth of the Bergen School and its flourishing off-set, the Chicago School.

So it happened that the problem of large-scale flow-patterns in the atmosphere was not tackled dynamically with any real success until about 1930, first by members of the Bergen School with a semi-Lagrangian method, and then more fully in 1938/40 by C.-G. ROSSBY on a rational Lagrangian basis.

Ever since 1919 the Bergen School had known the front-waves (the "short jet-waves" of inertia-type in Table I) and their behaviour, especially their development into vortices.[1] H. SOLBERG's theory of cellular inertia-waves 1928 provided an important preliminary dynamical interpretation of these phenomena. The work of J. BJERKNES & C. L. GODSKE 1936, and of GODSKE 1937, marked a further advance in this field.

However, a great intensification of the aerological network was sorely needed for describing satisfactorily and understanding better the cyclogenesis and other fundamental atmospheric structures and processes; cf. Sect. 6, principles 2—3, and Sect. 7 **M** (1).—A plan of securing, to this end, detailed vertical time-sections of special cases by one or more ascents an hour from a fixed station, was worked out at the Royal Belgian Meteorological Institute thanks to a collaboration between J. JAUMOTTE and J. BJERKNES in 1928—1930. Such *serial ascents* **O** were then made possible through JAUMOTTE's invention of the *light meteorograph*.[2] Thus J. BJERKNES from 1928, and later E. PALMÉN, could study the Bergen School models $\mathbf{M}_1$ three-dimensionally and confirm their assumed structure. Thereby PALMÉN 1933 could also prove definitely that the Polar front in principle extends at least to the tropopause, the temperature difference between Polar and Tropical air increasing up to or above the mid-troposphere. (The joint Central European opposition had, in fact, claimed that these models were either shallow and of little consequence—or already known!)—Already 1930 J. BJERKNES and E. PALMÉN began to study the connection between the Polar-front disturbances and certain waves in the upper flow-pattern. J. BJERKNES treated their mechanism by means of "isobaric channels" in 1937, and together with J. HOLMBOE in 1944 also taking account of the above factor β. Thus, they explained dynamically the short jet-waves (see Table I) or Polar-front disturbances and hinted their connection with the long waves.

The attack of the Chicago School, however, was more truly Lagrangian and consequently more fruitful, at least when applied to large-scale dynamics. The great simplifications introduced (cf. Sect. 9 **M**) made a first practical approach to the problem possible. As stated above, the beginning of daily and circumpolar aerology permitted an immediate testing of the new theories on a natural scale; it showed the long jet-waves in the field, and stimulated further research immensely.

The only remaining category of waves, the "long lee-waves" in Table I, was finally found at the Cirrus and nacreous-cloud levels (e.g. DIETERICHS 1950), and apparently also at the "low-cloud" level, reflected in the rain distribution (BERGERON 1949, p. 26—28).

*

Parallel to the different kinds and sizes of transversal atmospheric waves there is a spectrum of atmospheric vortices, from the smallest turbulent eddies over the cyclonic and anticyclonic vortices of various sizes to the large-scale circulations in our atmosphere. In most cases there will be a correspondence between a primary wave-stage and an ensuing vortex, though generally not so manifest and clearly demonstrated as with the front-waves (or "short jet-waves"), which regularly develop into typical vortices, the migrating cyclones.

Kinematically there is no essential difference between the just-mentioned waves and the vortices (cf. "Physikalische Hydrodynamik" § 43).—The motion in the very short HELMHOLTZ waves, just as in ROSSBY's long waves, consists in principle only in a periodic redistribution of preexisting energy. As soon as we ask for the energy balance at the transition wave→vortex, though, we

[1] Cf. i.a. T. BERGERON & G. SWOBODA 1924: "Wellen und Wirbel an einer quasistationären Grenzfläche über Europa."

[2] described by JAUMOTTE 1931.

meet a new problem, since this process is mostly connected with a transformation of potential energy into kinetic energy (and heat) that cannot be restored into potential energy within the life cycle of the same vortex.

The classical example of such a process is the formation of tropical hurricanes, which, however, falls outside the scope of this chronicle. But also with the extra-tropical cyclogeneses the problem is partly the same. During a century, the kinetic and the convective theory of the energy balance in cyclones contended for domination.

ESPY 1841, FERREL 1856, REYE 1872 and HELMHOLTZ were all in favour of the *convective*, or condensation, *theory*, and their main source of energy was the latent heat of water vapour. EXNER in his text-book of Dynamic Meteorology 1917 summarily dismisses this explanation, as to extra-tropical cyclones, by the following statement (l.c., p. 143), which is based on a wrong conclusion:

"Seitdem man weiss, dass die Depressionen unserer Breiten in den unteren 10 km kälter sind als ihre Umgebung, entfällt zunächst die Möglichkeit, diese Gebilde auf die angedeutete Art zu erklären. Dies schliesst aber nicht aus, dass die Kondensationstheorie anderswo, vielleicht bei den tropischen Zyklonen, anwendbar ist, wie HELMHOLTZ annimmt."

EXNER, it is true, accepts the rôle of the potential energy of adjacent cold and warm air according to MARGULES.[1] Yet, because of a misinterpretation, the "cold-core cyclone", based on the purely statistical aerological results of W. H. DINES 1912 and others, nearly gave the fatal blow to the convective theory.—Now, D. BRUNT 1951 (l.c., p. 8) tells us that this was also the case with LEMPFERT's & SHAW's cyclone model, thereby explaining why they never pursued their work on this problem, "and so missed the opportunity of finding the life history of the depressions". DINES' statistics even formed a serious obstacle to the recognition of the Bergen-School mechanism of extra-tropical cyclogenesis, which really also builds energetically on MARGULES' classical work of 1905.—In all these cases the opponents ignored the fact that the initial warm-core stage of an extra-tropical cyclone will be too short-lived to show up in values averaged over all cyclonic stages.

Already in 1902, on the other hand, M. JANSSON of the French-Scandinavian aerologic station at Hald,[2] N. Denmark (56°23′ N, 9°19′ E Gr.), had noticed that the upper air warmed with falling, and cooled with rising pressure; see M. JANSSON 1913, p. 232. Based on these observations, and on their extensive joint experience in the Swedish weather service, EKHOLM (1906, p. 239) made the pertinent statement that the core of moving cyclones ("rather rare in Europe"), and specially their katallobaric region, is warm, that of stationary (i.e. the completely occluded) ones cold—and *vice versa* in the anticyclones.

However, neither EKHOLM and M. JANSSON, nor V. BJERKNES, who stayed at the University of Stockholm till 1907, seem to have come in contact with LEMPFERT's and SHAW's cyclone model of 1906[1]; and the theoretician V. BJERKNES had little empiric knowledge of his own in this field (cf. V. BJERKNES, 1898, p. 5). Otherwise, BJERKNES' new hydrodynamics, in combination with this new cyclone model and MARGULES' energy studies might have led EKHOLM's and M. JANSSON's intense allobaric work into a very fruitful path, and there could have been a "Stockholm School" of, say, 1908.—EKHOLM also rightly opposed to the one-sided isobaric geometry (e.g. EKHOLM 1913, p. 17). But by unduly stressing the geometry and the primary rôle of the allobaric regions (l.c., p. 18, 19), instead of pursuing the just-mentioned idea of their connection with different air-masses, he, unfortunately, ended up in a *cul-de-sac*.

The competing *kinetic theory* was, in fact, first inaugurated by DOVE 1828, and later especially cherished by the Vienna School. On the basis of this theory, J. VON HANN in 1901 put the convective theory officially to death, i.a. on the argument that excessive convective rains usually bring a rise and not a fall of atmospheric pressure.

A. REFSDAL, in 1930—32, was the first again efficiently to break a lance for the condensation theory, thus continuing the line of thought of FERREL—REYE—MARGULES (cf. Table IIa). REFSDAL endeavoured to treat the basic problem of cyclogenesis, the energy balance, rationally and quantitatively. He showed that the effect on the wind and pressure field of a release of potential energy mainly depends on whether the mechanism in question implies a small-scale overturning of the atmosphere (convection→ Cumulonimbus) or a large-scale one (cyclogenesis → a Low), thereby also removing HANN's main argument against the convective theory of tropical cyclones. Un-

[1] Cf. above, p. 453, left col.—See also BIGELOW 1903.

[2] Cf. Travaux de la station franco-scandinave ... Viborg 1904.

[1] EKHOLM never quoted it, and it was unknown to V. and J. BJERKNES even in 1919.

Table II a. Stages in the Development of Weather Study and Weather Service

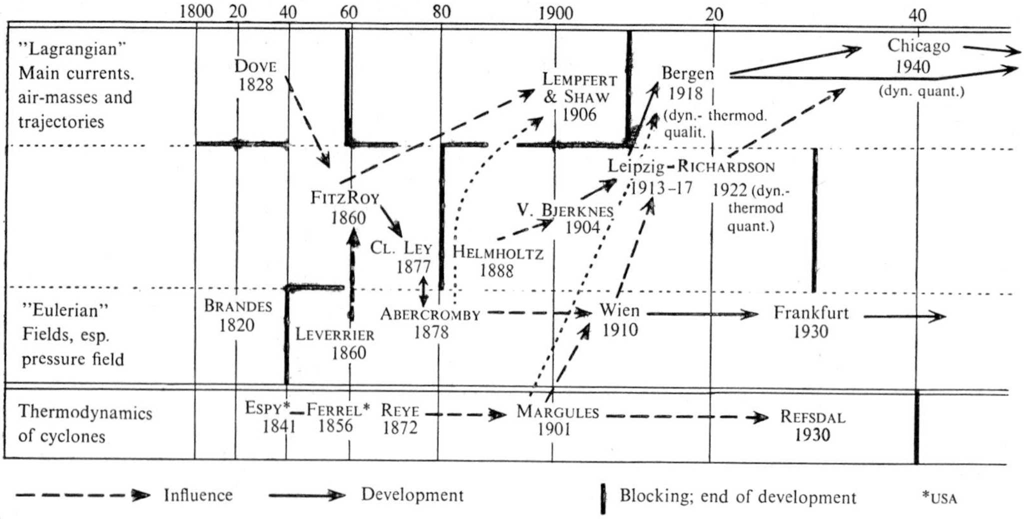

fortunately, REFSDAL (like his model MARGULES) left Meteorology prematurely, without having gained sufficient attention for his main points:

(1) the necessity of studying the production of kinetic energy in the atmosphere, and particularly within the most capricious weather systems, the cyclones;

(2) the rôle of moisture and conditional lability thereby;

(3) the fundamentally different effect of these factors in different kinds of mechanisms.

These problems—touched upon later by P. RAETHJEN and others—will probably have to be taken up rather soon for further treatment on a rational basis, the more as they may be of utmost importance for understanding and forecasting the apparently random developments mentioned by O. G. SUTTON, R. C. SUTCLIFFE and P. D. THOMPSON (cf. footnote on p. 440).

12. Historical trend of ideas

After the above somewhat rhapsodic and "subjective" exposition of the historical development of scientific Weather Study (especially within NW. Europe) a summary of this account may be needed. Table IIa contains the names of the main Schools or individual scientists treated here, arranged chronologically and as to their method: mainly Lagrangian, semi-Lagrangian, mainly Eulerian and energy-method. The arrows in the Table try to show the line of development of the different schools (or scientists) and their interdependence.

Apart from DOVE, the trend shown in Table IIa indicates a slow but general approach towards a true Lagrangian view and attack on the problems.—Reserve made for the author's personal notions having influenced the construction of the Table, it also indicates that the Bergen and Chicago Schools are still developing along these lines, and that a fusion of their methods will give the best promise for the future.

The more specialized Table IIb indicates the trend followed at the attack on the fundamental weather forecasting problem after 1865: the origin, structure and life cycle of atmospheric activity zones and disturbances. The following features are noteworthy, though not surprising:

(1) The discoveries in this field have proceeded continually to vaster and vaster entities, permitting longer and longer forecast periods (cf. SUTCLIFFE 1954, p. 14).

(2) There have been three considerable periods in the evolution mainly devoted to developing and utilizing the pioneer ideas of a previous relatively short epoch, and to consolidation of the new results: 1882—1917, 1928—1939 and since 1947 (abstracting from the discoveries in 1892 and 1906, since they never found their way into practice).

After the present period of awaiting one might hope for the next, maybe decisive, advance to come in the 1960:ies. Plausibly, this could result from a fusion of the best existing methods, as hinted in Sect. 13 and Table III, by close collaboration of active theoreticians and empiricists.

Table II b.—Discovery of Main Atmospheric Activity Zones and Disturbances after 1865

Model M_1	Author	Year
Local squall-lines—Cyclone model	CL. LEY	1878
Squall-line structure	W. KÖPPEN	1882
Cold-front	E. DURAND-GRÉVILLE	1892
Main air-currents—Cyclone model	SHAW & LEMPFERT	1906
Warm front—Cyclone model	J. BJERKNES & H. SOLBERG	1917—18
Polar front—Life-cycle of Cyclones (or "short jet-waves")	Bergen School	1919
Main fronts and air-masses—Cyclone series	" "	1920—28
Long upper-air waves—Wave formula	C.-G. ROSSBY	1939
Jet-stream—Life-cycle of Cyclone series (or "long jet-waves")	Chicago School	1947
? ?—Life-cycle of main fronts and jets	?	>1960

13. Applicability of main synoptic forecasting methods

We have now proceeded so far that we may list (Table III), compare and discuss the main different methods and kinds of models **M** hitherto used for scientific synoptic weather forecasting as to their practical usefulness.

1. & 2. The methods of *analogies* and of *formal extrapolation* (nos. 1 & 2 in Table III) may be of considerable assistance, especially when other methods cannot be advantageously applied. No. 2 was particularly elaborated by J. ANGERVO 1928/30 and by SV. PETTERSSEN 1933, 1940, 1956. Cf. also A. GIÃO 1929.—However, they can no longer form the basis of Weather Forecasting since they are mainly formal and not really physical.—N. EKHOLM, as a trained physicist and devoted synoptician, was fully aware of this last fact; yet he had to use both methods, no. 1 for weather prediction (stating 1904, p. 346/7, that "he knew of no better method" for this purpose), no. 2 for the wind.—Cf. also F. BAUR 1944 on "analogous cases".

3. The *complete theoretic-physical method* (no. 3 in Table III), represented by V. BJERKNES' program 1904, the Leipzig School work 1913—17 and L. F. RICHARDSON's famous prognostic trial 1922, is evidently in principle the ideal method. Due to lack of atmospheric models $\mathbf{M}_0$ or $\mathbf{M}_1$, and of appropriate mathematical methods, the work along these lines fell short in meteorological forecasting.—A renewed successful all-round attack on the problem according to this method is as yet not within sight.

4. The *front* and *air-mass,* or *Bergen methods* (no. 4 in Table III), even when extended into the stratosphere[1], cannot alone bring weather forecasting out of its present position. The main merit of this method lies in showing clearly, three-dimensionally and in detail all weather systems $\mathbf{M}_1$, their position, shape and structure, properties and mode of functioning[2], in short: the mechanisms that produce all the different kinds of *weather.* It also gives the clue to the trend of development inherent in each of these weather systems, i.e. their life history, when undisturbed by other systems.

On the other hand, this method does not in itself contain the dynamic and thermodynamic principles that can be used in practice for calculating quantitatively the steering and development of these weather systems over longer periods than two days, and their interaction with other, even far off systems.—Particularly, electronic computers have not yet proved useful with this method.

5. The *theoretic-dynamical* method as represented by the *Chicago School* (no. 5 in Table III) has the great merit of being both physical, quantitative and practicable. None of the older methods could claim to have these three advantages simultaneously.

Tentative numerical forecasting of the flow pattern at mid-troposphere level (which is assumed well to represent the mean atmospheric motion) according to this system have up till now mainly been based on a barotropic model of the atmos-

[1] For this extension, see E. PALMÉN 1933, A. NYBERG & E. PALMÉN 1942, and R. BERGGREN 1952, 1953.

[2] Provided that reliable humidity, cloud and other hydrometeor observations are available at all levels.

Table III. Main Synoptic Forecasting Methods
Listed chronologically

1. *Method of Analogies.*
When used quantitatively, it will from technical reasons chiefly be restricted to one or two meteorological elements.
Thus, incomplete and mainly empirical, qualitative and uncertain.

2. *Method of Formal (Non-physical) Extrapolation.*
Likewise restricted to the fields of a few elements (or even only the pressure field: EKHOLM 1904—SCHERESCHEWSKY & WEHRLÉ 1921/26—ANGERVO 1928—GIÃO 1929—SV. PETTERSSEN 1933).
Working quantitatively and yet practicable (i.e. relatively easy to handle technically), but incomplete, non-physical.

3. *Complete Theoretic-Physical Method.*
Utilizing all meteorological fields and working quantitatively. Thus, in principle, the ideal method (V. BJERKNES 1904—Leipzig School 1913/17—L. F. RICHARDSON 1922). No model **M**.
From technical reasons impracticable hitherto.

4. *Qualitative Practical-Physical Method*
Based on realistic, three-dimensional specialized synoptic models $\mathbf{M}_1$, taking account (in principle) of all meteorological elements (Bergen School), but not including certain fundamental large-scale dynamic processes (long waves etc.).
Practicable and directly rendering the future weather distribution sought for, but mostly only qualitatively, within a wide margin of errors and merely for one or two days.

5. *Quantitative Theoretic-Dynamic Method*
Based on general models $\mathbf{M}_0$ concerning wind, pressure (and temperature). Specialized synoptic models $\mathbf{M}_1$ not used; orography, radiation, friction, solenoid concentrations and/or water-vapour cycle hitherto mostly not taken into account (Chicago School etc.).
This practicable method works quantitatively (graphically or with computing machines), but with a wide margin of errors.—Efforts are being made to develop it into a complete theoretic-physical method (cf. 3. above) forecasting also the distribution of other elements than pressure and wind.

6. *Quantitative Practical-Physical Method*
Based on the most favourable combination of the above methods as fully developed (mainly 4 & 5), it might both be practicable and ensure an optimum of quantitatively reliable results, even as to forecasting the weather itself.

phere.—From reasons given above in Sect. 9 **M** it is doubtful *a priori*, though, whether such methods at present can on an average lead to tolerably correct forecasts even of the hypsography (or flow pattern) at that level. Still greater are the doubts as to forecasting the weather itself by such methods.

Moreover, the differences between observed and forecast developments during 24 (and 48 hours) turned out often to be of the same order when using these methods and the (formal or other) extrapolations made with "conventional methods" by an experienced forecaster.—The very fact that the barotropic model often produces as good results as analogous but more realistic models $\mathbf{M}_0$ ("three-layer model" etc., which are now being tried), seems also to indicate that *entirely new ways of tackling the dynamic-thermodynamical problems of the atmosphere are needed for a really efficient utilization of the observational data and a successful weather forecasting.*—Such efforts are, in fact, already being initiated, for instance by trying to incorporate humidity, radiation and statical stability in the computations, or by taking away the condition of geostrophic approximation.—SUTCLIFFE's *development method* (p. 463 above), in itself an off-spring of the Chicago-School methods, has in a way formed a starting point for studies of models with 2 or more parameters.

14. "Long-range forecasting" of Weather Forecasting

As stated in Sect. 1 "Everybody talks about better weather forecasts, but" . . . concrete remedies are mostly not discussed.—However, the present writer ventures to state that much could be gained at once and without any new methods or facilities, if we could realize at least part of the severe mistakes that, surely, are committed also within the present organisation of Weather Study and Weather Service.

Admittedly, it is extremely difficult to see one's own faults—otherwise one would be more ready to remove them. A mirror may help, though, to some extent. In the case of Science there is no other mirror than History to look into, and it gives only a dim and distorted image, i.e. the analogies will halt.

Yet, as already pointed out above, in our science the present conditions have important features in common with those 90—100 years ago.

Note for instance the analogy between (1) the interruption of the evolution started by DOVE-FITZROY's method, through the introduction of the isobaric-synoptic method 1860, and (2) a break in the Bergen-School work 1940—60, due to introduction of dynamic-synoptic methods aloft using mainly the pressure and wind-field.

Trying to make a "long-range forecast" of the natural development and possible control of Weather Study and Weather Forecasting on the basis of the above "epignosis" and "diagnosis" in Sections 2—12, we may start by the following comparison.

(1) In 1860 weather-men saw no point in using the local method and its detailed weather observations any longer, since they had then just got telegraphic reports **O**, synoptic maps **T**, and a *deus ex machina* $\mathbf{M}_1$: the Lows and Highs.

(2) In 1960, maybe, weather-men can see no point in getting reports of "local-method" character (i.e. from Key stations), and in performing a thorough synoptic analysis of the weather itself (primarily based on the composite map), since they now possess circumpolar upper-air reports of wind and pressure **O**, and two *dei ex machina:* the electronic computer **T** (to do most of the job for them) and the general dynamic models $\mathbf{M}_0$.

The *epignosis* may be expressed in these terms: Because of the evidently wrong course taken by Weather Study and Forecasting after 1865—due to the above opinion (1)—those activities were soon reduced to using crippled **O**, **T** and **M**. Strangely enough, meteorologists then for 50 years stayed satisfied with a loose network of reports in an inadequate code **O**, extremely poor synoptic maps **T**, and a one-sided model $\mathbf{M}_1$ for studying the weather systems.—*They used and were content with sterile isobaric-geometry at the 0-level for investigating and forecasting the weather.*—By rejecting DOVE's and FITZROY's ideas, because of the defects adhering to them, they had "thrown away the egg with the shell". This sad result was partly caused by falling into the different psychological pit-falls (A)—(D) listed on p. 443. Evidently it would be good to avoid them now, but who knows where they lie to-day?

The analogous *diagnosis*, cf. Sect. 13, would then read as follows. Because of a seemingly wrong course taken by Weather Study etc. to-day, its activities may not suffice for overcoming the present crisis in Weather Forecasting. Many meteorologists seem to stay content with upper-air probaritics for forecasting weather, although the correlation between a 500-mb hypsography and weather is feeble. Moreover, the small correlation existing is often derived from those vast parts of the atmosphere where, during a given period, a normal weather-type prevails, which generally implies quasi-stationary conditions and persistency—but *in those cases weather forecasts are trivial to the public.* Cf. R. B. CARSON 1954, p. 9.

The repeated cases of abnormal connection between upper-air flow and weather will not be caught by such forecasts. Nor are the electronic computers as yet able regularly to precalculate the great and sudden departures from the stationary state, i.e. abrupt intensifications and depletions of cyclones and anticyclones etc. But *those are the very cases more or less responsible for the weather vagaries that are important to the public:* the beginning or end of fine weather spells, or of rains, the major weather calamities, the extreme temperatures etc.

*

An attempt has been made above to retrace systematically some of the named deficiencies to objectively provable drawbacks, existing now or at one time. They shall be listed here for better survey. Progress has been unnecessarily obstructed or slowed down i.a. by:

(1) the factors (A) "blocking", (B) or (C) "underrating", and (D) "relabelling", mentioned on p. 443.

(2) lack of contact theory-empirie, and *vice versa.*

(3) lack of appropriate **O** or **T** for utilizing better **M**, and *vice versa.*

(4) one-sided emphasis on one element **O** or on one kind of model **M**.

The disastrous break in the evolution about 1860 was apparently caused by a most unlucky coincidence of a number of the above circumstances.

In 1860 we got the isobaric geometry on the 0-level maps. Shall we rest content in 1960 with an isobaric (or isohypsic) geometry aloft and geometry of isobars and "dry fronts" at 0-level? —Truly, there are many scientists now trying to avoid this alternative, but the meteorological world as a whole,—particulary its Weather Services, including all those at the aviation centers—is now not far from landing in the just-mentioned ditch.

It is not difficult to see why that is so.

The new weather-men of 1860/70 must have regarded DOVE's subjective observations of air-mass properties **O**, his lack of tool **T** and his partly defective models $\mathbf{M}_1$ with utmost pity. They had just got the new technical wonders: "numerous" exact, representative and objective barometer readings on an "extensive" synoptic map, where the isobars made it possible to discern the great currents in the chaos of local winds etc. (KÖPPEN 1921, p. 289); and the meteorological wonder: the Low, the real carrier of the weather.—Just as in 1860, Meteorology has now got observations **O** (the circumpolar upper-air data), tools **T** (the computers), and the general models $\mathbf{M}_0$ that seem so much more exact, representative and "objective" than the old or "conventional" ones.—Thus, it is quite natural when the new weather-men of to-day look analogously at those who toil with the "subjective" analysis of the composite map instead of using the new "objective" observations and wonder tools.[1]

Moreover, Man is after all a lazy creature. Thanks to these innovations Weather Service may become more and more mechanized, i.e. convenient to handle. We would not be human if we could resist this temptation. And why should we? In fact, it is there to be yielded to, provided that we utilize the new **O**, **T**, **M** for all that they can give, without giving up or forgetting to use older methods for what they can give—things that may after all lie outside the scope of the newest facilities.

Thus, the *prognosis* would read as follows:

Method 5 in Table III has seemingly given us the clue to the Life cycle of cyclone series and a necessary quantitative frame-work for all large-scale developments in the troposphere and lower stratosphere (the "weather-sphere"). This frame-work, among other things, supplies knowledge on the future steering and general development of the real weather systems $\mathbf{M}_1$ that determine the weather in the restricted sense of the word. This work can to a great extent be performed by the new **O**, **T** and **M** in a rather mechanical and "objective" way. Further, it is subject to a constant perfection in itself, particularly by continually introducing better models $\mathbf{M}_0$.

Method 4 in Table III gave the clue to the Life cycle of cyclones and disclosed the structure and functioning of such other important weather-systems that were not already known, i.e. all the entities $\mathbf{M}_1$ that are steered. This method, in emergency cases together with the most fruitful parts of methods 1—2, should be cultivated further and used as a necessary complement to method 5. —Shortly: *methods 4 and 5 should fuse into a higher unity, hinted as method 6 in Table III.*

Some ways in which method 4 can be perfected and better utilized were indicated by T. BERGERON 1952. In a later article an attempt will be made to show how Weather Service might be improved along such lines *even without any new* **O**, **T** *or* **M**, and also *what improvements of these factors seem to be most important at present.*

[1] Cf. two of T. E. W. SCHUMANN's "axioms", declared at Rome 1954: "Axiom II: Synoptic forecasting, mainly subjective as it is, holds out no prospects of any fundamental progress."—"Axiom III: The ideal to be striven for is the abolition of synoptic forecasting and its replacement as soon as practicable by objective methods." *Sic!*

Acknowledgements.

A general historical review in the field treated above—even when far from exhaustive or comprehensive—could hardly be achieved without aid from colleagues, among which the author would like specially to thank Dr. BERT BOLIN, Stockholm, for many helpful suggestions—not forgetting the valuable bibliographic and similar information received from several other scholars, both in and outside Sweden.

Obviously, the author has drawn considerably upon the meteorological philosophy of V. BJERKNES and C.-G. ROSSBY. The article is also meant as a homage to these two great school-founders in our science, and it tries to express some of their hopes for the future of Meteorology.

REFERENCES.

ABERCROMBY, R., 1878: On the general character and principal sources of variation, in the Weather at any part of a Cyclone or Anticyclone. *Quart. J. Met. Soc.*, **4**, p. 1.

— 1885: Principles of Forecasting by Means of Weather Charts. *Met. Council Off.*, No. 60, London 1885.

— 1887: Weather, a popular exposition of the nature of weather changes from day to day. *Intern. Sci. Ser.*, **59**. K. Paul Trench & Co., London 1887.

ABERCROMBY, R., MARIOTT, W., 1883: Popular Weather Prognostics. *Quart. J. Met. Soc.*, **9**, p. 27.

ANGERVO, J., 1928: Einige Formeln für die numerische Vorausbestimmung der Lage und Tiefe der Hoch- und Tiefdruckzentra. *Ann. Acad. Sci. Fenn., ser. A*, **28**, No. 10.

— 1930: Über die Vorausberechnung der Wetterlage für mehrere Tage. *Gerl. Beitr. z. Geophys.*, **27**, p. 258.

ASSMANN, R., 1901: Die modernen Methoden zur Erforschung der Atmosphäre mittels der Luftballons und Drachen. *Samml. pop. Schr. Ges. Urania Berlin*, No 57.

— 1902: Über die Existenz eines wärmeren Luftstromes in der Höhe von 10 bis 15 km. *Sitz.-Ber. Akad. Wiss. Berlin, Phys.-Math. Kl.*, **1902: II**, p. 495.

BAUR, F., 1944: Zur Methode der »ähnlichen Fälle«. *Met. Z.*, **61**, p. 28.

BEBBER, J. VAN, 1882: Typische Witterungserscheinungen. *Arch. d. Deutschen Seewarte*, **5**, No. 3. Hamburg 1882.

BERGERON, T., 1928: Über die dreidimensional verknüpfende Wetteranalyse, I. *Geof. Publ.*, **5**, No. 6.

— 1930: Richtlinien einer dynamischen Klimatologie. *Met.Z.*, **47**, p. 246 (English translation by H. C. WILLETT 1931: Ground Plan of a Dynamic Climatology. *Mo. Wea. Rev.*, **59**, p. 219).

— 1934 a: Трехмерно-связный синоптический анализ, II [Three-dimensionally combining synoptic analysis, II]. Ц. У. Е. Г. С. СССР., Moscow 1934.

— 1934 b: Лекции об облаках и практическом анализе карты. [Lectures on clouds and practical map analysis]. Ц. У. Е. Г. С. СССР., Moscow 1934.

— 1935: Sur l'utilisation des météorogrammes pour les recherches synoptiques. Ass. Gen. U.G.G.I. Lisbonne 1933. *U.G.G.I. Publ.*, *A.M.I.* [No. 5/c], p. 269. Paris 1935.

— 1937: On the Physics of Fronts. *Bull. Am. Met. Soc.*, **18**, p. 265.

— 1939: On a Manual of Weather Map Analysis. Ass. Gen. U.G.G.I. Edimbourgh 1936. *U.G.G.I. Publ. A.M.I.* No. 6/c. Paris 1939.

— 1949: The Problem of Artificial Control of Rainfall on the Globe. — II. The Coastal Orographic Maxima of Precipitation in Autumn and Winter. *Tellus*, **1**, No. 3, p. 15.

— 1952: Ways of Improving the Weather Service. *Weather*, **7**, p. 48.

— 1953: A General Survey in the Field of Cloud Physics. Ass. Gen. U.G.G.I. Bruxelles 1951. *U.G.G.I. Publ.*, *A.M.I.*, No. 9/c, p. 120. Bruxelles 1953.

— 1954: The problem of tropical hurricanes. *Quart. J. Roy. Met. Soc.*, **80**, p. 131.

— 1957: Föreläsningar i synoptisk-aerologisk analys. [Lectures on synoptic-aerologic analysis. Duplic.]. Uppsala 1957.

BERGERON, T., SWOBODA, G., 1924: Wellen und Wirbel an einer quasistationären Grenzfläche über Europa. *Veröff. Geoph. Inst. Leipzig, 2. Serie*, **3**, No. 2.

BERGGREN, R., 1952: The Distribution of Temperature and Wind Connected with Active Tropical Air in the Higher Troposphere and Some Remarks Concerning Clear Air Turbulence at High Altitude. *Tellus*, **4**, p. 43.

— 1953: On frontal analysis in the higher troposphere and the lower stratosphere. *K. Sv. Vet. Akad. Arkiv f. Geof.*, **2**, p. 13.

— 1958: Comparative Studies of 500 mb Barotropic Forecasts Based on Different Analyses. *Tellus*, **10**, p. 289.

BIGELOW, F. H., 1904: The mechanism of countercurrents of different temperatures in cyclones and anticyclones. *Mo. Wea. Rev. 1903*, **31**, p. 72.

BJERKNES, J., 1919: On the Structure of Moving Cyclones. *Geof. Publ.*, **1**, No. 2.

— 1932: Exploration de quelques perturbations atmosphériques à l'aide de sondages rapprochés dans le temps. *Geof. Publ.*, **9**, No. 9.

— 1935: Investigations of Selected European Cyclones by means of Serial Ascents. *Geof. Publ.*, **11**, No. 2.

— 1937: Theorie der aussertropischen Zyklonenbildung. *Met. Z.*, **54**, p. 460.

BJERKNES, J., GODSKE, C. L., 1936: On the Theory of Cyclone Formation at Extra-Tropical Fronts. *Astrophysica Norvegica*, **1**, No. 6.

BJERKNES, J., HOLMBOE, J., 1944: On the Theory of Cyclones. *J. Met.*, **1**, p. 1.

BJERKNES, J., PALMÉN, E., 1934, Aerologische Analyse einer Zyklone. *Beitr. z. Phys. fr. Atm.*, **21**, p. 53.

— 1937: Investigations of Selected European Cyclones by means of Serial Ascents. Case 4: February 15—17, 1935. *Geof. Publ.*, **12**, No. 2.

BJERKNES, J., SOLBERG, H., 1921: Meteorological Conditions for the Formation of Rain. *Geof. Publ.*, **2**, No. 3.

— 1922: Life Cycle of Cyclones and the Polar Front Theory of Atmospheric Circulation. *Geof. Publ.*, **3**, No. 1.

BJERKNES, V., 1898: Ueber einen hydrodynamischen Fundamentalsatz und seine Anwendung besonders auf die Mechanik der Atmosphäre und des Weltmeeres. *K. Sv. Vet. Akad. Handl.*, **31**, No. 4.

— 1902: Zirkulation relativ zur Erde. *Met. Z.*, **19**, p. 97.

— 1904: Das Problem der Wettervorhersage, betrachtet vom Standpunkte der Mechanik und Physik. *Met.Z.*, **21**, p. 1.

— 1913: Die Meteorologie als exakte Wissenschaft. Antrittsvorlesung [Leipzig, 8. Jan. 1913]. Verlag Vieweg, Braunschweig 1913.

— 1922: Wettervorhersage. *Phys. Z.*, **23**, p. 481.

— 1938: Bergen—Leipzig. Ueber die Entwickelung der Wettervorhersage. *Forschungen und Fortschritte*, **14**, p. 222. Berlin.

BJERKNES, V., BJERKNES, J., SOLBERG, H., BERGERON, T., 1933: Physikalische Hydrodynamik. Verlag Julius Springer, Berlin 1933.

BJERKNES, V., DEVIK, O., HESSELBERG, TH., 1911: Dynamic Meteorology and Hydrography, II. Kinematics. *Carnegie Inst. Wash. Publ.*, **88, II**.

BJERKNES, V., SANDSTRÖM, J. W., 1910: Dynamic Meteorology and Hydrography, I. Statics. *Carnegie Inst. Wash. Publ.*, **88, I**.

BLASIUS, W., 1875: Storms, their Nature, Classification and Laws. Philadelphia 1875.

BOLIN, B., 1950: On the Influence of the Earth's Orography on the General Character of the Westerlies. *Tellus*, **2**, p. 184.

BRANDES, H. W., 1820: Beiträge zur Witterungskunde. Leipzig 1820.

BRUNT, D., 1951: A Hundred Years of Meteorology (1851 —1951). *The Advancement of Science*, No. 30. London.

BYUS-BALLOT, C. H. D., 1860: Eenige Regelen voor anstaande weersveranderingen in Nederland. Utrecht 1860.

CALWAGEN, E. G., 1926: Zur Diagnose und Prognose lokaler Sommerschauer. *Geof. Publ.*, **3**, No. 10.

CANNEGIETER, H. C., 1936: 25 Jaar aerologie in Nederland. *Tijdschr. v. h. Kon. Ned. Aardr. Genootschap, 2e serie*, **53**, No. 6, p. 824. Leiden.

CARSON, R. B., 1954: Some objective quantitative criteria for summer showers at Miami, Florida. *Mo. Wea. Rev.*, **82**, p. 9.

— 1958: Observations on the utility, the limitations, and the didactic value of synoptic streamline analysis. *Trans. New York Acad. Sc., Ser. II*, **20**, p. 657.

CHARNEY, J., 1948: On the Scale of Atmospheric Motions. *Geof. Publ.*, **17**, No. 2.

CHARNEY, J., ELIASSEN, A., 1949: A Numerical Method for Predicting the Perturbations of the Middle Latitude Westerlies. *Tellus*, **1**, No. 2, p. 38.

Chromov, S. P., 1931: Dynamische Klimatologie nach Dove. *Das Wetter*, **48**, p. 312.

— 1933: Das meteorologische System des Admirals Fitz-Roy. *Das Wetter*, **50**, p. 123 & 148.

Dänisches Meteorologisches Institut und Deutsche Seewarte, 1884—1931: Tägliche Synoptische Wetterkarten für den Nordatlantischen Ozean und die anliegenden Teile der Kontinente. Dez. 1880—Febr. 1912. Kopenhagen 1884—1931.

Dieckmann, A., 1931: Fitz Roy. Ein Beitrag zur Geschichte der Polarfronttheorie. *Die Naturwissenschaften*, **1931**, p. 36. Berlin.

Dieterichs, H., 1950: Zur Entstehung der Perlmutterwolken. *Ber. d. Deutschen Wetterdienstes in d. US-Zone*, No. 12, p. 86.

Dines, W. H., 1912: Total and partial correlation coefficients between sundry variables of the upper air. *Geoph. Mem.*, **1**, No. 2, p. 31.

Dove, H. W., 1827: Einige meteorologische Untersuchungen über den Wind. *Pogg. Ann.*, **11**, p. 545.

— 1828: Ueber den Zusammenhang der Hygrometeore mit den Veränderungen der Temperatur und des Barometers. *Pogg. Ann.*, **13**, p. 305.

— 1828: Ueber mittlere Luftströme. *Pogg. Ann.*, **13**, p. 583.

— 1828: Ueber barometrische Minima. *Pogg. Ann.*, **13**, p. 596.

— 1837: Meteorologische Untersuchungen. Berlin 1837.

— 1840: Das Gesetz der Stürme. Berlin 1840. (Also in: *Pogg. Ann. d. Phys. u. Chem.*, **52**, p. 1.)

Durand-Gréville, E., 1892: Les grains et les orages. *Ann. Bur. Centr. Mét. de France*, **1**, p. 249.

— 1894: Les grains et les orages. *C. R. Acad. Sc. Paris*, **118**, p. 829.

— 1895: Le vent dans les grains. Anvers 1895.

— 1901: Les grains et les fausses dépressions secondaires. *Revue Scientifique, 4e série*, **15**, p. 263. Paris.

— 1906: Les cartes d'isobares par millimètres et la prévision du temps. *Ann. Soc. Mét. de France*. Janv. 1906.

— 1911: La loi des crochets de grain. *Ann. Soc. Mét. de France*. Nov.—Déc. 1911.

Ekholm, N., 1891: Cartes synoptiques représentant la densité de l'air. *Bih. K. Sv. Vet. Akad. Handl.*, **16: I**, No. 5.

— 1904: Wetterkarten der Luftdruckschwankungen. *Met. Z.*, **21**, p. 345.

— 1906: Die Luftdruckschwankungen und deren Beziehungen zu der Temperatur der oberen Luftschichten. *Met. Z.*, **Hann-Band**.

— 1913: Das Wetter auf der Nordsee während der ersten Hälfte vom Januar 1911. *Conseil Int. p. Expl. de la Mer, Publ. de Circ.*, No. 64. Copenhague. 1913.

Ekman-Danver, K., 1941: Vintergatan och Noaks ark. [The Milky Way and "Noa's Ark".] *RIG*, **24**, No. 3. Stockholm 1941.

Espy, J. P., 1841: Philosophy of Storms. Boston 1841.

Exner, F. M., 1906, 1907, 1910: Grundzüge einer Theorie der synoptischen Luftdruckveränderungen [I]—III. *Sitz.-Ber. Wiener Akad. Wiss., Phys.-Math. Kl.*, **115**, p. 1171; **116**, p. 819; **119: I**, p. 697.

— 1911: Über die Entstehung von Barometerdepressionen höherer Breiten. *Sitz.-Ber. Wiener Akad. Wiss., Phys.-Math. Kl.*, **120: II**, p. 1411.

— 1917: Dynamische Meteorologie. Leipzig & Berlin.

Ferrel, W., 1856: An Essay on the Winds and the Currents of the Ocean. *Nashville J. Med. & Surgery*, **12**, No. 4 & 5.

Ficker, H. von, 1910: Die Ausbreitung kalter Luft in Russland und Nordasien. *Sitz.-Ber. Wiener Akad. Wiss., Phys.-Math. Kl.*, **119: II**, p. 1769.

— 1911: Das Fortschreiten der Erwärmungen (der »Wärmewellen«) in Russland und Nordasien. *Sitz.-Ber. Wiener Akad. Wiss., Phys.-Math. Kl.*, **120: II**, p. 745.

— 1923: Polarfront, Aufbau, Entstehung und Lebensgeschichte der Zyklonen. *Met. Z.*, **40**, p. 65.

— 1927: Das meteorologische System von Wilhelm Blasius. *Sitz.-Ber. Preuss. Akad. Wiss.*, **1927**, p. 248.

FitzRoy, R., 1863: The Weather Book. A Manual of Practical Meteorology. Second edition. London 1863.

Fjørtoft, R., 1952: On a numerical method of integrating the barotropic vorticity equation. *Tellus*, **4**, p. 179.

Fujita, T., 1955: Results of Detailed Synoptic Studies of Squall Lines. *Tellus*, **7**, p. 405.

Galton, F., 1863: Meteorographica, or Methods of Mapping the Weather, ... Macmillan & Co. London & Cambridge 1863.

Gião, A., 1929: Mécanique Différentielle des Fronts et du Champ isallobarique. *Mém. O. N. M. de France*, No. 20.

Godske, C. L., 1937: Zur Theorie der Bildung aussertropischer Zyklonen. *Met. Z.*, **53**, p. 445.

Godske, C. L., Bergeron, T., Bjerknes, J., Bundgaard, R. C., 1957: Dynamic Meteorology and Weather Forecasting. Boston & Washington 1957.

Guldberg, C. M., Mohn, H., 1876, 1880: Etudes sur les mouvements de l'atmosphère, I & II. Christiania [Oslo], I 1876, II 1880.

Hann, J. von, 1901: Lehrbuch der Meteorologie, I. Aufl. Leipzig 1901.

Helmholtz, H. von, (1875) 1884: Wirbelstürme und Gewitter. *Vorträge u. Reden*, **2**, p. 141. Braunschweig 1884.

— 1888 a: Über atmosphärische Bewegungen. Erste Mitteilung. *Sitz.-Ber. Preuss. Akad. Wiss.*, **1888**, p. 647.

— 1888 b: Über atmosphärische Bewegungen, I. Mitt. *Met. Z.*, **13**, p. 329.

— 1889: Über atmosphärische Bewegungen. Zweite Mitt. *Sitz-.Ber. Preuss. Akad. Wiss.*, **1889**, p. 761.

— 1890: Zur Theorie von Wind und Wellen, II. Mitt. *Met. Z.*, **15**, p. 81.

Hildebrandsson, H. H., 1875: Essai sur les courants supérieurs de l'atmosphère dans leur relation aux lignes isobarométriques. *Nova Acta Reg. Soc. Sc. Ups., Ser. III*, **9**, Fasc. 2, No. 3.

Hildebrandsson, H. H., Teisserenc de Bort, L., 1900, 1907: Les bases de la météorologie dynamique. Tome I, Paris 1907.—Tome II, Paris 1900,

Hoffmeyer, N., 1876—80: Cartes synoptiques journalières, embrassant l'Europe et le Nord de l'Atlantique; sept. 1873—nov. 1876. Copenhague 1876—80.

— 1880: Etudes sur les tempêtes de l'Atlantique septentrional et projet d'un service télégraphique international relatif à cet océan. Copenhague 1880.

Howard, L., 1820: The Climate of London, deduced from Meteorological Observations, made at different places in the neighbourhood of the Metropolis, Vol. II. London 1820.

— 1833: The Climate of London, deduced from Meteorological Observations made in the Metropolis and at various places around it, Vol. I, 3rd ed. London 1833.

Jansson, M., 1913: Ur vår tids aërologi. [From Modern Aerology]. *Pop. Naturvetensk. Revy*, **1913**, p. 223. Stockholm.

JAUMOTTE, J., 1931: Un nouveau météorographe pour ballon-sonde. *Mém. Cl. Sc. Acad. Roy. Belgique, 2e série*, **10**, fasc. 4.

JINMAN, G., 1861, 1865: Winds and their Courses, 1st. ed. 1861, 3rd. ed. 1865, G. Philip and Son. London.

KÖPPEN, W., 1879: Beiträge zur Kenntnis der Böen und Gewitterstürme. *Ann. Hydr. u. marit. Met.*, **7**, p. 324.
— 1882 a: Der Gewittersturm vom 9. August 1881. *Ann. Hydr. u. marit. Met.*, **10**, p. 595, 714.
— 1882 b: Ueber den Einfluss der Temperaturverteilung auf die oberen Luftströmungen und auf die Fortpflanzung der barometrischen Minima. *Ann. Hydr. u. marit. Met.*, **10**, p. 657.
— 1914: Über Böen, insbesondere die Böe vom 9. September 1913. *Ann. Hydr. u. marit. Met.*, **42**, p. 303.
— 1921: H. W. Dove und wir. *Met. Z.*, **38**, p. 289.
— 1932: Anfänge der deutschen Wettertelegraphie 1862—1880. *Beitr. z. Phys. fr. Atm.*, **19**, p. 27.

KÜTTNER, J., 1938: Moazagotl und Föhnwelle. *Beitr. z. Phys. fr. Atm.*, **25**, p. 79.
— 1939: Zur Entstehung der Föhnwelle. *Beitr. z. Phys. fr. Atm.*, **25**, p. 251.

LAPLACE, P. S., 1799: Traité de Mécanique céleste, Tome I. Paris 1799. (English translation by NATHANIEL BOWDITCH. Boston, Mass. 1829.)
— 1814: Essai philosophique sur les probabilités. 2e éd. Paris 1814.

LE VERRIER, [U.J.J., 1867]: Travaux des treize dernières années. Obs. Impér. de Paris.

LEY, W. CLEMENT, 1872: The Laws of the Winds prevailing in Western Europe, Part I. London 1872.
— 1877: The Relation between the Upper and Under Currents in Areas of Barometric Depressions. *Quart. J. Met. Soc.*, **3**, p. 437.
— 1878: The Euridice Squall. *Symons's Met. Mag.*, **13**, p. 33.
— 1879 a: Clouds and Weather Signs. Modern Meteorology, lecture IV. London 1879.
— 1879 b: On the Inclination of the Axis of Cyclones. *Quart. J. Met. Soc.*, **5**, p. 167.

LYRA, G., 1943: Theorie der stationären Leewellenströmung in freier Atmosphäre. *Z. angew. Math. u. Mech.*, **23**, p. 1. Berlin.

MARGULES, M., 1901: Über den Arbeitswert einer Luftdruckvertheilung und über die Erhaltung der Druckunterschiede. *Denkschr. Math.-Naturw. Cl. Akad. Wiss. Wien*, **73**, p. 329.
— 1905: Über die Energie der Stürme. *Jahrb. k. k. Zentralanst. f. Met. Wien 1903, Anhang.* Wien 1905.

MCINTYRE, D. P., 1951: The Philosophy of the Chicago School of Meteorology. *Archiv f. Met., Geoph. u. Bioklim., Ser. A*, **4**, p. 24. Wien.

MÖLLER, M., 1882: Beziehungen zwischen dem Ober- und Unterwinde einer Depression und den aus diesen resultierenden Wolkenformen. *Ann. Hydr. u. marit. Met.*, **10**, p. 212.

MÜGGE, R., 1932: Die stratosphärische Steuerung während der Kälteperiode im Februar 1929. *Synoptische Bearbeitungen mitg. v. d. Wetterdienststelle Frankfurt a. M.*, No. 1. Frankfurt am Main 1932.

MYRBACH, O., 1921: Die Polarfront und — Dove. *Met. Z.*, **38**, p. 129.

NAMIAS, J., 1940: Air Mass and Isentropic Analysis. Am. Met. Soc., Milton, Mass.

NYBERG, A., PALMÉN, E., 1942: Synoptisch-aerologische Bearbeitung der internationalen Registrierballonaufstiege in Europa in der Zeit 17.—19. Oktober 1935. *Geogr. Ann.*, **24**, p. 51. Stockholm.

PALMÉN, E., 1930: Die vertikale Mächtigkeit der Kälteeinbrüche über Mitteleuropa. *Gerl. Beitr. z. Geophys.*, **26**, p. 63.
— 1931 a: Die Luftbewegungen im Zirrusniveau über Zyklonen. *Met. Z.*, **48**, p. 281.
— 1931 b: Die Beziehung zwischen troposphärischen und stratosphärischen Temperatur- und Luftdruckschwankungen. *Beitr. z. Phys fr. Atm.*, **17**, p. 102.
— 1931 c: Synoptisch-aerologische Untersuchung eines Kälteeinbruches. *Gerl. Beitr. z. Geophys.*, **32** (Köppen-Band I), p. 158.
— 1933: Aerologische Untersuchungen der atmosphärischen Störungen mit besonderer Berücksichtigung der stratosphärischen Vorgänge. *Soc. Sc. Fenn. Comm. Phys.-Math.*, **7**, No. 6.
— 1948: On the distribution of temperature and wind in the upper westerlies. *J. Met.*, **5**, p. 20.
— 1951: The rôle of atmospheric disturbances in the general circulation. *Quart. J. Roy. Met. Soc.*, **77**, p. 337.
— 1951: The Aerology of Extratropical Disturbances. Compendium of Meteorology. Boston, Mass. 1951.

PETTERSSEN, S., 1933: Kinematical and Dynamical Properties of the Field of Pressure, with Applications to Weather Forecasting. *Geof. Publ.*, **10**, No. 2.
— 1940, 1956: Weather Analysis and Forecasting. McGraw-Hill Book Co., New York 1940, 1956.

Quarterly Weather Report of the Meteorological Office, **1869**, Part I. London 1870.

QUENEY, P., 1936: Recherches relatives à l'influence du relief sur les éléments météorologiques. *La Météorologie*, **12**, pp. 334 & 453. Paris 1936.
— 1948: The Problem of Air Flow over Mountains: A Summary of Theoretical Studies. *Bull. Am. Met. Soc.*, **29**, No. 1.

RAETHJEN, P., 1953 a: Zur Morphologie und Dynamik der »lebendigen« Atmosphäre. *Naturwiss. Rundschau*, **6**, p. 320. Stuttgart.
— 1953 b: Dynamik der Zyklonen. *Probleme der kosmischen Physik*, **27**. Leipzig 1953.

REFSDAL, A., 1930: Der feuchtlabile Niederschlag. *Geof. Publ.*, **5**, No. 12.
— 1932: Zur Thermodynamik der Atmosphäre. *Geof. Publ.*, **9**, No. 12. (Abstract in *Met. Z.*, **50**, p. 212.)

Report of the Advisory Committee on Weather Services, 1953 [Summary of the Introduction]: *Weatherwise*, **7**, p. 16.

REYE, TH., 1872: Die Wirbelstürme, Tornados und Wettersäulen. Verlag Carl Rümpler, Hannover 1872.

RICHARDSON, L. F., 1922: Weather Prediction by Numerical Process. Cambridge 1922.

ROSSBY, C.-G., 1937/38: On the Mutual Adjustment of Pressure and Velocity Distribution in Certain Simple Current Systems. *J. Mar. Res.*, **1**, p. 15 & 239.
— 1940: Planetary Flow Patterns in the Atmosphere. *Quart. J. Roy. Met. Soc.*, **66**, Suppl., p. 68.

ROSSBY, C.-G., and COLL., 1937: Isentropic Analysis. *Bull. Am. Met. Soc.*, **18**, p. 201.
— 1939: Relation between Variations in the Intensity of the Zonal Circulation of the Atmosphere and the Displacements of the Semipermanent Centres of Action. *J. Mar. Res.*, **2**, p. 38.

ROSSBY, C.-G., EGNÉR, H., 1955: On the Chemical Climate and its Variation with the Atmospheric Circulation Pattern. *Tellus*, **7**, p. 118.

ROSSBY, C.-G., GRIMMINGER, G., PEKERIS, C. L., NAMIAS, J., WEXLER, H., 1938: Application of Fluid Mechanics to the Problem of the General Circulation of the Atmosphere. *Trans. Am. Geophys. Union*, 19th Ann. Meeting 1938.

ROTCH, L. A., 1898: The Exploration of the Free Air by means of Kites, at Blue Hill Observatory, Mass., U.S.A. *Quart. J. Roy. Met. Soc.*, **24**, p. 250.

SCHAEFER, V., 1958: Can we do it better? *Bull. Am. Met. Soc.*, **39**, p. 90.

SCHERESCHEWSKY, PH., WEHRLÉ, PH., 1921: Sur les mouvements des noyaux de variation de pression. *C R. Acad. Sc. Paris*, **173**, p. 1001.

— 1923: Les systèmes nuageux. *Mém. O. N. M. de France*, No. 1.

SCHERHAG, R., 1934: Die Bedeutung von Messungen der Richtung und Geschwindigkeit der höheren Wolken für das Entwerfen von Höhenwetterkarten im Wetterdienst. *Das Wetter*. **51**, p. 111.

— 1934: Die Bedeutung der Divergenz für die Entstehung der Vb-Depressionen. *Ann. Hydr. u. marit. Met.*, **62**, p. 152.

— 1935: Der aerologische Ausbau des täglichen Wetterberichts der Deutschen Seewarte. *Ann. Hydr. u. marit. Met.*, **63**, p. 216.

— 1948: Neue Methoden der Wetteranalyse und Wetterprognose. Springer-Verlag. Berlin . . . 1948.

SCHINZE, G., 1932: Untersuchungen zur aerologischen Synoptik. Hamburg 1932.

— 1932: Die praktische Wetteranalyse. *Arch. d. Deutschen Seewarte*, **52**, No. 1.

SCHUMANN, T. E. W., 1956: Proposal for a planned international research programme. Ass. Gen. U.G.G.I., Rome 1954. *U.G.G.I., Publ. A.I.M.*, No. 10/c, p. 237. London 1956.

SHAW, W. N., 1903: The meteorological aspects of the storm of February 26—27, 1903. *Quart. J. Roy. Met. Soc.*, **29**, p. 233.

— 1911, 1923 & 1940: Forecasting Weather. Constable & Co., London 1911, 1923 & 1940.

— 1934: The March of Meteorology. *Quart. J. Roy. Met. Soc.*, **60**, p. 101.

SHAW, W. N., LEMPFERT, R. G. K., 1906: Life History of Surface Air Currents. Meteorol. Committee, M.O. 174. London 1906.

SILBERSTEIN, L., 1896: Über die Entstehung von Wirbelbewegungen in einer reibungslosen Flüssigkeit. *Bull. Int. Acad. Sc. Cracovie*, **1896**, p. 280.

SIMPSON, C. G., 1955: FitzRoy and weather forecasts. *Met. Mag.*, **84**, p. 167.

SOLBERG, H., 1928: Integrationen der atmosphärischen Störungsgleichungen. *Geof. Publ.* **5**, No. 9.

Staff Members, Dept. of Meteorology, University of Chicago, 1947: On the General Circulation of the Atmosphere in Middle Latitudes. *Bull. Am. Met. Soc.*, **28**, p. 255.

STÜVE, G., 1926: Thermozyklogenese. *Beitr. z. Phys. fr. Atm.*, **13**, p. 23.

SUTCLIFFE, R. C., 1939: Cyclonic and anticyclonic development. *Quart. J. Roy. Met. Soc.*, **65**, p. 518.

— 1947: A contribution to the problem of development. *Quart. J. Roy. Met. Soc.*, **73**, p. 370.

— 1954: Predictability in Meteorology. *Arch. f. Met., Geophys. u. Biokl., Serie A*, **7**, p. 3.

SUTTON, O. G., 1951: Mathematics and the Future of Meteorology. *Weather*, **6**, No. 10.

Synoptische Darstellungen atmosphärischer Zustände. *Veröff. Geoph. Inst. Univ. Leipzig, Erste Serie*, Heft 1—4. Leipzig 1916—1919.

TEISSERENC DE BORT, L., 1889: Étude sur la synthèse de la répartition des pressions à la surface du globe. *Ann. Bur. Centr. Mét. de France*, **1887**, I Mémoires, p. C 1.

— 1902: Variations de la température de l'air libre dans la zone comprise entre 8 km et 13 km d'altitude. *Mém. Acad. de Sc. Paris*, **134**, p. 987.

The Weather Map. Meteorol. Off., M.O. 225 i, London 1916, 1930, 1939; M. O. 595, London 1956.

THOMPSON, P. D., 1957 a: Predictability: An Analysis of its Practical and Economic Aspects. [Address at 11th U.G.G.I.-IAM-meeting, Duplic.] Toronto 1957.

— 1957 b: Uncertainty of Initial State as a Factor in the Predictability of Large Scale Atmospheric Flow Patterns. *Tellus*, **9**, p. 275.

Travaux de la station franco-scandinave de sondages aériens à Hald 1902—1903. Viborg (Danmark) 1904.

WEHRLÉ, PH., 1926: Les noyaux de variation. *La Météorologie*, **2**, **(69)**, p. 49. Paris. (From Lexique Météorologique. *Publ. O.N.M.* Paris 1925.)

(Manuscript received November 1, 1958)

Hemispheric Nondivergent Barotropic Forecasting

By George P. Cressman
Joint Numerical Weather Prediction Unit, Washington, D.C.

Abstract

The initial results of the hemispheric barotropic forecasts computed by the Joint Numerical Weather Prediction Unit of the United States are described. The model uses a non-divergent, non-geostrophic wind, and includes the large-scale effects of terrain. Verifications and examples characteristic of the first few months' experience with the program are presented. The success achieved by a barotropic model of the atmosphere is regarded as a vindication of the opinions of Professor Rossby. The forecasts deteriorate noticeably by about three days as a result of inadequate treatment of very long waves, the neglect of baroclinic effects, friction, and other factors.

Introduction

Two well known and long held opinions of Prof. C.-G. Rossby could be represented as follows:

(1) The great majority of the flow pattern changes in mid-troposphere can be represented as a result of the horizontal redistribution of absolute vorticity.

(2) The most proper path for advance in numerical prediction should start with a complete exploitation of the barotropic model in order that the formulation of more complicated atmospheric models would not contain errors common to the barotropic one.

The wisdom contained in these views has been amply demonstrated by the experience of the Joint Numerical Weather Prediction (JNWP) Unit. All attempts so far at baroclinic forecasting have had only limited success because of the presence of certain types of error also found in the barotropic forecasts (Cressman, Hubert, 1957). In the meantime the barotropic forecasts have enjoyed a good success relative to standard subjective efforts at 500 mb forecasting. As a result, we have emphasized the improvement and extension of barotropic forecasting in order to increase the prospects of success with future baroclinic models.

This paper will describe the characteristic results of the barotropic model currently in use by the JNWP Unit. A number of members of the Unit have contributed to the development and programming of the model in its present form, especially Dr. Fred Shuman. The writer is merely describing some of the results.

The Model

The model computes the redistribution, in horizontal flow, of the conservative quantity q, such that

$$\frac{\partial q}{\partial t} + \mathbf{v} \cdot \triangle q = 0 \qquad (1)$$

where

$$q = \eta \exp\left(-a p_g / p_0\right) \qquad (2)$$

p_g being the standard atmosphere pressure at the ground, with p_0 set equal to 1,000 mb. The fraction a represents the ratio of surface to 500 mb winds, and is set at a value of 0.27. The absolute vorticity, η, is obtained from a stream function ψ given by the balance equation (Petterssen, 1953; Charney, 1955; Bolin, 1956)

$$\triangle^2 \psi = f^{-1}\left[\nabla^2 \phi + 2\left(\psi_{xy} - \psi_{xx}\psi_{yy}\right) - \nabla\psi \cdot \nabla f\right], \qquad (3)$$

where ϕ is the geopotential, f is the Coriolis parameter, and x and y are directions in the grid.

It can be seen that the result of the exponential in eq. (2) is to introduce a mountain effect giving a 500 mb divergence of the amount $-\omega_g/P_0$, where ω_g is the vertical velocity at the ground produced by a flow $a\mathbf{v}$ over the terrain, i.e.,

$$\omega_g = a\mathbf{v} \cdot \triangle p_g \qquad (4)$$

From the crudity of this approximation to the surface flow, one can expect only an approximate large-scale introduction of terrain effects.

The boundary conditions used during the forecast consist of taking $\partial\psi/\partial t = 0$ and $\nabla^2\psi = 0$ on the edges of the grid at all times. For the solution of the balance equation, $\nabla^2\psi$ is set equal to $f^{-1} \nabla^2 \phi$. Since the boundaries of the octagonal grid are at an average latitude of 14° N, the scaling of ψ yields boundary inflow and outflow of about one fourth of the corresponding geostrophic inflow and outflow.

The computation consists of an initial solution of the balance equation for ψ, after which the forecast proceeds in one-hour time steps. The balance equation is used to obtain ϕ, when desired, from ψ, for prints of the prognostic charts. The field of $\nabla^2\psi$ is smoothed every twelve hours by an operator which eliminates perturbations of wave length $2d$, while leaving those of wave length $5d$ practically intact (SHUMAN 1955) where d is the mesh length. The following running times are required for this program on the IBM EDPM 704 for the 1977 pt. grid.

Balance Equation (ψ from ϕ)	–	15 minutes
Forecast for 12 time steps	–	8 minutes
Inversion (ϕ from ψ)	–	3 minutes
Punch and print forecast	–	2 minutes

Characteristic Results of the Forecast Program

a. *Level of Accuracy*

Some of the verifications from November 1957 will be shown in illustration of the results obtained with the model described above. Verification of 48 hour forecasts will be used in order to bring out more clearly the nature of the errors.

Figure 1 shows the mean algebraic height error superimposed on the mean 500 mb chart for the month. The most prominent feature of the error chart is the area of positive error over East Asia, along with a slightly smaller error of the same sign over the Central Pacific. The larger of the two negative errors is centered just North of the British Isles. Broadly speaking, the errors show a very close phase relation to the mean monthly map, with positive errors found in mean troughs, and vice versa. WOLFF (1958) has shown that this large-scale error, which accounts for about half of all the height errors at 500 mb, is a result of the retrogression of waves of very large lateral scale in the forecasts and has proposed an empirical method of stabilization of these waves.[1]

The correlation coefficient of forecast vs observed height changes (fig. 2) shows, in general, maximum values at about latitude 50° N, where the greatest variability of the heights was found.

[1] This method of stabilization proposed by Wolff has been employed in the daily forecasts after the first draft of this paper was written.

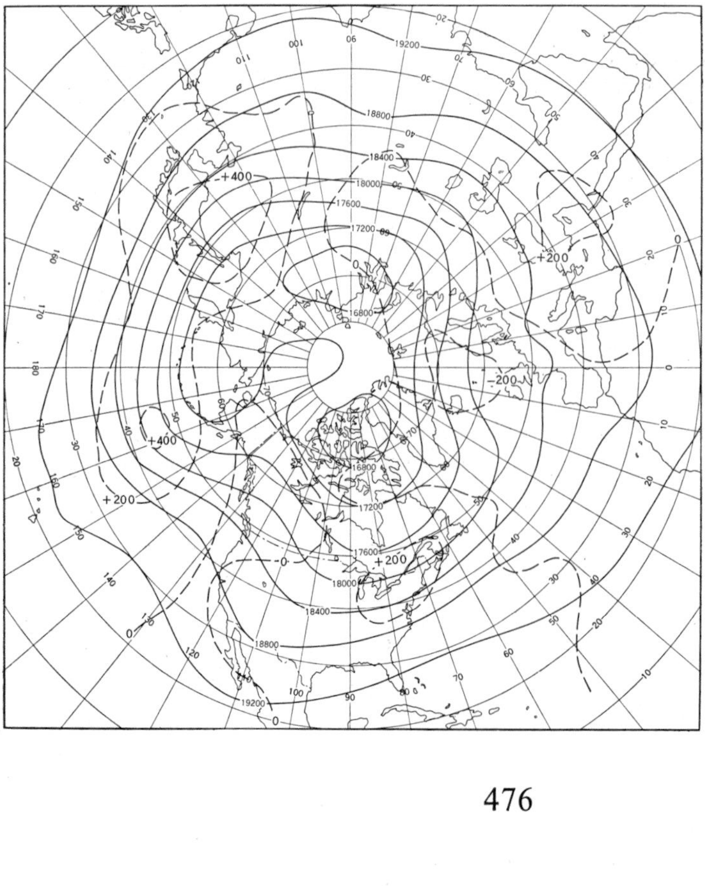

Fig. 1. Mean algebraic height error of barotropic forecasts for November 1957 (dashed lines) on mean 500 mb chart for November 1957 (solid lines). Heights are labelled in feet.

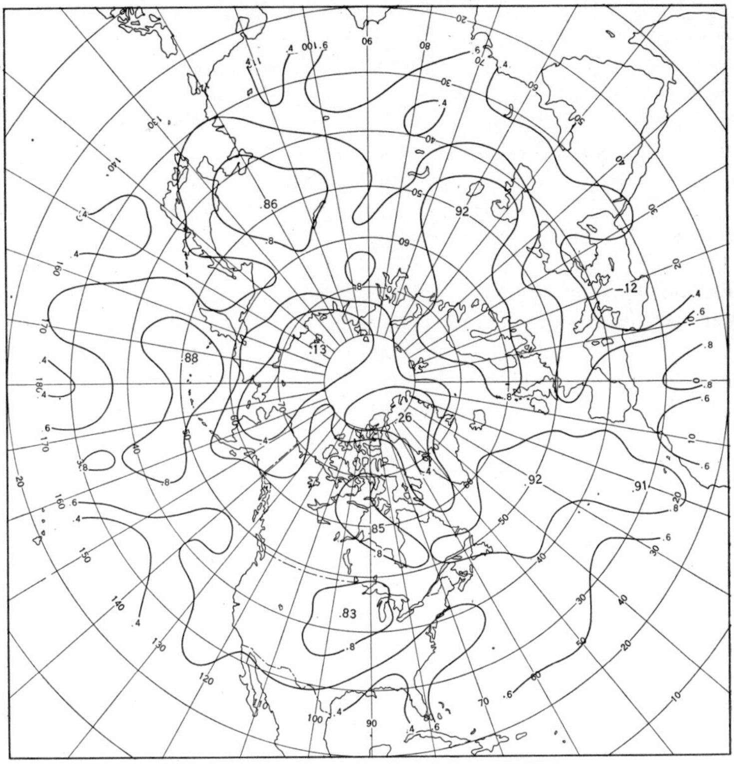

Fig. 2. Map of correlation coefficient of forecast 48 hour height changes vs. observed 48 hour height changes for November 1957.

The minima of correlation coefficient over the Gulf of Mexico, Northern Greenland, and North Siberian coast were also locations of minima of height change, the root mean square values of the 48 hour change at those locations being 70, 160 and 170 feet respectively.

b. *Sources of Errors*

The largest single source of height error, mentioned above as associated with retrogression of very long waves in the forecasts, has appeared the most clearly in the hemispheric grid, where lateral boundary errors are insignificant. This problem was discussed in the literature nearly twenty years ago, when Rossby (1939) diagnosed a weakness of the nondivergent barotropic model arising from its failure to allow for a proper adjustment of wind and pressure fields. He described two atmospheric models not having this weakness, one a single-layer fluid with a free upper surface and the other consisting of a double-layer atmosphere with one layer active and the other inert. These models were presented as giving a mechanism for the mutual adjustment of wind and pressure fields. Rossby discussed this problem with great clarity in 1945 (Rossby, 1945) in relation to the problem of energy propagation. In 1956, Bolin (1956) applied Rossby's theory in the development and use of a tropopause model. Since the inauguration of hemispheric forecasts it is clear that we have paid too little attention to this aspect of barotropic forecasting. The application of the type of divergence arising from these considerations will be equally important in most formulations of baroclinic models as well.

Another type of error in the barotropic forecasts appears in the form of an erroneous strengthening and northward shift of the zonal wind maximum. At the same time the subtropical easterlies undergo an erroneous strengthening. The most adverse effects of this process are evident in the subtropics, where verifying positions of highs and lows are almost always west of the forecast positions.

The barotropic strengthening of the mean flow, a consequence of the conversion of kinetic energy of the eddys to that of the mean flow, as described by Starr (1953) and computed by Phillips (1956), is balanced in the atmosphere by lateral eddy

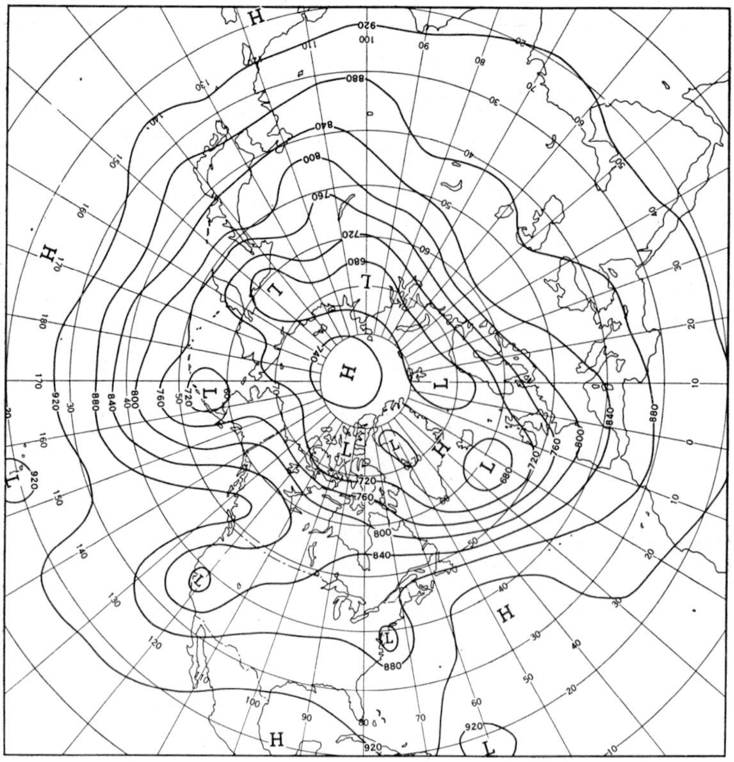

Fig. 3. 500 mb chart 00 GMT, 3 November 1957.

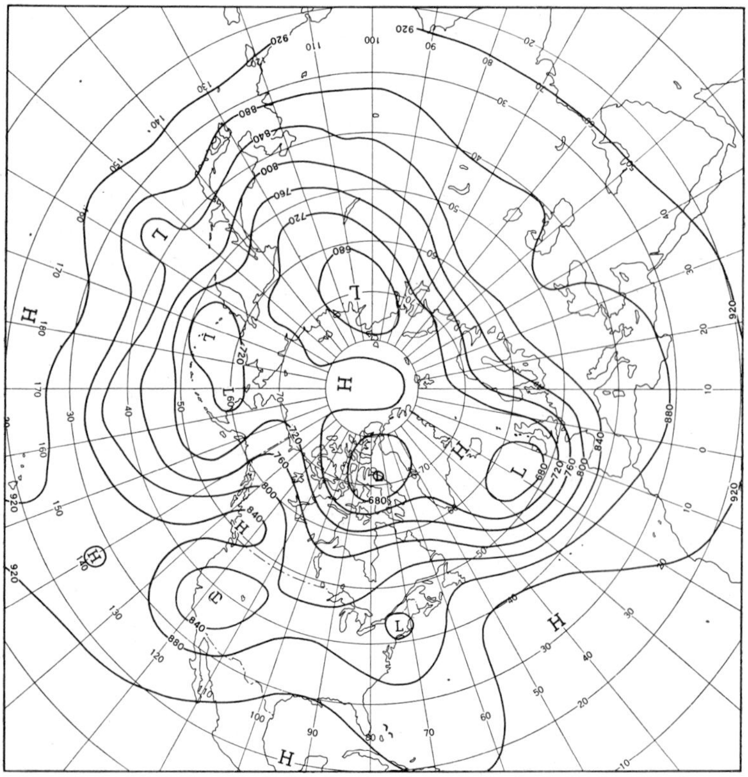

Fig. 4. 500 mb chart 00 GMT, 4 November 1957.

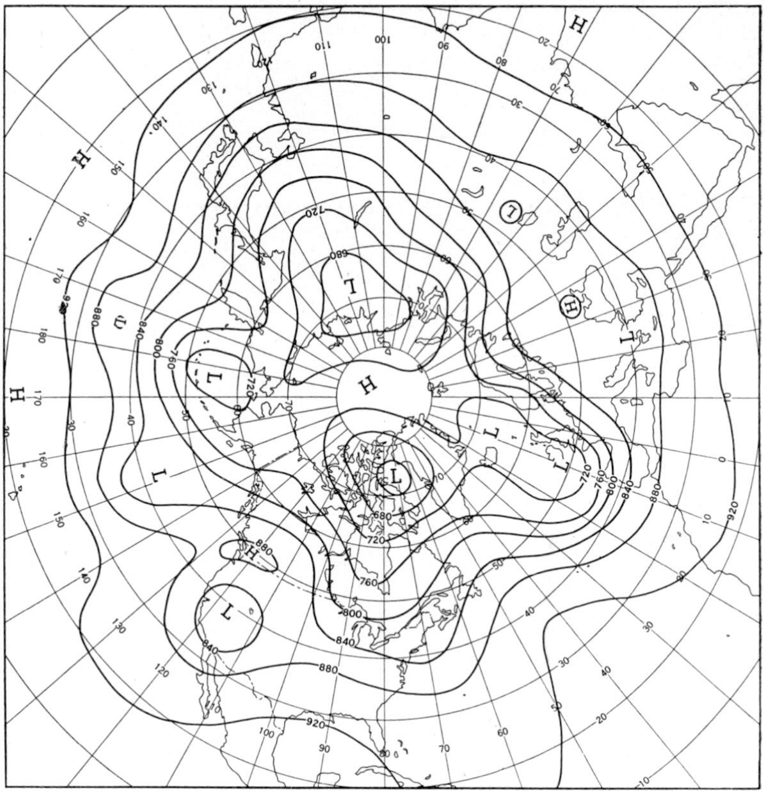

Fig. 5. 500 mb chart 00 GMT, 5 November 1957.

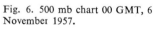

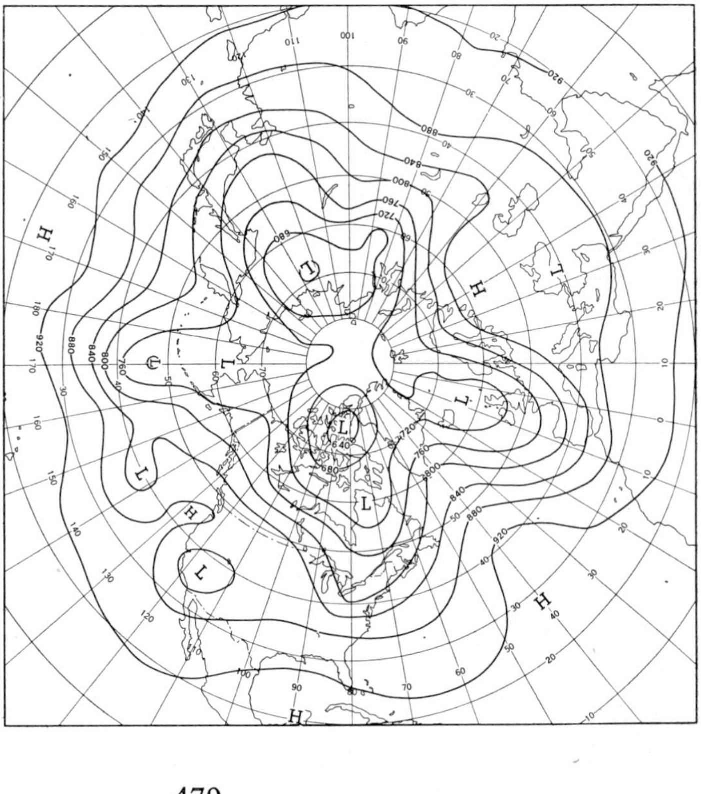

Fig. 6. 500 mb chart 00 GMT, 6 November 1957.

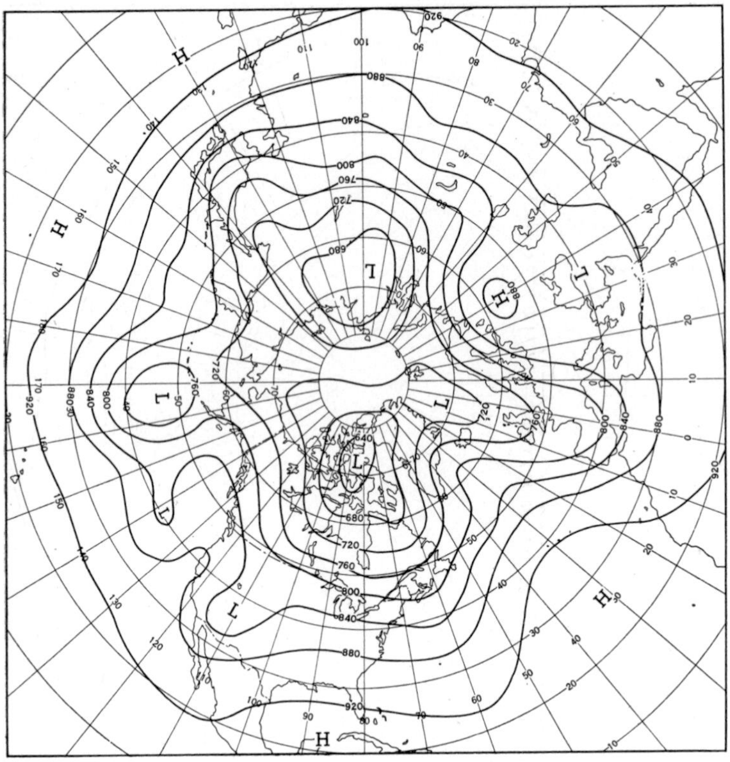

Fig. 7. 500 mb chart 00 GMT, 7 November 1957.

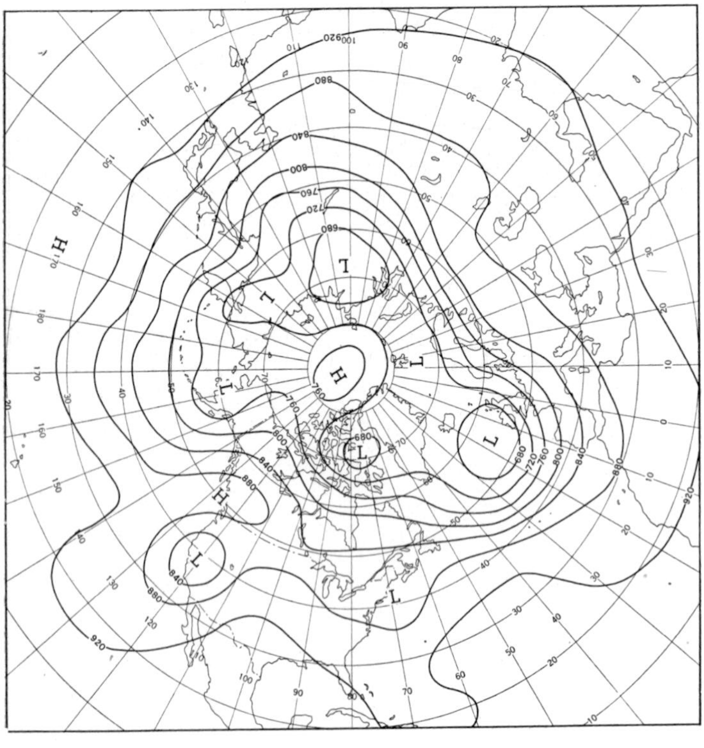

Fig. 8. 24 hr forecast from 00 GMT, 3 November 1957.

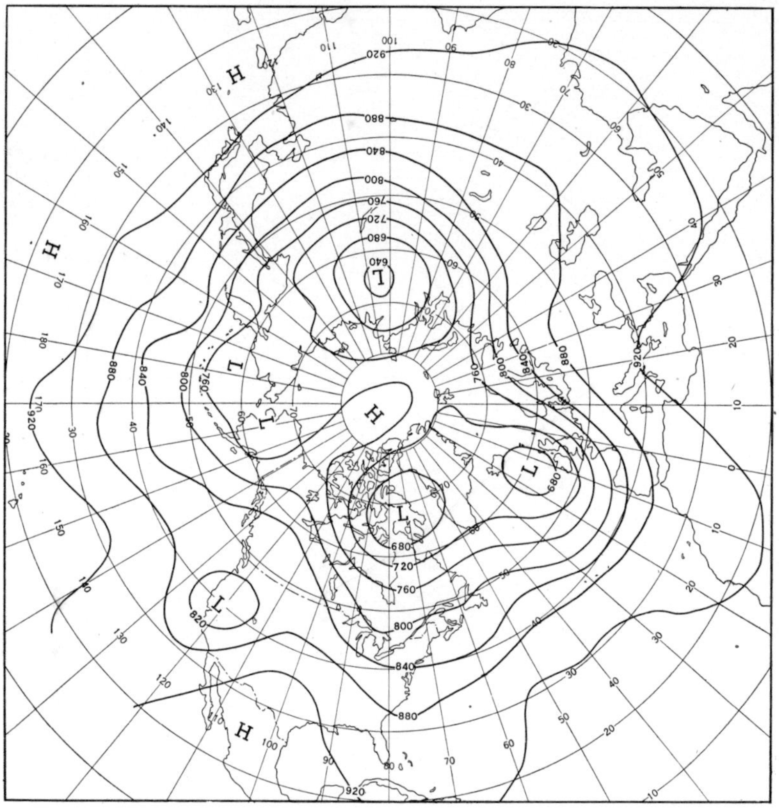

Fig. 9. 48 hr forecast from 00 GMT, 3 November 1957.

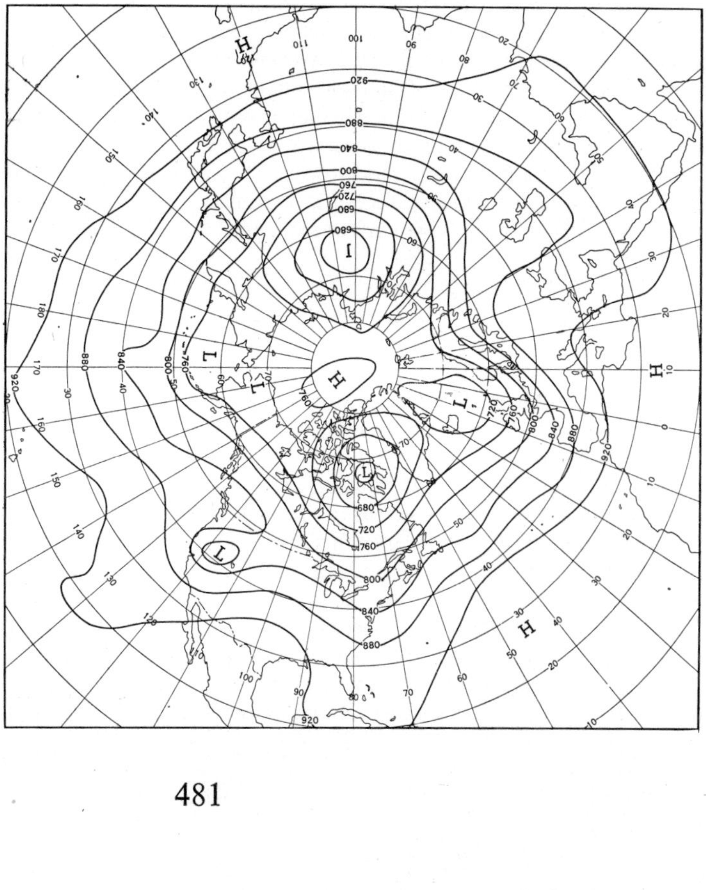

Fig. 10. 72 hr forecast from 00 GMT, 3 November 1957.

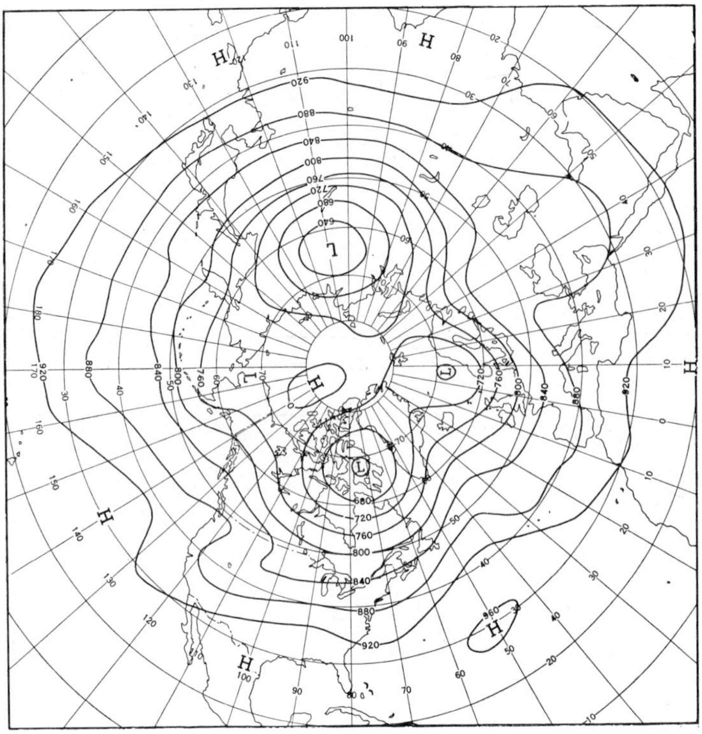

Fig. 11. 96 hr forecast from 00 GMT, 3 November 1957.

viscosity and by skin friction. In our barotropic forecasts, the smoothing operator acts in a manner qualitatively resembling the action of lateral eddy viscosity. A quantitative estimate is not available. It is questionable whether or not the effects of skin friction can successfully be incorporated into a barotropic model because of the difficulties of representing the surface wind without a continually evolving surface map.

Examples

An example of a successful barotropic forecast is shown in figs. 3—11. The forecast was the most successful over North America, the Atlantic, Europe, and the higher latitudes in general. The inadequate treatment of the very long waves in the forecast is clearly evident by 96 hours. Note also the tendency for the weak subtropical anticyclones to be predicted in positions too far west. However, in spite of its defects, this forecast could be most useful even to the fourth day for many areas.

The behaviour of the model in predicting the zonal wind in this situation is shown in fig. 12. The actual strengthening of the maximum at 32° N was forecast with modest success. However, the forecast obtained a very excessive zonal wind maximum at about 50° N by the fourth day.

During the two days after the period covered by this example, a baroclinic development occurred over the United States. This is illustrated in figs. 13—24. The increase of absolute vorticity at 500 mb is shown by the charts of absolute

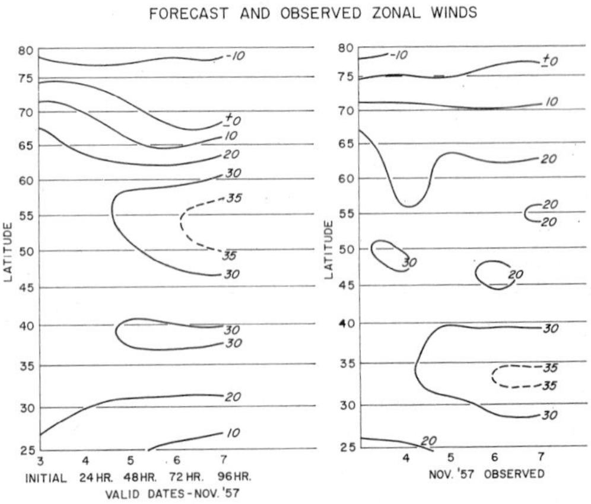

Fig. 12. Forecast and observed hemispheric zonal winds vs. latitude. Speeds in knots.

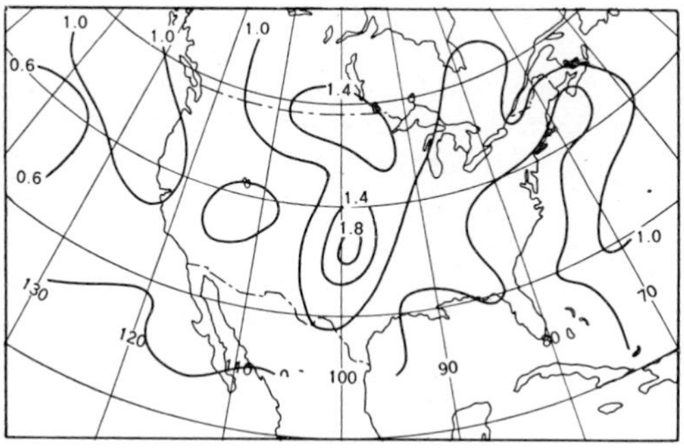

Fig. 13. Absolute vorticity at 500 mb., 00 GMT, 8 November 1957. Units in 10^4 sec^{-1}.

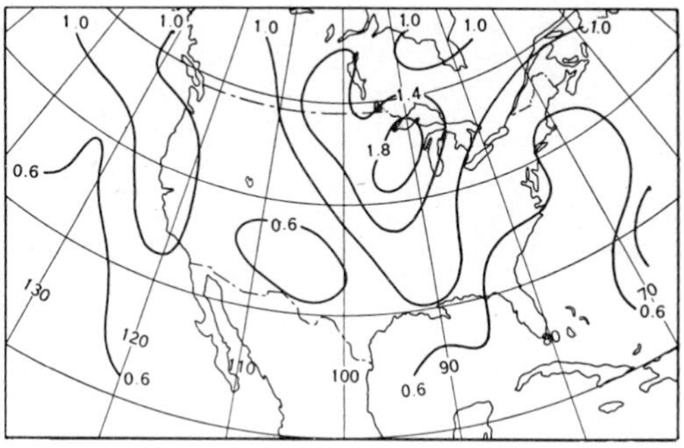

Fig. 14. Absolute vorticity at 500 mb., 12 GMT, 8 November 1957.

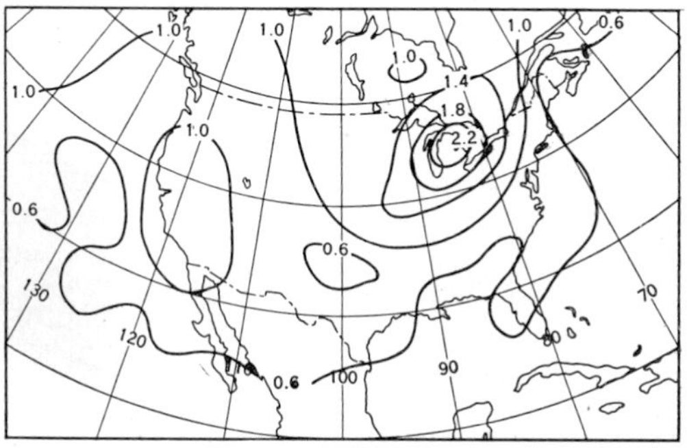

Fig. 15. Absolute vorticity at 500 mb., 00 GMT, 9 November 1957.

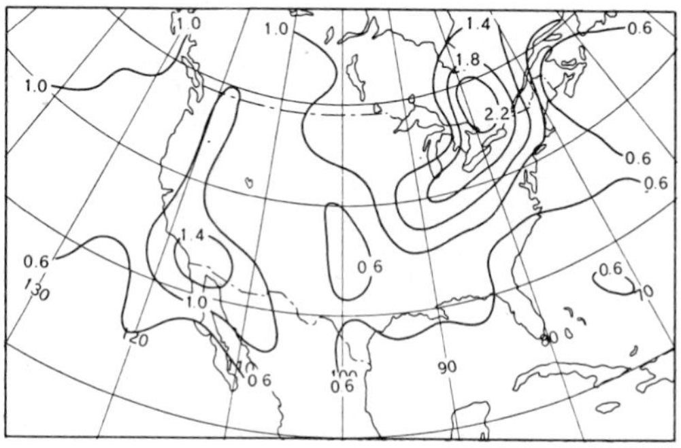

Fig. 16. Absolute vorticity at 500 mb., 12 GMT, 9 November 1957.

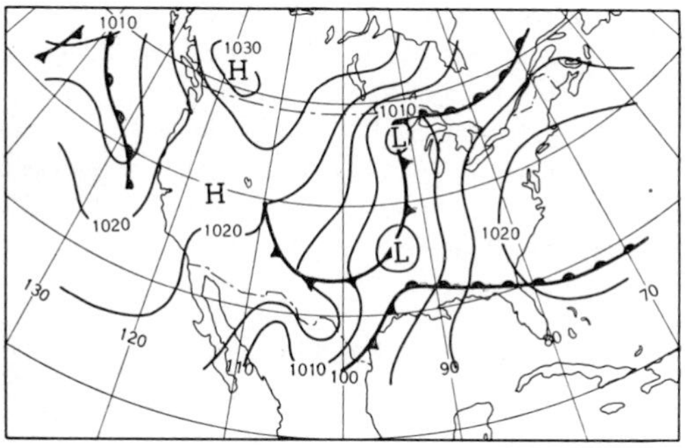

Fig. 17. Sea level pressure, 00 GMT, 8 November 1957.

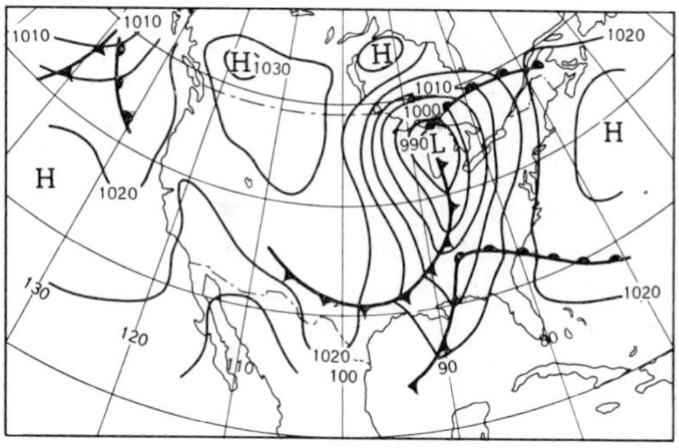

Fig. 18. Sea level pressure, 12 GMT, 8 November 1957.

vorticity (computed from the stream functions) in figs. 13—16. The center of maximum vorticity over the south central states on 00 GMT, 8 November expanded and intensified as it moved over the Great Lakes area. This was associated with a vigorous surface cyclogenesis illustrated in figs. 17—19. The 500 mb charts for the same period are shown in figs. 21—23. The 24 hr barotropic 500 mb forecast for 00 GMT, 9 November already reflects the errors resulting from the cyclogenesis. The error of the 48 hr forecast for the same time (fig. 20) is more extreme. The great similarity of the 48 hr errors

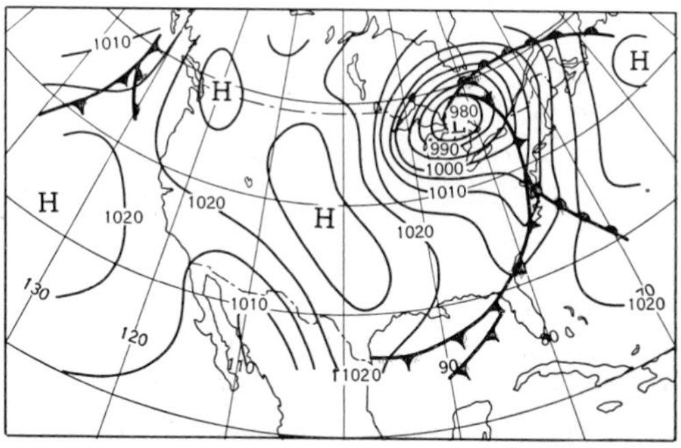

Fig. 19. Sea level pressure, 00 GMT, 9 November 1957.

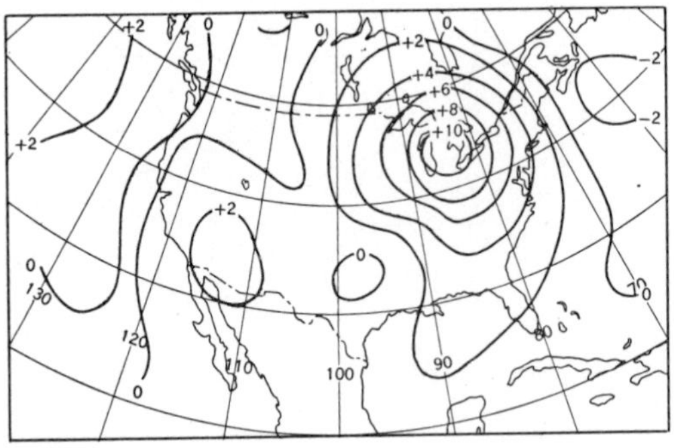

Fig. 20. Error (hundreds of ft.) of the 48 hr barotropic forecast from 00 GMT, 7 November, 1957.

of the barotropic forecast to the pattern of the surface cyclone at the same time is suggestive of an important role played by vertical vorticity transport in the increase of the 500 mb vorticity.

Conclusions

The relative success attained by the hemispheric barotropic forecasts of this type can be considered as a complete vindication of the opinions of Professor Rossby on this subject. Even after the large scale barotropic divergence is taken into account, processes operating in the general circulation of the atmosphere, i.e., baroclinic developments, skin friction, lateral eddy viscosity, etc., and not represented in a barotropic model must put an end to the usefulness of such forecasts after about three days. The symptoms of decay of accuracy of the forecast are a retrogression of the very long waves, loss of amplitude of the disturbances, and an uncompensated strengthening of the zonal currents. Further advances in short-range numerical prediction should be expected when the above mentioned processes are taken into account.

Acknowledgements

In addition to the work of Dr. Fred Shuman in programming the forecasts, it should be mentioned that the model was put into this form by Lt. Col. P. D. Thomson. Mr. C. L. Bristor made extensive computations and study of the trends in the zonal wind profiles. Dr. Norman Phillips gave us some illuminating discussions of the effects of friction in relation to the forecast errors. Cdr. Paul Wolff carried out the diagnosis of the very long waves.

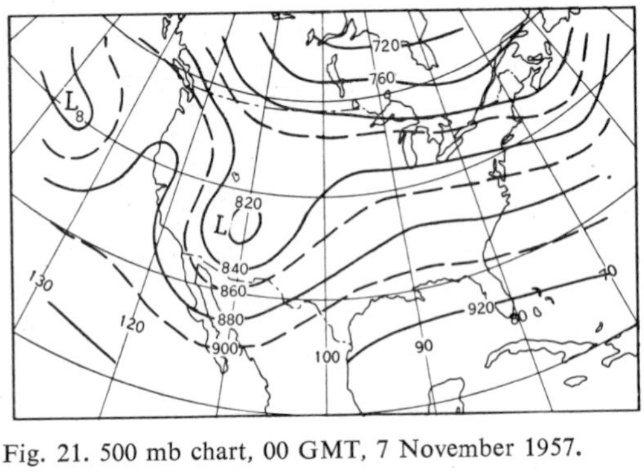

Fig. 21. 500 mb chart, 00 GMT, 7 November 1957.

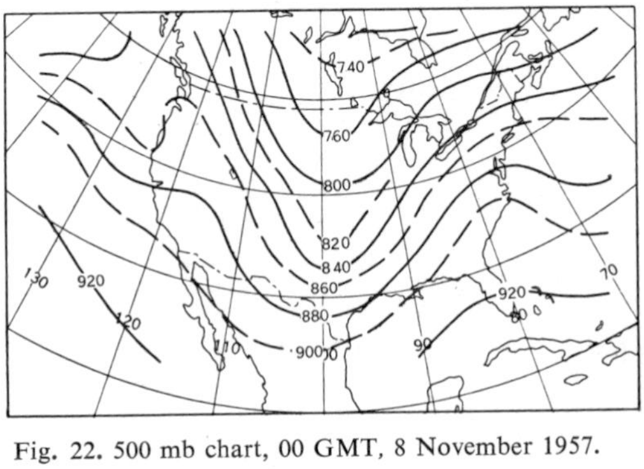

Fig. 22. 500 mb chart, 00 GMT, 8 November 1957.

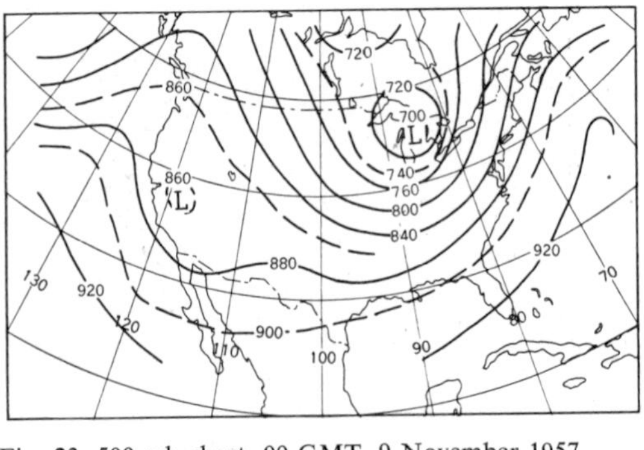

Fig. 23. 500 mb chart, 00 GMT. 9 November 1957.

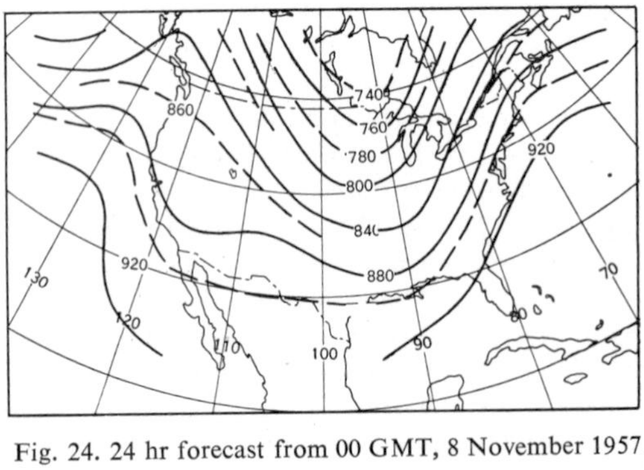

Fig. 24. 24 hr forecast from 00 GMT, 8 November 1957.

REFERENCES

Bolin, B., 1956: An Improved Barotropic Model and some Aspects of Using the Balance Equation for three-dimensional Flow, *Tellus*, **8**, pp. 61—75.

Charney, J., 1955: The Use of the Primitive Equations of Motion in Numerical Prediction, *Tellus*, **7**, pp. 22—26.

Cressman, G. P., and Hubert, W. E., 1957: A Study of Numerical Forecasting Errors, *Monthly Weather Review*, **85**, pp. 235—242.

Petterssen, S., 1953: On the Relation between Vorticity, Deformation, and Divergence, and the Configuration of the Pressure Field, *Tellus*, **5**, pp. 231—237.

Phillips, N. A., 1956: The General Circulation of the Atmosphere: A Numerical Experiment, *QJRMS*, **82**, pp. 123—164.

Rossby, C.-G., 1939: Relation between Variations in the Intensity of the Zonal Circulation of the Atmosphere and the Displacements of the Semi-Permanent Centers of Action, *Jour. of Mar. Res.*, **2**, pp. 38—55.

Rossby, C.-G., 1945: On the Propagation of Frequencies and Energy in Certain Types of oceanic and Atmospheric Waves, *Jour. of Met.*, **2**, pp. 187—204.

Shuman, F. G., 1955: A Method of Designing Finite-Difference Smoothing Operators to Meet Specifications, *Tech. Memo No.* **7**, Joint Numerical Weather Prediction Unit, 14 pages.

Starr, V. P., 1953: Note concerning the Nature of the Large-Scale Eddies in the Atmosphere, *Tellus*, **5**, pp. 494—498.

Wolff, P. M., 1958: The Errors in Numerical Forecasts Due to Retrogression of Ultra-Long Waves, *Tech. Memo No.* **13**, Joint Numerical Weather Prediction Unit, 21 pages.

(Manuscript received January 20, 1958)

Ein numerisches Experiment mit den primitiven Gleichungen[1]

Von K. HINKELMANN

Forschungsabteilung des Deutschen Wetterdienstes, Offenbach

Abstract

A short period numerical forecast is made with a multilayer nongeostrophic model for one and/or three days. In the used model sound waves and external gravitational waves have been filtered; combined inertial-internal gravitational waves, however, are still included in the equations.

Friction and non-adiabatic effects as well as those due to the earth's curvature and to orographical obstacles, are neglected.

Considered is the flow pattern within a channel being infinite with respect to the zonal coordinate, but bounded by rigid walls to the north and south.

The model defines and predicts horizontal wind components and temperature in the levels $p=100$, 300, 500, 700, 900 mb, the vertical velocity and the geopotential gradient in the levels $p=0$, 200, 400, 600, 800, 1000 mb at grid points at a distance of 300 km.

Initially a very simple sinusoidal barotropic disturbance, imbedded in an also simple basic zonal current, is specialized. The initial data are adjusted to each other quasigeostrophically to guarantee that no noise waves of appreciable amplitude will occur.

The developing flow patterns show a very s‘rong cyclo- and anticyclogenesis and a remarkable occlusion process of warm air within the cyclonic area, due to nongeostrophic temperature advection.

The tendencies of mean zonal momentum and temperature as well as some phenomena of meridional circulation processes are studied and briefly discussed.

The results show that the primitive epuations too, can serve as useful tools for predicting large scale weather developments.

I. Einleitung

Die bisher fast ausschließlich für numerische Vorhersagen benutzten sogenannten quasigeostrophischen Modelle weisen, insbesondere durch die Verwendung der geostrophischen Approximation als Lärmfilter, gewichtige Defekte auf, die es angezeigt erscheinen lassen, auch die primitiven Gleichungen, die von geostrophischen Einschränkungen frei sind, wenigstens an Hand von numerischen Experimenten auf ihre praktische prognostische Verwendbarkeit hin zu untersuchen.

Auf Mängel, die aus der Vernachlässigung nichtgeostrophischer Advektionsvorgänge resultieren, hat insbesondere HOLLMANN (1956) hingewiesen: Der Prozeß der Okklusion wird dadurch unterdrückt, mittlere vertikale Wärmeflüsse werden nicht einmal dem Vorzeichen nach richtig erfaßt. Darüber hinaus verlangt die geostrophische Approximation zur Wahrung der für die strengen Gleichungen gültigen integralen Beziehungen, die sich aus der Anwendung der Sätze von Gauß und Stokes ergeben, die Vernachlässigung weiterer synoptisch nicht unbedeutsamer Vorgänge, wenn nicht aufwendige Iterationen in Kauf genommen werden. So schließt z.B. die durch die geostrophische Approximation des Vorticity-Transports erzwungene Vernachlässigung des Terms $\zeta\nabla\cdot\mathbf{v}$ gegenüber $f\nabla\cdot\mathbf{v}$ in der Vorticity-Gleichung Unsymmetrien in der Entwicklung der Zyklone und Antizyklone aus. Außerdem verlangt die geostrophische An-

[1] Diese Untersuchung wurde unterstützt vom Air Research and Development Command, United States Air Force, durch Vermittlung dessen Europäischen Amts unter Kontrakt AF 61 (514)—1211-C.

näherung auch einschränkende Annahmen für das Verhalten der statischen Stabilität, die im allgemeinen eine Überschätzung der baroklinen Entwicklung zur Folge haben. Die Mitnahme des vertikalen Impulstransportes (Drehterm und vertikaler Vorticity-Transport in der Vorticity-Gleichung) bereitet im quasigeostrophischen System erhebliche mathematische Schwierigkeiten, so daß auch deren Einflüsse meist unberücksichtigt bleiben.

Wegen des völlig anders verlaufenden Lösungsprozesses der primitiven Gleichungen lassen sich alle diese Vorgänge ohne sonderliche Komplikationen erfassen.

Besonders schwerwiegend gegen die quasigeostrophische Theorie spricht jedoch der Umstand, daß diese die Stabilitäts- und Labilitätsverhältnisse für barokline Entwicklungen völlig unkorrekt wiedergibt. Während bei den geostrophischen Modellen die Amplituden von einem baroklinen Grundzustand überlagerten Störungen mit zunehmender Baroklinität (zunehmendem isobaren Temperaturgradienten bzw. zunehmender vertikaler Windscherung) unbegrenzt anwachsen, erweisen analytische Untersuchungen der linearisierten primitiven Gleichungen, vgl. z. B. EDELMANN (1958), daß bei diesen mit zunehmender Baroklinität das Amplitudenwachstum der Störungen zunächst einem Extremwert zustrebt, dann wieder abklingt, and daß oberhalb eines kritischen Baroklinitätswertes wieder stabile Verhältnisse angetroffen werden. Der Übergang von geostrophischen Modellen zu nichtgeostrophischen Modellen bringt also eine wesentliche Einschrumpfung des labilen Regimes barokliner Entwicklungen mit sich. Dies erklärt möglicherweise, daß in besonders stark ausgeprägten Frontalzonen die Zyklogenese zum Erlahmen kommt.

Erst nichtgeostrophische Differenzenmodelle mit mehr als zwei Parametern zur Beschreibung der vertikalen Struktur der Atmosphäre erfassen diese den nichtgeostrophischen Differentialgleichungen eigenen baroklinen Labilitätsverhältnisse.

Hauptsächlich scheut man sich vor der Verwendung der primitiven Gleichungen, weil diese bekanntlich unerwünschte Lärmvorgänge mitschleppen und deren numerische Lösung einen wesentlich kleineren Integrationszeitschritt erfordert, so daß die Zahl der Iterationen erheblich anwächst. Andererseits jedoch sind die primitiven Gleichungen mathematisch einfacher zu handhaben und zu programmieren und erfordern pro Zeitschritt einen geringeren Rechenaufwand als quasigeostrophische Modelle, der umso mehr ins Gewicht fällt, je mehr Gitterpunkte zur Beschreibung der vertikalen Abhängigkeit der Variablen benutzt werden, so daß insbesondere bei Mehrflächenmodellen der infolge des kleinen Zeitschritts erhöhte Zeitaufwand wenigstens teilweise wieder kompensiert wird.

Im folgenden wird ein einfaches numerisches Experiment mit einem nichtgeostrophischen Mehrflächenmodell beschrieben. Hauptzweck der Untersuchung war festzustellen, wie überhaupt die primitiven Gleichungen spezielle großräumige Wettervorgänge beschreiben und ob die Lärmvorgänge den synoptischen Trend überdecken.

Betrachtet wird der Prozeß der Zyklo- und Antizyklogenese in idealisierter Form. Die zur Beantwortung der Frage nicht entscheidenden Effekte der Reibung, nichtadiabatischer Prozesse, orographischer Hindernisse sowie der Kugelgestalt der Erde sind unberücksichtigt geblieben.

II. Modellgleichungen

Das verwendete Modell benutzt als prognostische Gleichungen für Wind und Temperatur die horizontalen Bewegungsgleichungen sowie die Adiabatengleichung in unmodifizierter Form, als diagnostische Gleichungen (Verträglichkeitsbedingungen) die hydrostatische Grundgleichung, deren Verwendung die Ausfilterung von Schallwellen bewirkt, sowie die über die Vertikale gemittelte Divergenzgleichung zur Errechnung des Geopotentials und die Kontinuitätsgleichung zur Errechnung der Vertikalgeschwindigkeit aus den zu fester Zeit vorgegebenen Werten des Windes und der Temperatur.

Benutzt wird ein kartesisches Koordinatensystem mit p (Druck) als vertikale Koordinate, als abhängige Variable werden betrachtet die horizontalen Geschwindigkeiten $\mathbf{v}\{u, v\}$, die im p-System sich anbietende generalisierte Vertikalgeschwindigkeit $\omega \equiv \frac{dp}{dt}$, das Geopotential $\phi = gz$ (z = Höhe über NN) und die potentielle Temperatur Θ.

Das später einzuführende Differenzenmodell definiert und sagt voraus u, v, Θ in den Flächen $p = 100, 300, 500, 700, 900$ mb, ω und $\nabla\phi$ (bzw. ϕ bis auf eine Konstante) in den Flächen $p = 0, 200, 400, 600, 800, 1000$ mb in Form von diskontinuierlichen Gitterfunktionen. Dem Modell liegen die folgenden Differentialgleichungen zugrunde:

Bewegungsgleichungen

$$\frac{\partial \mathbf{v}}{\partial t} + \nabla \cdot (\mathbf{v}\mathbf{v}) + \frac{\partial}{\partial p}(\omega \mathbf{v}) + f\mathbf{k} \times \mathbf{v} = -\nabla \phi, \quad (1,\ 2)$$

Adiabatengleichung

$$\frac{\partial \Theta}{\partial t} + \nabla \cdot (\mathbf{v}\Theta) + \frac{\partial}{\partial p}(\omega \Theta) = 0, \quad (3)$$

Kontinuitätsgleichung

$$\frac{\partial \omega}{\partial p} + \nabla \cdot \mathbf{v} = 0, \quad (4)$$

hydrostatische Grundgleichung

$$\frac{\partial \phi}{\partial p} = -\frac{1}{\varrho} = -\frac{R}{p}\left(\frac{p}{p_0}\right)^{\lambda} \Theta. \quad (5)$$

Als Randbedingung an der oberen und unteren Grenze der Atmosphäre wird benutzt:

$$\omega = 0 \quad \text{für} \quad p = 0, \quad (6\,\text{a})$$

$$\omega = 0 \quad \text{für} \quad p = p_0 = 1000 \text{ mb},$$

$$\text{bzw.} \quad \int_0^{p_0} (\nabla \cdot \mathbf{v})\, dp = 0 \quad (6\,\text{b})$$

Die Randbedingung (6 b), die anstelle der für eine ebene Erdoberfläche in 1000 mb geltenden exakten Randbedingung

$$\omega = \varrho \left(\frac{\partial \phi}{\partial t} + \mathbf{v} \cdot \nabla \phi\right)$$

tritt, filtert externe Gravitationswellen aus.

Als Lärmvorgänge verbleiben in den Gleichungen (1—6) somit noch kombinierte Trägheits-interne Gravitationswellen.

Die Symbole haben die übliche Bedeutung. R = Gaskonstante trockener Luft = 287,04 m^2 sec^{-2} °K^{-1}, $\lambda = R/c_p = 0{,}286$, f = Coriolis-parameter = const = ½ Std^{-1}, $\mathbf{k}$ = vertikaler Einheitsvektor, $\nabla \left\{\frac{\partial}{\partial x}, \frac{\partial}{\partial y}\right\}$ = horizontaler Nablaoperator. Punkt · als Multiplikationszeichen kennzeichnet das innere, Kreuz × das äußere Vektorprodukt.

Später wird ein seitlich abgeschlossenes Gebiet (Kanalströmung) betrachtet. Als seitliche Randbedingung fordern wir das Verschwinden der Normalkomponente des Windes.

III. Lösungsverfahren

Im Gegensatz zu den geostrophischen Modellen können im nichtgeostrophischen System mehrere meteorologische Funktionen beliebig vorgegeben werden. Wir spezialisieren zur Zeit $t = 0$ die potentielle Temperatur Θ sowie die horizontalen Windkomponenten, die jedoch wegen der Ausfilterung externer Gravitationswellen der Modellbedingung (6 b): $\int_0^{p_0} (\nabla \cdot \mathbf{v}) dp = 0$ unterliegen.

1. *Diagnostischer Teil:*

Aus der Vorgabe der u, v, Θ-Werte zu einer festen Zeit errechnet sich mittels der Verträglichkeitsbedingungen ω und ϕ.

ω erhält man aus der Kontinuitätsgleichung (4) zu

$$\omega = -\int_0^p (\nabla \cdot \mathbf{v})\, dp.$$

Mit der hydrostatischen Relation (5) erhält man aus Θ unmittelbar $\frac{\partial \phi}{\partial p}$ und damit ϕ bis auf eine lediglich von den horizontalen Koordinaten abhängige Integrationsfunktion. Wir berechnen zunächst das über die vertikale gemittelte Geopotential $\tilde{\phi} \equiv \frac{1}{p_0}\int_0^{p_0} \phi dp$ und benutzen hierzu die über p gemittelte Divergenzgleichung:

Anwendung des Divergenzoperators auf (1, 2) ergibt die Divergenzgleichung

$$\frac{\partial}{\partial t}(\nabla \cdot \mathbf{v}) + \nabla \cdot [\nabla \cdot (\mathbf{v}\mathbf{v})] + \nabla \cdot \frac{\partial}{\partial p}(\omega \mathbf{v}) +$$
$$+ \nabla \cdot (f\mathbf{k} \times \mathbf{v}) = -\nabla^2 \phi,$$

und Mittelung dieser Gleichung über p ergibt wegen (6 a, b):

$$\nabla^2 \tilde{\phi} = -\frac{1}{p_0}\int_0^{p_0} \{\nabla \cdot [\nabla \cdot (\mathbf{v}\mathbf{v})] + \nabla \cdot (f\mathbf{k} \times \mathbf{v})\}\, dp. \quad (7)$$

Die Lösung dieser Poisson-Gleichung für $\tilde{\phi}$ führt auf ein Randwertproblem 2. Art.

Da wir auf der seitlichen Berandung das Verschwinden der normalen Windkomponente voraussetzen, liefert die Normalkomponente der über p gemittelten Bewegungsgleichungen (1, 2) die zum vorliegenden Randwertproblem zugehörige Randbedingung. Sie führt bei krummliniger Berandung auf die Gradientwindbeziehung, für geradlinige Berandung auf die geostrophische Beziehung zwischen mittlerer Tangentialkomponente des Windes und normaler Ableitung des Geopotentials.

In unserem speziellen Ausschnitt einer Kanalströmung, wo die Berandungslinien mit Linien konstanten y zusammenfallen, $y = y_R = \text{const}$, erhält man als Randbedingung für (7):

$$\frac{\partial}{\partial y}\tilde{\phi} = -\frac{f}{p_0}\int_0^{p_0} u\,dp, \quad \text{für } y = y_R. \qquad (8)$$

Die Lösung ist damit bis auf eine unerhebliche Konstante bestimmt. Durch partielle Integration von $\frac{1}{p_0}\int_0^{p_0}\phi\,dp$ erhält man

$$\phi(p = p_0) = \tilde{\phi} + \frac{1}{p_0}\int_0^{p_0} p\frac{\partial\phi}{\partial p}\,dp, \qquad (9)$$

und damit schließlich Φ als Funktion von x, y, p

$$\phi(p) = \phi(p = p_0) + \int_{p_0}^{p}\frac{\partial\phi}{\partial p}\,dp. \qquad (10)$$

Damit sind ω und ϕ aus den vorgegebenen u, v, Θ Funktionen bestimmt.

2. *Prognostischer Teil*

Nachdem für den betrachteten Zeitpunkt die in den Gleichungen (1, 2) und (3) vorkommenden Funktionen $\mathbf{v}$, Θ, ω, ϕ mit ihren räumlichen Ableitungen vorliegen bzw. errechnet sind, werden diese drei Gleichungen unmittelbar zur zeitlichen Extrapolation der ursprünglich spezialisierten Quantitäten $\mathbf{v}$, Θ benutzt, womit diese Funktionen zu einem späteren Zeitpunkt bekannt werden und der angegebene Lösungsprozeß iteriert werden kann. Das Lösungsverfahren für die Differentialgleichungen ist lediglich in das numerische der entsprechenden Differenzengleichungen zu übersetzen.

IV. Differenzenmodell

Die numerische Lösungsmethode erfordert die Einführung eines räumlich-zeitlichen Gitternetzes und den Ersatz der kontinuierlichen Variablen durch Gittervariable, die nur an den Gitterpunkten definiert sind.

Wir orientieren $x \rightarrow E$, $y \rightarrow N$ und betrachten lediglich einen atmosphärischen Ausschnitt in Form eines Kanals der Breite $D = 5\,100$ km mit festen Wänden im Süden, $y = 0$, und Norden, $y = D$, wo die kinematischen Randbedingungen das Verschwinden der Meridionalkomponente v fordern. In der zonalen x-Richtung sei der Kanal unbegrenzt, jedoch sollen alle abhängigen Variablen in x periodisch sein mit der Periodenlänge $L = 6\,600$ km, so daß für eine beliebige Funktion α gilt $\alpha(x+L) = \alpha(x)$. Es genügt somit, in der Horizontalebene lediglich das rechteckige Gebiet $0 \leq x \leq L$, $0 \leq y \leq D$ zu betrachten.

Zur Formulierung der Differenzengleichungen führen wir diskontinuierliche Variable i, j, k, τ ein, mit

$$\begin{array}{llll} x = i\Delta_i, & \Delta_i = 300\text{ km} = \Delta, & i = 0, 1, 2 \ldots & I-1 \\ y = j\Delta_j, & \Delta_j = 300\text{ km} = \Delta, & j = 0, 1, 2 \ldots & J \\ p = k\Delta_k, & \Delta_k = 100\text{ mb}, & k = 0, 1, 2 \ldots & K \\ t = \tau\Delta_\tau, & \Delta_\tau = 1/4\text{ Std}, & \tau = 0, 1, 2 \ldots & \end{array}$$

$$I = 22 \qquad J = 17 \qquad K = 10$$

Die versuchsweise Erhöhung des Zeitschrittes Δ_τ auf 1/2 Stunde führte zu numerischer Instabilität.

Wegen der Periodizität ist $\alpha(i+I) = \alpha(i)$. $j = 0$ und $j = J$, $k = 0$ und $k = K$ geben die Begrenzungsflächen wieder. Das Gebiet umfaßt demnach einschließlich der Randpunkte 18×22 Gitterpunkte.

Die abhängigen Variablen sind definiert und werden vorhergesagt für alle i, j einschließlich der Randpunkte, die Variablen u, v, Θ jedoch nur in den Flächen mit ungeradem k; $k = 1, 3, 5, 7, 9$; die Variablen ω, ϕ nur in den Flächen mit geradem k; $k = 0, 2, 4, 6, 8, 10$; do daß das Modell lediglich als 5-Flächenmodell anzusprechen ist.

Zur einfacheren Schreibweise definieren wir die folgenden zentralen Differenzenoperatoren, die zur finiten Approximation erster Ableitungen nach den unabhängigen Variablen x, y, p, t dienen:

$$(\delta_x\alpha)_{i,j,k,\tau} \equiv \frac{1}{2\Delta}(\alpha_{i+1} - \alpha_{i-1})_{j,k,\tau} \approx \left(\frac{\partial\alpha}{\partial x}\right)_{i,j,k,\tau}$$

$$(\delta_y\alpha)_{i,j,k,\tau} \equiv \frac{1}{2\Delta}(\alpha_{j+1} - \alpha_{j-1})_{i,k,\tau} \approx \left(\frac{\partial\alpha}{\partial y}\right)_{i,j,k,\tau}$$

$$(\delta_p\alpha)_{i,j,k,\tau} \equiv \frac{1}{2\Delta_k}(\alpha_{o+1} - \alpha_{o-1})_{i,j,\tau} \approx \left(\frac{\partial\alpha}{\partial p}\right)_{i,j,k,\tau}$$

$$(\delta_t\alpha)_{i,j,k,\tau} \equiv \frac{1}{2\Delta_\tau}(\alpha_{\tau+1} - \alpha_{\tau-1})_{i,j,k} \approx \left(\frac{\partial\alpha}{\partial t}\right)_{i,j,k,\tau}$$

Wo Mißverständnisse ausgeschlossen sind, werden wir jedoch die Indices wieder fortlassen. Zur Annäherung des Laplace-Operators definieren wir konsequenterweise

$$(\nabla^2\alpha)_{i,j,k,\tau} \equiv (\delta_x\delta_x + \delta_y\delta_y\alpha)_{i,j,k,\tau} = \frac{1}{4\Delta^2}(\alpha_{i+2,j} + \alpha_{i-2,j} + \alpha_{i,j+2} + \alpha_{i,j-2} - 4\alpha_{i,j})_{k,\tau} \approx \approx (\nabla^2\alpha)_{i,j,k,\tau}$$

Man beachte, daß der Operator ∇^2 den Aufpunktswert an der Stelle i, j mit Nachbarwerten verknüpft, die um zwei Maschenweiten Δ vom Aufpunkt entfernt sind. Würde man in der Divergenzgleichung (7) den dort auftretenden Laplaceoperator durch einen Differenzenoperator mit der einfachen Maschenweite approximieren, so zerstört man die Konsistenz des Differentialgleichungssystems, erzeugt entgegen der Modellannahme über p gemittelte nicht mehr verschwindende Divergenzen, was zu absurden numerischen Resultaten führt.

Wegen der unterschiedlichen Belegung der Flächen konstanten Druckes mit Werten der abhängigen Variablen, ist es noch zweckmäßig, folgenden Mittelwertoperator einzuführen

$$\left(\overset{M}{\alpha}\right)_{i,j,k,\tau} \equiv \frac{1}{2}(\alpha_{k+1} + \alpha_{k-1})_{i,j,\tau}.$$

Zur Approximation vertikaler Mittelwerte durch finite Summen benutzen wir die Tangentenformel. Es ist

$$(\overline{\alpha})_{i,j,\tau} \equiv \frac{1}{5}(\alpha_{k=1} + \alpha_{k=3} + \alpha_{k=5} + + \alpha_{k=7} + \alpha_{k=9})_{i,j,\tau} \approx \frac{1}{p_0}\int_0^{p_0} \alpha dp.$$

Anwendung des Operators $\overline{(\ )}^{M}$ auf eine Größe α führt dann zur Annäherung des vertikalen Mittels durch die Trapezformel:

$$(\overline{\alpha}^{M})_{i,j,\tau} = \frac{1}{5}\left(\frac{1}{2}\alpha_{k=0} + \alpha_{k=2} + \alpha_{k=4} + \alpha_{k=6} + + \alpha_{k=8} + \frac{1}{2}\alpha_{k=10}\right) \approx \frac{1}{p_0}\int_0^{p_0} \alpha dp.$$

Mit den soeben definierten finiten Operatoren ersetzen wir nunmehr die Differentialgleichungen (1—6) durch die entsprechenden Modelldifferenzengleichungen und schreiben

$$\delta_t u = -\left[\delta_x(u^2) + \delta_y(uv) + \delta_p\left(\omega \overset{M}{u}\right) - fv\right] - \delta_x \overset{M}{\phi} \tag{11}$$

$$\delta_t v = -\left[\delta_x(uv) + \delta_y(v^2) + \delta_p\left(\omega \overset{M}{v}\right) + fu\right] - \delta_y \overset{M}{\phi}, \tag{12}$$

$$\delta_t \Theta = -\left[\delta_x(u\Theta) + \delta_y(v\Theta) + \delta_p\left(\omega \overset{M}{\Theta}\right)\right], \tag{13}$$

$$\delta_p \omega = -(\delta_x u + \delta_y v), \tag{14}$$

$$(\delta_p \phi)_k = -\frac{R}{k\Delta_k}\left(\frac{k}{K}\right)^{\lambda}\Theta_k, \tag{15}$$

$$\delta_x \overline{u} + \delta_y \overline{v} = 0; \quad \omega_{k=0} = \omega_{k=K} = 0. \tag{16}$$

Die Gleichungen (11—15), angeschrieben für alle i, j einschließlich der Randpunkte $j = 0$, $j = J$ und in den Flächen $k = 1, 3, 5, 7, 9$ bilden zusammen mit den noch zu formulierenden Randbedingungen das algebraische Gleichungssystem des Differenzenmodells. Die Anwendung des Mittelwertoperators $\overset{M}{(\ )}$ auf ϕ und u, v, Θ in den vertikalen Ableitungen in den Gleichungen (11—13) bewirkt, daß die abhängigen Variablen nur an solchen Gitterpunkten miteinander verknüpft werden, an denen sie definiert sind.

Die der Stromimpulsform angepaßte finite Differenzenschreibweise garantiert, daß keine fiktiven Impulsquellen durch truncation-Fehler erzeugt werden, daß vielmehr die zeitliche Änderung des Gesamtimpuls, summiert über sämtliche Gitterpunkte und Randpunkte, wie im Differentialgleichungssystem lediglich von den im Inneren wirkenden Corioliskräften sowie den auf die seitlichen Wände wirkenden Druckkräften abhängt.

Der Lösungsprozeß ist völlig analog dem in Abschnitt III für das kontinuierliche System beschriebenen Verfahren. Die konsequente Benutzung zentraler Differenzenquotienten erfordert lediglich eine Ergänzung der Randbedingung an den nördlichen und südlichen Begrenzungsflächen $j = 0, J$, wenn an diesen Rändern nicht von nach innen gerichteten Differenzenquotienten Gebrauch gemacht werden soll. Schreibt man nämlich die Gleichungen (11—14) an den Randpunkten $j = 0$, J an, so erkennt man, daß über die den Operator δ_y enthaltenden Terme auch Funktionswerte an Gitterpunkten eingehen, an denen diese nicht definiert sind. Diese Schwierigkeit wurde dadurch umgangen, daß zusätzlich für die außerhalb des Gebiets liegenden Randnachbarflächen $j = -1, J+1$ ebenfalls das Verschwinden der Normalkomponente v postuliert wird. Diese lediglich durch die Differenzenschreibweise bedingte zusätzliche Randbedingung garantiert die Eindeutigkeit der Differenzen-Lösung für alle abhängigen Variablen innerhalb und auf dem Rand ($j = 0, j = J$) des Gebiets.

Aus der Vorgabe der u, v, Θ-Werte in Flächen mit ungeradem k erhält man mit (14) und (15) und wegen $\omega_{k=0} = 0$ unmittelbar ω und $\phi_k - \phi_{k-2}$ für $k = 2, 4, 6, 8, 10$ bzw. $(\delta_p\phi)_k$ für k ungerade.

Zur Bestimmung von ϕ selbst in den Flächen $k = 0, 2, 4, 6, 8, 10$ berechnen wir uns vorerst $\overline{(\phi)}^{M}_{i,j}$.

Anwendung des Differenzenoperators δ_x auf (11), δ_y auf (12), und Addition und Mittelung über k unter Beachtung von (16) führt auf ein elliptisches Differenzengleichungssystem für $\overline{(\phi)}^{M}$, das anstelle der Poisson-Differentialgleichung (7) tritt:

$$\nabla^2\overline{(\phi)}^{M} = -\delta_x\left[\overline{\delta_x(u^2) + \delta_y(uv) - fv}\right] - \delta_y\left[\overline{\delta_x(uv) + \delta_y(v^2) + fu}\right] \quad (17)$$

und wiederum für alle $i, j = 0, 1 \ldots . J$ definiert werde.

In den Zeilen $j = 0,\ 1,\ J-1,\ J$ erfaßt (17) wiederum Funktionswerte außerhalb des Gebiets, insbesondere $\overline{(\phi)}^{M}$-Werte in den Zeilen $j = -2$, -1, $J+1$, $J+2$, wo diese weder benötigt werden, noch überall berechenbar sind. Auch hier beseitigt die zusätzliche Randbedingung $v = 0$ für $j = -1,\ J+1$ diese Schwierigkeit. Mit dieser sowie der normalen Randannahme $v = 0$ für $j = -1,\ 0,\ J,\ J+1$ erhält man aus (12) durch Mittelung über k:

$$\delta_y\overline{(\phi)}^{M} = -\left[\overline{\delta_x(uv) + \delta_y(v^2) + fu}\right] \text{ für } j = -1, 0, J, J+1, \quad (18)$$

Schreibt man Gleichung (17) in der Form:

$$\delta_x\delta_x\overline{(\phi)}^{M} + \frac{1}{2\Delta}\left[\delta_y\overline{(\phi)}^{M}_{j+1} - \delta_y\overline{(\phi)}^{M}_{j-1}\right] = -\delta_x\left[\overline{\delta_x(u^2) + \delta_y(uv) - fv}\right] - \frac{1}{2\Delta}\left[\overline{\delta_x(uv) + \delta_y(v^2) + fu}\right]_{j+1} + \frac{1}{2\Delta}\left[\overline{\delta_x(uv) + \delta_y(v^2) + fu}\right]_{j-1}, \quad (17\text{a})$$

und beachtet (18), so sieht man, daß alle Terme, die in Gleichung (17) undefinierte Funktionswerte enthalten, gerade herausfallen. Das sind für $j = 0{,}1$ jeweils die Terme mit dem Index $j-1$, für $j = J-1,\ J$ jeweils die Terme mit dem Index $j+1$.

Nach Kürzung dieser Ausdrücke in den Zeilen $j = 0{,}1,\ J-1,\ J$ entsteht in (17) ein algebraisches Gleichungssystem, das ebensoviele Gleichungen wie Unbekannte $\overline{(\phi)}^{M}$-Werte enthält. Die rechten Seiten sind aus den gebietseigenen vorgegebenen Funktionswerten u, v errechenbar.

System (17) wurde durch Relaxation gelöst. Bei verschwindenden Residuen garantiert die Lösung $\overline{(\phi)}^{M}$ automatisch, daß die Modellforderung $\delta_x\bar{u} + \delta_y\bar{v} = 0$ bzw. $\omega_{k=K} = 0$ erfüllt bleibt. Zur Kontrolle wurden die ω-Werte in der Fläche $k = K$ mitberechnet. Sie wachsen mit der Zeit an, verbleiben jedoch selbst gegen Ende der dreitägigen Vorhersage unterhalb 0,1 mb/Std., d.h. unterhalb 3 % ihrer in der jeweiligen Vertikalen auftretenden Maximalwerte. Allerdings wurden pro Relaxation 50 Iterationen verwendet.

Analog zu (9) erhält man für

$$\phi_{k=10} = \overline{(\phi)}^{M} + \frac{\Delta_k}{5}\left[(\delta_p\phi)_{k=1} + 3\,(\delta_p\phi)_{k=3} + 5\,(\delta_p\phi)_{k=5} + 7(\delta_p\phi)_{k=7} + 9\,(\delta_p\phi)_{k=9}\right] \equiv \phi^*, \quad (19)$$

und analog zu (10)

$$\phi_{k-2} = \phi_k + (\phi_{k-2} - \phi_k), \text{ mit } \phi_{10} = \phi^*. \quad (20)$$

Im prognostischen Teil ist bei der ersten zeitlichen Extrapolation der Variablen u, v, Θ z.Zt. $t = 0$ ein vorderer zeitlicher Differenzenquotient anzuwenden, da nicht zu zwei aufeinanderfolgenden Zeiten $\tau = 0$ und $\tau = 1$ Anfangswerte beliebig vorgegeben werden sollen, was an sich die Differenzengleichungen (11—13) zulassen. Zur Vermeidung schwacher numerischer Instabilität wurden für die ersten drei zeitlichen Extrapolationen kürzere Zeitintervalle als $\Delta_\tau = 1/4$ Std. benutzt. Für die erste Extrapolation mit vorderem Differenzenquotient wurde $\frac{1}{4}\Delta_\tau$ angesetzt, so daß

$$(u, v, \Theta)_{\tau=1/4} = (u, v, \Theta)_{\tau=0} + \frac{1}{4}\Delta_\tau[\delta_t(u, v, \Theta)]_{\tau=0},$$

Durch zweimalige Verdopplung des anfangs benutzten Zeitschritts und Verwendung zentraler zeitlicher Differenzenquotienten erhält man nach insgesamt 3 Extrapolationen die Werte u, v, Θ z. Zt. $\tau = 1$, bzw. $t = \Delta_\tau$, von da an beginnt das mit Gleichungen (11—13) definierte normale Extrapolationsverfahren.

V. Maschinenzeit

Die Rechnungen wurden auf der 704-IBM-Maschine in Paris durchgeführt. Trotz der 50 Iterationen bei der Relaxation der Gleichung (17) betrug die Rechenzeit, einschließlich Schreibens der Werte u, v, Θ, ϕ, ω auf Magnetband pro Zeitschritt nur 45 sec., eine 24-stündige Vorhersage erforderte etwa 72 Minuten. Die Funktionswerte u, v, Θ, ϕ wurden in zweistündigen Abständen, die Vertikalgeschwindigkeit ω in halbstündigem Abstand ausgedruckt.

VI. Anfangsdaten

Als Anfangssituation ($t = 0$) wurde ein sehr einfaches baroklines Grundfeld angesetzt: ein zonaler von den horizontalen Koordinaten unabhängiger Grundstrom U, linear von p abhängig, der am Erdboden verschwindet und für $p = 0$ auf 150 km/Std. anwächst. Der zugehörige geostrophisch adaptierte nord-südlich gerichtete Temperaturgradient ist ebenfalls homogen in Flächen konstanten Druckes und nimmt mit p ab. Zur Vervollständigung des Grundfeldes sind noch Temperaturangaben in einer Fläche $j =$ const erforderlich. In der Mitte des Kanals $y = D/2$, bzw. $j = 8{,}5$ wurde, unabhängig von x, Θ als Funktion von p vorgegeben und zwar so, daß die statische Stabilität $\left(-\frac{\partial \Theta}{\partial p}\right)$ oberhalb 300 mb (Stratosphäre) wesentlich höhere Werte annimmt als unterhalb 300 mb (Troposphäre). Die statische Stabilität nimmt wegen des von p abhängigen Temperaturgefälles nach Süden hin ab und wird in der unteren Troposphäre am Südrand $y = 0$, bzw. $j = 0$, leicht negativ (überadiabatische Schichtung). Das führt nach 3 Tagen zu abnormen vertikal-zonalen Zirkulationen in der Zonalebene $j = 0$, so daß die tiorhersage nach 3 Tagen abgebrochen werden mußte. Die den Grundanfangszustand definierenden Werte sind der am Seiten schluss abgedruckten Tabelle zu entnehmen.

Da die mit dem Modell durchgeführten Vorhersagen lediglich Experimente darstellen, wurden die unrealistisch hohen Temperaturdifferenzen zwischen nördlicher und südlicher Begrenzung in der unteren Troposphäre in Kauf genommen. Andererseits hätte bei von x, y unabhängigem Grundstrom die vertikale Windscherung (Baroklinität) herabgesetzt werden müssen. Zur Erzeugung extremer Entwicklungsvorgänge langwelliger Störungen waren jedoch hohe Baroklinitätswerte erwünscht.

Dem Grundanfangsfeld wurde eine Störungsströmung auf zweierlei Weise superponiert:

Fall A

Vorgegeben wurde z. Zt. $t = 0$ eine sinusoidale barotrope (von p unabhängige) divergenzfreie Störungsströmung in Form einer Gitterstromfunktion:

$$\psi_{i,j} = \frac{A}{2} \sin\left(\frac{2\pi}{I} i\right)\left\{1 + \cos\left[\frac{2\pi}{J+1}(j - 8{,}5)\right]\right\},$$

$$j = -1, 0, \quad 1 \ldots J+1,$$

die genau zwischen den beiden seitlichen Doppelrändern, also an den Stellen $j = -\tfrac{1}{2}$, $j = J + \tfrac{1}{2}$, verschwindet. Sie definiert z. Zt. $t = 0$

$$u_{i,j} = -\delta_y \psi, \quad j = 0, 1, 2 \ldots J$$

$$v_{i,j} = \delta_x \psi, \quad j = 1, 2 \ldots J-1; \quad v_{i,j} = 0$$

$$\text{für } j = -1, 0, J, J+1.$$

Die Amplitude der Stromfunktion A wurde so bestimmt, daß die maximale meridionale Windkomponente 42 km Std^{-1} beträgt:

$$|v|_{\max} = \frac{A}{\Delta} \sin\frac{2\pi}{I} = 42 \text{ km Std}^{-1}.$$

p [mb]	U [km Std^{-1}]	$\delta_y T$ [°K (300 km)$^{-1}$]	$\delta_y \Theta$ [°K (300 km)$^{-1}$]	Θ ($j = 8{,}5$, i) [°K]
100	135	0.61	1.17	430
300	105	1.81	2.56	314
500	75	3.02	3.68	296
700	45	4.23	4.68	289
900	15	5.44	5.61	273

Da die Störung barotrop ist, verschwindet das geostrophisch zugehörige Temperaturstörungsfeld.

Mit Fall *A* (ω z. Zt. $t = 0$ verschwindet) wurde eine dreitägige Vorhersage gemacht.

Fall B

Dem im Falle A spezialisierten divergenzfreien Windfeld wurde noch ein divergentes wirbelfreies Windfeld in Form eines Geschwindigkeitspotentials χ überlagert, so daß

$$u_{i,j,k} = -(\delta_y\psi)_{i,j} + (\delta_x\chi)_{i,j,k}, \quad j = 0, 1 \ldots . J$$

$$v_{i,j,k} = (\delta_x\psi)_{i,j} + (\delta_y\chi)_{i,j,k}, \quad j = 1, 2 \ldots . J - 1;$$

$$v_{i,j} = 0 \text{ für } j = -1, 0, J, \ J + 1.$$

χ wurde vermittels der Poissongleichung $\nabla^2\chi = -\delta_p\omega$ aus einem Vertikalgeschwindigkeitsfeld berechnet, das selbst wieder mithilfe quasigeostrophischer Gleichungen aus einem Geopotentialfeld ϕ berechnet wurde, wobei $\phi = f(\psi - uy)$ gesetzt wurde.

χ ist von der Form

$$\chi_{i,j,k} = \cos\left(\frac{2\pi i}{I}\right) \cdot$$

$$\left\{(\delta_p M)_K + (\delta_p N)_K \cos\left[\frac{2\pi}{J+1}(j - 8{,}5)\right]\right\},$$

$$\text{mit } \overline{\delta_p M} = \overline{\delta_p N} = 0,$$

jedoch wurden die Anfangswerte $\chi_{i,j,k}$ durch die Maschine selbst berechnet.

Fall B spezialisiert sozusagen z. Zt. $t = 0$ ein geostrophisch adaptiertes Vertikalgeschwindigkeitsfeld, das bewirkt, daß die Amplituden der Lärmwellen (Trägheits- und Gravitationswellen) gegenüber Fall A reduziert werden.

Mit Fall B wurde eine eintägige Vorhersage durchgeführt.

VII. Ergebnisse

Fig. 1 zeigt die mit Fall A berechnete Anfangsstörung ϕ in 1 000 mb sowie die z. Zt. $t = 0$ vorgegebenen potentiellen Isothermen in 900 mb. Die ϕ-Störung ist barotrop, d. h. in allen Niveaus die gleiche, allerdings in höher gelegenen Flächen $k < K$ einer homogenen Grundströmung $U(p) = -\frac{1}{f}\delta_y\phi$ superponiert. Die leichte Asymmetrie zwischen Hoch und Tief, das letztere ist geringfügig intensiver, erklärt sich daraus, daß die bei der Berechnung der ϕ-Störung benutzte (über p gemittelte) Divergenzgleichung über den Term $\nabla \cdot [\nabla \cdot (\mathbf{vv})]$ auch zentrifugale Kräfte berücksichtigt, also die völlig symmetrischen Winde der Zyklone und Antizyklone nicht geostrophisch, sondern als Gradientwinde interpretiert, so daß der Gradient von ϕ in zyklonalen Gebieten stärker ausfallen muß als in den entsprechenden antizyklonalen Bereichen.

Im Falle B erhält man nahezu die gleiche barotrope ϕ-Anfangsstörung, da die überlagerten divergenten Windkomponenten gegenüber den divergenzfreien Komponenten vernachlässigbar klein sind und sich lediglich im Vertikalgeschwindigkeitsfeld auswirken, das im Falle B auf der

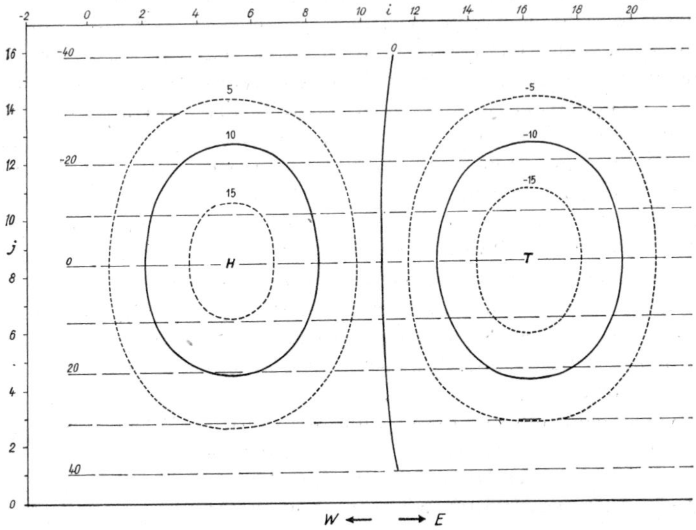

Fig. 1. Anfangsstörung. Isohypsen in 1000 mb (ausgezogene und punktierte Linien) in 5 Dekameterintervallen, Isolinien der potentiellen Temperatur in 900 mb (gestrichelte Linien) in 10° K-Intervallen.

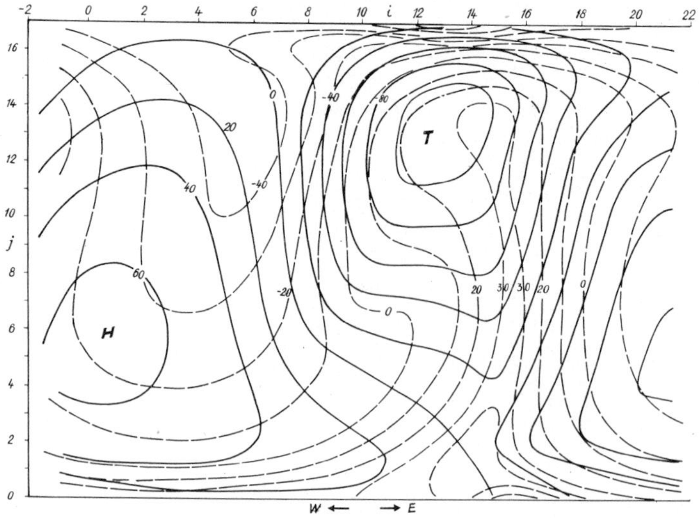

Fig. 2. Isohypsen in 1000 mb (ausgezogene Linien) in 20 Dekameterintervallen (ausgezogene Linien), Isolinien der potentiellen Temperatur in 900 mb (gestrichelte Linien) in 10° K-Intervallen nach 3 Tagen (Fall A).

Vorderseite des Tiefs Aufsteigen, auf der Rückseite Absinken aufweist mit Extremwerten zwischen den Störungszentren im Niveau 600 mb.

Die Störung in Fig. 1 denke man sich nach Westen und Osten periodisch fortgesetzt. Die Störung verlagert sich im dreitägigen Mittel in 1 000 mb mit einer Geschwindigkeit von etwa 70 km/h ostwärts, also etwa mit der mittleren Grundströmung. Die Verlagerungsgeschwindigkeit nimmt jedoch bis etwa 300 mb ab und nimmt oberhalb 300 mb bis auf nahezu 100 km/h wieder zu. Infolge des in der ganzen Kanalbreite stark baroklinen Grundzustandes der Atmosphäre entwickelt sich die langwellige Störung außerordentlich heftig. Nach drei Tagen ist in 1 000 mb das Tief von ursprünglich 18 dm (Dekameter) auf 100 dm, das Hoch von anfangs 17 dm auf 60 dm angewachsen — vgl. Fig. 2 —, wobei die Zahlenwerte nur relativ zu werten sind, da derartig langwellige Störungen in einem großräumig gleich intensiv baroklinen Felde in der realen Atmosphäre nicht angetroffen werden. Die Entwicklung nimmt mit zunehmender Höhe wegen der zunehmenden statischen Stabilität rasch ab. Oberhalb der Tropopause wird während der ersten beiden Vorhersagetage die Störung sogar gedämpft. Erst infolge der mit der Zeit einsetzenden Labilisierung und sich verstärkenden Baroklinität in der Stratosphäre — vgl. Fig. 5, 6, 11 — setzt sich am 3. Tag auch dort Entwicklung durch.

Gleichzeitig mit der Entwicklung neigen sich die ursprünglich senkrechten Achsen der Störungszentren in der Troposphäre nach rückwärts (westwärts), in der Stratosphäre nach vorwärts (ostwärts) — siehe Fig. 4 —. Dadurch gelangt das Bodentief unter eine Höhenströmung mit Südkomponente und schert nach Norden aus, das Bodenhoch unter eine Höhenströmung mit Nordkomponente und schert demzufolge nach Süden aus — Fig. 2 —.

Die Verteilung von potentieller Temperatur in 900 mb (gestrichelte Linien) sowie die ϕ-Bodenstörung (ausgezogene Linien) nach 3 Tagen (Fall A) sind der Fig. 2 zu entnehmen. Die Abbildung zeigt das typische Bild weitgehend verwirbelter Störungen mit einer deutlich ausgeprägten okkludierten Zyklone. Die auf der Vorderseite des Tiefs nach Norden vorgestoßene aufsteigende Warmluft hat sich abgeschnürt, während die nach Süden auf der Rückseite der Zyklone ausgebrochene Kaltluft in bodennahen Schichten sich ausgedehnt hat. Die Mitteltemperatur in 900 mb ist innerhalb von 3 Tagen um über 5° K abgesunken — Fig. 11 —.

Die in Fig. 2 südlich des Tiefdruckkerns ausgeprägten zyklonalen Isohypsen-«knicke» markieren zusammen mit der Warmluftzunge den Verlauf der Okklusion. Die ebenfalls am Südrand des Gebiets erkennbaren antizyklonalen Knicke dürften auf Randwerteffekte zurückzuführen sein.

Der Okklusionsprozeß wird durch nichtgeostrophische Temperaturadvektionen eingeleitet und resultiert analytisch aus der negativen Korrelation zwischen Temperatur und horizontaler Winddivergenz in bodennahen Schichten, wo

$$\int_0^L \int_0^D (T \nabla \cdot \mathbf{v})\, dx dy < 0.$$

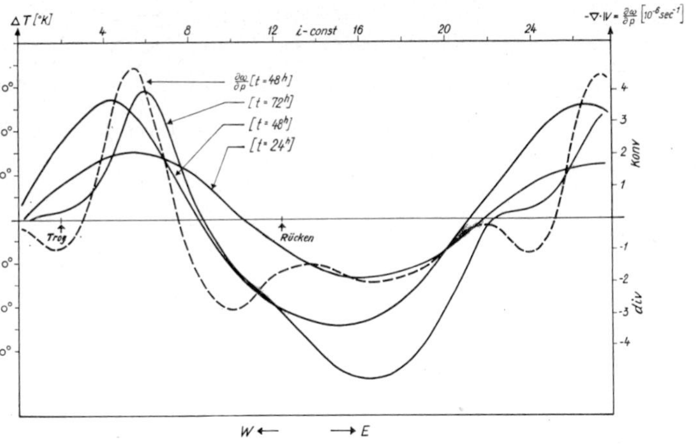

Fig. 3. Verläufe der potentiellen Temperatur (ausgezogene Linien) in Kanalmitte ($j = 8$), 900 mb, nach 24, 48, 72 Stunden, Verlauf der horizontalen Winddivergenz (gestrichelte Linie) 900 mb nach 48 Stunden, bezogen auf ein mit dem Trog mitbewegtes Koordinatensystem.

Dieser Term verschwindet bei geostrophischer Approximation der Adiabatengleichung. Die hohe Korrelation zwischen Temperatur und Windkonvergenz veranschaulicht Fig. 3, die gleichzeitig den Temperaturverlauf in der Kanalmitte 900 mb nach 1, 2 und 3 Tagen relativ zur Lage des Tiefdruckkerns anzeigt. Man erkennt, daß in unserem speziellen Beispiel der Kern des Tiefs während der ersten 2 Tage sich erwärmt, da er in die auf seiner Vorderseite advehierte Warmluft hineinläuft, und sich erst am 3. Tage, allerdings kräftig, abkühlt.

Markante Frontlinien bilden sich während der dreitägigen Entwicklung nicht aus und können wahrscheinlich erst bei Einschluß der Bodenreibung erwartet werden. Auch die in dem von PHILLIPS (1956) vorgeführten Experiment deutlich erkennbare nierenförmige Verformung der Bodendruckgebilde mit nordwestlicher Neigung der Trog- und Rückenachsen im nördlichen Teil und mit südwestlicher Neigung im südlichen Teil des Kanals wird nicht beobachtet. Voraussetzung für diese Verformung, die einen zur Mitte des Kanals gerichteten mittleren Impulsstrom beinhaltet, ist eine meridionale Scherung der Grundströmung, die in unserem Experiment z. Zt. $t = 0$ nicht angesetzt wurde.

Nach 66 Stunden stellenweise auftretende geringfügige Undulationen (wiggles) in Isohypsen und Isothermen wurden in Fig. 2 weggeglättet.

Einen zonalen Vertikalschnitt durch die Zentren der Störung (Kanalmitte, $j = 8$) nach 24 Stunden zeigt Fig. 4 (Fall B). Fall B wurde gewählt, weil bei diesem wegen der geringeren

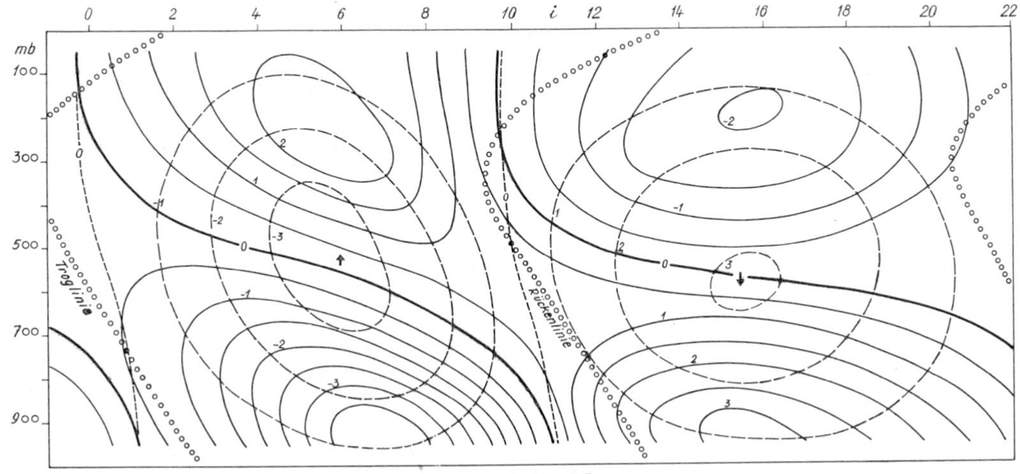

Fig. 4, Zonaler Vertikalschnitt (Fall B) durch die Zentren der Störung ($j = 8$) nach 24 Stunden. Trog- und Rückenlinien oooo, Divergenzfeld (ausgezogene Linien), Einheit 10^{-6} sec^{-1}, Vertikalgeschwindigkeit ω (gestrichelte Linien, Absinken positiv), Einheit mb Std^{-1}.

Amplituden der Lärmwellen die Felder der Vertikalgeschwindigkeit und die daraus abgeleiteten Horizontaldivergenzen zeitliche Mittelwerte besser repräsentieren. Die Abbildung veranschaulicht die bereits erwähnte vertikale Neigung der Trog- und Rückenachsen sowie das Aufgleiten auf der Vorderseite des Tiefs und das Absinken auf der Vorderseite des Hochs (gestrichelte Linien). Die Umkehr in der Achsenneigung oberhalb 300 mb ist ein Effekt der hohen statischen Stabilität in der Stratosphäre, die ein nahezu barotropes Verhalten und damit eine Verlagerung der Störung mit nahezu flächeneigener Grundströmung bewirkt.

Die ausgezogenen Linien verdeutlichen die Verteilung der horizontalen Winddivergenzen. Z. Zt. $t = 0$ fallen die Nullinien der Divergenz zusammen mit den anfangs senkrechten Störungsachsen sowie mit einer Fläche $p =$ const (zwischen 600 und 500 mb). Nach 24 Stunden ist dieses divergenzfreie Niveau zerstört.

Die Tröge und Rücken haben sich so verlagert und das Divergenzfeld hat sich so deformiert, daß der größte Teil der Trogachse im Gebiet der Konvergenz, der Rückenachse im Gebiet der Divergenz zu liegen kommt. Dies ist eine notwendige Voraussetzung für die weitere Entwicklung der Störungszentren. Lediglich oberhalb der Schnittlinien zwischen Achsen und Divergenz-Nullinien wird die Störung gedämpft. Überhaupt stimmt die Abbildung 4 qualitativ, wenigstens im troposphärischen Bereich, mit der von CHARNEY (1947) theoretisch abgeleiteten Feldverteilung völlig überein. Das demonstriert eindrücklich, daß auch die primitiven Gleichungen bei sorgfältiger Adjustierung der Anfangsfelder den meteorologischen Trend, weitgehend ungestört durch Lärmprozesse, zu beschreiben vermögen, selbst in den für Gravitationswellen höchst empfindlichen ω- und $\nabla \cdot \mathbf{v}$-Feldern.

Die nächsten Abbildungen 5—10 zeigen meridionale Vertikalschnitte. Die eingezeichneten Isolinien stellen die Verteilung zonal gemittelter Quantitäten dar, zur Abkürzung wird für die zonale Mittelung benutzt: $\hat{\alpha} \equiv \frac{1}{L} \int_0^L \alpha dx$.

Fig. 5 illustriert die Änderung der Mitteltemperatur $\hat{T}$ innerhalb des 3-tägigen Vorhersagezeitraums (Fall A). Infolge der sich entwickelnden Störungen wird in der Troposphäre sensible Wärme nach Norden transportiert. Man beobachtet kräftige Erwärmung in der nördlichen Hälfte, entsprechend starke Abkühlung in der südlichen Hälfte des betrachteten Kanals, ein Prozeß, der eine Nivellierung des mittleren Temperaturgradienten in der Mitte des Kanals und eine Aufsteilung an den Rändern bewirkt. Oberhalb 300 mb findet der umgekehrte Prozeß, allerdings wegen des mit p abnehmenden Temperaturgradienten wesentlich schwächer, statt, da in der Stratosphäre wegen der hohen Stabilität die advektiven Temperaturänderungen durch konvektive Temperaturänderungen überkompensiert werden.

Die advektiven Prozesse in der Troposphäre erzeugen meridionalvertikale Zirkulationen mit Absink- und Aufgleitvorgängen, die den advektiven Temperaturänderungen entgegenwirken. So entstehen (Fall B) drei Zirkulationszellen, ein indirektes Rad in der Mitte des Kanals, zwei direkte Zirkulationsräder an den Rändern des Kanals — Fig. 6 —. Da die mittlere Vertikalgeschwindigkeit $\hat{\omega}$ sowie die mittlere Meridionalgeschwindigkeit $\hat{v}$, die im nichtgeostrophischen

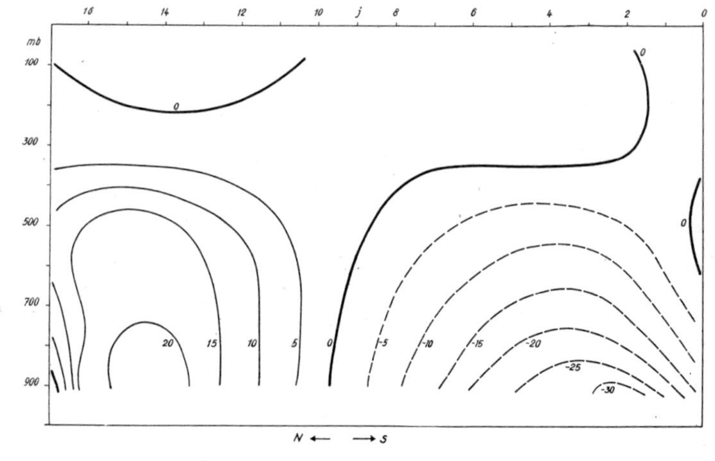

Fig. 5. Mittlere Temperaturänderung innerhalb 72 Stunden. $\hat{T}(t = 72) - \hat{T}(t = 0)$, Einheit °K.

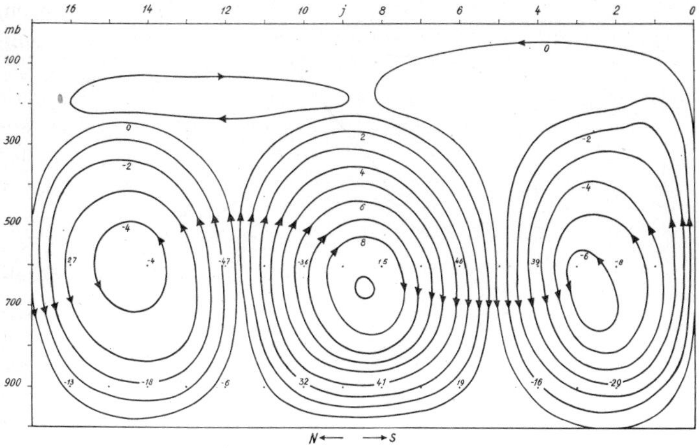

Fig. 6. Stromfunktion für mittlere meridionale—vertikale Zirkulation. Zahlen an Gitterpunkten 900 mb: $\hat{v}$, Einheit cm sec^{-1}. Zahlen an Gitterpunkten 600 mb: $\hat{\omega}$, Einheit 10^{-2}mb Std^{-1}. Fall B, Anfangsvertikalgeschwindigkeitsfeld quasigeostrophisch adjustiert, nach 24 Stunden.

Modell explizit berechnet werden kann, wegen ihrer Divergenzfreiheit einer Stromfunktion ψ: $\hat{\omega} = \frac{\partial \psi}{\partial y}$, $\hat{v} = -\frac{\partial \hat{\psi}}{\partial p}$ genügen, wurde diese zur Veranschaulichung der Zirkulationen verwendet.

Wie stark diese Vertikalzirkulationen auf Trägheits- und interne Gravitationswellen ansprechen, veranschaulichen die Fig. 7—9, die für den Fall A die meridionale-vertikale Zirkulation im Abstand von 12 Stunden (z. Zt. $t = 0$ ist $\hat{v} = \hat{\omega} = 0$) wiedergeben.

In der bodennahen Fläche $p = 900$ mb (z. Zt. $t = 0$ war die Grundströmung 15 km/h) verstärkt sich innerhalb der dreitägigen Vorhersage (Fall A) die Westwinddrift innerhalb eines breiten mittleren Gürtels, dagegen entstehen an den Rändern des Kanals zwei Ostwindgürtel — Fig. 10 —. Gleichzeitig bildet sich am Boden im Süden ein Hochdruckgürtel, im Norden eine Tiefdruckfurche aus, etwa an den Stellen, wo die Nullinien der Momentenänderung in Fig. 10 die 900 mb-Fläche schneiden. Im Gegensatz zu den Ergebnissen von Phillips (1956) wird jedoch oberhalb 700 mb, mit Extremwerten im Niveau der Tropopause, eine Abnahme der Zonalgeschwindigkeit in der Kanalmitte beobachtet, dagegen bilden sich an den Rändern des Kanals zwei jetähnliche Arme stärkerer Zonalgeschwindkigkeit aus, was sich geostrophisch aus der Änderung des mittleren Temperaturgradienten in der Troposphäre interpretieren läßt. In unserem benutzten nichtgeostrophischen Modell resultiert die Momentenänderung wesentlich aus dem Term $f\hat{v}$, wie die hohe Korrelation zwischen mittlerer Meridionalgeschwindigkeit und Momentenänderung — vgl. Fig. 6, 10 — unmittelbar veranschaulicht. Gegen diesen Effekt der meridionalen Zirkulation treten Divergenzen des Zonal-Impulsstroms $\frac{\partial}{\partial y}(uv)$ zurück; der Grund dafür dürfte

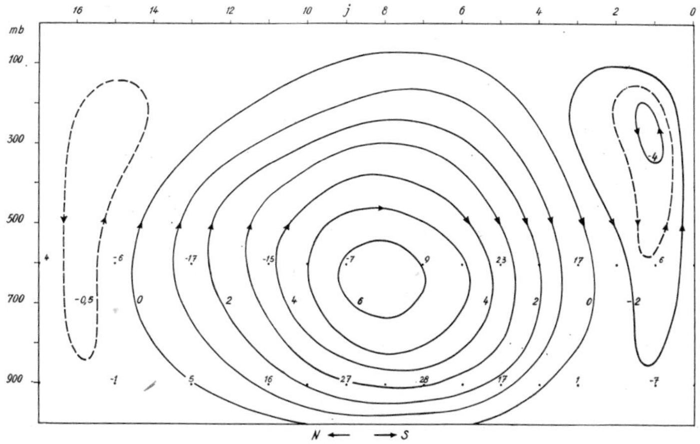

Fig. 7. Text wie Fig. 6, Fall A, Anfangsvertikalgeschwindigkeit = 0, nach 12 Stunden.

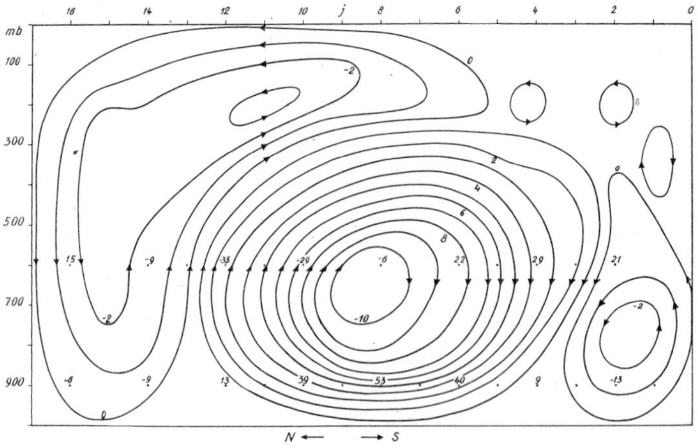

Fig. 8. Text wie Fig. 6, Fall A, Anfangsvertikalgeschwindigkeit = 0, nach 24 Std.

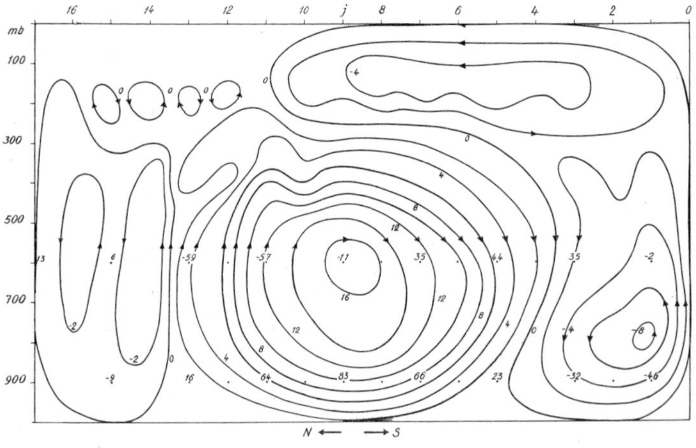

Fig. 9. Text wie Fig. 6, Fall A, Anfangsvertikalgeschwindigkeit = 0, nach 36 Std.

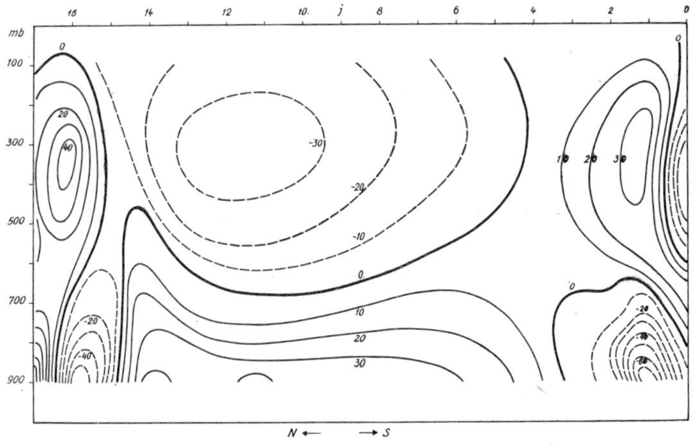

Fig. 10. Änderung der mittleren Zonalgeschwindigkeit innerhalb 72 Stunden, $\hat{u}\,(t=72) - \hat{u}\,(t=0)$, Einheit km Std^{-1}.

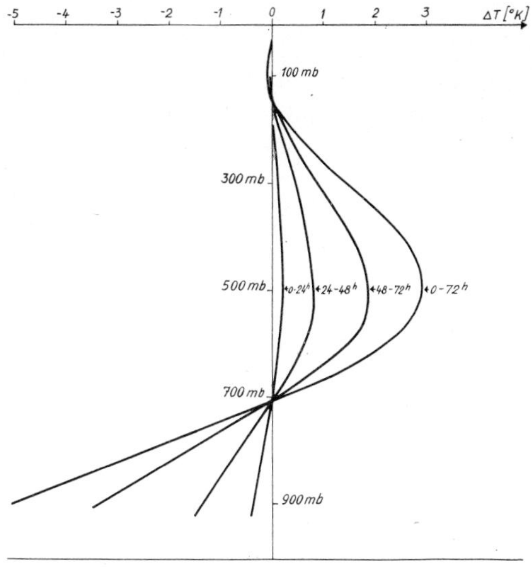

Fig. 11. Änderung der Temperatur, gemittelt über gesamtes Gebiet $\frac{1}{D}\int_0^D \hat{T}\,dy$ innerhalb 24, 48, 72 Stunden. Einheit °K.

einmal in unserer speziellen Annahme einer von der meridionalen Koordinate unabhängigen Anfangsgrundströmung zu suchen sein, zum anderen darin, daß in dem hier verwendeten Fünfflächenmodell die baroklinen nichtgeostrophischen Prozesse, auf die die meridionalen mittleren Zirkulationen wesentlich zurückzuführen sind, gegenüber den auch in barotropen Modellen wirksamen Momentenflüssen mehr betont werden, so daß auch die zeitliche Änderung der vertikalen Windscherung gegenüber der Änderung des über die Vertikale gemittelten Zonalwindes intensiver in Erscheinung tritt als bei Zweiparametermodellen.

Die mit der in Fig. 10 veranschaulichten Momentenänderung verbundene troposphärische Abnahme der Baroklinität in mittleren Breiten und Zunahme in hohen und niedrigen Breiten läßt erwarten, daß im weiteren Verlauf der Entwicklung die Störungstätigkeit nach Norden und Süden verlagert wird, dagegen in mittleren Breiten abklingt. Dies würde zu einem Abbau der Jet-Arme an den Kanalrändern und zu einer Jet-Erzeugung in der Kanalmitte führen. Es darf dabei jedoch die Variation des Coriolisparameters in der realen Atmosphäre sicher nicht außer Betracht gelassen werden. In südlichen Breiten wirkt die Abnahme von f für barokline Entwicklungen stabilisierend, so daß der südliche Jet-Arm beständiger sein wird. In höheren Breiten wird dagegen eine ständige gegenseitige meridionale Verlagerung von Jet-Gebieten und Zonen starker Entwicklung einsetzen, so daß in südlichen Breiten im zeitlichen Mittel der Jet markanter in Erscheinung tritt als in nördlichen. Inwieweit dies den tatsächlichen Vorgängen entspricht, werden erst detailliertere langfristige Vorhersageexperimente, die insbesondere die Kugelgestalt der Erde in Rechnung stellen, erweisen können.

Die aus nichtgeostrophischen Advektionen resultierenden Änderungen der Temperatur, gemittelt über das gesamte Gebiet, in Abhängigkeit von der vertikalen Koordinate, sind der Fig. 11 zu entnehmen. Die Abbildung zeigt infolge der in bodennahen Schichten sich ausbreitenden

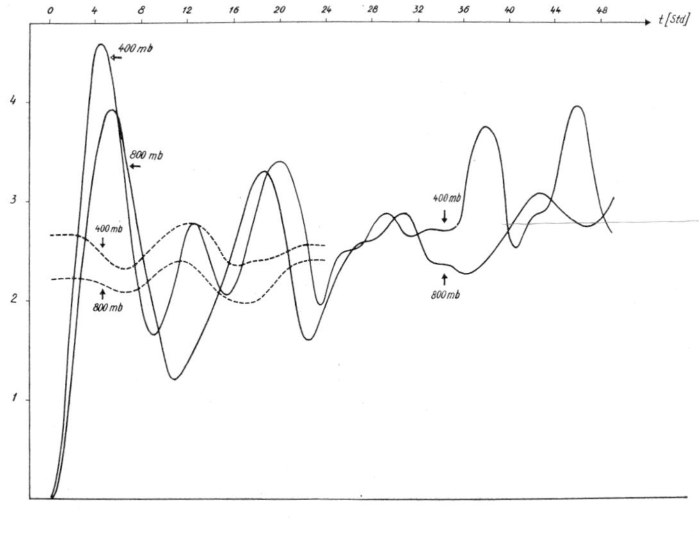

Fig. 12. Verläufe der Extremwerte der Vertikalgeschwindigkeit (Absinken) in 800 und 400 mb als Funktion der Zeit, Einheit mb/Std. Ausgezogene Linien: Fall A (Anfangsvertikalgeschwindigkeit = 0).
Gestrichelte Linien: Fall B (Anfangsvertikalgeschwindigkeit quasigeostrophisch adjustiert).

Kaltluft und der sich kontrahierenden Warmluft Abkühlung unterhalb 700 mb, infolge der umgekehrten Vorgänge in der oberen Troposphäre Erwärmung oberhalb 700 mb. Im Ganzen wird dadurch die Atmosphäre unterhalb 500 mb stabilisiert, oberhalb 500 mb labilisiert. Dieser aufwärts gerichtete großturbulente Wärmefluß infolge der Störungstätigkeit in mittleren Breiten ist lediglich mit nichtgeostrophischen Mehrparametermodellen erfaßbar.

Innerhalb der betrachteten 3 Tage kühlt sich die Gesamtatmosphäre um etwa 1°K ab. Diese Abnahme der inneren bzw. potentiellen Temperatur kompensiert das Anwachsen der kinetischen Energie der Störungen, da in unserem nichtgeostrophischen p-Modell die Energiebilanz folgendermaßen lautet:

$$\frac{\partial}{\partial t}\int_0^L\int_0^D\int_0^{p_0}(K+c_pT)\,dx\,dy\,dp=0 \quad \text{mit } K\equiv\frac{\mathbf{v}^2}{2}.$$

Wegen der Divergenzschreibweise der Adiabatendifferenzengleichung verschwindet die zeitliche Änderung der potentiellen Temperatur, gemittelt über alle Gitterpunkte, auch im Differenzenmodell.

In der Fig. 12 ist der zeitliche Verlauf der Extremwerte (Absinken) des ω-Feldes in den Flächen 400 und 800 mb aufgetragen, und zwar sowohl für Fall A wie für Fall B (gestrichelte Kurven). Man erkennt, daß im Fall B, wo anfangs das vertikale Windfeld quasigeostrophisch angepaßt wurde, die Amplituden der Lärmprozesse erheblich reduziert werden. Die Schwingungsdauer der einem Trend überlagerten Lärmwellen nimmt mit zunehmender Höhe wegen der zunehmenden statischen Stabilität ab.

Bei Einschluß von Effekten, die wesentlich auf das Vertikalgeschwindigkeitsfeld ansprechen (Kondensationsprozesse) wird eine Reduktion der Lärmvorgänge durch spezielle Anfangsbedingungen oder durch zeitliche Glättungen erforderlich sein.

Schlussbemerkung

Die mit dem nichtgeostrophischen Mehrflächenmodell erhaltenen Resultate erweisen, daß auch die primitiven Gleichungen für praktische Vorhersagezwecke brauchbar sind. Speziell das Vertikalgeschwindigkeitsfeld wird durch Lärmvorgänge wesentlich beeinflußt, während in den übrigen Feldern überlagerte Trägheits- und Gravitationswellen unmerklich sind. Eine sorgfältige Anpassung der Anfangsdaten ist erforderlich.

Für wertvolle Mitarbeit darf ich meinen Kollegen Dr. Edelmann und Dr. Reiser sowie Frl. C. Hübner danken, die nicht nur das Maschinenprogramm geschrieben und ausgeprüft haben, sondern auch wesentlich an der Abfassung des Differenzenverfahrens beteiligt waren.

LITERATUR

Charney, J. G., 1947: The dynamic of long waves in a baroclinic westerly current. *J. Met.* **4**, p. 135.

Edelmann, W., 1958: Vergleich verschiedener nichtgeostrophischer Modelle der Atmosphäre mit Hilfe von Lösungen der linearisierten Modellgleichungen. *Met. Abhandlungen Fr. Univ. Berlin*, Bd. VI, Heft 1.

Hollmann, G., 1956: Über prinzipielle Mängel der geostrophischen Approximation und die Einführung ageostrophischer Windkomponenten. *Met. Rdsch.* **9**, p. 73.

Phillips, N., 1956: The general circulation: a numerical experiment. *Quart. J. Roy. Met. Soc.* **82**, p. 123.

(Manuscript received August 14, 1958)

An Example of Non-Linear Computational Instability

By NORMAN A. PHILLIPS

Massachusetts Institute of Technology, Cambridge, Massachusetts

Abstract

A particular example is constructed to demonstrate that the finite-difference solution of the non-linear barotropic vorticity equation may have instabilities of a different nature than those caused by either an incorrect choice of the time increment or incorrect lateral boundary conditions. This instability arises because the grid system cannot resolve wave lengths shorter than about 2 grid intervals; when such wave lengths are formed by the non-linear interaction of longer waves, the grid system interprets them incorrectly as long waves. The seemingly successful use of a smoothing process to eliminate this difficulty is described.

1. Introduction

Suppose we are applying the barotropic non-divergent vorticity equation to the two-dimensional flow of an ideal fluid contained in a channel between parallel walls located at $y = 0$ and $y = W$, using the finite-difference methods now employed in numerical weather prediction. To make matters simple, let us restrict the initial flow patterns to those which have both the streamfunction ψ and vorticity ζ identically zero on both lateral boundaries ($y = 0$ and $y = W$), and to patterns which are periodic in x, so that $\psi(x, y, 0) \equiv \psi(x \pm L, y, 0)$. It is then clear that these boundary conditions will be valid for all time, and that the flow will maintain its periodic character in x.

We introduce as usual a finite-difference grid,

$$\begin{aligned} x &= j\Delta, & j &= 0, 1, 2, \ldots, J-1. \; (J \text{ even}) \\ y &= k\Delta, & k &= 0, 1, 2, \ldots, K \\ t &= \tau \Delta t, & \tau &= 0, 1, 2 \ldots \end{aligned}$$

where Δ is the space increment and Δt the time increment, and we suppose that W and L are such that $L = J\Delta$ and $W = K\Delta$.

The vorticity equation is

$$\frac{\partial \zeta}{\partial t} = J\left(\frac{\zeta, \psi}{x, y}\right); \quad \zeta = \nabla^2 \psi \tag{1}$$

(We are not here concerned with the variation of the Coriolis parameter.)

The finite-difference analogue of this which would normally be used, is

$$\nabla^2(\psi_{\tau+1} - \psi_{\tau-1})_{jk} = \frac{\Delta t}{2\Delta^2} \cdot$$

$$\cdot \left[\delta_j(\nabla^2\psi) \cdot \delta_k(\psi) - \delta_k(\nabla^2\psi) \cdot \delta_j(\psi)\right]_{jk\tau} \tag{2}$$

Here δ_j and δ_k are the usual simple centered difference operators in the x and y directions:

$$\delta_j(\psi) = \psi_{j+1k} - \psi_{j-1k},$$

$$\delta_k(\psi) = \psi_{jk+1} - \psi_{jk-1}.$$

$\nabla^2\psi$ represents the finite-difference approximation for the Laplacian:

$$\Delta^2 \nabla^2\psi \approx \nabla^2\psi =$$

$$= \psi_{j+1k} + \psi_{j-1k} + \psi_{jk+1} + \psi_{jk-1} - 4\psi_{jk} \tag{3}$$

(2) would be applied at the interior points $j = 0, \ldots, J-1$, and $k = 1, 2, \ldots, K-1$. At the boundary points where $k = 0$ or K, ψ and $\nabla^2\psi$ are both taken to be identically zero for all time. At the points for which $j = 0$ and $j = J-1$, the cyclic condition that $\psi(j, k) \equiv \psi(j \pm J, k)$ would be used.

The streamfunction field defined in this manner at the grid points j, k can then be represented by the finite sum:

$$\psi_{jk\tau} = \sum_{l=0}^{J/2} \sum_{m=1}^{K-1} \left[a_{lm\tau} \cos\frac{2\pi jl}{J} + b_{lm\tau} \sin\frac{2\pi jl}{J}\right] \cdot \sin\frac{\pi mk}{K}, \tag{4}$$

where the coefficients $a_{lm\tau}$ and $b_{lm\tau}$ are functions of τ. In this formulation, we take $b_{0m\tau} = b_{J/2m\tau} \equiv 0$, so that there are $J(K-1)$ degrees of freedom in the grid point values of ψ_{jk} and also in the coefficients a_{lm} and b_{lm}. We see from this representation that the smallest wave length in x recognized by the grid system is for $l = J/2$ and corresponds to a wave length of 2Δ. In y, the smallest wave length is for $m = K-1$, and corresponds to a wave length of $2\Delta(K-1)/K \sim 2\Delta$.

Equation (2) is non-linear. If we consider the interaction of 2 components ψ_1 and ψ_2, which are characterized by the wave numbers (l_1, m_1) and (l_2, m_2), it can be seen from (2) that they will contribute to the time rate of change of the 4 components with wave numbers (l_1+l_2, m_1+m_2), (l_1+l_2, m_1-m_2), (l_1-l_2, m_1+m_2), and (l_1-l_2, m_1-m_2). This non-linear interaction determines the transfer of kinetic energy between different parts of the spectrum in this type of flow, and, in the meteorological problem, becomes very important when forecasts are to be made for any extended period of time.

We now recall that any distribution of ψ on the grid network jk can be resolved into the Fourier sum (4), containing only wave numbers $l = 0, 1, \ldots, J/2$ and $m = 1, 2 \ldots, K-1$. It is then clear that the interaction of ψ_1 and ψ_2 with each other will not be interpreted correctly when $l_1 + l_2 > J/2$ and/or when $m_1+m_2 > K-1$. For example, if $l_1+l_2 = J-r$, with $r < J/2$, we would find the following type of misrepresentation to occur:

$$\left.\begin{aligned}\cos\frac{2\pi j}{J}(l_1+l_2) &= \cos\frac{2\pi j}{J}(J-r) = \cos\frac{2\pi j}{J}r,\\ \sin\frac{2\pi j}{J}(l_1+l_2) &= \sin\frac{2\pi j}{J}(J-r) = -\sin\frac{2\pi j}{J}r.\end{aligned}\right\} \tag{5}$$

Thus, instead of affecting wave number $J-r$, the components ψ_1 and ψ_2 will affect wave number r. A similar misrepresentation will occur in the m wave numbers whenever $m_1+m_2 > K-1$.

2. An example of instability from this source

The potential seriousness of this misrepresentation can be seen by constructing an artificial example.

We take only 2 components:

$$\left.\begin{aligned}\psi_1 &= \left[C_\tau \cos\frac{\pi j}{2} + S_\tau \sin\frac{\pi j}{2}\right]\sin\frac{2\pi k}{3},\\ \psi_2 &= U_\tau \cos\pi j \sin\frac{2\pi k}{3},\end{aligned}\right\} \tag{6}$$

Thus $l_1 = J/4$, $m_1 = 2K/3$, and $l_2 = J/2$, $m_2 = 2K/3 = m_1$. The misrepresentation which occurs is of the form

$$\left.\begin{aligned}l_1 + l_2 &= \frac{3J}{4} = J - \frac{J}{4} = J - l_1, \text{ and}\\ m_1 + m_2 &= \frac{4K}{3} = K - \frac{2K}{3} = K - m_1.\end{aligned}\right\} \tag{7}$$

Since $l_1 - l_2$ in this case is equal to l_1, and $m_1 - m_2$ is equal to zero, no new harmonics are generated by the finite-difference interaction of ψ_1 and ψ_2. The *exact* finite-difference solution of this particular example is then described by the three ordinary non-linear difference equations:

$$\left.\begin{aligned}&C_{\tau+1} - C_{\tau-1} = \sigma U_\tau S_\tau,\\ &S_{\tau+1} - S_{\tau-1} = \sigma U_\tau C_\tau,\\ &U_{\tau+1} - U_{\tau-1} = 0,\\ &\quad(\sigma = \sqrt{3}\Delta t/5\Delta^2).\end{aligned}\right\} \tag{8}$$

These are the result of inserting (6) into (2) and (3). Although non-linear, they are simple enough to be solved. We first find that U_τ has the constant value A for even τ and the constant value B for odd τ. C_τ (or S_τ) then satisfies the difference equation:

$$C_{\tau+2} - 2\cosh\Theta\, C_\tau + C_{\tau+2} = 0,$$

where $\cosh\Theta = 1 + \frac{1}{2}\sigma^2 AB$ is a constant. This difference equation has four solutions:

$$e^{\frac{\Theta\tau}{2}},\ (-1)^\tau e^{\frac{\Theta\tau}{2}},\ e^{-\frac{\Theta\tau}{2}},\ (-1)^\tau e^{-\frac{\Theta\tau}{2}}$$

If A and B have the same sign, Θ is a real number, and two of the solutions will amplify exponentially. *This "instability" cannot be eliminated by reducing Δt.*

If A and B are of opposite sign, but small enough in magnitude so that $1+\frac{1}{2}\sigma^2 AB > -1$, Θ is pure imaginary and we have four neutral solutions. However, if A and B are of opposite sign but large enough in magnitude so that $1+\frac{1}{2}\sigma^2 AB < -1$, the solutions are again of the form $\exp \pm \Phi\tau/2$ where $\cosh\Phi = |1+\frac{1}{2}\sigma^2 AB|$. These again will amplify with time, since Φ will be real. Thus, when A and B are of opposite sign, the instability can be eliminated by reducing Δt.

We may investigate the magnitude of the unavoidable instability as follows. From the form of ψ_2, we can think of A and B as equal to $\frac{1}{2}v\Delta$, where v is the velocity due to the difference in ψ_2 at the points $(j+1, k)$ and (j, k). Introducing this definition we find

$$\cosh \Theta = 1 + \frac{3}{200}\left(\frac{v\Delta t}{\Delta}\right)^2.$$

The ordinary linearized analysis of computational stability would have led us to a choice of $(v\Delta t/\Delta)$ less than 1. For small $(v\Delta t/\Delta)$, $\Theta \approx 0.17 \cdot$ $\cdot (v\Delta t\Delta) \sim 0.1$, say, and only 20 time steps will produce an e-fold amplification.

The above analysis is of course only a very particular example. A more thorough analysis of the general case is perhaps too difficult to make, but it seems unlikely that the mere presence of more than 3 degrees of freedom would remove this instability.

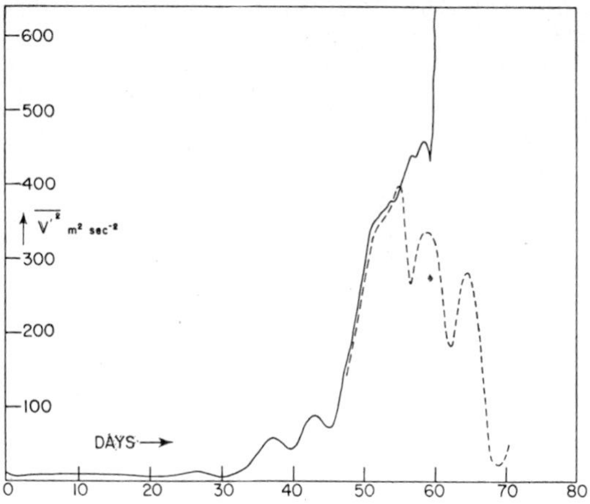

Fig. 1. Disturbance kinetic energy as a function of time. The solid curve was obtained without smoothing, the computations breaking down at about 56 days. The dashed curve was obtained by periodically introducing a filtering procedure.

3. Elimination of the instability by smoothing

Several years ago, the writer applied the techniques of numerical prediction to the study of the general circulation of the atmosphere (PHILLIPS, 1956). This was done by making a forecast for an extended period with a 2-level geostrophic model. The equations included a crude representation of heating and friction, and were applied to a simplified geometrical model of the atmosphere—the so-called "β-plane". After a period of several weeks, the appearance of large truncation errors caused an almost explosive increase in the total energy of the system.

In an attempt to explore this type of computation error, a similar set of equations has recently been solved again, using a smaller horizontal grid interval —166 ²/₃ km compared to the grid intervals of $\Delta x = 375$ km and $\Delta y = 625$ km in the earlier experiment. Although enough changes were also made in the differential equations (e.g. the representation of friction and of the heating function) to prevent a complete comparison between the two computations with respect to truncation error, the same catastrophic errors appeared again, and at a time when the disturbance kinetic energy was about the same magnitude as it was when the breakdown occurred in the first computation. Thus, the reduction in the grid distance, Δ, which should have reduced the truncation error, did not appreciably postpone the breakdown.

The graph of $\overline{\mathbf{v}'^2}$ —proportional to the kinetic energy per unit mass of the disturbance—for this second computation is shown by the full line in fig. 1. The truncation errors became significant around 56 days, just prior to the explosive increase in $\overline{\mathbf{v}'^2}$.[1]

The dashed line in the figure is the curve obtained by redoing the computations (beginning at 48 days) and *periodically eliminating all components with wave lengths smaller than* 4Δ. This was accomplished by performing a Fourier analysis on the grid point data every Nth time step, and then reconstituting the smoothed field, retaining only wave numbers $l = 0, 1, \ldots, J/4$, and $m = 1, 2, \ldots, K/2$. (N was variously chosen so as to give either a 2-hr or 6-hr interval between smoothing operations, little difference being found in the results for the two intervals.)

This smoothed forecast satisfied the energy budgets very well. Let δ be the difference between (a) the observed change in total energy over a one day interval and (b) the theoretical change in total energy computed from the gains due to non-adiabatic heating and the losses due to friction. The root mean square value of δ during the smoothed forecast (48—70 days) was only 0.23 joules sec^{-1} m^{-2}, and the mean value of δ was close to zero. (This was also typical of the value in the unsmoothed forecast *before*

[1] For example the *difference* between the observed change in total energy over one day and the change computed from the energy transformation integrals first exceeded 1 joule sec^{-1} m^{-2} at 55 days.

the sudden breakdown in that forecast at around 56 days.) This suggests that these geostrophic equations do not readily transmit energy to horizontal wave lengths shorter than 700 km—a result already familiar from the analysis by Fjørtoft (Fjørtoft, 1953) — since otherwise the smoothing process would have taken a noticeable amount of energy out of the system. However, the discussion above of the non-linear instability mechanism, and the success of the smoothing procedure, together indicate that even this small rate of energy transfer may be sufficient to activate non-linear computational instabilities in wave lengths shorter than 4 grid intervals if these components are not artificially removed.

In conclusion it may be appropriate to point out that misrepresentation errors similar to (5) will be encountered in solving the non-linear "balance equation" by finite differences (Bolin, 1955; Charney, 1955). This has already been noted by Shuman, who has developed some useful approximations to the straightforward but time consuming Fourier smoothing (Shuman, 1957).

Acknowledgements

This research was sponsored by the Office of Naval Research and the Geophysics Research Directorate of the Air Force under contract Nonr 1841(18). The numerical computations were performed at the MIT Computation Center, Cambridge, Massachusetts.

REFERENCES

Bolin, B., 1955: Numerical forecasting with the barotropic model. *Tellus*, 7, 27—49.

Charney, J., 1955: The use of the primitive equations of motion in numerical forecasting. *Tellus*, 7, 22—26.

Fjørtoft, R., 1953: On the changes in the spectral distribution of kinetic energy for two-dimensional, non divergent flow. *Tellus*, **5**, 225—230.

Phillips, N. A., 1956: The general circulation of the atmosphere: a numerical experiment. *Q. J. Roy. Meteor. Soc.*, **82**, 123—164.

Shuman, F. G., 1957: Numerical methods in weather prediction: II. Smoothing and filtering. *Mon. Wea. Rev.*, **85**, 357—361.

(Manuscript received May 22, 1958)

On the Equivalency of Formulations of Weather Forecasting as an Initial Value Problem and as an "Evolution" Problem

By Koo Chen-Chao

Institute of Geophysics and Meteorology,
Academia Sinica, Peking

Abstract

Weather forecasting is formulated as an initial value problem in the work of numerical forecasting, while in routine forecasting in the conventional way it is formulated as an "evolution" problem of the weather processes, especially considering one specific level. It is shown in this paper that these two different formulations in fact are equivalent for large-scale motions under certain trivial conditions. It is also pointed out that for large-scale motions the three-dimensional structure of the baroclinic atmosphere at a certain moment is implicitly determined by and could be reconstructed from the evolution of the contour and temperature fields at a certain level before and after that moment.

1. The problem

Up to the present time the problem of weather forecasting is formulated as an initial value problem in numerical forecasting (Bjerknes, 1904, Richardson, 1922, Kibel, 1940, Blinova, 1943). Formally the solution of the initial value problem may in turn be solved as a boundary value problem (Charney et al., 1950), but the formulation is in principle that of an initial value problem. However, the routine forecasting in the conventional way is done mainly by the method of "evolution" especially the "evolution" of weather at the surface during the past days or hours. Thus the latter formulation may be regarded as sort of a boundary value problem and is fundamentally different from the former formulation.

Owing to this difference in formulation, a series of questions arise. For example, why can the same problem of forecasting be treated so differently with, at least at the present time, almost the same accuracy? Are these two formulations equivalent to each other? Could they be combined to arrive at a better formulation of the problem? As we have not yet used all the available "historical" data for the three-dimensional atmosphere in the work of numerical forecasting, (also for example, that 24-hours before the initial moment) the answers to these questions are most interesting. If we know the answer we may at least get some idea about the way of improving forecasting with full use of our available weather data, both those for the initial moment and those for the near past. Thus, for theoretical as well as practical reasons, it is interesting to explore the problem of equivalency of these two different formulations. Since the equivalency of formulation evidently depends closely upon the form of the differential equations representing the laws of the weather development which may be different for different scales of atmospheric motion, we shall at first treat large scale motions ($L = 10^8$ cm).

2. The condition of equivalency

It is well-known that the large-scale motion is very close to geostrophic balance. Up to the second approximation of Kibel (1940) or under the so-called quasi-geostrophic assumption (Charney, 1948) the large-scale motions are well described in x, y, p, t-system for short range forecasting purposes by

$$\left(\nabla^2 + a\,\frac{\partial^2}{\partial p^2}\right)\tau = = J\left(\frac{1}{f}\,\nabla^2\Phi + f,\,\Phi\right) + \frac{a}{f}\,\frac{\partial}{\partial p}\,J\left(\Phi,\,\frac{\partial\Phi}{\partial p}\right) \quad (1)$$

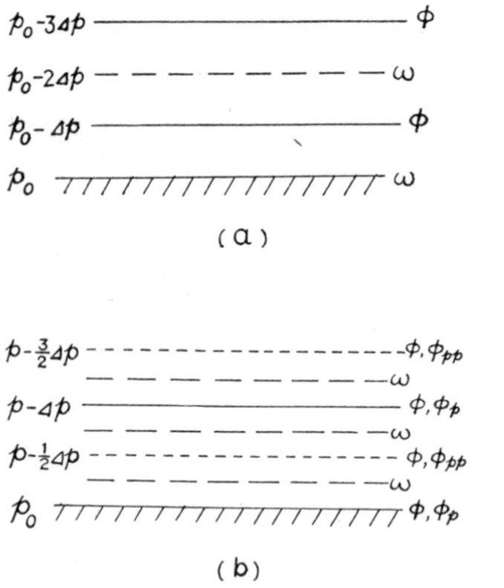

Fig. 1. The arrangement in the vertical direction.
a) for formulation I, b) for formulation II.

where Φ is the geopotential of an isobaric surface, $\tau \equiv \partial p/\partial t$ is the isobaric tendency, ∇^2 the Laplacian, J the Jacobian with respect to x and y, f the coriolis parameter, $a = f^2/\sigma$ a known parameter and the static stability $\sigma = f^{-2}[\partial^2\Phi/\partial p^2 + + k^{-1}p^{-1}\partial\Phi/\partial p]$ is assumed to be independent of the vertical coordinate p. The formulation of numerical forecasting is then generally as follows: To find the τ field at the initial moment $t = t_0$ from equation (1) with the initial condition

$$\Phi(x, y, p, t_0) = F(x, y, p) \tag{2}$$

and the vertical boundary condition for τ related to the condition of $\omega \equiv dp/dt$ at the upper and lower boundary:

$$\omega = 0 \qquad \text{at } p = p_0 \text{ and } p = 0 \tag{3}$$

for $t \geqslant t_0$. Then the Φ field at a later moment is obtained from τ by forward differences with respect to t. In routine forecasting, however, at least in the past, the forecasting problem has been solved from a knowledge of the evolution of the surface weather in the near past:

$$\left.\begin{aligned} \Phi(x, y, p_0, t) &= G_1(x, y, t) \\ T(x, y, p_0, t) &= G_2(x, y, t) \end{aligned}\right\} t \leqslant t_0 \quad \text{at } p = p_0 \tag{4}$$

The surface weather situation at later times, characterized by $\Phi(x, y, p_0, t)$ and $T(x, y, p_0, t)$ fields for $t > t_0$, is found by (kinematical) extrapolation. It is certain, however, as has been shown by experiments in numerical forecasting (MASHKOVICH, 1957) that equation (1) is suitable for description of the large-scale surface weather development. Thus we may regard this formulation as consisting of equation (1) with condition (4). Factors such as friction could be included in the equation without any difficulty in principle. It will be seen later that they are expressed in the equation by additional terms in which only horizontal derivatives are included, these factors will influence the discussion of equivalency below.

Apparently these two formulations differ not only in the conditions for solution but also in the level used for forecasting. However, if the conditions for the solution of the problem are equivalent to each other, the difference in object will be out of question, for, under the approximation used, $T \sim \partial\Phi/\partial p$. When $\Phi(x, y, p, t)$ for $t > t_0$ is forecast for different levels including $p = p_0$ level, by solving equation (1) in its finite difference form, $T(x, y, p_0, t)$ can be obtained from $\Phi(x, y, p, t)$ for $t < t_0$ by upward differences instead of central differences at $p = p_0$. Thus the difference in formulation is essentially a difference in the conditions for a solution. A proof for the equivalency could be completed by proving that any one of these two conditions for solution could be obtained from the other one with the aid of equation (1). It is easy to see that condition (4) can easily be obtained from the conditions (2) and (3) and equation (1), as $\Phi(x, y, p, t)$ including $\Phi(x, y, p_0, t)$ for $t < t_0$ could be computed by *backward* extrapolation with respect to time after τ has been computed. $T \sim \partial\Phi/\partial p$ could then also be computed by upward differences in the vertical direction for the level $p = p_0$. This is justified because the motion is still described by equation (1) as the fundamental laws of motion are not altered for different sense of progress in t, even if irreversible processes are involved. It should be pointed out here, however, that we are dealing with the whole atmosphere or at least one hemisphere, so that there are no difficulties concerning horizontal boundary conditions. The effect of the latter will be discussed in the last section.

Then it remains to see whether the conditions (2) and (3) could be obtained from condition (4) using equation (1). For this purpose, we are going to construct the field

$$\Phi(x, y, p, t_{-a})$$

for some past moment $t = t_{-a} < t_0$ from the condition (4) with the aid of equation (1). Let us at first construct the Φ field at the $p = p_0 - \Delta p$ level.

This could easily be done by the help of the hydrostatic equation, using *upward* differences for $\partial\Phi/\partial p$ at the surface $p = p_0$. But if we proceed to construct further upward for $p = p_0 - 2\Delta p$ level the $\Phi(x, y, p, t)$ field for the same instant $t = t_{-a}$, we have to know the $T \sim \partial\Phi/\partial p$ field at the $p = p_0 -$ $- \Delta p$ level which is not possible directly from the $\Phi(x, y, p_0, t)$ and $T(x, y, p_0, t)$ fields for $t \le t_0$. The question is then reduced to constructing $\partial^2\Phi/\partial p^2$ for the $p = p_0 - {}^1/_2\Delta p$ level, because if the latter is already known, $\partial\Phi/\partial p$ at $p = p_0 - \Delta p$ level could be obtained from the central difference approximation:

$$\frac{\partial\Phi}{\partial p}(x, y, p_0 - \Delta p,\ t_{-a}) = \frac{\partial\Phi}{\partial p}(x, y, p_0, t_{-a}) - $$
$$- \Delta p \times \frac{\partial^2\Phi}{\partial p^2}\left(x, y, p_0 - \tfrac{1}{2}\Delta p,\ t_{-a}\right)$$

Now $\partial^2\Phi/\partial p^2$ may be determined from equation (1) in the following way. Rewriting equation (1) as

$$\left(\frac{\partial}{\partial t} + \frac{1}{f}\frac{\partial\Phi}{\partial y}\frac{\partial}{\partial x} - \frac{1}{f}\frac{\partial\Phi}{\partial x}\frac{\partial}{\partial y}\right)\frac{\partial^2\Phi}{\partial p^2} =$$
$$= \frac{1}{a}\left[J\left(\frac{1}{f}\nabla^2\Phi + f, \Phi\right) - \nabla^2\frac{\partial\Phi}{\partial t}\right] \qquad (5)$$

and applying it to the level $p = p_0 - {}^1/_2\Delta p$, we get an equation for $\partial^2\Phi/\partial p^2$. As $\Phi(x, y, p, t)$ may be obtained in the same way for $p = p_0 - {}^1/_2\Delta p$ and $t = t_{-a}$ as for the $p = p_0 - \Delta p$ level, all quantities such as $\partial\Phi/\partial x$, $\partial\Phi/\partial y$, $\partial\Phi/\partial t$ etc. involved in the equation above can be considered to be known (a backward difference for $\partial\Phi/\partial t$ is used if $t_{-a} = t_0$). Thus the equation (5) is a first order partial differential equation for $\partial^2\Phi/\partial p^2$ with known coefficients and a non-homogeneous term (notice that $1/a = \sigma/f^2$ contains $\partial^2\Phi/\partial p^2$). According to the theory of partial differential equation of first order (see COURANT-HILBERT, 1937) $\partial^2\Phi/\partial p^2$ could be solved from equation (5) for $t = t_{-b}$ if $\partial^2\Phi/\partial p^2$ is known at a moment $t = t_{-b}$ on a curve C at the $p = p_0 - {}^1/_2\Delta p$ level, provided curve C is not one of the characteristics of equation (1). Physically a characteristic of the equation (1) is nothing but the geostrophic trajectory. Equation (5) simply states that $\partial^2\Phi/\partial p^2$ is propagated along the geostrophic trajectory and is subject to all the modifications represented by the terms on the right side of the equation (5). It is then very likely that the value of $\partial^2\Phi/\partial p^2$ a long time ago will not have any appreciable influence on the distribution of $\partial^2\Phi/\partial p^2$ at $t = t_{-a}$. Thus we take

$$\partial^2\Phi/\partial p^2 = \text{a known distribution}$$
$$\text{at } p = p_0 - \tfrac{1}{2}\Delta p \text{ level} \qquad (6)$$

as $t \to -\infty$. The distribution may be taken as the normal value of $\partial^2\Phi/\partial p^2$ for the level concerned or as a constant. Under this condition, we may solve $\partial^2\Phi/\partial p^2$ for the $p = p_0 - {}^1/_2\Delta p$ level at $t = t_{-a}$ (Fig. 1). Then in turn we compute $\partial\Phi/\partial p$ for the $p = p_0 - \Delta p$ level at $t = t_{-a}$. When Φ and $\partial\Phi/\partial p$ have been computed for the level $p = p_0 - \Delta p$, we can construct the Φ field further upwards. By proceeding successively upward in this way, we get a complete Φ field for all levels at the time $t = t_{-a}$. It should be noticed, however, that except for the level next to the top of the atmosphere, Φ and $\partial\Phi/\partial p$ must be constructed not only for $t = t_{-a}$ but also for the time before and after $t = t_{-a}$ as the equation contains $\partial\Phi/\partial t$. Thus the series of weather maps obtained for any level contains two maps less than the series at the level immediately below.

Thus we have constructed the $\Phi(x, y, p, t_{-a})$ field from the condition (4) and equation (5). It is of course not difficult to construct $\Phi(x, y, p, t)$ by using backward difference for $\partial\Phi/\partial t$ in equation (5) all the way up. However, $\Phi(x, y, p, t_{-a})$ becomes more accurate if central differences are used. In the first formulation of the problem it is

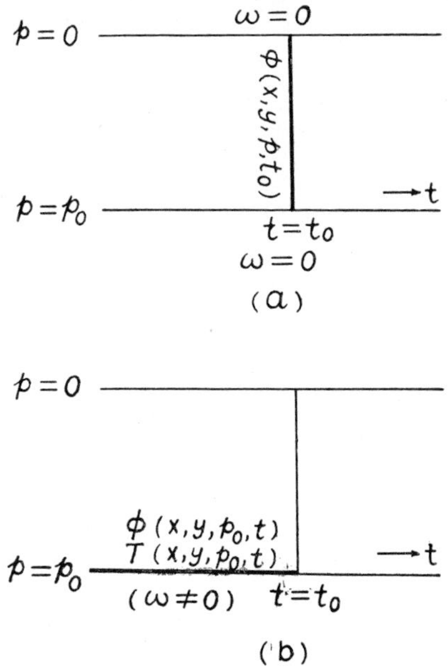

Fig. 2. a) Formulation I, b) formulation II.

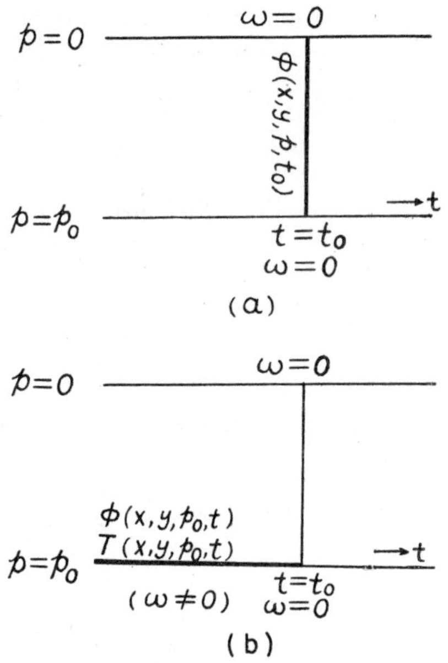

Fig. 3. a) Formulation I′, b) formulation II′.

thus better to forecast $\Phi(x, y, p, t_0)$ from $\Phi(x, y, p, t_{-a})$ using equation (1) with the condition (3) for $t_{-a} \leqslant t < t_0$. Furthermore, condition (3) in the first formulation can not be derived from the condition (4) and (6) using equation (1). In order to make a forecast from $\Phi(x, y, p, t_0)$ with the aid of equation (1), condition (3) must hold also for $t < t_0$. On the other hand, in constructing the field $\Phi(x, y, p_0, t)$ and $T(x, y, p_0, t)$ from the condition (2) with equation (1) for $t < t_0$ condition (3) must be valid for all time $t < t_0$. Thus the original formulations (Fig. 2)

(I)	(II)
Equation (1) with condition (2) and condition (3) for all $t \geqslant t_0$	Equation (1) with condition (4)

are not strictly equivalent. But a formulation slightly modified (Fig. 3) as

(I′)	(II′)
Equation (1) with condition (2) and condition (3) for all t.	Equation (1) with condition (4), condition (3) for $t \geqslant t_{-a}$ $(t_{-a} < t_0)$ and condition (6) as $t \to -\infty$.

are equivalent to each other.

It is easy to see that the Φ and T fields in condition (4) for the second formulation are not necessarily the fields at the earth's surface. The evolution of the Φ and T fields at any level serves just as well as those at the surface. The only difference is that the upward and downward differences should be used respectively when we construct the Φ field upward and downward. Thus condition (4) may be replaced by

$$\left.\begin{aligned}\Phi(x, y, p_a, t) &= H_1(x, y, t)\\ T(x, y, p_a, t) &= H_2(x, y, t)\end{aligned}\right\}\text{for } t \leqslant t_0 \text{ at } p = p_a \tag{4'}$$

In the above discussion, the main thing is to construct the three-dimensional pressure and temperature fields for $t \leqslant t_0$ upward from the same fields at the $p = p_0$ level using a temperature lapse rate determined by the dynamical process as expressed in the equation (1)[1].

It should be pointed out that the equivalency of these two different formulations has some very interesting implications. Physically it means that as the evolution of the Φ and T fields is nothing but the result of the baroclinic development of the three-dimensional pressure and temperature fields of the atmosphere, the evolution of the surface fields necessarily reflect and imply the baroclinic structure of the three-dimensional atmospheric motion. Roughly speaking, for the large scale motions a series of weather maps (Φ and T fields) at different time intervals for the same level is theoretically equivalent to a series of weather maps for different levels at the same instant. Of course there must be some relation between the time interval in the first series and the vertical interval in the second series, which may be found by other considerations.

It is also clear that just because of the baroclinicity we need the knowledge of evolution in the second formulation, because in the barotropic atmosphere, the Φ fields at different levels are not independent of each other. Thus only the Φ field at one level at $t = t_0$ is necessary in the first formulation and accordingly the evolution of the field for all $t < t_0$ is not needed.

[1] With the geostrophic assumption we have $\omega = dp/dt = \partial p/\partial t$ for a horizontal earth surface. As $\partial p/\partial t$ for $t \leqslant t_0$ is prescribed in condition (4), ω is also prescribed for $t \leqslant t_0$. Apparently this is in contradiction to the condition (3), but this causes no real troubles. The same thing happens in the first formulation i.e. $\omega = \partial p/\partial t$ determined from the forecasted $\Phi(x, y, p, t)$ field is different from zero in spite of the prescribed condition (3).

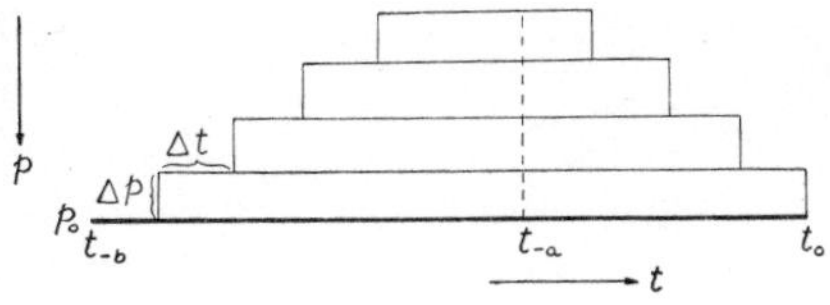

Fig. 4. Constructing upwards in formulation II.

3. The horizontal boundary condition

Now let us turn to the effect of the horizontal boundary conditions. From equation (1) it is seen that though the forecast may formally be made for an area as large as that in which the Φ field is given (analysis area) by the horizontal boundary condition

$$\tau = 0 \quad \text{on horizontal boundary} \qquad (7)$$

the accuracy of the forecasted Φ field is poor near the boundaries. The error will be particularly large at the side where the air flows into the area. In constructing $\Phi(x, y, p, t_{-a})$ using equation (1) with conditions (4) and (3), the horizontal boundaries cause still more trouble. In this case the boundary condition (6) should be modified as part of the trajectory and must be lying outside the horizontal boundary in the time interval $-\infty < t \leq t_{-a}$. For this reason, the horizontal boundary must be shifted upstream in such a way that all air parcels arriving at the forecasting area at the time $t = t_{-a}$, have entered into the area of analysis a sufficiently long time ago, so that the original distribution of $\partial^2\Phi/\partial p^2$ has already been smoothed out through some sort of diffusion. Letting the time $t \to -\infty$ for condition (6) may thus be changed into $t = t_{-b} \ll t_{-a}$ and the construction of Φ upward becomes possible. Furthermore, as the condition (6) is necessary for each step when constructing the $\partial^2\Phi/\partial p^2$ field upward, the region of analysis for a certain level must be larger than that for the level immediately below. The size of this area is equal to the one from which air parcels come into the analysis area during the time interval Δt further backward. It is seen, therefore, that the series of weather maps constructed for a lower level extends further than that for the upper level not only in time but also, for the case of a finite area of analysis, in the horizontal direction at the upstream side. In order to get the right size of the region (the forecast area P) for the weather maps at the uppermost level, the area of analysis (A) for the lowest level must be larger. Then the equivalent formulations for a finite region are approximately as follows

(I″)

Equation (1) with
- condition (2) for region (P)
- condition (3) for all t in (P) and
- condition (7) on the horizontal boundary of (P)

(II″)

Equation (1) with
- condition (4) for region (A)
- condition (3) for $t \geqslant t_{-a}$ in (P) and
- condition (6) for $t = t_{-b}$ in (A)
- condition (7) on the horizontal boundary of (P)

These formulations are however, not strictly equivalent to each other, as a series of weather maps obtained by marching backward in the formulation I″ is semi-infinite in time but smaller in area than those given for the condition (4) in the formulation (II″), besides the distortions close to the horizontal boundaries.

REFERENCES

BJERKNES, V., 1904: Das Problem von der Wettervorhersage, betrachtet vom Standpunkt der Mechanik und der Physik, *Met. Zeits.*, **21**, 1—7.

BLINOVA, E. N., 1943: A hydrodynamical theory of pressure and temperature waves and of centers of atmospheric action, *Comptes Rendus (Doklady) de l'Acad. Sci. d l'URSS*, **39**, 284—287.

CHARNEY, J., 1948: On the scale of atmospheric motions, *Geofys. Publ.*, **17**, 2, 17 pp.

CHARNEY, J., *et al.*, 1950: Numerical integration of the barocline vorticity equation, *Tellus*, **2**, 237—254.

COURANT, R. and HILBERT, D., 1937: *Methoden der Mathematischen Physik*, Bd. 2, Berlin, Springer Verlag, 549 pp.

KIBEL, I. A., 1940: Prilozheniek meteorologii uravnenii mekhaniki baroklinnoi zhidkosti. *Izvestiia Akad. Nauk. SSSR*, No. 5, 627—538.

MASHKOVICH, S. A., 1957: Prognoz nazemnogo davleniia s pomoshchiiu bystrodeischtvuiuschikh elektronnykh vychslitelnyhk mashin, *Meteorologiia i Gidrologiia* No. 1, 8—18.

RICHARDSON, L. F., 1922: *Weather prediction by numerical process, Cambridge*, Camb. Univ. Press, pp. 236.

(Manuscript received December 28, 1957)